AN INTRODUCTION TO
HUMAN GEOGRAPHY

AN INTRODUCTION TO
HUMAN GEOGRAPHY

FIFTH EDITION

Edited by

PETER DANIELS
School of Geography, Earth and Environmental Sciences,
University of Birmingham

MICHAEL BRADSHAW
Warwick Business School, University of Warwick

DENIS SHAW
School of Geography, Earth and Environmental Sciences,
University of Birmingham

JAMES SIDAWAY
Department of Geography, National University of Singapore

TIM HALL
Department of Applied Social Studies, University of Winchester

PEARSON

Harlow, England • London • New York • Boston • San Francisco • Toronto • Sydney
Auckland • Singapore • Hong Kong • Tokyo • Seoul • Taipei • New Delhi
Cape Town • São Paulo • Mexico City • Madrid • Amsterdam • Munich • Paris • Milan

Pearson Education Limited
Edinburgh Gate
Harlow CM20 2JE
United Kingdom
Tel: +44 (0)9
Web: www.pearson.com/uk

First published 2001 (print)
Second edition 2005 (print)
Third edition 2008 (print)
Fourth edition 2012 (print and electronic)
Fifth edition published 2016 (print and electronic)

ISBN: 978-1-292-08295-0 (print)
       978-1-292-08298-1 (PDF)
       978-1-292-12939-6 (ePub)

British Library Cataloguing-in-Publication Data
A catalogue record for the print edition is available from the British Library

Library of Congress Cataloging-in-Publication Data
Names: Daniels, P. W., editor.
Title: An introduction to human geography / edited by Peter Daniels [and four others].
Description: Fifth edition. | New York : Pearson, 2016.
Identifiers: LCCN 2016003272 | ISBN 9781292082950
Subjects: LCSH: Human geography--Textbooks.
Classification: LCC GF41 .I574 2016 | DDC 304.2--dc23 LC record available at http://lccn.loc.gov/2016003272

10 9 8 7 6 5 4 3 2 1
20 19 18 17 16

Print edition typeset in 9.5/12pt Sabon MT Pro by SPi Global
Print edition printed in Slovakia by Neografica

NOTE THAT ANY PAGE CROSS REFERENCES REFER TO THE PRINT EDITION

Dedicated to Jasmin Leila Sidaway
(see www.rgs.org/ourwork/grants/research/jasmin+leila+award.htm)

Brief contents

Contents in detail

Lecturer Resources

For password-protected online resources tailored to
support the use of this textbook in teaching, please visit
www.pearsoned.co.uk/daniels

Contributors

Manuel B. Aalbers   Associate Professor of Geography, Department of Earth and Environmental Sciences, KU Leuven/University of Leuven, Belgium. Urban and financial geography; political economy and financialization; housing, mortgages and real estate; neighbourhood change, exclusion and gentrification.

Dimitris Ballas   Senior Lecturer, Department of Geography, University of Sheffield. Regional science; economic geography; social and spatial inequalities, geoinformatics and the social sciences.

Heather Barrett   Principal Lecturer in Human Geography, Institute of Science and the Environment, University of Worcester. Urban geography; urban morphology, planning and conservation; pedagogic research; employability, learning spaces.

Michael Bradshaw   Professor of Global Energy, Warwick Business School, the University of Warwick. The geopolitical economy of energy, economic geography and energy security.

John R. Bryson   Professor of Enterprise and Competiveness, Birmingham Business School, University of Birmingham. Economic geography; expertise-intensive industries; industrial design; manufacturing and competitiveness; spatial divisions of expertise; sustainability and innovation.

Neil M. Coe   Professor of Economic Geography, National University of Singapore. Global production networks and local economic development; geographies of local and transnational labour markets; geographies of innovation; institutional and network approaches to economic development.

Ian Cook   Associate Professor of Geography, University of Exeter. Cultural geography; long-standing interests in material geographies, multi-sited ethnographic research, connective aesthetics and critical pedagogy, combined in/as the 'follow the thing' approach.

Philip Crang   Professor of Cultural Geography, Department of Geography, Royal Holloway, University of London. Cultural and economic geography, especially commodity culture.

Peter W. Daniels   Emeritus Professor of Geography, School of Geography, Earth and Environmental Sciences, University of Birmingham. Geography of service industries; services and globalization; trade, foreign direct investment and internationalization in services.

Shari Daya   Lecturer in Human Geography, Department of Environmental and Geographical Science, University of Cape Town. Culture; identity; modernity; geographies of production and consumption.

Klaus Dodds   Professor of Geopolitics at Royal Holloway, University of London. Geopolitics and international relations; Arctic and Antarctic; geography and popular culture.

Danny Dorling   Halford Mackinder Professor of Geography, School of Geography and the Environment, University of Oxford. Social and spatial inequalities; housing, health, employment, education and poverty.

James Evans   Senior Lecturer in Geography, School of Environment, Education and Development, University of Manchester. Environmental governance; urban sustainability; mobile methods.

Carl Grundy-Warr   Senior Lecturer in Geography, Department of Geography, National University of Singapore. Geopolitics; forced migration; political ecology; and transnational resource politics.

Tim Hall   Professor of Interdisciplinary Social Studies and Head of Department of Applied Social Studies, University of Winchester. Urban geography; economic geography of organized crime; higher education and pedagogic research.

Rachel A. Howell   Lecturer in Sociology/Sustainable Development, School of Social and Political Science, University of Edinburgh. Lower carbon/sustainable lifestyles; pro-environmental behaviour change; social movements for sustainability; climate change communication.

Phil Hubbard   Professor of Urban Studies, School of Social Policy, Sociology and Social Research, University of Kent. Geographies of sexuality; urban consumption and gentrification; geographies of higher education.

Andrew Jones   Dean and Professor of Economic Geography, School of Arts and Sciences, City University London. Globalization; transnational firms; business services; economic practices; knowledge economy; international voluntary work.

Clare Madge   Reader in Human Geography, University of Leicester. Postcolonial geographies; creative geographies; everyday online communities.

Virginie Mamadouh   Associate Professor of Political and Cultural Geography, University of Amsterdam, The Netherlands. Geopolitics and critical geopolitics; political geographies of European integration; multilingualism; new media and transnationalism.

Damian Maye   Reader in Agri-food Studies, Countryside and Community Research Institute, University of Gloucestershire. Agri-food restructuring; alternative food networks; short food chains; geographies of food security; sustainable food transitions; agricultural biosecurity and animal disease governance.

Cheryl McEwan   Professor of Human Geography, Department of Geography, Durham University. Feminist and cultural geographies; post-colonial theory and development; geographies of transformation in South Africa.

Warwick E. Murray   Professor of Human Geography and Development Studies, School of Geography, Environment and Earth Sciences, Victoria University of Wellington, New Zealand. Development geography; globalization; rural change; Latin America and Oceania.

Jenny Pickerill   Professor of Environmental Geography, Department of Geography, University of Sheffield. Environmental and social justice; eco-housing and eco-building; geographies of activism; indigenous geographies.

Jane Pollard   Professor of Economic Geography, Centre for Urban and Regional Development Studies and School of Geography, Politics and Sociology, Newcastle University. Geographies of money and finance; political economy and regional economic development.

Marcus Power   Professor of Human Geography, Department of Geography, Durham University. Post-socialist and post-colonial transformations in Southern Africa; critical geographies and genealogies of (post)development; vision, visuality and geopolitics; 'clean development' and low-carbon transitions; and the growing presence of (re)emerging powers in Africa.

Bill Pritchard   Associate Professor of Economic Geography, School of Geosciences, University of Sydney, Australia. Geography of food and agriculture; global trade rules in agriculture; food security and rural development.

Denis Shaw   Honorary Senior Research Fellow, School of Geography, Earth and Environmental Sciences, University of Birmingham. Historical and contemporary geographical change in Russia; history of geographical thought.

James D. Sidaway   Professor of Political Geography, Department of Geography, National University of Singapore. Political geography; finance, cities and borders; history of geographic thought.

Terry Slater   Honorary Senior Research Fellow, School of Geography, Earth and Environmental Sciences, University of Birmingham. Historical geography; urban morphology; topographical development of medieval towns; urban conservation.

David Storey   Principal Lecturer in Geography, Institute of Science and the Environment, University of Worcester. Nationalism, territory and place; sport and national identity; rural development, heritage and place promotion.

Chih Yuan Woon   Assistant Professor, Department of Geography, National University of Singapore. Critical geopolitics; geographies of peace and non-violence; security; Southeast Asia; China geopolitics

Richard Yarwood   Associate Professor (Reader) in Geography, School of Geography, Earth and Environmental Sciences, Plymouth University. Citizenship; social geography; rural geography; crime; military geographies.

Acknowledgements

As ever, the on-going success of this project relies on the goodwill and enthusiasm of the contributors. We would also like to thank the panel of reviewers who assessed the fourth edition and made suggestions on the ways in which it might be improved. This edition therefore includes some new chapters that reflect the feedback from the panel and which continues to ensure a lively collection of contributions: from those who have contributed from the outset, from those who joined as new contributors to the second, third or fourth editions, and from those who are new to the fifth edition. All have enthusiastically responded to the editors' edict that they should seek to adopt an accessible writing style that will engage readers and encourage them to make connections between many of the issues discussed in the book and their day-to-day experiences. This is achieved by using contemporary/everyday examples that makes the material more meaningful and less abstract. The importance of developing global perspectives is retained while also encouraging the contributors to include as wide a range of examples as possible, especially from Europe. We have again sought to ensure good integration between the case studies/artwork and the text so that the reader can see why a particular feature is situated at a particular point in a chapter, what it is there to illustrate, how it can provoke readers to think through the issue, and how it relates to the main narrative. It has also been very important to ensure that the fifth edition continues to offer readers perspectives on recent debates, issues and controversies that were a feature of the earlier editions. The contributors have risen to all these challenges and we would like to acknowledge their constructive response to the dialogue that this has necessitated along the way.

The editors and contributors are indebted to Patrick Bond (then at Pearson) who initiated the discussions that led to the decision to prepare a fifth edition. Just as the process was getting underway he handed over to Lina Aboujieb, who then offered invaluable support and encouragement during the process of pulling together the final manuscript and liaised with the contributors over contracts and queries associated with the artwork and illustrations. There are other members of the editorial and production staff at Pearson that the Editors do not meet, such as those tasked with preparing the artwork or undertaking the copy-editing and proofreading; we owe them all a debt of gratitude for seeing this project through to completion. Thanks are also due to Peter Jones, Department of History, University of Birmingham, for advice concerning Section 1 of the book.

Those who have used earlier editions will note that this one includes a new editor. For the fifth edition a new (fifth) member of the editorial team (Tim Hall) brings fresh ideas, energy and insight. The old hands are very pleased that Tim so readily agreed to join us! For all of the editors, production of the fifth edition has taken place at a time when we have all been facing numerous challenges and demands on our time, whether as a result of moving to pastures new, family commitments, making the transition to formal retirement, or simply coping with the ever-changing landscape of higher education. However, we have continued to work closely together as a team. Sticking to the task has again been made easier by the continuing enthusiasm shown by all the contributors and the team at Pearson; this has ensured that we have produced a fifth edition that we can all be proud of.

The School of Geography, Earth and Environmental Sciences at the University of Birmingham kindly offered us temporary office space, where sections of this edition could be assembled during the spring and early summer of 2015 and where an early draft of the Introduction was first hammered out by James and Tim. We are all grateful for this and James also thanks them for the wider hospitality during his sabbatical visit to Birmingham in 2015. James would also like to thank colleagues and students at the University of Amsterdam and National University of Singapore, where many of the ideas in Section 5 were rehearsed.

As with all the past editions, the most important motivation, of course, is our hope that the ideas, perspectives and challenges discussed in this book will encourage readers to connect with human geography; after all, the vitality of the discipline depends on students being enthused and critically, as well as creatively, engaging with human geography within and beyond the classroom.

PWD
MJB
TH
DJBS
JDS
Birmingham, July 2015

The editors and publishers would like to thank the following reviewers of the fourth edition for their invaluable input into the shaping of ideas for this fifth edition:

John Stubbs, University of Derby
Daniel Hammett, University of Sheffield
David Bell, University of Leeds
Samarthia Thankappan, University of York
Ed Hall, University of Dundee
Isla Forsyth, University of Nottingham
David Haigh, Leeds Beckett University
Annie Hughes, Kingston University London
Ruth Healey, University of Chester
Agatha Herman, University of Reading
Andrew Power, University of Southampton
Allan Watson, University of Staffordshire
Eifiona Thomas Lane, Bangor University
Michelle Newman, University of Coventry
Tim Brown, Queen Mary University of London
David Featherstone, University of Glasgow
Stephen Burgess, University of Cardiff

Publisher's acknowledgements

Figures

Figure 2.2 from *Descricao da Fortaleza de Sofala e das mais da India*, Fundacao Oriente, Lisbon (Carneiro, A de M 1990); Figure 2.6 from *Yorkshire Textile Mills 1770–1930*, 1 ed., HMSO (Giles, C. and Goodall, I.H. 1992) p. 102, MD94/04156, © Crown copyright. NMR; Figure 2.7 from *Yorkshire Textile Mills 1770-1930*, HMSO (Giles, C. and Goodall, I.H. 1992) p. 102, Courtesy of the Ironbridge Gorge Museum Trust; Figure 4.1 from http://www.worldmapper.org, Benjamin Hennig, © 2006 SASI Group (University of Sheffield) and Mark Newman (University of Michigan); Figure 4.3 from *United Nations, 2013*, p. xv, © United Nations, New York, Reprinted with the permission of United Nations; Figure 4.6 after *Human Population: Fundamentals of Growth: Future growth*, Population Reference Bureau (2007) Available at http://www.prb.org/Educators/TeachersGuides/HumanPopulation/FutureGrowth/TeachersGuide.aspx?p=1; Figure 4.7 from http://esa.un.org/unpd/wpp/publications/Files/WPP2012_HIGHLIGHTS.pdf—Page 12, 2012, © United Nations, Reprinted with the permission of United Nations; Figure 4.9 from *Vienna Yearbook of Population Research*, L Lutz, W. Goujon, A., Samir, K.C. and Sanderson, W., 2007; Figure 4.10 from Projection of populations by level of educational attainment, age and sex for 120 countries for 2005- 2050, Samir, K.C., Barakat, B., Goujon, A. et al., *Demographic Research*, 22, p.432, 2010, Available at http://www.demographic-research.org/volumes/vol22/15; Figures 4.13, 4.15 from http://www.worldmapper.org, © Copyright 2006 SASI Group (University of Sheffield) and Mark Newman (University of Michigan); Figure 5.1 from *Natural Resources: Allocation, Economics and Policy*, 2 ed., Rees, J., © 1985, Routledge, reproduced by permission of Taylor & Francis Books UK; Figure 5.2 from *Global Change and Challenge: Geography in the 1990s*, Rees, J. in Bennett, R. and Estall, R. (eds) , © 1991, Routledge, reproduced by permission of Taylor & Francis Books UK; Figure 5.3 from *Natural Resources: Allocation, Economics and Policy*, 2 ed., Rees, J, © 1985, Routledge, reproduced by permission of Taylor & Francis Books UK; Figure 5.9 from *BP Statistical Review of World Energy 2015 (2015:15)*; Figure 5.11 from *Environmental Resources*, 1 ed., Mather, A.S. and Chapman, K., © Prentice Hall, 1995, Reproduced by permission of Taylor & Francis Books UK; Figure 9.1 from *United Nations (UN-HABITAT 2008)*, © United Nations, New York, Reprinted with the permission of United Nations; Figure 14.1 extracted from *World Bank Development Indicators data* (http://data.worldbank.org/indicator, accessed 17 December 2014); Figure 14.2 from *http://www3.weforum.org/docs/GITR/2013/GITR_OverallRankings_2013.pdf*, GITR, Overall Rankings, World Economic Forum, Switzerland, 2013; Figure 15.1 from Forging linkages in the commodity chain: the case of the Chilean salmon farming industry, 1987-2001, *Sociologia Ruralis*, 43, pp. 108-27 (Phyne, J. and Mansilla, J. 2003), Reproduced with permission of Blackwell Scientific; Figure 15.2 from Alternative (shorter) food supply chains and specialist livestock products in the Scottish-English borders, *Environment and Planning A*, 37, pp. 823-44 (Ilbery, B. and Maye, D. 2005); Figure 16.1 republished with permission from Sage Publications Ltd, from *Global Shift: Mapping the Changing Contours of the World Economy*, 5 ed., Fig. 1.4c, Dicken, P., © 2007 Sage Publications Ltd; permission conveyed through Copyright Clearance Center, Inc.; Figure 16.3 from *Technology and organizational factors in the notebook industry supply chain*, The Personal Computer Industry Center publication, Figure 2 (Foster, W., Cheng, Z., Dedrick, J. and Kraemer, K. L. 2006), UC Irvine; Figure 16.7 from *Commodity Chains and Global Capitalism*, Praeger (Gereffi, G. in Gereffi, G. and Korzeniewicz, M. (eds.) 1994); Figure 16.8 from Globalization and paradoxes of ethical transnational production: code of conduct in a Chinese workplace, *Competition and Change*, 9, pp. 181-200, Figure 1 (Sum, N-L. and Ngai, P. 2005); Figure 17.1 from *Service Worlds: People, Organizations, Technologies*, Bryson, J. R., Daniels, P.W. and Warf, B, © 2004, Cengage, Reproduced by permission of Taylor & Francis Books, UK; Figure 17.2 from *Input-Output Analysis: 2005*, ONS (Mahajan, S. (ed) 2005) p. 23, Office for National Statistics licensed under the Open Government Licence v.3.0.; Figure 17.3

from Transnational Corporations and Spatial Divisions of 'Service' Expertise as a Competitive Strategy: The Example of 3M and Boeing, *The Service Industries Journal*, Bryson, J. R. and Rusten, © 2008, Routledge, Reproduced by permission of Taylor & Francis Books UK.

Maps

Figure 1.1 adapted from *Changing the Face of the Earth: Culture, Environment, History*, 2nd ed., Wiley Blackwell (Simmons, I. G. 1996) p.48; Figure 1.2 after Sherratt, A., Cambridge Encyclopedia Archaeology (1980), Cambridge University Press; Figure 2.3 after *Atlas of the British Empire*, 1st ed., (Bayley, C. 1989), © Octopus Publishing Group; Figure 2.5 after *The Hamlyn Historical Atlas*, (Moore, R. I. (ed) 1981); Figure 2.8 after Pounds, N.J.G, *An Historical Geography of Europe*, Cambridge University Press (1990); Figure 5.7 from *BP Statistical Review of World Energy 2015*, BP (2015:19); Figure 5.8 from *BP Statistical Review of World Energy 2015*, BP (2015:29); Figure 20.1 after *The Fate of the Forest: Developers, Destroyers and Defenders of the Amazon*, Verso (Hecht S. and Cockburn A. 1989) p.127; Figure 20.2 adapted from *Political Geography*, John Wiley (Glassner M.I. 1993) p.498, Reproduced with permission of Blackwell Scientific; Figure 20.4 from Arquivo Histórico Militar (Galvão, H. 1934) Archival Ref: PT/AHM/DIV/3/47/AV2/2325; Figure 20.6 after Political geography and panregions, *Geographical Review*, 80, pp. 1-20 (O'Loughlin J. and van der Wusten, H. 1990).

Tables

Table 2.1 from *The Hamlyn Historical Atlas*, (Moore, R.I. (ed), 1981), p. 57, Copyright © Octopus Publishing Ltd., 1981; Table 4.2 from from Population Division of the Department of Economic and Social Affairs of the United Nations Secretariat World Population Prospects: The 2012 Revision, © United Nations, New York. Reprinted with the permission of United Nations; Table 5.1 from Global Change and Challenge: Geography in the 1990s, Rees, J. in Bennett, R. and Estall, R. (eds), © 1991, Routledge, reproduced by permission of Taylor & Francis Books UK; Table 5.2 from *BP Statistical Review of World Energy* (2015: 41); Tables 5.4, 5.5 from *OECD/ IEA (2014) Key World Energy Statistics 2014*. Also available at: www.iea.org/statistics, © OECD/IEA 2014, IEA Publishing. Licence: www.iea.org/t&c/termsandconditions; Table 6.1 from *The Politics of the Environment: Ideas, Activism, Policy*, Cambridge University Press (Carter, N. 2001) p. 15; Table 6.2 from *The shallow and the deep, long-range ecology movement*, Inquiry 16 (Naess, A. 1973) pp. 95-100, Oslo; Table 6.3 from *The Politics of the Environment: Ideas, Activism, Policy*, Cambridge University Press (Carter, N. 2001) p. 4;

Table 6.4 from *Environmental Politics: Britain, Europe and the Global Environment*, 2 ed., Macmillan (Garner, R. 2000) p. 11, Robert Garner, Environmental Politics, Reproduced with permission of Palgrave Macmillan; Table 10.2 from *Dangerous Disorder: Riots and Violent Disturbances in Thirteen Areas of Britain, 1991-1992*, Joseph Rowntree Foundation (Power, A. and Tunstall, R. 1997); Table 10.3 from The changing dynamics of community opposition to human service facilities, *Journal of the American Planning Association*, 63(1), pp. 79-93 (Takahashi, L.M. and Dear, M.J. 1997); Table 14.1 from *World Bank, World Development Indicators* at http://data.worldbank.org/data-catalog/world-development-indicators [accessed 4 January 2015]; Table 14.2 from *World Tourism Highlights, 2010 Edition*, United Nation World Tourism Organization (2010), UNWTO, Madrid, © UNWTO, 9284405315; Table 14.3 from Major FDI Indicators, UNCTAD (2010)—United Nations Conference on Trade and Development (UNCTAD) Major FDI Indicators (extract from table at http://unctad.org/sections/dite.dir/docs/WIR11_web%20tab%202.pdf) [accessed 8 January 2015], 2010, © United Nations. Reprinted with the permission of United Nations; Table 14.4 from *Yeandle and Davies (2013)*, Table 11, p. 35; Table 14.5 from *Internet usage, by world region, 2010*, www.internetworldstats.com/stats.html; Table 16.2 from *The growing power of retailers in producer-driven commodity chains: a 'retail revolution' in the US automobile industry?*, (Kessler, J. and Appelbaum, R. 1998) unpublished manuscript, Department of Sociology, University of California at Santa Barbara, USA; Table 17.1 from *OECD, 2014*, based on data from Employment in Manufacturing and Service, 2012 and 2013, accessed on 14/01/2015; Table 17.2 from A 'Second' Global Shift? The Offshoring or Global Sourcing of Corporate Services and the Rise of Distanciated Emotional Labour, *Geografiska Annaler (Bryson, J.R. 2007)*, Reproduced with permission of Blackwell Scientific.

Text

Poetry on page 4 from *Geography is Everywhere* by Dr. Clare Madge; Poetry on page 64 from 'Slough', from *Collected Poems*, by John Betjeman © 1955, 1958, 1962, 1964, 1968, 1970, 1979, 1981, 1982, 2001. Reproduced by permission of John Murray, a division of Hodder and Stoughton Limited.

Photographs

(Key: b-bottom; c-centre; l-left; r-right; t-top)

Alamy Images: David R. Frazier Photolibrary, Inc 450, ITAR-TASS Photo Agency 112tl, Justin Kase 425, Lordprice Collection 69, MARKA 311, Alan Payton 118, The Art Archive 41; **Archant Norfolk**: 221; **Banksy**: 252b;

Bridgeman Art Library Ltd: Mr and Mrs Andrews, c.1748-9 (oil on canvas), Gainsborough, Thomas (1727-88)/National Gallery, London, UK/Bridgeman Images 252t; Corbis: Bettmann 367, 411bl, 411br, Stefano Bianchetti 30, Sherwin Crasto/Reuters 354, Angelo Hornak 60; T. Paul Daniels: 289; Mike Deaton: 198; Fotolia.com: Carabay 114, EyeMark 426, fotomuhabiri 471, Leonid Ikan 482, Juulijs 478, karenfoleyphoto 411tl, labalajadia 422, Monkey Business 344, Oksana Perkins 432, tanjalagicaimage 11, TheStockCube 440, Vacclav 452; Getty Images: Anadolu Agency 473b, Boston Globe 269, Jean-Pierre Fouchet 475, Spencer Platt 377, Popperfoto 112br, Mark Ralston/AFP 193, Chris Scott 431; Tim Hall: 199t, 199b, 202; Phil Hubbard: 214; PARS International Corp, Time Inc: from TIME, 15 January 1979 © 1979 Time Inc. Used under license. TIME and Time Inc. are not affiliated with, and do not endorse products or services of, Licensee. 412; John F. Kennedy Presidential Library and Museum, Boston: Cecil Stoughton. White House Photographs 174; LBJ Library Photo: by Yoichi Okamoto 177; Paul Lunnon: 248, 248bl, 248br; Warwick E. Murray: 227t, 227c, 228, 229, 232, 233, 234t, 234b, 238bl, 238br, 240 /John Overton 227b; NASA: 7; Panos Pictures: Paul Lowe 176; PhotoDisc: 248tl; Jenny Pickerill: 134, 135t, 135b, 139, 141, 147, 150, 153; Press Association Images: AP/John Froschauer 356, AP/Remy de la Mauviniere 213; Reuters: Toby Melville 472, Eduardo Munoz 159; Rex Shutterstock: courtesy of Everett Collection 415, 481bl, 481br, SIPA PRESS 401; Ronald Grant Archive: 20th Century/Lionsgate Film 257; Shutterstock.com: 1000 Words 380, 360b 67br, ArtWell 330, Asianet-Pakistan 458, Diego Barucco 24cl, Bikeworldtravel 463, Caminoel 410, cdrin 287, Malcolm Chapman 93, Jeffrey J Coleman 388br, coloursinmylife 461, ermess 383bl, Everett Historical 66, 348, 447, Iakov Filimonov 63tl, 67bl, peter jeffreys 63br, johnbraid 24cr, Joshua Rainey Photography 383br, Matej Kastelic 435, KieferPix 322, thomas koch 100, Daniel Korzeniewski 312, Alexander Kuguchin 28, kisa kuyruk 473t, Laborant 201, Daryl Lang 466, littleny 166, meunierd 384, Michaelpuche 388tl, Jan Mika 457, Slobodan Miskovic 34, Luciano Mortula 263, Gilles Paire 109, pcruciatti 21b, PhotoSmart 390, Ppictures 70, Pyty 299, Radiokafka 464, Dr. Morley Read 341, Joseph Sohm 385, TCJ2020 451, urbanbuzz 381, 386, Jeff Whyte 274; Terry Slater: 45, 55 (a), 55 (b), 55 (c), 55 (d), 57 (a), 57 (b), 57 (c), 57 (d); SuperStock: © Salvador Dali, Fundació Gala-Salvador Dalí, DACS, 2016. 413; The Independent: 393; TopFoto: 414; UNOG Library, League of Nations Archives: 483.

GEOGRAPHY: FINDING YOUR WAY IN THE WORLD

Introduction

James Sidaway
Michael Bradshaw
Peter Daniels
Tim Hall
Denis Shaw

Geography is indispensable to survival. All animals, including American students who consistently fail their geography tests, must be competent applied geographers. How else do they get around, find food and mate, avoid dangerous places?
(Yi-Fu Tuan 2002: 123)

We believe that our everyday lives are simply teeming with the kinds of issues and questions that are often pigeon-holed as theory. Much of the excitement and value in Human Geography lies in addressing these issues and questions by thinking through aspects of our own lives and of the world(s) in which we live.
(Cloke *et al.* 2014: 2)

This book is the fifth edition of *An Introduction to Human Geography*. The first edition was published in 2001. The task of compiling the first edition therefore dates back to 1997–98 so that it is now approaching 20 years since we wrote the first introduction. While the fifth edition incorporates further changes to the structure and contents and one new editor, we have retained the original goal, which was to provide an introduction to human geography that focuses upon contemporary *issues* and approaches. What introductory textbooks in human geography choose to include and foreground (and what is excluded or neglected) some years ago became the subject of heated debate in a leading disciplinary journal (*Transactions of the Institute of British Geographers*). According to one of the protagonists, textbooks (in part via their influence on a prospective new generation of geographers) become part of what shapes the dominant themes for research and scholarship in a discipline. Textbooks are thereby implicated 'in strategies to mobilize support for a particular set of disciplinary practices' (Johnston 2007: 437).

Textbooks also reflect *where* they are written and where they are read. For example, most textbooks written in North America devote a significant number of words to explaining what geography is and what constitutes a geographical approach. Early on in one of the most widely used American human geography introductions, Marston *et al.* (2011: 2) noted that:

> The power of geography comes from its integrative approach, which addresses global connections, historical trends, and systemic political-economic and socio-cultural relations by drawing on the intellectual tradition in both the natural and social sciences.

The reason why introductory textbooks in the United States need to explicitly consider definitions of human geography and devote space to explaining what a geographical approach amounts to is that many of the students taking a module in introductory human geography are not geography majors; that is, they will not go on to specialize in geography, and they will usually have experienced limited or no exposure to it as a discipline at high school. Geography is seldom taught in the American 'K–12' (kindergarten to pre-university) school system. The institutional setting within which the present textbook has been put together is different. The editors and most of the contributors are currently attached to (or associated with) British or continental European universities, or in countries where the influence of a British style educational system is more evident. Many of their students have chosen to specialize in geography at a secondary school or college and have made a choice to read for a degree in geography. Consequently, students from these countries often have ideas about the subject matter of the discipline (although this may turn out to be rather different from much of what they will subsequently encounter at university: see Bonnett 2003 and Stannard 2003). Further, the departmental contexts within which geography is taught and learnt within universities varies a great deal between different institutions and national systems of higher education. The fact that the discipline is being reproduced across a variegated international institutional landscape may be having an impact on geography's immediate futures (see Spotlight box I.1).

Moreover, human geography and the world that it seeks to interpret and represent are dynamic. In the years since we embarked on the first edition of this book a great deal has changed in the world; ongoing processes of migration, urbanization and economic transformations (such as the fast pace of development in parts of China, the Persian Gulf and India) are producing new spaces, connections and flows that require new maps and geographical narratives. New divisions are also being created, old conflicts revived and, on first appearances, the world might appear to be more fragmented and contested than it was at the start of the twentieth century. For example, the aftermath of the 2008 global financial crisis, which is still being felt in many economies across the world, seems to have accelerated the shift in the centre of geo-economic power further towards parts of Asia; although such shifts are uneven and there are some countervailing trends.

Spotlight box I.1

Departments and the reproduction of geography: where do you fit?

University geography departments are very diverse entities. As Noel Castree (2011, 5) has noted, 'A century ago, a small number of university geographers in England and elsewhere worked hard to create a subject that is, today, far larger and more buoyant than they could possibly have imagined'. The scale and complexity of geography as an academic discipline is apparent in a number of ways, one of which is the complexity of its management arrangements, the ways in which it is organised into departments in universities. Some geography departments are single subject, autonomous units but increasingly, in the UK at least, and for much longer in other countries, geography is managed alongside other subjects such as archaeology, sociology, environmental science, geology and a host of others from across the sciences, social sciences, arts and humanities. One of the editors, along with a number of other colleagues mapped the changing management of geography within UK higher education, interpreting these trends within the wider political economies of UK and international higher education systems (Hall *et al.* 2015). And all five editors were once either postgraduate students or staff at what was in the 1990s (when the first edition of this textbook was planned) a single subject geography department (founded in 1924, although the subject was taught from the 1890s in Mason College, which became the University of Birmingham in 1900), but is now a larger School of Geography, Earth and Environmental Sciences at the University of Birmingham.

These different departmental configurations and management arrangements reflect a number of things including traditions of academic management, national systems of higher education, fluctuations in student numbers, financial and administrative pressures as well as disciplinary and intellectual fashions, trends and aspirations. For example, in most North American universities geography courses are required to meet the needs of non-geography students who are taking geography as an option or elective. Single subject, autonomous geography departments are therefore the exception rather than the rule, and in many continental European countries, physical and human geography are separate departments.

Think about the university department at which you are studying geography. Understanding the administrative place of academic geography can tell you a lot about the institutional pressures that it has to confront, its security, the wider structures that the discipline is located within and the possibilities for its immediate futures. Reflect upon the place of geography within your university and what this reveals. For example, is geography the only subject in your department or is it managed alongside other subjects? If it is the latter, what are the other subjects in

your department? Does it differ from the management of geography in other universities? Most importantly, though, does this management of geography in your university matter? Does it impact upon the geography you study? For example, are you able to take courses taught with students from other subjects, perhaps that are taught by non-geography staff? How does this affect your emerging geographical imagination (see page 6)? Does your exposure to perspectives from beyond geography enrich or diminish your own geographies? If you are in a single subject autonomous geography department look at the publications produced by your lecturers (usually their homepages indicate some of these, but they can also be searched on Google Scholar and the like). Do they conduct research and publish with non-geographers? Who are these collaborators, why have these collaborations arisen and what sort of geographies are being produced through them? Very quickly you will discover that geography is not a hermetically sealed discipline but it overlaps with other fields in many ways and for many reasons.

Think also about the history of geography in your university. Can you find out if the management of geography has changed over time? This information is not always readily available – but it may be worth looking into. Asking your lecturers may be a starting point or finding out if there is a published history of your department (such as the one for Birmingham by Giles, 1987). The issue of why has it changed and who got to decide geography's institutional position is often complex, however. Was this the result of decisions made by geography staff or university managers, most of whom were probably not geographers by background? You will find that geography is not just an intellectual pursuit that exists in a vacuum but is impacted by its immediate disciplinary, institutional and wider socio-economic contexts. The geography you will learn and the geographer you will become will also be a product of these and the many other contexts within which geography is reproduced here and around the world. You can start to understand and unpack the reproduction of geography by turning your critical eye on your own geography department and the geographies it is producing.

Changing worlds: changing human geographies

Geographical knowledge is not – and should not attempt to be – static and detached from what is going on in the world, but is rather dynamic and profoundly influenced by events, struggles and politics beyond university life.

(Blunt and Wills 2000: x–xi)

The root of the word 'geography' combines *geo* (earth) and *graphy* (writing). To engage in geography is to write about the earth (which includes its lands and seas, resources, places and peoples) or, more widely perhaps, to represent the earth in text (which includes maps: some of the most complexly crafted of all texts). Of course, many other branches of knowledge such as history, anthropology, sociology, oceanography, politics and geology (from which geography draws) and many other sciences are also in some way or other about the world. Traditionally, what has been distinctive about human geography is that it puts an emphasis on people in *places* and *spaces*, on *landscapes* modified by human interventions, human relationships with *nature* and *environment* and on complex *spatial* connections. The terms italicized in the last sentence have been enduring topics in human geography. However, approaches too them have shifted radically over the decades. Moreover, human geography is not just about 'out there', it is also about 'in here' (see Spotlight box I.2). Thus, you all create your own personal geographies derived, for example, from where you live, where you work or when you travel.

Spotlight box I.2

Geography is everywhere
By Clare Madge

Willow fell and swallow soar

In my back garden
there were two
    beautiful
                wispy
                          emerald
      willow
    trees.
where pigeons roosted
and swallows soared.
One day
Two men
Climbed
The trees
And
Felled
Them
Whole.
In life there are many things
that can bring us to our
           knees,
fell us sure as any tree.
But, like the willow stump,
we can grow shoots
and again start sprouting
to journey with swallows.

Geography is everywhere. The poem might not immediately appear to be 'geography as you know it'. I wrote the poem as I was sitting in my garden recovering from chemotherapy. In the poem I was meditating about my cancer diagnosis and my will to survive. At that moment I felt a resonance with the felled tree, its life being truncated and its future unknown, although I also drew strength from the tree, knowing it would grow back through its 'irrepressible vitality'. So, if geography is everywhere, how is this poem geographical? What can it tell us about geographical worlds and how those worlds might be expressed?

Geography is everywhere, emerging out of our lived lives. As the poem shows, these lived lives are not simply about our human world but are infused with animals, plants and atmospheres. Moreover, these geographical worlds may at the same time be about death, dying and vulnerability as well as life, living and vitality: spaces of dissolution and fragility circulate beside spaces of regeneration, challenging simplistic oppositions of life/death. The poem also reveals that therapeutic landscapes exist far beyond medicalised places (hospital wards), and that these landscapes can be metaphorical and spiritual. Those experiencing life-threatening illnesses can create a vision of the world – an active place-making – that helps them sculpt out a way of being in the world that makes a life worth living. So although perhaps not instantly apparent, this poem touches upon those well-versed geographical themes of place, space, landscape and nature. But it is about more than that too.

Geography is everywhere and geographical worlds can be emotional, sentient and visceral. They can be about minded-bodies that feel. The poem is deliberately and unashamedly intimate and it paints a picture from 'the inside', from a one minded-body going through a particular experience of a cancer diagnosis. Such intimate expression can be used to counter disembodied accounts, disclosing detailed knowledge and candid feelings – a sort of finely tuned life-writing – thus being a means to insert the ill minded-body into geographical publishing space, populating geographical texts with the diverse bodies that are still sometimes forced to its margins. Poetic encounters can act as a portal into such inner lifeworlds, bringing alive a fleshy, fine-grained emotive analysis of everyday lived life, albeit from a specific framing or perspective.

So . . . geography is everywhere, and it can be expressed in a multitude of ways. While the vast majority of geographic texts are written in conventional academic style, there are also alternative ways of expressing geography. Examples include creative writing, theatre, photography, painting, films, music and poetry. Thus geography is a subject that can be expressed in multifaceted, multisensory creative formats (Madge 2014a, 2014b).

However, while geography is everywhere, it is everywhere differently. This poem is written from the frame of someone experiencing one specific illness, located in a precise place, with its particular system of health care, embedded in specific social and political networks and experienced through a distinct minded-body. Cancer is, however, a prevalent worldwide disease. As a health issue of (differential) global significance, it is therefore a topic of important consideration, but the experience of cancer varies enormously across the globe. Poetic expression can carve out space for 'other' stories about cancer from 'other' places, illustrating the intense social and spatial inequalities in health outcomes and experiences. As poetry is also emotive and embodied, it has the potential to 'show' another person how it is to feel or experience something beyond their specific world perspective, enabling appreciation that the world is made up of manifold, heterogeneous geographies, which are constantly changing.

Thus, geography is everywhere and is continually emerging: it is a living subject. The poem was a response to my changed life circumstances, but it was also a reflection on living on and shaping a world in which I was part. It is on this point that I wish to finish. Geography is a living subject and in its liveliness we all have potential to shape the world in which we live. Geography is not simply a static, flat canvas which we describe and interpret as scholars, but we can shape the contours and terrain of that geographical landscape too. It is exciting to think about all those diverse geographies not yet expressed, waiting to emerge out of your (multiple) experiences, voices and visions.

Through such myriad social–cultural, political and economic geographies, we inhabit a world, as John Pickles (2004: 5) pointed out:

> that has, in large part, been made as a geo-coded world; a world where boundary objects have been inscribed, literally written on the surface of the earth and coded by layer upon layer of lines drawn on paper.

Those geo-codes have increasingly become digital. They are stored, transformed, transmitted and negotiated electronically; as in the signal that your mobile phone is transmitting regarding your current location (unless you have turned it off) or the data about you that is in archives, online or within that phone (be it on or off).

Such complexity, connections and challenges (as well as diverse 'geo-codes') are evident when we consider the idea of 'globalization'. As many of the chapters spell out, a combination of technical, political, ideological, cultural and economic transformations throughout the twentieth century enhanced the sense of global interconnection. Take the case of this book. The copy that you are reading may well have been printed far from where you picked it up. Or you may be reading it as an e-book. Either way, it was published by a multinational company, whose ownership and 'home' location may not be immediately evident. The shares of the publisher (Pearson) are traded in London, part of the daily turnover on the world's largest stock exchange. In addition to textbooks such as this, Pearson publishes Penguin books and, until 2015, also published the daily *Financial Times* and the weekly *Economist*. The company found itself in the headlines in March 2011, when it was revealed that the holdings of the Libyan Investment Trust (LIT), who held 3.2 per cent of Pearson's shares, had been suspended, along with the freezing of other assets belonging to the then government of Libya (and the Qaddafi family who formed its core). This followed the outbreak of a civil war – in which Britain and other outside powers had taken military sides with the anti-Qaddafi rebels, who soon after overthrew the regime leading to protracted civil war. In turn, Pearson's stake in the LIT reflects the flows of money associated with geographies of resources (oil and gas) and the modern financial system that are considered in later chapters. But, in turn, Libyan economic and political geographies cannot be understood without reference to colonial histories (the then Ottoman Turkish lands that today comprise Libya were invaded by Italy in 1911, in a bloody war that cost thousands of Arab lives), nationalism, revolution and geopolitics. It can be argued that these led the post-colonial Libyan state (established in the early 1950s in the debris of Italian fascist imperialism and the Second World War) into violent conflict with the West, with some of its neighbours (whose boundaries themselves were drawn by competing European colonialists) as well as with more conservative Arab regimes. Such colonial histories continue to be contested elsewhere in the Middle East, with ongoing consequences for Libya and the wider world.

To describe contemporary technological, economic, cultural or political tendencies as 'globalization' is to invoke a certain *geographical imagination*: a vision of the growing significance of a global scale of action, of the world as a single place. Yet, we know that many people and places remain relatively marginalized, sense dangers or face threats from these supposedly hypermobile ways of living and working. And some people and places benefit from them more than others. Of course, such power and inequality are not themselves new. Consider the profits and consequences of the transatlantic slave trade between the sixteenth and nineteenth centuries, for example (see Chapter 2). Cheap sugar and cotton for northern hemisphere markets and manufacturers in Europe and America enabled new links, markets and economies. But the humans traded as unpaid workers (slaves) and objects of exploitation who did the work did not see it that way (if they lived long at all). Today, a low-paid worker (or self-employed prospector) in a diamond mine might experience the global trade in these minerals rather differently to the companies that dominate the jewellery business. Certainly the benefits of globalization are uneven. This is not new.

As an alternative to the term 'globalization', we might use other terms: 'imperialism', 'power' or 'capitalism', for example. Each carries particular connotations. In this way, 'globalization' serves as a particular concept that is used to make sense of the world whereby a certain geographical imagination, of an increasingly connected and 'shrinking' world for example, is emphasized. Yet just because something is *imagined* and interpreted in particular ways and by reference to particular geographies, it does not make it any less *real* to those caught up in it. Globalization is seen by some as a broadly positive force, breaking down barriers, making capitalism more efficient and spreading its benefits throughout the world. For others it is a more negative process enabling another round of exploitation, often with the further destruction of local cultures and identities and further commodifying life and nature. Everything is for sale, everything has a price. Obviously, globalization has been contested, in terms of both the meanings attributed to it and the evaluation of its consequences. Judge for yourself, but as you do so, do not make the mistake of assuming that everyone everywhere shares your vantage point and experiences of the world. And having boomed as a term and way of talking about the world in the 1990s, recent years have seen use of the term begin to decline. Although based on a selective sample of books published in English since 1900, data provided by Google's scanning of books indicates that the number using the term 'globalization' peaked in the mid-2000s after a steep rise from almost zero in the 1980s (see Figure 1).

Some events and moments have had global coverage as an iconic image likened by some to the moment when the American Apollo 8 spacecraft in 1968 captured the first image of the earth as a whole from space, or the reception of photographs of the earth from space by subsequent NASA missions (see Plate 1). These images have since circulated widely and are credited with reshaping human perceptions of the planet (see Cosgrove 2001). Yet the way that some events become 'significant' or 'global' reflects where they happen and who they affect. The spectacular losses of thousands of lives in Manhattan on '9/11', for example, became a global media event and subject of debate in the way that the death of several million people through a decade of war from the mid-1990s in the Democratic Republic of Congo never did.

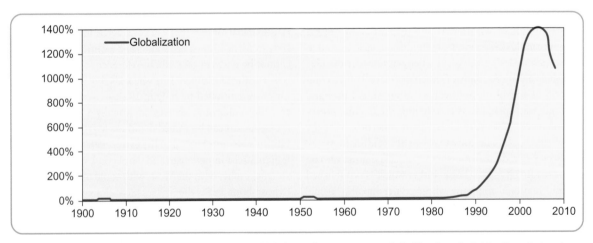

Figure 1 Use of the term 'globalization', 1900–2009, based on a survey of digitized material in Google books.

Source: http://ngrams.googlelabs.com/graph?content=globalization&year_start=1900&year_end=2008&corpus=0&smoothing=1

Plate 1 'The Blue Marble'. Photograph taken by a crew member aboard Apollo 17 on 7 December 1972. (NASA)

The evolution of academic geography

A brief glance at the available disciplinary histories of geography gives an indication of a long association between geography and the militarized attempts to claim territory on behalf of a particular imperial project.

(Nayak and Jeffrey 2011: 5)

Consider how the contents and style of this text, like those others, is marked by *where* it was written. Geography, as a subject, has both history and its own geography; it has varied in space and time. As a student of the subject, you might want to venture online, or into the recess of a library, to discover past textbooks, such as Haggett (1972) which over 40 years ago was a ground-breaking text. It is important to appreciate this – and the longer-term – intellectual heritages of geography.

As a distinct subject (with students reading for a degree in it) geography has been present in European universities since the mid- to late-nineteenth century. Before then, however, geographical knowledge was studied and taught in many universities (not only those in Europe, but in the great centres of learning in the predominantly Islamic world, such as Baghdad and Cairo), as part of a variety of programmes of study – sometimes alongside mathematics and geometry for example, or as part of (or alongside) natural history, astronomy or cosmography (see Withers and Mayhew 2002). In the second half of the nineteenth century, universities were reorganized around modern disciplines, increasingly with discrete departments and separate degree schemes. This happened as the old curriculum – based on classical learning in philosophy and sciences – began to break down with the rise of science, commerce and new capitalist rationalities. The fact that the late nineteenth century was also a time when many European states (chief amongst them Britain, France and the Netherlands) were engaged in overseas colonization and empire-building, and all were keen to foster their sense of national identity and territorial coherence, gave geography a new practical relevance. Children needed to be taught, it was argued, about their nation and its place in the world and their teachers thus required a degree in geography. At the same time, geographical knowledge had direct strategic and military relevance (this was the moment too of the birth of geopolitics, as detailed in Chapter 20) as well as commercial and imperial relevance, such as in schemes to exploit the perceived agricultural potential of colonies in Africa and Asia, for example. Nineteenth-century ideas about the relations between climate, environment and 'race', and (to use the language of that time) 'civilization' and progress, were caught up with the emergence of the discipline, but so too were the impacts of Darwin's ideas about evolution (which influenced physical geography too: in the conception of the way that landforms evolve).

The early years of the modern discipline were therefore inescapably tied up with nationalism and empires. This continued into the early twentieth century, with a growing number of geography departments being established at universities in the USA and Canada, in many Latin American countries, in the European colonies and dependencies and in Japan. In some instances, such as Russia, the earliest departments were organized in the 1880s and this was tied to nation-building rather than overseas expansion. Such was also the case in Germany and in Scandinavia. By the time of the Second World War, geography was relatively well established – and the practical knowledge (as part of military 'intelligence', for example) it yielded in wartime helped to consolidate the discipline's place in universities in many countries. After 1945 new challenges arose as other disciplines expanded, but (with some exceptions such as the closure of a few departments in the United States), geography benefited from the first big post-war expansion in the number both of universities and of students in the 1960s. Human geography increasingly reoriented itself to the technological and scientific spirit of the times, fed by a new phase of military competition in the Cold War (on this, see Barnes and Farish 2006).

In an age of formal decolonization, where the old imperial disciplinary role was waning, human geography also found new fields of study and outlets for its graduates (such as conservation, development and planning: but also many others, by virtues of the broader skills they would acquire within a geography degree). There were, however, fierce debates about the appropriate focus (for example over the status of regional geography) and methods (such as the role of statistical analysis), which meant that what undergraduate students were exposed to (and thus had to learn) to pass a geography degree continued to change (though unevenly, depending on where they studied).

By the 1960s and 1970s, the world was changing and so was human geography. At first it led geographers to adopt statistical techniques, seeking to render the discipline more scientific. But other, more radical social and political changes (think of the hippies, the rise of feminism and gay liberation, or the movements against the American war in Vietnam and for civil rights in America and the wider spirit of revolution that came to the fore in the late 1960s) kindled interest in the underlying economic causes of inequality, turmoil and conflict in capitalist societies. An early 1990s textbook, introducing the ensuing theoretical debates in human geography, noted how, by the 1970s, 'human geography as an academic discipline had just entered into a period of considerable turmoil' (Cloke *et al.* 1991: viii). They go on to note how:

> One of the most obvious characteristics of contemporary human geography is its diversity of approach. Within human geography today there is an unprecedented liveliness to the engagement with issues of method and theory. Rarely, if ever before, has the subject seen such a plurality of research methodologies and encompassed such a broad sweep of topics of investigation.
>
> (Cloke et al. 1991: 1)

This liveliness has continued, reflecting both changes in the world (including political, economic and cultural shifts) and accompanying technical developments, theoretical exuberance and shifting funding arrangements for, and ways of, running universities. Cloke *et al.* (1991) looked back to what one particularly creative geographer had once termed a geographical imagination. They thus cited David Harvey (1973: 24):

> This imagination enables the individual to recognize the role of space and place in his own biography . . . to relate to the spaces he sees around him, and to recognize how transactions between individuals and between organizations are affected by the spaces that separate them. It allows him to recognize the relationship which exists between him and his neighbourhood, his territory, or, to use the language of the street gangs, his 'turf' . . . It allows him to fashion and use space creatively and to appreciate the meaning of the spatial forms created by others.

Nearly 40 years later, another leading geographer claimed that:

> it is worth affirming the importance of the geographical imagination, as a matter of both practical wisdom and scholarly reflection, and not least for its pleasure and enchantment, for people's love of learning about the world and their place within it.
>
> (Daniels 2011: 186)

Today though, the taken-for-granted 'him' of Harvey's (1973) quote would be qualified with 'him or her': and with this perhaps a recognition of significant gender differences in experiences and assumptions. For example, where do men and women experience space differently and how does this relate to spaces of power, sexuality, work and reproduction? Such sensitivity has evolved out of the ways that by the 1970s geographers, David Harvey amongst them and later joined by others from many different backgrounds, started to ask more difficult questions about inequality, power, exploitation and difference. In turn, capitalism entered a phase of heightened restructuring (shaped by economic recessions, new technologies and new forms and places of production and regulation, as detailed in Section 4). Reflecting the times, human geographers became more concerned with inequality, economic and political crises and contradictions. Feminist, humanistic, ecological and other critiques also started to impact on human geography and feed into re-evaluations both of its history (the way that early twentieth-century imperial geography was shaped by racism and sexism, for example) and contemporary contents. Moreover, the boundaries between many of human geography's subdisciplines, such as urban, political, historical or cultural geography, became more blurred. However, along the way, the modelling, data processing and visualizing capabilities of geographic information science continued to be refined (Fairbairn and Dorling 1997; Fotheringham *et al.* 2000; Schuurman 2004) and the Internet, digitisation and mobile technologies produced new capacities for communication and altered relations and perceptions of proximity and distance (see www.zooknic.com for work on the geographies of the Internet). For some, outside the discipline, the decline of the Cold War in the late 1980s brought the 'end of history'. For others, the development of technology and the globalization of the economy were creating a 'borderless world'; some even proclaimed the 'end of geography'.

Yet the fact that social and economic processes take place across space matters. Indeed the way they do so is vital to how they operate. Human geography is not just about *describing* the spatial manifestations of economy and society: it is about *explaining* how space is configured and shapes economies, societies and social processes. Thus, geography is not a passive outcome; it is a critical component of dynamic social and economic processes. More than that, geography in its broader definition provides an interface between the human and the natural worlds. We would argue that geography is a *key* subject for the twenty-first century, in part because many of the challenges that face humanity are at the interface between human societies and natural environments. One of the oldest themes of human geography (and indeed of geography as a whole, including its physical side) – human–environment relations – has become an urgent agenda for the twenty-first century.

Human geographers have also become more aware of the ways that knowledge is socially constructed. This is complex, reflecting ideology. But in the simplest terms, the way you see the world is partly a function of who you think you are and, hence, *where* you see yourself as coming from. Human geographers have come to realize that much of the knowledge and understanding that they claimed to be universal is in various ways Eurocentric: it comes from somewhere and any idea that it is universally true (for all and everywhere) might be challenged. Similarly, Eurocentrism has been associated with a very 'white' view of a multi-ethnic world such as the fairly widespread self-perception that white folk are not really themselves members of a particular 'ethnic' group, except amongst racists and white supremacists. Yet in global terms they are arguably a distinctive 'ethnic minority' whose identity has been forged through comparisons and interactions with other people classified as non-white. In turn, however, such ideas about race and ethnicity are rooted in colonial histories (and hierarchies) that are evidently themselves particular (imperial) ways of knowing, ordering and interpreting the world. These resurface in contemporary racism, and have their own historical geography. Ideas about race, which today may seem self-evident and obvious, would not have been present in, for example, the Roman Empire, which had other ways of ordering and stratifying society and demarcating insiders, barbarians, citizens and slaves. All this means that geographers must now reconsider the ways in which assumptions and value judgments shape the way they view the world. They must accept that *all* descriptions of the world are culturally determined, often politically motivated, and can always be contested.

So, think about your position; realize that this book presents the views of human geographers working at particular places and times. We have set out to challenge readers to think about the ways that human geography interprets the major social, cultural, economic,

environmental and related issues that face the world in the early years of the twenty-first century. It is for you to use this book to inform your own insights and opinions as geographers; and to read beyond it. In other words, reading this textbook is the beginning of your introduction to human geography, not the end.

Today, human geography is characterized by a wide variety of approaches; there are many ways of writing geography and approaches to doing so (see Spotlight box I.2). The idea of a single, all-encompassing geographical approach (which may have been evident in times past) is not convincing anymore. Since we have adopting an *issue-based* approach, there is not the scope here to say much more about the evolution of debates in human geography. You can further explore their trajectory using some of the other readings listed at the end of this chapter. Alternatively, track down and read Chris Philo's (2008) fluent summary alongside his 'map' of changing approaches in human geography. But at this point please accept our word that this story (like Philo's 'map') becomes immensely complex, intertwined and convoluted, reflecting the intellectual trends and social changes mentioned earlier.

However, it is important to appreciate some shared concepts. Most disciplines have their central concepts and ideas that define what it is they study and how they study it. Human geography is often accused of borrowing ideas from elsewhere, rather than generating its own; but it is possible to identify a set of concepts that make it distinct and different. We might disagree on what they might mean (and each is the subject of a vast literature), but ideas of place, space, and scale are certainly central to human geography and have been for a long time, as has an interest in landscape, difference, connectivity and unevenness. All of the core ideas of human geography can be deployed to interrogate and explain the places where we live and the places where we travel. As geographers, we seek explanations as to why something came to be where it is, how places are experienced, connected and represented, or how the physical environment and nature are transformed by society. Chapter 12 notes how the planetary scale of such transformations has been re-conceptualized as a human-influenced geological epoch (the Anthropocene). At a more personal scale, in Spotlight box I.3, one of the editors explains his engagements with a particular place – or set of places connected on a path. It is our hope that, as a practising human geographer, you will also find your own literal or metaphorical paths through this discipline and be inspired to think geographically. For us, then, human geography is a way of seeing, enquiring and understanding past, present and potential future worlds.

Spotlight box I.3

James' wanderings

One of us especially likes walking. It is a deeply geographical practice. For (even enabled by the geo-technologies of GPS and mobile Internet) it is easy to get lost, or find oneself in the 'wrong' place, or feel 'out of place', or discover new places. Walking requires an intimate encounter with place, whilst negotiating space and landscape. James has done this often in different cities and written scholarly geographies about it, linking it to the geopolitics and memories in/of a particular one: the English city of Plymouth (Sidaway 2009). He is far from

alone in this of course and his paper draws on an enormous literature about walking in cities from many sites and a vast range of authors. But sometimes it is nice to get away from the city (even the one he currently lives in: Singapore) and walk in more remote places. So over the years since the third edition of this book, he has bit by bit been walking one of the routes there that is commonly referred to as the Camino de Santiago (Way of St James), mapped in Figure 2. As the account of another who walked this way has noted:

the Camino de Santiago is really a network of routes, many of Roman origin, extending throughout Europe

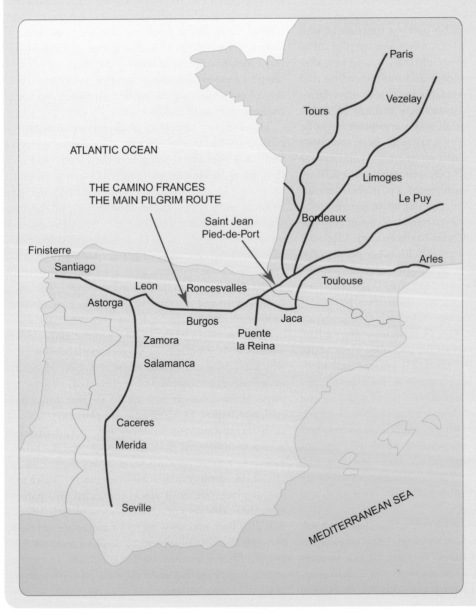

Figure 2
A map of the routes known as Camino de Santiago.

that have been used by pilgrims since the eleventh century to reach Santiago de Compostela [whose Cathedral houses the shrine dedicated to the Apostle St James] . . . The early medieval pilgrimage played an important role . . . fostered by the reigning political forces.

(Frey 1998: 5)

Frey's book also describes how, with the lessening of Christian influence in the latter half of the twentieth century, the ancient pilgrimage routes declined, before undergoing a rapid renaissance in recent years. Today many thousands walk these routes daily (Plate 2). Not all are pilgrims. Some go mostly for the exercise, others for a change of scene, as a holiday, or as a personal or even spiritual journey that may not be grounded in a formal religion. But to walk it is to experience everyday geographies of slow movement – as on any other popular long-distance walking trail, such as those in Appalachia, the UK, Germany, New Zealand or on grander scales and higher altitudes in, say, Nepal or Peru.

Long-distance walkers must negotiate and become, sometimes painfully, aware of scale, topography and landscape. When you are walking, distances, pace, elevations and inclines matter fundamentally. Weather, food and water become things that may not be taken for granted, as must what you decide to carry or decide to leave behind (as in other travel of course: including those using sophisticated technologies like aircraft). Economic geographies and cultural geographies are evident: place names and language differences for starters; carrying enough money; where to eat and sleep; and who gains from all that expenditure? So are political geographies, if you know where to look. But glance up and see an aircraft far overhead – during a long day of remote walking perhaps – and encounter other walkers from across the world, or discuss where you started from with them, and the question of scale

Plate 2 Signalling the *Camino* to Santiago de Compostela.

tanjalagicaimage/fotolia

becomes more complicated. This is because, when you pause to think about it, any place on the path becomes part of a vast network extending in many directions. To make such a journey also links mind, body, landscape and movement in ways that are hard to capture in words: geographical imaginations may be rich, but some things you can only learn – or fully appreciate – by doing them. Moreover, others walk long distances not for pleasure or spiritual gain, but simply to collect water, seek a living or escape conflict. And other demands, injuries, age or disability, or preferences mean that hiking long distances is not something that everyone can, or might want to, do.

Approach of the book

The major sections of this book focus on important issues facing the world, but they also relate to major sub-disciplines in human geography. Section 1 provides historical context for the four issue-oriented sections that follow. While it is natural for us to proclaim that geography matters, it is also the case that historical geography matters. A cursory examination of an atlas printed at the start of the last century will show you that the world has changed

a great deal. Many of the contemporary issues discussed in this book, such as the geographies of development and of inequality, owe much to the way the world looked in 1900, or considerably earlier. A sense of history is critical to an understanding of contemporary human geography. However, if we cast our minds even further back into the records of antiquity we are reminded that societies are transitory; nothing lasts forever. States and civilizations have come and gone and this should teach us that there is little permanent about the current world order. At the same time, what is past, and not always immediately visible, often has a profound influence on the world we live in now. Section 1 highlights some of these issues and then focuses on the emergence of capitalism and its relationship with the making of the modern world.

It probably makes sense to work with Section 1 first; after that each section can be utilized in whatever order you see fit. It starts with a brief summary of the important issues covered by each of the chapters and there is logic to the order in which the chapters are presented. Section 2 examines the interrelationship between population change, resource production and consumption, global economic development and the environment. Section 3 focuses on social and cultural issues within urban and rural contexts and at a global scale and includes a chapter on the social construction of nature and what this means for the analysis and interpretation of how, for example, to manage the global environment in a sustainable way. Section 4 examines the globalization of economic activity, production networks, the emergence of a global financial system and means of exchange (which has played an increasingly visible role in recent decades), and the importance of consumption to an understanding of the geography of economy. Section 5 considers a variety of political geographies at differing scales and how they interface and intertwine. Here too the sense of continuity and change is evident, as in shifting global geopolitical scenarios since the decline of the old superpower Cold War confrontation between the Soviet Union and the USA that had lasted for 50 years from the 1940s to the 1990s and whose legacies remain active today.

So, where else do you go from here? As a geography student (or any other kind of student for that matter), you may be faced with choices, for example between human and physical geography or between more specialized subjects within one of those traditions. It is in the nature of academic disciplines to subdivide and to compartmentalize knowledge. Geography is unusual in that it sits at the intersections between the humanities, social sciences and natural sciences. This means that it internalizes both the disadvantages of disciplinarity and the potential advantages of multidisciplinarity. In other words, as Harrison (2009: 163) notes:

> it incorporates perspectives from a very wide range of diverse subjects from the social sciences (including history, sociology, politics, economics, and psychology) and from the natural sciences (including physics, biology, ecology and geology). To some, this diversity has been regarded as a sign of weakness, suggesting a subject with such a broad range of research fields must treat those in a superficial manner. Others have seen it as a sign of strength, arguing that geography has avoided the intellectual trap of increased specialization and held on to a holistic view.

Much of the promise of geography lies on the margins between the sub-disciplines, between human and physical geography or, for example, between economic and cultural geography. In your studies you should make the most of this promise, seek out the space on the margins and look for the connections between the human and natural environments, the economic, the social and the cultural. Many of the challenges that face humanity also occupy these margins. The emphasis on places and spaces and how they are interconnected, imagined and represented (the hallmarks of human geography) is itself promising. Engaging with such promise will deepen, stretch, enrich and challenge your understanding of the world. Geography is a worldly discipline. At once grounded and practical, human geography can sometimes be also deeply theoretical, abstract and philosophical; it mobilizes words, maps and numbers, and articulates social sciences and the humanities, in a symbiotic relationship with the science of physical geography. Wherever geography takes you intellectually and professionally, we hope that the chapters and arguments brought together in this book will (when supplemented by further reading, critical thought, writing and conversation) encourage you to continue to engage with the promise inherent in geography.

Further reading

This first set of readings points you towards two other textbooks that you can use to enrich your perspectives on human geography. Individual chapters from them are sometimes cited elsewhere as references in this book, but they are also worth browsing to get a sense of the different ways in which human geography is presented.

Cloke, P., Crang, P. and Goodwin, M. (eds) (2014) *Introducing Human Geographies,* 3rd edition, Routledge, Oxford.

The third edition of an innovative text: 59 inviting short chapters that reflect the diversity of approaches in contemporary human geography. Well worth delving into wherever you may be.

Marston, S.A., Knox, P., Liverman, D., Del Casino, V. and Robbins, P. (2013) *World Regions in Global Context: People, Places, and Environments,* 4th edition, Prentice Hall, Upper Saddle River, NJ. A comprehensive and accessible text written principally for the North America market with lots of pictures and diagrams. Probably the best US textbook.

Research and study guides, readers and further insights into human geography

This section is dedicated to publications that will assist you in conducting geographical research and/or expand your knowledge of debates and approaches in the discipline. The list comprises dictionaries, and books on methodology, approaches and theory in human geography as well as a few (such as auto-biographies of influential geographers) that are hard to categorize. You should also seek out the various 'readers' (comprising reprints of influential papers that usually first appeared in journals) that have been produced. Led by publishers, these have proliferated in recent years, along with encyclopedias, dictionaries and companions to the discipline, or for specific sub-disciplines. Some bring together the most influential readings in a particular area of human geography, whilst others are collections of specially commissioned review essays that assess the status of particular areas of research.

Agnew, J. and Duncan, J.S. (eds) (2011) *The Wiley-Blackwell Companion to Human Geography,* Wiley-Blackwell, Oxford. Comprising commissioned original essays, this is a rich starting point to get a feel of how the discipline has evolved and what it includes today.

Atkin, S. and Valentine, G. (eds) (2014) *Approaches to Human Geography: Philosophies, Theories, People and Practices, 2nd edition,* Sage, London, New Delhi and Thousand Oaks, CA. A good way into the range of theoretical (and methodological) debates in human geography.

Benko, G. and Strohmayer, U. (eds) (2004) *Human Geography: A History for the Twenty-First Century,* Arnold, London. Republished by Routledge in 2014, this book sought to address histories of continental European and Anglophone geography and the relations between them. It only scratches the surface.

Blunt, A. and Wills, J. (2000) *Dissident Geographies: An Introduction to Radical Ideas and Practice,* Prentice Hall, Harlow. This book is worth tracking down. The geographies explored all share political commitments to critique and to challenging prevailing relations of power: from gay and lesbian geographies to geographies of anarchism and anti-racism, it brings out some of the ways in which the production of geographical knowledge is tied to politics and struggles outside, as well as within, universities.

Boyle, M. (2014) *Human Geography: A Concise Introduction,* Wiley Blackwell, Chichester. Structured around the idea of geographic imaginations, this is an ambitious, though inviting and accessible text.

Castree, N. (2005) *Nature,* Routledge, London and New York. A challenging introduction to how geographers have studied nature and what this tells us about the nature of academic geography.

Clifford, N. and Valentine, G. (eds) (2010) *Key Methods in Geography,* 2nd edition, Sage, London. Covers the methods used in both human and physical geography, including those they share.

Cloke, P., Crang, P., Goodwin, M., Painter, J. and Philo, C. (2002) *Practising Human Geography,* Sage, London. A more advanced (but very readable and inviting) guide to research methods and writing strategies in human geography. An inspiring guide to the use of qualitative methods. You will need to look elsewhere if you are interested in using quantitative techniques or GIS.

Couper, P. (2015) *A Student's Introduction to Geographical Thought: Theories, Philosophies, Methodologies,* Sage, London. A superb introduction to ideas and theories across both human and physical geography. The companion website offers rich student resources. Sample them: https://study.sagepub.com/couper.

Crampton, J.W. (2010) *Mapping: A Critical Introduction to Cartography and GIS,* Wiley-Blackwell, Oxford. One of a series of 'Critical Introductions to Geography'. A fantastic guide to maps and mapping.

Cresswell, T. (2004) *Place: A Short Introduction,* Blackwell, Oxford. Explores how human geographers have studied, debated and complicated a concept that may seem self-evident and familiar, but which turns out to be dependent upon a range of assumptions, ideologies and contests.

Cresswell, T. (2012) *Geographic Thought: A Critical Introduction,* Wiley-Blackwell, Oxford. Another survey of the history of geographic thought that is especially good on developments in recent years.

Daniels, S. and Lee, R. (eds) (1996) *Exploring Human Geography: A Reader,* Arnold, London. Includes articles not intended primarily for a student audience, but the collection provides a useful survey of human geography in the 1980s and 1990s.

Dorling, D. and Fairbairn, D. (1997) *Mapping: Ways of Representing the World,* Prentice Hall, Harlow. Maps have always been associated with geography and geographers. This text will help you to understand how maps express the will to describe, understand and control.

Flowerdew, R. and Martin, D. (2005) *Methods in Human Geography: A Guide for Students Doing a Research Project,* 2nd edition, Longman, Harlow. A guide to a wide variety of the research techniques used by contemporary human geographers.

Gould, P. and Pitts, F.R. (eds) (2002) *Geographical Voices: Fourteen Autobiographical Essays,* Syracuse University Press, Syracuse, NY. A collection of autobiographies that chart the experiences and insights of some of leading geographers of the past 70 years.

Gregory, D., Johnston, R.J., Pratt, G., Watts, M. and Whatmore, S. (eds) (2009) *The Dictionary of Human Geography,* 5th edition, Wiley-Blackwell, Oxford. Over a thousand pages. We think it is an indispensable reference. But, like vintage wines, some prefer earlier editions (each one thicker and weightier than the last). If you want to spend an afternoon learning a lot about academic geography, track down older ones and look at how the entries have changed.

Clifford, N.J., Holloway, S.L., Rice, S.P. and Valentine, G. (eds) (2009) *Key Concepts in Geography,* 2nd edition, Sage, London. Worth reading alongside this text, especially if you are taking introductory classes in human and physical geography – this collection addresses both.

Hubbard, P., Kitchin, R. and Valentine, G. (eds) (2008) *Key Texts in Human Geography,* Sage, London. A starting point, designed to lead you beyond textbooks into classic texts in the field. Many were not written for a student audience but as entrée it is especially helpful.

Johnston, R.J. and Sidaway, J.D. (2016) *Geography and Geographers: Anglo-American Human Geography since 1945,* 7th edition, Arnold, London. First published in 1979, the seventh edition of this book provides an updated and fairly comprehensive survey of the major trends in human geography since 1945 in the English-speaking world. Includes a discussion of geography as a discipline that will help you to better understand what academic geographers do and how the discipline is structured.

Livingstone, D. (1992) *The Geographical Tradition: Issues in the History of a Contested Enterprise,* Blackwell, Oxford. On publication this immediately became a landmark scholarly study of the long-term history of human geography. It still is.

Nayak, A. and Jeffrey, A. (2011) *Geographical Thought: An Introduction to Ideas in Human Geography,* Pearson, Harlow. This does what it says in the title.

Thrift, N. and Kitchin, R. *et al.* (eds) (2000) *The International Encyclopedia of Human Geography,* Elsevier, Oxford. This A–Z is a comprehensive survey of human geography. You can lose yourself inside it for hours and only scratch the surface.

Tuan Yi-Fu (1999) *Who am I? An Autobiography of Emotion, Mind and Spirit,* University of Wisconsin Press, Madison, WI. The autobiography of a Chinese-American who arrived in the United States as a 20-year-old graduate student in the 1950s and went on to become one of America's most original and respected geographers.

Women and Geography Study Group (1997) *Feminist Geographies: Explorations in Diversity and Difference,* Longman, Harlow. Republished by Routledge in 2013, this remains a great way to begin to understand how feminist geographies have reshaped the study of human geography.

Wylie, J. (2007) *Landscape,* Routledge, London. A fascinating text that examines how human geographers (and others) have conceptualized and narrated landscape.

As this introduction has sketched, human geography (understood as the subject, and those who study and teach it) has its own geography (understood as locations), in so far as it is unevenly developed (in some countries it is studied as part of the school curriculum, in other places – most significantly perhaps in the USA – it is hardly studied at schools). How and why this has come about is a complex reflection of wider

histories and geographies, including the historical geography of empires (see Chapter 2), which meant that aspects of a British-style educational system were long imposed on many territories in Africa and Asia (and in Ireland). For more systematic reflections on the relative position of geography in the academy in a range of countries, see the set of papers in the *Journal of Geography in Higher Education,* 31(1), compiled by and following a brief introduction by Kong (2007) (see also Spotlight box I.1). Browsing other issues of the *Journal of Geography in Higher Education* can be instructive, since it is full of ideas and guides to research and geographical learning.

This and other material from scholarly journals must usually be downloaded whilst logged in to a university network; since university libraries pay the subscription costs to publishers of such journals. However, the following is free to all: Barder, H. and Engel-Di Mavro, S. (eds) (2008) *Critical Geographies: A Collection of Readings,* Praxis (e)Press: www.praxis-epress.org. This reprints a collection of classic and inspiring geographies; starting with an 1885 essay by an anarchist Russian geographer on 'What Geography Ought to Be'. We suggest you start here.

But why stop with the Earth? If you read the following book, you will soon see how geography of Mars is, in the end, more about the Earth than Mars. With time, you might begin to agree with us that all geographies of other places tell as much about where they are written as that which they purport to describe:

Lane, M.D.K. (2011) *Geographies of Mars: Seeing and Knowing the Red Planet,* University of Chicago Press, Chicago, IL.

If Martian geographies are not to your taste, but you are also taking classes in physical geography, see if you can impress those who seek to teach you physical geography by asking them what they think about:

Clifford, N. (2009) 'Globalization: a physical geography perspective', *Progress in Human Geography,* 33(1), 5–16.

Finally, one of the key unfolding areas of debate in contemporary geography is how the discipline might engage with the Anthropocene idea. This recent forum, organized by two editors but with contributions from six other scholars, provides a way into these debates:

Johnson, E. and Morehouse, H. (eds) (2014) 'After the Anthropocene: politics and geographic enquiry for a new epoch', *Progress in Human Geography,* 38(3), 439–56.

Useful websites

This section provides access to the sites of some of the major geographical societies in the United Kingdom and North America. Visit the sites of other university geography departments across the world and discover how geography is represented and taught in different places. With the partial exception of the Canadian Association of Geographers, the links below focus on the Anglophone world.

www.aag.org   The website of the Association of American Geographers. Founded in 1904, the AAG is the primary academic geography organization in the United States. This site provides a wealth of information on the Association's activities, as well as access to its two scholarly journals: the *Annals of the Association of American Geographers* and *Professional Geographer.*

www.amergeog.org   The website of the American Geographical Society. The Society was established in 1851 and is the oldest professional geographical organization in the United States. The society publishes the *Geographical Review* and *Focus.*

www.cag-acg.ca   The website of the Canadian Association of Geographers. Founded in 1951, the CAG-ACG is the primary academic organization in Canada. The association publishes *The Canadian Geographer* and organizes national and regional meetings.

www.geography.org.uk   The website of the Geographical Association, which was founded in 1893 and is the national subject teaching organization for all geographers in the United Kingdom. The Association publishes three journals: *Primary Geographer, Teaching Geography* and *Geography.*

www.iag.org.au   The website of the Institute of Australian Geographers. The IAG was founded in Adelaide in 1958 and is the principal body representing geographers and promoting geography in Australia. The institute publishes the journal *Geographical Studies.*

www.nationalgeographic.org   A public face of geography in the English-speaking world. Home to the *National Geographic* magazine, the site also provides access to the maps and photographs that appear in its magazine, as well as a searchable index.

www.rgs.org   The home of the Royal Geographical Society (with the Institute of British Geographers). The RGS was originally founded in 1830 and the RGS-IBG is still the primary academic organization in UK geography. The website provides information on the societies as well as a route to its three key journals: *Area,* the *Geographical Journal* and *Transactions.*

As you will probably already know, there are dozens of commercial websites that will help you to try to short-cut and circumvent learning and scholarship, by buying putatively top-grade custom-written essays for almost any assignment. Like other even seedier sides of the Net, these have their own geography, in terms of by whom and *where* they are produced, *where* the money goes, plus the spatiality of the wider economies, trends and technologies that enable them. In the words of a geographical account of these published more than a decade ago:

> The technology of the Internet has connected remote places and facilitated the diffusion of any number of economic activities such as call centers, off-shore banking, and data processing. The Internet adult industry is yet another example of how a combination of regulatory issues, lower costs for content, and low barriers to entry results in a restructuring of production and consumption. While allowing access to a whole new range of people, the Internet is still shaped by existing structures of regulation, power, and hegemony. In short, the space of flows cannot be understood without reference to the 'space of places' to which it connects.
>
> (Zook 2003: 1283)

As for those commercial essay-writing websites, although some pretend otherwise, they rest on a specialist form of fraud known as plagiarism, severely sanctioned in all universities when detected.

WORLDS IN THE PAST:
CHANGING SCALES OF EXPERIENCE AND PAST WORLDS IN THE PRESENT

Edited by Denis Shaw

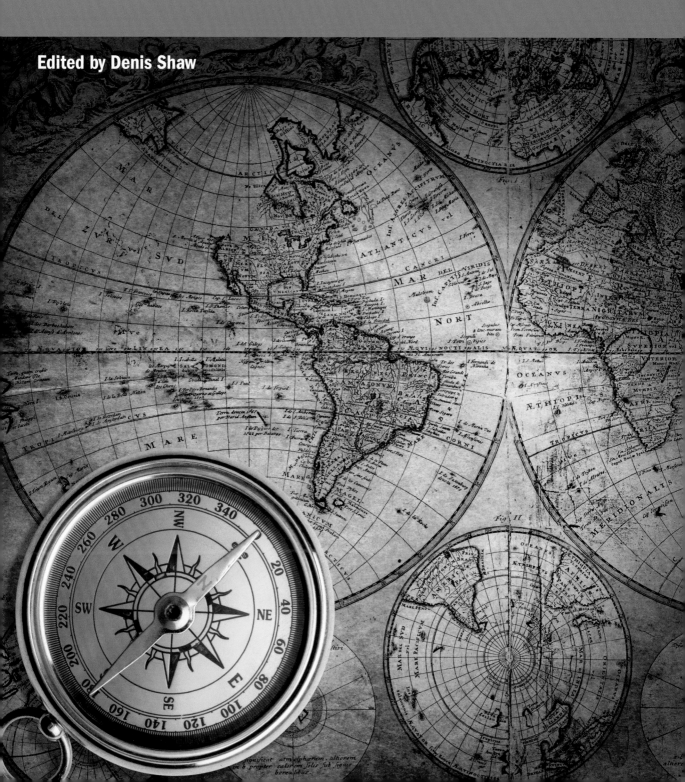

The world in which we live today has been moulded and is constantly being remoulded by the forces of capitalism (defined in Chapter 2, pp. 38–9). As modern capitalism spread across the globe it inevitably changed the societies which preceded it. But the pre-capitalist societies, while adapting to capitalism, did not necessarily lose all their distinctive features, and capitalism itself was configured through the process of interacting with them. The fact that human societies in the modern world differ among themselves in all kinds of ways is only partly the result of the way global capitalism works and of the ways in which societies are now adapting to the various forces affecting them. Societies also differ because of their past histories, histories that stretch back into pre-capitalist times. The world into which modern capitalism spread was itself already enormously varied and had been changing in innumerable ways over thousands of years. This section presents a brief survey of that long history and argues that the human geographer cannot understand the present-day world without knowledge of the worlds which have existed in the past.

Chapter 1 of this section considers what the world was like before capitalism and what if any generalizations can be made about this long period of human history. Chapter 2 analyses the rise and spread of modern capitalism down to the end of the nineteenth century. Its history during this period is intimately linked to the rise of the European powers and to the worldwide spread of their influence. This, of course, is not to deny that capitalism probably sprouted, and then died, in other societies in other periods, or that it might have gained worldwide significance on the basis of a non-European core had circumstances been different. During the twentieth and twenty-first centuries, which are the subject of Chapter 3, capitalism became a truly global phenomenon and radically changed in the process. This chapter thus provides a more immediate background for the sections that follow.

In summary, this part of the book emphasizes the variety and complexity of the world before globalization. And it demonstrates that only by knowing something about that world can we understand globalization itself.

PRE-CAPITALIST WORLDS

Chapter 1

Denis Shaw

Topics covered

- Why geographers need to know about the past
- Ways of classifying past and present societies
- Bands, tribes, chiefdoms, regulated states, market-based states
- Hunting and gathering
- The invention and spread of agriculture
- The rise of cities, states and civilizations
- Medieval feudalism
- Problems of studying past societies

Much of this book is about how capitalism has spread across the globe and even now is remoulding human societies in new and unexpected ways. This chapter is about what the world was like before capitalism. In other words it is about how human beings have lived during most of their existence on this planet. It will also say something about why it is important for human geographers to be aware of that past.

Capitalism has changed the world profoundly and often very quickly. In the first half of the twentieth century it was still possible for geographers and others to travel to regions where its influence was minimal and where people still lived in pre-capitalist societies. Today this is much less true. Even so, the geographer can still find numerous areas where the way of life has many pre-capitalist traits, though perhaps increasingly influenced by the modern world. Let us consider some examples.

About 2 per cent of the population of Australia identifies as Aboriginal; whose ancestors first settled the continent up to 50,000 years before white Europeans (Broome 2002). Today their way of life ranges from that of suburban professionals to remote outstations and homelands where people live partly off the land in traditional style. When the British established their first penal colony on Australian soil in 1788, more Aborigines lived on the continent than today, and they were divided into some 500 groups displaying a wide variety of languages, cultures, economies and technologies. All were hunters and gatherers leading a semi-nomadic existence and using some similar tools, like stone core hammers, knives, scrapers and axe heads as well as wooden implements like spears, digging sticks and drinking vessels. However, there was also a variety in technology and economy that reflected the diverse environments in which Aboriginal peoples lived. Whether living on coasts, riverbanks, in woodland or desert regions, they were efficient and skilled at exploiting the flora and fauna of their surroundings. Aboriginal peoples who hunt and fish today are often using skills honed by their ancestors over thousands of years. Their languages and cultures similarly reflect the experiences of many hundreds of generations.

The Inuit or Eskimo peoples living in the Arctic, mainly coastal, territories of Greenland, northern Canada, Alaska and the extreme eastern tip of Russia, are another group who in the past lived almost entirely by hunting and gathering (Sugden 1982; Bone 2009). Hunting and gathering still plays an important role in many of the remoter communities. Like the Australian Aborigines, the Inuit showed a remarkable ability to exploit the **resources** of what, in their case, is an extremely harsh environment. Because of their environment, Inuit communities demonstrated less economic variation than the Aborigines but they were far from uniform. There were

marked seasonal movements depending on the character of the local resources as groups moved between exploiting the fish and mammals of the open ocean, hunting seals on the ice, and seeking caribou, musk ox and similar fauna inland. The rich Inuit culture is also varied but by no means as varied as the Aboriginal (there are only two interrelated languages, for example). Considering the vast geographical spaces that the Inuit occupy, the latter fact is remarkable and may reflect a relative ease of communication by sledge and boat as well as the frequency of migrations. Like the Aborigines, the Inuit have had to adapt in the recent period to an intrusive, mainly white culture, but are still sufficiently conscious of their distinctive histories and life-styles to have a strong sense of identity.

The Australian Aborigines and the Inuit are but two of many human groups existing either now or in the recent past who have lived by hunting and gathering (see Figure 1.1). The present-day world also contains other groups whose way of life to a greater or lesser extent reflects pre-capitalist characteristics. **Pastoral nomads**, for example, live mainly by raising and herding domestic animals (cattle, sheep, goats, camels, yak, reindeer and others), that provide them with food, clothing and other necessities. Pastoralists are particularly found in marginal (semi-arid, sub-arctic, sub-alpine) lands in parts of Eurasia and Africa (see Plate 1.1). Another example is the many peasant farmers still to be found in parts of sub-Saharan Africa, southern Asia and elsewhere. Some still grow much of their own food and market relationships have yet to become of central importance to their lives (Wolf 1966). To the extent that such people eat and otherwise depend on what they grow and raise rather than on what they can sell or earn outside the farm, their way of life is similar to that of peasants over the centuries. Of course, nowadays the number of peasants is declining and they are increasingly exposed to the influences of the outside world. But again they remind us of a world before capitalism.

The point, then, is that today's world still contains many societies whose ways of life differ from those lived by most of this book's readers and which recall earlier periods in human history. In order to understand those ways of life and the world as it is now, the geographer must know something about the world before capitalism. Learning about that world helps us to see how capitalism has changed the world and the pluses and minuses of that process.

A number of arguments can be advanced to suggest why it is important to know something about the world before capitalism:

Understanding the past helps geographers and others to understand themselves and their societies. Societies

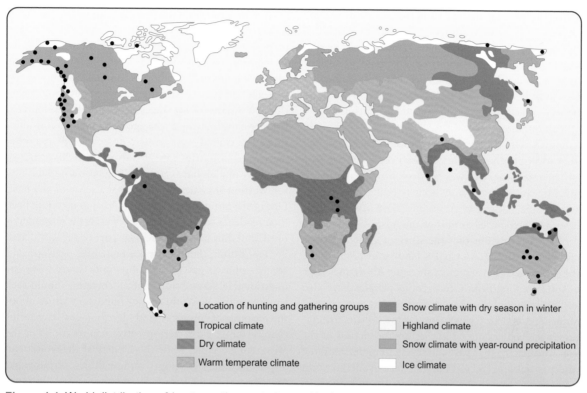

Figure 1.1 World distribution of hunter-gatherers today and in the recent past, with indication of their habitats (based on a classification of climate).

Source: adapted from Simmons (1996: 48)

Plate 1.1 Nomadic herders unloading their yaks on high-altitude pastures near Tso Moriri, India.

(pcruciatti/Shutterstock)

and individuals are products of the past, not just of the present. The present cannot be understood in ignorance of the past. Studying the past provides answers not merely to questions about how things were but also about how things are now (and, more tentatively, about how things will be in the future).

An example of the latter is the character of the physical environment in which people now live. Human beings have lived on this planet for so many thousands of years that over vast areas the physical environment has been profoundly modified. The world today is the product of thousands of generations of human activity. In fact, can any of the world's landscapes now be said to be truly 'natural'? (The implications of this are explained in Chapter 12.) This shows us that it is likely that human activity will continue to modify our environment into the future. Keeping the environment exactly as it is now is a very unlikely option. But how far we can control those changes, or keep them within acceptable limits, is a more difficult question.

A further important point is that Aborigines, Inuit and other **indigenous peoples** (those peoples native to a particular territory that was later colonized, particularly by Europeans) have recently been asserting their rights. For example, Australian Aborigines have asserted their right to be recognized as part of the Australian national identity, pointing out that the story of Australia does not begin with Captain Cook's landing in 1788, as the whites have so often assumed, since the Aborigines were in Australia long before. Indigenous peoples have also been claiming rights to local resources long ago usurped by outsiders and are trying to protect their distinctive cultures. Such peoples often feel they are the victims of the past. By studying that past and trying to understand the variety of cultures and ways of life that exist in the world and how they came to be, geographers are more likely to understand and respect such feelings.

Thus, while human geography is primarily about the present, it cannot afford to ignore the past. Some of the above points will be illustrated in the following pages.

1.1 Making sense of the past

Despite the spread of capitalism and globalization, the world of today remains immensely varied and complex. The same is true of the world in the past. The question for the geographer is how to make sense of this complex past; how to make it amenable to geographical analysis and understanding.

Different scholars have tried different ways of answering this question, but all suffer from shortcomings. For example, the economist W.W. Rostow, in his famous theory of economic growth typical of capitalist development, simply described the pre-industrial period as 'traditional society' (Rostow 1971: 4–6). Yet the fact is that pre-industrial human societies ranged from the smallest communities of hunters and gatherers to societies as sophisticated and geographically extended as the Roman Empire, ancient China and feudal Europe. Inasmuch as such societies existed in the past, and not today, it is not possible to observe them directly. But the more scholars learn about them, the more they realize how unlike one another these early societies were.

One reason why Rostow oversimplified the pre-industrial past was that he was not much interested in it. He was really interested in modernity, as exemplified by the United States and its Western allies. Furthermore, his theory can be described as 'unilinear evolutionary' inasmuch as it suggested that all societies should pass through a series of set stages of economic development before finally arriving at the age of 'high mass consumption'. The United States (where Rostow lived) and other 'developed' countries have already reached this age. Evolutionary models have certainly long been a popular way for Western societies to try to make sense of the past. One of the attractions of such models has no doubt been their tendency to suggest that the West is the most 'developed' and thus most 'progressive' part of the world and, by implication, the best (and a model for development: see Chapter 8, pp. 177–9). But quite apart from the questionable assumption that all societies should seek to imitate the West, this raises important issues about the meaning of 'progress' and 'development', two terms that certainly carry very positive connotations in the West. For example, while those parts of the world usually deemed most developed and wealthiest certainly use most energy (see Chapter 5) and enjoy access to more material goods, they also make huge demands on the environment, perhaps ultimately to everyone's undoing. Thus, what is progress in this context? Similarly, it has often been noted that the price people tend to pay for more 'development' and wealth is that they have to work harder and for more hours. Unless hard work is regarded as a virtue in itself, this again raises questions about the meaning of progress. The point here is not to disparage all forms of evolutionary theory or idea (for example, to deny that human societies have, by and large, become more complex and spatially extended through time; see Dodgshon 1987). Rather, it is to suggest that what is most recent or new or complex is not necessarily best. Thus, in what follows, words like 'modern' do not imply 'better', nor do 'ancient' or 'primitive' imply 'worse'.

An alternative method of trying to make sense of the past, and one that does not have the unilinear evolutionary structure of, say, Rostow's theory, is to classify human societies into a series of types. Classification can be described as a way of simplifying a complex world by grouping together phenomena that are regarded as having some common feature or property, particularly where the latter is deemed especially significant. Thus Marxists have commonly grouped societies in accordance with their prevailing mode of production, or in other words with the way in which material production is related to social structure (Hindess and Hirst 1975). As a geographer, primarily interested in spatial structure, Robert Sack classified societies in accordance with their use of **territoriality** (Sack 1986) (a theme taken up in Chapter 21). The point is that there is no right or wrong mode of classification. It all depends on what the purpose of the classification is. Most social theorists have wanted to claim that their mode of classifying societies is particularly significant for understanding how and why societies differ. The problem is that there is a large measure of disagreement about what the best mode is, and each has its shortcomings.

1.2 A classification of human societies

As an example of the kinds of difficulties that face any attempt to classify past and present human societies, this chapter will focus on one mode of classification that has had widespread appeal not only for human geographers but also for anthropologists and other scholars. This is the mode of classifying human societies into bands, **tribes**, chiefdoms and states (regulated and market-based) (see Bobek 1962; Dodgshon 1987). Spotlight boxes 1.1 to 1.5 describe, in simplified form, the major characteristics of each type of human society according to this classification. It will quickly be seen that the classification describes a range of societies from the simplest and most primitive to the capitalist societies of today. What it does not suggest is the circumstances under which one kind of society may change into, or be succeeded by, another.

One reason why this mode of classification has had such appeal is because it suggests that over the course of human history larger and more complex societies have tended to appear. It also relates size and complexity to the way societies occupy space and their relationships to their physical environment. However, it is worth reiterating that this is only one way of classifying human societies. Indeed some scholars reject the whole idea of classifying human societies because they feel it leads to misapprehensions about how societies are formed and survive, and even to dangerous notions of unilinear evolution. It thus needs to be remembered that this scheme is suggestive only, and does not necessarily describe the way any given society has actually changed through time. In particular, it does not stipulate that societies must develop through a series of set stages, or that one type of society necessarily leads to the next.

Subsequent sections will outline some of the social processes that might have helped to produce, change and perhaps destroy the different kinds of human society described in Spotlight boxes 1.1 to 1.5. In so doing, some of the limitations of the classification system used will become apparent. Before proceeding, however, it is worth making one important point. Our knowledge of **prehistoric societies** (societies which have left no written records) derives mainly from archaeological data, or material left by such societies and the traces of their environmental impacts. Methods for analysing such data have become ever more sophisticated, but the data themselves obviously become scarcer the older they are. Moreover, there are many kinds of questions, for example about the way early people viewed the world around them, which cannot be answered directly from the archaeological evidence. New discoveries are always liable to change our understanding of past societies, and especially of the earliest ones. Our knowledge of the latter societies, and of the dates attaching to them, must therefore be regarded as especially tentative.

1.3 Hunting and gathering

The time when the first human-type species (hominids) first appeared on earth is very uncertain, but a date of at least two and a half million years ago is often given. Homo erectus, believed by some to be the forerunner of the modern human species, is thought to have appeared around 1.9 million years ago, and the modern species (Homo sapiens sapiens) at least 40,000 years ago (but see Foley 1995 for a contrary view). Since agriculture appears to have arisen about 12,000 years ago, hunting and gathering in **bands** have been the basic occupations for much of humanity's existence (see Spotlight box 1.1).

As noted already, only a limited amount is known about early human societies (see Plate 1.2). In addition to archaeological evidence, much has to be inferred, for example from hunter-gatherers who are still in existence or who existed until quite recently. Needless to say, such inference can be dangerous because modern hunter-gatherers have probably been influenced by other, more 'advanced', societies that now share their world. Their way of life is thus unlikely to be identical with those who existed in the remote past (Barnard 2004).

The distribution of hunter-gatherers in the recent past shows that they have existed in every major climatic zone and have practised enormously varied economies, depending on the nature and potentials of the local environment (Figure 1.1). This fact alone suggests that a simplistic evolutionary model of human societies will fail to do justice to their complex histories. Some generalizations do seem possible, however – for example, that in recent times groups living in the highest latitudes (above 60 degrees) have relied largely on hunting, and those below 39 degrees on plant collecting. Fishing seems to have played an important role for many groups living in intermediate latitudes (Lee 1968; Oppenheimer 2012).

Spotlight box 1.1

Bands

- Bands are societies of hunter-gatherers. Most of human history has been lived in this way.
- Bands live by hunting wild animals and gathering food from the surrounding flora.
- Because of the pressures they place on the surrounding environment, bands are almost always nomadic.

- Bands are the smallest and simplest of human groups.
- Bands rarely exceed 500 people.
- For most of the time band members generally live in smaller groups of 25–100 people, which allows for efficient exploitation of the environment.
- Bands usually have a minimum of social differentiation and functional specialization.

Plate 1.2 Artefacts from early human sites: (a) Prehistoric stone tool dating back some 400,000 years; (b) The much more recent Neolithic settlement of Skara Brae, Orkney, Scotland, dating from about 3000 BC.

((a) Diego Barucco/Shutterstock (b) johnbraid/Shutterstock)

Hunter-gatherers have lived in this world for such a long period that today's environment is the way it is partly as a result of their activities. For example, any notion that early human beings lived in complete harmony with their environments or always had 'sustainable' economies is simply untrue. Thus hunter-gatherers are credited with the extinction of many animals. An outstanding case is North America where perhaps two-thirds of the large mammal fauna living there just before the arrival of the ancestors of modern native Americans (via the Bering land bridge, possibly about 12,000 years ago) subsequently disappeared. The most likely explanation is the effects of hunting. The discovery of fire, its use by hominids long predating the appearance of Homo sapiens sapiens, was also an important instrument whereby human beings changed their environments. Some scholars have argued that the present-day appearance of such

major biomes as the African savannas and the prairies of North America is the result of the human use of fire over thousands of years (Simmons 1996). More recently, contacts between hunter-gatherers and agricultural and industrial societies frequently had even more far-reaching environmental effects. At the same time, other scholars have asserted that the relations between such groups and their physical environments were rarely if ever exploitative in the modern sense. Hunter-gatherers lived in an intimate relationship with their environment and frequently regarded it, or aspects of it, as sacred. Some scholars have thus described their relationship as 'organic' in a way which has been forgotten by our modern societies, much to the detriment of today's global environment (Merchant 2005).

Scholars have wondered about processes whereby bands evolved into tribes, or hunter-gathering economies into agricultural ones (Harris 1996a, 1996b). It has been pointed out, for example, that where the natural environment was especially favourable, the packing of bands tended to be denser, leading to less mobility and perhaps to semi-permanent settlement and closer interaction between bands. There may also have been a much greater degree of manipulation of the environment and its resources than might be expected in a pure hunter-gatherer economy. Altogether the life of bands was much more variable and a good deal less stable than the above classification scheme suggests. The boundary between band and tribe is thus blurred.

1.4 Human settlement and agriculture

Just as the boundary line between band and tribe may not always be easy to define in practice, the same can be said of the boundary between tribe and chiefdom. Some

scholars, for example, doubt whether the category 'tribe' (Spotlight box 1.2) is particularly helpful, implying as it does the lack of a hierarchical social structure (Friedman and Rowlands 1977). Such scholars tend to believe that the appearance of agriculture will have sparked off competition for access to the best land, or at least rules whereby such land was allocated and inherited, and that some people and groups will inevitably have lost out. They therefore see a social hierarchy (characteristic of chiefdoms and states – see Spotlight boxes 1.3 and 1.4) beginning to emerge even as agriculture and the process of permanent settlement began.

Be that as it may, it is now widely accepted that the traditional picture of agriculture being invented in a small number of 'hearths' and then spreading across the globe is far too simple. Bands of hunters and gatherers are known to develop an often intimate knowledge of their local environments, and no doubt human beings understood much about the factors influencing plant and animal development long before they began to practise

Spotlight box 1.2

Tribes

- Tribes appeared with the invention and spread of agriculture.
- Agriculture usually demands considerable investment of human effort into a relatively small area. This reduces the propensity to migrate (but pastoral nomads are an exception).
- The appearance of agriculture usually allows more people to live in a smaller space.

- Agricultural societies thus tend to be bigger than bands, with higher population densities.
- Settlements tend to become more fixed than in bands.
- The greater spatial fixity of society encourages intermarriage and the development of extended family networks. Tribes thus develop a sense of kinship and of common descent.
- Socially, tribes are relatively egalitarian, at least as between kinship groups.

Spotlight box 1.3

Chiefdoms

- Chiefdoms arose with the emergence of 'ranked and stratified' societies.
- 'Ranked' societies are societies where groups and individuals have, on a relatively permanent basis, different degrees of status and power.
- 'Stratified' societies are societies where groups and individuals have, on a relatively permanent basis, different degrees of material wealth.
- A chiefdom implies the presence of a permanent ruling group and/or individual, though kinship

remains the chief bond between ruler and subject.
- Chiefdoms imply a greater degree of centralization and control within society than in a tribe (shown, for example, in the imposition of taxes and tribute on the ordinary subjects). Spatially this might be reflected in the greater importance accorded to a central settlement (proto-city) where the ruler resides.
- The first chiefdoms began to appear about 3000 BC in Europe, but earlier elsewhere.

Spotlight box 1.4

Regulated (pre-modern) states

- Whereas the chiefdom is organized around the principle of kinship, the state is organized on the basis of territory (viz. one is subject to the state if one resides in the territory of that state).
- States, whilst also based on social inequality, tend to be larger and administratively more complex than chiefdoms. This implies greater functional specialization and greater probability of the rise of urban forms.

- Pre-modern states existed in a world before modern capitalism. The market was not central to their functioning and was often controlled ('regulated') in various ways. Thus economic relationships were generally subordinated to political, social and religious considerations.
- Other forms of social relationship, for instance landholding, also often tended to be controlled (regulated) rather than being determined by the market.

Spotlight box 1.5

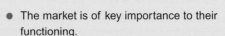

Market-based states

- Market-based states are modern states whose development is closely linked to that of capitalism and thus of the world economy.

- The market is of key importance to their functioning.
- In the last two centuries these states have been associated with colonial and national projects (see Chapters 2, 3 and 22).

full-blown agriculture. David Harris (1989, 1996a, 1996b) argued that the development of agriculture was a long drawn-out affair and that there must have been much trial and error before it finally emerged in some places in a fully recognizable form. Some prehistoric northern Australian Aborigines, for example, knew about agriculture, but never adopted it.

Something can, however, be said about when, and perhaps why, agriculture appeared. The archaeological evidence makes it possible to detect and date the remains of domesticated varieties of plants and animals. According to Simmons (1996: 93) there were probably three foci for the initial surges of domestication: around 7000 BC (to use the Christian chronology) in south-west Asia, around 6000 BC in south-east Asia, and around 5000 BC in Meso-America. Different species of plants were associated with each, for example: wheat, barley and oats in south-west Asia; rice in south-east Asia; and maize, squash and gourds in Meso-America. Domesticated animals also began to appear about the same time (though the dog, domesticated from the wolf, appeared before agriculture). Sheep, goats, pigs and cattle are all associated with south-west Asia (Simmons 1996: 87–134), though pigs may also have been domesticated independently in eastern Asia.

As to why agriculture was adopted, scholars differ. The simple answer, that it was more efficient than hunting and

gathering, hardly applies to naturally productive environments where it clearly involved much greater effort relative to the return achieved. Some scholars favour population pressure. Others, however, argue that this view is over-deterministic and point out that even hunter-gatherers had the means of controlling population growth. Such scholars tend to favour more complex explanations that embrace cultural preferences and choices as well as environmental and population pressures (Maisels 1993: 25–31).

Just as the factors that led up to the appearance and spread of agriculture are by no means straightforward, the same is also true of its further development. No simple evolutionary model can account for how agriculture has changed and developed throughout the world. Everywhere traditional agriculturalists showed a remarkable ability to adapt their practices to local environmental conditions. Eventually they largely displaced the hunter-gatherers (Figure 1.2) and gave rise to an enormous variety of agricultural systems.

Agriculture's effects on the landscape were much greater than the effects of hunting and gathering. It changed the vegetation cover of wide areas as forests and grasslands disappeared under fields, practices like terracing and irrigation were introduced, and the effects on soil composition abetted erosion in some places. The grazing of animals and other forms of resource use frequently

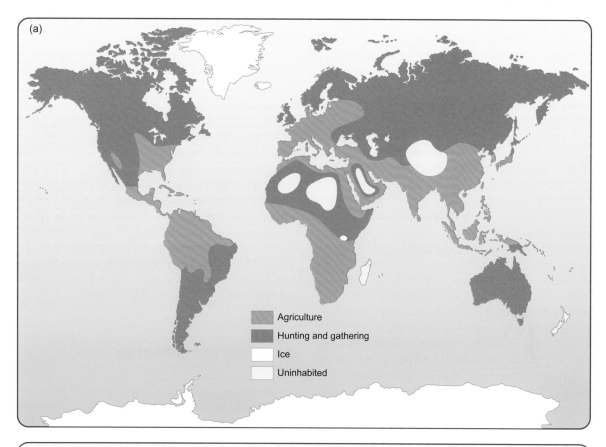

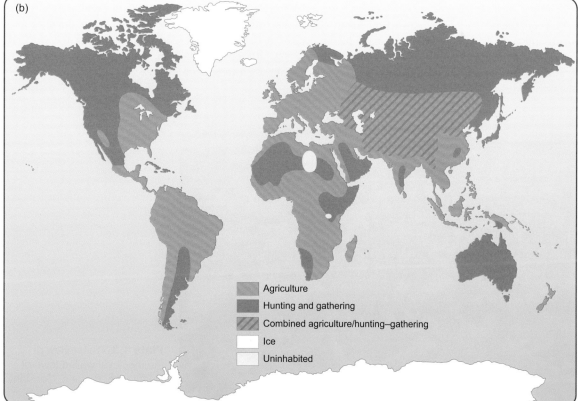

Figure 1.2 World distribution of agriculture and hunter-gathering about AD 1 (a) and AD 1500 (b).

Source: Sherratt (1980: 97, 117)

changed the species composition of forests, grasslands and other areas. Agricultural systems, crops and domesticated animals spread way beyond their initial locations. An outstanding example is the cultivation of rice, which may have started in east Asia around 5000 BC, if not before, and spread as far as Egypt and Sicily by Roman times. Such developments long preceded the European overseas expansion beginning in the fifteenth century AD, which was to have even more far-reaching consequences both for the geography of agriculture and for the environment (see Chapter 2, pp. 42–7; Crosby 2004).

There is no doubt that the spread of agriculture (whether as a result of migration or through cultural diffusion) had far-reaching effects on human society, encouraging permanent settlement and the emergence of tribal systems (though Crone, 2003, questions the nature of the link between agriculture and tribes). Tribal members, living permanently side by side, almost inevitably developed similar cultural traits such as common languages. As suggested in Spotlight box 1.2, tribes also typically develop myths of common ancestry (indeed, this seems to be part of their definition). In the late nineteenth and early twentieth centuries, a period much influenced by ideas based on Darwinian evolution as well as by myths of European racial and cultural superiority bolstered by European overseas imperial expansion, it became fashionable, on very limited evidence, for scholars to imagine that modern ethnic differences have a biological basis and that certain '**races**' or ethnic groups are inherently superior to others. In Britain, for example, many historians and archaeologists regarded the modern English as deriving almost entirely from Anglo-Saxon invaders with both racial and cultural characteristics which equipped them to dominate the 'inferior' Celtic peoples. Similar ideas, of course, reached their ultimate absurdity in the racist theories propounded by Adolf Hitler and the Nazis. Nowadays, with the availability of new scientific approaches like molecular archaeology and DNA studies, we know that the origins of the English and of other peoples are much more complex than was once thought and that 'different' peoples are in fact remarkably similar in their capabilities (Miles 2006: 18–31; Oppenheimer 2012). Different human groups, settling in the same region, may gradually have adopted similar languages and cultural patterns, thus slowly fusing into one people or ethnic group even though they were not originally closely interrelated. In this way the study of even the remote past can cast light on issues which cause contention today and, as in this case, help to discredit theories based on crude racist prejudices and a misreading of history.

1.5 Cities and civilization

The invention of agriculture was only one of the events that moved human societies along a road that ultimately led to the kinds of societies which predominate in the world today. Others included the appearance of cities, states and civilizations. Cities and states usually go together. Maisels (1993: 302), for example, argues that the functional specialization associated with cities allowed rulers to rule more effectively and also to put a greater social distance between them and their

Plate 1.3 Winter view of the medieval walled town of Nordlingen, Bavaria, Germany.

(Alexander Kuguchin/Shutterstock)

subjects. The gathering of specialists around the person of a state's ruler fostered urban life, commerce and the many other things (such as writing, technology, religion and speculative thought) with which is associated the word 'civilization'. Indeed, the very words 'city' and 'civilization' have a common Latin root (civitas, meaning 'state').

As is the case with the appearance of agriculture, the processes that eventually gave rise to cities and civilizations are far from straightforward. It is clear that the development of a social hierarchy was a necessary precursor, but what produced that? Different scholars have debated the merits of alternative potential causes such as land shortages, inheritance rules, or the emergence of particularly strong or charismatic individuals. But while these and other factors may have produced **chiefdoms** (see Spotlight box 1.3), something more seems to be required to explain the rise of cities, states and civilizations. As Maisels writes, chiefs enjoy only 'hegemony' over their peoples, and are bound by rules of kinship which imply mutual obligations. Chiefdoms were notoriously unstable. Kings and other state rulers, by contrast, exercise 'sovereignty' (ultimate power) over a **territory** and its peoples (Maisels 1993: 199). Thus scholars have cast around for particular factors which enabled individual leaders to have their power recognized as legitimate by subject peoples and persuaded the latter to pay over the tribute, food surpluses and services which cities and rulers required to maintain themselves in existence. Such particular factors might have included religious sanctions, military skills or organizing power. The problem is to show how the kind of social inequality that might be produced by such processes then transforms itself into the stable and legitimate power that a ruling group exercises in the state. Some scholars, therefore, have proposed that states came into being as a result of different processes working together in a contingent way rather than being caused deterministically by a single overriding process (Maisels 1993: 199–220).

Whatever may be the explanation for the initial development of states and associated cities, they gave rise to major changes in human societies (see Spotlight box 1.4). Rather than being organized around the principle of kinship like the tribe and the chiefdom, for example, states were organized on the territorial principle. This means that the rulers of states exercised their rule over defined territories and their inhabitants, no matter who the latter happened to be. This proved an extremely powerful way of organizing human societies. States thus appeared in different parts of the globe. The first organized states are believed to have developed in Sumer in present-day Iraq around 3000 BC. According to Maisels, these took the form of **city-states**. In China the first state, associated with the Shang dynasty, arose about 1500 BC, and by about 1000 BC the Maya civilization had appeared in Meso-America. In Europe the first **states** are commonly taken to be the Greek city-states that began to develop in eastern Greece and the neighbouring islands about the eighth century BC. Whether the state arose independently in different places across the globe, or whether the idea of the state was somehow diffused from one or two initial foci, is uncertain.

Early states took many different forms. All faced difficulty in enforcing and maintaining their territoriality in the context of poor communications, and different states approached this problem in different ways. The Greek city-states, for example, typically occupied only small areas and restricted their population sizes. When population in any one state exceeded a certain threshold, that state would found a self-governing colony elsewhere on the sea coast. Travel by sea was generally easier than overland travel and thus settlements could keep in touch (see Plate 1.4). In this way the Greeks eventually colonized much of the eastern Mediterranean coast (Figure 1.3). The huge Roman Empire, by contrast, could not rely solely on sea travel. This was a much more centralized polity and only by having superb military organization, an elaborate system of roads and fortifications, good administration, and a state-controlled religion centred on the person of the emperor, could it survive for several centuries (Figure 1.4 and Case study 1.1). The Mongol Empire was also very extensive, controlling much of Asia and a good slice of central and eastern Europe in the thirteenth and fourteenth centuries AD. The Mongols were pastoral nomads whose formidable warrior skills were based on their horsemanship and their ability to outmanoeuvre their enemies. But nomadic empires had a tendency to contract as quickly as they arose. It was difficult for the emperor to maintain control over his swift-moving armies of mounted warriors. Finally, medieval Europe's answer to the problem of territoriality was to decentralize political power through kings to territorial lords and minor nobles (see Case study 1.2). In return for their rights to their land and other privileges, lesser nobles owed their lords a duty of military support in time of need, which meant having to appear with an army of knights, retainers and other soldiers when ordered to do so. The lords in turn owed loyalty to their overlords, and so on in a hierarchy that ended with kings or other rulers. Medieval European states were thus quite decentralized and unstable, as regional lords and their underlings were often tempted to rebel (Figure 1.5). Only after centuries of struggle between rulers, lords and ordinary subjects did the European states of today finally appear.

What all this tells us is that the present-day pattern of states is contingent on and the outcome of quite random

Plate 1.4 A Classical Greek ship of the kind which plied the Mediterranean in Antiquity.

(Stefano Bianchetti/Corbis)

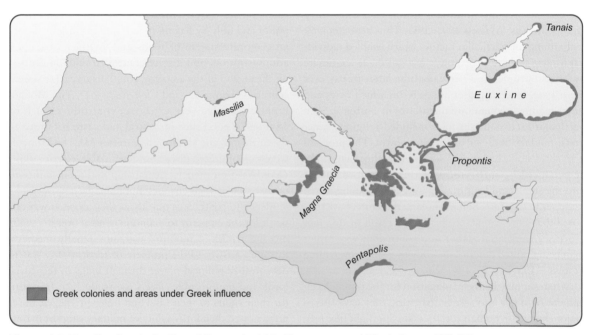

Greek colonies and areas under Greek influence

Figure 1.3 The Greek colonization of the ancient Mediterranean and Black Sea *c.* 550 BC.

Source: after Pounds (1947: 49)

historical processes. Had other processes taken place, the outcomes might have been totally different. In other words, there was no historical inevitability about the emergence of states like the United Kingdom, France, China or Nigeria, whatever present-day nationalists might like to think. Often enough state-building has

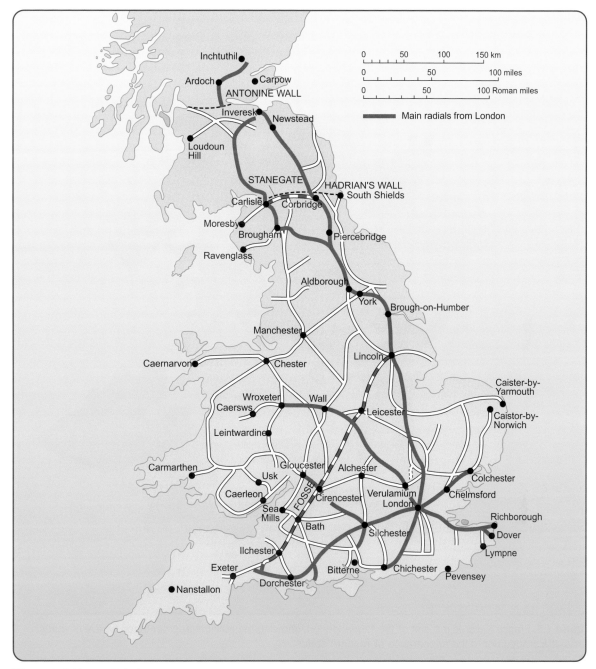

Figure 1.4 Roman Britain.

Source: © Oxford University Press 1984. Redrawn from map VI from Roman Britain in *Oxford History of England*, edited by Peter Salway (1984), by permission of Oxford University Press

been a murky and messy business in which many innocent people have suffered, and it was rarely characterized by the glorious victories and heroic deeds so often celebrated in modern national mythologies. And if the existence of modern states is the product of historical chance, why should things be any different in the future?

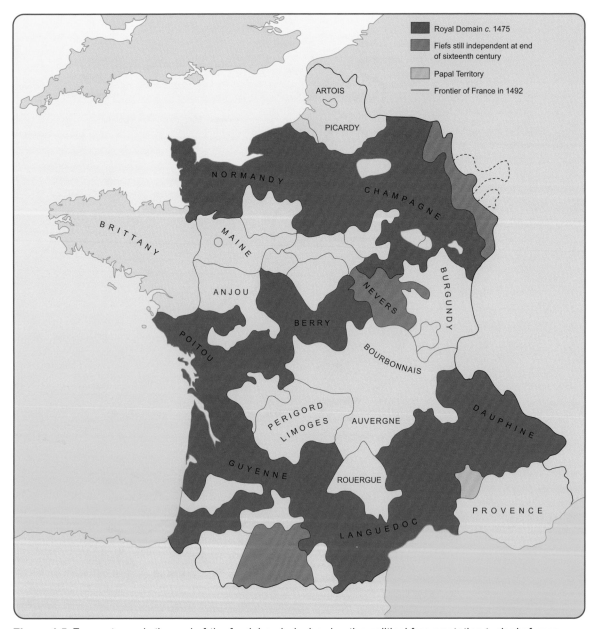

Figure 1.5 France towards the end of the feudal period, showing the political fragmentation typical of many parts of Europe prior to the appearance of modern states.

Source: based on *The Times Atlas of World History* (1989: 15.1). © Collins Bartholomew Ltd 1989, reproduced by permission of HarperCollins Publishers

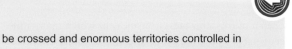

Case study 1.1

The Roman Empire at its zenith (first to fourth centuries AD)

The Roman Empire was one of the greatest achievements of state-building in the pre-modern period and is testimony to the way in which huge distances could be crossed and enormous territories controlled in spite of the absence of modern industrial technologies. At its greatest extent the empire's east–west axis stretched from the Caucasus to Cape Finisterre in north-west Spain, a distance of about 2,800 miles. North–south it reached from Hadrian's Wall, near the present-day Anglo-Scottish border, to the fringes of the Sahara in North Africa, some 1,600 miles. The empire was characterized by two major languages (Latin and Greek), low tariff barriers, a common currency, a common code of laws, and the basis of a common system of education and culture for the Romanized elite. Rome was a truly 'universal state', which lasted in its mature form for half a millennium, and in its eastern (Byzantine) manifestation until the capture of Constantinople by the Turks in 1453.

Like all early states, Rome had problems in enforcing its territoriality – the sheer scale of the empire meant that there were always difficulties in maintaining control over its far-flung provinces. That the empire was able to endure for so long (albeit with many vicissitudes) was a tribute to its highly developed capacity for organization and an astuteness in gaining and retaining local loyalties. The acquisition of new territories proceeded by a mixture of conquest, colonization by Roman and Latin colonists, the establishment of vassal kingdoms and powers, alliances (often forced) and other means. The Roman army, reformed by the Emperor Augustus after 13 BC, was a masterpiece of military organization superior to any of Rome's enemies in this period. The seas and waterways were patrolled by the navy, protecting merchant shipping. Towns and military bases were interconnected by a network of fine roads, and an official transport system (the *cursus publicus*) with inns and posting stations at regular intervals speeded official communications. There were even roadbooks (*itineraria*) for the guidance of the many travellers, including some tourists. Fortified lines, of which Hadrian's Wall is the most celebrated, protected the most vulnerable frontiers. But the empire was not held together only by military force. It was also by judicious extensions of Roman citizenship and other privileges to local elites, and by fostering helpful religious practices like emperor worship, that local loyalties were ensured.

The empire's economic and cultural achievements were many. Long-distance trade in such items as grain, metals and luxury goods was important, for example, though there were many hindrances to commerce and most people depended on local agriculture and manufacture. It must also be remembered that there was a heavy dependence on slavery. In the end the Romans could never be assured of political stability, even in their heartlands. Reliance on the army contributed to the empire's eventual undoing – generals and their armies competed for political power, the economy was undermined by overtaxation and other factors, and growing military weakness invited rebellion, and invasion by 'barbarians'.

Case study 1.2

European feudalism

- Feudal society was hierarchical – ranked and stratified.
- The majority of the population were subsistence farmers, engaged in extensive forms of agriculture (for example, by cultivating strips in open fields shared with others, raising some livestock) and exploiting local resources like pastureland, woodland and fish.
- Many of the rural population were obligated to their lords and landholders, for example not to move away from their villages, to work the lord's land, to pay the tribute and taxes the lord and the state required, to serve the lord militarily and to perform other services.
- Lords held their land conditionally from their overlord and ultimately from the king or other ruler. Land could not easily be sold. Lords exercised jurisdiction over those living on their estates.
- Lords owed allegiance to their overlords (and they in turn to their overlords and so on), for example in supporting them with their military forces and performing other services as required.
- Feudal states were quite decentralized, parcelled out into lordships and they in turn into jurisdictions of various kinds.
- Towns were generally small and few and far between (see Plate 1.3). Most were centres of trade and crafts. Their residents (merchants, burgesses) often enjoyed freedoms and privileges ('liberties') denied to most rural dwellers.
- Merchants and itinerant traders joined together networks of local and long-distance trade, linking local fairs and markets with towns, ports and so on. Craft production and trade were generally subject to a variety of restrictions and controls, and often played only a minor role in the lives of rural dwellers.
- The medieval world-view was strongly influenced by the Church, whose priests and officials were among the few educated people and were universally present.

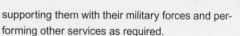

1.6 Pre-capitalist societies

It should be clear by now that pre-capitalist societies were by no means simple. They differed among themselves in all kinds of ways. At the same time, when compared with present-day capitalist societies, they appear to have had a number of distinguishing features. This section will consider some of the more obvious ones.

Geographers and others have sometimes been tempted to think that past societies, lacking modern communications, were essentially small in scale and localized, with life based around the community. It is hoped that enough has been said already to suggest how over-simplified this view is. Huge **empires** had to be administered and defended, great cities like classical Rome had to be fed. Classical Rome imported some 17 million bushels of wheat each year from Egypt, North Africa and Sicily (Simmons 1996: 109). In the Roman Empire and other societies, high-value goods often travelled much greater distances. Even the Inuit, living the lives of hunters and gatherers, sometimes travelled hundreds of miles each year on hunting trips, and their geographical knowledge frequently covered an even wider span. Enough has been said above about migrations and the diffusion of artefacts and practices across great distances to suggest how space could be overcome even if individuals were immobile, at least by today's standards.

There was, however, no avoiding the problems of communication in pre-modern societies. Most people in agricultural societies lived lives which were bound to their villages and the surrounding regions. Their work consisted essentially in winning the means of subsistence for themselves and their families from their environment, as well as paying the taxes and meeting the other demands which were made upon them. From the time of the appearance of states down until the twentieth century the lives of most people were lived in the context of such **peasant** communities. As mentioned earlier, such communities are still characteristic of parts of the world today, though increasingly eroded by commercialism and growing contacts with modernity.

Scholars researching traditional peasant societies have frequently pointed to the many cultural differences between such rural dwellers and the cities that ruled over them and which they might occasionally visit. A case in point is religion. Religion has been a fundamental factor in social organization and in outlook in virtually every human society down to the twentieth century. Early states were generally associated with an official religion that legitimized the established order and which was often practised in cities but was rarely fully understood by the peasants, most of whom were probably illiterate (see Plate 1.5). Even where the peasants officially followed the same religion as the elite, as in medieval Europe, they almost always interpreted its teachings in their own ways, mixing them with their own superstitions and 'pagan' beliefs. The life and outlook of the ruler and the elite, if not of all cities, were entirely alien to them. And equally their way of life was alien to the cities.

For this reason, it would be completely misleading to think of the subjects of pre-capitalist states as 'citizens' in the modern sense. Traditional rulers knew little of the countryside, where most of their subjects lived, and cared even less (except, perhaps, where they had landed estates, and even then the running of the estate could be left to officials). What mattered to rulers was law and order, and extracting the taxes and tribute the state needed to maintain itself in existence. The idea

Plate 1.5 Icons of the Virgin Mary, Jesus and saints of the Eastern Orthodox Church. Such images would have impressed the peasants of the Christian Orthodox parts of eastern Europe and the Middle East, even if they did not fully understand the icons' significance.

(Slobodan Miskovic/Shutterstock)

that rulers should care for the welfare of their ordinary subjects, let alone consult them about their policies, is very modern indeed.

It is difficult for most people living in a world dominated by capitalist relationships to conceive of societies where this was not the case. Before capitalism, most people were engaged in subsistence activities: hunting, gathering, farming, fishing or whatever. They might have to pay taxes or tribute, and they might trade some of what they gathered or produced, but market trade, generally organized by a small minority of merchants and traders, was often quite marginal to them. Where market trade did exist in early societies, it was frequently hedged about by laws and restrictions of various kinds. There might be laws against the taking of interest on loans, for example, regulations on price, or restrictions on where and when trade might take place or who might engage in it. Only with the rise of modern capitalism did the market become central to the way societies functioned.

It is very difficult to generalize about pre-capitalist societies and almost any generalization is open to objection. Case study 1.2 describes the main features of the feudal society that existed in medieval Europe which, according to many scholars, was the seedbed for the development of world capitalism (see Chapter 2). Even here, however, one must be careful – the features described would be more or less true, depending on the date and the place being considered.

1.7 The heritage of the past

Nowadays the past, or what is commonly referred to as **heritage**, is big business. Medieval cities and cathedrals, historic villages and battlefields, monuments, gardens and ruined temples are objects sought out by international tourists and cultural visitors, whilst tourist providers and also those charged with the conservation of the past compete to sell the past to visitors. What cannot be viewed out of doors is gathered together into museums which become ever more elaborate and ever more tied to the leisure industry rather than to the educational role which defined them in the past. Cities which are in the business of selling themselves to international investors and global companies use their cultural resources, including heritage, to do so. Altogether, it seems, our age is obsessed with the past, and nostalgia has become part of almost everyone's life.

Not surprisingly, perhaps, the present-day significance of heritage has not escaped the notice of human geographers and other students of society (Graham *et al.* 2000; Johnson 2003; Benton 2010). Geographers have been concerned to know what it is about the past which appears to attract so much public interest and how people understand those facets of the past which they encounter. More specifically, since the past is no longer with us and cannot be encountered directly, scholars have begun to ask about which particular past is being viewed under the guise of heritage, and about the ways in which the past is manipulated for public consumption. For the fact is that there are many pasts, depending on the viewpoints of those who wish to describe them and on the messages which those in control of heritage wish to purvey. Whether it be politicians wishing to convey some lesson about 'the nation' (such as the recent discussion in the UK about so-called 'British values'), museum curators trying to explain particular historical events or epochs, or the guardians of historic sites aiming to entertain and titillate tourists, the scope for historical distortion (even if it means only telling one side of the story) is immense. History, in other words, is all around us, and history is controversial. Only by knowing something about the past can the geographer hope to avoid ignorance about the present.

Learning outcomes
Having read this chapter, you should begin to appreciate that:

- The surviving evidence necessarily limits our knowledge of past societies, since they cannot be observed directly. In general, the further back in time past societies existed, the more uncertain our knowledge about them becomes.
- People in the past lived very different lives from those of most people alive today. But it is important not to oversimplify or overgeneralize about past societies that varied enormously in their structures and ways of life and in their degree of complexity.

- Classifying societies into types is a way of making sense of the past and of trying to understand the geographical characteristics of varied societies. But all classifications have their shortcomings.
- Overcoming the friction of space was a severe problem in pre-capitalist societies. But it is important not to exaggerate its effects – people often travelled, and often migrated, long distances even in 'primitive' societies, ideas and artefacts travelled vast distances, and empires were successfully established.
- The landscapes that can be seen today have been profoundly influenced by past societies, including hunter-gatherer ones. Our world is the product of generations of human activity.

- Change and progress are two different things. Social change almost always means winners and losers. The human record suggests that the latter have often been the majority.

- We must not assume that our present-day society is the world's most successful or progressive. We should be prepared to learn from others and to allow for the possibility that other ways of organizing society might be better at coping with some problems (for example, that of environmental degradation) than our own.

- There are many pasts depending on the viewpoint of the observer. Many assumptions adopted by people alive today are based on misunderstandings or distortions of the past. We should always be prepared to test our ideas and assumptions against the historical evidence. We should be prepared to do the same with the ideas and assumptions of others.

- Only by knowing something about the past can the human geographer hope to avoid ignorance about the present.

Further reading

Benton, T. (ed.) (2010) *Understanding Heritage and Memory,* Manchester University Press, Manchester. A set of essays exploring the contentious nature of heritage and memory, including the idea of cultural landscape, arguing that it is never possible to impose a single set of values or interpretations on acts of remembering.

Crone, P. (2003) *Pre-Industrial Societies: Anatomy of the Pre-Modern World,* Oneworld, Oxford. An excellent introduction to the character of pre-industrial societies, from the invention of cities and civilization. Written for undergraduates.

Dodgshon, R.A. (1987) *The European Past: Social Evolution and Spatial Order,* Macmillan, Basingstoke. An original examination of European prehistory and history, taken from a geographical perspective. Based on the social classification system highlighted in this chapter. Very detailed, but repays careful study.

Dodgshon, R.A. and Butlin, R.A. (eds) (1990) *An Historical Geography of England and Wales,* 2nd edition, Academic Press, London. An historical geography of the region from prehistoric times to 1939. Chapters 4 and 5 illustrate the issue of feudalism.

Jones, R. (2007) *People/States/Territories: The Political Geographies of British State Formation,* Blackwell, Oxford. People, power and places in the making of the British state.

Jones, R. and Phillips, R. (2005) Unsettling geographical horizons: explaining pre-modern and non-European imperialism, *Annals of the Association of American Geographers,* 95(1), 141–61. This article argues for longer term historical perspectives in human geography.

Simmons, I.G. (1996) *Changing the Face of the Earth: Culture, Environment, History,* 2nd edition, Blackwell, Oxford. A history of the impact of humans on the natural environment from the earliest times to the present. Contains excellent chapters on pre-capitalist societies, especially from the environmental point of view, but tends to be a little technical in places.

The Times Archaeology of the World (1999), new edition, Times Books, London. A lavishly illustrated survey of archaeology.

The Times Atlas of World History (1999), new edition, Times Books, London. A highly acclaimed survey of world history beginning with human origins. This is in fact more a history book with maps than a true atlas and fails to provide detailed maps despite its large format. But it is lavishly illustrated and contains a wealth of factual and explanatory material. Other similar atlases are available.

Useful websites

www.britishmuseum.org   The British Museum, London. The museum holds a unique collection of art and antiquities from ancient and living societies across the globe. The website gives details of the museum's holdings and current exhibitions, hosts discussions on prehistory and past civilizations, and gives guidance on how to find further information.

www.si.edu   The Smithsonian Institution, Washington, DC. The Smithsonian is a focus for many kinds of scientific and cultural endeavour in the United States. The website contains much that is useful for readers of this chapter, especially in relation to the history and prehistory of North America.

www.jorvik-viking-centre.co.uk   The website of the Jorvik Viking Centre in York, England, famed for its reconstruction of life in York in the Viking period.

http://english-heritage.org.uk   The website of English Heritage, which is responsible for the upkeep of many prehistoric and historic sites in England, many of which are open to the public.

www.besthistorysites.net Entitled 'Best of History Websites', a comprehensive guide to history-oriented resources online, starting with prehistory. For teachers, students and others.

www.british-history.ac.uk   British History Online is a digital library of key printed primary and secondary sources for the history of Britain and Ireland. The accent is on the period between 1300 and 1800.

http://whc.unesco.org/   The official world heritage site of UNESCO, which designates and seeks to protect 'World Heritage', defined as 'cultural and natural heritage around the world considered to be of outstanding value to humanity'.

THE RISE AND SPREAD OF CAPITALISM

Chapter 2

Terry Slater

Topics covered

- Definitions of capitalism
- The cyclical nature of capitalism
- The transition from feudalism to capitalism
- The beginnings of European imperialism
- Colonial commerce
- Transatlantic migrations and the slave trade
- European colonial empires and racism
- Industrial and agricultural transformations
- New modes of transportation
- Industrial urbanism

Between 1500 and 1900 there was a fundamental change in the way an increasingly large part of the Western world was organized. Beginning in particular in parts of England, and spreading to other parts of Europe, the capitalist economic system was to change, or influence substantially, not only the economies, but also the political, social and cultural dimensions of newly powerful **nation-states**. By 1900, capitalism was the dominant socio-economic system over a large part of the world, a by-product of the colonial empires of those nation-states.

2.1 What is capitalism?

A number of writers have provided theoretical frameworks for understanding the workings and ramifications of the capitalist system. The first was devised by the Scottish philosopher, historian and father of classical economics, Adam Smith, in his book *An Inquiry into the Nature and Causes of the Wealth of Nations* (1776). Like all theoretical models, Smith's is a simplification of reality, but it introduced a terminology and series of conceptualizations that are still familiar to us today. Smith assumed the model was driven by people's selfish desires for gain and self-interest. Thus, production takes place to generate profit; surplus profits are accumulated as capital; and the basic rule of the system is 'accumulate or perish'. Integral to the system is the determination of prices which, in a free market, said Smith, are determined by the supply of, and demand for, the **factors of production**. In order to maximize their profits, industrialists will always seek to minimize their costs of production, including the wages that they pay their workforce, so as to outcompete other producers by having lower prices. One way of doing this was through the **division of labour**, dividing manufacturing tasks into simple, repetitive operations that could be performed by unskilled, and therefore cheap, labour. Another important way in which manufacturers could seek **competitive advantage** over their fellows was to be first in the use of new technology. The significance of the invention and adoption of new ways of doing things, whether through science and technology, or ideas and organization, has often been crucial to firms, industries and regions in getting ahead of competitors. This is still very clearly so today in technological 'hotspots' like the Milano and Stuttgart regions of the European space economy. Most scholars agree that the capitalist system began to cohere into an integrated whole in a particular place (England), at a particular time (the seventeenth century), and that it then took another long period (until the mid nineteenth century) before it matured in the states of north-west Europe and in North America (Green and Sutcliffe 1987: 6–7) (Spotlight box 2.1). We do need to note, however, that recently this viewpoint has been challenged by some historians who believe that it is too Eurocentric and that greater attention should be given to developments in China and the East more generally (Section 2.2.3).

2.1.1 Cyclical characteristics of economic development

Smith went on to model the workings of a national economy over a year (macroeconomics) to elucidate the way in which capitalism works in a series of interconnected cycles. These cycles have been studied subsequently by other economists, most notably the Russian N. Kondratieff (1925), whose name is now used for the roughly

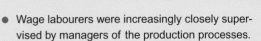

Spotlight box 2.1

Characteristics of states with a mature capitalist economy and society

- The majority of the population in these countries were wage labourers forming a 'working class' who sold their labour power for wages in cash or kind so as to purchase food and other commodities to survive.
- The majority of these wage labourers were male and worked outside the home; females increasingly 'worked' in the home, both in the domestic care of their families and by 'selling' surplus labour time for minimal wages.

- Wage labourers were increasingly closely supervised by managers of the production processes.
- The means of production of wage labourers was owned by capitalists whose aim was to make a profit on their investment.
- There was an increasing disparity between the 'profit' of capitalists and the 'wages' of workers with an increasing propensity for conflict between the two.
- The vast majority of goods and services, including fixed property like land, were distributed through monetary exchange.

50-year-long cycles of boom and depression that have characterized the capitalist world since the mid eighteenth century.

In seeking the explanation for these cycles of growth and stagnation, Schumpeter (1939) argued that technical innovation leading to the development of new industries was the key to understanding the growth phase of the cycle. Because technical innovation is spatially uneven, then so too has been the geography of economic development under capitalism. The question then arises as to why the geography of innovation is uneven. Recent research has suggested that the socio-institutional structures of regions of innovation, or of those lacking innovation, are the key to explanation; in other words, whether educational, governmental and social organizations encourage or discourage enterprise and change. Others have criticized the technological determinism of these theories (Mahon 1987).

2.2 Other perspectives, other stories

2.2.1 Marxism

The viewpoints of orthodox economics are not the only interpretation of the transformation of large parts of the world over the past 300 years. Karl Marx, in his book *Das Kapital* (1867), took a very different perspective in his analysis of capitalism (see Spotlight box 3.2). He proposed that profit arises out of the way in which capitalists (the bourgeoisie) dominate labour (the workers) in an unequal class-based relationship. This unequal class relationship was perceived by Marx to lead inevitably to class conflict. In his later writing he sketched out ways in which labour could gain control of the means of production and thereby 'throw off their chains'. This was to have dramatic long-term consequences for the socio-political organization of the world through most of the twentieth century between the Russian Revolution and the upheavals of 1989 (see Chapter 3, pp. 65–7). We need to note, however, that Marx's writing is dominated by an historical, but not a geographical, perspective: it traces class relationships in time but not in space. Marxist interpretations of capitalist development have therefore always had difficulty in conceptualizing uneven spatial development. It is also highly Eurocentric in its perspective.

2.2.2 World systems theory

Another way of conceptualizing the nature of these changes is to be found in the writings of Immanuel Wallerstein (1979), whose 'world-systems theory' provides a threefold categorization of historical socio-economic systems. Wallerstein proceeded to delimit the spatial characteristics of the capitalist world economy into **core**, **periphery** and **semi-periphery**. These terms are not used in the everyday sense but signify areas in which particular processes operate. For Wallerstein, core processes are those characterized by relatively high wages, advanced technology and diversified production; periphery processes are characterized by low wages, simple technology and limited production. Between the two is the semi-periphery: areas that exploit the periphery but which are exploited by the core, so that they exhibit a mixture of both core and peripheral processes (Taylor 1989: 16–17). In the period between the seventeenth and the end of the nineteenth century some regions of the world were in the core (north-west Europe, for example) or periphery (central Africa) throughout the period. Other regions moved from the semi-periphery into either the core (the southern states of the USA, for example) or the periphery (the states emerging from the ruins of the Ottoman/Turkish empire). Wallerstein's theory has been very influential in explanations of the growth of globalization, but it is an explanation only at the 'structural' level. It says little about the complexities of the social and economic networks that enable the system to work, or of the resistance by groups or individuals trying to change it (Ogborn 1999).

2.2.3 Eurocentrism

In recent decades, a significant group of scholars (mostly historians) have claimed that most of the theories discussed above are 'Eurocentric'. That is they tell the story of these three centuries as being about the 'rise of the West' owing to its developing humanism, scientific rationalism and democratic politics. The story of the East is relegated to a few footnotes because it was perceived as passive, unchanging and despotic. This new group of scholars, beginning perhaps with Edward Said (1978) and his concept of 'Orientalism', have tried to show that, in fact, the story of East and West is fundamentally intertwined and that capitalism would not have emerged without the import of eastern technology, ideas and resources along long-established long-distance trade routes developed by eastern merchants and connecting to Europe through the Middle East. Eurocentrism was deeply embedded in the West (at least from medieval times onwards) and also led to a distinctive, socially constructed European 'identity' that was Christian and 'civilized' and could be set against the so-called 'primitive' peoples of North America, Africa and Australasia who could be exploited as European states began to develop their empires (Hobson 2004).

2.3 The transition from feudalism to capitalism

The transformation of the European economy into a capitalist one was a long drawn-out process and historians continue to argue the precise causes of the changes that took place. Writers using an avowedly Marxist frame of reference (Dobb 1946; Kaye 1984) have made many of the most significant contributions in this debate. To them, the development of a class of wage labourers is crucial, together with the assumption of political power by the new class of capitalists. Geographers have been particularly concerned to trace the outworking of these historical processes of social and economic transformation in the particular space economies of local regions (Gregory 1982; Langton 1984; Stobart and Raven 2004).

The disintegration of **feudalism** (see Case study 1.2), with its carefully controlled market system, was considerably speeded by the after-effects of the Black Death in mid-fourteenth-century Europe. The European population was reduced by between one-third and a half, and towns were especially hard hit. The resulting labour shortage meant that enterprise and new ways of doing things were more likely to be rewarded, since the feudal elite required more revenue to maintain their power. At the same time, the slackening of social and cultural controls meant that new ways of thinking could flourish, especially in the growing towns.

By the later fifteenth century, larger European towns were dominated by what has come to be called **merchant capitalism**. Merchants were both the providers of capital and principal traders in a regionally specialized, complex, Europe-wide trading nexus based not on luxury goods as in the medieval period, but on bulky staples like grain and timber, and on an increasing array of manufactured products. Towns that flourished economically in fifteenth- and sixteenth-century Europe were those whose inhabitants were able to copy and manufacture imported products more cheaply than the exporting regions, and develop a constant stream of new, innovative, marketable products (Knox and Agnew 1994: 154–61) (Spotlight box 2.2). For most commentators, the key question then becomes: why did these processes of transformation coalesce first in sixteenth- and seventeenth-century England?

We can begin to answer this question by suggesting that, since land was one of the key factors of production, critical in the sixteenth century was the enormous transfer of land in England from conservative ecclesiastical ownership to secular ownership. This was the consequence of the dissolution of the monasteries by Henry VIII in the later 1530s. Even the monastic buildings could be adapted by capitalist manufacturers, as the Wiltshire clothier William Stumpe showed at Malmesbury Abbey where he installed 300 weavers in the 1540s (Chandler 1993: 487–9). Land was also being transformed in the sixteenth and seventeenth centuries

Spotlight box 2.2

Characteristics of the period of merchant capitalism in Europe

- Increasing numbers of people sold their labour for money wages. They ceased to work on their own land. This led to increased consumer demand for food, clothing and household goods; in many places there was a notable rise in living standards.
- More producers of both agricultural and craft-manufactured products began to accumulate capital as they produced for this growing market. These prosperous yeoman farmers and manufacturers were the foundation of a new class of capitalists.
- The removal of feudal market restrictions and controls by guilds on production led merchants to invest in the reorganization of production on a capitalist basis.

- Technical innovations transformed industries; the most significant was probably the development of the printing press by Gutenberg, in Mainz, enabling knowledge to be diffused cheaply and rapidly. However, we need to note that paper-making, block printing, and the movable metal-type press all originated earlier in China/Korea.
- The rediscovery of Classical knowledge led to new ways of seeing the world and, consequently, to its rebuilding to reflect these new images, especially in towns.
- Ultimately, these changes led to religious upheaval and political revolution whereby the new capitalist class became dominant in the governance of nation-states.

through the process of enclosure. This enabled live-stock to be raised more efficiently for the urban meat markets and experimentation in new agricultural techniques to be undertaken by yeoman farmers (Butlin 1993: 178–9).

In the seventeenth century it was the social, religious and political transformation of England that was critical, according to Dobb (1946). The struggles between Crown and Parliament during the Civil War and Commonwealth (1642–60) are seen as a conflict between landowners, and capitalist yeomen and manufacturers. Though this struggle was continued through the Restoration (1660) and Glorious Revolution (1688), by the end of the seventeenth century the capitalist bourgeoisie were politically predominant and were able to transform the state to their own advantage.

Elsewhere in Europe landowners remained pre-eminent over a predominantly peasant agricultural workforce and this period is known as the 'Age of Absolutism'. Landowners, especially the rulers of small states, amassed enormous wealth from their control of land. This wealth was expended on increasingly spectacular landscapes of display: huge palaces, filled with works of art and every luxury, set in carefully designed, and often very intricate, landscapes reliant on vast inputs of labour for their maintenance (Figure 2.1). King Louis XIV of France had set the model at his palace of Versailles, outside Paris, using the resources of a much larger state. Such conspicuous displays of wealth and privilege by the few led, ultimately, to a much bloodier revolution than in England. The French Revolution saw the slaughter of not simply the royal house, but of the landowners, intellectuals and the bourgeoisie, since this was the first of the workers' revolutions, with its cry of '*Liberté, egalité, fraternité*'. However, it led rapidly to the totalitarian militarism of Napoleon.

Figure 2.1 The palace of Versailles in 1662 by Pierre Patel. Louis XIV's mansion already has vast formal gardens stretching to the horizon, reservoirs to supply the fountains (to the right of the palace) and a *patte d'oie* of avenues (in the foreground) to provide processional routes. The growing town (left and right) gave accommodation to government officials and military officers.
Source: The Art Archive/Alamy

2.4 An expanding world

As the European economic and cultural world was gradually transformed, European travellers began to voyage beyond the shores of Europe. They travelled overland into Asia, drawn both by a thirst for greater knowledge and, more significantly, by the rewards that could be reaped from direct exploitation of scarce commodities for European consumption. These included spices, sugar, silk, muslins, porcelain and the like, which had previously been traded through the eastern Mediterranean. In the late fifteenth century, however, this region was coming under Turkish (Ottoman) control. The Portuguese, funded by Italian bankers, were the first Europeans to navigate round Africa into the Indian Ocean, using the existing Arab-dominated sea-based trading networks (Arabs had already rounded the Cape in the other direction), whilst soon after (in 1492), Christopher Columbus, again funded by Italian (Genoese) merchant capital, sailed westwards across the Atlantic to open the Americas to European exploitation using African labour.

For Spain and Portugal, this is the heroic 'Age of the Navigators', as they moved rapidly to take control of these new maritime trade routes looking out to the Atlantic. The merchants of Lisbon and Seville grew rich on this trade. For the rest of the world it marks the beginning of the European colonial empires that were to dominate and control almost every aspect of life for the next 400 years. The Portuguese established a far-flung network of small fortified port bases around Africa and the Indian Ocean, many of them based beside existing Arab ports, through which they were able to link western Europe into the trade in gold, spices and textiles (Figure 2.2). Equally significant was their use of African slaves to produce sugar on plantation farms in their Brazilian territory. The Spanish founded a more militaristic, oppressive and exploitative empire in central and south America which saw the decimation of local populations through warfare and the catastrophic effects of European diseases, especially smallpox and measles. It also brought enormous inflows of gold and silver bullion into Spain and, ultimately, onwards into the European economy. Blaut (1993) sees this as the event that more than any other kick-started the European capitalist world system.

Fairly quickly, control of the products of this new Western maritime world economy moved from southwest to north-west Europe. The Dutch began to compete successfully with the Portuguese in the Indian Ocean and the centres of European capital moved from Lisbon and Seville first to Antwerp by the mid sixteenth century, and then to Amsterdam at the end of the century. The merchants of these ports successfully integrated the Atlantic trade with that flowing from the Baltic and from central

Figure 2.2 The Portuguese fortress and trading station of Sofala, in modern Mozambique, in 1558. For a time it was the administrative centre for all Portuguese trading with India. Note the well-defended Portuguese fortress, the warehouses and accommodation of the merchants, with a Catholic church, defended by a moat, and the houses of local people in the forest landscape beyond.

Source: Carneiro (1990)

Europe via the Rhine valley. It was at Antwerp that the first stock exchange was established, enabling capital raised in one business to fund investment in another. Amsterdam's rise was based on having greater military and naval power than its neighbours and using it to enforce the privileges of a distinctive trading **monopoly**: the state-licensed joint-stock charter company (the Dutch East India Company) (Dodgshon 1998: 74–83).

At the same time, French and English fishermen had followed John Cabot's exploratory voyage across the North Atlantic to begin to exploit the rich fishing grounds off Newfoundland and, subsequently, to trade with native Americans for fur pelts. From these small beginnings French and English merchant influence began to expand through the seventeenth century in the Indian Ocean (using similar company trading monopolies to the Dutch); in the Caribbean, where sugar plantations and slave labour were copied from the Portuguese; and in North America. They superseded the Dutch in the early eighteenth century through superiority of arms, but it was not until the later eighteenth century that the British emerged dominant in the developing Western world economy. Consequently the primary city of the European

capitalist system moved once more, from Amsterdam to London (Dodgshon 1998).

The colonialist trading systems that developed in the period up to 1770 have often been described in simple dualist, oppositional, terms (core–periphery; dominant–subordinate; metropolitan–colonial, for example). Blaut (1993) is especially critical of the Eurocentric character of this type of argument. More recently, a more complex, multi-layered interpretation has been posited. We need to note, first, that different parts of the developing world economy operated in somewhat different ways, were based on different product interactions between raw materials, manufacture and consumption, involved complex transportation flows, and required different politico-military frameworks to make them function properly. Meinig's (1986) model of the Anglo-French mid-eighteenth-century North Atlantic economy uncovers some of these complexities in terms of the commercial, political and social systems that were required for the geography of colonial capitalism, and Ogborn (1999) has added details of networks of individuals and patterns of resistance (Figure 2.3). The North Atlantic 'triangular trade' is certainly the best-known of these colonial trading systems.

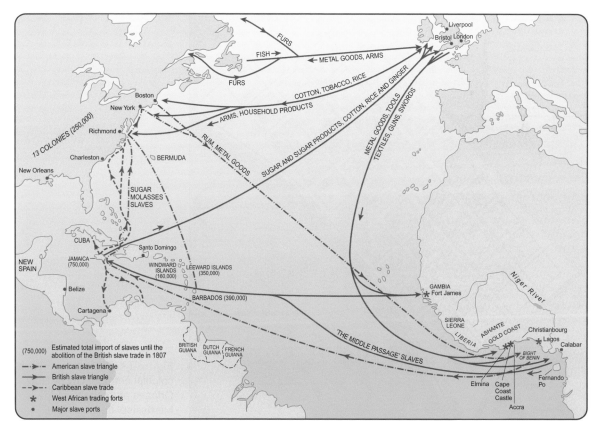

Figure 2.3 The eighteenth-century North Atlantic trading system between Britain, Africa and North and Central America.

Source: Bayley (1989: 46–7)

2.4.1 Colonial commerce

In Meinig's North Atlantic commercial system, London and Paris acted as the source of finance, commercial intelligence and marketing (London's Royal Exchange was founded in 1566). The expanding industries of particular regions of western Europe were growing, in part because they supplied a developing colonial market with manufactured goods such as textiles, tools, armaments and household necessities. These goods were assembled in Atlantic ports such as Bristol, Liverpool, Bordeaux and Le Havre. After crossing the Atlantic they were stored, disassembled and distributed from colonial ports such as New York, Charleston and New Orleans (Figure 2.4, Plate 2.1) by major traders. They sold on to local traders towards the colonial frontier. At the frontier a barter system of **exchange** was as likely to be found as a money economy. Nonetheless, fur, fish, timber and agricultural produce flowed in the opposite direction for storage and transhipment back to Europe (see Figure 2.3).

In North America, tobacco, rice, sugar, rum and cotton were the major export products. All were produced on the plantation system using slave labour. By 1750, some 50,000-60,000 people were being forcibly transported across the Atlantic each year from all parts of the western African seaboard. Many died en route or shortly afterwards but, altogether, some 3.8 million Africans had been transported by 1750, just over half to Latin America, the remainder to English, French and Dutch North America and the West Indies. These

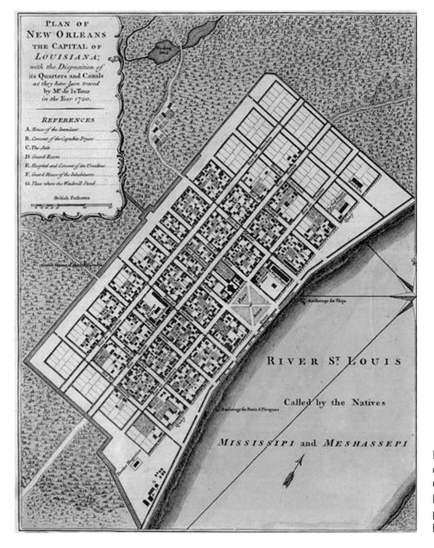

Figure 2.4 Plan of the French colonial entrepôt city of New Orleans at the head of the Mississippi delta in 1720, published in London in 1759 by Thomas Jefferys.

Plate 2.1 Madame John's Legacy, c.1788. One of the oldest houses in New Orleans, it was built during the Spanish colonial period (1765–1803). Commercial functions occupy the brick-built ground floor, residence the balcony floor.

(Terry Slater)

staggering figures meant that African-Americans were easily the largest new culture group to be established in both North and South America in the colonial period (Meinig 1986: 226–31).

The African abolitionist Olaudah Equiano, who gained his freedom in England, wrote forcefully from his own experience about the horrors of the 'middle passage' voyage from West Africa to the West Indies. He said:

> The stench of the hold while we were on the coast was intolerably loathsome ... but now that the whole ship's cargo were confined together, it became absolutely pestilential ... The air soon became unfit for respira-tion... and brought on a sickness among the slaves, of which many died ... This wretched situation was aggravated by the galling of the chains ... and the filth of the necessary tubs (toilets) into which the children often fell and were almost suffocated. The shrieks of the women and the groans of the dying, rendered the whole scene of horror almost inconceivable.
>
> (1789)

By 1750, the trade in slaves was dominated by large European companies using specially constructed and fit-ted ships, but many smaller traders from the Atlantic ports would sail first to African trading stations to exchange manufactured products, including guns, tools and chains, for slaves. The slaves would then be taken to the West Indies or Charleston, with ships returning to Liverpool or Bristol with a cargo of sugar, tobacco, rum or rice, and sometimes slaves such as Equiano, too. Most of the latter were destined for domestic service in aristocratic households (see Figure 2.3).

2.4.2 Colonial society

The slave trade was perhaps the most significant aspect of the cultural transformation effected by the eight-eenth-century capitalist world economy in the Ameri-cas and, it should not be forgotten, in Africa. One of the distinctive features of this transformation in the Americas was the 'othering' of Africans by Europeans. They were regarded as in every way inferior to Euro-peans; they were legally and socially defined as differ-ent; and they therefore lived their lives separately from white settlers. The social consequences of this were to reverberate through the next 250 years, into our own times, where spatially segregated city neighbourhoods based on **ethnicity** are still a commonplace in North American cities, whilst from the 1950s West Indian migration to Britain saw similar ethnic areas develop in many British cities. Where Africans were in the majority in the eighteenth-century colonies, as they were in the West Indies, and in the Carolinas and Louisiana, this enabled distinctive African-American cultures to develop within the confines of political and economic enslavement.

There were, of course, other trans-Atlantic migrations throughout the time period covered in this chapter. The earliest included those seeking to escape religious persecution in Europe, or to establish religious utopias in the new continent. The Puritan 'Founding Fathers' of New England were in this category and, right through to the Mormon migration in the early nineteenth century, such groups continued to leave Europe's shores for what was perceived to be a better new world. Religious faith also inspired another group of settlers who came to convert the native people of the Americas to Christianity. The competition in Europe between Catholic and Protestant versions of the faith – between Reformation and Counter-Reformation – was exported to the colonies since both native Americans and African slaves were perceived as being in need of conversion. Consequently, Jesuit monasteries or Franciscan friaries often stand at the heart of Spanish colonial towns and cities, whilst

their dedicatory saints gave name to many of today's largest cities: San Francisco, Los Angeles and San Diego, for example (Conzen 1990).

By the beginning of the eighteenth century, significant migrations of Scots, Irish, French, Germans, Dutch, Swiss and Moravians had taken place, but the dominant migrant group were the English. Between 1700 and 1775 the population of the eastern colonies grew tenfold to some 2.5 million and, by 1820, the population of the United States surpassed that of Britain (Lemon 1987: 121). The losers were native Americans who were dispossessed of their lands east of the Appalachians and often taken into slavery.

2.4.3 Colonial politics

There were major differences in the way European states governed their colonial empires. The Spanish developed a highly centralized system in which all aspects of policy were laid down in Madrid. The Laws of the Indies, which laid down in meticulous detail how colonization should take place and how new towns should be planned, are symptomatic of this centralization (Nostrand 1987) (Case study 2.1). The French governed through a similar centralized structure of military,

Case study 2.1

Summary of the Laws of the Indies by Philip II of Spain, 1573

Laws 1–14
Establish that exploration cannot take place without royal permission; that governors should learn all they can about their territory; they should consult with and negotiate with local 'Indians'. 'Discoverers' should take possession of land and should name rivers, hills and settlements.

Laws 15–31
Lay down that Spaniards should treat 'Indians' in a friendly manner; they should help priests in their work of conversion.

Laws 32–42
Concern the type of region that should be explored, pacified, settled and brought under Spanish mandate; the siting of towns in such regions, and the establishment of local government.

Laws 43–109
Establish the legal and taxation regimes for new colonies and lay down that each town should have at least 30 families. The ideal size of house plots, farms, herds, and commons is established.

Laws 110–128
Provide details of the plans of new towns, including the size of the plaza, the orientation and breadth of the streets, the location of churches and public buildings, and the allocation of house plots by lot.

Laws 129–135
Describe provision for common land and farms and the character of domestic buildings.

Laws 136–148
Lay down relationships with local 'Indians' and the way in which they should be converted to Christianity so that they 'can live civilly'.

Source: Crouch *et al.* (1982: 6–19)

administrative and ecclesiastical strands of authority linked to government departments and the Crown in Paris. The English, in contrast, allowed each colony to be virtually self-governing and the links to London were many and various. English colonial plantation owners and merchants were not averse to threatening a governor if their capitalist trading relations were endangered. It should occasion no surprise that it was the English colonies that eventually first rebelled and fought for their independence. Overlapping these colonial territories were the older territorial patterns of native groupings, those of the Iroquois and Creeks remaining well into the eighteenth century (Meinig 1986: 262). That was to change dramatically after 1815 when, over the next 15 years, the south-eastern United States was 'ethnically cleansed' of its native American inhabitants. The resultant land sales of millions of acres of 160-acre 'quarter sections' saw the first great economic boom in the United States, in much the same way as the sale of monastic lands had done in Britain in the mid sixteenth century (Johnson 2013).

2.5 Imperialism and racism

A second phase of colonial expansion, through the nineteenth century, was geographically distinct in that it was focused on Asia and, especially after 1880, on Africa. It is also marked by the development of a much more virulent **racism** in the 'othering' of all non-Europeans. The consolidation of European states in the nineteenth century, especially of Germany and Italy, and the increasing economic competition they offered to the eighteenth-century leaders of the world economy, Britain and France, led them to seek new opportunities through the colonial exploitation of hitherto economically peripheral lands. Britain seized the Dutch Cape Colony at the tip of southern Africa in 1806 to prevent its use by Napoleon's navy. By 1820, 4,000 British settler graziers were in conflict with African pastoralists, despite the fact that the low-wage labour of those same Africans was essential to maintain the farms (Lester 1999). At much the same time, the first British farmers were beginning to establish themselves in Australia as its period as a convict colony began to draw to a close. The recent novel by Kate Grenville, *The Secret River* (2006), gives a perceptive, imaginative account of the struggle for land between farmers and Aborigines at this time and the consequences for both cultures of that struggle. Meanwhile, in Britain itself, Christian-inspired reformers succeeded in bringing an end to the slave trade in

1807, and then to slavery in 1833. Sadly, the invective of both populist and bourgeois writing opposed to abolition characterized Africans, Australian Aborigines, Indians and native Americans as not only unchristian and therefore 'uncivilized' but also as less than human; inferior to Europeans in every way; both savage and yet child-like, and therefore needing to be controlled and disciplined. By the middle of the nineteenth century, these attitudes were widespread amongst all classes in Britain and were fuelled further by popular antagonism to events such as the Indian Mutiny (1857), the Zulu rebellion (1879) and the Maori wars (1860s). By the late nineteenth century, Darwin's ideas on evolution were being misused to give a scientific veneer of respectability to this 'othering' of non-Europeans, to the extent that Australian Aborigines were being shot as 'vermin' rather than seen as fellow humans.

In the United States the institution of slavery continued to flourish, especially in the lower Mississippi valley where it was an essential part of the cotton-growing plantation economy. In 1800 there were some 100,000 slaves in the present states of Louisiana and Mississippi; by 1860 there were more than 750,000. The slave trade had been successfully internalized and American firms with jails and large yards walked slaves from the south-eastern states to the Mississippi, bred children for sale and, as the recent film *12 Years a Slave* (2013), based on the 1853 autobiography of Solomon Northup, so graphically showed, kidnapped men, women and children from freedom into slavery (Johnson 2013).

The mid nineteenth century marked both the deliverance of one continent from colonialism to self-government, as South America broke free from Spanish and Portuguese control, and the colonizing of another, as European powers raced to divide Africa amongst themselves. The interior of Africa remained largely unknown to Europeans until the 1860s except for Christian missionaries. But by the end of the century, borders had been delineated and fought over, natural resources were being rapaciously exploited, and the polities, cultures and economies of native peoples had been disrupted or destroyed (Figure 2.5). Again, this period of history reverberates down to the beginning of the twenty-first century because the boundaries drawn to the satisfaction of European soldiers, administrators and traders did not correspond to African ethnic, cultural and political divisions. In some respects the origins of the genocides of Biafra (1960s' Nigeria) and Rwanda (1990s), and the long civil war in Sudan, which is still ongoing in Darfur and South Sudan, can be laid at the door of the 'scramble for Africa' in the later nineteenth century.

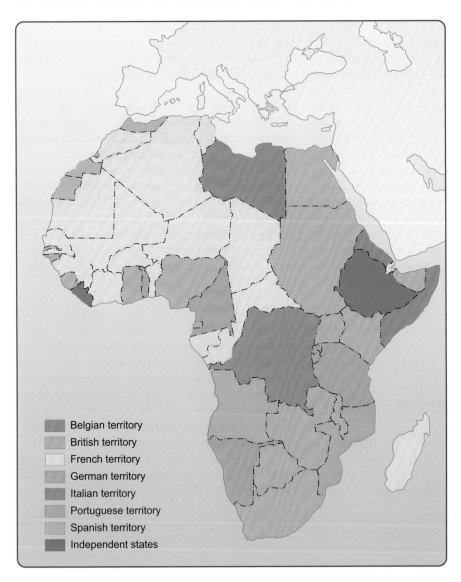

Figure 2.5 Africa in 1914 after the European imperial contest to divide the continent.

Source: Moore (1981: 74)

Belgian territory
British territory
French territory
German territory
Italian territory
Portuguese territory
Spanish territory
Independent states

2.6 Industrialization

2.6.1 Proto-industrialization

The early phases of capitalist industrial development in Europe, up to about 1770, are categorized in various ways. To some writers this is the period of merchant capitalism (see Spotlight box 2.2), to others this is the period of **proto-industrialization**. Both terms have generated a substantive academic debate as to precisely what processes of transformation were involved. Proto-industrialization is characterized by some type of 'domestic' production system whereby the capitalist merchant provides the raw materials and often the machinery for producers who worked in their own

homes. These producers generally worked in family units and were paid piece rates on a weekly or monthly basis. Their 'time geography' was therefore under their own control. As long as the contracted number of items were made each week then recreation or other activities could be fitted into the week. Many early industrial processes were located in the countryside to avoid problems with urban guild restrictions and to enable machinery to be water-powered.

Textile manufacture is the most studied production process of this period. Its transformation began in several parts of Europe as early as the fifteenth century. By the early eighteenth century, more and more of the production processes were being mechanized and industrialists were concentrating their machinery into single, multi-floor buildings. By the 1770s, the mechanization of spinning had been completed and weaving followed in the 1820s. The logic of this transformation was completed by steam power and the factory was established as both a building (Figure 2.6) and a system of production (Spotlight box 2.3). Different sectors of the textile industry went through this transformation at different times, and some sectors declined absolutely as capital was diverted to the most prosperous sectors. The textile industry, more than any other, had a relentless tendency to geographical specialization and concentration with the result that many towns and regions were dangerously dependent on a single industry (Laxton 1986). By the 1770s in Britain, west Yorkshire was beginning to dominate light worsted woollen cloth, Lancashire and the north Midlands cotton cloth production, the Welsh borders flannel, and the east Midlands hosiery.

I began work at the mill in Bradford when I was nine years old . . . we began at six in the morning and worked until nine at night. When business was brisk, we began at five and worked until ten in the evening.

(Hannah Brown, interviewed in 1832).

Legislation dating from this time remains effective in controlling the age at which children and young people can work and their hours of employment.

The complex interaction of resources, labour skills, technological innovation, and capital circulation in particular regional economies, which increased production and lowered prices, meant that new markets had to be developed and transport improved. Market opportunities were to be found both in the growing urban markets at home, and among the colonial populations overseas. Thus, cotton textiles were first imported to Britain from

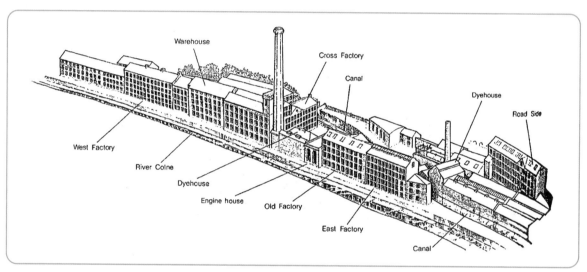

Figure 2.6 Starkey's woollen textile mill, Huddersfield, c.1850. Though this mill was steam-powered, by mid-century its powerlooms were still housed in multi-storey buildings rather than a single-storey shed, since the site was a restricted one.

Source: Giles and Goodall (1992: 102) © Crown Copyright. NMR

Spotlight box 2.3

The factory system of production

Under the factory system the capitalist:
- Had complete control of the production process from receipt of raw materials to finished product.
- Had control of the labour force on whom a new, disciplined time geography could be imposed (early factories often worked day and night).

- Could apply capital to the development of new machinery to simplify processes and reduce labour costs through mechanization; and,
- By dividing the tasks of the production process, could reduce labour costs further by employing women and children.

India; the techniques of production were learnt; manufacture commenced; factory production lowered costs; cotton textiles were exported to India; there they undercut and destroyed the Indian industry.

A key transformation of the transport infrastructure, so essential to industrialization, was the improvement of links with growing towns, and with the ports. Canals and turnpike (toll) roads, which were the principal innovations before the 1820s, also lowered the costs of raw materials, especially of coal. This is graphically illustrated by the way in which urban populations celebrated the opening of new canals, not for their industrial potential, but because they dramatically reduced the cost of domestic heating. In Britain, the construction of better roads, and of the canal network, mostly between 1760 and 1815 (the growth phase of the first **Kondratieff cycle**) was financed by private capital. The state was involved only in providing the necessary legislation to enable construction to take place and fees or tolls to be levied. Thus Josiah Wedgwood (china and pottery), Abraham Darby (iron manufacturer) (Figure 2.7) and Matthew Boulton

(jewellery and silver plate), as well as the Duke of Bridgewater (landowner and coal owner), all invested some of their capital in canal companies to improve the distribution of their products (Freeman 1986). A similar pattern is observed in New England. In France and Germany, by contrast, new roads were seen to have a military function in the centralization of state control and were therefore largely financed by the state through taxation.

2.6.2 Agricultural change

It was not just industries such as textiles, metal manufacturing and pottery that were transformed by early capitalist production: society needed food production to keep pace with a rising population that was increasingly employed full-time in manufacturing. Consequently, the eighteenth century saw the transformation of agriculture into increasingly capitalistic modes. In parts of Europe, especially in Britain, self-sufficient peasant farming began to come under pressure from landowners who used state legislation to remove common rights to land in

Figure 2.7 The world's first iron bridge, constructed across the River Severn, east Shropshire, in 1788 by Abraham Darby III's Coalbrookdale Company, was part of the transport infrastructure improvements financed by local industrialists.

Source: The Ironbridge Gorge Museum

favour of private ownership through enclosure. Ownership was increasingly concentrated into fewer hands, and farms were consolidated from scattered strips to single-block holdings, again especially in Britain and, rather later, in Scandinavia and northern Germany. Elsewhere in Europe this process was delayed until the twentieth century. In northern and western Europe, landowners invested in transforming production for the new urban markets, using technology and new techniques and crops first developed in the Low Countries in the seventeenth century. In eastern Europe, the semi-periphery, this period saw a reversion to serfdom and near-feudal relations of production. Capital was also deployed to increase the area of land under intensive, rather than extensive, production. Fenland and coastal marshes were drained; heathland soils improved for cultivation, and the moorland edge of improved pastures pushed higher up hill and mountain slopes.

In the nineteenth century, European agriculture continued to increase production but was unable to keep pace with the demand from the growing urban industrial population. In 1840, Britain repealed the Corn Laws, which had protected local grain producers, and opened its markets to colonial and American producers. New methods of extensive grain farming were used in mid-western North America, and in the new British colonies in Australasia and South Africa. The invention of the steam ship, allowing more rapid transport, and of refrigeration and meat canning from the 1870s, led to similarly extensive ranch grazing of sheep and cattle in these countries. Together with the Pampas grasslands of Argentina,

all became an important part of the semi-periphery of Britain's global economy. This export-dominated agriculture was reliant on overseas investment by British capital in new railway networks to transport these products to slaughterhouses and industrial packing plants at the port cities whilst, in the USA, Chicago was growing rapidly on the same economic foundations (Cronon 1991; Miller 1997). It was accompanied, too, by new waves of migration to the colonies and the mid-west of the USA (Table 2.1), especially from Ireland and Scotland, where the Great Famine and the Highland Clearances, respectively, were other manifestations of capitalist agricultural change in the British Isles. The United States absorbed enormous numbers of European migrants throughout the nineteenth century. Irish migrants predominated in the 1840s and 1850s, followed by Scots and English, Scandinavians and Germans through the second half of the century, with Russians, Italians and south-central Europeans from the 1880s onwards (Table 2.1) (Ward 1987).

This later colonization, and the internal colonization of the United States mid-west in particular, were grandly characterized as a moving frontier of settlement by the American historian, F.J. Turner, writing in 1894, who suggested that it also transformed the 'character' of frontier settlers, making them self-reliant, opportunistic, individualistic and democratic. Recent commentators have noted that Turner's hypothesis says little about the continued sweeping aside of the rights of the native populations of these lands who fought a long and ultimately unsuccessful attritional battle to retain it for their own use (the land was regarded as 'open' or

Table 2.1 European emigration 1881–1910

Source countries	Destination countries	Numbers of migrants
Great Britain	N. America, S. Africa, Australasia	7,144,000
Italy	USA and N. Africa	6,187,000
Germany	North and South America	2,143,000
Austria/Hungary	North and South America	1,799,000
Russia	USA	1,680,000
Scandinavia	North America	1,535,000
Spain	Central and S. America; N. Africa	1,472,000
Ireland	USA	1,414,000
Portugal	South America	775,000
S.E. Europe	USA	c.465,000
France	Central and S. America	223,000
Low Countries	USA	171,000

Source: Moore (1981: 57)

'free' for white settlement); nor does it give any credit for the settlement process to women, who provided both the domestic labour and, often, especially in the initial phase of settlement, much of the farm labour too. The advancing frontier of capitalist agriculture was as much small-scale, incremental and domestic as it was wide-sweeping and large-scale.

2.6.3 Factories and industrial production

Some commentators have seen the 'Industrial Revolution' in Britain as a short period, between 1770 and 1830, of rapid transformation whereby the country's economy moved from an agricultural to an industrial manufacturing basis. More recent writers see the transformation as much more drawn out, extending from the seventeenth century and into the early twentieth century. They also see it as much more regionally diversified and geographically uneven, with particular regions specializing in particular products which transformed their production systems at different times. Most attention has been given to the textile and iron and steel industries, both of which are characterized by large factories requiring massive capital investment in buildings and machinery, driven by steam power, with manufacturing processes increasingly vertically integrated, and employing a large, and increasingly disciplined labour force (see Figure 2.6). The same forces were at work in New England. By 1855, there were 52 cotton mills in Lowell, Massachusetts, employing more than 13,000 people, two-thirds of them women (Groves 1987). In Europe, Lille (France), Ghent (Belgium), Łódź (Poland) and the Wupper valley of Germany developed as centres of cotton textile manufacture (Pounds 1990: 402).

Recently, Johnson (2013), in an avowedly Marxist interpretation, has suggested that historians have viewed the cotton trade (the largest single sector of the global economy in the first half of the nineteenth century) through the wrong end of the telescope. It was not Lowell, Liverpool and Łódź that were the foundation stones of the capitalist economy, but the Mississippi valley, where the raw cotton was produced, where the planter's capital was human bodies (slaves) which were more valuable than all the machinery, infrastructure, manufacturing and free labour elsewhere in the United States. The 'industry' of slave-based plantation cotton production in the Mississippi valley was what tied together the fortunes of cotton planters of Louisiana, the cotton brokers of Liverpool and the cotton manufacturers in Manchester. What kept the slaves from revolt and crushed slave resistance was the use of the state's military might to ensure that the system was maintained (Johnson 2013).

Many other industries were developed in the same way as new markets arose on a national and international basis and production expanded. Food and drink, for example, is rarely thought of as a factory-based industry, but brewing, once the prerogative of almost every village inn, became increasingly an urban, large-scale industry with regional markets for its beers. In England, Burton-upon-Trent developed rapidly as the 'brewing capital' of Britain, with huge factory-scale breweries, on the basis of its colonial contracts to supply bottled 'India Pale Ale' to troops and civilians stationed in the Indian sub-continent as a substitute for local water. For other industries, however, including many manufacturing industries, 'factories' remained small-scale workshops employing fewer than 50 people (the Sheffield cutlery industry in northern England, and wire-drawing in the eastern Ruhr in Germany are good examples). Indeed, many industries remained almost domestic in scale well into the twentieth century (for example, the Birmingham jewellery and Coventry watch industries, both in central England).

The nineteenth century is characterized not only by this enormous variety in the scale of production, but also by an equally enormous variety of manufactured products. The tag 'The Workshop of the World' is as true of nineteenth-century Britain in general as it is of several of the country's manufacturing cities. In other British, European and American regions there was an increasing specialization so that local economies were dependent on maintaining market advantage on a single industry: the Polish textile city of Łódź and Lancashire's cotton mill towns were of this kind. Such places also produced distinctive working-class cultures, which, in the case of Łódź, was also predominantly Jewish (Koter 1990). Again, in those same mill towns much factory employment was female (see the example of Lowell above), whereas in heavy industry centres, such as ship-building in Newcastle and Sunderland, in the north-east of England, waged employment was male-dominated and women's roles were primarily domestic. E.P. Thompson, in his classic Marxist interpretation of *The Making of the English Working Class* (1963), is especially sensitive to the variety of experiences of working people in this period of aggressive industrial capitalism. There are, however, some common features of nineteenth-century industrial development in Britain and, subsequently, in Europe and North America. First was the fact that the power supply for the majority of industries came to be dominated by steam. There was therefore a move by many industries to the coalfield regions to reduce the cost of fuel (Figure 2.8). The development of the Ruhr region of Germany (Pounds 1990: 412–29), and of western Pennsylvania in the USA

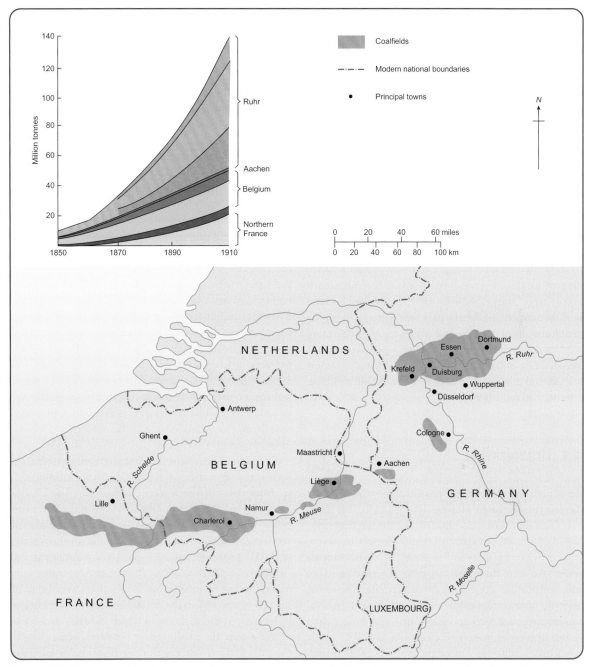

Figure 2.8 The coalfields of north-west Europe saw a concentration of new industrial enterprises after the 1780s as steam-powered machinery became normal in textile manufacturing, iron and steel making and metal goods manufacturing.

Source: Pounds (1990: 44)

(Meyer 1990: 256–8), are good examples of this process. The reason for this change in fuel supply was the invention and commercial development of the rotative steam engine by James Watt and Matthew Boulton in 1769–75.

Secondly this, in its turn, was fundamental to the invention and development of railways that transformed the transport costs of both raw materials and finished products almost as dramatically as it reduced the friction of distance. The Western and, increasingly, the colonial worlds saw a new time geography from the 1840s onwards, whereby journeys previously requiring several days to accomplish could be undertaken in a few hours. This was especially important in the industrialization of North America with its vast transcontinental distances (the first transcontinental line was completed in 1869). It was also significant in Britain's imperial control of India, and of Russia's colonization of the interior of Siberia and central Asia. In all three cases the railways enabled industrial-scale exploitation of natural resources (from timber to metalliferous ores) to take place, the profits from which could, in turn, be invested in further industrial, urban or railway development. The rapid expansion of San Francisco following the California gold and Nevada silver discoveries in 1849 and 1859 respectively is a good example of this (Walker 1996). Railways were also major industries in their own right, of course; the Indian railways employed three-quarters of a million people by the 1920s, for example.

Third was the fact that, as capitalists sought **economies of scale**, the transformations of the nineteenth century were largely urban. By 1851, Britain had become the first country anywhere in which a majority of its inhabitants lived and worked in towns. By 1900 there were sixteen cities in the world with a population that exceeded one million, as against one (Peking [Beijing]) in 1800, and another 27 places which had half a million or more (Lawton 1989).

2.7 Urbanization

The urbanization of capital has been theorized from a Marxist perspective by Harvey (1985a, 1985b). He notes that, as capitalists over-accumulate, the surplus flows into secondary circuits of capital, of which the principal is the built environment (in its widest sense). As in the primary industrial circuit, these flows are cyclical according to the perceived profitability of such investment. Because of the longevity of the built environment these 'building cycles' (sometimes called Kuznets cycles) are much longer than the business cycles, somewhere between 15 and 25 years. Crises may lead to the loss of profitability of an investment, but they do not often lead to the loss of building fabric. Western cities are therefore made in the image of past capitalist decisions and subsequent adaptations to fit new circumstances. Harvey goes on to suggest ways in which class struggle is written into the landscape of the Western city (1985a: 27–31), which he explores in more detail in an analysis of Paris in the third quarter of the nineteenth century. More recently, Dodgshon (1998: 148–61) has built on these arguments to show how the built environment of towns and cities is a major source of inertia in capitalist economies and societies.

There are perhaps two major phases of development in Western industrial cities before 1900, and the beginnings of a third. The first phase, which began in Britain in the 1770s, was characterized by the need to provide homes for workers once the production process was separated from home. Initially, such housing was provided by a process of 'densification' whereby more and more living spaces were crammed into the existing built-up area. Gardens and yards were used for increasingly high-density basic accommodation, much of which was multi-occupied. By the 1770s in larger British cities this process could go no further and housing began to be provided on the city fringe where it proved a profitable 'crop' for small landowners. Such housing was brick-built, basic, unplanned and unregulated, and regionally distinctive in its plan forms (Plate 2.2(a)). The most notorious of these forms was the back-to-back dwelling originating in the Yorkshire textile towns (Beresford 1988). The lack of regulation meant that these housing areas lacked effective water supplies, sewage and waste disposal systems, social and educational facilities, and connected road systems. The consequences, when combined with the **poverty** of low wages, were ill health, disease and very high urban death rates, especially among children. European and North American cities were also characterized by unregulated slum housing areas as urban populations rose from the 1820s onwards (Pounds 1990: 368–91; Homburger 1994: 110–11).

The second feature of this first phase of industrial cities was the separation of the residences of the bourgeoisie from those of the workers. Industrial cities became class-divided cities, though the working classes, especially young females, were recruited to provide domestic services by the elite (Dennis 1984). In the southern states of the USA that servant class was African-American and still slaves until the 1860s. Thirdly, the capitalist land market began to value more highly the accessibility of the city centre and so the central business district began to emerge, as did districts in which industry and warehousing were the predominant land use, often close to the port facilities of canal, river frontage or harbour. One of the classic portrayals of this phase of urban development in Britain is Engels' (1845) *The Condition of the Working Class in England*. Warehouse districts, of course, have recently been 'revalued' in many cities to become today's loft apartments or high-tech offices (Zukin 1989).

The second phase of development, from 1840 to the 1890s, was one of increasing regulation in towns and cities. New forms of local government and the collection of statistical information led to building regulations; the provision of sewerage and better water supplies; the

Plate 2.2 English nineteenth-century industrial housing. (a) Back-to-back courtyard house, Birmingham *c.*1840. The door on the right leads on to a court of 12 identical houses fronting a narrow courtyard. Such houses were found in the Midlands in the period 1770–1860. (b) Tunnel-back bye-law houses, Teignmouth, Devon *c.*1880. The distinctive rear elevation resulted from bye-laws derived from the 1875 Public Health Act. These houses are found in all cities in the period 1875–1914. (c) Harborne Tenants Association, Birmingham, 1908. These houses derive from the garden city movement. Experimental estates of the Edwardian period provided the model for twentieth-century municipal housing. (d) Improved industrial dwellings, east London *c.*1885. Industrial Dwellings Associations experimented with tenement blocks with open galleried staircases.

(All photographs Terry Slater)

provision of new cemeteries and parks; and better urban transport, especially tramways. All this led in turn to the increasing **suburbanization** of the better-paid elements of the urban workforce in the last quarter of the nineteenth century. These transformations occurred in most European core economies, and in North American cities, but with temporal variations. Thus, in England, the characteristic late-nineteenth-century dwelling was a suburban, brick-built, tunnel-back, terraced house (Plate 2.2(b)). In North America, excepting only the largest cities, the vast majority of urban housing was timber-built; in much of the rest of Europe, from Stockholm to Naples (as well as in Scotland), the apartment or tenement block was the norm (Plate 2.2(d)). The North American city, from the 1840s, was also characterized by the ghettoization of immigrant populations: first Irish and Germans, then freed slaves from the southern states after the Civil War, then Italians, and finally, from the 1890s, Jewish migrants from the Russian empire of eastern Europe (Ward 1987) (Plate 2.3(d)).

Central business districts were modified by two other major transformations in the capitalist system in this second phase. First, banking services were increasingly required to enable surplus capital to be safely stored, efficiently invested and recycled towards new opportunities; such banks were but one aspect of developing office quarters, including, for example, insurance offices, land agents and other property services, and legal services. Many of these well-constructed buildings have been found alternative uses today, as cafes, pubs or homes, because they have become valued parts of city conservation areas. This tertiary employment sector grew rapidly in the second half of the nineteenth century and 'the office' developed as both a specialized building type and a means of production (Daniels 1975). It was increasingly characterized by female employees using typewriters (the key technological invention) supervised by male managers. In North America the building type showed an increasing propensity to both large floor areas and height at the end of the century. The skyscraper was born in Chicago and relied on the development of steel-frame construction methods and the invention of the elevator (Gad and Holdsworth 1987) (Plate 2.3(a) and (b)). Second was the growth of consumption. This led to the development of a variety of new retail spaces in city centres, including department stores and arcades (Plate 2.3(c)), as well as an enormous growth in the variety of specialized shops.

The incipient third phase of urban development reflected a minority interest in improving the living conditions of workers by industrialists. Model settlements have a history that dates to the beginning of the factory system. Modern commentators note both the generally higher standard of accommodation in these places, and the capitalist control of the home life as well as the working life of their workers. At the century's end the experimental garden suburb settlements at Bournville and Port Sunlight in England (Plate 2.2(c)) were widely admired and imitated in Germany (Margarethenhöhe in Essen, for example) and the USA (Radburn, New Jersey). At the same time, the first experiments in the large-scale provision of social housing were underway in London using apartment-block housing. These two themes, the garden suburb and social housing, were to combine powerfully in the development of modern planning to shape the urban environment in the first half of the twentieth century in Europe and its empires, but not in North America.

2.8 Conclusion

Within three centuries, Western capitalism had utilized its ill-gotten gains from its first colonial adventures to develop a series of specialized industrial regions supplying worldwide markets. Food production, industrial manufacture, service provision, consumption and transportation were all radically transformed by the capitalist enterprise. Cultures, societies and governments were necessarily impelled to change, too. States became more centralized and powerful. The difference between rich and poor both at the level of individuals and between countries became more marked. For some individuals and groups capitalism brought prosperity, improved living conditions and greater freedom; for others it brought destruction of local cultures, impoverishment, degradation and slavery. At the end of the nineteenth century the South African Boer War gave the first glimpse of the industrialization of warfare which was to scar the twentieth century so deeply.

Plate 2.3 American nineteenth-century city buildings. (a) Reliance office building, Chicago; architect: Daniel H. Burnham & Co (1895). This is the nearest that a steel-framed building got to being sheathed almost entirely in glass in the nineteenth century. (b) Flat Iron office building, New York; architect: Daniel H. Burnham (1901–2). This famous skyscraper of 22 storeys is in the style of an elongated Renaissance palazzo. The steel frame is clad in limestone and terra cotta. (c) Carson Pirie Scott & Co store, Chicago: architect: Louis H. Sullivan (1899–1904). Department stores were an important retail innovation in large city centres. (d) New York tenement building; 97 Orchard Street (1863–4), now the Lower East Side Tenement Museum. There were two shops in the sub-basement with four three-room apartments on each of the five floors. Seventy-two mostly German immigrants lived there in 1870; in 1900 there were 111 mostly Russian Jewish residents.

(All photographs Terry Slater)

Learning outcomes

Having read this chapter, you should know that:

- Scholars have interpreted and theorized the development of capitalism in different ways.
- The European colonialist enterprise was critical in the evolution of capitalism.
- Industrial capitalism transformed all sectors of the economy, including the built environment and social relations between individuals and classes.
- Industrial capitalism was essentially urban.

Further reading

Blaut, J.M. (1993) *The Colonizer's Model of the World: Geographical Diffusionism and Eurocentric History,* Guilford Press, New York and London. This is a very readable and thought-provoking polemic of post-colonial writing, providing an alternative explanation of the 'success' of European capitalism.

Dodgshon, R.A. (1998) *Society in Time and Space: A Geographical Perspective on Change,* Cambridge University Press, Cambridge. A more advanced text which provides much more detailed arguments and evidence for the themes of this chapter.

Hobson, John M. (2004) *The Eastern Origins of Western Civilisation,* Cambridge University Press, Cambridge. Challenges the Eurocentric interpretation of this period of the world's developmental history.

Johnson, Walter (2013) *River of Dark Dreams: Slavery and Empire in the Cotton Kingdom,* Belknap Press, Cambridge MA. This recent scholarly book melds the institution of slavery, the cotton plantation economy of the Mississippi valley, and the global cotton trade in the nineteenth century to present a new way of seeing what we previously thought of as familiar.

Knox, P., Agnew, J. and McCartney, L. (2014) *The Geography of the World Economy,* 6th edition, Edward Arnold, London. A well-written and popular textbook which will give readers another perspective on this period and much else besides.

Langton, J. and Morris, R.J. (eds) (1986) *Atlas of Industrializing Britain, 1780–1914,* Methuen, London and New York. Historical atlases usually treat this period very well with innovative cartography and thought-provoking texts. This one deals with Britain in considerable detail.

Mitchell, R.D. and Groves, P.A. (eds) (1987) *North America: The Historical Geography of a Changing Continent,* Hutchinson, London. There are a number of good historical geographies of North America. This one is well written, thoughtful and copiously illustrated.

Ogborn, M. (2007) *Indian Ink: Script and Print in the Making of the English East India Company,* University of Chicago Press, Chicago, IL. This book explores the geographies of power and knowledge in the rise of the British Empire in India.

Watts, M. (2001) *Late Victorian Holocausts: El Niño Famines and the Making of the Third World,* Verso, London. An account of the interactions between imperialism, ecology and famine in the nineteenth century. It is worth reading in tandem with Crosby, A.W. (1986) *Ecological Imperialism: The Biological Expansion of Europe, 900–1900.* Cambridge University Press, Cambridge.

Useful websites

www.besthistorysites.net Entitled 'Best of History Websites', a comprehensive guide to history-oriented resources online. For teachers, students and others.

www.british-history.ac.uk British History Online is a digital library of key printed primary and secondary sources for the history of Britain and Ireland. The accent is on the period between 1300 and 1800.

THE MAKING OF THE TWENTIETH- AND TWENTY-FIRST-CENTURY WORLD

Chapter 3

Denis Shaw

Topics covered

- The second industrial revolution
- Fordism – new patterns of production and consumption in the twentieth century
- Fordist capitalism
- Challenges to liberal capitalism: Nazism, communism
- The end of European imperialism; informal imperialism
- Globalized capitalism
- The world in the early twenty-first century

The twentieth century could be said to have been the period when capitalism finally triumphed over most of the globe. But it was neither a straightforward triumph nor an unchallenged one, and capitalism itself was changed in the process. This chapter is concerned with the various spaces created by and in response to twentieth- and twenty-first-century capitalism – spaces of resistance and reinterpretation as well as spaces of adaptation and acceptance. The patchy and unequal world in which we now live reflects the erratic and conflict-laden nature of the processes that have produced it, and we need to know something about those processes to understand the world as it is now.

3.1 The changing capitalism of the early twentieth century

In the autumn of the year 1933 the writer and journalist J.B. Priestley set out by bus on a trip that was to take him the length and breadth of England and which he later described in his *English Journey* (Priestley 1937). As he left London by the Great West Road, Priestley noted how the road 'looked odd. Being new, it did not look English. We might have suddenly rolled into California.' What struck Priestley as particularly odd was 'the line of new factories on each side' of the road. 'Years of the West Riding', he explained (he was born and raised in Bradford in northern England), 'have fixed forever my idea of what a proper factory looks like: a grim, blackened rectangle with a tall chimney at one corner. These decorative little buildings, all glass and concrete and chromium plate,

seem to my barbaric mind to be merely playing at being factories.' Armed with a copy of the now celebrated textbook, *The British Isles: Geographic and Economic Survey* by Stamp and Beaver (1933), which was later to be used by generations of geography undergraduates (including the present writer), Priestley went on to make some astute geographical and social points about these factories: 'Actually, I know, they are tangible evidence, most cunningly arranged to take the eye, to prove that the new industries have moved south. You notice them decorating all the western borders of London. At night they look as exciting as Blackpool. But while these new industries look so much prettier than the old, which I remember only too well, they also look far less substantial. Potato crisps, scent, tooth pastes, bathing costumes, fire extinguishers; those are the concerns behind these pleasing facades' (Priestley 1937: 3–5).

In these few words, Priestley summarized some of the major ways in which the industrial world of the twentieth century was to differ from its nineteenth-century predecessor. The fact that he was making his journey by road was itself significant; 30 years before he would have had to go by rail. The new factories he observed were the products of the technological changes that had been transforming industrial capitalism since the late nineteenth century, and many had clearly developed to serve an expanding consumer market (see Plates 3.1 and 3.2). And the location of the factories by the new arterial highway leading westwards out of London was the result not only of a revolution in transport and communications but also of the locational freedom deriving from the availability of electricity and other fuels. The textile industries that Priestley remembered from his childhood

Plate 3.1 The Hoover factory, Perivale, west London. This splendid example of Art Deco architecture, designed by Gil Wallace in 1932, reflects the new consumer industries which were being established in the years after the First World War.

(© Angelo Hornak/CORBIS)

in Bradford were tied to the coalfields; the newer industries that were appearing in London by the 1930s no longer needed coal, and were much cleaner and brighter in consequence.

Of course, what Priestley saw along the Great West Road was by no means representative of all the technological changes that had been affecting the industrial economies of Britain and other countries for the previous few decades. What had been happening in these countries was that a whole series of new industrial branches had been developing to supplement, and eventually to eclipse, the traditional activities based on coal, iron and textiles. Not all of these were as pleasing to the eye as those observed by Priestley. In the second half of the nineteenth century, for example, the metallurgical industries had been transformed as a result of a series of inventions allowing the production of cheap steel. Next came the rapid development and proliferation of different branches of the chemical industry (alkalis, dyestuffs, pharmaceuticals, explosives, lacquers, photographic plates and film, celluloid, artificial fibres, plastics). The electricity generation industry, which began to flourish by the end of the nineteenth century, was dependent on earlier inventions, like the steam turbine. About the same time came the rise of the motor industry, which was in turn associated with other industries like oil and rubber. When Priestley set out on his journey, society was already beginning to adjust to the impact of the many new activities catering to the consumer (most notably, domestic appliances – see Plate 3.2) and to new means of transportation (car, bus, aircraft). Of course the full impact of such developments was to come later, after the Second World War, while some technologies, like regular TV broadcasting, the jet engine, nuclear power and the microchip, still lay in the future.

So profound were the technological and accompanying social changes that affected industrial capitalism from the late nineteenth century that some historians have described them as a '**second industrial revolution**' (Landes 1969: 4). But it is important to remember that the older industries – coal, textiles, railways, some forms of engineering – did not die immediately or indeed quickly. One of the features of the changing industrial geography of the late nineteenth and early twentieth centuries was that countries like the USA and Germany, whose industrialization came later than Britain's, now began to forge ahead on the basis of the newer industries described above. Britain remained overdependent on the older and less dynamic branches (Figure 3.1).

For the first half of the twentieth century, the industrial changes described above only directly affected certain parts of the world, notably Western Europe, North America, Japan, and by the 1930s the Soviet Union and

Plate 3.2 Admiring one of the new consumer products which were becoming available for more affluent groups by the 1930s.
(Everett Collection/Shutterstock)

some other areas. Much of what was later to become known as the Third World, or the developing world, was still agricultural. Yet, in continuation of earlier processes (see Chapter 2, pp. 42–5, 50–2) many colonies and other regions were now being organized commercially to supply the industrial countries with raw materials and tropical products – for example, bananas and sugar from Central America and the Caribbean, Brazilian coffee, Indian tea, Malaysian rubber. They were thus being tied in to the capitalist world economy. Gradually certain of these countries began to adopt the technologies of the industrialized world – the rise of the Indian textile industry is one example – but only later in the twentieth century did industrialization become more widespread.

Thus the foundations of what is now known as a global economy were already being laid in Priestley's day, or even earlier. By the beginning of the twentieth century capitalism had become a world phenomenon, tying far-flung countries together by means of international trade and fostering international capital flows through major financial centres like London and New York. The first multinational corporations were already appearing. All this was aided and abetted by the new systems of communication and transport – telegraph, telephone, radio (from the 1900s), fast steamships, aircraft – which were beginning to provide services that spanned the globe. Of course, none of this bears comparison with the forces of globalization that were to become so significant later in the century. Yet the world was already becoming a smaller place (see Plate 3.8). J.B. Priestley himself suggested this when he compared the Great West Road to 'California'. What might this mean to the average English reader in the 1930s? The answer is – a great deal. The Hollywood film industry in Los Angeles

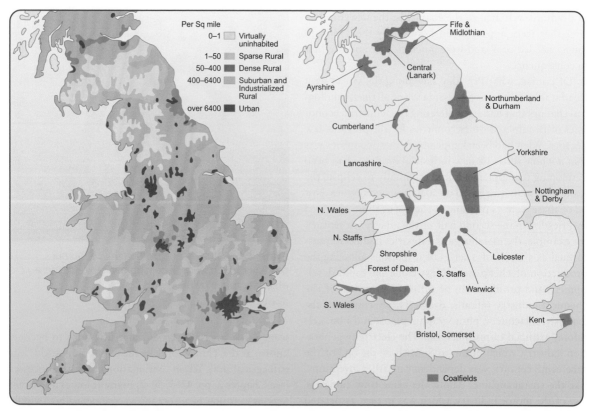

Figure 3.1 The geography of the UK population and coalfields compared. With the significant exception of London, there is a strong correlation between the geography of population and that of coalfields, reflecting both the early stage at which Britain industrialized and urbanized, and the country's long dependence on nineteenth-century industries.

Sources: population, based on Mitchell (1962); coalfields, Stamp and Beaver (1963: 286)

was in its heyday and the people, homes and landscapes it portrayed were being viewed, and copied, the world over.

3.2 Fordist capitalism

It would be a mistake to suppose that the advance of capitalism in the twentieth century was a story of unmitigated triumph. On the contrary, its fluctuations and misfortunes were such that one historian felt constrained to call the period the 'Age of Extremes' (Hobsbawm 1995). The first half of the century – Hobsbawm's 'Age of Catastrophe' – was particularly disturbed, with two world wars (1914–18 and 1939–45) and a deep world economic depression (1929–33).

By contrast, the years between 1945 and 1973 were ones of growing prosperity across much of the globe (Hobsbawm's 'Golden Age') only to be followed once more by a disturbed period in the wake of the oil price rise shocks of the 1970s.

It was Karl Marx who originally emphasized the unplanned, competitive and even chaotic nature of capitalism's development. But one of the features of the twentieth century has been the attempt, by both national governments and private agencies, to regulate and even to control it. The reasons for this phenomenon are many, but they are no doubt linked both to the precipitate nature of technological change during this period and to the severe fluctuations mentioned above. Attempts to 'organize' capitalism have taken a number of different forms. For example, already in the late nineteenth century, and especially in the USA and Germany, there were moves towards the formation of inter-firm agreements, cartels and larger companies and corporations. Large corporations could more easily marshal the huge capital resources which modern industry requires, and also influence their markets more effectively. As noted already, the first multinational corporations appeared at this time, those based in the USA being most notable. Nineteenth-century examples include the German electrical firm, Siemens, and the US Singer sewing machine company (see

Plate 3.3 The former Singer building on Nevsky Avenue, St Petersburg, Russia. Constructed in 1904 by the architect P. V. Suzor in the art nouveau style fashionable at the time, this building symbolizes the globalized economy which was beginning to appear by the early twentieth century. The property was confiscated after the 1917 Russian Revolution and subsequently served as one of the city's main bookshops, a function it still performs today.

(Iakov Filimonov/Shutterstock)

Plate 3.3). Twentieth-century examples include US-based Hoover, Ford, Coca-Cola, Pepsi Cola, Nabisco (Shredded Wheat), and Kellogg's, all of which invested in Britain in the 1930s. Most of the major international oil firms also date from this period.

A further way in which capitalism became more 'organized' was the phenomenon of mass production, linked especially to the growing consumer market. Here two Americans are regarded as particularly significant. F.W. Taylor (1856–1915) is especially associated with time-and-motion studies, whereby complex tasks on the factory floor could be completed more efficiently and productivity increased. The other is Henry Ford (1863–1947) who organized car production in his Dearborn, Michigan plant using modern methods like the assembly line and interchangeable parts. The result of his centralized approach was a significant reduction in the time and cost of producing cars, meaning they could now be manufactured on a mass basis. These production methods and associated patterns of mass consumption are frequently referred to as **Fordism**, hence the capitalism of this period is often referred to as *Fordist capitalism*.

Governments were also affected by the desire to 'organize' capitalism and to tackle the many problems to which it seemed to give rise. At the international level, the USA, which emerged after the Second World War as the undisputed leader of world capitalism, took the lead in establishing a series of institutions like the **World Bank**, the International Monetary Fund (IMF) and the General Agreement on Tariffs and Trade (GATT) to ease international monetary payments, promote trade and encourage economic development. At the national level, numerous countries, especially some of those in Western Europe, pursued democratic agenda of various kinds, such as attempts to construct 'welfare states' to tackle social problems like unemployment, ill health, old age and social inequity. Arguably the experience of government planning and controls in wartime (and possibly also a fear of **communism** – see below) helped pave the way for the optimistic belief in the benefits of planning and large-scale social engineering that characterized the postwar period. In Western Europe especially this was the era of bold experiments in new town and city development, slum clearance and ambitious social housing schemes, regional planning, and extensive controls over land use (Hall 2014). No doubt the success of these schemes was dependent on the spreading affluence that accompanied Hobsbawm's 'Golden Age'. Across Western Europe and North America a tide of suburbanization signalled not only a growing ability to own one's own home in a desirable location but also the availability of the social and physical infrastructure, the private cars and the many new consumer products which now made such a goal possible for many (see Plate 3.4).

The writers Scott Lash and John Urry have described the era ushered in by the methods of Ford and Taylor that reached its apogee during the period 1945–73 as 'organized capitalism' (Lash and Urry 1987). Some of its

Plate 3.4 Brick and render middle-class housing built in the suburbs of a West Yorkshire town in the 1930s. The suburbanization of the inter-war period was a product of the affluence and increased mobility of some middle-class groups at the time. Suburbanization was to become even more prominent after the Second World War.

(peter jeffreys/Shutterstock)

Spotlight box 3.1

Fordist or 'organized' capitalism

- Extractive and manufacturing industries are the dominant economic sectors.
- There is an accent on economies of scale, leading to the importance of large industrial plants. Such plants may structure entire regional economies around themselves. Examples might include (in the United Kingdom): the West Midlands, based on cars and engineering; Lancashire, based on cotton textiles; the North-East, based on mining, shipbuilding and heavy engineering; and (in the USA): Detroit, based on cars and engineering; and Philadelphia, based on textiles and port-related activities.
- Manufacturing plants are controlled centrally by big industrial corporations – there is an emphasis on mass production and standardization.

- There is state regulation of the economy to overcome problems generated by the market, for example regional unemployment problems.
- Big industrial cities are the spatial expression of large-scale manufacture.
- There is state-controlled welfare provision to even out social inequalities, address unemployment problems and raise health standards.
- In culture and social provision, there is an accent on mass provision, for example in housing, consumer goods, TV programming and newspapers. The emphasis on mass coverage and standardization leaves relatively little choice, reflecting a modernist perspective.

Source: after Lash and Urry (1987)

principal features (which were especially characteristic of the developed world) are described in accordance with their views in Spotlight box 3.1.

Needless to say, such generalizations would be more or less true, depending on the time and location being considered. Capitalism had different histories in different places, and the exact form it took had much to do with the long-term evolution of each society affected by it.

3.3 Challenges to liberal capitalism: Nazism, communism

Come, bombs, and blow to smithereens,
Those air-conditioned, bright canteens,
Tinned fruit, tinned meat, tinned milk, tinned beans,
Tinned minds, tinned breath.
Mess up the mess they call a town –
A house for ninety-seven down
And once a week a half-a-crown
For twenty years

From 'Slough' by John Betjeman (1937)[1]

John Betjeman's famous fulminations against the town of Slough, situated just west of London and experiencing developments similar to those observed by J.B. Priestley a few years earlier, are in fact a hymn against modernity. Betjeman was railing against many of the social repercussions of the profound twentieth-century changes noted earlier in this chapter. In this he was by no means alone. Similar attitudes have been characteristic of many commentators living in countries where modernity (here defined as the spectrum of economic, social, political and cultural changes associated with twentieth-century capitalism) has brought problems of adaptation.

It has already been noted that the twentieth century cannot be described as a century of uninterrupted progress for capitalism, particularly in its Western 'liberal' form. Capitalism has been subjected to a series of challenges and political struggles that greatly affected the course of twentieth-century history, and in various parts of the world there have been attempts to create spaces in which alternatives to liberal capitalism can flourish. Interestingly enough, in terms of Wallerstein's world systems theory (discussed in Chapter 2; see p. 39), most of these attempts have been associated with countries outside the core, or with those like Germany after its

[1]Poem: 'Slough' from *Collected Poems* by John Betjeman © 1955, 1958, 1962, 1964, 1968, 1970, 1979, 1981, 1982, 2001. Reproduced by permission of John Murray (Publishers)

defeat in the First World War struggling to rejoin the core states. Particularly important for the political geography of the twentieth century were the attempts by Marxists and others to reject the capitalist development model entirely and to reconstruct society on a new basis. This issue will be discussed below. First, however, attention will be paid to another twentieth-century movement that challenged Western-style capitalism without discarding it entirely: Nazism, together with its close relative, **Fascism**.

Although they had nineteenth-century antecedents, both Fascism and Nazism were essentially products of the inter-war years. Fascism, under its leader Benito Mussolini, ruled in Italy from 1922 until its final defeat in the Second World War in 1945. Nazism under Adolf Hitler ruled Germany from 1933 until it too was defeated in 1945. Various Fascist or neo-Fascist groups ruled or were active elsewhere in Europe, and in some other regions, during this period, and to a lesser extent since.

There is no doubt that Nazism was by far the most influential Fascist movement after 1933, and so the following brief remarks will be devoted to it (Kershaw 2000). One of the problems of discussing Nazism or other forms of Fascism is their lack of a consistent ideology or philosophy. However, certain general points can be made. Like certain Western intellectuals and others, the Nazis were moved by a dislike of facets of capitalist modernity, such as commercialism, materialism, individualism, threats to the traditional family like the rise of female employment (see Plate 3.4), and similar tendencies that they associated with the 'decadent' Western democracies. They also despised Western-style parliamentary democracy, with its plurality of political parties and class divisions. In its place, they advocated the concept of a single national community, a *Volksgemeinschaft,* headed by a single Leader or Führer (Hitler), who was regarded as representative of, and chosen by, the people (this was the Nazi concept of 'democracy'). The Leader's power was absolute. Such a creed, however, seemed exceedingly unlikely to come to power in Germany in the early 1930s had it not been for the extreme circumstances reigning there. One was a general sense of resentment at Germany's defeat in the First World War and subsequent national humiliations. As extreme nationalists, the Nazis promised to avenge this defeat. Another was the dire economic and social straits to which many of the middle class had been reduced by post-First World War inflation and the Depression that began in 1929. There was also the fear of the many strikes and disorders perpetrated by communists and other left-wing groups (as well as by the Nazis) that were, of course, encouraged by the selfsame economic difficulties.

One of the oddities of Nazism was that it was, at one and the same time, both reactionary and modernizing (Herf 1984). On the one hand, the Nazis looked backwards to an imagined heroic and rustic Germany of the past, to Nordic myths, Germanic towns and landscapes (see Rollins 1995; Hagen 2006) and happy peasants tilling the fields in traditional costume. They tried to bolster the 'traditional' family: women were to remain at home and raise children for the fatherland. There were even attempts to build villages and garden settlements to reflect such ideals. On the other hand, the Nazis were also modernizers who built the autobahns, fostered industry and spent vast sums on the military, organizing their capitalist economy to these ends. Their aim was to turn Germany into a superpower, able to dominate the European continent and regions beyond (see Chapter 20, pp. 407–10).

Nazism's central and most notorious feature was its racism. Building on common European assumptions of racial and cultural superiority (prejudices which have by no means disappeared, even today), they taught that the Germans and related Aryan **races** were equipped by nature to dominate the globe. All non-Aryan peoples were regarded as inferior, particularly the Jews who, because of their culture, religion and cosmopolitan ways, seemed to represent all that the Nazis feared and hated. As time went on, it became clear that the Nazis meant to exterminate the Jews (they killed six million of them) as well as others (Roma peoples, homosexuals, the mentally ill, certain religious groups) who could have no place in the world they intended to reconstruct. The Nazi death camp at Auschwitz in Poland, which has been researched by geographers (Charlesworth *et al.* 2006; Knowles *et al.* 2014), is kept as a memorial to the huge numbers who were murdered and as a solemn warning to today's world of the horrific consequences of racial prejudice.

Perhaps the most significant challenge to liberal capitalism in the twentieth century, however, came from Marxist-style communism (Calvocoressi 1991). By the 1960s and 1970s up to one-third of humanity was living under communist governments that explicitly rejected capitalism as an acceptable way of organizing society. The reasons for that rejection and why it largely failed must now be considered.

An outline of some of the principal features of Marxism is given in Spotlight box 3.2. An important point is that Marx's teachings failed to change those societies at which they were initially aimed – the industrial societies of Western Europe and North America. Marx himself had expected that communism would find support among the growing industrial working classes of countries like Germany and Britain, where factories

Spotlight box 3.2

Marxism

- Marxism, which derives from the teachings of Karl Marx (1818–83), is related to other forms of socialism that seek to moderate or reform the injustices of capitalism.
- Unlike some other forms of socialism, Marxism regards capitalism as an innately unjust and exploitative system.
- According to Marxism, capitalism divides society into antagonistic classes: those who own the main sources of wealth (the capitalists) and those who must live by selling their labour to the capitalists (the proletariat).

- Marxism teaches that the capitalists are forced by the very nature of capitalism to maximize the profits they obtain at the expense of the workers.
- Marx thought that eventually capitalism would become so exploitative and prone to crises that its downfall was inevitable.
- It would then be replaced by a much more just, classless society (socialism, gradually maturing into communism).
- In the meantime Marx exhorted the world's workers (especially the industrial workers) to organize politically to hasten capitalism's downfall.

were bringing such groups together in increasing numbers. However, it was by no means obvious, as the years passed, that the workers of those countries were necessarily being increasingly exploited, as Marx seems to have expected (later, these countries were accused by Marxists of exporting exploitation to colonies and other less developed regions). Instead, Marxism triumphed in Russia (in 1917), in what was in fact the least industrialized of Europe's great powers. Thus, whereas in terms of Wallerstein's world systems theory Marxism was expected to find favour in the core countries, in fact it initially triumphed in a semi-peripheral one. That it did so changed the character of Marxism, which was now faced with the challenge of building socialism in a peasant society, and in virtual isolation from the rest of the world.

What happened after 1917 in Russia (or the Soviet Union as it was now to be called) was of profound importance for the other countries that later adopted communist systems, if only because Russia was the pioneer. What happened there began to assume something of the character of orthodoxy (Sakwa 1999). In view of the difficulties they faced, and in all likelihood because of their own inclinations, the Bolsheviks (as the Russian or Soviet communists were called) adopted a highly centralized political system that brooked no opposition and entailed the destruction of the previous ruling and capitalist class. Eventually, from the late 1920s, they implemented a fully centrally planned economic system. This involved the abolition of private enterprise and virtually all forms of market relations, and the collectivization of agriculture. The purpose

Plate 3.5 Women workers in an American armaments plant during the First World War. The labour shortage during the First World War gave women job opportunities which were increasingly taken as the twentieth century advanced.

(Everett Historical/Shutterstock)

of this extraordinary economic system was both to speed the process of economic development and to build up the country's military resources. As the 1930s advanced, it became clear that what had earlier seemed a rather vague threat from the outside capitalist world was beginning to take a concrete and menacing form in the guise of Nazi Germany. The centrally planned or command economy (which involved much suffering on the part of the Soviet people) eventually proved equal to this challenge. In the ensuing war with Germany

(1941–5), the Soviet Union emerged victorious, but only after sustaining enormous losses.

Soviet victory in the Second World War greatly enhanced that country's prestige. Moreover, because the Soviet armies were now in occupation of much of central and eastern Europe, they were able to ensure that regimes friendly to the Soviet Union (that is, communist regimes) would assume power in those regions. Communism soon spread into other countries, notably China (in 1949), south-east Asia and beyond: in other words, into Wallerstein's 'periphery'. All these countries initially followed the Soviet development model, but soon found that it was necessary to adapt it to their own needs. In the meantime the spread of communism, and Soviet ambitions, excited the suspicions of the capitalist West. After 1945, therefore, the world was split into two armed camps, both equipped with nuclear weapons. The ensuing confrontation, known as the **Cold War**, profoundly influenced both sides and encouraged their militarization (see Chapter 20, pp. 410–13). However, many countries, especially in the developing world, tried to avoid taking sides, while China, though communist, began to pursue its own version of communism outside the Soviet sphere.

While the actual form that communism took in the Soviet Union and other countries may have been a modification of Marx's own ideas, it did represent a radical departure from the capitalist development model. Not only was the command economy a very different, state-centred approach to economic development (and one which was copied in many parts of the developing world after the Second World War, with varying degrees of success), it regarded itself, and was regarded, as a threat to the whole idea of capitalism (Sakwa 1999). Internally, whilst it led to attempts to reconstruct society on a different basis, it did in fact give rise to new forms of spatial inequality (Bater 1986). Interestingly enough it also had certain spatial features in common with Nazism and Fascism, such as an emphasis on creating urban spaces specifically for the purpose of mass ceremonial and display (Plate 3.6). The creation of 'spaces of terror', such as concentration camps for the incarceration or elimination of those deemed unacceptable to the regime, was also a feature of the two systems (Moran 2004; Pallot 2005).

In the end, communism failed to prove itself a successful, viable challenger to capitalism. Especially from the 1970s, the Soviet Union and its eastern European allies fell behind their capitalist rivals in terms of productivity, flexibility and innovation. Whether this was because of problems inherent to command economies as such, or whether it has more to do with mistakes made by the various political leaderships, is hard to say. Whatever the reasons, by the end of the 1980s practically the whole of the communist world was in a state of economic and political crisis. The subsequent fall of communism in eastern Europe, and the splitting of the Soviet Union into 15 separate states in 1991, signalled the end of the Cold War. Since then the post-communist states, plus China which continues to pursue its own version of socialism 'with Chinese characteristics', have been struggling to adapt to the market economy and in other ways to cope with the problems of post-communist transformation (Gwynne *et al.* 2003: 59–72, 101–8).

Plate 3.6 Red Square, Moscow, one of the open spaces enhanced by the Soviet dictator Joseph Stalin for official communist demonstrations and ceremonial display.

(Iakov Filimonov/Shutterstock)

Plate 3.7 A section of the Berlin Wall in central Berlin in October, 1988. The fall of the wall in the following year signalled the end of communism in the Soviet bloc and the removal of a major twentieth-century challenge to world capitalism.

(360b/Shutterstock)

3.4 The end of imperialism?

Father, Mother, and Me
Sister and Auntie say
All the people like us are We,
And everyone else is They.
And They live over the sea,
While We live over the way,
But – would you believe it? – They look upon We
As only a sort of They! –

From 'We and They' by Rudyard Kipling
(1912: 763–4)[2]

At the beginning of the twentieth century Britain and several other European powers sat proudly at the centre of a series of empires that spanned the globe (Figure 3.2). As noted in Chapter 2, these empires were the products of a long period of European exploration, settlement, economic exploitation and imperial rivalry. Something of the complacency and condescension with which Europeans commonly regarded their empires at this period is nicely captured by Rudyard Kipling in his comic poem 'We and They', quoted above.

However, the future of European imperialism was already being questioned even before the First World War. The English liberal J.A. Hobson, and later the Russian revolutionary V.I. Lenin, popularized the idea that Europe's overseas colonies were being economically organized and exploited mainly for the benefit of the European 'mother countries', forming an undeveloped periphery to the European core. Lenin taught that imperialism was an inevitable consequence of capitalism – its 'highest stage'. In the meantime various rumblings of discontent were being felt in various parts of the European empires.

But it was the three great episodes of the first half of the twentieth century – the First World War, the Great Depression (1929–33) and the Second World War – that fatally undermined European imperialism. **Nationalism**, which had had such an impact on the political geography of Europe (see Chapter 22), had also influenced the colonial world where 'national liberation movements' began to demand independence for their countries. Starting with the independence of India in 1947, the next quarter

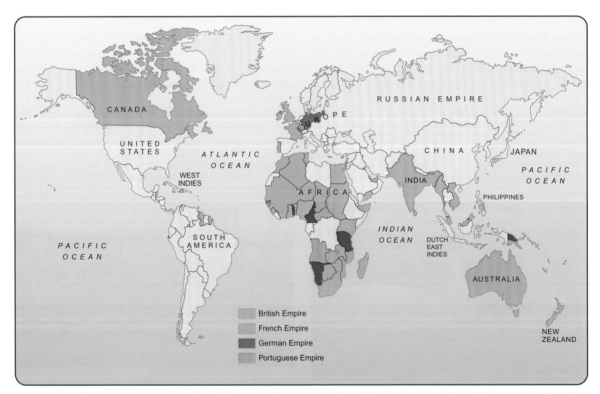

Figure 3.2 The world in 1914 showing British, French, German and Portuguese empires. Note, too, the Russian empire, the Dutch East Indies, and other colonial territories under Belgian, Italian and Spanish rule.

[2]Poem: 'We and They' by Rudyard Kipling, with permission of A.P. Watt Ltd on behalf of Gráinne Yeats

Plate 3.8 Imperial Airways flies to Australia. Imperial Airways was the major British airline company which operated at ever more ambitious international and intercontinental scales during the 1930s.

(Lordprice Collection/Alamy)

of Western models was not always a suitable response to their problems. For example, many of the new states attempted to copy the European idea of the **nation-state**, hoping to unite their peoples around a common sense of national identity. But the old colonial boundaries had generally been drawn up to suit imperial convenience rather than that of local communities. Thus these boundaries, now the boundaries of independent states, frequently grouped peoples into one state who had no common culture or history while dividing others who did so. This contributed little to the political stability or unity of many new states. Another problem was the feeling among many citizens of the new states that the capitalist economy was responsible for the underdevelopment of their countries. This set off a search for socialist or communist alternatives, much to the annoyance of the West, and encouraged debates about the meaning of 'development' (see Chapter 8, pp. 176–9). Finally, fundamental questions were frequently posed about how far modernization, as generally understood, was compatible with the traditions of the former colonial peoples. The Islamic revival, discussed below, can be seen as one response to this dilemma.

Just as imperialism had a profound impact on the political and social geographies of enormous areas in Africa, Asia and the Americas, it equally affected the imperial countries themselves. One of the most important manifestations of this in the twentieth century was the flow of migrants from colonies and former colonies, especially in the tropics and sub-tropics, to take up jobs in the former imperial states. This naturally had a far-reaching cultural impact in cities and regions in Western Europe. In fact the whole experience of imperialism led to the mixing of peoples and cultures on a grand scale. It also led to widespread questioning of long-held assumptions about European (and often male) cultural superiority (see Chapter 2, p. 47).

Many scholars have argued that the end of European colonialism did not mean the end of exploitative relationships between the core countries of the world economy (including the former imperial powers) and what was now increasingly referred to as the 'Third World'. According to such thinkers, the formal imperialism of the colonial era had merely been replaced by a more 'informal' alternative, but the basic situation of the core exercising hegemony over the periphery had not really changed (Wallerstein 1980; Frank and Dutt 2002). From the 1970s, however, some fundamental changes seemed to affect the world economy which, in the opinion of certain scholars, demanded that international relationships be viewed in a new way. Lash and Urry have described these changes as 'the end of organized capitalism' (Lash and Urry 1987).

of a century witnessed the break-up of all the European empires (though the Soviet Union, successor to the old Russian empire, finally disappeared only in 1991). Many new, independent states appeared on the map of Africa, Asia and other regions, though not, unfortunately, without considerable turmoil in some cases. The world's political geography was transformed.

In giving (or being forced to give) independence to their colonies, the former imperial powers hoped that they would adopt European-type political systems and capitalist economic systems, partly because these appeared the best basis for future development, and partly because they seemed a reasonable way of upholding European influence. The elites who were now to hold power in the new states were often sympathetic to these aims, since they had frequently been educated by Europeans and wished to see their countries modernized along European or Western lines. However, the adoption

3.5 Globalized capitalism

In 1960 the industrialized areas of Western Europe and North America produced almost 80 per cent of the world's industrial output. Even Japan accounted for only around 4 per cent. Much of the Third World remained agricultural. Only after this time did industrialization spread beyond its traditional centres (which since the 1930s had included the Soviet Union). Meanwhile many of the older industrial countries began to lose industries, even some of those which had arrived with the twentieth century.

Of course, some areas of the 'Third World' benefited far more from this industrial spread than did others. Most spectacularly, the **newly industrialized countries** of East Asia, Brazil, Mexico and certain others soon seemed set to join the industrial core. Yet others, like certain Middle Eastern states, earned huge revenues from their energy exports. But there remained many areas, especially in Africa, which missed out on the new developments (even so the latter part of the twentieth century was a period of unprecedented population growth and urbanization across much of the developing world – see Chapters 4 and 9). The term 'Third World', used to group together countries with such disparate economic characters, seemed increasingly redundant, and the world as a whole seemed as unequal as ever (Sidaway 2012).

How is one to explain the changes affecting the world's economic geography in the last third of the twentieth century and at the beginning of the twenty-first? Geographers and others argued that such changes are part of the process of globalization. Speedier communications meant that the world was becoming a much smaller place as the twentieth century drew towards its close. Capitalism itself was now a truly global phenomenon as markets were internationalized and finance became fully mobile. Before 1960, despite the importance of international trade, the world economy was structured around individual states. After 1960, the world economy became in effect transnational as the boundaries of individual states became ever less important to its functioning. Thus this period witnessed the rise to global importance of the transnational corporations, commercial conglomerates which became major players on a world scale (see Chapters 14 and 16). Because of the wealth and political influence they wielded, such huge companies became increasingly free to switch their operations from country to country as economic circumstances dictated. States, which had previously seemed unchallenged within their own frontiers, found it ever more difficult to control their own economies and began to bid against one another to attract footloose investment and the favours of the **transnational corporations**. Many manufacturing and service firms now began to locate in parts of the Third World, where costs were lower, whilst core industrial countries began to experience **deindustrialization** and a switch into services and 'control' functions (the headquarters of the transnational corporations still tended to be located in the traditional core countries). A further important result of the development of information technology was that production became much more flexible than before and more geared up to highly specialized markets, changing fashion and the whim of the individual consumer. This new, more flexible approach to production is sometimes known as **post-Fordism**.

Later chapters of this book will explore some of the specific economic and social implications of these changes. Meanwhile, it is worth stressing here how unsettling such developments have been, especially for the core countries. The years of growing affluence after 1945 were succeeded, from the mid-1970s, by a period of greater uncertainty as deindustrialization gathered pace (see Plate 3.8), unemployment rose, insecurity became more widespread, and social inequality became more apparent. By the century's end it seemed that Western-style capitalism and democracy were increasingly threatened and, if anything, the feeling of threat and uncertainty has grown into the new century. The last part of this chapter will briefly survey some of the factors that lie behind that uncertainty.

Just as Lash and Urry used the term 'organized capitalism' to describe the years down to about 1973 when Fordism reached its apogee, so they have described the closing years of the twentieth century as those of 'disorganized capitalism'. Some of its more prominent features are listed in Spotlight box 3.3, once again paying particular attention to how the changes have affected the core countries of the world economy.

Plate 3.9 Inside the hall of a coal mine abandoned in the wake of 1980s deindustrialization.

(Ppictures/Shutterstock)

Spotlight box 3.3

Globalized or 'disorganized' capitalism

- The onset of 'disorganized capitalism' is marked by a decline in the relative importance of extractive and manufacturing industries.
- There is a relative increase in the importance of service and consumer industries, especially in employment.
- The use of flexible technologies encourages a reduction in the average size of manufacturing plants with more accent on labour-saving investments and more flexible employment processes, all induced by competition.
- Because of the need for flexibility and cost-cutting, industrial firms tend to 'hive off' many of the services and supporting activities they need to other firms and organizations. There are thus more opportunities for small firms, changing the traditionally specialized nature of the regional economy.
- Regional economies are also affected by the greater emphasis on non-standardized production – traditional regional specializations become less marked.

- The global economy reduces the effectiveness of state attempts at economic regulation – from the state's point of view, the economy becomes less predictable.
- Rising costs, demands for reduced taxation, and growing social inequality challenge the idea of a centralized welfare state.
- Smaller, more footloose industries, the rise of services, better communications and other factors reduce the traditional importance of big, industrial cities by comparison with small towns and rural areas.
- There is a rise in importance of the educated social strata needed to work in the new administrative, control, service and related activities – the so-called 'service class' – with more sophisticated and individualized tastes in consumption and other areas. The age of mass cultural provision is replaced by greater cultural fragmentation and pluralism (sometimes referred to as post-modernism). There is a commensurate decline in faith in large-scale planning and similar activities associated with **modernism**.

Source: after Lash and Urry (1987)

3.6 The world in the early twenty-first century

In 1992, some three years after the fall of the Berlin Wall, an event which is regarded as marking the end of the Cold War (see Plate 3.7), the American political scientist Francis Fukuyama published a book entitled *The End of History and the Last Man* (Fukuyama 1992). Here Fukuyama made some startling claims regarding what he saw as the recent global triumph of 'liberal democracy'. The end of the Cold War, Fukuyama asserted, meant that liberal democracy had now 'conquered rival ideologies like hereditary monarchy, fascism and . . . communism' and that this triumph marked 'the end point of mankind's ideological evolution'. He went on to announce that 'while earlier forms of government were characterized by grave defects and irrationalities that led to their eventual collapse, liberal democracy [is] arguably free from such internal contradictions'. Hence 'the ideal of liberal democracy could not be improved on'. A close reading of Fukuyama's text reveals that what he had in mind by 'liberal democracy' was not only a specific political system but also a way of organizing the economy, namely

through 'free markets'. Just how 'free' markets were meant to be he did not say. But in the opinion of many, what Fukuyama was celebrating at the dawn of the new millennium was in effect the final triumph of Western-style capitalism, and of the Western way of life, over the rest of the world – an awesome claim indeed.

Now in the second decade of the new millennium, and more than 20 years since Fukuyama published his book, it is probably true to say that relatively few people are as optimistic about the prospects for liberal democracy as he evidently was. In fact the future seems as uncertain as ever and 'liberal democracy' (whatever that might mean in practice) is faced with new challenges, some of which were perhaps only dimly discernible when Fukuyama wrote. Understanding these challenges forms the substance of the chapters which follow. Here we can only summarize the most significant among them.

3.6.1 Economic challenges

Fukuyama published his book at a time when most Western states, and many others as well, had strongly espoused the economic doctrine known as **neoliberalism**. This was a reaction to the disappointing economic record of the 1970s and promised to achieve high and sustainable economic growth through freeing up markets, privatizing as much of the economy and associated activity as possible, and restructuring the state (see Hendrikse and Sidaway 2010). In the event the actual record of economic achievement was much more modest than had been hoped for (Harvey 2006: 30, 42; Dicken 2015) and there was much volatility on the world market. Furthermore, the removal or absence of regulation over much economic activity seemed to encourage financial speculation and even corruption in many places, culminating in a major international banking crisis in 2008, and precipitating economic recession and a crisis in the Eurozone in 2011. As a result many countries found themselves deeply in debt and were forced to make major cuts in public spending which especially disadvantaged the poorer elements in society. As we have seen, this was not the first occasion that Western-style capitalism has been seized with crisis. But this recent occurrence has caused many to question whether the way in which the world economy has been managed recently has been sensible and whether some alternative policy should now be adopted, particularly as some countries like China have very successfully pursued rather different (and more state-centred) economic policies. Indeed, some economic analysts have suggested that the West can no longer assume economic dominance over the rest of the world with rising economic powers like China and India now entering the fray. The West's days as the centre of the global economy may thus be numbered. Some of these issues are discussed further in Chapters 14 and 16.

There is an additional reason why many people have begun to question the wisdom of a neoliberal approach to economic policy. This is the growing inequalities that it seems to engender. For example, many countries that have adopted neoliberal economic and social policies have experienced the emergence of huge gaps between rich and poor. Indeed, according to a report issued by the charity Oxfam in January 2015, 1 per cent of the world's population will soon own more wealth than the remaining 99 per cent! Thus, at one end of the scale, many people now enjoy previously unimaginable income levels, benefiting among other things from low levels of taxation, allowing them to escape the consequences of the reductions in public expenditure which are the hallmark of neoliberalism. In the UK and other countries the public concern expressed at the levels of payments and bonuses being made to bankers and others whose activities are widely regarded as having precipitated the 2008 banking crisis (which resulted in huge investments of public money to rescue the faltering banks) is symptomatic of a broader dissatisfaction. And, at the other end, many of the poor, who are most dependent on public welfare and

public expenditure of various kinds (whose reduction is partly associated with the neoliberal policy of lowering taxes) suffer deprivation as well as the unemployment and other problems invariably associated with a volatile economy (see Chapter 10).

Many wonder whether such levels of inequality are compatible with the maintenance of free and democratic polities. Meanwhile, at an international scale, numerous scholars regard neoliberal attitudes as being partly responsible for the growing economic inequalities and other disparities between countries in different parts of the world (Stiglitz and Charlton 2007; see Chapter 8). It is argued that the factors encouraging this include the inappropriate ways in which the rules governing international trade have been applied to developing countries, and the hypocritical way in which many Western countries, having espoused free trade principles as applied to other countries, actively seek to avoid their full application in their own case. In consequence, whilst Western countries pump huge amounts of aid into poorer countries, this is more than counteracted by the trade policies they pursue.

3.6.2 Geopolitical challenges

At the time Fukuyama published his book it seemed safe to assume that, with the collapse of communism and the Soviet Union, the United States would be left as the only remaining superpower, well placed to dominate the rest of the globe. Thus there dawned the vision of a world organized in accordance with a *Pax Americana,* whereby the benefits of American democracy and of the Western way of life more generally might spread to the rest of the globe. Again, however, in the second decade of the twenty-first century, this vision now seems too simplistic for a number of reasons. One, mentioned above, has been the phenomenal rise of China and of other parts of East Asia in the recent period (Dicken 2015). Economic power, of course, invariably means political power, and in this situation the United States' geopolitical dominance is no longer assured (see Chapters 20 and 23), especially since, according to some estimates, China is now the world's biggest economy. A symptom of the changing situation lies in the growing competition and disagreement between the USA and China in such areas as trade relations, currency policy and industrial policy as well as disputes over such matters as human rights and public access to the Internet. A further symptom erupted in 2014 when civil war in Ukraine, arising out of disputes over whether the country's future lay with the EU and NATO to the west or with its eastern neighbours including Russia, resulted in Western sanctions against Russia and the threat of a much wider conflict (Sakwa 2015a). Thus the blithe assumption that the USA can order the world according to its wishes and that the rest of the world will gladly adopt American values is questionable. This is quite apart from the problem of the numerous poor and peripheral states across the world (Afghanistan and Somalia, for example) which neither the USA nor China nor anyone else seems able to control.

Given the rising significance of China and other parts of Asia in the recent period, it has become fashionable among certain scholars to attempt to explain this phenomenon from a long-term, historical perspective (see, for example, Frank 1998; Darwin 2007). Andre Gunder Frank's book, *ReOrient* (Frank 1998), is a case in point. Contrary to the ideas of Wallerstein and others (see Chapter 2, p. 39), his thesis is that by the year 1500 there was already a single global economy in existence centred on Asia whose roots went back many thousands of years. In this global system Europe was both relatively and absolutely marginal and continued to be so until about 1800 when it assumed dominance over Asia, partly because of its successful conquest of the Americas. Thus, according to Frank, there is nothing particularly surprising about Asia's recent resurgence. Hence he is challenging the rather Eurocentric perspective adopted in the first three chapters of this book as well, it might be said, as that adopted by the overwhelming majority of Western historians and other scholars.

3.6.3 Environmental challenges

In the opinion of many people, the most urgent problem facing the world today is that of environmental change, and in particular climate change. As we saw in Chapter 1, there is nothing new about the idea of human beings changing the environments in which they live. Indeed they have probably done so ever since they first appeared on earth. But what has become particularly worrying in the most recent period is the notion that such changes are now becoming unsustainable and are beginning to threaten not only our way of life but also, perhaps, our very existence. Concern about such matters goes back many years, to the nineteenth century at least, but became more pressing from about the 1960s when some of the environmental consequences of continuous economic growth became more noticeable. Thus alarm began to be expressed about the possibility of the world running out of its most significant resources, especially energy resources, a worry that has hardly diminished as the search for oil and gas now impinges on the Polar and sub-Polar regions, some of the most ecologically fragile regions on earth. Likewise, there is concern over the loss of biodiversity, associated among other things with the pressure to intensify agriculture and to expand food production to feed the world's rapidly growing population (itself a problem of the utmost importance; see Chapters 4 and 15). Needless to say, the impoverishment of the web of life, or the **biosphere** as it is often called, which sustains life on earth could have catastrophic consequences for everyone. A related issue, one that has been vividly illustrated during 2013–15 by the Ebola crisis in West Africa, is the spread of new diseases or the revival of old ones. Thus the apparently reducing effectiveness of antibiotics exacerbated by their overuse might in future result in bacterial-borne diseases like tuberculosis becoming major killers once again.

The issue of climate change has come on to the agenda recently as data have become available showing that the continuous emission of carbon dioxide and other **greenhouse gases** into the atmosphere, which is a hallmark of industrial societies, may already have led to marked (and in some opinions unstoppable) climate change. Increases in the incidence and intensity of hurricanes, bush fires, floods, droughts, heat waves are, in the opinion of some, symptoms of climate change. In the more extreme scenarios, the complete melting of the polar icecaps, the flooding of much of the earth's low-lying (and most densely populated) regions, and catastrophic changes elsewhere, are predicted.

There is no need to emphasize the point that the more dramatic predictions regarding the dire consequences of continuous and unsustainable environmental change threaten the entire basis of our modern way of life. We must either change our entire mode of life, it seems, or hope, through further technological development for example, to solve some of the most pressing problems. But even then it is difficult to envisage the model of continuous economic growth in the way we understand it now being sustainable in the longer term, at least on this planet. Not surprisingly, given the rhetoric surrounding environmental issues (and, perhaps, the vested interests who might be threatened if the more dramatic scenarios are taken seriously), there are those who discount such claims, questioning some of the evidence supporting climate change and other predictions. The whole question is therefore controversial. Some of the ramifications of the environmental debates, and their political implications, are explored in Chapters 4–7.

3.6.4 Value and identity issues

On the first anniversary of the 9/11 attack on the World Trade Center in New York, US President George W. Bush made the following declaration:

> We will use our position of unparalleled strength and influence to build an atmosphere of international order and openness in which progress and liberty can

flourish in many nations. A peaceful world of growing freedom serves American long-term interests, reflects American ideals and unites America's allies . . . We seek a just peace where repression, resentment and poverty are replaced with the hope of democracy, development, free markets and free trade . . .

(quoted in Harvey 2006: 11).

In this declaration, President Bush clearly implied that such 'ideals' are not only American but also need adopting by the rest of the world.

But what exactly is 'freedom' in a world in which, for example, the USA has felt able to imprison so-called 'terrorists' in its Guantanamo Bay prison camp without trial and allegedly even used torture on them? Or what is 'democracy' in a world where the USA and its allies back numerous repressive regimes in their own security interests, or where politicians, having made certain promises to their electorates, appear to feel free to do the exact opposite once they are elected as well as engaging in corrupt practices in certain cases? No wonder that such vaunted 'values' are being questioned in many quarters rather than simply being accepted as presented.

In fact the whole area of values, what they mean and whose interests they serve, seems to be an increasingly contested one (witness the ongoing debate about 'British values' in the UK). This is linked to the issue of identity. Perhaps related to feelings of social injustice and/or loss of certainty and personal autonomy in an increasingly globalized world, more and more people appear to feel the need to assert their distinctiveness and their freedom either as individuals or as groups. Movements like feminism, gay liberation and animal rights are a case in point. Another is the recent rise of fundamentalist religious movements among many established faiths, whether it be among Christians, Muslims, Hindus or others (sometimes, it must be said, in reaction against some of the movements mentioned above, and sometimes against the materialism and secularism which are such a feature of modern life). In many Western countries, for example, the problem of 'radicalization' of some Muslim youth, whereby, apparently under the influence of the Internet, some have been travelling to join militant groups in the Middle East, has been a cause of concern to politicians. Rising nationalism also seems to be a problem in many parts of the world. Thus whereas Fukuyama airily assumed that, in Western Europe at least, nationalism was being 'tamed', the demands for regional or ethnic autonomy, or recognition, seem by no means to be abating. For example, the September, 2014 referendum on whether Scotland should become an independent state saw a voter turnout of almost 85 per cent with nearly 45 per cent of voters supporting independence. The

long-term consequences of this strong pro-independence vote for the stability of the United Kingdom have yet to be seen. Elsewhere in the world, nationalism has often been an even more significant issue.

Unfortunately the debates over issues of values and identity have sometimes given rise to disorder and even outright violence. Some of these points are explored further in Chapters 13 and 22.

3.6.5 Security issues

The horrifying attack on the offices of *Charlie Hebdo*, a French satirical magazine, in January 2015, an attack which caused the deaths of 12 people and injuries to 11 others, was a sharp reminder to the West of a phenomenon which is all too common elsewhere in the world. The Paris attack, horrific as it was, pales by comparison with other terrorist activities elsewhere in the world. For example, the actions of Boko Haram in Nigeria and some neighbouring countries are believed to have caused the deaths of more than 5,000 civilians up to June 2014. In this case there are clear links with Islamic fundamentalism. But the link between Islam and terrorism should not be overstressed as it involves only a tiny minority of Muslims. The fact is that the Islamic revival, which is associated with the desire to return to traditional Muslim values on the part of many who reject Western values based on secularism and materialism (and thus Western-style capitalism), is a far more broadly based movement than any misleading attempt to link it with terrorism might imply (Park 1994; Esposito 1995). In the opinion of the majority of scholars, Islam and the adoption of terrorist tactics are incompatible.

Clearly, however, the dangers and apparent frequency of terrorist acts are a sharp reminder of the limits to the power of states in an increasingly globalized world. They are a challenge to the democratic freedoms enjoyed in many states (despite the caveats about the meaning of the term 'democracy' outlined above), not least because they encourage governments to adopt more and more stringent security measures. But terrorism in the above sense is by no means the only security threat to menace states and communities as the twenty-first century advances. One might mention the spread of weapons of mass destruction, including chemical and biological weapons, and the possibility of cyber-terrorism, as two that are particularly worrying (see Chapter 20). Many states and citizens are also concerned about the issue of international migration as a security concern. Encouraged by such events as wars and disturbances, ecological catastrophes and economic hardship, such movements are often most unfortunately targeted by right-wing political elements eager to warn of the danger of national cultures being 'swamped' and of the need to defend national identity.

3.7 Conclusion

The twentieth century was a period of rapid economic and social change over most parts of the world. It was also a period when the world seemed to become smaller and most regions were gradually drawn into an ever more embracing global system. Yet it would be a mistake to imagine that this was an uncontested process, or one that threatens to bring about a global uniformity. The legacy of the twentieth century for the twenty-first is a world that is both dynamic and uneven, and therefore very uncertain. The rest of this book tries to grapple with this uncertainty.

Learning outcomes

Having read this chapter, you should know that:

- Capitalism is inherently dynamic and unstable. It was so throughout the twentieth century, and is likely to continue to be so in the future.

- The concepts of Fordist or 'organized' and Globalized or 'disorganized' capitalism are ways of trying to make sense of the changes that affected capitalist societies during the twentieth century.

- 'Fordism' and 'post-Fordism' (concerning production and consumption) and 'modernism' and 'postmodernism' (concerning culture) similarly try to make sense of twentieth and twenty-first century change. No concepts, however, can do justice to the complexity of change during this period.

- Western-style liberal capitalism is only one variant of capitalism. It has been challenged in various ways in the twentieth century, some of which have had long-term consequences for different parts of the globe. Future challenges might prove more successful than past ones.

- The twentieth century has been an era of nation-states and of nationalism. Towards the end of the twentieth and into the twenty-first centuries the role of the nation-state seems increasingly challenged by globalization. Nationalism, however, may yet flourish as a response to globalization.

- Modernity may not lead to the disappearance of traditional cultural practices. The Islamic revival, and similar religious revivals across the world, are a case in point.

- Despite the view of some that globalization is leading to the emergence of a global culture, it might actually increase the differences between places and hence the importance of geography.

Further reading

Dicken, P. (2015) *Global Shift: Mapping the Changing Contours of the World Economy,* 7th edition, Sage, London. A comprehensive overview of developments in the global economy up to the present time. Chapter 2 considers the longer-term development of that economy with particular emphasis on the period since 1960. It is therefore particularly relevant to the second half of the present chapter.

Frank, A.G. (1998) *ReOrient: Global Economy in the Asian Age,* University of California Press, Berkeley, CA. A rather idiosyncratic book that seeks to challenge the Eurocentric assumption of many scholars that the global economy (and other signifiers of modernity, including 'capitalism') had their origins in Europe and then spread to the rest of the world. Frank argues that the rise of Asia preceded that of Europe with the latter only becoming predominant after about 1800. Thus the recent rise of Asia is only a return to its former preeminence.

Hall, P. (2014) *Cities of Tomorrow: an Intellectual History of Urban Planning and Design since 1880,* 4th edition, Wiley-Blackwell, Chichester. A splendid account of urban development in the late nineteenth and twentieth centuries in different parts of the world. The accent is on urban planning and design, but there are many social insights.

Hobsbawm, E. (1995) *Age of Extremes: The Short Twentieth Century 1914–1991,* Abacus, London. What quickly became a classic account of twentieth-century history, written by a doyen of British Marxist historians. Any chapter is worth reading, but geography students will find those dealing with economic, social and cultural change especially revealing.

Piketty, T. (2014) *Capital in the Twenty-first Century,* Belknap Press, Cambridge, MA. A world best-seller, this book examines the long-term evolution of social inequality, the concentration of wealth and prospects for economic growth. The author argues that, over the long term, returns on capital tend to exceed the rate of economic growth. Therefore those who already have capital have an inherent advantage over those who are dependent on wages only. This situation threatens to generate extreme inequalities in wealth, abetting discontent and the undermining of democratic values.

Useful websites

www.si.edu The Smithsonian Institution, Washington, DC. The Smithsonian is a focus for many kinds of scientific and cultural endeavour in the United States. The website is a very useful source for twentieth-century history and developments, with particular emphasis on the United States.

www.besthistorysites.net Entitled 'Best of History Web-sites', a comprehensive guide to history-oriented resources online. For teachers, students and others.

POPULATION, RESOURCES, FOOD, THE ENVIRONMENT AND DEVELOPMENT

Edited by Michael Bradshaw

Writing in 2009, John Beddington, the Chief Scientific Adviser to the UK government, noted that by 2030 the world would need to produce 50 per cent more food and energy, together with 30 per cent more fresh water, while at the same time mitigating and adapting to climate change. He warned that this combination of challenges threatened to create a 'perfect storm' of global events. As Lester Brown (2011: ix) notes in the preface to his book *World on the Edge,* Jonathon Porritt, then Chair of the UK Sustainable Communities Development Commission (which was subsequently axed by the then Coalition Government), endorsed Beddington's analysis, but suggested that the storm was more likely to strike closer to 2020 than 2030 (Porritt 2009). Recent events might suggest that Porritt is right: we seem to be experiencing extreme climatic events with increasing frequency and energy price volatility now seems the new reality. However, there is also reason for optimism: in 2015 the Millennium Development goals were reset on the basis of significant progress and there is hope for a global agreement on climate change. The world's leaders agreed collective action at the COP-21 meeting in Paris in late 2015 to limit global warming to less than 2 degrees. While this section does not deal explicitly with the issues of climate change and water security, which are normally covered elsewhere in a geography curriculum, it does deal with the issues of population, food, energy, environment and development. Thus, it provides an essential background to understanding many of the issues that contribute to the 'perfect storm' scenario.

This section makes clear both the scale and the complexity of delivering the more sustainable approach to development needed in the face of storm warnings. The chapters highlight the diversity of problems that exist at the global, interstate and local level. In this era of heightened globalization, developments in one locale, region or state can have global impact. For example, the so-called 'developed world' has achieved high levels of consumption, but in doing so has exhausted indigenous sources of energy, raw material and food supply, making consumers increasingly reliant on global supply chains. The same regions now face high production costs, a shortage of skilled labour and an increasingly elderly and dependent population. Elsewhere in the majority of the world there are regions and states that suffer from an absence of economic development and an inability to compete in the global marketplace for much needed resources: a problem often compounded by the fact that they have to export food and natural resources to generate income to support the trappings of statehood. All too often, local political elites misappropriate the national surplus to support their own livings standards and safeguard their control over power. Events in the Arab world in the spring of 2011 reflect in part the peoples' frustration with this situation. At the same time, despite the recent global economic crisis, the continuing rapid growth of new centres of demand in the emerging economies of, for example, Brazil, China and India, highlights the dynamic nature of the global system and the fact that new sources of demand for resources are placing additional stress on the planet's ability to support global capitalism. The analysis presented in this section suggests that there can be no doubt that the storm clouds are gathering and that urgent action is needed to change the relationship between environment, society and development.

DEMOGRAPHIC TRANSFORMATIONS

Chapter 4

Dimitris Ballas and Danny Dorling

Topics covered

- The geographies of population growth
- Changes in life expectancy and fertility
- Population projections
- Migration
- The geography of disease, natural disasters and wars
- The challenges of an ageing population in Europe

4.1 Introduction

Demographic processes are relevant to almost every topic discussed in this book. For example, changes in population size and structure can have an impact on the environment (including consumption patterns that affect climate change) as well as on the economy of countries and regions. They may also influence the formation of government policies and strategies at all geographical levels. Events such as environmental disasters, wars, economic shocks and rising inequality can alter a whole populations' **life expectancy** and lead to significant demographic shifts. This chapter draws on recent work by the authors (Dorling 2013) to explore the geography of global population growth trends and processes. It also presents traditional demographic concepts and models that were developed to better understand such processes (drawing on and updating relevant sections in earlier versions of this chapter written by John Round 2012). Further, we critically reconsider such models in the context of a global environment where countries, regions and cities and their populations are increasingly interdependent and at a point when there are growing numbers of people moving over national and international borders. We also discuss more recent events and demographic transformations in the context of official population projections that suggest that the world population is now stabilizing. The chapter then considers case study examples where factors such as wars and environmental disasters can be seen to be strongly associated with demographic processes and can have a significant impact on the population structures of many countries and within countries. The chapter concludes by providing a summary of the issues discussed and also a brief discussion of the impact of income and wealth inequality upon life expectancy (which in recent years in Europe and the USA have been exacerbated for some groups of the population by the implementation of austerity measures that disproportionally affect them).

4.2 Geographies of population growth

Before 1851 the world's population experienced relatively slow growth for most of human history, with the exception of the period that is known as the Neolithic revolution (which is thought to have taken place around 11,500 years ago). In particular, just before the Neolithic revolution, which is also known as the Agricultural Demographic Transition, the global population of humans has been estimated to have been around 6 million people, with a huge amount of error associated with that estimate. According to estimates of the United Nations Population Division (see Table 4.1) the global population in year zero (just over 2,000 years before today) was estimated to have been around 300 million. However, other estimates of the world population at that time vary between 170 and 400 million. Up to the end of the first millennium the world's average population growth rate was under 0.1 per cent. During the second millennium population growth rates were slow and at times of plague and the spread of diseases to the new world they were negative, but despite such setbacks the global human population reached one **billion** in 1820. From then it went up to 1.3 billion by the early twentieth century and then rose rapidly to a staggering 6 billion by 1999. On 31 October 2011 the United Nations declared that the global population reached 7 billion (United Nations 2011). Table 4.1 shows how the population changed throughout the last 2,000 years.

Table 4.1 World population 0–2011 (in billions)

Year	Billions
0	0.30
1000	0.31
1250	0.40
1500	0.50
1750	0.79
1800	0.98
1850	1.26
1900	1.65
1910	1.75
1920	1.86
1930	2.07
1940	2.30
1950	2.52
1960	3.02
1970	3.70
1980	4.44
1990	5.27
1999	5.98
2000	6.06
2010	6.79
2011	7.00
2015	7.32

Source: United Nations Population Division (1999, 2012); Population Institute (2011)

The numbers in Table 4.1 and discussion of world population growth do not tell us anything about the geographical distribution of that growth. We can explore the changing geography of the global population with the help of maps and cartograms from the Worldmapper project (see Useful websites section at end of chapter). In the context of this project the world is categorized in 12 Worldmapper regions, which are geographically contiguous territories of population groups (containing at least 100 million people per region) classified by the UN Human Development Index and colour coded accordingly, with different shades for individual countries. Visit the Worldmapper website for a further explanation of the regional definition. Using a rainbow scale, ranging from violet for the best-off region (consisting of Japan alone) to dark red for the poorest region comprising countries in the centre of the African continent, Figure 4.1 presents a series of Worldmapper cartograms highlighting the changing geographies of population growth over the last 2,000 years, based on past population estimates (from the Angus Maddison Project; see Useful websites at end of chapter for more details).

These maps are cartograms in which the territories are drawn in proportion to their population at the different moments in time. In year one (around when it is thought that Christ was born), the population of what is now China, Mongolia and Korea combined was the same as the population of the United Kingdom today, around 62 million people. Hardly anyone lived in what is now the UK, just enough for it to be worth the Romans invading (a few years after Christ is thought to have died in what is now Israel). The population of what is now India, then at the centre of the (known) world, was, at 78 million, less than that of Germany today. Across all of the rest of the planet the remaining 90 million humans were unevenly spread out. As can be seen in the first cartogram, the largest territories are China (bright green) and India (orange), where an estimated 135 million people, more than half of the then total global population, were thought to live. At that time there were 40 million people in Europe, 18 million in the Middle East and 11 million in Northern Africa, whereas North and South America as well as Asia Pacific were very sparsely populated. Generally the colder areas in Northern latitudes tended to have lower populations whereas the territories that now encompass the Ganges, Tigris, Yangtze, Nile and Po rivers were the most populous.

The second map in the figure shows the distribution of the population in year 1500, the time of the Spanish conquest in South America. Although the global population

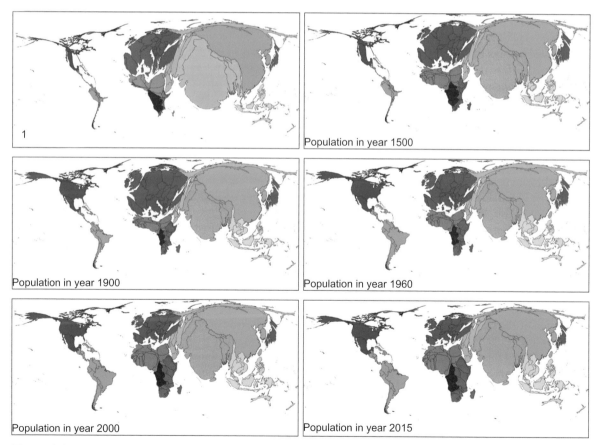

Figure 4.1 The geography of population growth by Worldmapper regions (worldmapper.org).

Source: cartography by Benjamin Hennig (viewsoftheworld.net).

nearly doubled from year 1 to year 1500, its geographical distribution remained largely the same, with Southern and Eastern Asia remaining the most populous world regions. It is also interesting to note that at this time the combined population of Mexico and Peru was greater than the total of the land now labelled as all other American countries. This pattern was about to change in the following centuries. In particular, the encounter of the New World in 1492 was accompanied by the exposure of its inhabitants to germs and illnesses to which they did not have immunity. This had a devastating effect upon the indigenous population that died far faster from those diseases than from the colonial wars and atrocities committed by the Old World powers (Diamond 1997; Mann 2011; Dorling 2013). Back across the Atlantic, the shock was so great that the economy of the Old World was transformed; riches plundered from the New World turned the social order of continents on their head. Suddenly, the underdeveloped far west of Asia (called Europe) became the centre of the world; and China was peripheral. Trade flows altered, colonization began, the taking of slaves accelerated in Africa and for most people in the world within a few centuries everything that was solid had melted into air. From continent to continent human populations began to multiply rapidly as the established social orders were overturned. The first, fastest and most destabilizing population explosion was within Europe itself. Africa was depopulated through both slavery and 400 years of forced migration, mostly to the New World. India was colonized (twice), Chinese empires were destroyed, partly through the British Empire-orchestrated opiate trade. A nascent North American empire was conceived. Between 1500 and 1900 the global population tripled to 1.5 billion and the geographical distribution changed significantly, as shown in the fourth map. During this period, which was characterized by imperial rule and territorial expansion, the populations of Britain and North America increased more than ten-fold. Also, by comparing the second and third maps we can observe the devastating impact of slavery upon Africa. The fourth map in the series reproduced here shows the geography of the global population in 1960, when it reached 3 billion. South America has increased its proportion of the world's population living in that continent rapidly since 1900. In contrast, the Western European proportion of the world population began to decline in relative terms in 1900 when it was 15 per cent, to 11 per cent in 1960 and then 6 per cent in 2000. The fifth cartogram shown in Figure 4.1 portrays the geographical distribution of the estimated 6.1 billion global population in 2000, one year after it reached 6 billion, whereas the sixth and last cartogram shows how the 7.32 billion people in 2015 are geographically distributed in our own time.

As noted above, after a long period of stability there was a great demographic change. A key milestone was

1820 when the world population reached 1 billion. It can be argued that this change was the long-term result of the encounter between the Old and the New World in 1492, which led to a new demographic transition and a new human equilibrium as described above, and as will also be discussed in more detail in the next sections of this chapter.

The 120-year period between 1851 and 1971 is charted in Figure 4.2 and is known as the era of global population acceleration. After 1851 the population was not just growing, *the growth itself was growing*! In particular, the rate of global population growth experienced a rapidly increasing trend itself throughout this period with the notable exceptions of periods associated with the two World Wars and a small number of other significant events. The world's average population annual growth rate rose from 0.1 per cent to over 0.5 per cent between 1851 and 1900 and went up to over 1 per cent in the beginning of the twentieth century, with the brief drop to 0.3 per cent during the First World War and the influenza pandemic that followed (1918–1919). It then went up to 1.3 per cent during the 1920s, before falling again to 0.8 in the era of the Great Depression from 1929 to 1936. It then briefly rose to just over 1 per cent again in the late 1930s, before falling dramatically during the Second World War. After that first truly global war there was a further and rapid acceleration to 1.8 per cent by the mid-1950s, briefly interrupted in the three years of the Great Chinese Famine (between 1958–1961, when up to 45 million premature deaths occurred) and peaking at 2.1 per cent in 1971. The period of global population acceleration ended in that year and annual growth fell to 1.6 per cent in 1982, jumped to 1.9 per cent in 1983 and has been falling continuously since then. It should be noted that all these increases are compound (the annual increase are in addition to previous growth) and therefore a growth of 2 per cent means that the world population doubles every 35 years – if that rate continues.

The review and analysis of past trends in population growth can be used by demographers in order to try to project what the future population growth rates might be. In countries without population registers, such as the UK and USA, the population census, which records demographic and socio-economic information at a single point in time and is normally carried out every ten years (Rees *et al.* 2002), is an essential instrument that is used in order to obtain reliable estimates of population numbers. Censuses were taken in ancient times by kings, pharaohs and emperors to estimate the size of the population they had to keep suppressed and the number of soldiers they could raise, as well as to estimate their tax base. However, the first modern-day repeated census taking took place in Prussia in 1719 and in the USA in 1790, whereas the first census in Britain was not held until 1801. Census datasets describe the state of the

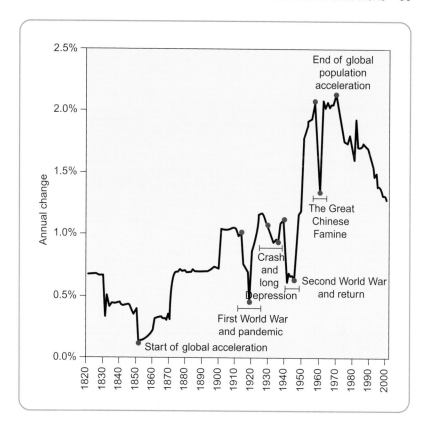

Figure 4.2 World annual population growth, 1821–2001.

whole national population and are extremely relevant for the analysis of a wide range of socio-economic issues and related policies. In addition to the census there is an increasingly wide range of administrative and private sector sources of suitable socio-economic data that can be used for demographic research.

The data collected from censuses of populations can be used in order to provide estimates of population in the past as well as projections into the future. In particular, once a census is taken, it is possible to calculate birth and death rates and once these rates are calculated it becomes possible to project population numbers both backwards and forwards in time, including estimates of future and past migration flows.

On the basis of the past demographic trends reviewed above it is expected that in coming decades the global population growth rates will continue to decline, as they have for the last four decades. In particular, the United Nations predicts a fall in growth rates to below 1 per cent by around 2020, declining further thereafter to 0.3 per cent by 2050 (which will be the lowest growth level recorded since the mid-eighteenth century). However, even these more modest growth rates will see the world's population grow by over 35 million a year until 2050. Even such slowed growth results in an overall population of 9.5 billion, 2.5 billion more than present. Given the compound nature of population growth, as we shall see below, it takes only small changes in fertility/death rates to have major consequences for population totals over a long period. However, it is population ageing that will be responsible for most population growth in coming decades, but high fertility would alter this. Thus, as Figure 4.3 shows, the UN produces a range of predictions based on different **fertility rates** for 2050, with those made in 2012 ranging from 8.3 billion to 10.8 billion.

It is instructive to break down the UN estimates and predictions by country and world regions. One of the classifications used by the UN to classify world regions and countries is that of 'more developed countries' or 'less developed countries' which (as discussed in Chapter 8) is problematic; nonetheless these terms are used in this chapter (as well as other socio-economic and political classifications), as they are routinely and widely employed by organizations such as the UN and the World Bank. Figure 4.4 shows the official UN estimated past and projected future growth rates in so-called 'more developed' and 'less developed' countries. As can be seen, population size in the **'more developed countries'** has remained relatively stable since the late 1950s, at around 1 billion. In contrast, the total population of the **'less developed countries'** has increased rapidly from approximately 1 billion to 5 billion since 1950.

This difference in growth rates is depicted starkly in Figure 4.4, which shows that the rates of population growth in less developed regions, although declining rapidly, will continue to be far above those in more

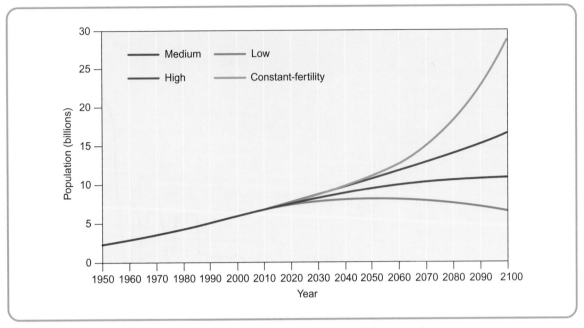

Figure 4.3 How changes in fertility rates might impact on future population growth.

Source: United Nations (2013: xv)

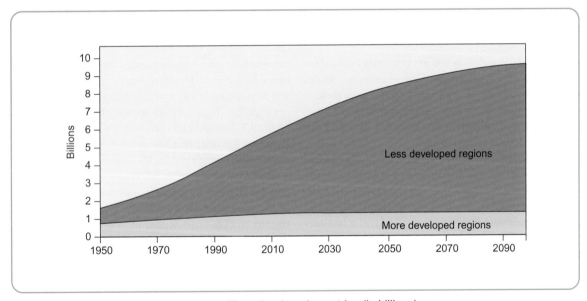

Figure 4.4 Population growth by more and less developed countries (in billions).

Source: based on data from *World Population Prospects: The 2012 Revision* (United Nations 2014a)

developed regions for the foreseeable future. The most striking aspect of the geography of population change is how population size in the 'more developed countries' has remained relatively stable since the late 1950s, at around 1 billion. In contrast, the total population of the 'less developed countries' has increased rapidly from approximately 1 billion to 6 billion since 1950. Also, as can be seen in Figure 4.4, the rates of population growth in 'less developed regions' are projected to be far above those in 'more developed regions' for the foreseeable future.

Even within the category of 'less developed' there are still further variations, the reasons for which will become more apparent below. The 48 least developed countries, according to UN data, experienced the greatest increases in population growth. This group only held 8 per cent of the world's population in 1950 but in the subsequent half-century, as a result of their rapid population growth, they contributed around 15 per cent of the overall global growth. Such differences in population growth rates have altered the relative distribution of the world's population. For example, the 'more developed' countries in 1950 combined to provide approximately a third of the world's population. By 2010 this had fallen to around 18 per cent (this global shift is discussed in Chapter 5 in relation to global energy demand and carbon emissions). As Table 4.2 shows, this has meant that significant changes have occurred in overall population share by region. Consequently, as Table 4.2 demonstrates, Europe's share of the world's population fell from approximately a quarter to around an eighth between 1900 and 2000, with Africa contrasting most as the biggest continental gainer in percentage terms. What is most significant here is how this has happened, with most of the changes taking place since 1950.

By 2050 Europe's share of the world's population is likely to have fallen to 7 per cent, while Africa's share is expected to be nearly three times that. Over the period 2003–2050 Africa's population is projected to grow by just under 1 billion people, representing over one-third of all global growth in humanity (36.4 per cent) compared to only one-sixth (16.6 per cent) for 1950–2003. Meanwhile, Asia seems destined to remain the main contributor in absolute terms, adding a further 1.4 billion up to 2050, but this is a marked reduction in the pace of growth compared to its 2.4 billion gain between 1950 and 2003.

4.3 Geographies of changing birth and death rates and the demographic transition model

To explain changes in population growth rates demographers often use the **demographic transition model**. According to this model there are five stages through which most countries have passed in their demographic history. Figure 4.5 summarizes the model and shows the stages (see Lee 2003 for an overview of its development). During stage one, health care is rudimentary and many people die from what are now easily treatable diseases, leading to very high crude death rates (CDR – deaths per 1000 people). **Birth rates** (CBR – births per 1000 people) were also high as large families were the norm, possibly as insurance against uncertainty and to ensure that parents will have support when they can no longer work. With birth and death rates relatively equal, overall population size does not increase dramatically during this stage.

Countries move to stage two, as their political, economic and social organization evolves and leads to the development of health care and sanitation systems, so that fewer people die from easily preventable diseases. However, there is usually a period during which birth rates remain high. This might be due to a delayed adjustment to the new

Table 4.2 Changes in overall population share (%) by region

Major area	1950	1975	2010	2050 Low	2050 Medium	2050 High	2050 Constant
More developed regions	32.2	25.7	17.9	13.8	13.6	13.5	11.4
Less developed regions	67.8	74.3	82.1	86.2	86.4	86.5	88.6
Least developed countries	7.7	8.5	12.1	19.1	19.0	18.8	23.0
Less developed regions, excluding least developed countries	60.1	65.7	69.9	67.1	67.4	67.7	65.6
Less developed regions, excluding China	45.9	51.3	62.0	71.4	71.5	71.6	76.3
Africa	9.1	10.3	14.9	25.4	25.1	24.7	29.0
Asia	55.3	58.6	60.2	53.7	54.1	54.4	52.3
Europe	21.7	16.6	10.7	7.5	7.4	7.4	6.1
Latin America and the Caribbean	6.6	8.0	8.6	8.1	8.2	8.3	8.0
Northern America	6.8	6.0	5.0	4.7	4.7	4.6	4.1
Oceania	0.5	0.5	0.5	0.6	0.6	0.6	0.6

Source: Population Division of the Department of Economic and Social Affairs of the United Nations Secretariat, *World Population Prospects: The 2012 Revision*, United Nations, New York (United Nations 2014a).

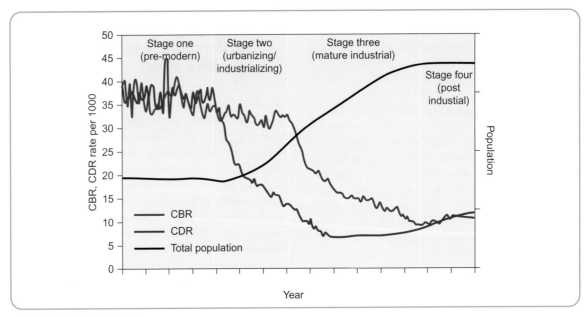

Figure 4.5 The demographic transition model.

Source: http://pages.uwc.edu/keith.montgomery/Demotrans/demtran.htm

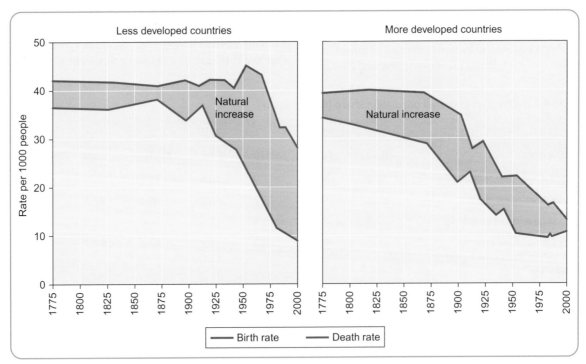

Figure 4.6 How changes to birth and death rates can lead to changes in natural population growth.

Source: Population Reference Bureau (2007)

situation, or because economic growth sees an increasing demand for family labour. This gap between death and birth rates results in an increasing population. As death rates can fall rapidly this can often cause a rapid rise in population growth. Figure 4.6 demonstrates how this occurs.

From these figures we can see that, in less developed countries, from the middle of the previous century death rates fell dramatically as health care began to improve. However, birth rates, although declining, did not converge with death rates, resulting in a rapid increase in the rate of natural

more and more work harder to ensure that their offspring are better educated than they were.

A recent projection (Samir *et al*. 2010) of educational changes has suggested that future trends for India and China will result in the numbers in any form of education in India not peaking until 2050, but the absolute numbers in various categories of learning falling in China from 2020 onwards. This will occur as the numbers of young people most likely to attend educational institutions continues to fall there even as the proportion attending higher education rises. The report accompanying the projection ends with the following salutary note: 'A historical example is provided by South Korea. In the 1960s, based on historical growth data, the economic outlook would have been modest, but projections of its future educational attainment profile may have indicated that it was about to enter a window of opportunity combining high qualifications with low dependency ratios' (Samir *et al*. 2010). When the rapid current uptake in educational opportunities is taken into account, then an even more rapid future population slowdown would appear yet more likely in both India and China. Women in particular tend to have fewer children when educated to secondary level, and fewer still if university educated. Figure 4.10

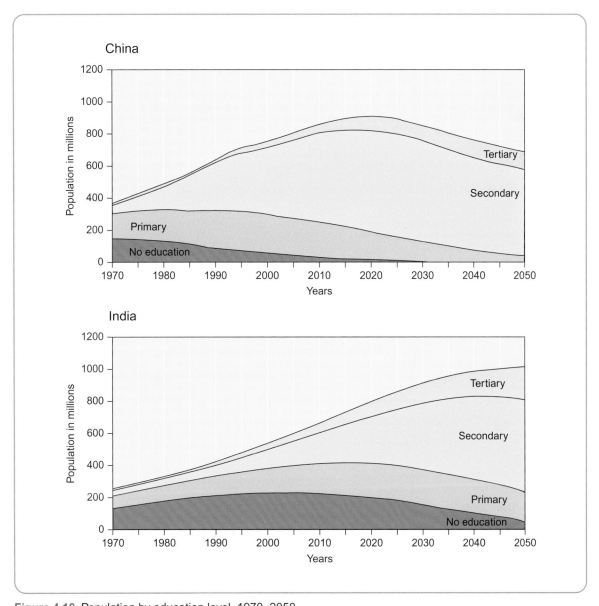

Figure 4.10 Population by education level, 1970–2050.

Source: Samir, K C, Barakat, B, Goujon A. *et al.* (2010: 432) Projection of populations by level of educational attainment, age and sex for 120 countries for 2005–2050, *Demographic Research,* 22, 383–472, www.demographic-research.org/volumes/vol22/15/

shows the highest level of education achieved or projected to be achieved by adults in India and China. Children are not included in these figures. Even in countries as affluent as the United States, educational changes are still linked to fertility changes.

4.5 Migration and population change

A world in which fertility's contribution to population growth is declining will see future population change within any region and country being attributed far more often to migration. In addition, there is an increasing movement of people between regions and countries so these patterns are changing. As the world urbanizes, more will move more often and further. Far more often than before those moves will be over international borders, simply because it has become easier to move slightly longer distances (and to video-call back home), while

the number of borders tends to remain fixed. According to recent data from the World Bank and the United Nations, approximately 3 per cent of the global population (213 million people) in 2010 lived in a country different from their country of birth. This compares to 2.4 per cent (72 million) of the total global population having permanently crossed a border in 1960. Table 4.3 shows the trends from 1960 to 2010 for the world as well as selected major regions and political and socio-economic groupings, whereas Figure 4.11 shows the changes over this period of 50 years for world regions by income level (as classified by the World Bank).

As can be seen in Figure 4.11, the number of immigrant residents as a percentage of total population tends to be higher in more affluent countries with nearly 12 per cent of the population in the high income countries (as classified by the World Bank) born abroad (in 1960 it was 3.9 per cent). This can be attributed to 'pull factors' in such countries such as better job opportunities or higher pay rates, but it should also be noted that immigrants

Table 4.3 Number of people born in a country other than that in which they live as a percentage of total population

International migrants (% of total population)	1960	1980	1990	2000	2010
World	2.4	2.1	2.9	2.9	3.1
By supra-national membership grouping					
Arab World	3.6	5.9	7.0	6.4	7.4
Euro area	2.3	3.5	6.4	8.4	10.9
European Union	2.8	3.6	5.7	7.3	9.4
By Human Development Index, income category and other status					
Fragile and conflict affected situations	3.9	4.3	3.5	2.7	2.6
Heavily indebted poor countries (HIPC)	3.9	3.6	3.5	2.6	2.1
Latin America & Caribbean (developing only)	2.7	1.6	1.5	1.1	1.1
Latin America & Caribbean (all income levels)	2.8	1.7	1.6	1.2	1.2
Least developed countries: UN classification	2.8	2.3	2.2	1.6	1.4
OECD members	3.9	4.6	6.0	7.6	9.0
High income	3.7	4.9	7.7	9.4	11.2
High income: non OECD	1.9	3.9	11.6	12.5	14.2
High income: OECD	4.1	5.1	6.8	8.7	10.5
Upper middle income	1.0	0.7	1.2	1.1	1.1
Lower middle income	2.7	1.6	2.0	1.5	1.3
Low & middle income	1.8	1.2	1.6	1.3	1.2
Low income	2.6	2.1	2.0	1.6	1.4

Source: authors' calculations using data from the United Nations Population Division (2015) and The World Bank (2015b)

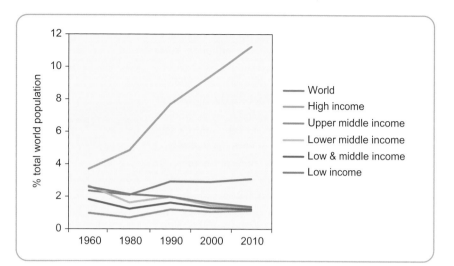

Figure 4.11 Trends (global and by income region) between 1960–2010 of number of people born in a country other than that in which they live as a percentage of total population.

Source: authors' calculations using data from the United Nations Population Division and The World Bank (2015b)

themselves contribute to the economic growth and prosperity of the destination countries. And destination countries often actually desperately need immigrants to replace the babies that have not been born as fertility declined rapidly two or three decades earlier. However, this is often an unfair trade. In particular, immigrants bring in skills but have been educated at the expense of the taxpayer in their home country. This is the case even with those who may be unskilled or have no formal education qualifications, as when they are employed they paid contributions to social insurance and pension schemes and in many cases they are doing jobs that existing residents do not want to do. Migrants also bring benefits in non-monetary ways that are more difficult to quantify, as they expose their new country to different cultures.

Overall, there needs to be a change of thinking towards understanding that just as gaining migrants is usually positive, for the migrant leaving a country is often a positive move too. In particular, the conditions in destination counties are generally good and this applies to both poorer countries and within the richer world. The large majority of migration in the world occurs where the large majority of people are, in the poorer areas of the world. Often called south–south migration, this is when people leave one country within a continent such as Africa to move to another, usually neighbouring, country. Such moves are can be viewed as problematic: 'The assessment of development progress is based on measurements within national boundaries. The emigration of people is still seen as a symptom of development failure' (Bakewell 2011). Similarly, emigration to the rich world is often seen as a failure of immigration control, rather than a success story of mass human endeavour. This also applies to situations where people are forced to leave their homes and become refugees as

Plate 4.1 A Greek Coastguard ship having picked up refugees who have crossed from Turkey to Europe near Mytilene, Lesvos on 11 June 2015. Lesvos is now a hotspot for refugees.

(Malcolm Chapman/Shutterstock)

well as economic migrants, as is the case with the recent events in the Mediterranean sea, which is often seen as a failure of immigration control rather than an opportunity to celebrate humanity, offering a better future to those in need and at the same time benefiting European countries with their rapidly ageing populations (see also Case study 4.3 and Section 4.8).

It should also be noted that it is more sustainable to build up population where there is already infrastructure, an abundant water supply, flat land and a demand for new labour, as compared to where many of these things are lacking. For existing cities that see their populations expanding often the only way is up, and more apartments are the future. For example, it would make little sense for Europe and Japan to depopulate. If migration to them from poorer areas were to increase, their population growth would help slow down total world population growth even faster than it is already slowing, possibly resulting in a global population which never exceeds 9 billion (because fertility falls faster than predicted). It should also be noted that when people move countries they, or their children, tend to quickly adopt the fertility rates of the places they are moving to. However, these facts tend to be overlooked in debates about migration in developed countries and especially by the tabloid press that publish misleading and alarming stories about 'immigrants taking our houses, our school places and our hospital beds' (Rowe 2014) and by far-right political parties (especially in Europe) which – just as their fascist forebears did – use immigrants and people seen as different (such as the Jews) as a scapegoat, blaming them for the rise of unemployment and representing them as a threat, when in fact, as argued above, the overall

impact can be extremely positive, especially when societies are properly prepared to welcome them. For more discussion, arguments and examples of why and how migration is beneficial to host countries see Rowe (2014).

4.6 Geographies of mortality and life expectancy

One of the key messages of the discussion above is that there has been a significant improvement of life expectancy across the world over the past 200 years and that unless there is a terrible disaster, a new plague or widespread famine, examples of where whole countries experience life expectancy below 50 years should soon

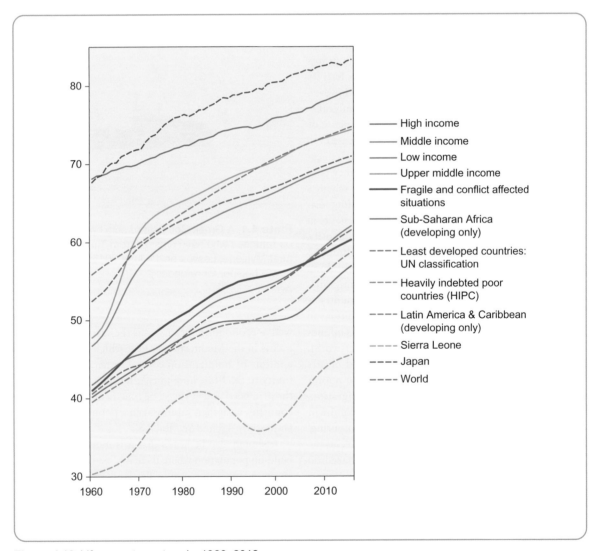

Figure 4.12 Life expectancy trends, 1960–2013.

Source: graph drawn based on data from The World Bank (2015c)

be relegated to the historical record, along with examples of countries where the average couple has four or five children.

According to the most recent data from the World Bank, the global population life expectancy at birth in 2013 was 71 years. Figure 4.12 shows the trends from 1960–2013 for world regions (using geographic, economic and political criteria) as well as for Japan and Sierra Leone, which are the countries with the highest and lowest life expectancy in 2013 respectively.

There has been a significant increase in life expectancy in most regions, although the rates of increase vary considerably between the different categories of countries as well as over different time periods. In particular, there was significant progress in the 1960s and 1970s in all countries. The rates of increase were higher in countries and regions where they were already extremely low. For example, as seen in Figure 4.12, life expectancy in sub-Saharan African countries went up from 40.2 years in 1960 to 56.9 in 2013. In addition, according to data from the World Bank (2015c), life expectancy in the world region of Middle East and North Africa went up from 46.6 in 1960 to 72.4 in 2013. In the same period the increase for countries in East Asia and the Pacific went up from 48 to 74.9 years. There were smaller increases in higher income countries where life expectancy was

already relatively high, such as Western Europe and North America. For instance, life expectancy in North America went up from 69.9 to 79.1 years and in countries that now make up the European Union it went up from 69.3 to 80.4 years. Worldwide the increase was 18.5 years between 1960 and 2013. However, life expectancy remains stubbornly low in the 'least developed' countries and especially in sub-Saharan African countries, where HIV/AIDS has been a major cause of death. In particular, in several of these countries there was no change in life expectancy or a decline (also see discussion in the next section). Other causes of significant declines in life expectancy include major environmental disasters such as the recent earthquake in Nepal but also armed conflict, such as the 1990s genocide in Rwanda, or the more recent wars in Syria, Afghanistan, Iraq, and Sudan.

There is also a high but rapidly falling **infant mortality rate** in the least developed regions: whereas the IMR for the period 2005–10 was just over 4 per 1,000 live births in North America, most of Europe and Australia/New Zealand, it averages 22 in Latin America, 56 in south-central Asia and 80 in sub-Saharan Africa (also see Figure 4.13). It was one of the United Nation's Millennium Development Goals to reduce by two-thirds the mortality rate among children under five (www.undp.org) (see Case study 4.1).

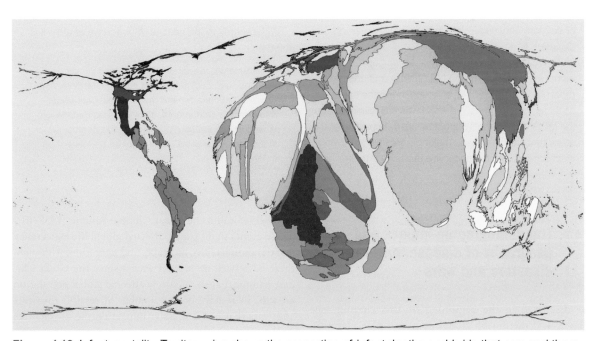

Figure 4.13 Infant mortality. Territory size shows the proportion of infant deaths worldwide that occurred there in 2002. Infant deaths are deaths of babies during their first year of life.

Source: www.worldmapper.org

Case study 4.1

United Nation's Millennium Development Goal number 4: reduce by two-thirds the mortality rate among children under 5

The Millennium Development Goals are eight develop-ment objectives that were set to be achieved by the end of 2015 (see discussion in Chapter 8). They were adopted by 189 nations at the UN Millennium Sum-mit in September 2000 (see www.undp.org/mdg for a full overview of the goals). Goal number 4 aimed to reduce by two-thirds the mortality rate among children under 5.

Progress was to be measured by the following indica-tors: under-5 mortality rate; infant mortality rate; and the proportion of one-year-old children immunized against measles. UN data shows, however, that in the first four years of the scheme little progress had been made in sub-Saharan Africa. Few countries there saw infant mortality decrease significantly and some had even seen rates increase. Some countries had experienced a rise in immunization rates but this is not universal to the region (for an excellent database on Millennium Devel-opment Goal data go to http://unstats.un.org/unsd/mdg). Elsewhere though there had been great progress, but these achievements was averaged down by the deaths of so many very small children in the very worse-off places.

Overall, according to the latest Millennium Develop-ment Goals Reports by the UN (2014a) and another report by UNICEF (2014), although there has been considerable progress, the world was still falling short of the MDG child mortality target by 2014. In particular, it is noted that there has been major progress in improving child survival with the under-five mortality rate declining by almost half since 1990 (but not yet to two-thirds of that rate). In addition, the rate at which under-five mortality is declining has more than tripled during the same period, with Eastern and Southern Africa having the highest annual rate of reduction in the world once East Asia and the Pacific are excluded from the com-parisons. It is also noted that under-five mortality is fall-ing among the poorest children. However, the progress has been insufficient to meet goal number 4 by the end of 2015 and if current trends continue the target will only be reached by 2026, 11 years behind schedule. Further, without rapid increases in funding to prevent easily preventable child deaths, the UN estimates that in some parts of sub-Saharan Africa the goals will not be reached until 2115. Despite the progress the toll of under-five deaths over the past two decades is stagger-ing, as 223 million children worldwide died before their fifth birthday during that period. Most of these deaths continue to occur in sub-Saharan Africa and South Asia. As pointed out in by UNICEF (2014):

> Sub-Saharan Africa continues to shoulder the greatest burden: 1 in 11 children born there still die before age 5, nearly 15 times the average in high-income countries (1 in 159). The recent momentum achieved in sub-Saharan Africa needs to be sustained and accelerated.

With regards to the causes of under-five deaths, it is noted that:

> although under-five deaths from leading infectious diseases have declined significantly, pneumonia, diar-rhoea and malaria are still the main killers of under-fives. In 2013, pneumonia, diarrhoea and malaria caused about one third of all under-five deaths. Impor-tantly, neonatal deaths account for 44 per cent of all under-five deaths.

4.7 The demographic impact and geography of disease, natural disasters and wars

As discussed in the beginning of this chapter (see Figure 4.5) the era of global population acceleration between 1851–1971 was interrupted by four major events: the First World War through to the end of the influenza pandemic (1914–19); the economic crash of 1929 through to the end of depression in 1936; the Second World War (1939–1945); and the Great Chinese Famine (1958–61). These events significantly affected global life expectancy and trends in fertility, mortality and migration. Although, there have been no similar events since the Great Chi-nese Famine that so massively affected global population growth, there have been a number of terrible disasters and wars that had a massive impact on the life chances and demographic processes of particular world regions and countries. For example, as discussed in the previous section, most of the countries in the world that expe-rienced a decline in life expectancy over the past few decades were in sub-Saharan Africa, where HIV/AIDS

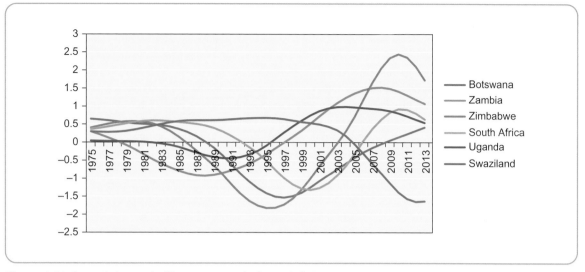

Figure 4.14 Annual change in life expectancy in five sub-Saharan countries.

Source: authors' calculations using data from The World Bank (2015c)

has been a major cause of death, despite the fact that the AIDS pandemic has been subsiding in recent years. According to the World Health Organization there were an estimated 1.5 million deaths from AIDS in the year 2013 alone. This cause of death is now declining in importance. These were 22 per cent fewer deaths in 2013 than in 2009 and 35 per cent fewer than the peak year of 2005 (World Health Organization 2011). However, over two-thirds (1.1 million) of these deaths were in Africa (World Health Organization 2014). Soon more people will die each year in road crashes than from HIV/AIDS. That, of course, is not much cause for celebration. But perhaps then we will begin to treat so many avoidable deaths from car crashes worldwide as seriously as we view pandemics?

According to UNICEF (2013) and UNAIDS (2010) there were then nine countries with HIV prevalence rates of over 10 per cent and the worst affected country at that time was Swaziland, which had the highest rate in the world (26 per cent), followed by Botswana (23.4 per cent), whereas in terms of absolute numbers South Africa was home to the world's largest epidemic with 5.6 million people living with HIV (17.3 per cent of its total

population). The figures will not be that dissimilar today, if you are reading the book shortly after its publication.

Figure 4.14 shows the trends in life expectancy in a number of selected countries that have experienced very high HIV/AIDS prevalence rates and numbers of deaths. During the 1970s and 1980s there were significant improvements of health care and life expectancy across the world (including the least developed regions) due to the successful introduction of sustained programmes curbing easily preventable diseases. For example, life expectancy in Botswana rose to approximately 65 by the mid-1980s and it was predicted that it would have reached 69 by 2011, but for HIV/AIDS. Instead, in 2011 male life expectancy was 55. In Swaziland life expectancy is now 46; without HIV/AIDS it is estimated that it would be 64. As Figure 4.14 shows, there have been dramatic falls in life expectancy throughout the period when the HIV/AIDS epidemic affected each of these countries. However, there has been a gradual improvement in the more recent years for some countries that can be attributed to the use of antiretrovirals and increased education levels about the transmission of HIV and the increased use of condoms, despite the attempts of some religious groups to stop this.

Case study 4.2

HIV/AIDS

HIV (Human Immunodeficiency Virus) is a virus that can develop into AIDS (Acquired Immunodeficiency Syndrome). This syndrome leads to the failure of the

immune system, making minor infections life threatening. There is currently no cure for this disease. The virus is most commonly passed on by sexual contact and the sharing of infected needles and can also be transmitted during pregnancy and through breastfeeding. While the scale of the pandemic is clear, the origins of HIV/AIDS are not easily identifiable. There are many competing theories as to why and where the disease began, but it first came to the attention of the medical profession in the early 1980s when groups of patients started to suffer from diseases rarely seen within their age group and which were extremely resistant to treatment (see www.avert.org or www.unaids.org for further details). By the mid-1980s the disease was named, tests became available and public awareness campaigns on how to avoid infection began. Despite this, the number of people becoming infected grew rapidly. One of the main causes of this is the fact that HIV is asymptomatic and can be carried for many years before AIDS develops, therefore a carrier can infect many other people before they become ill themselves.

Today HIV/AIDS affects every country in the world. According to the World Health Organization (WHO), since the beginning of the epidemic, almost 78 million people have been infected with the HIV virus and about 39 million people have died of HIV. WHO estimates that globally, 35.0 million people were living with HIV at the end of 2013. Sub-Saharan Africa is the region of the world worst affected with nearly 1 in every 20 adults living with HIV and accounting for nearly 71 per cent of the people living with HIV worldwide.

While there is no cure there are drugs, known as antiretrovirals, that can slow down the progression of the disease. This can greatly improve the health and life expectancy of people living with HIV/AIDS and they can block the transmission of the virus from mother to child. According to a UNAIDS report antiretroviral therapy averted 5.5 million deaths in low and middle-income countries from the peak in 1995 until 2012 (UNAIDS 2013). However, these drugs are not a cure and if treatment is missed or a patient develops resistance to the drug then the disease reverts to its normal course. Also, due to the cost of the drugs many people in low and middle-income countries have not been able to access them at all. At the beginning of the 21st century there were very few people in low and middle-income countries with access to HIV treatment. This was to some extent due to the very high prices of antiretroviral drugs and the international patents that stopped them from being manufactured at cheaper prices. However, since 2001 drug manufacturers in developing countries began to manufacture generic drugs under special terms in international trade law and this resulted in a significant reduction in price, enabling the expansion of treatment on a global scale (AVERT 2014). According to UNAIDS the cost of first-line antiretroviral therapy in some low- and middle-income countries has been reduced to around US$140 per person per year by 2013, from US$10,000 per person per year which was the estimated cost in the mid-1990s.

In late 2006 UNAIDS estimated that out of over 7 million people living with HIV in these countries less than 2 million had access to antiretroviral medication. In 2012 this number was estimated to be 9.7 million and there was an overall 40-fold increase in access to antiretroviral therapy between 2002–2012 (UNAIDS 2013). In addition, UNAIDS estimated that there was an overall 33 per cent decrease in new HIV infections between 2001 and 2012 and a 29 per cent decrease in AIDS related deaths between 2005 and 2012. However, in many sub-Saharan African countries less than half of expectant mothers with HIV receive the medication they require to reduce the risk of transmission to their child. While there is still the will to increase access to medication, the current prolonged global economic downturn (as we write in 2015) means that even though the cost of the drugs continues to fall many governments are struggling to purchase them in sufficient quantities or to maintain the health care infrastructure needed for their effective delivery. Overall, UNAIDS highlights that there has been remarkable progress over the last decade, but also that significant challenges remain.

World demography is still altered by several major infectious diseases. Malaria is another disease that has significantly affected life expectancy in several African countries. In 2003 there were an estimated 110 million deaths from Malaria and 92 per cent of them were recorded in Africa, with the rest mainly in Asia Pacific and Southern Asia. Deaths from Malaria when estimated globally are now found to be falling (United Nations 2014b).

Other possible causes of significant declines in life expectancy, as well as disease, include human mobility and displacement especially following major environmental disasters including epidemics, droughts, famines, earthquakes, volcanoes, storms, fires and events caused by accidents or indirectly caused by wars. There is a very uneven geography of such deaths that reflects the relative vulnerability of the population (Affifi and Jäger 2010). With regards to the people affected by disaster and requiring external assistance (such as shelter, water, sanitation, medication and food) to survive, 43 per cent were in Southern Asia, 41 per cent in Eastern Asia and 5 per cent in Southern Africa (Worldmapper 2015a).

The ability of countries to deal with disasters and to minimize the loss of human life heavily depends on the local infrastructure, which includes good communications and early warning systems and adequate planning as well as the readiness of the international community to provide support. Again, there is an uneven geography of the potential of countries and regions to address the impact of disasters, leading to higher number of deaths in some areas that could have been prevented (e.g. see Worldmapper 2015b). For instance, the 2015 earthquake in Nepal had a devastating effect upon the country's population and economy and there was an urgent and very strong need for international assistance. In contrast, Japan was in a much better position to deal with the Great Eastern Earthquake and tsunami disaster in 2011 with minimum international assistance.

It is also increasingly argued that natural disasters are now more and more likely to be the result of **climate change** and there is a great amassing of evidence in relation to the processes at play and mitigating the environmental impact that human activity has on the planet. At the same time there are increased calls for action from humanitarian agencies such as the Office of the United Nations High Commissioner for Refugees (UNHCR). Such agencies are increasingly developing climate-change scenarios that envisage massive environmental disasters which would result in direct or indirect human displacement (and **environmental migration**, which includes **climate migration**) including hydro-meteorological disasters (flooding, hurricanes, typhoons, cyclones, mudslides etc.), environmental degradation and slow onset disaster (e.g. reduction of water availability, desertification, recurrent flooding), the possibility of 'sinking' small states and violent conflict triggered by a decrease in essential resources (such as water, land, food) owing to climate change (UNHCR 2014). UNCHR have already been involved in operations aimed at mitigating the impact of disasters for which there are strong reasons to believe are caused by climate change, such as the flooding of Somali refugee camps in north-eastern Kenya in November 2007 resulting in 12,000 **refugees** losing their shelters and displacing another 80,000 (UNHCR 2014).

Related to climate change is the increased use of cars for commuting in the world and traffic – one of the causes of death expected to rise (Dorling 2011). According to the latest data from the World Health Organization there were 1.24 million deaths from road traffic accidents in 2010.

After road crashes the next highest source of traumatic death is war. War has a huge impact on the demographic structure, life expectancy and migration patterns of whole countries and regions. Ever since the Second World War there has been no military conflict that would have such an impact on global population growth. However, since then there have been a number of smaller wars and armed conflicts resulting in more than 50 million deaths, and these have had a devastating effect on the populations of particular countries and world regions. Figure 4.15 shows the geographical distribution of deaths resulting from wars between 1945 and 2000. China, Vietnam and the Democratic Republic of Congo and Sudan had the highest number of war

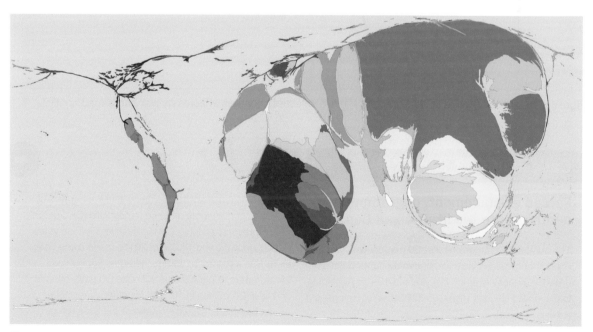

Figure 4.15 War deaths, 1945–2000.
Source: www.worldmapper.org

Plate 4.2 Unidentified Syrian people in refugee camp in Turkey on 18 June 2011 on the Turkish–Syrian border.

(thomas koch/Shutterstock)

deaths during this period, whereas there were very few war deaths affecting the populations of Japan, Western Europe and North America. There were relatively few war deaths in Eastern Europe (including the wars in former Yugoslavia) and South America (mainly in Bolivia, Colombia and Guatemala).

Figure 4.16 shows the annual changes in life expectancy of five selected countries affected by war and armed conflict. War and other disasters result in population displacement and forced migration, which has a demographic and socio-economic impact on the structure of regions and countries that are the destinations of immigrants (see Case study 4.3).

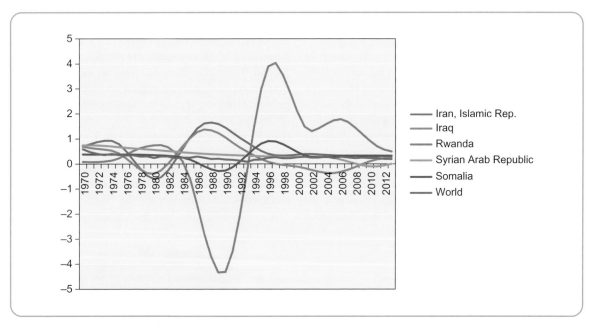

Figure 4.16 Annual change in life expectancy in five selected countries affected by war and armed conflict.

Case study 4.3

Forced displacement, migration and deaths in the Mediterranean Sea

The number of refugees caused by persecution, war and conflict, generalized violence, or human rights violations grew significantly over the five years 2010–15. According to the United Nations High Commissioner for Refugees (UNHCR) report, during 2013 an average of 32,200 individuals per day were forced to leave their home and

seek protection elsewhere, either within the borders of their own country or in other countries (UNHCR 2015a). This represents a significant increase to previous years (23,400 in 2012 and 14,200 in 2011). In the same year, there was a record 1.1 million individual applications for asylum or refugee status submitted to governments and UNHCR offices in 167 UN countries or territories. As put by António Guterres, head of the UN's refugee agency 'We are witnessing a quantum leap in forced displacement in the world' (*The Guardian* 2015). Overall, an estimated total of 51.2 million individuals were forced to flee their homes around the world by the end of 2013 and this is the highest recorded level since the Second World War. If all these people had their own country it would be the 24th most populous in the world. UNHCR identifies seven population categories of forcefully **displaced people**: refugees; asylum-seekers; internally displaced persons (IDPs); refugees who have returned home (returnees); IDPs who have returned home; persons under UNHCR stateless mandate; and others who do not fall under any of these categories.

The largest source country of refugees is Afghanistan (and has been for over three decades) as a result of long-term conflicts and war. It is now closely followed by Syria, which became the second largest origin of refugees within just five years and has moved from being the second largest refugee-hosting country to being the second largest refugee source country. The civil war that broke out there in the spring of 2011 has resulted in the uprooting of half the country's pre-war population. According to UNHCR more than 4 million Syrians are refugees in neighbouring countries and an additional 7.6 million internally displaced (BBC 2015). Other countries that are in the top origins of refugees include Somalia, Sudan and the Democratic Republic of Congo (UNHCR 2015a). More details and statistical data (including data on historical trends by region and by country) are available via the UNHCR's statistical website (www.unhcr. org/statistics).

The overwhelming majority (86 per cent) of the global refugee population is hosted by developing countries (UNHCR 2015b). The country with the largest number of refugees is Pakistan (1.6 million), followed by Iran, Lebanon, Jordan and Turkey. A relatively small proportion (15 per cent) of refugees are located in Europe (UNHCR 2015b). However, there is a very large (and rapidly increasing) number of people risking (and losing) their lives in order to seek refuge there. According to 'The Migrants Files' (www.detective.io/detective/the-migrants-files/), a project set up by a pan-European consortium of journalists and the European Network Against Racism 'United for Intercultural Action' (www.unitedagainstracism.org/), there have been at least 29,000 deaths of people (including hundreds of babies and children) attempting to reach Europe since 2000. A lot of these deaths occurred in the Mediterranean sea, as desperate people attempt to cross it in often rickety and unseaworthy boats, dying on an almost daily basis (Rice-Oxley and Mahmood 2014). According to a recent report by the BBC (2015)

drawing on data by the International Organization for Migration (www.iom.int/) more than 1,700 people are believed to have died in the first four months of 2015, compared with 96 up to the end of April in 2014.

At least 800 people drowned in a single incident on 19 April 2015 after the boat they were travelling in capsized in the Libyan waters south of the Italian island of Lampedusa on 19 April 2015. According to UNHCR, in the first five months of 2015 more than 42,000 people (most of them refugees) arrived by sea in Greece, six times the level of the same period in 2014 and almost the same as the total for all 2014. Over 90 per cent of these people originated from refugee-producing countries, principally Syria (over 60 per cent of arrivals in the first five months of 2015), Afghanistan, Iraq, Somalia and Eritrea (UNHCR 2015b).

The increasing numbers of people trying to seek refuge in Europe and the recent deaths of thousands of migrants trying to cross the Mediterranean prompted the European Union to prepare an emergency response to stave off a worsening of the humanitarian crisis. This includes proposals for all member states to host a set number of migrants, partly to relieve the pressure on southern states like Italy and Greece. However, they also include controversial proposals (that were heavily criticized by human rights activists and organizations such as Amnesty International) for military action to identify, capture and destroy boats that carry migrants before they embark to Europe (Traynor 2015). So far, as we write in 2015, protestors have manged to prevent the military powers of rich nations from carrying out such inhuman acts. It should also be noted that there are also now strong anti-immigration sentiment and views in some regions and countries of Europe that oppose the welcoming and integration of immigrants and refugees. These are similar to the anti-refugee sentiments in the 1930s and early 1940s that resulted in Jewish people being barred entry into countries such as the UK. At the same time, there are emerging movements and activist networks calling for open welcoming spaces, such as the 'all together' initiative in the Greek island of Lesvos (http://lesvos. w2eu.net/). Similarly, over 70 years ago activists managed to help Jewish children escape mainland Europe on the kinder-transports – if not their parents. Given knowledge of refugees situations in our recent past it is surprising that such initiatives are not more warmly embraced and supported by the European Union and by local and national governments, given the potential benefits (see Section 4.5) and the expedient challenges of aging populations in Europe (also see Section 4.8).

4.8 The challenges of ageing populations

According to UN calculations (Population Reference Bureau 2014) in 1970 just under half (48 per cent) of the global population was younger than 20. Another 47 per cent was aged 20–64 and the remaining 5 per cent was aged 65 and older. The age structure of the world's population has now significantly changed as a result of lower fertility rates and longer life expectancy. The population under age 20 is now approximately just 35 per cent and is falling most rapidly, whereas the population aged 20–64 is 58 per cent, falling in numbers more slowly and the population aged 65 and over is 7 per cent and rising as a share of the total. However, there is considerable variation across world regions and countries.

Europe and North America have populations that are much older than the global average. It can be argued that this is the result of them entering the final stage of the transition model discussed in Section 4.2. Whereas, in contrast, Africa's current youthful age structure is similar to the global average in 1970 (Population Reference Bureau 2014). These differences in population structures are illustrated in the diagrams shown in Figure 4.17. These diagrams, known as population pyramids, show the distribution of the men and women in the world and different world regions by age groups in 1970 and 2014. It is worth noting the difference in the shape between Europe and North America and the other continents (and especially Africa). The shape of these diagrams for Europe and North America (and especially by 2014) is often described as a 'constrictive pyramid' typical for affluent societies with low fertility and mortality rates and relatively older populations. As can be seen in the first pyramid shown in Figure 4.17, there is a trend for the world population pyramid to become 'constrictive'. In addition, the 2014 pyramids for Europe and North America clearly stand out from the rest

Soon most countries in Europe and North America are going to be faced with a demographic and pension crisis as there will be fewer people of working age and fewer taxpayers, making it impossible to provide current levels of support, especially in areas of net out young migration and fertility below 1.5 children per potential couple. A possible solution to these issues could include increasing the retirement age (and this has already happened in some countries, including the UK), as this would result in additional working years and tax revenues and a reduction in the time that a person might receive a state pension. Another possible solution often discussed is for governments to try and stimulate birth rates so that more

young people enter the economy in the future. A few governments are therefore resorting to incentive schemes to try and arrest the declining birth rates experienced by many European countries. For example, the German government introduced in January 2007 a 'parents' money' law, which means that parents who remain at home to look after their child will receive 67 per cent of their previous income for a year (up to €1800 per month). Those on a low income will receive 12 monthly payments of €450. This is extremely generous when compared to the British system wherein a new mother receives 90 per cent of her previous pay for 6 weeks and then a flat €150 for 26 weeks only. Men can take 2 weeks paid paternity leave at €150 per week for 2 weeks. In Norway mothers receive 10 months at full pay and men *have* to take 4 weeks paternity leave at full pay, helping the country to the third highest birth rate in Europe. Poland and Italy have recently introduced an incentive of a one-off payment for each child born.

The more obvious solution of encouraging international migration into countries with ageing populations is also a way of increasing their workforce and slowing down population growth in poorer countries. In addition, increased migration into countries like the UK would help reduce current debts, and also help in caring for a growing elderly population. It would also reduce global population growth faster than even the current very fast rate of growth slowdown. That is because young migrants from poorer countries who move to countries like the UK tend to have fewer children than they would have had had they not migrated. Although many other factors will influence the future level of public sector debt in the UK, increased immigration reduces debt, while emigration of younger adults from Britain will increase it.

4.9 Conclusion

Throughout human history the global population experienced relatively slow growth, with the exceptions of the Neolithic Revolution and the most recent era of global population acceleration from 1851 to 1971, leading to a population explosion from 1 billion in 1820 to 7 billion in 2011. The most significant increase occurred in the past 60 years, when the population went up by 4 billion, from 3 billion in 1950 to 7 billion in 2011. However, it is vital to realize that for the majority of those past 60 years population growth rates have been rapidly decelerating everywhere. During this period the population of the more affluent world (described by the UN as 'developed regions') increased from 800 million in 1950

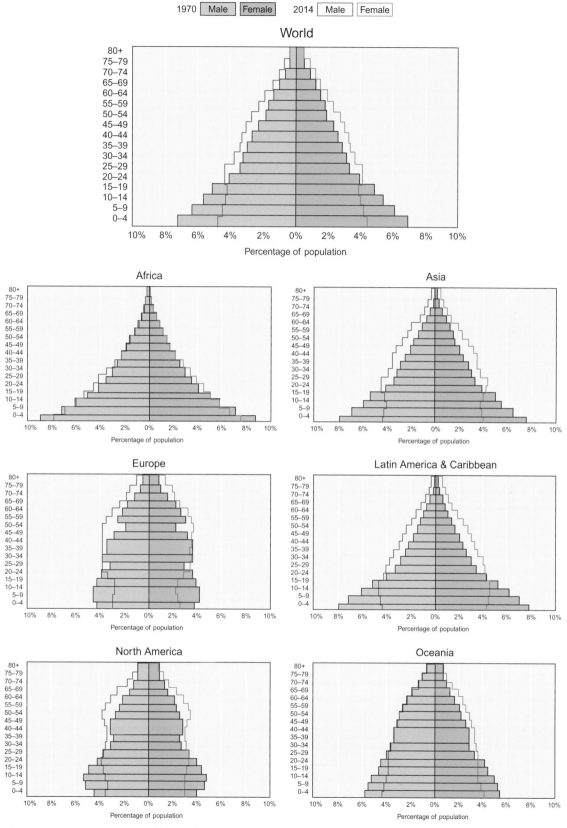

Figure 4.17 Age structure, 1970–2014.

Source: Population Reference Bureau (2014: 10)

to only 1.2 billion in 2011 (and it is now only stabilized by in-migration), whereas the population of the poorest ('least developed') regions more than trebled, going up from 1.7 billion to 5.8 billion. That global division is due to deceleration in the growth rate having been earliest and fastest in the richest of places and, at the other end of a continuum, latest and slowest in just a few parts of Africa.

The overall planetary population increase has been placing a strain on environmental, food, housing and welfare infrastructures. However, it should be noted that it is not just the number of people that has an impact on these infrastructures, but how people live. For instance, the so-called 'developed countries' have been polluting the environment and contributing to **global warming** and climate change far more compared to the most populous poorer parts of the world (see Chapter 6). The strain is not from those who are greatest in number, but from those whose greed is most great, in both rich and poor countries alike. Greed control is now much more important than population control.

This chapter has highlighted as especially important the fact that since 1971 the world has entered an era of global deceleration of population growth rates. There is projected to be an even more significant slowdown in population growth very soon, which is expected to lead to a world human population peak of, at most, ten billion being reached by around 2100. Average fertility rates worldwide are rapidly falling and are predicted to continue to fall and converge to just below the population replacement level rate of 2.1 by 2100 in all world regions. Estimates, of course, vary greatly although few people talk as seriously as they should about the future low-fertility scenarios in which fewer than 9 billion people might be the peak. In contrast, in 2015 talk of 11 billion humans by 2100 was more common. The uncertainty is important to acknowledge. We humans think we know so much but we don't even know how many grandchildren we are likely to have, even in aggregate.

As fertility's contribution to population growth is declining, migration is playing a more and more important role in the growth and social and economic development of countries and regions, and there have been increasing numbers of international migrants crossing borders in recent years. At the same time, there has been a dramatic increase in average life expectancy across the world over the past 200 years. In 1800 all countries around the world had an average life expectancy at birth of less than 45 years (according to the Gapminder; see Useful websites section); by 2013 the estimated global average life expectancy was 71 years.

Averages only tell us so much. There are still significant social and spatial inequalities in life expectancy and life chances worldwide. In the so-called 'least developed

countries' the average life expectancy at birth was 61.5 years in 2013, whereas in sub-Saharan African countries it was 56.9 years. In contrast, in the affluent world (in the so-called 'high income countries' as classified by the World Bank) average life expectancy was 79.4 years and in particular parts of the regions of this richest section of the world it was even higher (e.g. 83.3 in Japan and 80.4 years when the European Union is averaged out). In contrast to such longevity, poorer countries are far more affected by disease, natural disasters (including disasters caused by climate change) and wars that have been disproportionally affecting all the poorest regions of the world, leading to the slow-down in gain, or even a short decline in life expectancy, as well as to human displacement. Mostly recently, countries such as Afghanistan and Syria have reported significant numbers of premature deaths due to conflict and huge numbers of people having to become refugees. The overwhelming majority of the world's refugees are hosted by developing countries and only a relatively small number are hosted by affluent countries. For example, only 15 per cent of global refugees are hosted in Europe and 7 per cent in the Americas.

Recently some groups within some of the more affluent countries have been facing decreases in life expectancy due to rising income and wealth inequalities as well as the introduction of severe and sometimes punitive austerity measures (O'Hara 2014; *The Guardian* 2015). Further, there have been a growing number of studies suggesting a very strong link between a number of factors relating to life expectancy, well-being and health of populations and income and wealth inequality, especially in more affluent societies. In particular, according to the groundbreaking book *The Spirit Level: Why Equality is Better for Everyone*, by epidemiologists Richard Wilkinson and Kate Pickett (2010), a wide number of indicators (including demographic indicators such as life expectancy) are related to inequalities in income and wealth.

Regions of the affluent world (in short especially Europe, North America and Japan) are facing the challenges of ageing populations and a potential demographic and pension crisis on top of all the trends already listed here. As we argued in this chapter, an obvious way to respond to this potential crisis is to encourage international migration, including a warmer welcome and integration of refugees. Net international migration tends to be into countries with ageing populations and is also a way of increasing their workforce and slowing down population growth in poorer countries. Migrants tend to have fewer children than people in the areas they leave, and to behave more like the population they join in terms of their fertility.

Overall, it is very important to understand demographic trends and processes as well as the interdependencies between countries, regions and cities and all their populations, but to also highlight the fact that the actual number of people on the planet is, to an important extent, incidental to the impact humans have on both the environment and each other. This is also illustrated in all other chapters of this book. It is not how many of us there are or will be that matters most, but how we all behave, think and act in future. Control greed and we can expect a healthy demographic future.

Learning outcomes

Having read this chapter, you should be able to:

- Recognize the dynamic nature of populations, not only in terms of size but also with respect to the geographies which exist within the overall growth.

- Explore how sudden economic changes, disasters or disease affects life expectancy and alters the course taken by countries through the demographic transition process.

- Acknowledge the increasing importance of migration as a component of national population change alongside fertility and mortality.

- Assess the significant problems that ageing populations will have in terms of social and economic development, as well as issues of selfishness, empathy and greed.

- Understand the potential impact of inequality upon demographic issues and life expectancy.

Further reading

Bailey, A.J. (2011) Population geographies and climate change, *Progress in Human Geography,* 35(5), 686–95.

Bailey, A.J. (2010) Population geographies, gender, and the mitigation-development nexus, *Progress in Human Geography,* (3), 375–86. The first of these articles connects the themes of this chapter with those of Chapters 5 and 6, the second with those of Chapters 7 and 8.

Castles, S. and Miller, M.J. (2009) *The Age of Migration: International Population Movements in the Modern World,* 4th edition, Palgrave Macmillan, Basingstoke. This book, now in its fourth edition, provides a comprehensive survey of past trends and current developments in international migration. See the companion website at: www.age-of-migration.com/UK/index.asp.

Dorling, D. (2013) *Population Ten Billion: The Coming Demographic Crisis and How to Survive It,* Constable, London.

Harper, S. (2005) *Ageing Societies,* Hodder Arnold, London. This book explores the issues of population in both developing and mature countries. It examines the necessity for people to extend their working lives, the changes ageing societies have on families, the challenges it poses for state social provision and the impact these issues will have on developing regions.

Hennig, D. B. (2013) *Rediscovering the World: Map Transformations of Human and Physical Space,* Springer, Heidelberg.

Hughes, B. (2010) *Too Many Of Whom and Too Much Of What? What the New Population Hysteria Tells us About the Global Economic and Environmental Crisis, and its Causes,* A No One Is Illegal discussion paper, www.noii.org.uk/2010/01/13/too-many-of-whomand-too-much-of-what/.

Hugo, G. (2007) Population geography, *Progress in Human Geography,* 31(1), 77–88. One of a series of articles looking at developments in population geography in the Southern Hemisphere. This article looks at population vulnerability and migration.

Jones, H. (1990) *Population Geography,* Paul Chapman, London. A clear introduction to geographical perspectives on population. Look especially at the chapters on population growth and regulation, international variations in mortality, fertility in developed countries, fertility in less developed countries, and international migration.

National Research Council (2000) *Beyond Six Billion: Forecasting the World's Population,* National Academy Press, Washington, DC. This presents the findings of a US National Academy of Sciences panel on population projections. It contains detailed examinations of transitional and post-transitional fertility, mortality and life expectancy, and international migration, together with assessments of the accuracy of past projections and of the uncertainties in current population forecasts.

UNAIDS (2010) *UNAIDS 2011–2015 Strategy: Getting to Zero.* Available to download at www.unaids.org/en/media/unaids/contentassets/documents/unaidspublication/2010/JC2034_UNAIDS_Strategy_en.pdf. This report gives a comprehensive overview of the challenges that countries and international organizations face when confronting the epidemic. It also details many success stories and the development of good practice as well as providing country and regional statistics.

United Nations (2010) *World Population to 2300.* Available to download at www.un.org/esa/population/publications/. . ./WorldPop2300final.pdf. The report provides an overview of global demographic trends and explores in detail population size and growth, urbanization and city growth, population ageing, fertility and contraception, mortality and international migration.

Vlassopoulos, C. (2013) Defining environmental migration in the climate change era: problem, consequence or solution?, in Faist, T. and Shade, J., *Disentangling Migration and Climate Change: Toward an analysis of Concepts, Methodologies, and Policies,* Springer, New York.

Useful websites

www.worldpopulationatlas.org A collection of world maps, where territories are re-sized on each map according to the subject of interest.

www.gapminder.org An online interactive visualization of data resource promoting sustainable global development and achievement of the United Nations Millennium Development Goals.

www.iom.int Provides access to the International Organization for Migration publications and statistics.

www.un.org/esa/population/unpop.htm Provides access to extracts from the United Nations' population-related publications and statistics.

www.census.gov/ipc/www/idb US Census Bureau (online) International Data Base, United States Bureau of the Census, Washington, DC. This is a computerized source of demographic data.

www.neighbourhood.statistics.gov.uk/dissemination The Neighbourhood Statistics website provides access to a wealth of UK Official Statistics, including data from the 2001 and 2011 Censuses.

www.unhcr.org Provides access to publications and data of the United Nations Refugee Agency.

http://data.worldbank.org Free and open access to data about development in countries around the world (including a wealth of demographic data).

www.ggdc.net/maddison/maddison-project/home.htm The Maddison Project, providing information (including population data sets) in relation to the work of Angus Maddison, who was a world scholar on quantitative macro-economic history.

RESOURCES, ENERGY AND DEVELOPMENT

Chapter 5

Michael Bradshaw

Topics covered

- The nature of natural resources and ways of defining and classifying them

- The factors that influence resource availability

- Types of renewable energy

- The changing geography of oil and gas production and consumption

- Global energy dilemmas

Resources are defined by *society*, not by nature.
(Adapted from Rees 1985:11)

Resources are not, they become; they are not static but expand and contract in response to human wants and actions.
Zimmerman (Peach and Constantin 1972:16)

The large-scale exploitation of the planet's resource base is one of the defining characteristics of the age in which we live (McNeill 2000); fortunately, we are increasingly aware of the finite nature of the planet's resource base (see Chapter 6). The explosion at the Deepwater Horizon drilling platform in April 2010, and the subsequent oil leak that poured oil into the Gulf of Mexico for three months, provides a stark reminder that the exploitation of natural resources usually results in environmental degradation. There are also many tragic reminders of the human cost of resource extraction, such as the continuing high death toll of coal miners in China. Indeed, all energy sources carry risks, as the crisis in March 2011 at the Fukushima Daiichi nuclear power station in Japan following the devastating earthquake and tsunami showed. This chapter explores the nature of natural resources and considers the relationship between resource production and consumption, economic development and climate change (see Gautier 2008 for a discussion of climate change and the role of energy). The chapter is divided into three sections, each with a distinct task. The first section examines the nature of 'natural resource', it evaluates the various ways of classifying resources and analyses the diverse factors that influence their availability. The second section analyses the specific case of energy resources, and reviews the various types of **renewable energy** and the changing geographies of oil and gas production and consumption. The third section considers the interrelationship between energy consumption, economic development and climate change. The chapter concludes by discussing the energy dilemmas that currently face the different regions of the world and the emerging global energy paradox in relation to continued investment in fossil fuels.

5.1 Natural resources

The Earth holds a finite stock of resources, the resource base. However, what human societies consider a resource has varied through time and across space. As both Zimmerman and Rees acknowledge above, something is a resource because human society attaches value to it. Many of the things we value today as 'resources' held no value in the past and may hold no value in the future. Followers of science fiction, such as *Star Trek*, see a future based on resources and technologies that have yet to be created.

5.1.1 Defining resources

In his seminal work *World Resources and Industries*, Zimmerman (Peach and Constantin 1972: 9) states: 'The word "resource" does not refer to a substance, but a function that a thing or a substance may perform, or to an operation in which it might take place.' He also notes that 'resources are . . . as dynamic as civilization itself'. In fact, one can suggest that each major human civilization was sustained by a particular set of resources and technologies for their exploitation (Smil 1994; Simmons 1996); the archaeological record includes the *Stone Age*, the *Bronze Age* and the *Iron Age*. In reference to the Industrial Revolution of the nineteenth century, Simmons (1996: 208) states that 'industrialization based on fossil fuel energy represents a turning point in the history of human–nature relations'. If the nineteenth century was based on the era of coal, then the twentieth century will been seen as the era of oil. Clearly, the changing notion of what constitutes a 'resource' is an important factor in shaping the relationship between human societies and the natural environment. As Blunden (1995: 164) observed, 'Because definition as a resource depends on usefulness to human society, natural materials may be required as resources by societies in some times and places but not in others.' While it is still the case that people in many parts of the world live in what Mather and Chapman (1995: 139) call 'low-energy societies' (dependent upon plants, animals and human labour), one of the defining characteristics of our age, and a consequence of the processes of globalization, is that the majority of societies now have some shared notion of what sorts of things constitute resources. The Inuit living in northern Canada are as dependent on gasoline for their skidoos as the commuters for their cars in Los Angeles or London are. Furthermore, echoing Lenin's famous edict that 'Communism is electrification plus Soviet labour power', the provision of electricity is central to the modernization process in all types of societies. There are still 1.4 billion people around the world that lack access to electricity (IEA, UNDP and UNIDO 2010). There is increasing acknowledgement of the centrality of energy access to poverty alleviation and 2014 marked the beginning of the UN's decade of 'Sustainable Energy for All'.

If the notion of resource is dynamic and intimately linked to the evolution of human society, it follows that so-called 'technological progress' both creates and destroys resource value. As new technologies emerge, dependent on particular resources, so old technologies and their associated resources become redundant. For example, today flint has limited value as a building material, yet in the Stone Age it was an essential resource for making tools. Because such resources had 'use value' they were also objects of trade. Other resources that were valued in the Bronze Age, such as copper and zinc, are still valued today as new ways of using them are discovered. New technologies also create new demands and concerns, such as the availability of so-called rare

Plate 5.1 The use of firewood for cooking in a 'low energy' consumption society.

(Gilles Paire/Shutterstock)

earth metals used in many 'green' technologies or lithium that is needed for rechargeable batteries. The use value of resources also means that control over their supply is an important part of political and economic power. In theory at least, resource-rich regions are able to exploit this natural advantage in their dealings with resource-poor regions. Consequently, gaining control over particular resources has been at the heart of many wars and much conflict (Klare 2002; Le Billon 2007). The European colonization of the 'developing world' was motivated by a desire to discover and control new sources of resources. It is also no surprise that even today five of the world's ten largest corporations are oil

and gas companies – Shell, Exxon Mobil, BP, Sinopec (China Petroleum and Petrochemical Company) and CNPC (China National Petroleum Company) (Dicken 2015: 395–422). Our discussion so far has implied that all resources share the same characteristics. However, we know that there are many different types of natural resource and the various ways of classifying them is the subject of the next section.

5.1.2 Classifying resources

Natural resources are commonly divided into two types: **non-renewable** or **stock resources** and renewable or flow resources (Figure 5.1). Stock resources are those, mainly mineral, that have taken millions of years to form and so their availability is finite. Hence, we also refer to them as non-renewable as there is no possibility of their being replenished on a timescale of relevance to human society. Within the category of stock resources, it is useful to distinguish between those that are consumed by use, such as fuel minerals, those that are theoretically recoverable and those that are recyclable, such as aluminium. A further characteristic of stock resources is that they tend to be highly localized, that is they are found in relative abundance only in specific places, such as ore deposits and coalfields. Some stock resources are more abundant than others and their relative scarcity affects their value. For example, aggregate minerals, like sand and gravel, are relatively abundant, while precious metals, such as gold and silver, are relatively rare.

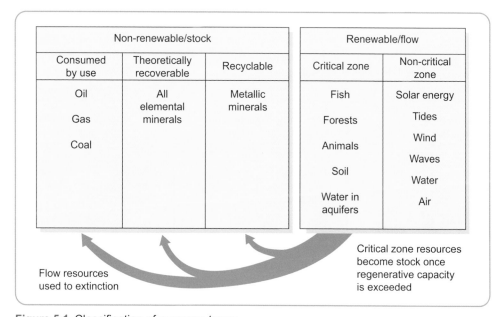

Figure 5.1 Classification of resource types.

Source: J. Rees, *Natural Resources: Allocation, Economics and Policy,* 2nd edition, Routledge, 1985, p. 15

Renewable or flow resources are those that are naturally renewed within a sufficiently short time-span to be of use to human society. Again we can distinguish between different types of stock resource. Figure 5.1 divides flow resources into 'critical zone' and 'non-critical zone' resources. The distinction here is between those flow resources whose continued availability is dependent upon management by society (critical zone) and those that will continue to be available independent of the actions of society (non-critical zone). As indicated by the arrows, it is possible for critical zone flow resources to become stock resources if they are mismanaged and their regenerative capacity is exceeded. Thus, resource management aims to ensure that exploitation of a particular renewable resource does not damage its capacity to replace itself. In recognition of the increasing challenge, and the numerous failures, to manage renewable resources, Rees (1991: 8) has developed an alternative to the conventional two-part typology of natural resources: 'All resources are renewable on some timescale . . . what matters for the sustainability of future supplies is the relative rates of replenishment and use . . . it seems better . . . to think in terms of a "resource continuum" than the conventional two-part typology' (Figure 5.2). Water might once have been considered a relatively abundant resource, but the combined impact of population growth and industrialization is placing increasing stress on the planet's finite supply of fresh water. Millennium Development Goal 7 (see www.developmentgoals.org) is to ensure environmental sustainability, and a target was set to halve by 2015 the proportion of people without sustainable access to safe drinking water and basic sanitation. In their 2014 assessment (United Nations 2014c), the UN noted that:

> The target of halving the proportion of people without access to an improved drinking water source was

achieved in 2010, five years ahead of schedule. In 2012, 89 per cent of the world's population had access to an improved source, up from 76 per cent in 1990. Over 2.3 billion people gained access to an improved source of drinking water between 1990 and 2012.

However, a large rural–urban divide still exists with access still an issue in rural areas. By comparison, far less progress has been made on the sanitation goal, and here the situation is much worse in urban than rural areas. The resource continuum recognizes that access to (clean) air and water supply now have scarcity value and should be considered as finite.

In our discussion so far we have highlighted the complexity of the notion of natural resource and considered the various ways of classifying resources, but what factors affect the availability of particular resources?

5.1.3 Resource availability

As was noted earlier, at any moment in time there is a finite stock of natural resources on the planet, the resource base. Each stock resource has its own resource base, the total quantity of a substance or property on the planet, for example, the total amount of oil geologically present today. However, that total resource base is not the amount available for human exploitation. Figure 5.3 illustrates the relationship between the resource base and the various sub-divisions of resource availability. The term proven reserve is applied to those deposits that have already been discovered and are known to be economically extractable under current demand, price and technological conditions. However, the extent of a proven reserve is dynamic and dependent upon a host of interlinked factors. These include the availability of the technology and skills to exploit the resource, the level of demand, the cost of production

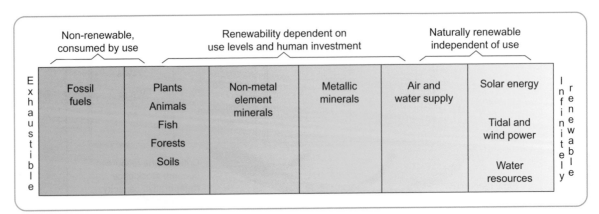

Figure 5.2 The Resource continuum.

Source: J. Rees, Resources and environment: scarcity and sustainability, in Bennett and Estall (eds) *Global Change and Challenge: Geography for the 1990s*, Routledge, 1991, p. 9

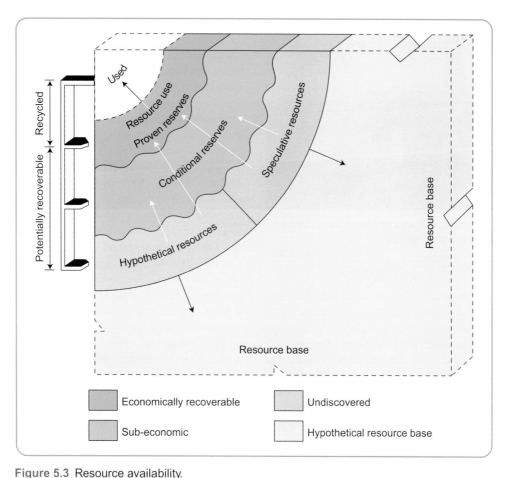

Figure 5.3 Resource availability.

Source: J. Rees, *Natural Resources: Allocation, Economics and Policy,* 2nd edition, Routledge, 1985, p. 20

and processing, the price it can command in the marketplace, the availability and price of substitutes, and the environmental and social costs of developing the resource. The extent to which each of these factors influences resource development also varies across space and time. Today we have the technological ability to recover resources in geological and environmental conditions that were previously uneconomic. For example, the Deepwater Horizon drilling rig in the Gulf of Mexico that was destroyed by an explosion in April 2010 was designed to operate in waters up to 2,400 metres (8,000 feet), to a maximum drill depth of 9,100 metres (30,000 feet). It was pushing the limits of offshore production into ever-deeper waters and deeper fields. The recent growth of shale gas production in North America relies on new techniques of horizontal drilling and fracturing that release the oil and natural gas trapped in shale deposits far below ground at a competitive cost, resulting in a dramatic surge in natural gas production in the USA, but also a reassessment of the scale of global natural gas reserves.

The category of conditional reserve refers to deposits that have already been discovered but are not economic to work at prevailing price levels using currently available extraction and production technologies. The boundary between **proven** and **conditional reserves** is dynamic and bi-directional (that is, resources that change from conditional to proven reserves can, if conditions change, revert to conditional status). Canada's oil sands are at this boundary. High production costs require an oil price of US$65 or higher to be economic, when the price falls below this level investment in oil sands production falls substantially. This has happened more than once before and the most recent fall in the oil price has again resulted in a reduction in investment in oil sands projects. One of the reasons that OPEC (Saudi Arabia in particular) is allowing the oil price to fall is that they want to test how sensitive unconventional oil and gas production in North America is to a low-oil-price environment.

The two remaining categories of resource are not readily available to society. **Hypothetical resources**

Plate 5.2 Offshore technology advances, so more remote resources can be exploited.

(ITAR-TASS Photo Agency/Alamy)

are those that we may expect to find in the future in areas that have only been partially surveyed and developed. Thus, the US Geological Survey has suggested that the Arctic accounts for 13 per cent of the world's undiscovered oil and 30 per cent of its undiscovered gas. There are also hypothetical resources in regions such as Antarctica, but the international community has placed a moratorium on resource development, for the time being at least. **Speculative resources** are those that might be found in unexplored areas that are thought to have favourable geological conditions. Finally, there remains a large part of the earth about which we have no information on its potential resource base. The strength of this classification is that it stresses the highly dynamic nature of the concept of resource reserve. Its weakness is that it lends itself to the idea that we will never run out of resources; there will always be more to discover and new technology will continue to make new resources available for exploitation. Even if that was the case, and clearly it is not, the planet now faces the additional problem that the consumption of resources, such as hydrocarbon fuels, produces wastes that threaten the stability of the global ecosystem. Thus, there is a need to rethink the whole notion of resource scarcity to take into account the ecological cost of our current 'fossil fuels society'.

Given the highly dynamic nature of resources, at any moment in time, it is very difficult to estimate the level of resource availability. It is even more difficult to speculate about future levels of production and consumption and, thus, the possibility of resource scarcity. Nonetheless, the supporters of 'peak oil' maintain that the world will soon reach the point of maximum oil production (Deffeyes 2001), which is highly contested, not just because extrapolation on the basis of current trends is often misleading, but also because there are a whole variety of

factors that can promote resource scarcity (Table 5.1). The resource crisis of the 1970s was motivated by geopolitics, but by increasing the price of energy, it brought about other forms of scarcity. For example, the increased price of oil had a major negative impact upon those countries in the 'developing world' that had embarked upon industrialization and had become increasingly dependent upon imported oil. However, it also shocked the 'developed world' into the realization that energy resources were finite, energy conservation was worthwhile and that alternative sources of energy were required. The 'developed world', and particularly the United States, then recognized the strategic importance of securing 'energy independence', which is now seen by many as achievable thanks to unconventional oil and gas.

In July 2008 the oil price peaked at US$144 a barrel, only to fall below US$40 by November 2009 as a global economic crisis took hold. Despite continued geopolitical tensions in the Middle East and North Africa, we still have a relative abundance of oil, in large part because the global economic recession reduced demand. The oil price soon rebounded and found a new equilibrium around the US$100 mark; however, in the summer of 2014 the price started another dramatic decline, falling to less than US$50 a barrel. At the time this book went to press the price had fallen below $30 a barrel. This time the cause is over-supply relative to global demand. But there is no scope for complacency; the rapid growth of energy demand in the emerging economies, especially China and India, is causing concern that high energy prices will eventually return. This coincides with increasing societal concerns about the ecological consequences of increased energy consumption (for the most recent analysis of the causes of anthropogenic change see IPCC 2014). The prospect of increasing demand as a result of

Plate 5.3 The energy crisis of 1973 brought queues at the petrol pumps in many western countries and a three-day week in the UK.

(Popperfoto/Getty Images)

Table 5.1 The dimensions of resource scarcity

Type of scarcity	Concern
Physical scarcity	• Exhaustion of minerals and energy. • Human populations exceed the food production capacity of the land. • Depletion of renewable resources such as fish, soils or timber. • Growing demand for water for human use threatens aquatic ecosystems and the ability of river systems to replenish themselves.
Geopolitical scarcity	• Use of minerals exports as a political weapon. • Shift in the location of low-cost minerals sources to 'hostile' or unstable blocs of nations.
Economic scarcity	• Demand at current price levels exceeds the quantity supplied, resulting in shortages. • Needs exceed the ability of individuals or countries to pay for resource supplies (resource poverty). • Rich economies can always outbid the poor for essential resources, creating unequal patterns of resource use. • Economic exhaustion or falling demand for specific minerals or renewable resources causes economic and social disruption in producer regions or in nations dependent on them.
Renewable and environmental resource scarcity	• Distribution of essential biogeographical cycles (e.g. the carbon cycle and the greenhouse effect) threatening sustainability of life on earth. • Pollution loads exceeding the 'absorptive' capacity, causing economic health and amenity problems. • Loss of plant and animal species (biodiversity) and landscape values, with wide, but poorly understood, long-term consequences.

Source: Adapted from J. Rees (1991) Resources and environment: scarcity and sustainability, in Bennett and Estall (eds) *Global Change and Challenge: Geography in the 1990s*, Routledge, London, p. 6

economic development in the 'global south', combined with the challenges of climate change, has led to the idea of a 'New Energy Paradigm' that combines traditional concerns about security of energy supply at reasonable prices with the need to devise energy policies that reduce carbon emissions (Helm 2007).

5.2 Fuelling the planet

Of all the different types of resource that we have discussed so far, in recent history it is those that provide energy services (we transform energy resources to obtain services such as heating, light, transportation, etc.) that have been the most sought after. For most of human history societies have utilized renewable sources of energy; flow resources such as wood that can be depleted, sustained or increased by human activity; and continuous resources, such as water to drive watermills or the wind to turn windmills, that are available irrespective of human activity (Figure 5.4). They have also used draught animals, horses, buffalo, etc., but these need to be fed and housed.

The Industrial Revolution changed the way in which certain parts of the world powered their economies, leaving the remainder dependent upon renewable resources.

5.2.1 The dominance of fossil fuels

Since the invention of the steam engine about 200 years ago, much of human society has become ever more dependent upon the exploitation of non-renewable energy resources (see Smil 2010 for an introduction to the energy system and energy transitions). According to BP (2015), in 2014 fossil fuels (coal, oil and gas) still accounted for 86.3 per cent of the primary commercial energy consumed on the planet. These resources were formed from the decomposition of organic materials millions of years ago and have been transformed by heat and pressure into coal, oil and natural gas. The advantage of fossil fuels as a source of energy is that they are readily accessible, a highly concentrated source of energy, easy to convert using proven technologies, and cost-efficient in production and use. Unfortunately, the combustion of fossil fuels is also the single largest source of greenhouse gases (GHG).

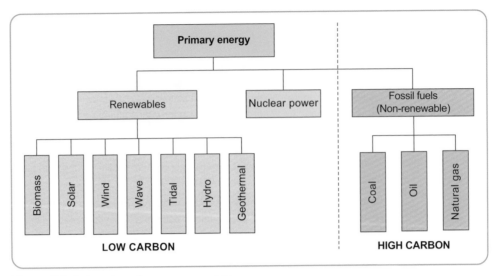

Figure 5.4 Categories of energy resources.

Oil is the most versatile fossil fuel while coal, even though it is relatively bulky, is still used in many industrial processes, as a source of heat, and is the most important fuel for electricity generation. The great advantage of oil is its transportability over long distances in large volumes using pipelines, ocean tankers, or smaller rail and road tankers. It has spawned a huge petrochemical industry producing a vast range of products, including plastics and textiles, that have substituted products based on renewable resources, such as wood and cotton, for those based on non-renewable resources. In addition, oil has created many resources, such as jet engine fuel, for which commercially viable substitutes have yet to be developed. Consequently, advanced industrial societies are totally dependent upon the continued supply of oil at a reasonable price, which explains the importance that governments attach to energy security (for a comprehensive discussion of oil see Bridge and Le Billon 2012).

In recent years, natural gas has become an increasingly important source of energy and a feedstock for petrochemicals. In many advanced industrialized economies it has replaced coal as the favoured resource for electricity generation and domestic heating. However, the transport flexibility of natural gas is inferior to oil; pipeline transport is most economic but the infrastructure investment needed requires sizeable reserves, a secure source of production (security of supply) and stable markets (security of demand). Liquefied natural gas (LNG), produced via cooling and high pressure, is an option but the process requires substantial investment in plant and consumes large quantities of energy. Nevertheless, LNG production is becoming an increasingly important fuel, particularly

Plate 5.4 Special LNG tankers are used to distribute liquefied natural gas to markets worldwide.
(Carabay/fotolia)

in the Asia-Pacific region, while the European Union sees LNG supplies as a means of compensating for declines in domestic production and diversifying its sources of supply away from Russia.

5.2.2 Alternative sources of energy

Given the finite nature of hydrocarbon fuels, the problems of scarcity and the environmental consequences of burning fossil fuels, it is no surprise that alternative sources of energy have been sought. There are two alternatives (see Figure 5.4): first, developing new ways of harnessing renewable energy sources, and second, developing nuclear power. At present all commercial nuclear power stations use so-called fission reactors that release energy, mainly in the form of heat, which is then used to generate electricity. In the 1950s, nuclear energy was heralded as a cheap and clean alternative to fossil fuels, but safety issues discouraged the expected expansion of the nuclear industry (see Case study 5.1). In recent years, since it does not generate CO_2, the nuclear option for electricity production has been back on the agenda even though many of the concerns about high costs, safety, the disposal of radioactive waste and the decommissioning of power stations remain. The disaster at Fukushima Daiichi power plant in Japan has reopened the debate and there is renewed uncertainty about the role that nuclear power can play in meeting the growing demand for energy and mitigating climate change.

The other alternative to fossil fuels is the development of 'new' or 'modern' renewable sources of energy (Evans 2007: 81–114). Many of these renewable sources involve applying new technologies to historic sources of energy supply and scaling them up to provide an alternative source of electricity generation and fuel. While no single source is likely to provide an alternative to fossil fuels, collectively they can start to reduce our reliance on hydrocarbons. A review by the Swedish Academy of Sciences (Destouni and Frank 2010: 19) maintains that, by 2050, renewable energy can be expected to provide up to 35 per cent of global energy supply and nearly half of electricity production, which still means that 65 per cent of global energy will come from fossil fuels and nuclear power.

Case study 5.1

Nuclear power remains in the mix

During the 1950s the peaceful use of nuclear power was heralded as the great hope for the world's energy needs. Harnessing the power of the atom promised a cheap and clean source of electricity. The energy crisis of the 1970s increased interest in a nuclear solution. By developing a nuclear power industry, the developed world hoped that it could reduce its reliance upon OPEC-supplied oil. The 1970s and 1980s saw a rapid expansion in the generating capacity of the world's nuclear power plants. Between 1960 and 1990 total global electrical generating capacity had grown from zero to 328 gigawatts. In the last decade or so growth has stalled (in 2008 the total global capacity was 372.5 gigwatts) with the real possibility of a decline in total capacity. What went wrong and have conditions changed such that a return to nuclear power is now back on the agenda?

In short, as the nuclear power industry developed, expanded and matured it became increasingly apparent that the supposed benefits were far outweighed by the environmental problems it posed. Reddish and Rand (1996: 79) listed four criticisms levelled at nuclear power by environmental groups and these remain the major concerns today:

1. Abnormal radiation levels from normal operations will cause cell damage, malignant cancers, genetic diseases, etc.
2. Reactor operations and transport of irradiated fuels cannot be guaranteed safe against catastrophic accidents.

3. Radioactive waste has to be disposed of safely and reactors have to be decommissioned, all of which is extremely costly.
4. The radioactive materials needed to fuel the reactors need to be kept safe and secure from theft or misappropriation to make nuclear weapons (the so-called proliferation problem).

Over the years public trust in nuclear power has been significantly eroded by a number of serious accidents, such as those at Windscale, Cumbria (United Kingdom) in 1957, Three Mile Island (USA) in 1979, Chernobyl in the Ukraine in 1986 and most recently Fukushima in 2011. Furthermore, as the true cost of building, maintaining and decommissioning nuclear power plants has become apparent, many have questioned the economics of nuclear power relative to other sources of energy.

Despite these problems, in 2008 nuclear power accounted for 15 per cent of global electricity generation, but until recently it has been very much an option for the developed world, partly because of cost and technology, but also because of concerns over the proliferation of nuclear weapons. In 1996, OECD member states accounted for 86.6 per cent of total nuclear power production, but by 2005 that share had fallen slightly to 83.8 per cent (IEA 2006: 437). In 2008 the top three countries in terms of nuclear capacity were the United States (27.1 per cent), France (17.0 per cent) and Japan (12.4 per cent). In the same year, nuclear power accounted for 76 per cent of total domestic electricity generation in France and 42 per cent in Sweden. Sweden had decided to phase out its nuclear power stations and switch to conventional thermal power stations, but in 2009 it reversed this policy. Germany, by contrast, has decided to phase out nuclear power by the early 2020s. However, concerns about climate change and the associated desire to reduce CO_2 emissions, plus worries about fossil fuel energy security, means that many countries remain committed to nuclear power. Hedberg *et al.* (2010: 3) report that at present 55 new reactors are being built in 30 countries, 137 are planned and a further 295 are proposed for the future; there are currently nearly 440 fission reactors in operation in 30 countries (for further details visit www.world-nuclear.org).

For the emerging markets of China, India and Russia the expansion of nuclear power is seen as a key element of policies to meet the energy demand associated with rapid economic growth. Russia, for example, has a programme to increase the share of nuclear power in electricity generation from 15 per cent now to 25 per cent by 2020 and it is also exporting nuclear power stations to emerging markets. China has set a target to build 40 gigawatts of nuclear generating capacity by 2020 and India has a target of 40 gigawatts by 2030. Many OECD countries are also reconsidering the nuclear option because, first, it addresses the need to reduce greenhouse gas emissions and second, increased reliance on imported oil and gas is raising concerns about energy security. In particular, following supply disruptions in 2006 and 2009 and now the conflict in Ukraine and the imposition of sanctions following the annexation of Crimea, the European Union wishes to reduce its reliance on supplies of natural gas from Russia. Given the high costs and long lead times to build nuclear power plants, a decision needs to be made now to avoid energy shortages in the future. The environmental movement remains vehemently against nuclear power as it argues that none of the long-standing problems have been adequately addressed. Thus, the nuclear debate is being revisited in the United Kingdom and elsewhere in the OECD, as the disadvantages of the nuclear option are set against the possible benefits it might bring in terms of addressing climate change and promoting energy security (see Case study 5.2). The UK government is now committed to building a new generation of ten nuclear power stations, all on the site of existing soon-to-be-decommissioned nuclear stations, but progress is very slow and a new fleet of power stations now seems unlikely until the mid-2020s at the earliest. The United States' Energy Information Administration (EIA 2010: 4) predicts that electricity generation from nuclear power will increase from 2.6 trillion kilowatt-hours in 2007, to 3.6 trillion kilowatt-hours in 2020 and 4.5 trillion kilowatt-hours by 2035. The strongest growth will be in non-OECD Asia, where nuclear power electricity generation is projected to grow at an annual rate of 7.7 per cent a year from 2007 to 2035. However, the disaster at Fukushima has increased public concern about the safety of nuclear power and the lessons learnt may increase the costs of nuclear power further, calling into doubt its viability. If nuclear power has fallen from favour again it may result in even higher levels of fossil fuel consumption as power companies turn to coal and gas as a low-cost alternative. Alternatively, it could spur investment in renewable energy, but that will also require advances in storage technologies.

- **Biomass** energy was the very first form of energy used by humans and involves the burning of plant and animal residue to produce heat. In much of the world it is still the traditional source of energy. The IEA, UNDP and UNIDO (2010: 20) maintains that there are currently 2.7 billion people in developing countries who rely for cooking primarily on biomass used in inefficient devices. In industrially developed economies, wood waste from pulp and paper mills is used to generate heat and electricity, and in some households wood-burning fires are used for space heating, although often more as a lifestyle choice than out of necessity. More recently, the use of biomass to produce alternative fuels, so-called biofuels, has gained popularity in the developed world; but it is increasingly apparent that if not properly managed biofuels production creates as many problems as it solves. The land being taken up to produce crops for biofuel production is either a natural habitat supporting biodiversity or agricultural land that could be used for food production. At the same time, increased demand for crops such as corn is increasing the cost of animal fodder and basic foodstuffs. Further, much of this production requires the use of fertilizers and pesticides that are hydrocarbon-based and consume considerable amounts of energy when they are produced. The net result is that many 'first generation' biofuels may actually consume more energy to produce than they generate when used to run a vehicle. So-called 'second generation' biofuels aim to use non-food feedstock, organic waste and algae and may become a viable alternative to fossil fuels. Finally, on a small scale, gas from landfill sites and from the anaerobic digestion of vegetable waste is also being developed to produce bio-methane.

- *Solar energy* is ultimately the source of all energy, with the exception of nuclear power. Solar energy usually involves capturing the sun's rays in order to produce thermal energy to warm buildings, heat hot water or generate steam to produce electricity. Alternatively, photovoltaic cells turn the sun's rays directly into electricity (solar PV). As the efficiency of solar panels increases and their cost declines, so solar energy is becoming a viable small-scale local solution at the household or building level. However, it is subject to daily or seasonal variations and is weather-dependent, but it can provide an efficient supplemental source of energy for heating domestic hot water, and so on (visit the website of the International Solar Energy Society at www.ises. org). There are now some very ambitious large-scale projects aimed at harnessing the sun's energy and transmitting it via high-voltage transmission lines to centres of demand. The so-called 'Desertec Concept' is based on the proposition that 'Within 6 hours the deserts receive more energy from the sun than humankind consumes in a year' (www.desertec.org) and it proposes the development of a network of concentrating solar power installations in North Africa to generate electricity for export to Europe. However, the current political instability in North Africa precludes immediate progress with this project. As the technology improves, energy costs increase and the costs of solar energy decrease, it will increasingly become part of the low-carbon energy solution.

- *Wind power* is of historical significance and has now made a return in the form of 'wind farms'. Improved design has increased the efficiency of modern windmills and they are becoming an increasingly common sight in exposed coastal and upland locations in the developed world. Wind farms can generate electricity for local use or for the power grid. However, some would argue that modern wind farms lack the aesthetic qualities of traditional windmills and therefore many see them as a source of both visual and noise pollution. In Europe, Germany, Spain and the UK currently lead the way in wind power (EWEA 2014). In September 2010, Vattenfall opened the Thanet Offshore Wind Farm, which has 100 wind turbines and covers an area of 35 square kilometres. At that time it was the largest operational offshore wind farm anywhere in the world and has a capacity of 300 megawatts, which has boosted UK offshore wind capacity by 30 per cent, producing on average enough electricity to supply more than 200,000 homes. The UK has plans for further offshore wind farms to be built off the coast in the Thames Estuary, the Greater Wash and the Northwest, and the energy from them is expected to power 15 per cent of UK households; however, onshore wind is meeting increased opposition and government subsidies are being withdrawn early. In terms of total installed wind capacity in 2014, China is first with 31 per cent, followed by the United States with 17.8 per cent and Germany with 10.6 per cent (REN21 2015: 135). China is developing renewable energy at an astonishing pace, as it badly needs new sources of energy that will not aggravate already substantial energy-related environmental problems. It also sees the supply of equipment, such as wind turbines and solar PV, as a new growth area for industry for both domestic consumption and export.

- *Hydropower generation* also pre-dates the industrial revolution, but dams and hydroelectric schemes have now replaced the watermills that powered the early machines. In many regions of the world hydroelectricity has become an important source of energy, but, in all but a few cases, Norway being one, it cannot offer a large-scale solution to a country's energy needs. The building of dams to store water and build a 'head' to drive the turbines that generate the electricity floods large areas of land; it also starves river systems of flow and damages deltaic and riverine environments. The construction of Three Gorges Dam on the Yangtze River in China involved the displacement of 1.2 million people and the creation of a reservoir occupying 111,000 hectares. Other forms of waterpower, such as wave and tidal power, are also being developed. At present, there is only one large-scale commercial tidal power station in the world, the La Rance Tidal Power Plant in Brittany, France. In the UK a proposal to create a tidal lagoon in Cardiff bay to generate power is being backed by the Government. New forms of wave power and tidal power are being developed, such as the Pelamis Wave Energy Converter, but these are still at the developmental stage.

- The final form of renewable energy is *geothermal energy*. As the name suggests, this form of energy uses naturally occurring heat in the earth's crust and is only really viable in areas of volcanic activity. There are two forms of geothermal energy. One is wet-rock geothermal energy where steam or hot water is trapped from boreholes or surface vents and used to heat buildings or generate electricity. The other is hot–dry geothermal energy, which is accessed by boreholes drilled into hot dry rocks. Water is then forced down and the steam used to generate electricity. At present geothermal energy accounts for about 10 per cent of New Zealand's electricity production. In global terms, it is the United States that produces the most electricity with geothermal power. In 2009, US geothermal power plants produced 15.2 billion kilowatt-hours, or 0.4 per cent of total US electricity generation, and seven states have geothermal power plants. At a very local scale there is growing interest in using ground-source heat pumps to heat individual buildings. This technology does not require a geothermal source, but makes use of renewable energy stored in the ground.

Plate 5.5 Thanet Offshore Wind Farm.

(Alan Payton/Alamy)

In nearly all of the above cases, renewable energy is already providing localized, small-scale solutions to energy needs but, at present, does not provide a viable alternative to fossil fuels. That said, the share of renewable energy in the global energy system is growing rapidly, albeit from a low base and there are places where it is making significant inroads – for example in Germany, where its growth follows a decision to move away from nuclear power. In 2013 renewable energy, including large-scale hydroelectricity, accounted for 19.1 per cent of global final energy consumption, this includes 10.1 per cent for modern renewables and 9 per cent for traditional biomass (REN21 2015: 6). The challenge is to 'scale up' modern renewable energy production to provide a low-carbon alternative. This can take the form of large-scale centralised systems, like an offshore wind farm or a concentrating solar array, or decentralised generation within individual households and buildings. At present, most of these alternatives require considerable capital investment and access to advanced technology and they do not, therefore, offer an obvious solution to the fast-growing energy needs of the 'developing world'. To provide a more global solution, those technologies, and the finance to purchase them, will need to be made available to the regions experiencing the most rapid increases in energy demand, i.e. the global south. The rapid fall in solar PV costs thanks to the expansion of production in China is already having a significant impact on the growth of solar power across the world. If similar developments can deliver low-cost electricity storage, then a renewable solution to energy access in the global south may be possible.

5.2.3 The changing energy mix

The balance between the various sources of energy is known as the energy mix. During the last century it has changed substantially, but substantial regional variation

remain, as shown in Table 5.2. Simply because it accounts for most of the world's energy consumption, the evolution of the energy mix tends to be linked to the development of the industrialized world where coal was by far the most important energy resource at the start of the twentieth century. The oil industry was still in its early stages; the first modern oil well was drilled in the US state of Pennsylvania in 1859. Natural gas was not recognized as a resource at all. Hence, the dominance of coal was not threatened. Advances in transportation technology, such as the invention of the jet engine, and the emergence of a petrochemicals industry triggered a rapid increase in the demand for oil in the boom years after the Second World War. In 1950 coal accounted for 61 per cent of the world's commercial energy consumption with only 27 per cent coming from oil, by 1970 it was 30 per cent from coal, 44 per cent from oil and 20 per cent from natural gas. Even so, the absolute level of global coal production continues to increase at the same time as economic growth in the developed world is increasingly underpinned by oil and, more recently, by natural gas. The recent 'dash-for-gas' in the developed world was driven by a desire to reduce dependence on oil imported from the Middle East and the fact that electricity generation using natural gas generates less greenhouse gases. Thus, in the past hundred years, the energy mix in the industrialized world has undergone two major transitions, from coal to oil and from oil to gas. In 2014, in the OECD, oil accounted for 37 per cent of **primary energy** consumption, natural gas 26.1 per cent and coal 19.1 per cent (BP 2015: 41).

The energy mix in the developing world is somewhat different (see Table 5.2). For the most part it remains more reliant upon oil for its commercial energy and in some regions coal remains the dominant resource. For example, China in 2014 accounted for 50.6 per cent of global coal consumption that produced 66 per cent of its primary energy consumption (BP 2015). Over the past few years China has met its growing energy needs by burning even more coal, raising obvious concerns about climate change. Elsewhere, dependence upon oil has made countries in the developing world particularly vulnerable to sudden periodic increases in oil price over the past three decades, but they lack the capital and technology to develop their own energy potential or to diversify their energy mix. However, as it depletes its own sources of oil and gas the developed world has become increasingly dependent upon supplies from the developing world. Historically, the international oil companies (IOCs) were the key actors delivering the energy resources of the developing world, but increasingly the governments of the oil-producing states have seized control over their oil and gas industries. Now IOCs, such as BP, ExxonMobil, Chevron, Total and Shell, work in

Table 5.2 Regional variations in energy balance, 2014 (per cent of total consumption)

	Oil	Natural gas	Coal	Nuclear	HEP	Renewables	Per cent of total world
European Union	36.8	21.6	16.7	12.3	5.2	7.4	12.5
OECD	37.0	26.1	19.1	8.2	5.7	3.9	42.5
NON-OECD	29.3	22.0	38.1	1.7	7.6	1.4	57.5
North America	36.3	30.7	17.3	7.7	5.4	2.6	21.8
Europe & Eurasia	30.3	32.1	16.8	9.4	6.9	4.4	21.9
S. & C. America	47.1	22.1	4.6	0.7	22.4	3.1	5.4
Africa	42.7	25.7	23.5	0.9	6.6	0.7	3.2
Middle East	47.5	50.6	1.2	0.1	0.6	–	6.4
Asia-Pacific	26.8	11.4	52.0	1.5	6.4	1.8	41.3
World	32.6	23.7	30.0	4.4	6.8	2.5	100.0

Includes commercially traded fuels only. Therefore excludes wood, peat and animal waste as fuels. Also excluded is wind, geothermal and solar power.

Source: *BP Statistical Review of World Energy* (2015: 41) (also available at: www.bp.com)

partnership with regimes whose human rights records are condemned by governments and NGOs in the developed world – the most high-profile case being Shell in Nigeria. Furthermore, the most attractive oilfields are reserved for the national oil companies (NOCs) of the reserve-holding states. The age of 'easy oil' is over for the IOCs and they must now make do with access to the most technologically and environmentally challenging fields. Rising costs and falling prices are leading many to question the future prospects for the IOCs.

5.2.4 The changing geography of energy production and consumption

Whereas in 1950 North America, Europe and the Soviet Union accounted for nearly 90 per cent of world energy demand, by 1990 their share had fallen to two-thirds (Jones and Hollier 1997: 181). In 1997 the member states of the Organization for Economic Cooperation and Development (OECD) accounted for 58.4 per cent of global energy consumption but by 2006 this had fallen to 50.1 per cent and by 2014 to 42.5 per cent (Table 5.2). The redistribution of energy consumption has not been due to decline in the developed world, although during the 1990s this was the case in the so-called 'transition economies', but to increased demand in the developing world (Table 5.3). There are substantial variations in terms of level of per capita energy use and energy and carbon intensity, with high-income countries having by far the highest level of energy use. The high usage levels in the middle-income countries and in Europe and Eurasia

reflect the energy legacies of the post-socialist states in Central Europe and the former Soviet Union while in the developing world China and India are the new major emitters. The past decade has seen a global shift in the energy system. Population growth and economic development in countries like Brazil, India and China is driving up energy demand, while the developed economies are seeking reduced levels of energy consumption. This differential growth rate, together with the decline in indigenous production in the developed world, has major implications for global geopolitics (Klare 2008).

There are three elements to the geography of energy production: the global distribution of reserves and production, the distribution of consumption, and the resultant pattern of trade between energy-surplus and energy-deficit regions. As noted earlier, the potential to produce coal, oil and natural gas is geologically determined, but the actual exploitation of a deposit depends on numerous factors (for a more detailed discussion, see Bradshaw *et al.* 2015). Reserve to production ratios (how long current reserves would last at current rates of production) for the three fossil fuels show that coal is the most abundant fossil fuel, followed by natural gas and then oil. World reserves of coal at the end of 2014 would last 110 years at current rates of consumption, current oil reserves would last 52.5 years, and natural gas reserves 54.1 years (BP 2015). While the OECD countries have more than sufficient coal to meet their needs, it is these economies that have most reduced their reliance upon coal, making the developed world dependent upon the very fuels for which it has the lowest reserve to

Table 5.3 Energy consumption, efficiency and carbon intensity in 2011

	GDP per unit of energy use (2011 ppp $/kg oil equivalent) 2011	Energy use per capita (kg oil equivalent) 2011	CO_2 emissions per unit of GDP (kg per 2011 $ of GDP) 2011
World	7.3	1,890	0.4
Low income	--	40.2	0.2
Middle income	6.8	74.2	0.4
Lower middle income	7.9	64.0	0.3
Upper middle income	6.4	79.5	0.5
High income	7.9	4,877	0.3
East Asia & Pacific	5.6	1,671	0.6
Europe & Central Asia	6.3	2,080	0.4
Latin America & Caribbean	10.6	1,292	0.2
Middle East & N. Africa	8.3	1,376	0.3
South Asia	8.1	555	0.3
Sub-Saharan Africa	5.6	681	0.3
Euro Area	10.7	3,485	0.2
China	4.9	2,029	0.7
United States	7.1	7,032	0.4
United Kingdom	12.3	2,973	0.2
India	7.8	614	0.4

Source: *World Bank (2015d)* World Bank Development Indicators 2015 (also available at: www.worldbank.org)

production ratios, i.e. oil and gas. This has been reduced in North America by the development of unconventional oil and gas, but Europe and Asia are likely to become ever more dependent upon imported oil and gas. The Middle East still accounts for the majority of the world's oil reserves – 47.7 per cent at the end of 2014, with a reserve to production ratio of 77.8 years (BP 2015: 6). Natural gas reserves are dominated by the Middle East and the former Soviet Union where three countries, Iran, Russia and Qatar, account for 48.7 per cent of global reserves (BP 2015: 20). Thus, a large share of the world's oil and gas reserves are in regions that are presently perceived to be politically and/or economically unstable by the major importing states.

The diagrams shown in Figures 5.5 and 5.6 compare the share of world production and consumption of oil and gas by major region. Asia-Pacific, Europe and North America are the major deficit regions, Africa, the Middle East, the former Soviet Union and South and Central America are the major surplus regions. Despite being the second largest producer in 1997, the United States still imports almost as much oil as it produces (Table 5.4).

Likewise, North Sea production falls well short of meeting Europe's demand for oil and is now past its peak production. The result is a movement of oil production dominated by Middle Eastern supply to Europe and North America and substantial movements to China and Japan (Figure 5.7).

The major exporters and importers of natural gas are listed in Table 5.5, while Figure 5.8 shows the movements of natural gas. The less 'transportable' nature of natural gas is clearly shown in Figure 5.8; for the most part there is a balance within each region, excepting Africa and the former Soviet Union (Russia and Turkmenistan), which have a surplus of natural gas, and Europe, which has a deficit. Natural gas supply into Europe is via pipeline from West Siberia (Russia) and North Africa or as LNG from North Africa. At present most of this LNG originates from the Asia-Pacific region, but this is changing as supply from the Middle East (Qatar) to Asia and from the west coast of Africa to Europe increases, and as new projects come online in Australia. The recent rapid growth of unconventional gas production, which has seen the US pass Russia as the world's largest gas producer, has

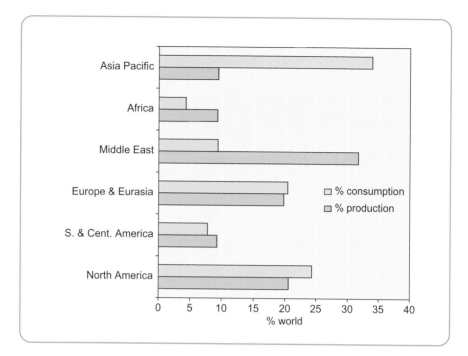

Figure 5.5 Distribution of oil production and consumption in 2014.

Source: *BP Statistical Review of World Energy 2015* (2015: 10–11) (also available at: www. bp.com)

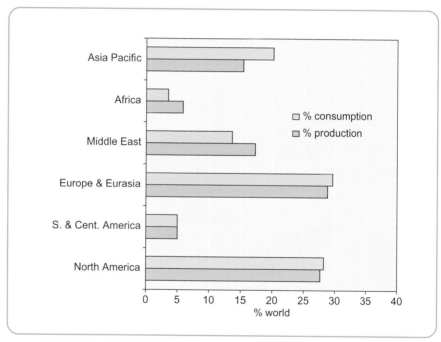

Figure 5.6 Distribution of natural gas production and consumption in 2014.

Source: *BP Statistical Review of World Energy 2015* (2015: 22–3) (also available at: www.bp.com)

dramatically reduced the need for the US to import gas and the US should be exporting LNG by the end of 2015.

These geographies of production and consumption arise from a complex interaction of economic and political factors. Not surprisingly, there are substantial regional differences in the cost of oil production. The record-low oil prices of the late 1990s focused attention upon the actual cost of producing oil and Cambridge Energy Research Associates put the cost of production in the Middle East as low as US$2/barrel (*The Economist*, 4 March 1999: 29). That same report estimated the cost of production in Indonesia at US$6, Venezuela and Nigeria at US$7, Mexico at US$10, the United States and the North Sea at US$11 and Russia at US$14. The recent period of high oil price promoted exploration activity in high-cost locations, such as the deep water offshore in the

Table 5.4 Producers, exporters and importers of crude oil (million tonnes)

Producers in 2013	Mt	% of world	Exporters in 2012	Mt	Importers in 2012	Mt
Saudi Arabia	540	13.1	Saudi Arabia	371	United States	442
Russia	525	12.8	Russia	239	China	269
United States	440	10.7	Nigeria	124	India	185
China	208	5.1	Iraq	119	Japan	179
Canada	193	4.7	UAE	118	Korea	128
Kuwait	16	4.0	Kuwait	103	Germany	93
Venezuela	155	3.8	Venezuela	93	Italy	74
UAE	153	3.7	Canada	90	Spain	60
Iraq	153	3.7	Angola	84	Netherlands	57
Iran	151	3.7	Mexico	66	France	57
Rest of World	1,434	34.7	Rest of World	578	Rest of World	507
World	4,117	100	World	1,985	World	2,051

Source: OECD/IEA (2014) *Key World Energy Statistics 2014* (also available at: www.iea.org)

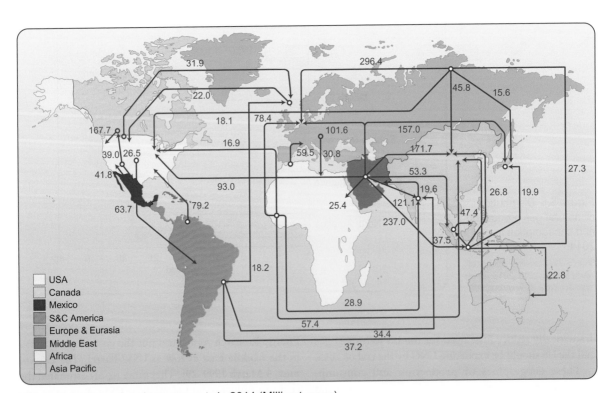

Figure 5.7 Major oil trade movements in 2014 (Million tonnes).

Source: *BP Statistical Review of World Energy 2015* (2015: 19) (also available at: www.bp.com)

Table 5.5 Producers, exporters and importers[1] of natural gas (billion cubic metres)

Producers in 2013	BCM	% of world	Exporters in 2013	BCM	Importers in 2013	BCM
United States	689	19.8	Russia	203	Japan	123
Russia	671	19.3	Qatar	121	Germany	76
Qatar	161	4.6	Norway	103	Italy	62
Iran	159	4.6	Canada	54	Korea	53
Canada	155	4.5	Algeria	45	China	49
China	115	3.3	Turkmenistan	45	Turkey	45
Norway	109	3.1	Netherlands	40	France	43
Netherlands	86	2.5	Indonesia	35	United Kingdom	39
Saudi Arabia	84	2.4	Australia	26	United States	37
Algeria	80	2.3	Nigeria	22	Spain	30
Rest of World	1170	33.6	Rest of World	156	Rest of World	279
World	3479	100.0	World	850	World	836

[1]Exports and imports include pipeline gas and LNG

Source: OECD/IEA (2014) *Key World Energy Statistics 2014* (also available at: www.iea.org)

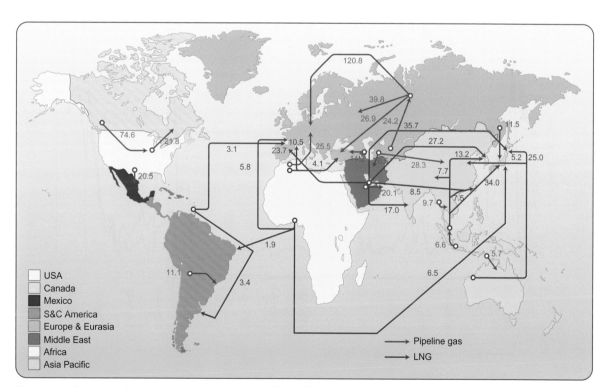

Figure 5.8 Major trade movements in natural gas 2010 (billion cubic metres).

Source: *BP Statistical Review of World Energy 2015* (2015: 29) (also available at: www.bp.com)

Gulf of Mexico and off the coast of Brazil. It was also essential to the dramatic development of unconventional oil and gas in North America, which itself is relatively expensive to produce. This prompts two questions: why develop high-cost fields and unconventional resources when the Middle East has massive reserves and very low production costs, and what will be the consequences of a prolonged period of lower oil and gas prices?

The answers lie in the realms of geopolitics as much as economics (see Klare 2008). Prior to the first oil shock of 1973–4 the industrialized world had become increasingly dependent upon supplies of cheap oil from the Middle East (Odell 1989). When the Middle Eastern oil producers formed OPEC (the Organization of Petroleum Exporting Countries, see www.opec.org)

and used the oil embargo to punish the industrialized West for supporting Israel in the Arab–Israeli war the price of oil rapidly escalated. The first oil shock was followed by another in 1979–80 following the Iranian Revolution and a mini-shock in 1990–1 because of the Gulf War (see Figure 5.9). Following the second shock prices started to decline. There were at least three reasons: first, high energy costs promoted conservation; second, the high price of oil and the actions of OPEC promoted production by high-cost non-OPEC producers; and third, recession and economic restructuring reduced the growth of demand in the developed world. As a response to very low prices, OPEC members agreed to cut back production, which, combined with global economic recovery, saw prices recover by 1999. However,

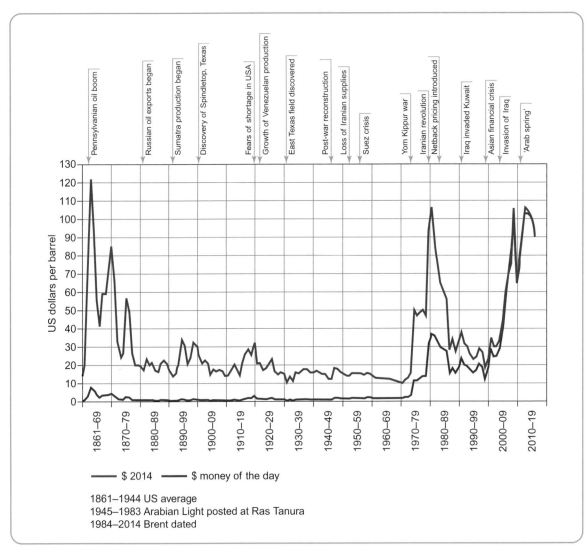

Figure 5.9 Historical trends in world crude oil prices, 1861–2014.

Source: *BP Statistical Review of World Energy 2015* (2015:15) (also available at: www.bp.com)

subsequent events dramatically illustrate the volatile nature of oil and gas markets.

In the aftermath of 11 September 2001, a global economic downturn kept oil prices low. Then the global geopolitical situation changed dramatically with the war in Afghanistan and then the second Iraq War. But despite this, a surge in demand from emerging markets, principally China and India, plus tight supply as a result of underinvestment in the previous decade and continued instability in the Middle East all contributed to a short-term 'supply gap'. By mid-2008 a combination of tight markets and financial speculation in oil futures pushed the price to a record US$147 a barrel. Then the collapse of Lehman Brothers triggered a global financial crisis,

Case study 5.2

Energy security

At present, the United States – with something less than 5 per cent of the world's total population – consumes about 25 per cent of the world's total supply of oil. In 2025, if current trends persist, we will be consuming half as much petroleum again as we do today; however, domestic production will be no greater than it is today, and so the entire increase in consumption – approximately 10 million barrels of oil a day – will have to be supplied by foreign producers. And because we can't really control what goes on in those countries, we become hostage to their capacity to ensure an uninterrupted flow of petroleum.

Klare (2004: 11)

A generally accepted definition of 'energy security' is the reliable supply of energy at reasonable prices. As we know from discussions earlier in this chapter, resource scarcity is seldom about the physical shortage of a particular resource: this is particularly true of oil and gas. When the first edition of this book was in preparation we were in a period of very low oil prices; today we face sustained higher oil prices. Furthermore, there seems to be a growing consensus that in the longer term we have to reduce our reliance on the consumption of hydrocarbons to avoid the more catastrophic consequences of climate change.

Despite the global economic crisis, we seem to be experiencing a period of pressure on global oil supplies because of increased demand from growing economies, such as China and India, combined with supply interruptions caused by hurricanes and oil leaks in the Gulf of Mexico, labour unrest in Nigeria, declining production in long-established fields and delays in bringing on new fields. Thus, there is increased competition for access to supplies of oil and gas. Furthermore, an increasing share of the oil and gas consumed by the developed world (OECD) is imported from non-OECD and OPEC suppliers, particularly in the Middle East. In such a context, it seems that it is the business of national governments to devise policies to promote energy security. These may take the form of seeking to promote energy conservation, promoting other sources of energy supply, promoting cooperation with, and investing in, oil- and gas-producing states (often via support for the activities of state and private oil companies) and *in extremis* taking military action to protect the supply of oil. Many would argue that since the so-called 'Carter Doctrine' of 1979, when President Jimmy Carter, in the wake of the Soviet invasion of Afghanistan (see Spotlight box 20.1, p. 412), 'declared that any move by a hostile power to acquire control over the Gulf region would be regarded "as an assault on the vital interests of the United States of America", which would be opposed "by any means including military force"' (quoted from Rutledge 2006: 48), US foreign policy in the Middle East has been all about oil (Harvey 2003; Klare 2004). Both President Bush and Prime Minister Blair denied that the invasion of Iraq was motivated by a desire to secure Iraqi oil production; even if it was, it failed as Iraqi production is now lower than before the war and this is helping to keep the oil price up. Whatever the motivations for military intervention in the Middle East and North Africa, it is a fact that the international oil market is dependent on supplies of oil from that region. Thus, even if the USA is less dependent on physical imports of oil, it is still exposed to volatility in the global oil market, which determines the price of its own crude oil. The civil war in Syria and the emergence of the so-called Islamic State poses a new threat to the stability of the oil-exporting states in the region. At the same time, Europe is seeking to reduce its reliance on imported energy from Russia, a determination that has been further advanced by Russia's annexation of Crimea and the continuing conflict in eastern Ukraine that has resulted in sanctions being imposed on Russia.

The combination of concerns about the geopolitical dimension of energy security, becoming increasingly reliant on unreliable and potentially hostile sources of supply, climate change, and the need to reduce levels of hydrocarbon consumption, have created a new energy paradigm (Helm 2007) and have also prompted a need to rethink the concept of energy security (Yergin 2006). As Daniel Yergin (2006: 70) put it in a highly influential article in the journal *Foreign Affairs*: 'a wider approach [to energy security] is now required that takes into account the rapid evolution of global energy trade, supply-chain vulnerabilities, terrorism, and the integration of major new economies in the world market.' According to Yergin, this new approach or framework must abide by the following principles:

- Diversification of supply to reduce the impact of a disruption in supply from one source.
- A 'security margin' in the energy supply system that provides a buffer against shocks and facilitates recovery after disruptions.
- Recognition of the 'reality of integration', that there is only one global oil complex and a worldwide system that moves 86 million barrels of oil every day. For

all consumers stability resides in the stability of this market.
- The importance of information that underpins well-functioning markets.

In addition to these principles, Yergin (2006: 70) maintains that there is a need to recognize the globalization of the energy security system, which means that the developed world must engage with the likes of China and India, and a need to expand the concept of energy security to include the entire energy supply chain and infrastructure. In the longer term, it may be the case that the solution lies in developing an alternative to today's hydrocarbon economy; however, for the next 30 years or more we will depend on oil and gas for the majority of our energy needs and the competition for increasingly scarce resources means that concerns about energy security can only grow. Next time you switch on the light think about the complex set of issues that now lies behind keeping the lights on!

demand fell and by the end of the year the price was below US$40 a barrel. It then recovered and for a while was relatively stable around the US$100 a barrel mark. The average price between 2011 and 2014 was US$ 107.65; however, in mid-2014 the price started to fall to a low of US$45 in January 2015. In early 2016 it was less than $30 a barrel with little prospect of a revival. The cause of the latest slump is at least three-fold: the growth of unconventional oil production in North America; the unwillingness of Saudi Arabia to cut back production; and the continued weak demand for oil. The current situation is a challenge for many oil exporting states, but a bonus for oil importing states and consumers; it also highlights the complex relationship between energy consumption and economic development and the volatility of energy prices.

5.3 Energy and development

The experience of the developed world suggests that in the initial phases of industrialization there is a direct link between increased energy consumption and economic development. That is, as industrial activity grows it consumes more and more energy. However, in the past 40 years it has become increasingly apparent that in the developed world the relationship between economic development and energy consumption has changed. This is largely due to the processes of de-industrialization and economic restructuring that have seen the less energy-intensive service sector replace heavy industry and, to a lesser degree,

manufacturing as the major generators of wealth. At the same time, conservation and technological change has made industry more energy-efficient. Similarly, a change in transportation technology has increased energy efficiency; as a result, today's post-industrial societies have decoupled the link between economic growth and increased energy consumption. That said, it is still the case that the developed world consumes a large amount of the world's energy, although non-OECD primary energy consumption surpassed that of the OECD for the first time in 2008.

5.3.1 Energy consumption, economic development and climate change

The relationship between energy consumption and economic development is usually depicted as a scatter plot showing the level of per capita energy consumption on one axis and **gross national product (GNP)** per capita on the other (Figure 5.10). The chart shows that the higher the level of GNP per capita the higher the level of energy consumption. Obvious outliers are easily explained away: some countries, such as the Soviet-type economies that had a bias towards heavy industry and were notoriously wasteful in their use of energy traditionally had higher levels of energy consumption than GNP. Others, such as Japan, have low levels of energy consumption but high GNP because they introduced energy-saving technologies at an early stage and moved energy-intensive industry offshore. Finally, there are some countries, such as Canada, where climatic extremes (both hot and cold) require a large amount of energy to be used for heating or for air

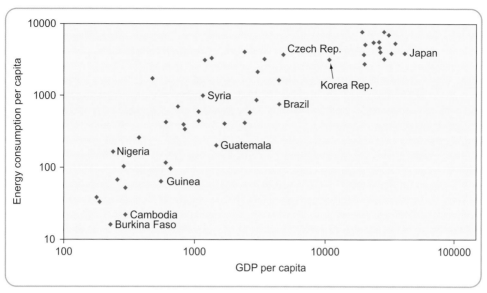

Figure 5.10 Relationship between energy consumption and economic growth.

conditioning. There are also other factors, for example the more urbanised a country the higher its level of per capita energy consumption. Finally, the size of a country may determine the amounts of energy that are required to move between places. Such an argument could be marshalled to explain the very high levels of energy consumption in the United States, as could climatic factors, but the average American household also consumes more energy than anywhere else in the world.

On the face of it the relationship between energy consumption and economic development seems unproblematic. However, the whole question of what stands for 'development' is itself contested (as Chapter 8 reveals). The measurements used in Figure 5.10 systematically understate the relative position of the developing world. First, because the use of commercial energy as a measure of energy consumption ignores the role of non-commercial biomass energy sources, it therefore only measures the 'modern' sectors of the economy. Second, the monetary measure of GNP per capita inadequately measures the 'human condition' in many of the world's poorest countries. That said, a more representative measure would only move them slightly 'up the curve' and it would not modify the clear relationship between industrialization and energy consumption. The Stern Review (2006: xi) into the economics of climate change notes:

CO_2 emissions per head have been strongly correlated with GDP per head. As a result, since 1950, North America and Europe have produced around 70 per cent of all the CO_2 emissions due to energy production, while developing countries have accounted for less than

one-quarter. Most future emissions growth will come from today's developing countries, because of their more rapid population and GDP growth and their increasing share of energy-intensive industries.

It suggests that we need to 'decarbonise' development so that the developing world can enjoy the benefits of economic growth without substantially increasing global CO_2 emissions. A report on 'Development and Climate Change' echoes this sentiment and highlights the importance of ensuring that the developing countries do not get 'locked in' to the development of high-carbon energy infrastructures (World Bank 2010: 190).

The historical relationship between industrialization and energy consumption implies that all the countries of the developing world will eventually follow an energy and development trajectory similar to the developed world. Thus, the patterns of energy and development can be equated to a stage model of the kind proposed by W.W. Rostow (Figure 5.11). This model examines the change in the **energy ratio** (the relationship between the rate of change in energy consumption and the rate of change in economic growth) over time as an economy develops (Mather and Chapman 1995: 154). In the pre-industrial phase the energy ratio is less than one, as these are 'low-energy' societies mainly dependent on subsistence agriculture. As discussed earlier (also see Chapter 2), the industrial revolution resulted in a change in the relationship between society and resource consumption; harnessing new sources of energy was at the heart of this process. As economies industrialize, the energy ratio begins to exceed one. In the early phases of

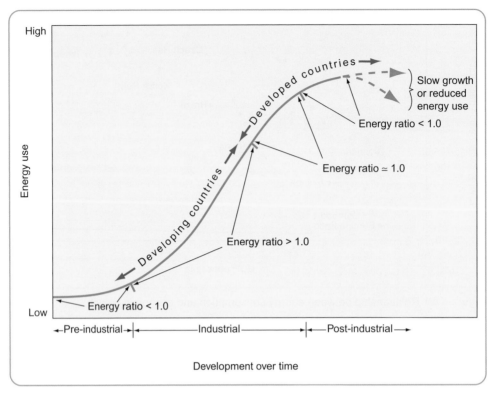

Figure 5.11 Energy ratios and economic development.

Source: *Environmental Resources,* Mather, A.S. and Chapman, K., Pearson Education Limited © Prentice Hall (1995)

industrialization energy efficiency is low and economies are dominated by energy-intensive industries. As the industrial economy matures so the energy ratio declines due to increased efficiency, increased energy costs, or the actual decline in the level of economic activity. This stage is typified by the developed world during the 1970s. Eventually, the economy moves into a post-industrial phase and the ratio falls below one. If the model seems very familiar, it is much like that for demographic transition (see Chapter 4) because it describes the evolution of the energy economy as it actually occurred in Western Europe and the United States.

What evidence is there that the rest of the world will inevitably pass through the same stages? It could justifiably be argued that the newly industrialized countries (NICs) of Asia have followed this pattern of industrialization; however, the time taken has been compressed as the NICs have tried to diversify their economies and promote service sector growth without the advantage of substantial indigenous energy resources, a fact that has made them vulnerable to the effects of energy price volatility. At present it is the rapidly growing energy demands of the emerging economies such as China, India and Brazil that is driving the growth in global

energy demand and sustaining energy prices. With that have come increased CO_2 emissions, making the energy needs of these emerging economies a major obstacle in global climate change negotiations. There are signs that China is now moving out of this energy-intensive phase as its economy restructures and in 2014 demand for coal fell 3 per cent and emissions fell for the first time since 1999 (IEA 2014). Meanwhile, as noted earlier, a much bigger question mark hangs over the developing world. Is it inevitable that it will have to industrialize to improve living standards? If so, then access to energy resources and/or energy-saving and low-carbon technologies will have to be a central component of the development agenda in the twenty-first century. Furthermore, as we have seen in this chapter, many of those same countries are also likely to be the major suppliers of oil and gas and other minerals and there is plenty of evidence to suggest that such resource-based development often fails to provide a sustainable basis for improving living standards (see Case study 5.3) and can generate conflict and instability. The first decade of the twenty-first century suggests that the global shift in economic growth and energy demand is generating a whole series of new challenges to the existing world order.

Case study 5.3

Resource abundance: blessing or curse?

From all that has been said in this chapter, one would assume that having a relative abundance of natural resources would convey an advantage in terms of prospects for economic development. However, the reality is somewhat different. There is now substantial evidence to suggest that resource-abundant economies have actually performed worse in terms of rates of economic development than resource-poor economies. The geographer Richard Auty (1993, 2001) was the first to term this phenomenon the 'resource curse thesis'. Sachs and Warner (2001) have weighed up the evidence and conclude that there is sufficient evidence to suggest that 'high resource intensity tends to correlate with slow growth'. In other words, economies that have a high degree of dependence on the resource sector tend to grow more slowly than resource-poor economies. While the 'resource curse thesis' is now generally accepted, there are exceptions to the rule, those usually cited being Botswana, Chile and Malaysia, and there is no single explanation for this underperformance. Sachs and Warner suggest that most forms of explanation follow some form of 'crowding out' logic, whereby the dominant resource sector inhibits the development of the non-resource sector. Resource economies are particularly susceptible to fluctuations in income because of the volatility of resource prices, added to which, as we know from earlier discussions, the resource base itself is often soon depleted. Once the 'resource boom' is over, the economy is not sufficiently developed or diversified to sustain living standards and a period of 'bust' often follows. Such a 'boom and bust' cycle is by no means inevitable: effective government policy can use resource income to promote a more diversified economy that can sustain living standards once the boom has passed. A review of the literature (Stevens 2003) suggests that there are number of dimensions to the 'resource curse' (though Stevens favours the term 'resource impact'):

- In many resource-rich economies there has been a failure to save income during boom periods to cover periods of bust (some states have created so-called 'stabilization funds' to save for a rainy day), plus a tendency to spend income on consumption (usually through increased imports) and on prestige projects.
- There is also a failure to redeploy income from the resource sector to promote a more sustainable

pattern of economic development. In some instances there is also a tendency to use resource income to subsidize and protect the activity of inefficient producers in the non-resource sector. Later, when the resource income dwindles and the economy is opened up to international competition, these inefficient producers then fail.

- In many instances, often as a consequence of a colonial heritage, the resource economy remains relatively isolated from the rest of the economy. This minimizes the multiplier impact of large-scale resource-based investment projects, beyond their payment of taxes. One solution is to impose a 'local content' requirement on the resources companies, forcing them to use local suppliers of goods and services. However, given the relative lack of 'economic development' in many resource economies it is often difficult to source goods and services locally.
- The increase in export income associated with a resource boom tends to result in a strengthening of the value of the domestic currency of the resource economy. This can have the effect of making the cost of domestic production in the agricultural and manufacturing sectors higher than the cost of imports. This is known as 'Dutch Disease' following the experience of the Netherlands; the net result is a decline in the competitiveness of the non-resource sector, which aggravates the problems discussed above.
- Finally, there is increasing evidence that suggests that a sudden influx of resource income tends to promote crime and corruption, armed conflict and an abuse of human rights. Such problems not only have a direct impact on the welfare of individuals, but also promote increased social inequality and undermine the effectiveness of the state (see Ross 2001; Renner 2002; Le Billon 2007).

The continuing underperformance of resource-rich economies has led the World Bank and the major resource companies to reassess the impacts of resource development. The World Bank through its Extractive Industries Review (www.eireview.org) is reconsidering whether it should be promoting resource-based development as a means of improving living standards and promoting sustainable development. The EIR's final report, called *Striking a Better Balance,* concludes: 'the Extractive Industries Review believes that there is still a role for the World Bank Group in the oil, gas and mining sectors – but only if its intervention allows extractive industries to contribute to poverty alleviation through sustainable development and that can only happen if the right conditions are in place'. The EIR was prompted by the World Bank's decision to finance the construction of the Baku–Tbilisi–Ceyhan (BTC) pipeline from landlocked Azerbaijan to the Mediterranean coast of Turkey. The collapse of the Soviet Union has prompted a dash to gain access to new energy resources in the Caspian and Central Asia, and more recently in Siberia and the Russian Far East (Kleveman 2003). The BTC pipeline also prompted the UK government to champion the Extractive Industries Transparency Initiative (http://eiti.org/), which is 'a coalition of governments, companies, civil society groups, investors and international organizations. The EITI now includes 23 countries and supports improved governance in resource-rich countries through the full publication and verification of company payments and government revenues from oil, gas and mining.' High oil and gas prices and concerns about energy security have also promoted increased oil and gas activity off the shores of West Africa and elsewhere (Gary and Karl 2003; Rowell *et al.* 2005; Ghazvinian 2007) as the developed and emerging economies (China in particular) seek to gain control of sources of energy (Bradshaw 2009). Sustained high energy prices are resulting in a new influx of resource revenues and the expansion of oil and gas production into new areas will create a new set of resource-abundant economies and regions; NGOs such as Revenue Watch (www.revenuewatch.org) are now closely monitoring the flow of revenues arising from these new resource projects (see Caspian Revenue Watch 2003). The dangers of the resource curse are now well recognized, but only time will tell if the international community can assist the newly resource-rich economies to avoid the pitfalls of the past.

5.4   Conclusions: global energy dilemmas

This chapter has considered the nature of resources through a detailed study of the relationship between energy and economic development. We conclude by considering the world's energy dilemmas. It is not just a matter of whether or not there is access to sufficient energy resources to meet demand; rather, it is a question as to whether the global ecosystem can absorb the consequences of continued increases in energy production and consumption. Put simply, at the global scale and to avoid catastrophic climate change, can an energy system that delivers secure, affordable and equitable energy services that are also environmentally benign be created? The exact nature of the energy dilemma varies across the globe, so there is no single energy dilemma, nor a universal solution (for further discussion of global energy dilemmas, see Bradshaw 2014).

In the developed market economies (including the Asian NICs), the energy dilemma relates to the economic and political costs of geopolitical scarcity and the environmental impacts of high levels of GHG (greenhouse gas) emissions (see Table 5.1). Increasingly, these economies are finding themselves dependent upon what they perceive to be 'hostile' and 'unstable' sources of energy supply. The response has been to develop high-cost conventional and unconventional resources close to home, to promote increased efficiency and conservation and to seek low-carbon alternatives, such as renewable energy.

The unconventional oil and gas revolution in North America has certainly reduced import dependence, but it is also creating a new set of environmental problems, particularly oil sands in western Canada. The developed world can afford to seek technological solutions to its energy dilemma and it is essential that it achieves very substantial reductions in fossil fuel consumption and GHG emissions to create the atmospheric 'headroom' needed for the developing world to improve its living standards and constrain global warming to 2°C.

In the original global energy dilemmas framework presented in previous editions and elsewhere (Bradshaw 2009, 2014), the post-socialist transition economies were identified as a separate group. However, it is more than 25 years since the collapse of the Berlin wall and being 'post-socialist' no longer unifies this group of countries. In Central Europe most have joined the European Union and are fast becoming 'high-energy societies' with their attendant problems. The southern periphery of the Caucasus and Central Asia now rank among the low- and middle-income economies of the world and some of them are resource-abundant economics. Both Belarus and Ukraine find themselves caught between an expanded European Union and an increasing belligerent Russia, whose annexation of Crimea has heightened tensions with the international community and resulted in economic sanctions, some of which are targeted at the energy sector.

Russia faces its own particular set of energy dilemmas (Bradshaw 2014). It remains the world's largest producer and exporter of hydrocarbons, but its domestic economy is still woefully inefficient and the state is dependent upon oil and gas revenues. It could pursue a path of economic modernisation, diversification and energy efficiency, but it seems more likely to continue its path of fossil fuel dependence, which will mean investment in both unconventional oil and Arctic oil and gas. However, it will also need to find new markets as Europe seeks to reduce it consumption of fossil fuels and its reliance on Russia in particular. This is well understood in Moscow and Russia's 'Asian Energy Pivot' is well underway with an oil pipeline to the Pacific and a new pipeline – the Power of Siberia – to deliver gas to China.

The resource-abundant economies of the emerging and developing world face particular challenges as a consequence of their resource wealth. For many, but not all, access to revenue from oil exports has proved a mixed blessing. However, it would be wrong to label all energy-exporting economies as victims of the resource curse. There is a world of difference between the oil and gas exporting states of the former Soviet Union, the Middle East and West Africa. They all have their peculiarities, but all are vulnerable to the volatility of energy prices (though some far less so than others). Thus, for the present at least, their energy dilemma relates to the challenge of using energy exports to finance a more sustainable model of economic development. In the longer run, these states must deal with the fact that climate change policies will reduce the demand for their principal source of revenue, which makes economic diversification all the more imperative.

Over the last decade or so, a group of rapidly industrialising economies has emerged and their rate of economic development, population growth and urbanization is driving rapid growth in demand for energy services. Although economies such as China and India possess substantial energy resources of their own, they tend to be reliant upon coal; at the same time, the rate of demand growth has outstripped the capacity of their domestic energy industries to match demand. The net result has been a rapid increase in energy imports, particularly oil and increasingly gas. This growth in energy consumption is also associated with increasing GHG emissions. As discussed earlier, energy- and carbon-intensive types of industrial activity dominate their current economic structures, and they have yet to decouple economic growth from growing energy demand. Somewhat paradoxically, because of their very large populations, their per capita levels of energy consumption and CO_2 emissions are still low. As individual incomes increase there is

huge potential for consumption-driven energy demand to increase, through car ownership, for example. Thus, the energy dilemma for these fast-growing economies relates, on the one hand, to securing the necessary energy to fuel continued economic development; while, on the other hand, ensuring that increased energy consumption does not result in further environmental degradation and rapid growth of GHG emissions.

In the developing world a dualistic pattern of resource consumption seems to have developed in relation to energy. On the one hand, there remains a 'low-energy' rural society dependent upon biomass energy and subsistence agriculture, in which the majority of people exist. Here population pressure is leading to environmental problems as forests are stripped for fuel wood and land ploughed up or over-grazed. On the other hand, there exists a growing 'high-energy' society linked to increasing commercial agricultural (see Chapter 6 for more on this), industrial activity and the spread of urbanization. In common with the colonial past, much of this activity is aimed at supplying natural resources and agricultural products (including biomass for energy production) to the developed and emerging economies. The two sectors of society combine to create an increasing demand for energy services, and increased pressure on the environment. The balance between the sectors also varies greatly among the countries of the developing world. Paradoxically, solutions to the problem of rural poverty will inevitably be increased demands for energy services, though the absolute levels of per capita energy consumption will remain low.

Given that the majority of the world's population lives in the emerging and developing worlds that are also experiencing population increase and rapid urbanization, the growth in energy demand in global south will be the major factor contributing to increases in GHG emissions over the coming decades. More than a decade ago, in its *Global Environment Outlook 2000*, the United Nations Environment Programme (UNEP 1999: 2) concluded that: 'A tenfold reduction in resource consumption in the industrialized countries is a necessary long-term target if adequate resources are to be released for the needs of developing countries.' It is this increasing energy demand in the developing world that now raises the spectre of scarcity in any number of forms. To address the many global energy dilemmas, the developed world must address its own energy profligacy and at the same time help the developing world to shape an entirely new relationship between energy and development.

Learning outcomes

Having read this chapter, you should understand that:

- The notion of what is a resource is socially constructed and varies through time and across space.
- There is a variety of different ways of classifying natural resources.
- There is a complex set of factors that influence the availability of natural resources.
- There are substantial regional variations in energy production and consumption and a growing mismatch between the countries that consume most of the world's energy and those that produce it.
- There is a complex and increasingly challenging relationship between energy consumption, economic development and climate.
- Different types of energy dilemmas confront the different regions of the world.

Further reading

Bradshaw, M.J. (2014) *Global Energy Dilemmas: Energy Security, Globalization and Climate Change,* Polity, Cambridge. A book-length analysis using the global energy dilemmas framework introduced at the end of this chapter.

Bridge, G. and Le Billon, P. (2012) *Oil,* Polity Press, Cambridge. An analysis of the geopolitical economy of the global oil industry, written by two geographers.

Dicken, P. (2015) *Global Shift: Mapping the Changing Contours of the Global Economy,* 7th edition, Sage, London. The latest edition of this excellent textbook has a new chapter on the extractive industries.

Ekins, P., Bradshaw, M. and Watson, J. eds. (2015) *Global Energy: Issue, Potentials and Policy Implications,* OUP, Oxford. A key reference source that covers many of the issues raised in this chapter in much greater detail.

Gautier, C. (2008) *Oil, Water and Climate: An Introduction,* Cambridge University Press, Cambridge. An introduction to the essential background on climate change needed to understand the relationships between energy, population and environment.

Robbins, P., Hinstz, J. and Moore, S.A. (2014) *Environment and Society,* 2nd edition, Wiley-Blackwell, Oxford. Has lots of material relevant to this chapter and others in this section.

Useful websites

There is a huge amount of material available on the Web that relates to the issues discussed in this chapter. Some of the key reference sources are listed below; additional websites have been referenced in the text.

www.bp.com Home of the BP *Statistical Review of World Energy* and the *BP Energy Outlook.* This website, which is updated on an annual basis, has a wealth of statistical information on the energy sector, much of which is downloadable in Excel format or as PowerPoint slides.

www.iea.org The official site of the International Energy Agency. The site contains information on the Agency's operations and publications, as well as statistics on energy production and consumption. Also has links to other international organizations.

www.eia.doe.org The official site of the US government's Energy Information Administration. In addition to information on US energy matters, it contains reports on individual countries and a massive list of links to other US government agencies, international agencies, foreign governments and commercial company sites.

www.ipcc.ch The official site of the Intergovernmental Panel on Climate Change (IPCC), established by the UN Environment Programme (UNEP) and the World Metrological Organization (WMO) to provide the world with a clear scientific view on the current state of knowledge on climate change and its potential environmental and socio-economic impacts. The site hosts all of the IPCC's Assessment Reports and supporting documentation.

www.worldbank.org The official site of the World Bank. The site contains information on World Bank operations and publications, as well as downloadable statistics and briefing documents.

www.wri.org The World Resources Institute is an independent centre for policy research and technical assistance on global environmental and development issues. Its website provides information on its own activities and publications, some of which are downloadable, as well as links to other organizations in the same area. The Institute, together with the UNEP, UNDP and World Bank, produces the biennial *Resource Report,* which is an indispensable reference guide to the state of the Earth's resources.

www.ren21.net REN21 is the global renewable energy policy network that connects a wide range of key actors. REN21 facilitates the collection of comprehensive and timely information on renewable energy. It produces an annual report on the global status of renewable energy. Its activities are managed by a Secretariat, based at UNEP in Paris, France.

THE ENVIRONMENT AND ENVIRONMENTALISM

Chapter 6

Rachel Howell and Jenny Pickerill

Topics covered

- How we value 'the environment' and perceive environmental issues

- The evolution of sustainable development

- The complexity of scale of environmental problems

- Different strategies for action

- Challenges to how we conceptualize 'environmental issues'

- Positive steps towards a sustainable future

No one is untouched by the emerging environmental agenda; everyone has an interest in shaping the development of environmental politics (for good and bad).
(Connelly and Smith 2003: 358)

The language 'It's too late' is very unsuitable for most environmental issues. It's too late for the dodo and for people who've starved to death already, but it's not too late to prevent an even bigger crisis. The sooner we act on the environment, the better.
(Environmental Philanthropist Jeremy Grantham in an interview with Leo Hickman, 2013)

When asked if I am pessimistic or optimistic about the future, my answer is always the same: If you look at the science about what is happening on Earth and aren't pessimistic, you don't understand data. But if you meet the people who are working to restore the Earth and the lives of the poor, and you aren't optimistic, you haven't got a pulse.
(Environmentalist Paul Hawken, commencement speech at Portland State University, 2009, www.up.edu/commencement/default.aspx?cid=9456)

6.1 What kind of world do you want?

What kind of world do you want? If we don't act now, we won't have a choice. Do you want a world where climate change continues to devastate our environment?

(Friends of the Earth flyer, June 2006)

Environmentalists are often accused of being unrealistic and demanding the impossible. Yet people seldom ask the question 'What kind of world would we like?' If we considered this a little more we might be taking bigger steps towards curbing our environmental impact and seeking environmental justice. Environmental issues affect all places and societies – the urban and the rural, the rich and the poor, nobody is unaffected. The environment matters and our impact upon it is often damaging, from pollution of the air that we breathe to degradation of the soils we rely on to grow food.

The rise of environmental activism has highlighted the importance of environmental protection, with some notable successes. In 2010, the British government cancelled plans to expand Heathrow airport, as well as refusing permission for new runways at Gatwick and Stansted, and the logging of old-growth forests has been all but stopped in Western Australia. Britain has the 'oldest, strongest, best-organized and most widely supported environmental lobby in the world' (McCormick 1991: 34), but there are examples worldwide of people taking a stand and making changes to protect the environment. However, 'there is no doubt that environmental issues have had a big impact on contemporary politics, and yet the frequency with which governments adopt a business-as-usual response to environmental problems raises the cynical thought that perhaps nothing much has really changed' (Carter 2001: 2). Thus, despite high levels of environmental concern and an active environmental movement, we are faced with a wide array of environmental problems – from global **climate change** to river pollution, from water supply issues to nuclear power. To understand why this is, we need to explore: different approaches to environmental issues and how we value the environment; limits to growth; the complexity of scale and responsibility; various strategies for action; what a focus on 'the environment' ignores; and finally what positive steps we should take.

6.2 How we value the environment and perceive environmental issues

We each value the environment in different ways and for different ends. Historically we have always debated how various parts of our human and non-human world

Plate 6.1 Old-growth forests in north eastern Tasmania.
(Jenny Pickerill)

should be valued. These values are used to answer ethical questions about the environment and non-human life; for example, whether we should eat meat, or whether it is justifiable to cut down a tree in order to burn it to heat a house. Understanding values helps us understand why some people care greatly about the environment and others less so.

We can use three categories of value when talking about the environment: intrinsic, inherent and instrumental values (see Table 6.1). An object or living being has an **instrumental value** when we view it as a resource, of use to us for a specific end. For example, a forest has an instrumental value if we view it just as a source of wood for fuel. At the other end of the continuum an element has **intrinsic value** if we view it as important in and of itself, with no reference to how we might use it or to how it might make us feel. For example, people generally view human life as intrinsically valuable.

In between these, **inherent value** (sometimes referred to as 'weak' instrumental value) refers to how we value something beyond its use as a resource but still relate value to how the thing makes us feel. For example, we might value a woodland because we enjoy walking through it and feel less stressed after doing so.

We can understand this better if we consider the rule of no-substitution. If something is instrumentally valuable, its value will disappear if there is a preferable substitute. For example, wind and water power was replaced by steam engines in mills in nineteenth-century Britain because they were more reliable, efficient, and flexible in terms of where mills could be located. But if something is inherently valuable for itself, and not as an end, it is not substitutable in this way. Hinchliffe and Belshaw (2003) use the example of the wild tiger to illustrate the consequences of these values. The wild tiger population is threatened by the international trade

Table 6.1 Defining value

Instrumental value	Value which something has for someone as a means to an end
Inherent value	Value something has for someone, but not as a means to a further end
Intrinsic value	Simply the value something has. No appeal need be made to those for whom it has value

Source: Carter (2001: 15)

in tiger parts, often for use in Chinese medicine. One solution is to establish tiger farms. However, if we find such farms acceptable that implies an instrumental valuation of tigers. If tigers' inherent value is paramount, then the notion of farming becomes objectionable. The implications of such values are also explored in Case study 6.1.

We can also consider the values we accord the environment by understanding the terms 'anthropocentrism' and 'ecocentrism'. At its most extreme, an **anthropocentric** approach views only humans as having intrinsic value and the environment as having only instrumental value. In other words, the environment is only useful as a resource for humans, and environmental sustainability is only considered for the sake of human welfare. **Ecocentrism** critiques anthropocentrism and suggests that non-human entities have intrinsic value. However, for many people the situation is not this black and white. There is a large range of intermediate views, within which some non-human entities have value, others do not, but humans are valued as *more* important than the environment. Thus there is a continuum between these approaches, just as there is between 'deep' and 'shallow' ecology (Naess 1973). Shallow ecology is an anthropocentric position. **Deep ecology**, as defined by Naess, is a form of ecocentrism but one where everything has intrinsic value (see Table 6.2 for the eight basic principles of deep ecology). The approach asks us to consider humans not only as part of nature but also of *equal* value to non-human entities. This is a holistic vision whereby all human and non-human entities are interconnected and interdependent. A holistic perspective enables us to understand that if we upset one element it will have an impact on all other elements. If we were to adopt such an approach it would require us to make radical changes to the way we live.

How we value the environment is not the only influence on how we relate to it and perceive environmental issues. There is evidence for **gender** differences associated with environmentalism; for example, a review by Zelezny *et al.* (2000) showed that stronger pro-environmental attitudes and behaviour among women than men are found in Spain and 13 countries in North and South America. They suggest that gender differences in **pro-environmental behaviour (PEB)** arise because of the

Plate 6.2 Logging in Styx Valley, Tasmania, Australia.

(Jenny Pickerill)

Plate 6.3 Styx Valley, Tasmania, Australia.

(Jenny Pickerill)

Case study 6.1

Old-growth logging in Tasmania, Australia

The logging of old-growth forests is a particularly controversial issue in Australia, with views sharply polarized (Hutton and Connors 1999). Old-growth forests have experienced only minimal human interference, take hundreds of years to grow and contain the tallest plants on earth. They are often considered to be of high conservation value.

The state government of Tasmania has shown little inclination to curb the logging of old-growth forests. This is despite a consultation process (Tasmania Together) where the population voted to end deforestation. In May 2003 the government lifted a ban on logging in the Tarkine – the single greatest stretch of temperate rainforest in Australia. The forests of the south-east and north-east are also threatened by expanding logging operations. Every year approximately 15,000 hectares of old-growth forest are logged in Tasmania.

In a country which draws much of its wealth from its natural resources (forests, minerals, uranium, fishing and agriculture), logging is often justified by the need to provide jobs in rural areas and earn export revenue. Loggers argue that Australia has limited resources and therefore needs to make the most profitable use of them; that they have historically 'managed' forests through selective logging, consequently arguing that all forests in Tasmania have been influenced by humans for generations.

Environmentalists have argued that logging is simply a waste of resources. Logging in Tasmania is heavily subsidized and uneconomical (not only in the price obtained for products but in its negative impact upon tourism). Most of the wood is sold as woodchips to be made into paper. Moreover it is unsustainable and irreversible and many of the trees destroyed would take over 300 years to regrow, e.g. the Houn Pine in the south-west of the island takes 3,000 years to grow to full size. Old-growth forests cannot simply be replaced; their destruction results in the loss of biodiversity of a barely understood and fragile ecosystem. Deforestation does not only have localized effects but also plays a key role in reducing carbon dioxide absorption and can upset hydrological systems beyond the area of logging. Environmentalists also believe that the largest trees are important in and of themselves. The Wilderness Society, a key environmental group in the

Australian logging debate says, 'our forests are places that inspire and rejuvenate us all – nurturing us as well as the delicate ferns and mosses on the forest floor, or connecting us to timeless grandeur as we touch the tallest flowering plants on Earth' (2006).

The campaigns to save the old-growth forests have ranged from small-scale local protests to garnering international support. The Styx Valley in the south-east is an example of an iconic campaign. It contains the world's tallest hardwood trees – *Eucalyptus regnans*. Many are taller than a 25-storey building. The forest is also home to many native species of wildlife, including the majestic Wedge-tailed Eagle and the Yellow-tailed Black Cockatoo. While a few of the largest trees in the valley have been protected, between 300 and 600 hectares are being logged each year. Furthermore the main form of logging is destructive clear felling and burning (not selective logging).

Action on a local level has involved occupying threatened trees and targeting the woodchip mills. Regionally, environmentalists have been using their research to argue against clear fell logging, and to prove the environmental implications of logging. Environmentalists have appealed to the federal government and the Australian populace for support through media campaigns and advertising. In 2013 there was an historic breakthrough in the 30-year-long campaign against old-growth logging, when environmentalists, timber communities, forest unions, state government and the logging industry jointly signed the Tasmanian Forests Intergovernmental Agreement on how a sustainable timber industry could be created while also protecting the remaining old-growth forests. The agreement would protect key old-growth forests like the Tarkine and Styx Valley, amongst others. The main logging company – Gunns – promised to end its operations in the state. The agreement requires the state government to financially support workers and contractors to stop logging, and to implement legal changes to safeguard forests as formal reserves to the same level of protection as national parks. This is the first time that all the protagonists have come to an agreement, and it is likely to signal the end of old-growth logging in Tasmania.

Analysis of the conflicts about protection of forests enables us to understand how the environment is valued differently within a community; in other words, why some argue for its protection and others choose its destruction. The state government and logging companies clearly view the forests as a resource for use by humans, thus they believe they have an instrumental value. They will only be interested in managing forests sustainably if that will add value to their use and exploitation in years to come. For environmentalists it is more complex. On one level, many acknowledge the instrumental value of forests (for making furniture, for example) but think the current methods of forestry are wasteful. But in addition environmentalists believe the environment has an inherent value (as demonstrated

by the Wilderness Society's recognition of the rejuvenating effects of being in forests), and an intrinsic value which is not related to human need. Therefore many believe old-growth forests should be protected from all but recreation, and left untouched for future generations to enjoy.

Q How do you value forests like those in Tasmania and how does that affect your perspective as a geographer?

Table 6.2 The eight basic principles of deep ecology

1	The well-being and flourishing of human and non-human life on Earth have value in themselves (synonyms: intrinsic value, inherent value). These values are independent of the usefulness of the non-human world for human purposes.
2	Richness and diversity of life forms contribute to the realization of these values and are also values in themselves.
3	Humans have no right to reduce this richness and diversity except to satisfy vital needs.
4	The flourishing of human life and cultures is compatible with a substantial decrease of the human population. The flourishing of non-human life requires such a decrease.
5	Present human interference with the non-human world is excessive and the situation is rapidly worsening.
6	Policies must therefore be changed. These policies affect basic economic, technological and ideological structures. The resulting state of affairs will be deeply different from the present.
7	The ideological change is mainly that of appreciating life quality (dwelling in situations on inherent value) rather than adhering to an increasingly higher standard of living. There will be a profound awareness of the difference between big and great.
8	Those who subscribe to the foregoing points have an obligation directly or indirectly to try and implement the necessary changes.

Source: Naess (1973: 95–100)

greater socialization females experience to be socially responsible and to care about others. Older people also score higher for various types of PEB (Olli *et al.* 2001). This may be due to the social conditions which shaped their habits; many older people in Britain, for example, experienced rationing and grew up with a 'waste not, want not' mentality that is less prevalent now.

Cultural theory asserts that there are different 'cultural types' of people, differentiated by whether they have a preference for – or feel bound by – strong or weak societal rules and hierarchical structures, and strong or weak 'group' features of society (ties to others; sense of community). The theory posits that each of the four cultural types – hierarchists, egalitarians, individualists, and fatalists – has a different view (or 'myth') of nature and a different preferred management style for dealing with environmental (and other) problems (Steg and Sievers 2000). Dake and Thompson (1999) showed that

different cultural types demonstrate different patterns of consumption. These views and consumption patterns are shown in Figure 6.1.

Cultural theory and the associated myths of nature can help explain why individuals vary in their perception of the risks of environmental issues such as climate change, and their responses to them (Hulme 2009). For example, Steg and Sievers (2000) found that individuals who regard nature as finely balanced (the egalitarian view) showed more awareness of the problems of car use, felt more responsibility for those problems, were more likely to agree that reducing car use is necessary, and stated more support for policy measures to reduce car use than other types, particularly those who view nature as 'benign' (the individualist view). Marshall (2007) uses the theory to suggest that different messages are needed to motivate individuals to adopt lower-carbon lifestyles, depending on their consumption preferences. While egalitarians

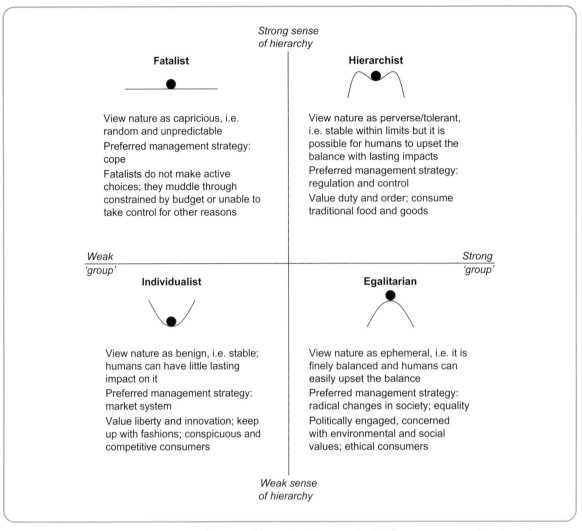

Figure 6.1 Cultural theory and myths of nature. (Note: the diagrams in this figure represent the view of nature held by each type.)

Sources: based on diagrams and information from Michaelis (2007) and Steg and Sievers (2000).

(whom he names strivers) will respond to typical environmental messages to 'save the planet', individualists (he calls them winners) will find these kind of appeals off-putting, and instead need to be persuaded that high-carbon lifestyles will go out of fashion and that savvy consumers buy low-carbon technologies such as electric cars. We should stress to hierarchists, or traditionalists as Marshall calls them, that climate change will threaten things they value such as the countryside, but solutions to climate change will be actions they already support, like holidaying in Britain and buying British food. And because fatalists (or 'survivors') feel little control over their own lives and often have little money, the message for them needs to emphasize that energy saving measures save money and that being prepared for climate change will mean it doesn't make life even harder.

One of the main factors that differentiates beliefs about climate change is political affiliation, with conservatives more likely to be sceptical about the reality of human-induced climate change than others. This is particularly true in the USA, where there has been a widening gap between Democrats and Republicans in terms of attitudes and beliefs about climate change in the last few years (Dunlap and McCright 2008). Feygina *et al.* (2010) argue that the 'conservative white male' effect of denial of environmental problems occurs because conservative white men are more likely to defend and justify the societal status quo when faced with the threat posed by environmental issues, since they have a stronger preference for things as they are than other people (women, liberals, and ethnic minorities). But it is possible to combat the negative effects of system justification on environmentalism by presenting PEB as patriotic and as a means of preserving the status quo.

The conservative white male effect reveals something very interesting about the way individuals think about environmental issues. While we might expect beliefs and risk perceptions about a problem to affect what people consider we should do about it, and how they themselves are willing to respond, the political split about various environmental issues shows that the reverse is also true. Views on action in response to environmental problems (e.g. whether or not it is patriotic) can influence whether people believe the problem exists, and how concerned they feel about it. This is one of many reasons that simply giving people information about a problem does not necessarily lead them to change their behaviour or campaign for government action in response. If they do not want to accept the implications of the issue for their own lifestyle, or do not support government legislation to tackle the problem, they are likely to ignore or reject the information.

The 'information-deficit model' – the idea that people who do not feel concerned about an environmental problem, or are not acting in response to it, simply don't know enough about it and therefore more information is the answer – has been criticised for many other reasons. For example, people do not tend to take action unless they feel a sense of agency, which has two aspects. The first is the belief that it is possible to take action oneself; people who have this sense of personal control are more likely to engage in PEB than those who see control residing in an external source beyond their influence (Jonsson and Nilsson 2014). The second aspect of agency is a belief that taking action will make a difference and therefore is worth doing. Evaluating the UK government's 'Helping the Earth Begins at Home' campaign, Hinchliffe (1996) noted that many people he spoke to expressed a sense of futility about taking individual action because they didn't believe others would do so. Acting together with others in a group helps to create a feeling of agency (see Case study 6.4 for an example). The social norms that operate in our society and peer groups are another important influence on our perceptions of environmental issues and the way we respond to them (Smith *et al.* 2012). By engaging in PEB we help to change what is perceived as 'normal' in society and therefore our actions can have bigger effects than we might think.

6.3 Limits to growth and the challenge of capitalism

The rejection by environmentalists of the anthropocentric approach whereby the environment is viewed purely instrumentally, and the belief that individuals can make a difference by engaging in pro-environmental behaviour, are cornerstones of modern environmental thought. Another key insight is that there are **limits to growth**. The earth is a finite system and thus growth in use of resources and production of wastes cannot continue indefinitely. This was highlighted by Meadows *et al.* in 1972 with the publication of *Limits to Growth*. Using computer models they sought to project trends in resource use and population growth into the future. They predicted natural limits on future growth and two of their simulated scenarios ended in environmental catastrophe by the mid to latter part of the twenty-first century. Although the report has been criticized for being overly pessimistic, defenders say that elements of the projections are similar to observed data so far, and the idea of limits and finitude (scarcity rather than abundance) has remained important.

However, it also became apparent, for people in the minority world at least, that it was possible to maintain economic growth and reduce resource consumption per unit of wealth created. This argument resulted in the emergence of an alternative view to **ecocatastrophism**: a view that would develop into the concept of sustainable development (see Spotlight box 6.1).

Connelly and Smith (2003) identify two broad interpretations of what an environmentally sustainable society would look like: a deep green approach, and the more reformist **ecological modernization**. The deep green interpretation is a radical approach that calls for change and restructuring at all levels of society in political, economic and social arenas. In essence it is a critique of everything about the way we currently live today, a critique of contemporary consumerist society and free-market capitalism. In this understanding of sustainable development, accepting that there are limits to growth means changing our notions of what makes a good life and learning to live more simply (thus slowing growth):

Plate 6.4 Low-impact house: Tony's Roundhouse, Brithdir Mawr, Wales.

(Jenny Pickerill)

Spotlight box 6.1

Sustainable development

The 1987 Brundtland Report adopted the position that it was possible to pursue economic growth without compromising the environment, and it provided the first, still widely used, definition of sustainable development: 'development which meets the needs of the present without compromising the ability of future generations to meet their own needs'.

However, this definition is highly contested and vague, leading to weak interpretations. For example, how can present and future needs be determined, and whose needs does it refer to? Many attempts have been made to refine the concept, which have led to numerous, often contradictory, definitions. The result is that 'sustainable development' is often little more than a sound-bite, signalling recognition that the environment matters but failing to provide substance.

The real success of the Brundtland Report was the emphasis it placed on the relationships between economic growth, social conditions and environmental degradation, an emphasis that placed sustainable development firmly on the global political agenda. Sustainable development is therefore often understood as involving three elements: economic, social, and environmental sustainability. These are sometimes conceptualized as three separate but equally necessary 'pillars' of sustainability, but another perspective

is to view the economy as a subsystem of human society, which in turn is dependent on the biosphere. This is represented by a diagram of three nested circles, economy inside society, inside environment, emphasizing that these are not separate domains of action (see Figure 6.2). Product standards that refer to these three elements of sustainable development include the Fairtrade mark and Rainforest Alliance certification. Culture is now increasingly recognized as a fourth aspect of sustainable development.

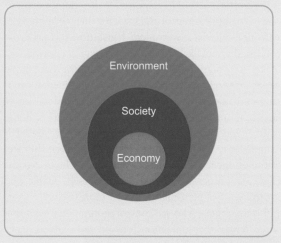

Figure 6.2 Three elements of sustainable development.

Case study 6.2

Low-impact living in Britain

Low-impact living (LIL) is a form of living that enables people to reduce or even minimize the environmental impact of their daily lives. Those advocating LIL often build houses from local, natural and recycled materials and in rural areas ensure they have a low visual impact by blending with their surroundings. Many developments aim to generate their own renewable energy and deal with their own waste (through recycling and composting). In addition LIL is about more than just environmentally friendly buildings: it is about a *way* of life. Implicit in the LIL approach is an emphasis on minimizing vehicle use, reducing consumption and purchasing goods locally, growing food, and, in rural areas, creating livelihoods largely from the land.

In Britain there is a growing number of LIL projects. Hockerton Housing Project in Nottinghamshire is an earth-sheltered, self-sufficient terrace of five single-storey houses. Built into the side of a hill with large windows to the south, they rely solely on passive solar heating and generate all their electricity through wind turbines and photovoltaic systems. The houses are highly energy-efficient and waste is disposed of through a reed-bed system into a large lake. They also grow their own vegetables and generate income through education. Another example is Tony Wrench's roundhouse at Brithdir Mawr, south-west Wales (Plate 6.4). This is built from home-grown timber, straw and earth. It is built into the earth with a turf roof so that, from behind, you can hardly see it. It is highly insulated, has recycled windows and uses a wood burner and passive solar heating.

It has often been very difficult to get planning permission in Britain for LIL projects. Many rural communities have secretly constructed their dwellings or fought long retrospective planning battles to keep their homes. However, on 13 July 2006, eight years after the discovery of ecohouses at Brithdir Mawr and the ensuing planning controversy, Pembrokeshire County Council and Pembrokeshire National Park adopted an innovative policy on low-impact development. This explicitly allows rural greenfield development under a number of conditions aimed to ensure developments remain low impact. Development must be highly sustainable, using local, renewable, recycled and/or natural materials and built to high standards of eco-design, with the emphasis on 'low impact', including visual effects. Moreover, the proposal must offer positive environmental, social and/or economic contributions with public benefit. These could include services to the community, economic diversification for the area, opening paths for walkers or improved biodiversity. Furthermore, residents must prove a need to be on the land (rather than clustered within existing rural settlements). In 2009 the first large-scale new eco-village was approved under

this policy. Lammas eco-village (www.lammas.org.uk) is a low-cost nine-house community on 76 acres of mixed pasture and woodland next to the village of Glandwr, Pembrokeshire.

LIL projects don't have to be in rural areas. LILAC (Low Impact Living Affordable Community; www.lilac. coop) was built in Leeds in 2013, and includes 20 households and a common house. The buildings are made of locally sourced super-insulated straw bale and timber panels. Residents grow food on their allotments next to the buildings, share tools and resources, and get together for shared meals and events to build a sense of community. Beddington Zero Energy Development (BedZED) in London consists of 82 homes plus work space, built in 2000–2002. Although there have been some problems (e.g. with the biomass Combined Heat and Power plant), BedZED residents use 45 per cent less electricity and 81 per cent less gas for heating per year than the average for the borough they live in, and less than half the local average of mains water (Hodge and Haltrecht 2009).

Q What measures should we put in place to ensure our buildings, and the way we live in them, have minimal environmental impact?

Plate 6.5 The Dales house, Tir y Gafel eco-village, Wales.

(Jenny Pickerill)

for example, consuming less overall but more locally produced goods, generating less waste, travelling less and being conscious of our impact on the environment in our daily lives. The result is an emphasis on 'localization', living small-scale, perhaps more communally to share the load of everyday tasks, in energy-efficient buildings, and often with importance attached to producing for your

own needs, e.g. through growing your own vegetables. See Case study 6.2 for a British example of low-impact living.

The ecological modernization interpretation is far less radical and has been adopted by many more in mainstream politics. Supporters of ecological modernization criticize the deep green vision as naive and utopian with an unnecessary and ineffective focus on localization. In essence this approach argues that economic growth does not need to be slowed to ensure environmental protection. It does not undermine the limits to growth thesis entirely, but suggests that we can 'reorient' economic growth and find technological solutions for environmental problems, or 'decouple' economic growth from increased energy use, pollution and waste, thus overcoming the environmental impact of growth. It is a very weak interpretation of sustainable development that allows for a reformist response where the current dominance of free-market capitalism is not challenged; 'the future of environmental politics on this reading is a technical question of how to make capitalism more environmentally sensitive' (Connelly and Smith 2003: 359).

The **Environmental Kuznets Curve** (EKC) hypothesis states that although pollution and environmental degradation initially increase with increasing per capita income, once a country becomes rich enough it begins to implement environmental protection measures and the damage is reversed. Thus ecological modernizers argue that economic growth is necessary, to ensure both a decent material standard of living *and* environmental protection. But the theory appears to hold true only for some local pollutants and measures of air quality (Dinda 2004). Ecological footprint measures are highest in the richest countries of the world, for example, and Dietz and Adger (2003) found that an EKC does not exist for biodiversity loss. It may be that the EKC hypothesis only works when industrialization, urbanization and economic development cause environmental problems that have very obvious local impacts, such as the pollution of rivers by sewage and chemicals. As people become richer they have higher expectations regarding their local environment and urge protection of it, but environmental problems that are less obvious, or have impacts far from home, do not gain so much attention or response.

The EKC hypothesis has also been criticized on the grounds that the apparent improvement in measures of environmental health may be due to rich countries 'exporting' their pollution and energy consumption abroad (Suri and Chapman 2008). The reduction in UK greenhouse gas emissions has been achieved partly through the decline in British manufacturing and increased reliance on imported goods; emissions associated with the latter are not counted as part of the UK's carbon footprint but may be higher in poorer countries with more lax environmental regulations. Thus globalization and free-market capitalism pose a real challenge to our ability to adjust to the reality of limits to growth.

and Nature, George Perkins Marsh presented evidence for negative consequences of tropical deforestation. Carter (2001) has categorized the evolution of environmental issues (Table 6.3) into three key periods. Pre-1960s a great deal of environmental concern was focused upon small-scale localized problems such as local pollution and wildlife protection. In the 1960s concern grew about the interrelation between human actions and more complex environmental impacts. For example, *Silent Spring,* written by the biologist Rachel Carson in 1962 is generally regarded as a milestone in modern **environmentalism**. Carson pointed out the long-term ecological consequences of intensive agriculture, particularly the ways in which synthetic pesticides (notably **DDT**) persist in the food chain and poison birds and mammals (including humans). At the same time there were growing concerns about **overpopulation**. Paul Ehrlich, Garrett Hardin and Barry Commoner were considered **neo-Malthusian** because they saw environmental problems as a consequence of population growth, following the arguments set out by Thomas Malthus in the late eighteenth century. The misguided simplicity of neo-Malthusian explanations of environmental problems is shown in studies that have tried to explain land degradation in terms of population dynamics (Boserüp 1990). Not only is the evidence contradictory, for example increased land degradation in northern China has been linked to population growth (Takeuchi *et al.* 1995), whereas in northern Yemen (Carapico 1985) and Kenya's Machakos Hills (Tiffin *et al.* 1994) it has been related to population decline, but also it is clear from these studies that linking land degradation to one explanatory parameter – population size – masks

6.4 The complexity of scale and responsibility

The scale of response to environmental issues is a key point of debate. As we have seen, deep greens argue that localization is one of the most important elements to enacting environmental sustainability. If we adopt a more localized lifestyle then we can minimize our environmental impact. However, our environmental problems are far more complex, and global, than the notion of 'localization' suggests. To understand this we need to explore the evolution of environmental concern from one of local problems to global environmental issues.

There is no clear beginning to environmental concern. Plato, Lucretius and Caesar all noted the problems of soil erosion. Many of today's most pressing environmental issues were first identified in the nineteenth and early twentieth centuries. For example, in his 1869 book *Man*

Table 6.3 Evolution of environmental issues

First generation: Preservation and conservation (pre-1960s)	Protection of wildlife and habitats Soil erosion Local pollution
Second generation: 'Modern environmentalism' (from 1960s)	Population growth Technology Desertification Pesticides Resource depletion Pollution abatement
Third generation: Global issues (late 1970s onwards)	Acid rain Ozone depletion Rainforest destruction Climate change Loss of biodiversity Genetically modified organisms

Source: Carter (2001: 4)

the complexity behind population dynamics and labour-land relationships (Millington *et al*. 1989). Environmental problems are in fact a function of consumption of resources and production of wastes, as well as population and other factors.

By the early 1970s there was recognition not just of the interconnectedness of environmental issues, and of the problems of cumulative damage, but also that these were global problems that needed internationally coordinated responses. Environmental scientists identify two types of global environmental change. On the one hand, systemic change occurs when there is a direct impact on a physically interconnected, global system, e.g. the atmosphere or the oceans: for example, the effects that increased emissions of greenhouse gases have on global climate. Cumulative change, on the other hand, occurs when many discrete events become significant because their distribution is global or because, added together, their impact is felt across a large proportion of the globe. For example, across the Americas, Africa and Asia-Pacific, the relatively small amounts of tropical forest lost in each area being converted from forest to farmland, or being lost to a mining operation, add up to a global-scale problem affecting humid tropical forests, one of the most biodiverse biomes found on earth, of vital significance to the global water and carbon balances. Recognition of this duality is important in formulating policies and strategies. Addressing systemic issues need to be a global effort, with all countries agreeing and adhering to action. Focusing on cumulative issues requires both global approaches (e.g. in the fields of data exchange and comparative research) and local strategies (to reduce the impacts of a problem because different causes may exist in different geographical locations) (Middleton 2003).

In 1992, after five years of negotiations and preparatory meetings, the UN Conference on Environment and Development (also known as the **Earth Summit**) was held in Rio de Janeiro. It brought together 172 government delegations, 108 heads of state or government, 2,400 **NGO** representatives and a press corps of nearly 10,000. The parallel NGO Forum, which had consultative status, was attended by 17,000 people (see www.un.org/geninfo/bp/enviro.html). A rift opened up between the representatives of the majority world and the minority world countries, the former being worried that environmental concerns would be used by the minority world to limit their development. Shifting tensions between geopolitical blocs developed over issues such as biodiversity, climate change and desertification. But whatever its failings, the key point is that the Earth Summit resulted in a number of specific agreements that now form the basis of a global strategy for sustainable development and it had

a wider, less quantifiable impact on environmental issues worldwide, particularly in that:

- it elevated the importance of the environment on the political agendas of most countries (the majority now participate in the conventions that were agreed to at Rio, and many have used these conventions to pass new environmental legislation);
- the multilateral negotiations led to some issues gaining internationally important status (perhaps most notably biodiversity loss, which had only been recognized by scientists some 12 years earlier), and which changed long-standing, often ineffective attitudes to nature conservation;
- legislation at the international scale was negotiated, heralding an era of global environmental policy-making;
- there was recognition that many stakeholders had legitimate voices in environmental policy-making (the recognition of the stakeholder principle was vital in allowing actors outside government to become effective in bringing about changes in environment and development, a point that proponents of the bottom-up approach to development had long argued for).

Each of the three main conventions agreed at Rio has been followed by annual conferences of the parties (i.e. the countries that have signed a convention), at which progress towards ratification and implementation of the conventions has been discussed. Whilst the Convention to Combat Desertification and the Convention on Biological Diversity proved relatively straightforward to ratify and implement, negotiations arising from the Framework Convention on Climate Change have been beset by disagreements (see Case study 6.3).

The Earth Summit was followed by the World Summit on Sustainable Development ('Rio+10') in 2002 and the United Nations Conference on Sustainable Development ('Rio+20') in 2012. These conferences were not as groundbreaking as the original; in 2002 the USA did not attend, and the main outcome of Rio+20 was a non-binding document, *The Future We Want*. In it the heads of state of the 192 governments attending reaffirmed their commitment to sustainable development and to previous action plans.

Although a few governments have found it difficult to ratify conventions and make efforts to achieve targets, the implementation of sustainable development actions by local administrations – **Local Agenda 21**s – has been far more successful. The International Council for Local Environment Initiatives (2002) reported that 6,416 LA21s were underway or committed to in 113 countries, that national campaigns were underway in 18 countries, and that formal stakeholder groups had been established in 73 per cent of administrative units with LA21s.

Case study 6.3

Negotiating and implementing an international convention: the obstacles faced in tackling climate change

The latest scientific report by the Intergovernmental Panel on Climate Change states that warming of the climate system is 'unequivocal'. Atmospheric concentrations of the greenhouse gases (GHGs) carbon dioxide (CO_2), methane and nitrous oxide are higher than they have been for at least the last 800,000 years. Their effects are 'extremely likely' (95–100 per cent probability) to have been the main cause of observed climate change since the mid-twentieth century (IPCC 2014).

The United Nations Framework Convention on Climate Change (UNFCCC) was created at the Rio Earth Summit in 1992 and came into force on 21 March 1994 (see www.unfcc.int for further details). The ultimate objective of the UNFCCC is to 'stabilize greenhouse gas concentrations in the atmosphere at a level that will prevent dangerous anthropogenic (human induced) interference with the climate system. Such a level should be achieved within a time-frame sufficient to allow ecosystems to adapt naturally to climate change, to ensure that food production is not threatened and to enable economic development to proceed in a sustainable manner'. Annual conferences of the parties (COPs) are attended by all the states that have ratified or acceded to the Convention (196 as of November 2014).

The third COP, held in Kyoto, Japan, in 1997 saw agreement on the **Kyoto Protocol**, which was intended to commit all industrialized nations to reduce their emissions compared to 1990 levels by 2008–12. Although the Protocol was signed in Bonn in July 2001, it did not come into force until 16 February 2005 after Russia ratified it, therefore ensuring the requirement was met that it was ratified by at least 55 countries producing at least 55 per cent of global emissions in 1990. However, the USA, the world's second- largest emitter of CO_2 after China, has never signed up to the Kyoto Protocol, and the original targets were reduced during the Bonn meeting to ensure that Japan, Canada and Australia would agree. Ultimately, 37 industrialized nations (and the European Community as a whole) were bound by targets during the first Kyoto commitment period. These varied between countries, to reflect the ease or difficulty of reducing emissions, what had already been done, and what countries would accept. Japan and Canada had a 6 per cent reduction target

while Norway, Australia and Iceland were actually allowed to increase their emissions from 1990 levels. The European Union committed to an 8 per cent reduction, to be shared out between members; Germany and Denmark promised to reduce emissions by 21 per cent each, while the UK agreed to 12.5 per cent and poorer countries such as Portugal and Greece were allowed to increase emissions. Not surprisingly, a complex set of rules and regulations surrounds the targets, making it possible to trade 'emissions reductions' between states. One means of doing this is the **clean development mechanism (CDM)**, through which minority world countries are able to earn credits towards their own reduction targets by investing in emission reduction projects in the majority world. In other words, the minority world will have to help the majority world implement the CDM and this will require transfer of considerable amounts of capital and technology. Thus O'Riordan (2000: 202) notes that:

> the CDM mechanism denies the right of Third World nations to select their own CO_2 future. This is 'ecological colonialism' by another name. While the minority world has access to the capital and technology to achieve the Kyoto targets, it still requires the political will. In the majority world, political will amounts to little without the material requirements to balance the economic growth with environmental needs.

There are now significant concerns as to the efficacy of this mechanism. The Copenhagen Accord agreed in 2009 has done little to quell these fears, being widely regarded as too weak and vague to really tackle these key concerns. Although there were similar criticisms of the outcomes of the Cancun climate talks in 2010, progress was made in establishing a new Green Climate Fund. This is intended to raise and distribute £64 billion a year by 2020 to assist in technology transfer and low-carbon development for the poorer countries.

Overall the Kyoto Protocol should have achieved an average reduction in GHG emissions of 5 per cent from 1990 levels by the end of 2012, for those countries involved. Whether this has been accomplished depends on exactly how emissions are counted. Under the rules of the Protocol, only emissions produced in a country count towards its total, and using this 'production perspective' many countries (including the UK) have met their targets. However, from a 'consumption perspective', which assigns GHGs associated with imported goods to the country consuming them rather than the producer country, emissions reductions are more than cancelled out by the GHGs 'embedded' in imports from the majority world (Peters *et al.* 2011).

COP15 in Copenhagen in 2009 was supposed to result in a new set of post-2012 binding reduction commitments. This didn't happen; all that was agreed was the Copenhagen Accord, a set of non-binding, voluntary targets. Furthermore, Canada withdrew from the Kyoto Protocol in 2011 to avoid heavy financial penalties that it would otherwise face as it would not meet its emissions reductions targets, while Japan and Russia stated that they would not take on further targets. 'The Kyoto Protocol does not cover the world's largest two emitters, the United States and China, and therefore cannot work,' argued Canadian Environment Minister Peter Kent. In 2010 UK Prime Minister David Cameron had blamed the USA and China for obstructing the discussion process when he said that he doubted further international agreement on emissions reductions was likely. The essence of the problem is that the USA is unwilling to accept binding targets while rapidly industrializing countries do not; China and other majority world countries argue that, historically, the industrialized world is responsible for the vast majority of emissions, so they should not have to accept emissions reductions yet that would hamper their economic growth and ability to reduce poverty. However, in November 2014 China and the USA announced a joint plan to tackle climate change, involving a commitment by China to ensure its emissions peak by 2030 at the latest, while the USA will reduce its emissions by 26–28 per cent from 2005 levels by 2025.

At COP21 in Paris in 2015 it is intended to create a new global climate agreement with binding targets from 2020 for all parties to the UNFCCC. However, some commentators argue that rather than continue to seek to agree Kyoto-style targets and pledges, there is an increasing need to explore alternatives such as a global carbon tax (see, for example, this blog by Dieter Helm, Professor of Energy Policy at the University of Oxford: http://e360.yale.edu/feature/forget_kyoto_putting_a_tax_on_carbon_consumption/2590/).

Why has it been so difficult to negotiate a climate change treaty, compared to the process that resulted in the Montreal Protocol to prevent depletion of the ozone layer, often cited as a successful example of international policymaking? Key features of the 'ozone hole' problem were that the scientific evidence of damage was relatively clear and simple to understand; it would affect rich countries through increased cancer rates, which the public was concerned about; ozone depletion was caused by relatively few chemicals which were therefore fairly easy to regulate; and rich-world industries had already started producing non-ozone depleting substitutes so it was in their interests for a treaty to be agreed that would speed up adoption of these alternatives. In contrast, evidence for climate change causes and impacts is extremely complex; most people in the rich world see climate change as a problem that will impact other people, distant in time and space; climate change is caused by GHGs associated with a huge range of human activities, affecting many aspects of our everyday lives; reducing energy-related GHGs is seen as putting a break on economic growth, which is not acceptable to the majority world; and many industries regard emissions reduction policies as contrary to their interests and so have been involved in trying to obscure climate science, promote scepticism and inhibit mitigation action.

Q **What will it take for all countries and elites everywhere to cast aside their domestic concerns and privileges in favour of the global and collective good?**

The problem of scale can make it hard to determine how to take the best action. Not only do we need to unpack the causes of environmental change and identify likely solutions, but also 'those making decisions concerning global environmental problems need to consider the ramifications for national economies and local populations' (Harris 2004: 13). In other words, we (individuals, businesses, nations, etc.) need to take responsibility for our environmental impacts *and* understand the consequences of mitigating these problems (for other people, the economy, and so on). The problem of climate change is thus 'a local and social problem as much as it is a global environmental problem' (Barnett 2007: 1361). For example, if we want to reduce the negative consequences of driving cars we can reduce individual use, encourage companies to design more fuel-efficient vehicles, and lobby governments to increase the price of petrol through tax rises, subsidize eco-alternatives and introduce road pricing. However, in practice, governments of countries like the USA have argued in the past that it would damage their economy, making them less globally competitive (leading to job losses).

All these complexities are shaped by how we value the environment, at what scale we view these problems, and thus whose responsibility we believe it is to make changes. While many individuals, NGOs and governments argue that we all need to take responsibility for our actions, a solely localized approach by some of us will allow the harmful environmental consequences of others to go unchecked. Multi-scalar action is required, from local to international, involving all of us in the processes of change. But how have people sought to make such change happen and how does it work in practice?

6.5 Strategies for change

There are a wide variety of ways in which action is taken, through international agreements, the legislature (i.e. formal party politics), lifestyle changes, community living, and through direct action (Dobson 2001). We can broadly conceive of these as a continuum between reformist and radical approaches (see Table 6.4). Both approaches are part of the broad and diverse environmental movement, and many people hold positions somewhere between the extreme ends of the continuum. We can use some examples to explore these strategies in practice: in national party politics (the German Green Party), political lobbying (Friends of the Earth UK), direct action (Earth First!), individual actions, and business responses.

The German Green Party – Die Grünen – made its entrance into formal politics in 1983 with 5.6 per cent of the national vote and 27 seats in Federal Parliament (Doyle 2005). The party emerged from a vibrant environmental movement that was particularly active on antinuclear issues. When it was first launched Die Grünen was closely aligned to those seeking radical change. Petra Kelly, an early leader of the party, described Die Grünen as 'half party and half local action group – we shall go on being an anti-party party' (Kelly 1984: 21). Thus the party aimed to be part of formal politics but simultaneously subvert the process by looking to practise more **participatory democracy** and pushing for fundamental change. They did this through the legislation they sought, funding environmental groups and organizations, and structurally by rotating their representatives sitting in parliament, limiting the length of office of their leaders and practising participatory decision-making processes.

However, over time 'the party has been colonized by the demands and temptations of parliamentary activity' (Dobson 2001: 127). It has dropped many of its earlier commitments (environmental sustainability, disarmament, social justice and participatory democracy) and abandoned 'their experimental attempt at institutionalizing direct democratic structures within the framework of **representative democracy**' (Poguntke 1993: 395). The radical faction lost out to those in the party who believed in reformist change. This led to the party forging coalitions with other parties, eventually forming an alliance with the Social Democrats to form the national government in 1998, consequently weakening their stance on war and nuclear power, and taking a stance *against* those undertaking environmental direct action (Doyle 2005). The German experience is a cautionary tale about the difficulties of implementing change through formal political arenas.

Environmental NGOs and related groups serve two key roles in society: they often identify environmental problems and, importantly, they seek to translate environmental concern into practical strategies for change. In 1971 Friends of the Earth (FoE) was launched in London; it has become one of the biggest and most influential of the British environmental NGOs, and is part of an international FoE network. Its formation reflected a frustration with the staid conservation movement's lack of action against perpetrators of environmental degradation (Rawcliffe 1998). They have a five-pronged strategy:

Table 6.4 Reformist and radical approaches to environmentalism

Reformist	Radical
1. Modified sustainable economic growth/ ecological modernization.	1. Limits to, and undesirability of, economic growth.
2. Large role for technological development as a provider of solutions for environmental problems.	2. A distrust of scientific and technological fixes.
3. Environmental solutions can co-exist with existing social and political structures.	3. Radical social and political change necessary: either authoritarian or decentralized and democratic political organization.
4. Anthropocentrism and a commitment to intragenerational and intergenerational equity.	4. Intrinsic value of nature or, at least, a weaker version of anthropocentrism; a commitment to social justice within human society and between humans and non-human nature.

Source: from Robert Garner, *Environmental Politics,* published 2000, (Macmillan) reproduced with permission of Palgrave Macmillan

to lobby those in political power and industry, often using legislative activity to press for change; to generate scientific research and publish it in accessible formats; to employ the media to attract attention to particular issues; to mobilize the public through local groups; and to coordinate and cooperate with other groups to run large-scale campaigns.

By the early 1990s, however, FoE had evolved from a radical group to one that seemed less keen to press for far-reaching change. In effect it had become reformist – pragmatically seeking inclusion of environmental concern within the current political and social system. Many saw this reformist approach as being ineffectual, slow and hierarchical, though it has achieved some successes, such as influencing the creation and passing of the UK Climate Change Act of 2008. Drawing inspiration from other movements and other countries, smaller, more radical environmental groups (or informal networks) began to proliferate. They pose a systematic challenge to existing societal practices, often rejecting 'representative' democracy and formal politics and promoting grassroots participation in environmental decision-making and a 'do-it-yourself' approach. The tactics employed reflect their belief in the need for radical change and often involve the use of non-violent direct action such as road blockades and office occupations. Direct action is 'intended to have an immediate effect on a situation, as distinct from political activity which might have a roundabout effect through representatives, or demonstrative activity whose effect was to get publicity' (Rooum 1995: 27).

One such group, Earth First! (EF!), formed in the United States in 1979 and spread to the United Kingdom in 1991. Based upon anarchist ideology, it is a network of autonomous groups that eschew formal membership and hierarchy (and thus leadership) and espouse consensus decision-making structures and non-violent direct action: one of their slogans is 'If not you, then who?' (Wall 1999; Doherty 2002). EF! has been influential in British anti-roads protests, e.g. Twyford Down (1992), Newbury (1995–6) and the A30 in Devon at Allercombe and Fairmile (1994–7). They used protest camps with tree-sits, tunnels and lock-ons with the aims of (i) physically preventing road construction; (ii) generating media publicity; (iii) educating the public; and (iv) acting as a catalyst for mass mobilization. The defining characteristics of such activism are the continuously evolving creativity in tactics coupled with a broad concern for a variety of issues; for example 'they see exploitation of the Third World, the global poor, women, animals and the environment as a product of hierarchy, patriarchy, anthropocentrism, racism and, most prominently, capitalist economic relations' (Seel and Plows 2000: 114).

Such actions have been influenced by many others and replicated worldwide. In Australia, environmentalists have employed direct action since the late 1970s. Tree sits and roadblocks at Terania Creek (New South Wales), Daintree (Queensland) and surrounding the Franklin Dam (Tasmania) all focused on preventing the logging of old-growth trees. India has an even more extensive history of *satyagraha* (non-violent action) inspired by Mahatma Gandhi. In the early 1970s, villagers (mostly women) from Uttar Pradesh physically began to try to prevent local logging – resulting in the Chipko Andalan movement (McCormick 1989). More recently, villagers threatened with losing their land, homes and livelihoods by the construction of the Narmada Dam have committed to drowning rather than forced resettlement (Shiva 2002).

A key tenet of many environmental approaches is the need for individuals to take action. With a grassroots movement of individuals making changes, bigger changes can occur: 'the only possible building blocks of a Greener future are individuals moving towards a

Plate 6.6 An anti-car stunt calling for radical environmental activism.

(Jenny Pickerill)

Case study 6.4

Reducing fossil fuel consumption through personal carbon allowances

Personal Carbon Trading (PCT) has been proposed as a means of reducing individuals' fossil fuel consumption. As a strategy for change, it is a gradualist approach that allows people choices in how they respond, but proponents argue that it would create the necessary conditions for a radical transformation to a low- or zero-carbon society. The policy would involve allocating every eligible citizen a 'personal carbon allowance', their free, equal share of a country's permitted carbon emissions, which they would have to use when buying certain fossil-fuel related goods. The allowances would decrease over many years, in order to meet emissions reduction targets.

Every eligible adult would have a 'carbon account' (and associated 'carbon card'), similar to a bank account, which would be automatically credited with their free carbon allowance (composed of 'carbon units') at regular intervals. Parents might receive an extra allowance for children or else higher child benefit payments to compensate for the costs of buying extra credits to cover their family's energy use. Fossil fuels for home and vehicle use (principally gas, oil, coal, petrol and diesel), electricity generated from non-renewable sources, and possibly travel tickets would be assigned a carbon rating, based on the amount of CO_2 emitted by using these goods. We would be required to pay in carbon units as well as money for these purchases (e.g. an electricity bill or tank of petrol). Fuel and travel tickets are the only goods that would be carbon-rated; for simplicity, PCT schemes are not designed to cover 'embedded' emissions in products such as food and clothes.

Carbon units would be legally tradable between individuals. Those with spare credits could sell them on a regulated market to people who required more than their free allocation. This is an important aspect of PCT, since the allowance necessary to cover current CO_2 emissions varies considerably between individuals. It would prevent a black market and also provide an incentive for us to cut our emissions below the allowance level, which would not exist if we could not sell spare credits.

People would be able to check their carbon accounts and buy or sell credits at post offices and banks, by phone, or using the internet. They would also be able to buy carbon units at point-of-sale when purchasing carbon-rated fuels and travel tickets, so you wouldn't end up stranded on the petrol station forecourt if you suddenly realized you had no credit remaining on your carbon card, or had left it at home.

Advocates of PCT argue that it would increase carbon literacy and be a fair and effective way to create a more sustainable society in which everyone would be interested in energy-efficient products, supportive of renewable energy, and motivated to change their lifestyles. Many details of how PCT would work would still need to be clarified before it could ever become a reality. The UK Department for Environment, Food and Rural Affairs (Defra) conducted a study to assess the proposal and concluded that although it would be technically feasible, PCT is 'ahead of its time', particularly because of the high costs of implementing it and lack of public acceptability (Defra 2008). However, others suggest that the costs would be lower and the benefits greater than Defra's calculations, and that Defra's own research shows that PCT is preferred to other policies such as a carbon tax (Fawcett 2010).

From 2006, Carbon Rationing Action Groups (CRAGs) were formed in the UK and then in a few other countries including the USA, Canada and China. These were grassroots voluntary groups of people who put some of the PCT proposals into practice by setting themselves a carbon allowance each year. Some groups operated basic trading, with a financial penalty for over-emitters that was shared out to members who used less than the allowance, but most groups didn't do this and instead emphasized supporting each other to cut their carbon emissions from home energy use and personal transport. People involved in CRAGs showed that it is possible to make significant reductions by changing their behaviour, installing insulation and renewables (e.g. solar-powered hot water systems) at home, and buying more efficient appliances. An especially popular action was to cut down or give up flying, which is very carbon-intensive. Being part of a CRAG helped people by offering support and a sense of accountability to the group, and encouragement, because they could see that their individual reductions put together added up to something more significant. CRAG members also shared information, resources like energy monitors, and social time together.

Source: adapted from Howell (2012)

For more information on Personal Carbon Allowances (also called Tradable Energy Quotas) see www.teqs.net.

Q 'If something cannot be manufactured, built or grown without causing irreparable ecological damage, can't we strive to create something to take its place, or simply decide to do without it?' (Tokar 1994: 80). What could you do without in your consumption and what would make you willing to give it up?

Greener way of life *themselves* and joining together with others who are doing the same' (Bunyard and Morgan-Grenville 1987: 336). Thus individuals are encouraged, for example, to 'reduce, reuse, recycle'. The three R's are deliberately in the order of magnitude of impact. So reducing our fossil fuel energy consumption (see Case study 6.4) will have a far greater environmental benefit than recycling, which is time, energy and financially inefficient. In recent years there has been a rapid rise in 'green consumerism' – purchasing goods such as eco-friendly washing powder or 'natural' shampoos that are intended to be less damaging to the environment than alternatives. While this is a step in the right direction, green consumerism is not about buying *less,* just purchasing different products. Potentially more sustainable ways to meet our needs include swap shops, Freecycle and similar online recyling networks (which enable people to get unwanted goods for free, thus reducing waste and demand for new products), Local Exchange Trading Systems and Time Banks (which use alternative currencies to encourage non-monetary exchanges of goods and services), and 'Buy Nothing Day' (www .buynothingday.co.uk). However, unfortunately at present, 'it seems unlikely that a massive number of individuals will experience the conversion that will lead to the necessary changes in their daily behaviour' (Dobson 2001: 131) so it is also necessary to campaign for legislation to change the infrastructure and social norms that create unsustainable ways of living.

Finally, businesses can play a key role in strategies for environmental change, both good and bad (Doyle and McEachern 2007). Businesses have sought to develop technologies that reduce environmental impacts (wind farms are one example), support ecological projects through providing financial services (e.g. Triodos Bank and the Ecology Building Society), and practise Corporate Social Responsibility throughout their operations. Globally the United Nations Global Compact attempts to encourage such action by asking businesses to sign up to ten universally accepted principles in the areas of human rights, labour, environment and anti-corruption. However, some companies have lobbied hard against legislation that they perceive would impact upon their profits. The Global Climate Coalition was formed by (mainly USA) companies involved in energy-intensive industries such as coal, oil, automobile, electricity generation, cement, and paper to cast doubt on climate change science and campaign against government measures to limit GHG emissions (Jeswani *et al.* 2008). Some companies also face accusations of 'greenwashing' – appearing green while changing none of their fundamental approaches. Spotlight box 6.2 discusses one practice that has attracted this kind of criticism. Moreover, businesses' entry into green markets can lead to a dilution of the original principles and eventually subvert the environmental benefits. For example, a core element of organic food production is to reduce pollution. This principle is enhanced when people purchase organic food locally (for example, through a box scheme from a local farm). However, when supermarkets saw organics as a market opportunity, they began to import organically produced food from Africa and Latin America, undermining many of its environmental benefits (Hughes 2005, 2007). Here supermarkets failed

---

Spotlight box 6.2

Carbon offsetting

Carbon offsetting is the practice of buying carbon credits from projects which are intended to reduce greenhouse gas emissions. The credits are then 'offset' against the purchaser's carbon footprint. In other words, counted as a reduction in their actual carbon emissions. Individuals, companies and countries increasingly seek to buy carbon credits through funding energy efficiency, reforestation or renewable power projects, often in majority world countries. In 2005 HSBC, one of the world's biggest banks, asserted that it had gone 'carbon neutral' by buying carbon offset credits from renewable energy projects in New Zealand, Australia, India and Germany.

Critics of carbon offsetting argue that it is a poor substitute for actually reducing our carbon emissions and is another way that companies and individuals can buy their way out of responsibility for the environment. There is significant debate as to its validity and effectiveness, with arguments about measurement and 'additionality' (i.e. whether projects would have happened anyway, in which case the payments for carbon credits are not responsible for extra emissions reductions). Tree-planting offset schemes have been especially criticised because of the time it takes for new trees to absorb carbon dioxide, and because they only 'offset' emissions for as long as the trees don't burn or die and rot. The website www.cheatneutral.com explores some of the criticisms of carbon offsetting in an amusing way by comparing it to paying others to be monogamous or celibate so as to offset cheating on your partner.

to take account of the importance of reducing the 'air miles' that food has travelled as part of the measure of the environmental impact of food consumption.

The dilemma remains how best to enact change, be it through NGOs that are able to lever access to the halls of power but in doing so can appear elitist, or through radical direct action which encourages grassroots participation and individual responsibility but which in turn can be small in scale and effect. For now, the answer appears to lie in the vibrancy of environmental movements composed of a variety of contesting, challenging and supportive groups, incorporating international NGOs alongside more radical small-scale groups.

What can one person, one household, one community or one administrative unit do when governments of some of the world's most economically powerful states cannot be brought onside? The environmentalist's answer is to be a good global citizen, to put pressure on administrations, governments, corporations and supranational organizations through political and non-political means, and to educate, encourage and work with others. We have gone some way down this route in the past four decades, but significant problems remain.

6.6 What is missing from our focus on 'the environment'?

One of those problems is the way in which we conceptualize the environment and 'environmental issues' as separate from other aspects of our lives and concerns. 'Environmentalists' are stereotyped as 'treehuggers' who care more about animals than people, and it is assumed that they are not the same people as those who campaign about human rights and social justice. However, we are beginning to acknowledge the complex web of relationships between humans and the environment, and the relation of 'environmental' problems to poverty, development, human health, injustice and issues of democracy. In reality, environmental issues are social issues, as shown by the increasing focus of development NGOs such as Oxfam and Christian Aid on 'environmental' concerns like climate change.

At the level of international policymaking, too, the emphasis has changed since the Rio Earth Summit to one that seeks to integrate environment and development more closely and for the environmental agenda to include concerns about poverty. These lines of thinking are underpinned by the World Bank's Poverty Alleviation Strategies and the Millennium Development Goals which were agreed by the UN General Assembly in September 2000 (www.un.org/millenniumgoals) in response to lack

of progress on poverty and debt in the Third World (see Chapter 8 for more discussion on this theme). For many in the majority world the links between poverty, development and the environment are explicit. It is not a simple case of poverty leading to environmental damage: there are countless examples of poor people being key actors in environmental campaigns in India, Indonesia, the Philippines and across South America. Certain forms of development have significant environmental consequences – such as dam building, fossil fuel power generation and natural resource extraction (see Chapter 5 for further information). But we should understand these developments within the context of a history of colonial exploitation and contemporary processes of competitive economic globalization.

Ecological modernization has failed to consider international justice (Connelly and Smith 2003). Where industrialized nations have sought to reduce their environmental damage they have in many cases simply exported their environmental problems to less industrialized countries: for example, the export of harmful

Plate 6.7 Teaching Indigenous knowledge about the land, Australia.

(Jenny Pickerill)

computer wastes to China (Shabi 2002). Environmental injustice also occurs within countries (see Spotlight box 6.3). Furthermore, environmental protection as well as environmental damage has resulted in the dispossession of Indigenous peoples from their land, to make way for national parks for example (see Case study 6.5). This practice results from two mistaken beliefs: first, that humans will only ever have a detrimental impact on their surroundings and second, that preservation of an environment is more important than human ties to a particular place, and in some cases, human survival.

Thus the industrialized world's approach to 'the environment' often fails to understand majority world experiences, the need to incorporate humans *into* our understandings of the environment, and to acknowledge that some people have limited environmental choices. Recent work has sought to change how we view the environment, suggesting that the division between human and non-human is an artificial and unhelpful one (see Chapter 12). Environmental concerns have been recast as issues of social survival. For example, the impact of

sea-level rises on Pacific Islanders will be so catastrophic that it will potentially wipe out entire nations. People who take action on climate change are often motivated not so much by concerns about 'the environment' for its own sake, as by the plight of poor people in the majority world who have contributed least to the problem but will suffer most (Howell 2013). Rather than being seen as a hindrance to wildlife preservation, Indigenous people's environmental knowledge and management skills are slowly beginning to be valued. The 2004 *Arctic Climate Impact Assessment,* for example, portrays Indigenous people as both at risk of losing their ways of life, *and* as holders of valuable knowledge about the impacts of climate change (see www.acia.uaf.edu/). Moreover, Indigenous peoples' often alternative ways of viewing the environment, as being a melding of culture, land and sky in the case of Indigenous Australians for example, challenge our conceptualizations. The need to understand the psychology behind environmental concern and to promote behavioural changes are becoming priority areas for environmental research (Hulme 2004).

Spotlight box 6.3

Environmental justice

The environmental justice movement calls for acknowledgement that it is often the already marginalized who suffer most from environmental degradation. Robert Bullard in his book *Dumping in Dixie* (1990) argued that toxic dump sites were more likely to be near neighbourhoods of black Americans than whites – race being a major factor in the quality of a person's environment. The African National Congress asserted that 'poverty and environmental degradation have been closely linked' in South Africa (McDonald 2004: 2). These are forms of environmental injustice.

It is also a critique of environmentalists' focus on wilderness preservation rather than the plight of the underprivileged, and 'has dragged other parts of the US environmental movement into a political place where the social ramifications of being green have to be confronted' (Doyle and McEachern 2001: 69). Understanding environmental problems as rooted in inequality is helpful in understanding some of the contemporary issues in dealing with climate change. Parks and Roberts (2008) argue that 'global inequality may be a central impediment to interstate cooperation on climate change policy' (p. 621) and therefore that we need to tackle this injustice first.

Case study 6.5

Wilderness and conservation debates in Australia

Environmental campaigns worldwide are often framed as conserving 'wilderness' and preventing exploitation of natural resources. Organizations lobbying for protection of vast tracts of Alaska, Canada and Australia

employ an emotive language using words such as 'pristine', 'untouched', 'undisturbed', 'intact expanse' and 'wild frontiers' to rally support. Photographs of lands empty of people or any human structures often accompany these words. Whether directly, through hunting for example, or indirectly through their development activities, people are usually held responsible for wildlife losses. Until the 1980s, conservationists' solutions relied on strategies like hunting bans and establishing protected areas through World Heritage status or as National Parks.

However, there is increasing recognition not only that Indigenous people have historic rights of possession to some of that land, but also that Indigenous environmental knowledge and land management practices can be beneficial for conservation outcomes. This recognition and the legal changes that have accompanied it (such as the development of Native Title in Australia) have forced environmental and conservation groups to reconsider their approach, although many have been slow to change their language or practices when it comes to viewing areas as 'wilderness' devoid of people.

Language is a key articulation of power in understandings of the 'environment'. The term 'wilderness' and its relation 'wild' are highly problematic when talking of any landscape, but especially so in Australia, a land inhabited by the Indigenous population for tens of thousands of years. Yet these terms are still employed. Such a romanticization of the environment draws upon the writings of Henry David Thoreau, John Muir and Miles Dunphy, and is used to sell Australia and garner support for environmental protection.

Indigenous people have been highly critical of the use of such words. They have colonial and racist connotations, and the narrow vision, propagated by environmental groups, of what 'wilderness' entails is dualistic. Indigenous Australians argue that there can be no such division between the environment and culture and that 'land is a much more energetic configuration of earth and air, water and minerals, animals and plants, as well as people, than a surface area contained by lines on a map' (Whatmore 2002: 71). It is precisely because of these interrelations between environment and culture that Indigenous people need to live on their land in order to care for their country; 'the land needs the people and the people need the land ... these are important cultural environments that require people to manage them according to tradition and culture, to maintain ... and to encourage species' (Damian Britnell, Mossman Gorge Aboriginal Community).

The Indigenous critique of 'wilderness' and approach to 'country', especially calls to live on land, is controversial. However, the majority of environmental groups in Australia now have (albeit only recently) a vague policy of supporting Indigenous rights. Some groups have attempted to go further and alter their language and practices to implement this policy. The Wilderness Society has shifted away from large-scale agreements and broad alliances with Indigenous groups to grounded community-level cooperation. Although they have not discarded the contentious goal of creating National Parks, they are working more in collaboration with traditional owners, supporting a class of National Park which is owned as Aboriginal Land but managed under the Nature Conservation Act, supporting attempts to gain Aboriginal Freehold land, and to establish Indigenous Protected Areas (Schneiders 2006: 27).

The Australian Conservation Foundation (ACF) has taken a different path. They have instigated a northern Australia Programme, which aims to take a long-term proactive approach towards creating a bicultural organization. It is focused on coming up with joint goals rather than finding campaign partners for issues the ACF think are important. To this end they have even opposed the creation of new National Parks when traditional owners have objected. ACF avoids the words 'wilderness' and 'biodiversity' altogether and instead talks about 'nature' and 'culture'.

Both these organizations have made progress in modifying their language and practices in response to the charge that they were party to 'a form of ecological imperialism' (Langton 1998: 18). However, two key problems remain. First, the majority of Indigenous engagement by these two groups has been confined to northern Australia. A view persists that there is no need to engage with Indigenous politics further south, perpetuating the myth that only those Indigenous people who have a more apparent and historic (according to non-Indigenous adjudicators) connection to their homeland need consultation. Second, although the language has changed, the underlying premise of why a landscape is of enough value to protect has not altered. Both still employ a biophysical-based and scientific method to determine value. We are a long way from bridging the gap between 'environment' and 'culture' and widening the ways in which we value landscape.

Source: adapted from Pickerill (2008)

Q Do you think later settlers should have any say in the environmental management of Indigenous land and the wildlife that inhabits it?

6.7 Environmentally sustainable futures

Society is taking action: policies are being designed and implemented at global, regional and local scales. But there are issues that still dog progress:

- The impacts of some environmental problems are distant in time and space from those who contribute most to causing them.
- Remediation and restoration of many types of environmental damage takes years.
- The costs of environmental remediation and protecting environments are often enormous.
- Our incomplete knowledge about many aspects of the environment, and how environment–society linkages work, can act as a barrier to finding effective solutions.
- The drive for economic growth is strong, while the negotiation and implementation of global and regional environmental policies is slow.

Despite these obstacles it is up to us to decide what kind of world we want and to work towards it. We have explored a range of ways in which we understand and value the environment, different ways in which we could 'reconceive the environment', and strategies for change. In summary, there are four key steps we can take towards reducing our environmental damage.

First, we need to understand our environmental impacts better: globally, regionally, locally and individually. At an individual level we can use an ecological footprint calculator (e.g. http://footprint.wwf.org.uk) to evaluate our resource use. Second, we can participate in environmental decision-making. Connelly and Smith (2003: 361), through their concept of **ecological democratization**, argue that the only way to achieve environmentally sustainable practices is through 'a commitment to both justice and participation'. They advocate extensive citizen participation and development of democratic institutions to tackle environmental issues at all scales. In many ways this is an extension of many pre-existing local initiatives. Third, we need to recognize and make use of innovative grassroots solutions. Seyfang and Smith (2007)

argue that it is the grassroots-community level where significant innovation occurs that can offer us inspirational visions of alternative futures. We have seen this in the case studies about low-impact living and Carbon Rationing Action Groups. Some of these innovations are small-scale in their approach, others, such as **permaculture**, are now being adopted globally. Fourth, and least radically, we need to improve our management of the current situation. There are existing environmental issues that we need to mitigate immediately, even while we begin to explore alternative futures. For example, in Britain there are growing numbers of car users. A 2006 government report, The Eddington Transport Study, supported road pricing, rather than more road building, in order to overcome existing congestion problems, and argued that 'all transport users should meet all their external economic, social and environmental costs' (Eddington 2006: 2). This approach has led to the introduction of the congestion charge in London. However, plans to implement similar schemes in Manchester and Edinburgh have been publicly rejected. We have to decide if road pricing is an appropriate management strategy, or whether an alternative policy such as having a travel allowance, akin to rationing, would be better. Given these choices, which pathways forward are you going to take?

Plate 6.8 A Reclaim the Streets demonstration in Hull, May 1999, which illegally occupied the streets for a day in protest at a car-obsessed culture.

(Jenny Pickerill)

Learning outcomes

Having read this chapter, you should understand:

- The concepts of limits to growth and sustainable development.

- That information about environmental problems is not necessarily enough to motivate action; responses depend on people's worldviews and how they value the environment.

- The complexity of scale when looking for solutions to environmental problems.

- The possibilities and limitations of different strategies for action.

- How we can begin to make progressive steps towards reducing our environmental impacts.

Further reading

Böhm, S., Pervez Bharucha, Z. and Pretty, J. (2015) *Ecocultures: Blueprints for Sustainable Communities,* Earthscan, London. A book packed full of global examples of environmentalism and environmental projects in action.

Dauvergne, P. (2009) *The A to Z of Environmentalism,* The Scarecrow Press, Toronto. A great dictionary of key terms, events and people related to environmentalism.

Doyle, T. (2005) *Environmental Movements in Majority and Minority Worlds: A Global Perspective,* Rutgers University Press, London. A good introduction to a variety of environmental movements in the USA, Australia, Britain, Germany, the Philippines and India, incorporating protection of forests, rivers and wilderness areas, and movements against mining, road building and nuclear power.

Harris, F. (ed.) (2012) *Global Environmental Issues,* 2nd edition, John Wiley and Sons, Chichester. Taking a global perspective this book examines environmental problems as complex issues with a network of human and biophysical causes.

Haq, G. and Paul, A. (2012) *Environmentalism since 1945,* Routledge, London. A brief history of how minority world environmentalism became a global movement.

Hulme, M. (2009) *Why We Disagree About Climate Change: Understanding Controversy, Inaction and Opportunity,* Cambridge University Press, Cambridge. This book seeks to reconsider how we perceive climate change and views it as an environmental, cultural and political phenomenon rather than simply a threat. It combines a scientific approach with social and political standpoints.

Klein, N. (2015) *This Changes Everything: Capitalism vs. the Climate,* Penguin Books, London. An incisive critique of our current response to climate change, with – unusually in books on this topic – a whole section on movements for change and reasons for hope.

Marshall, G. (2014) *Don't Even Think About It: Why Our Brains Are Wired to Ignore Climate Change,* Bloomsbury USA, New York. Engaging and easy-to-read discussion of why we ignore climate change and what to do to stop that happening.

McNeill, J.R. (2000) *Something New Under the Sun: An Environmental History of the World in the 20th Century,* Penguin, London. A very readable history of the impact of humanity on the planet and the rise of environmental concern.

Peet, R., Robbins, P. and Watts, M.J. (eds) (2011) *Global Political Ecology,* Routledge, London. This book includes a large variety of case examples exploring the relationships between environmental issues, economics, poverty and politics.

Peterson Del Mar, D. (2012) *Environmentalism,* 2nd edition, Routledge, Abingdon, Oxon. A short thought-provoking book which examines the complex relationship between prosperity and environmentalism.

Reynolds, M., Blackmore, C. and Smith, M.J. (2009) *The Environmental Responsibility Reader,* Zed Books, London. A good collection of essays and extracts on topics such as environmental ethics, ecological citizenship and individual and collective responsibility. It contains key pieces that have influenced environmental thinking, including extracts from *Silent Spring* by Rachel Carson, and Garrett Hardin's essay on the tragedy of the commons.

Robbins, P., Hintz, J. and Moore, S.A. (2014) *Environment and Society: A Critical Introduction,* 2nd edition, Wiley-Blackwell, London. An accessible introduction to the relationship between society and environmental challenges, usefully illustrated with a broad range of examples.

Stibbe, A. (ed.) (2009) *The Handbook of Sustainability Literacy: Skills for a Changing World,* Green Books, Dartington, Devon. A book of essays on the skills and values 'necessary for surviving and thriving in the declining conditions of the world in ways that slow down that decline as far as possible.'

Uekötter, F. (2014) *The Greenest Nation? A New History of German Environmentalism,* MIT Press, London. A concise and revealing history of the environmental movement in Germany.

Wapner, P. (2010) *Living Through the End of Nature: The Future of American Environmentalism,* MIT Press, London. This book explores the tension between environmentalism and nature, and explores the future of environmentalism.

Useful websites

www.climatecrisis.net   Provides additional information, science and 'take action' suggestions for Al Gore's film *An Inconvenient Truth* about climate change.

www.ipcc.ch   Provides information from the Intergovernmental Panel on Climate Change on the science of climate change and future change scenarios.

www.lowimpact.org   Low Impact Living Initiative. A non-profit organization whose mission is to help people reduce their impact on the environment, improve their quality of life, gain new skills, live in a healthier and more satisfying way, have fun and save money.

www.wilderness.org.au   The Wilderness Society Australia. Contains information on old-growth logging in Australia and the wide variety of other environmental campaigns with which this Australian environmental advocacy organization is involved.

www.foe.co.uk   Friends of the Earth is an international environmental organization which campaigns for action on climate change, food and biodiversity.

www.unep.org/geo   United Nations Environment Programme website, including links to their latest publications on the state of the environment and trends at regional and global scale, the *Global Environmental Outlook (GEO)* reports.

http://old.quaker.org.uk/extras/climateimpact/index.html Carbon Calculator: enables you to estimate your carbon footprint. This one is handy if you don't have figures from household energy bills; it lets you estimate based on the size of your house and how many people live in it. It also shows you results as you go along, so you can see very easily how making changes to your lifestyle will affect your footprint.

www.resurgence.org/education/carbon-calculator.html Another carbon calculator. This one is quite detailed and you will need information from energy bills to calculate your carbon emissions from home energy use, which should give an accurate figure.

FOOD SECURITY

Chapter 7

Bill Pritchard

Topics covered

- Famines
- Undernourishment
- Entitlements
- Green revolution
- Genetically modified foods and world hunger
- Food-aid dependency
- The Right to Food

Starvation is the characteristic of some people not having enough food to eat. It is not the characteristic of there being not enough food to eat. While the latter can be a cause of the former, it is but one of many possible causes.

(Opening words to Amartya Sen's *Poverty and Famines: An Essay on Entitlement and Deprivation*, 1981)

7.1 Introduction

Food security' is a term that is used in many different ways. The purpose of this chapter is to discuss this concept in a manner that is consistent with its usage at the international level by entities such as the UN Food and Agriculture Organization. We begin by placing contemporary debates about food security into an historical perspective.

7.2 Hunger in human history

Widespread hunger has stalked humankind perennially. Although this threat might seem far removed from the quotidian concerns of most people living in the global North during the early twenty-first century, the challenge to feed and sustain the human population has been a pre-eminent social, political and economic struggle across history, and remains central to the planet's circumstances today.

In Western Europe, battles over food and hunger were seminal to the cycles of political evolution and revolution which forged nation states. Rousseau's apocryphal description of a French princess (not Marie Antoinette, as commonly attributed) asking why the peasants would prefer bread to cake ['*Qu'ils mangent de la brioche!*' ('popularly translated as 'Let them eat cake!')] is a testament to the symbolic and material power of food in political and social life. Throughout the period right up until the twentieth century, periodic civil strife over food was a defining element of European life. In the British Isles, there was ongoing hunger and malnourishment for the working and agrarian classes throughout the onset of the industrial period, which erupted episodically into food riots, such as those affecting England and Wales in 1772–73. During the nineteenth century, a key element in the debate over the passage of the Corn Laws (which allowed cheaper, imported food into Britain) was the need to feed (and, thus, politically placate) the fast-growing urban working class. All the time, however, the threat of widespread hunger was ever-present. In Ireland, as is well known, the collapse in potato production because of *phytophthora infestans* (potato blight) instigated famine conditions over the period 1845–52. Perhaps less well known, similar conditions also afflicted the Scottish Highlands over this same period, with a level of death and out-migration which was of almost equal magnitude to the Irish famine.

As European peoples spread across the world, these challenges travelled with them. The American tradition of Thanksgiving traces its origins to the near-starvation of the Pilgrim settlers in 1620–21. Following a successful harvest that kept the settlers alive, a Thanksgiving feast was held. Comparably, in Australia, the First Fleet settlers of 1788 faced imminent starvation within two years of arrival due to the expiration of their rations and farming failures.

Amongst European peoples worldwide, the politics of hunger continued to hold important sway right up until the end of the Second World War, often associated with interruptions to seasonal harvests brought on by climate or war. Thus, in 1815 when the far-distant Tambora volcano erupted in the Dutch East Indies (now Indonesia) and sent a shower of ash into the upper atmosphere, a resultant global cooling of temperatures decimated food harvests in the northern hemisphere the following summer, creating a hunger crisis in cities on America's Atlantic seaboard. The author Simon Winchester describes this event as 'the last great subsistence crisis of the Western world' (2003: 295). Food insecurity remained a present threat in urban America through the nineteenth century, including New York's 'bread riots' in 1837, and food riots in many cities during the Civil War (1861–65). In Europe, the wars of the nineteenth and twentieth centuries were often accompanied by food shortages and hunger. Perhaps the last ever full-scale famine in Western Europe occurred in 1944–45 in the western Netherlands, when Dutch resistance to Nazi rule caused disruptions to food transports and an estimated 18,000 people died of hunger (van der Zee 1982). More recently (though perhaps less dramatically), the end of the Cold War saw heightened food insecurity in the former Soviet Union over several years as its economic system restructured to the logics of capitalism. Yet for all the importance of hunger within the record of Western civilization, non-European populations have been the overwhelming bearers of hunger across human history. An East India Company trader visiting (what is now known as) the state of Gujarat in India during the great famine of 1630–32 recorded that: 'from Suratt [sic] to this place [Agra] our noses were never free of the stinck [sic] of corpses' and 'the [roads] were so full of dead bodyes [sic] that we could hardlie [sic] pass them without treading on or going over some' (cited in Keay 1993: 115). The strengthening of British colonial rule in ensuing centuries exacerbated hunger vulnerabilities. Local politico-administrative systems were recomposed to fit within colonial logics, which had as their core the extraction of profit to service the Empire. A series of famines in India during the nineteenth century saw the deaths of an estimated 30–40 million people. The last major famine under British rule occurred in Bengal, in 1942–43, when a combination of war-induced decisions to restrict the transportation of rice and cyclonic devastation resulted in the starvation deaths of between 1.5 million and 4 million persons (see Case study 7.1).

Case study 7.1

The Bengal famine of 1942–43

Estimates of deaths from the 1942–43 Bengal famine remain disputed. The Famine Commission set up by the British authorities reported 1.5 million deaths. Amartya Sen has suggested the death toll was closer to 3 million, and some other Indian sources suggest it was higher still. Ó Gráda (2007: 19) adopts

a 'mid-range' estimate of 2.1 million deaths. For the Famine Commission estimate, see p. 68 in Weigold, A. (1999) Famine management: the Bengal famine (1942–44) revisited, *South Asia,* 22(1), 63–77. For Amartya Sen's discussion of the death toll, see p. 52 in Sen, A. (1981) *Poverty and Famines: An Essay on Entitlement and Deprivation,* Oxford University Press, Oxford.

Histories of China, other parts of Asia and Africa reap a similar story. In Ethiopia, for example, widespread crop failures and the related onset of hunger occurred with regularity once or twice a decade from recorded history many centuries ago until 1984–85, when a severe famine impelled global action. The United Nations defines a famine as occurring when three conditions are met: (1) at least 20 per cent of the population has fewer than 2,100 calories of food a day; (2) the prevalence of acute malnutrition exceeds 30 per cent of children; and (3) the death rate exceeds two deaths per 10,000 people, or four child deaths per 10,000 people per day. The arrival of these conditions in Ethiopia in 1984–85 provided the impetus for a major charitable intervention in the West through the 'Live Aid/Band Aid' initiative, and brought images of famine to many Western eyes for the first time. The economic historian Cormac Ó Gráda (2007: 5–6) observes that 'By the 1990s, famine-induced deaths were confined to poverty-stricken and often war-torn pockets of the globe'. At the time of writing, the most recent episodes of famine were in Somalia (2011–12) and West Africa (2012). In both cases, war and civil unrest were centrally implicated within the onset of famine conditions.

7.3 The present scale and geography of global hunger

Notwithstanding this receding of large-scale repeat famine cycles, chronic hunger remains at unacceptable levels across the world, and almost everywhere, exists side-by-side with a worsening incidence of overweight and obese populations. Many countries are now confronted with a double-burden of malnutrition, having to deal simultaneously with problems of hunger within some segments of their population and overweight/obesity in others. However, focusing on undernutrition and hunger, a key turning point in this recent history was 2008, when there was a confluence of rapidly rising prices for food (Figure 7.1) and energy (see Chapter 5). These trends sparked a dramatic increase in global hunger. In 2008, it was estimated (although see Spotlight box 7.1) that the number of people living in chronic undernourishment was estimated to have exceeded one billion people. Subsequent revisions to official data suggest that the spike in undernourishment was not as severe as

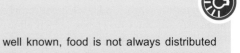

Spotlight box 7.1

How many hungry people are there in the world?

The FAO estimates that in 2014 there were 791 million undernourished people on the planet. In all probability, however, this is a lower bound estimate of global hunger. The methodology by which these data are collected (via national household surveys and modelling the effects of changes in incomes and food prices) tends to assume that if a household has the capability to acquire enough food to meet the daily minimum energy requirements of its members, then no-one in that household is hungry.

But, as is well known, food is not always distributed equitably within households (in many societies there is a prevalence of men being fed first and women often going hungry). Also, just because a household *can* feed itself doesn't mean it *does* feed itself; in many households across the globe, money that should be used for food is used for alcohol, drugs and gambling, for instance. Indeed, one of the world's leading food researchers, Per Pinstrup-Andersen, cites an estimate of two billion iron deficient people on the planet as evidence to suggest that global hunger is far greater than official estimates suggest (Pinstrup-Andersen 2009: 6).

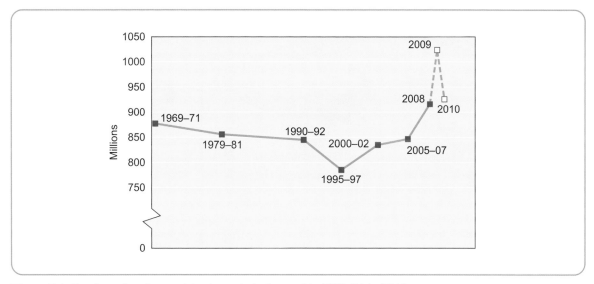

Figure 7.1 Number of undernourished people in the world, 1969–71 to 2010.

Source: adapted from FAO (2010) *State of Food Insecurity*, p. 9

originally thought (Pritchard and Choithani 2014) (Figure 7.1), however increased food prices triggered food riots across 60 countries, which saw at least one government (in Haiti) fall (Plate 7.1). Significantly, the events of 2008 arguably constituted the first-ever *global* food crisis. Because of the highly integrated international character of contemporary food commodity markets, ripple effects from one country to the next occurred in a rapid and coordinated fashion. With hunger a matter of global political and economic concern, international policy makers were shaken from their complacent assumptions about the world community 'winning the war' on undernutrition. Although the global number of

persons who are undernourished has fallen since 2008, it is still at an unacceptable level, and progress remains at the mercy of economic volatility and the limitations of our planetary resources.

Furthermore, global hunger is dispersed across the world in a highly uneven way, with 40 per cent of the world's undernourished people living in China and India. A further four countries (Bangladesh, Pakistan, Democratic Republic of the Congo, and Indonesia) account for a further 26 per cent (FAO 2010: 10). Moreover, with the exception of China, all of these countries failed to meet the Millennium Development Goal (MDG) for reducing hunger (see Figure 7.2 and Case study 8.1). The MDG for

Plate 7.1 Protests over food prices in Haiti in 2008.

(Eduardo Munoz/Reuters)

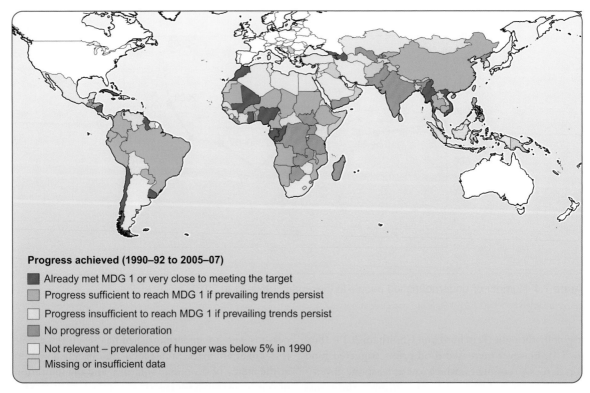

Progress achieved (1990–92 to 2005–07)

- ◼ Already met MDG 1 or very close to meeting the target
- ◻ Progress sufficient to reach MDG 1 if prevailing trends persist
- ◻ Progress insufficient to reach MDG 1 if prevailing trends persist
- ◼ No progress or deterioration
- ◻ Not relevant – prevalence of hunger was below 5% in 1990
- ◻ Missing or insufficient data

Figure 7.2 Progress towards Millennium Development Goal 1: hunger target.

Source: www.fao.org/fileadmin/templates/es/Hunger_Portal/MDG_Progress_Map.pdf

hunger aims to reduce by half (between 1990 and 2015) the proportion of people in the world suffering from hunger – measured statistically as (i) the prevalence of under-weight children under 5 years of age, and (ii) the proportion of the population below minimum dietary energy consumption. Clearly, this map paints a depressing picture of global food security; many of the world's countries with the highest rates of food insecurity are also those currently displaying worst progress in generating improvements to these situations. Moreover, it needs remembering that hunger and undernourishment also exist in the developed world. The recent global recession has exacerbated the extent of hunger: in 2008, 14.6 per cent of the US population was food insecure at some point in the year, including 5.7 per cent with 'very low food security', meaning 'that the food intake of one or more household members was reduced and their eating patterns were disrupted at times during the year because the household lacked money and other resources for food' (Nord *et al.* 2009: 1). Five years later, in 2013, these statistics remained unmoved, despite the considerable gains of the US economy since 2008 (Coleman-Jensen *et al.* 2013).

The rapid changes in the incidence of global undernourishment in recent years have triggered renewed debate amongst researchers and policy makers on the causes and manifestations of hunger. Central to these current debates is the newly articulated concept of **food security**. To a large degree, this concept has become the foundation stone for contemporary strategic interventions of international organizations (such as the FAO) and **non-governmental organizations (NGOs)** (such as Oxfam, ActionAid and Red Cross/Red Crescent). In the following section, the concept of food security is defined, and afterwards, its application to key issues relating to global hunger is discussed.

7.4 Defining food security

Until the mid-1990s, the prevailing perspective in international debates on food and hunger tended to prioritize production-centric explanations with the emphasis on maintaining food stocks in the context of an unpredictable world. Hence, in the case of the Irish famine of 1845–52, cited earlier, famine was seen to be caused by the unexpected threat of potato blight. In Ethiopia or the Indian subcontinent, famine vulnerability was tied to the unpredictability of the monsoon. Clearly, the implicit suggestion within these explanations was that such problems were premised on catastrophic and unavoidable circumstances – 'acts of God', as an insurance policy might say. Hence, in 1974, the World Food Conference defined food security as: 'Availability at all times of adequate world food supplies of basic foodstuffs to sustain a steady expansion of food consumption and to offset fluctuations in production and prices' (cited in FAO 2006: 1).

Fundamental aspects of this perspective remain important within present thinking. Rarely, if ever, are rapid descents into widespread hunger *not* associated with a food production shock of some kind (climatic, environmental, biological or human-induced, e.g. war). Such cataclysms obviously impact on people's abilities to feed themselves and, from a policy perspective, require an immediate response in the form of food aid. Nevertheless, since the mid-1990s there has been an increasing recognition of the need to build more sophisticated conceptual understandings of what causes hunger. Instead of seeing particular biological, climatic or environmental contexts as catastrophic events that define these problems, the emergent approach is to understand food production shocks as *triggers* that reverberate (in socially uneven ways) through populations. This approach refocuses the attention of researchers and policy makers to the broader systems that connect people to the food system. This perspective goes under the banner of the food security approach.

The chief and most influential proponent of such an altered perspective has been Amartya Sen, an Indian economist and philosopher. Sen was awarded the Nobel Prize in Economics in 1998 for a body of work that included landmark analyses of the causes of famine. Sen addressed the causes of hunger and famine from a radically different set of premises from that which prevailed in mainstream thinking. He saw that famines in different circumstances worldwide each could be understood as having a common socio-politico-economic themes. Whereas dominant contemporary explanations about these episodes looked to a fall in food production as the root causes of hunger, Sen documented a more complex reality. Hence in the Irish famine, the potato crop failed but Ireland remained a large exporter of foodstuffs across to England. In Ethiopia in the famine of 1972–73, food was trucked from famine areas to the capital of Addis Ababa. The great Bengal famines of 1942–43 and 1972–73 were associated with 'moderate' falls in production being translated into severe market shortfalls due to hoarding, speculation and 'administrative chaos' (Sen 1981: 76). Extending this further, Sen's approach asked why some 'poor years' of agricultural production produced widespread hunger or famine, whilst others did not. Clearly, other factors came into play. China's disastrous 'Great Leap Forward' of 1957 caused famine not just because of crop failures, but also through ill-conceived central state planning. Famine in Cambodia during the late

1970s was instigated by the brutal maladministration of the militaristic Khmer Rouge. The 1984–85 famine in Ethiopia was associated not only with drought, but in a context where the national government diverted a massive share of scarce national resources to the military. Famine in North Korea in 1998 was associated with crop failures in the context of an autocratic regime that prioritized national security and protection of the interests of the elite class.

From this analysis, Sen proposed the concept of **entitlements** as a way of understanding hunger. This concept sought to explain hunger and famine by way of asking questions about the social, cultural and economic frameworks that bestowed rights to ownership within populations. As Sen contended, even the seemingly straightforward notion of possessing a loaf of bread (and thus forestalling one's hunger) assumes a chain of entitlement relations:

> I own this loaf of bread. Why is this ownership accepted? Because I got it by exchange through paying some money I owned. Why is my ownership of that money accepted? Because I got it by selling a bamboo umbrella owned by me. Why is my ownership of the bamboo umbrella accepted? Because I made it with my own labour using some bamboo from my land. Why is my ownership of the land accepted? Because I inherited it from my father. Why is his ownership of that land accepted? And so on. Each link in this chain of entitlement relations 'legitimizes' one set of ownership by reference to another, or to some basic entitlement in the form of enjoying the fruits of one's own labour.
>
> (Sen 1981: 1–2)

Thus, in Sen's writings on this subject, he asserted that the ability of a person to avoid starvation depended on her/his entitlements, which, in turn, was constructed from her/his *ownership bundle* (the combination of labour powers, resources and assets s/he can use to acquire food) and the *exchange entitlement regime* s/he faced (the rights to resources s/he can access to transfer an ownership bundle into food). Or, in slightly more simplified language: 'Entitlements are defined as the set of all commodity bundles over which a person can establish command given the legal, political, economic and social arrangements of the community in which they live (including traditional rights such as access to common resources)' (FAO 2006: 1). Applying this framework to Ireland in 1845–52, Sen contended that famine was caused because the pre-eminent asset within the ownership bundle of the rural Irish poor (their control over small plots of land on which to grow potatoes, their staple food) became suddenly worthless with the onset of potato blight, and the population had few other rights over resources that could replace this loss (piecemeal social safety net efforts, such as the workhouse system, were associated with poor management and/or were hotbeds for infectious diseases (Ó Gráda 2007:17)). Hence, although potato blight was the trigger, it was this combination of ownership bundles and exchange entitlements amongst the poor that provided the ultimate cause of the Irish famine.

Sen's work was an important precedent for the ways that policy makers approached these issues at the 1996 World Food Summit (WFS), in Rome. This Summit is popularly credited with launching the concept of food security into mainstream food policy discourse. As defined at the WFS:

Food security exists when all people, at all times, have physical, social and economic access to sufficient, safe and nutritious food that meets their dietary needs and food preferences for an active and healthy life.

(FAO 1996)

Expressed in this way, the concept serves a dual purpose. At one level, it encapsulates a *normative goal*; an aspiration for the world community to attain this outcome for 'all people, at all times'. But also, it represents a *definitional signpost*. The clear focus of the quote above is that 'food security' is defined in terms of the extent to which a food system satisfies individuals' nutritional, livelihood

and social circumstances. Notably, unlike the 1974 World Food Conference definition, cited earlier, this does not equate 'food security' with maximizing food production, or having large stocks of food in reserve. These supply-side factors are obviously important, but the over-riding message in this definition is that the attainment of food security is primarily about the social, economic, cultural and political circumstances that either enable or restrict the provisioning of food to needy populations. Thus, the WFS definition of food security can be seen as a political enactment of Sen's notion of entitlements. Ultimately, what is important for addressing hunger is *not only* the ability to produce food, but a social-political-economic regime that enables people in need to gain that food.

In order to give this definition operational relevance, however, it needed elaboration. Accordingly, in the immediate years after the 1996 WFS, an FAO Working Group developed a framework for understanding the processes that created particular patterns of food security/insecurity. This framework – which is shown diagrammatically in Figure 7.3 – conceives food security as being an outcome from three dimensions of the food system:

● *Availability:* The supply-side factors that shape the availability of sufficient quantities of food of appropriate quality.

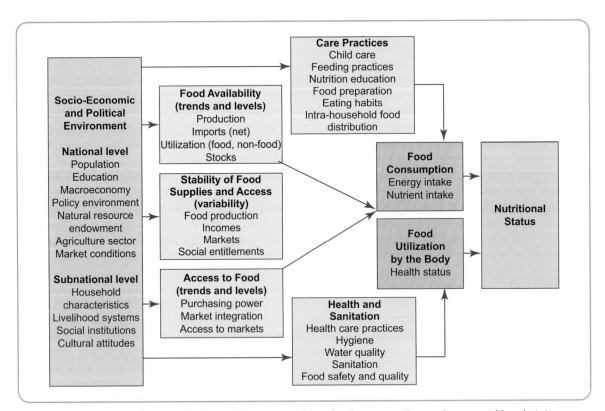

Figure 7.3 Conceptual framework of possible causes of low food consumption and poor nutritional status.

Source: adapted from FAO (2008) *Climate Change and Food Security: A Framework Document*, p. 4

- *Access:* The political, social, cultural and economic processes that connect supply-side processes to individuals.
- *Utilization:* The elements of clean water, sanitation and health care that ensure that food that is made available and is accessible (i.e. the two categories above) generates nutritional well-being for consumers.

Reflecting the importance of these three dimensions within contemporary debates on food security, the remainder of this chapter uses this framework as an organizing device to bring into focus a series of issues relating to food security in the contemporary world. We focus on the first two categories – availability and access – because the third relates primarily to nutrition and dietary science and, as such, is somewhat outside the scope of the current chapter.

7.5 Food availability

As noted above, the concept of food availability refers to the overall capacity of the planet to produce enough food to eliminate hunger. (Whether that food gets to the hungry, of course, is another matter – to be discussed in Section 7.6). By-and-large, the past century has witnessed unparalleled progress in this regard. Increases in the quantum of food being produced on the planet dramatically exceeded population growth, so that, during the twentieth century, food became cheaper. Figure 7.4

illustrates this trend. (The international wheat price is a good indicator of overall food prices.)

A myriad of factors were behind these production gains: more land put to agricultural use, improvements in water infrastructure and technologies; developments in post-harvest technologies and storage facilities; increased capitalization and economies of scale in farming (allowing machinery such as tractors and combine harvesters to be employed); innovations in livestock breeding and husbandry; and intensive protein production (fish, poultry and pork, in particular). However, two key factors stood out. The first was in the early decades of the twentieth century, when developments in plant genetics converged with the invention of synthetic, nitrogen-based fertilizers to enable agribusiness firms to match particular seed varieties with specific chemical inputs (see Goodman and Redclift 1991: 95–100 and Pritchard 1998: 66). These innovations generated profound boosts to agricultural productivity, especially in the 'new world' agricultural heartlands of the USA, Canada, Argentina and Australia. The second key shift occurred in the 1960s and 1970s, with the development of **green revolution** varieties of staple cereal crops, notably, rice and wheat (see Case study 7.2). Notwithstanding ongoing controversy about the social and environmental impacts of the green revolution, discussed in Case study 7.2, with the passage of time its legacy remains indisputable. It provided a boost to world food output precisely at a time when the global population was increasing very rapidly, thus forestalling worst-case eventualities of potential famine and undernourishment.

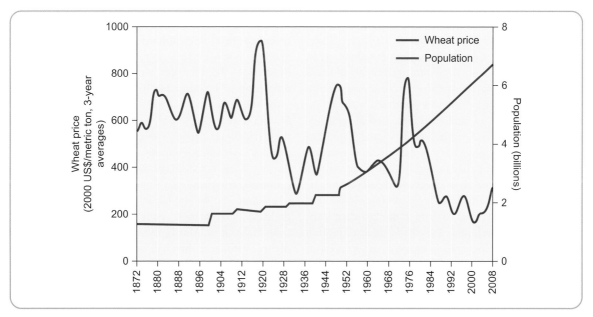

Figure 7.4 Wheat prices and population 1872–2008.

Source: adapted from Von Braun (2008) *Food and Financial Crises: Implications for Agriculture and the Poor,* p. 2

Case study 7.2

The green revolution

The start of the 'green revolution' is generally traced to the plant-breeding research of Norman Borlaug in Mexico, commencing in the late 1940s. By the early 1960s, Borlaug and his colleagues had developed and globally distributed a series of high-yield 'dwarf wheat' varieties with dramatically increased potentials. Also around this time, a series of parallel developments in rice research (undertaken mainly in the Philippines) saw new high-yield varieties developed. These innovations became the centrepieces for major international development assistance efforts during the 1960s and 1970s. Proponents argued that because of their undeniable capacities to boost global cereals production, they held the keys to eliminating world hunger. Additionally, these agendas enmeshed with the Cold War politics of the time – by assisting the rural poor, it

was argued, Communist sympathies would be muted. Thus, as one historian has contended: 'American plant-breeding science thus became part of the Cold War's defence of capitalist political economies' (Perkins 1997: 239). However, there were (and remain) many dissenting voices about the social and environmental implications of green revolution interventions. It put many rural societies onto a pathway of increasing inequality, because richer farmers were best able to exploit these technologies and, once they had captured the benefits, used the returns to buy more land (Atkins and Bowler 2001: 221). Ecologically, green revolution varieties were associated with increased pesticide use (often in poorly regulated contexts – thus leading to health and environmental problems), intensified water extraction and the replacement of multi- for mono-cropped agricultural systems, thus reducing local agro-biodiversity (see Shiva 1991).

Yet in meeting this challenge, new questions have been opened about 'what kind of food system' the world has created. During the last decade, in particular, the ethical basis of food production (in terms of animal welfare, social issues and environmental sustainability) has come under intensified scrutiny. Many have asserted that technology has bolstered global food production, but at what cost? The intensification of protein production systems has been associated with factory farm regimes that raise questions about animal rights and welfare. Renowned philosophers, such as Peter Singer, contend that there has been a moral vacuum at the heart of agendas to optimize global food production (see Singer 2009). Moreover, the boost to global agricultural production has occurred hand-in-hand with increased dependence on international food trade (see Fold and Pritchard 2005), raising questions about the labour standards and livelihood conditions that underpin global agriculture and food production. These concerns include such matters as low wages, hazardous working conditions (food workers are often exposed to dangerous agro-chemicals, especially in the developing world) and the exploitation of smallholder producers by commodity traders. Ensuing public debates have given rise to an expansion of fair trade initiatives, corporate social responsibility agendas, and various types of codes of conduct; however, legitimate questions still remain about the social ethics of the global food system.

Perhaps the harshest criticisms of the contemporary global food system, however, relate to its impacts on the environment. There is now heightened appreciation across the world that food production systems cannot be assessed independently from environmental systems – a perspective known as the food–water–environment Nexus approach. The huge boost to global agricultural production in the twentieth century depended on a massive injection of energy inputs into agriculture, with little regard to the ecological limits of natural resources (see Spotlight box 6.1). Thus, in the Indian State of Punjab – the nation's breadbasket and a key site for the green revolution – the demands from water-thirsty farming systems is seeing the water table fall at an average rate of 55 cm per year (Aggarwal et al. 2009). This issue shows the inevitable connections between food, water and energy security. Unless new solutions are proffered, the ability of Punjab's farmers to feed the nation will be seriously compromised, and thus India's poor record on food security (see Figure 7.2) will be harmed further. The problem of ecological limits is more severe still, however, with regards to animal protein. Marine fish stocks appear to be in rapid decline, with more than half of the world's catch coming from less than 7 per cent of the oceans, 'in areas characterized by an increasing amount of habitat damage from bottom trawling, pollution and dead zones, invasive species infestations and vulnerability to climate change' (Nelleman et al. 2009: 23). If the world's population is to continue to eat seafood at its current rate, consumption will need to be sourced increasingly from aquaculture. But the rub, here, is that aquaculture systems are more resource-intensive than marine capture, because they depend on fish being fed from manufactured foodstuffs. Hence, it seems that the only viable way to sustain the global appetite for seafood is to push production into more energy- and resource-intensive (i.e. unsustainable) ways. Comparable arguments can also be made with regards to meat production (see Spotlight box 7.2 and Case study 6.4).

So does the continued operation of the current global food system imply that to feed the world's population in the twenty-first century, the only option is to further degrade the global environment? As the journal *Nature* editorialized in 2010, the challenge of feeding the world was easy . . . 'Easy, that is, if the world brings into play swathes of extra land, spreads still more fertilizers and pesticides, and further depletes already scarce groundwater supplies' (*Nature* 2010: 531). According to many, a key element in resolving the Hobson's choice of food versus the environment is to embrace genetically modified foods (GMFs). In this chapter we cannot do justice to the debate on GMFs, which is complex and multi-faceted. However, in terms of the debate on food security, it can briefly be observed that advocacy of genetic modification needs to tackle the same kind of charges that confronted the green revolution; namely, it intensifies the high input–high output technological treadmill of farming, with potentially highly uneven social impacts (richer farmers are, in general, better placed than smallholders to

access genetically modified materials). Thus, whilst **genetic modification** may assist farmers to generate higher yields and/or enable lower pesticide use, its wider social and environmental implications remain an ongoing matter of contention.

In the early twenty-first century, sub-Saharan Africa is the cradle for debate on what role genetic modification could and should play in agricultural development. By and large, the green revolution of the 1960s and 1970s exerted relatively little influence on sub-Saharan African agriculture, because the key hybrid seed varieties were developed and trialled in Asia. Thus, in 2006, an agreement to fund a coordinated plan to develop a 'uniquely African' green revolution was established, under the name the Alliance for a Green Revolution in Africa (AGRA). The founding donors for AGRA were the Rockefeller Foundation and the Bill & Melinda Gates Foundation, with partnership support from a wide range of international development and agricultural research organizations. AGRA affirms that it has learnt from mistakes of the original green revolution, and professes to implement initiatives that assist the interests of smallholders (as opposed to large farms), but some NGOs have been critical of its activities (see Spotlight box 7.3). At the time of writing, AGRA says it 'is not funding the development of new varieties through the use of genetic engineering' (AGRA 2010); however, this does not preclude future involvement in these activities, 'when it is the most appropriate tool to address an important need of small-scale farmers and when it is consistent with government policy'.

Spotlight box 7.2

Meat and the environment

Increased consumption of meat is a central feature of the current global food system. As populations within developing countries become wealthier, their consumption of meat tends to rise dramatically. Researchers worldwide agree that the effects on the global environment of this consumption are overwhelmingly negative: '[T]he livestock sector is by far the single largest anthropogenic user of land. The total area occupied by grazing is equivalent to 26 per cent of the ice-free terrestrial surface of the planet. In addition, the total area dedicated to feedcrop production [i.e. crops grown to feed animals for meat production] amounts to 33 per cent of total arable land' (Steinfeld *et al.* 2006: xxi). Hence, the expansion of grazing lands for meat production (and the additional

land used for feedcrops that go into meat production) is a key factor driving global deforestation and reduced biodiversity. Further to these points, the feeding of crops to animals for meat production represents a diversion of output away from humans. On average, it takes 3 kg of grain to produce 1 kg of meat. It is estimated that if global per capita meat consumption could be stabilized at year 2000 levels, then by the year 2050 an extra 400 million tonnes of cereal would be available for human consumption: 'enough to cover the annual calorie need for 1.2 billion people' (Nelleman *et al.* 2009: 26–7). Even if it is unlikely that the world will move to a wholly vegetarian diet, there are many initiatives to reduce per capita meat consumption in different countries, such as the 'meat-free Monday' campaigns in Western countries. See also Jarosz (2009) and D'Silva and Webster (2010).

Spotlight box 7.3

The Alliance for a Green Revolution in Africa (AGRA)

The NGO ActionAid (2009) has published a broad critique of AGRA. It argues that: (i) too much faith is placed on technological solutions, rather than seeking to establish conducive and stable political, economic and social frameworks to underpin these investments; (ii) the program's enthusiasm for private sector-led solutions blinds it to the potential for smallholders to become dependent on technologies and seeds owned by large corporate interests; (iii) 'large private consulting firms' have played too great a role in project developments, rather

than African governments; (iv) not enough attention has been placed on smallholders' 'access to land, water, infrastructure, information and credit' (p. 12). In sum, ActionAid advocate a food sovereignty approach, which suggests that the best livelihood course for smallholders is to extract themselves from the potentially exploitative effects of involvement in the global economy. The NGO contends that the 'overall goal [of a restructured AGRA] should be to reverse the current dependence on global agricultural technological and commodity markets, which submerge local knowledge and technologies and deepen the extraction of farming surpluses (through the unfair pricing of food and inputs)' (p. 22).

7.6 Food access

The debates discussed above frame the question of whether there is global capacity to feed the world's population. However, for food production to actually reach the mouths of the needy requires a further set of considerations to come into view. As the scientific journal *Nature* (2010: 532) acknowledges: 'Nor are science and technology by themselves a panacea for world hunger. Poverty, not lack of food production, is the root cause'. This set of issues – which invoke the concept of *food access* – raises questions about the entitlement mechanisms that connect people with food.

In a general sense, people gain access to food in three ways. First, people can grow or procure their own food directly, either by cultivating crops, tending livestock or by hunting, fishing or foraging. Of course, for most of human history this has been the dominant food access regime for most people on the planet. Even today, a very large proportion of the world's population relies heavily on such mechanisms to ensure their day-to-day survival. Second, people can buy food through the use of money. (This is akin to Amartya Sen's example of the umbrella seller, quoted above.) Most of the readers of this book, one would imagine, obtain the vast majority (if not all) of their food through this method. Third, people can gain access to food through disbursement programs (such as food banks, food aid and food voucher welfare programs) operated by governments, international organizations (such as the UN's Food World Program) or charities/NGOs.

These three general mechanisms of food access do not operate separately to one another. Households across the world have diverse, multi-dimensional modes of food

access. The food security of a household in a coastal village of India might depend on fish being caught daily by one household member, fruits and vegetables to be bought at a local market using the cash income earned by another household member, and rice and cooking oil being acquired at a public distribution outlet operated as part of a government food program.

Comparably, in the developed world, self-sufficient production and food disbursement programs play an important (indeed, possibly increasing) role for many households. Urban agriculture schemes based around community gardens and individual allotments have grown steadily during the past decade, and media reports have suggested that this trend has accelerated since the onset of economic recession in 2008 (Plate 7.2). The symbolic development of a kitchen garden on the White House lawn by first lady Michelle Obama in 2009 tapped

Plate 7.2 A community garden/urban agricultural allotment.

(littleny/Shutterstock)

this zeitgeist. Likewise, the recession has also spawned increased demand for emergency food disbursements, across both sides of the Atlantic. In part, these efforts have been entwined also within the ethics of the food rescue movement, whereby excess and unused food from shops, restaurants and other facilities are acquired and redistributed to the needy – thus generating a double-benefit addressing both the environment and hunger.

Focusing on the developing world (where these issues tend to have more pressing livelihood implications), two vital debates are pertinent to contemporary discussions of how food access arrangements impact on food security outcomes. The first relates to the future of small farms; whether food security for the rural poor in developing countries is ultimately best served by seeking to maintain smallholder, self-sufficient production. The second relates to national food policies; the extent and character of governments' interventions in food markets to secure food security for the poor (a debate about food security via disbursements).

7.6.1 Food access via self-production or the market? Debate on the future of small farms

The future of small farms in the developing world is currently a topic of major discussion. In essence, what is at stake is the question of what works best for hungry people: a food entitlement regime based on people growing their own food, or one in which they buy food at local markets, shops and supermarkets.

The economist Paul Collier kick-started the most recent instalment of this debate with an influential article published in the journal *Foreign Affairs*, in the midst of the 2008 food crisis. Collier's chief charge was that 'the world needs more commercial agriculture, not less' (2008: 68), and that '[T]he first giant that must be slain is the middle- and upper-class love affair with peasant agriculture' (2008: 71). Collier asserted that foreign aid projects and 'rural-friendly' international financial programs from the West were inspired by a wrong-headed, allegedly 'romantic' attachment to support small-scale agriculture. In Collier's vision, food security is best attained by encouraging small farmers to abandon their plots of land, and then to aggregate those holdings into large-scale farms. Former peasants could then work on those farms, or move to cities where incomes are generally higher (see UNDP 2009). In 2009, the World Bank's *World Development Report* chimed in to support key aspects of this argument, arguing that the welfare of the world's hungry and poor would be best served by policies that encouraged the movement of people from rural to urban areas (a so-called 'three D's' strategy: encouraging population *density* (i.e. population growth in cities), *distance* (encouraging people to be mobile, in search of jobs) and *division* (removing barriers like tariffs and some restrictions on migration that inhibit the flow of goods and people)). The assumption of these visions is that (i) large-scale agriculture enables food to be produced at lower costs, and (ii) the higher wages paid in cities places more money in the pockets of the poor; a tandem process that generates quantum improvements in food security.

Yet many researchers question the assumptions that lie behind these visions. Encouraging rural smallholders to divest their land and move to cities makes sense only if countries are at a stage of development where sufficient numbers of city-based jobs are available. If this isn't the case, rural migrants add to the ranks of squatter-settlements with highly insecure food and economic prospects. A more reasonable approach, according to a number of leading geographers (see Wiggins *et al.* 2010) is to establish more gradualist, 'multi-track' strategies of rural poverty-reduction. According to the proponents of these views, smallholders' control over land has foundational importance in allowing own-production for basic sustenance. Hence, food security strategies should aim to bolster the livelihoods of the poor through constructing viable rural economies, rather than advocating abandonment of rural settlements for an uncertain urban life (see Case study 7.3). It should also be noted that smallholder-based agriculture is generally more climate-friendly, in that it is associated with lesser comparative greenhouse gas emissions than large-scale intensive agriculture (IAASTD 2009).

Case study 7.3

Small rural farms and food security

In many parts of the developing world, the majority of the food insecure population live in rural areas (FAO 2005: 5). Many of these people exist on small plots of land that are sub-economic (that is, on their own, they can't produce enough food or income to sustain a household). Thus, many agricultural smallholders in the developing world suffer chronic hunger, despite having the ability to grow their food. A good summary of the debate about the future of these populations can be found in a special issue of the journal *World Development* dedicated to this problem (Wiggins *et al.* 2010).

7.6.2 Food aid and provisioning programs

In many developing country contexts, food aid and food provisioning schemes provide important complements to peoples' access to food via own-production or the market. Usually this involves food programs (operated by national governments or international agencies, for example the World Food Program) warehousing and distributing major food staples (rice, wheat, etc.) to populations in need.

Such disbursements are crucial in preventing starvation deaths in times of crisis, but, long-term, have been criticized because of the potentially adverse implications of creating cycles of food-aid dependency. The crux of this criticism is the alleged *displacement effects* of food aid. This arises in contexts where the food security of rural populations is dependent upon the sale of agricultural outputs to cities and towns. In such cases, periodic large disbursements of food aid can swamp local markets, thus driving down prices and taking away the incomes of farmers who rely on market sales. Closely related to these criticisms is the charge that food aid disbursements can often be *donor-driven* (meaning that they serve the interests of the senders, not the recipients). For example, the decision by the US government to heavily subsidize its agricultural sector has gone hand-in-hand with policies to procure large amounts of staple food crops for international food aid. As many critics have argued, therefore, US policies to disburse food aid can be seen as strategies that help prop up the incomes of American farmers, as much as they are policies aiming to assist hungry populations. Notwithstanding these criticisms, however, an exhaustive study of these issues by the FAO (2006) concluded that the adversities of food-aid dependence tended to arise mainly when food aid was poorly managed: 'On balance, the report finds that food aid can support food security both in emergencies and in cases of chronic hunger *if it is properly managed*' (p. vii).

In many developing countries, international food aid plays a secondary role to food provisioning policies operated by national governments. India is a case in point. The national government operates the Food Corporation of India (which purchases and stores key food items from farmers) and the Public Distribution System (which distributes food to the poor at highly subsidized prices through a nationwide network of 'Fair Price' shops). In theory, these activities should ensure a basic level of nutritional subsistence to the poor. However, well-documented problems of maladministration and corruption have ensured that these arrangements work less than perfectly (see Programme Evaluation Organisation 2005; Ram *et al.* 2009). Hence, recent years have witnessed a keen public debate in India on how to restructure these schemes to ensure that people in need receive their full food entitlements. Technological innovations will play a key part in future arrangements, with bureaucrats seeking to use smart card and electronic monitoring systems to cut down on system 'leakage'.

Finally, in this regard, is debate over the **right to food**. The above discussion implicitly assumes that the task of getting food to people in need relies on the goodwill of the international community and/or national governments. However, it is increasingly recognized that governments have human rights obligations to feed their citizens. In 1948, the UN Declaration of Human Rights recognized peoples' Right to Food, but this was not clearly incorporated into any international legal framework until 1996 (when the Right to Food was adopted by the World Food Summit) and then 2000, when the UN Commission on Human Rights appointed (for the first time) a Special Rapporteur on the Right to Food (a person with overarching authority to report on international progress on the Right to Food). These initiatives triggered a shift in many countries to a rights-based approach to food, that is, the recognition by governments in many countries that their people had a legal right to be provisioned with food, which could be justiciable (that is, heard in court). Thus, in India in 2013 the national government enacted Food Security legislation that would have the purpose of enshrining people's legal *right* to food.

7.7 Conclusion

The issue of food security is extensive and complex. This chapter has sketched key themes in relation to this concept, but many more have remained outside its purview. For example, a crucial area for ongoing consideration is the question of how food security and climate change connect to one another. During the past few years, there has been widespread discussion of these issues using the notion of *food system stability* and the Nexus approach (see above) – the extent to which food systems are resilient to environmental and social change of various kinds.

The vital message of this chapter is that the *food security* needs to be understood as a social outcome. It exists when all people, at all times, have physical, social and economic access to sufficient, safe and nutritious food. Thus, the concept of food security should not be confused with debates on the technologies to maximize food production, or on whether any country (whether the UK, Japan or Botswana) is reliant on food imports. What matters are the socio-cultural, political, environmental and economic systems that link a food system to a population. To think about food security, thus, is to think about the environmental sustainability and social justice of the planet.

Learning outcomes

Having read this chapter, you should understand that:

- Food security is defined socially. It concerns not simply the amount of food that is produced, but the extent to which a food system is able to satisfy the nutritional requirements of everyone in a population. Therefore, food security research must focus on the three core elements of food access, availability and utilization.

- During the past half century, the world has been able to successfully address problems of famine, but levels of chronic malnutrition remain of major concern. Increases to global food prices since 2007–08 have exacerbated these problems.

- Proposals to increase world food supply through technologies such as genetic modification should be assessed in terms of how they address the needs of the most vulnerable and whose interests they serve.

- A key question in the world today is whether the long-term food security needs of the planet are better served by a shift to large-scale agriculture, or the maintenance of smallholder systems of farm production.

- Food security is a human right, and recent approaches to this issue have stressed peoples' Right to Food.

Further reading

Jarsoz, L. (2009) Energy, climate change, meat and markets: mapping the coordinates of the current world food crisis, *Geography Compass,* 3(6), 2065–83. This article relates to issues considered in Spotlight box 7.2 and other chapters in this section.

FAO (various years) *The State of Food Insecurity,* FAO, Rome. An annual report that provides the most up-to-date assessment of global conditions with regards to food security. Each year, a different aspect of this issue is highlighted in the report.

Shiva, V. (1991) The Green Revolution in the Punjab, *The Ecologist,* 21(2), 57–60. A famous article which provided a critical perspective on the Green Revolution and provided the foundation for alternative viewpoints on technology and agriculture.

Wiggins, S., Kirsten, J. and Llambi, L. (eds) (2010) The future of small farms: special issue, *World Development,* 38(10), 1341–526. Articles in this special issue of *World Development* summarize key aspects of debate around the fate of smallholders in ensuring global food security.

Sen, A. (1981) *Poverty and Famines: An Essay on Entitlement and Deprivation,* Oxford University Press, Oxford. This book changed the way that leading policy makers began to view the issue of food security. It was a major element in justifying Sen's subsequent award of the Nobel Prize for Economics.

Davis, M. (2000) *Late Victorian Holocausts,* Verso, London. This book traces the history of famine back to Colonial times and examines the roles of politics and economics for widespread hunger.

Useful websites

www.fao.org   The Food and Agriculture Organization of the UN. This is the pre-eminent global body charged with responsibility for international coordination of food and agricultural efforts.

www.ifpri.org   The International Food Policy Research Institute (IFPRA) is a policy and research arm of the Consultative Group on International Agricultural Research. It provides extensive information on international food prices and under-nourishment.

www.gatesfoundation.org/Pages/home.aspx   The Bill & Melinda Gates Foundation funds extensive research and extension activities in the areas of food, agriculture and hunger.

www.foodfirst.org   Food First is a US-based Non-Government Organization with a long track record in monitoring global food and hunger.

www.mssrf.org   The M.S. Swaminathan Research Foundation is a leading Indian Non-Government Organization in the area of food policy.

WORLDS APART?
THE CHANGING GEOGRAPHIES
OF GLOBAL DEVELOPMENT

Chapter 8

Marcus Power

Topics covered

■ Development as knowledge and power

■ The view from 'the South' and the view from 'below'

■ Alternative geographies of global development and inequality

■ North–South and South–South development cooperation

■ The 'rising powers' and 'emerging economies' of the global South

Development is one of the most complex words in the English language (Williams 1976) and little consensus exists around the meaning of this heavily contested term, yet many nation-states and international organizations claim to be pursuing this objective in some way and vast sums of money are spent every year in its name. Notoriously hard to define, the term 'development' often refers simply to 'good change', a positive word that in everyday parlance is practically synonymous with 'progress' and is typically viewed in terms of increased living standards, better health and well-being and other forms of common good that are seen to benefit society at large. Development also often simply means 'more': whatever we might have some of today we might or should have more of tomorrow (Wallerstein 1994). In many ways the strength of development as an idea comes from its power to seduce, in every sense of the term: 'to please, to fascinate, to set dreaming but also to abuse, to turn away from the truth, to deceive' (Rist 1997: 1).

A distinction can usefully be made here between 'big D' Development and 'little d' development (Hart 2001). The former refers to a post-Second World War project of intervention in the 'Third World' whilst the latter points to the development of capitalism as a 'geographically uneven, profoundly contradictory set of historical processes' (Hart 2001: 650). D/development can thus be viewed simultaneously as both a project and a process. In other words, development is both a continuous intellectual and ideological project as well as an ongoing material process. Historically the pursuit of 'development' has been focused on particular spaces and regions: most frequently on the space of the 'Third World', which was often seen to be characterized by common features such as poverty, famine, environmental disaster and degradation, political instability, regional inequalities and so on. A particular geography of the 'Third World' has thus been historically imagined around a powerful and negative set of images and a series of tragic stereotypes, along with a bewildering array of labels for people and places that are seen as 'deficient' in some way or that are not considered 'developed' and therefore require external intervention. In many ways this is the power of development: 'the power to transform old worlds, the power to imagine new ones' (Crush 1995: 2).

Development agencies often draw upon statistical indicators to produce certain stories about the peoples and places where they seek to intervene and to narrate the lives and geographies of aid recipients, but what constitutes 'knowledge' in development policy and practice is often defined in relation to quantitative measures, statistical data, formal academic research and Western 'science' and this often helps to reproduce the image of an underdeveloped, primordial, traditional and war-ravaged 'Third World' (Ahluwalia 2001). In other words, these narrations of the disparities between regions are space-producing practices that help to construct and imagine a world in need of development. As Escobar (1995) has argued, the idea of a 'Third World' gives enormous power to Western development institutions to shape popular perceptions of Africa, Asia or Latin America. The 'Third World' is thus partly defined by and becomes intelligible through the languages and representations of the agencies and institutions of global development.

In some ways the lack of an agreed set of international development indicators and measures or of common systems of data collection tells its own story of the failure of international development since 1945 (see Case study 8.1). A major problem with the geographies of development produced from these statistics is that they have allowed some observers to label whole areas as 'Third World' or 'lesser developed' as if the same could be said of all its constituents (Wood 1985). In emphasizing what people are deprived of (as is implied by poverty), statistics impose a negative uniformity upon non-Western societies as poor people are categorized and become objects of study or are labelled in ways that homogenize them, ignoring the complexity of their identities (which are then 'fixed' and reduced by imposing labels such as 'poor' or 'refugee'). Further, labelling whole regions and spaces as 'developed', 'lesser developed' or 'developing' (all of which are value-laden expressions) reduces and overlooks the political, economic, social and cultural *diversity* of the places and communities included within these gross generalizations, simplifications and aggregations.

Thus, the picture of unevenness and injustice in the contemporary world that comes to us through these labels is not always a sharp, coherent and precise one and often this unevenness is not effectively conveyed in the statistical measures that are taken as indices of what constitutes 'development'. Crucial then to the imagination of a world requiring development interventions is a process of setting worlds apart and a politics of labelling. All too often the 'developing world' has been defined as a 'problem' for Western governments that can only be resolved with the intervention of Western 'experts', donors, technology, expertise or ideology (see Case study 8.2). Moving beyond the labelling of 'Third World' peoples and places as a homogeneous group, it is important to grasp how places and peoples are spatially and socially *differentiated* through development and inequality, experiencing progress and 'good change' in a variety of ways.

Behind the tragic stereotype of the 'Third World' there is an alternative geography, one which demonstrates that the introduction of development has been a 'protracted, painstaking and fiercely contested process' (Bell 1994: 175). The chapter also argues that the use of

Case study 8.1

The Millennium Development Goals

One area where a consensus has been established by the international community is around the Millennium Development Goals (MDGs). These are eight international development goals that all 192 United Nations member states and at least 23 international organizations had agreed to achieve by the year 2015, following the Millennium Summit of the United Nations in 2000. They included: (1) eradicating extreme poverty and hunger; (2) achieving universal primary education; (3) promoting gender equality and empowering women; (4) reducing child mortality; (5) improving maternal health; (6) combating HIV/AIDS, malaria and other diseases; (7) ensuring environmental sustainability; and (8) developing a global partnership for development. Together with these eight goals were 21 targets and a series of measurable indicators for each target. There is broad agreement that while the MDGs provided a focal point for governments on which to hinge their policies and overseas aid programmes to end poverty and improve the lives of poor people – as well as provide a rallying point for NGOs to hold them to account – they have been criticized for being too narrow. The eight MDGs failed to consider the root causes of poverty, or gender inequality, or the holistic nature of development. No mention was made of human rights or energy issues, nor did the MDGs specifically address economic development. While the MDGs, in theory, applied to all countries, in reality, they were considered targets for poor countries to achieve, with finance from wealthy states. There was often a perception then that the MDGs were rooted in a Northern agenda and that countries of the North should thus pay for them (in other words that the MDGs were to be achieved through aid alone). As the MDG deadline approached, around 1 billion people were still living on less than US$1.25 a day – the World Bank measure on poverty – and more than 800 million people do not have enough food to eat. Women are still fighting hard for their rights and millions of women still die in childbirth. To take these targets beyond 2015 a set of 'Sustainable Development Goals' (SDGs) have been agreed that represent a new universal set of goals, targets and indicators that UN member states will be expected to use to frame their agendas and policies over the next 15 years. In total 17 goals have been agreed (and within them are a further 169 targets), although it remains unclear how they will be funded. Member states agreed the draft of 17 SDGs set at a UN summit in September 2015. They became applicable from January 2016 and must be met before the deadline of 2030. Their success or failure will have immense consequences, not only for the world's poor, but also for the credibility of collective action by the international community.

categories (such as 'developing world' or 'Third World') to demarcate world regions on the basis of their levels of development is increasingly disputed as these categories are beginning to break down and decompose (Sidaway 2012). This is happening partly as a consequence of the recent (re)emergence of a number of 'rising powers' in the global South such as Brazil, China and India which are shifting global economic power towards the South and unsettling the boundaries used to differentiate rich and poor, 'First' and 'Third' World, 'developed' and 'developing' countries.

The first section of the chapter examines the origins of the 'three worlds' schema during the Cold War and the emergence of a space called the 'Third World' that became a focal point for the ideological struggle between capitalism and communism, between the USA and the USSR and their different forms of aid and 'development'. The next section then discusses two of the most important conceptual perspectives that have been formulated on the relations between development and inequality: the *modernization* and *dependency* schools. Although there have been many other different strands of development thinking, both these perspectives have been widely influential and remain relevant to an understanding of theory and practice today. The next section then outlines the need to view development historically and to formulate a sense of how it has been redefined through time. How have historical forces shaped our understanding of the geography of development and in what ways are the legacies of the past important to understanding contemporary global economic difference and inequality? The penultimate section of the chapter then looks at the 'rising powers' and examines the emergence of new Southern donors, exploring the implications of their rise for contemporary geographies of development. The concluding section returns to the key themes of unevenness and inequality and challenges the notion that 'development' is just an issue for the global South.

8.1 Development and the geography of the 'Third World'

Definitions of the term 'Third World' have been contested, as have the origins of the phrase (Mountjoy 1976; O'Connor 1976; Auty 1979; Pletsch 1981; Wolfe-Phillips 1987), yet the concept of 'three worlds' can hardly be said to convey a precise meaning or to be characterized by a specific geography with clear boundaries. The three worlds schema posited a 'First World' of advanced capitalism in Europe, the USA, Australia and Japan, a 'Second World' of the socialist bloc (China's position within this has been much debated) and a 'Third World' made up of the countries that remained when the supposedly 'significant' spaces of the world had been accounted for. These terms thus have to be approached with some caution. For some observers the terms global 'North' and 'South' are preferable to the 'three worlds' scheme but again there have been problems with defining where the boundaries of this global divide can be drawn.

Following the fall of the Eastern Bloc (or Second World), many of its constituent countries were reclassified as 'developing', despite being geographically located in the 'North'. At the same time, geographically 'southern' nations previously considered to be part of the 'Third World' such as China, Brazil, India and South Africa, have experienced levels of economic growth that appear to bring them closer to the 'First World'. Furthermore, the lines that have so far divided North and South are now present within *every nation-state* and are making ever less appropriate the conventional language used to interpret the geography of development in the world economy (rich/poor, North/South, First World/Third World, developed/developing) (Power 2003).

Subscribers to the three worlds scheme have been criticized for the simplicity of these divisions and their failure to recognize diversity and difference within these spaces; the world does not consist of a series of discrete individual national or regional economies in the way often suggested in United Nations and World Bank reports and in the context of globalization it is important to attend the *interdependencies* that link and connect different places, peoples, nations and regions. We also need to remember that the pursuit of development is not exclusive to particular regions (such as the so-called 'Third World') and that issues of poverty and inequality are also highly pertinent in both the 'First World' and in the former socialist states that comprised the 'Second world'. The onset of a global economic downturn in 2007 has had implications for the livelihoods of almost everyone in an increasingly interconnected world and there has been evidence of rising levels of unemployment, poverty and homelessness in many supposedly 'advanced' and 'developed' Western economies.

'Development' has historically served in part as a kind of 'lighthouse' (Sachs 1992) or as a 'lodestar' (Wallerstein 1991) into which several different movements, governments and institutions have invested faith and meaning. The period 1955–75 was one of extraordinary global change and of confrontational political realignment as a result of the global ideological struggle between capitalism and communism (the Cold War), but it was also a period that saw an intensification of debates concerning the development of the 'Third World' and the beginning of collective political demands in the fields of 'development' and politics (see Case study 8.2). With the accelerating pace of decolonization and the creation of independent states in the South, geopolitical questions begun to be addressed from a set of new or 'Third World' perspectives and there was a growing perception that 'underdeveloped' countries had distinct geopolitical considerations from those of Western societies (see also Chapter 20).

The 'three worlds' schema is very much a Cold War conceptualization of space and is strongly associated with the global social and political conflict between capitalism and communism, between the USA and USSR, in the second half of the twentieth century. During this time both these superpowers used the giving of foreign aid as a way to promote their own wider political and strategic objectives and to promote their own particular ideological visions of the 'correct' pathways to development (capitalist or communist) (see Case study 8.2). For the USA, on the one hand, the idea of development was seen as the way to counter the spread of communism and of 'making the world safe for capitalism' (Westad 2006: 31) since the donation of foreign aid was often linked to a recipients acceptance of market access and the exclusion of communists and left-wing socialists from government. The USSR, on the other hand, saw foreign aid as a way of 'exporting' communist revolution to the periphery, of building a sphere of influence and creating a block in opposition to the West (Berzoets 2011). Both the USA and USSR identified vital national interests in 'Third World' territories and for both Washington and Moscow 'developing areas appeared critical to the achievement of basic strategic, economic, political and ideological goals' (McMahon 2001: 2). In both cases foreign aid was thus used to secure alignment between the politics of emergent 'Third World' countries and the wider geopolitical strategies of the USA and USSR (see Case study 8.3)

Case study 8.2

Bandung, non-alignment and the 'Third World'

The Bandung conference was a meeting of representatives from 29 African and Asian nations, held in Bandung (Indonesia) in 1955, which aimed to promote economic and political cooperation within the 'Third World' and to oppose colonialism. The conference was sponsored by Burma, India, Indonesia, Ceylon (Sri Lanka) and Pakistan and tried to cut through the layers of social, political and economic difference that separated nations of the 'Third World' in order to think about the possibility of *common agendas and actions*. The aims of the 29 nations that attended included a desire to promote goodwill and cooperation among Third World nations and to explore and advance their mutual as well as common interests. Bandung

was in many ways the 'launching pad for Third World demands' where countries distanced themselves from the 'big powers seeking to lay down the law' (Rist 1997: 86). It was not hard for countries with shared histories of colonial exploitation to find something in common, since the 'agenda and subject matter had been written for centuries in the blood and bones of participants' (Wright 1995: 14). In his opening speech to the conference on 18 April 1955, President Sukarno of Indonesia urged participants to remember that they were all united by a common 'detestation' of colonialism and racism (Sukarno 1955: 1) and pointed out that colonialism was not dead or in the past but also had its modern ('neo-colonial') forms. The conference was especially successful in hastening the arrival of new international institutions explicitly dealing with 'development' (Rist 1997).

---

underlining the importance of geopolitics to both the theory and practice of development.

In 1949, US President Harry Truman spoke of the emergence of an 'underdeveloped' world that presented a 'handicap and threat both to them and the more prosperous areas' (Truman 1949). Truman went on to explain the need for 'modern, scientific and technical knowledge' as a pathway to overcoming this 'handicap' of underdevelopment and announced the beginning of a 'bold new program' within the 'developed world' to resolve inequality and remedy impoverishment in 'backward' areas. This agenda was further advanced under the administration of President John F. Kennedy (1961–3) that oversaw the creation of the United States Agency for International Development (USAID) in 1961. In the same year Kennedy also proposed an 'Alliance for Progress', a 10-year US$20 billion programme that considerably increased economic and development cooperation between the US and Latin America as a way of stopping the spread of communism in its tracks.

The Soviet Union also sought influence through aid after the Second World War. Initially it offered modest amounts of subsidized oil and technical assistance along with weaponry and military training before moving to a much more extensive involvement in regional conflicts through the supply of military capabilities and the use of proxies, such as Cuba. After Eastern Europe, the Soviet Union progressively drew in Cuba, Vietnam, Laos and several African states (such as Angola, Ethiopia and Mozambique), drawing upon Lenin's argument that the peoples of the colonial world represented *de facto* allies of

Plate 8.1 President Kennedy introduces the First Lady at La Morita, Venezuela in 1961 as part of establishing his 'Alliance for Progress' in Latin America. The Kennedy administration underwrote all the economic policies of Venezuelan President Romulo Betancourt's government through the Alliance for Progress, which used Venezuela as the exemplar for all of Latin America.

(Photograph by Cecil Stoughton. White House Photograph. John F. Kennedy Presidential Library and Museum)

the proletariat and of the first proletarian state, the Soviet Union. Their struggle for independence from the imperialist West would contribute to the weakening of the major opponents of the Soviet Union, including ultimately the United States. In the early stages of Soviet involvement in the 'Third World' the model that clients were expected to

Case study 8.3

The 'strategic interests' of foreign aid

In many ways, examining the case for aid can tell us a great deal about the history of development theory and practice and provides a useful opening on to wider discussions of North–South relations. Most official development assistance (ODA) comes from the OECD's Development Assistance Committee (DAC) whose 28 members collectively contributed US$134.8 billion in 2013 (OECD 2014a) representing 0.30 per cent of DAC donors' combined gross national income. A further US$15.9 billion in ODA came from the European Commission in 2013 whilst non-DAC countries gave an additional US$9.4 billion. Only five members of the DACs 28 member countries, however, have met a long-standing UN target for ODA to comprise at least 0.7 per cent of a donor's gross national income (GNI) (Denmark, Luxembourg, Norway, Sweden and the UK). DAC aid to developing countries grew steadily from 1997 to a peak in 2010, but then fell in 2011 and 2012 as many governments took austerity measures and consequently sought to trim their aid budgets. Around two-thirds of DAC aid is government-to-government or *bilateral aid* and the remainder is *multilateral aid* disbursed by agencies like the World Bank group, the UN bodies and the European Union. Critics of foreign aid have argued that it has been less effective than private investments and commercial loans in stimulating long-term economic growth. Other critics point to the dubious Cold War record of foreign aid and its subsidizing of autocratic regimes and inflammation of regional conflicts. Foreign aid has sometimes been seen as a kind of political narcotic, fostering addictive behaviour among states that receive it and thus come to depend on it. States are thought to exhibit the symptoms of dependence – a short-run 'fix' or benefit from aid, but external support sometimes does lasting damage to the country. For Moyo (2009) limitless development assistance to African governments has fostered dependency, encouraged corruption and ultimately perpetuated poor governance and poverty. Thus, many critics of foreign aid have sought to highlight the 'strategic interests' at work in its distribution as well as the inequality and unpredictability of aid provision. During the 'War on Terror', for example, there is evidence that the USA used foreign aid donation to secure support from a number of states in the South such as Pakistan. Just as 'development' was once seen as a means of countering the spread of communism in the 1950s, shortly after 9/11 it was increasingly re-constructed as a means of countering terrorism. Strangely, except for a brief period during the mid-1970s, anti-poverty measures have not been an important focal point of foreign aid, whilst aid has led to many reversals as well as to advances. Seen as a (simultaneous) remedy to problems of growth, governance, poverty and inequality, it has become (not unlike the idea of development) overburdened with expectations (Sogge 2002) and an overambitious enterprise (Rist 1997). A report by ActionAid claimed that only 39 per cent of total overseas development assistance is 'real aid' and that the remainder is 'phantom aid', made up of overpriced technical assistance, double-counted debt relief and poorly targeted and uncoordinated aid (ActionAid International 2005). Although aid from OECD donors has increased in recent years, much of this is in the form of debt relief, or humanitarian or military aid, which does little to advance long-term development.

Not surprisingly (given the size of its economy) the United States remained the largest DAC donor in 2013 by volume with net ODA flows of US$31.5 billion, yet this constitutes only 0.19 per cent of US gross national income. Countries like Afghanistan and Iraq (in the reconstruction of which the USA has been heavily involved in recent years) have figured prominently in the list of major DAC aid recipients, yet interestingly so too have emerging economies like India which is itself increasingly active as an aid donor.

follow was that of the Soviet Union itself with its focus on state control of the 'heights' of the economy, heavy industrial projects, import substitution, reduction of ties with the capitalist West, and closer integration with socialist states (Valkenier 1983). An important aspect of Soviet policy toward countries across Asia, Africa and Latin America was the provision of equipment for infrastructure and industrial development projects as well as technical assistance and the education and training of local people to build the foundations of modern industrial and agricultural enterprises. Soviet aid almost always went for large and visible projects in the state sector that were expected to increase the productive capacities of the recipient country and reduce their dependence on the capitalist West. Over time, however, military support generally outweighed economic assistance in Soviet policy.

Plate 8.2 American Marines guarding food aid distribution in Mogadishu during 'Operation Restore Hope'. In 1991 President Barre was overthrown by opposing clans, but they failed to agree on a replacement and plunged the country into lawlessness and clan warfare. In December 1992 US Marines landed near Mogadishu ahead of a UN peacekeeping force sent to restore order and safeguard relief supplies.

(Paul Lowe/Panos)

China also used aid and development cooperation to further its socialist agenda and to compete with Soviet and US influence in regions like Africa, constructing itself as part of the 'Third World' and at the head of a united international proletariat battling against imperialism. Chinese leaders believed that by fomenting revolution in the various 'rural' areas of the world, eventually the liberation movements would surround and overrun the urban areas, just as they had in China during its civil war. Between 1967 and 1976 China's aid had reached an average of 5 per cent of government expenditure and at the start of the 1970s Chinese teams were building close to 100 different turn-key aid projects around the world (Brautigam 2009: 41). By 1978 some 74 countries were receiving aid from China, the largest group of which were in Africa, and by then China had aid programs in more African countries than the USA. The Chinese often made a point of supporting schemes that the West had rejected on narrowly economic grounds or which were important to African states for political or psychological reasons, and they also made a point of 'doing something' for districts that the Europeans had been content to leave as backwaters (Snow 1988). Aid was also an important geopolitical tool for the Chinese in the contest with Taiwan (also an aid giver) and the USSR (where the Chinese aimed to shame the Kremlin by stepping up their charity and economic aid and by providing fewer arms). Aid thus became an important way of exposing the limitations of China's opponents, both Western and Soviet.

8.2 Conceptualizing development

When considering the many ways in which development has been conceptualized it is useful to consider the history of 'Development thinking' (Hettne 1995), or the sum total of ideas about development theory, ideology and strategy. Development *theories* are logical propositions about how development occurred in the past and/or should occur in the future. Development *strategies* are the practical paths to development adopted by a wide range of actors, from the 'grassroots' to the international. Development *ideologies* are the different goals and objectives that underpin development theories and strategies. In many ways this 'development thinking' has often been caught in a 'Western' perception of reality or has been based around 'Western' philosophies, experiences and histories (Hettne 1995; Power 2003). Conceptualizing development is partly about the negotiation of what constitutes 'progress' and 'improvement' and the definition of what constitutes 'appropriate' intervention in the affairs of 'poor' or 'lesser developed' countries. Since all-encompassing definitions have been contested and controversial, little consensus exists today but some core conceptions have emerged, many of which have continued relevance in the contemporary world. Although there are many different strands of development thinking to explore, the modernization and dependency approaches have been two of the most influential in the twentieth century. Both approaches were far from being static, uniform or unified, however, and neither represents a singular commonly agreed approach. In discussing these different conceptions then it is important to think about where and when they emerged. Most reflect some of the priorities of development thinking characteristic of their era. The formation of development theories, therefore, depends on different perceptions of 'development challenges' at different times.

8.2.1 The modernization school: an anti-communist manifesto

With the end of the Second World War and after the United Nations was established, conceptualizations of development received a decisive stimulus. Between 1945 and 1981, UN membership rose from 51 to 156 nation-states (Berger 2001). With many new states being formed after the end of colonialism and in the context of the Cold War, theorizing development became a more complicated and contested enterprise. In some ways the task of development was seen by some as seeking to provide 'an ethos and system of values which can compete successfully with the attraction exercised by Communism' (Watnick 1952–3: 37). In this regard many observers called for the modernization of 'underdeveloped areas' and painted a picture (following President Truman) of 'underdeveloped peoples' confined to 'backwardness' but torn between the appeal of communism and the prospect of Western modernization. This was an essential characteristic of the *modernization school,* which was often dualistic, opposing 'traditional' to 'modern' life-styles, 'indigenous' to 'Westernized', as if no country or citizen could belong to both categories.

Albert Hirschmann (1958) was a key proponent of modernization ideas, voicing the optimistic view that the forces of concentration ('polarization') will 'trickle down' from the core to the periphery at national, regional and global scales. Hirschmann explained how development economics might 'slay the dragon of backwardness' (quoted in Rist 1997: 219). John Friedmann's (1966) core–periphery model adopts many of the same assumptions about the polarization of development in 'transitional societies' and the 'trickle-down' effect of development. Geographers at the time sought to contribute to the mapping of modernization geography, seeking to look at how progress trickled down along urban hierarchies, through transport systems or with the introduction of modern technology. The message from these modernization geographies was that underdeveloped countries could move briskly into the modern tempo of life within a few years, whilst the state (concerned with macro issues and the national economy) would be the key monitor and broker of development.

One of the modernization theorists who identified 'stages of growth' in the development process was the American economic historian and political theorist Walt Whitman Rostow. Subtitling his book *A Non-Communist Manifesto,* Rostow (1960) played a key role in the administrations of both John F. Kennedy and Lyndon B. Johnson in the 1960s and closely shaped US foreign policy in South-east Asia during this time. For Rostow Communism was 'an opportunistic virus that took out infant nations not yet blessed with a constitutional "maturity"' (Gilman 2003: 195) and he was the first to advise President Kennedy to send US combat troops to South Vietnam in 1965 and the first to recommend the bombing of North Vietnam in 1966. To Rostow, communism was not the agent of modernization but a side effect of it. It was a 'disease of the transitional process' likely to spread in any nation during the early, difficult stages of development and instead of accelerating growth communism 'disfigured' it, producing an unbalanced and dysfunctional modernity. Again the focus was on a top-down 'trickling'

of capitalist development from urban-industrial areas to other regions (Stöhr and Taylor 1981) as Rostow (1960) predicted that nations would 'take off' into development, having gone through five stages, which he likened to the stages an aeroplane goes through before take-off, from taxiing on the runway to mid-flight. Ranging from stage one, 'traditional society', to stage five, the 'age of high mass consumption', the theory takes our faith in the capitalist system for granted since Rostow assumed that all countries will be in a position to 'take off' into development. Further, in common with other modernization approaches, Rostow's model devalues and misinterprets 'traditional societies', which represent the 'lowest' form or stage of development. The advanced state of modernization was always represented as 'Western modernization'; traditional societies seem like distant, poor relations.

In America the Democratic administrations of the 1960s took Rostow's theory to mean that if the USA could help shepherd 'underdeveloped' countries safely through the take-off stage then the Communist 'contagion' could be arrested. Many social scientists like Rostow thus turned modernization theory's description of the modernity of Western societies into a prescription for transforming the Third World. It is important to remember, however, that theories of modernization were not an exclusively American enterprise – modernization was also a very influential idea within the Soviet Union. In part then the conflict between East and West in the Third World was an expression of two competing models of modernization, a democratic one led by the USA and a socialist one led by the USSR (Westad 2006). Geographies of inequality and development cannot be

Plate 8.3 Walt Rostow shows US President Lyndon B. Johnson a model of the Khe Sanh area in Vietnam in the 'situation room' in 1968.

(LBJ Library photo by Yoichi Okamoto)

neatly summarized as a set of prescriptive stages how-ever. Urban areas, for example, are themselves subject to uneven development and inequality (see Chapter 10). Modernization approaches have also largely failed to address the importance of gender, assuming that men and women occupied equal positions in terms of power relations and decision-making. Further, the 'trickle-down' effect has often failed to materialize among those who have been the subjects of modernization projects. This approach seemed to suggest that devel-opment could be mimicked, copied and replicated and that 'underdeveloped' countries should try to reproduce the development paths of richer 'developed' nations like Britain or the USA. As Gunder Frank has argued, this approach can also be understood as reflections of the 'Sinatra Doctrine':

> Do it my way, what is good for General Motors is good for the country, and what is good for the United States is good for the world, and especially for those who wish to 'develop like we did'.

(Frank 1997: 13)

In the modernization schema, it was implied that there is nothing before the beginning of development in a 'developing country' that is worth retaining or recalling, only a series of deficiencies, absences, weak-nesses and incapacities (Abrahamsen 2000; Andreas-son 2005). The approach was also in a sense very much based around a 'top–down' rather than a **bottom–up** approach, implying that the process could be brokered by states or development institutions rather than emerge from the 'grass-roots' struggles of 'Third World peoples' as had been called for in some more radical approaches. In terms of common criticisms, the division of the world into modern and traditional has often been seen as problematic (Pletsch 1981). Modern societies were much more fractured and were divided by ethnicity, class and politics and were not as united and respon-sive to the blueprints of planners as was often assumed. The scale of modernization programmes was also often a problem in that they assumed that 'big is beautiful' (involving large dam-building and irrigation projects, for example). Rostow was also able to say little about the 'final stage' of his organic model of development since his underlying principle was that growth had no limits (Rist 1997) and instead he simply discussed a number of very generalized scenarios. Like so many theorizations of development that followed, it ended with a creed, a set of principles about what was to be done, and heav-ily invested faith in the goals of mass consumption and Westernization.

8.2.2 The dependency school: beyond 'core' and 'periphery'?

One of the major weaknesses of the modernization approach was that the notion of a 'trickle-down' dif-fusion of development implied that there were precise demarcations available of where the 'core' ends and the 'periphery' begins when this has never really been the case. Radical **dependency** approaches that emerged in the 1960s and 1970s challenged this notion of positive core–periphery relations, identifying instead exploita-tion between 'satellites' and 'metropoles'. Whilst the modernization approach was taken up by many inter-national institutions and bilateral donors, dependency approaches comprised all those opposed to US post-war imperialism and allied in some way to the movement of 'third worldism'. The dependency school is most com-monly associated with Latin America, but also emerged in Africa, the Caribbean and the Middle East. Drawing upon Marx's writings about the unevenness of capitalist development, dependency scholars such as Celso Fur-tado (1964) and Milton Santos (1974) drew attention to the mode of incorporation of each country into the world capitalist system, identifying this as a key cause of exploitation.

The dependency school is most commonly asso-ciated with the work of André Gunder Frank who published a number of seminal pieces on 'The devel-opment of underdevelopment' in the late 1960s (Frank 1966). This thesis is relatively uncomplicated in that it views development and underdevelopment as opposite sides of the same coin; the development of one area often necessitates the underdevelopment of another. For the dependency scholars (or *dependentistas*), a big part of the economic development and wealth of the rich countries is wealth that has been directly imported from the poor countries as the world economic system actively *generates* inequality. Dependency on a metro-politan 'core' (e.g. Europe, North America) increases the 'underdevelopment' of satellites in the 'periphery' (e.g. Latin America, Africa). Unlike many moderni-zation approaches, the *dependentistas* sought to view development in historical context, and argued, for example, that colonialism helped to put in place a set of dependent relations between core and periphery. These peripheral satellites, they argued, were encour-aged to produce what they did not consume (e.g. primary products, including natural resources) and consume what they did not produce (e.g. manufac-tured or industrial goods). Thus, rather than likening the process of economic growth to an aeroplane setting off into a blue sky of urban-based, Western life-styles and consumption, the dependency school was arguing that many 'underdeveloped' areas had been stalled on the runway by unequal relations and a history of colonialism, denying them a chance of ever being airborne, 'modern' or 'industrialized'. A dependence on natural resources can lead to slower growth and patterns of development that are geographically uneven (see also Chapter 5 for a discussion of the 'resource curse' thesis).

In many ways, dependency approaches were so directly opposed to modernization approaches (almost point by point) that eventually both 'seemed to checkmate each other' (Schuurman 2001: 6). The dependency school even appeared to preserve the dualistic and binary classification of the world into 'developed'/'underdeveloped', 'First World' and 'Third World', core and periphery, and also lacked a clear statement of what 'development' actually is. Key criticisms directed at the *dependentistas* were that the theory represents a form of 'economic determinism' and also overlooks social and cultural variation within developed and underdeveloped regions. The dependency framework seemed to leave the simplistic impression of an 'evil genie who organizes the system, loading the dice and making sure the same people win all the time' (Rist 1997: 122) and like modernization approaches it also dealt in dualistic either/or scenarios and viewed poverty in deprivationist terms. Another point of contention was that the dependency theorists seemed to be calling for a de-linking from the world capitalist economy at a time when it was undergoing further globalization and economic integration. Elements of the dependency writings were, however, quite thought-provoking and remain relevant, particularly their contention that the obstacles to development equality were *structural*, arising not from a lack of will or poor weather conditions but from entrenched patterns of global inequality and 'dependent' relationships.

8.3 Development practice: the historical geography of development

Whilst both modernization and dependency approaches alluded to the importance of 'tradition', many early writings about development lacked a sense of historical perspective (Rist 1997). As Crush (1995) points out, development is primarily 'forward looking', imagining a better world, and does not always examine issues of historical and geographical context. Many recent histories of development have dated its beginnings as an area of theory and state practice to President Truman's speech of

1949, but the idea of development is much older than this (Cowen and Shenton 1996) and has much more diverse geographical origins. Development was not a simple 'gift' following contact with Europeans but predates the 'age of discovery' (1400–1550) and the 'age of empire' (1875–1914) (see Section 1 of this book). It is, however, particularly important to examine the significance of Empire in the making of international development. Between 1800 and 1878, European rule, including former colonies in North and South America, increased from 35 per cent to 67 per cent of the earth's land surface, adding another 18 per cent between 1875 and 1914, the period of 'formal colonialism' (Hoogevelt 1997: 18). In the last three decades of the nineteenth century, European states thus added 10 million square miles of territory and 150 million people to their areas of control or 'one fifth of the earth's land surface and one tenth of its people' (Peet with Hartwick 1999: 105).

Colonialism has been variously interpreted as an economic process of unequal exchange, as a political process aimed at administration and subordination of indigenous peoples, and as a cultural process of imposing European superiority (see Chapters 2 and 20). According to the dependency theorists it was in this period that the periphery was brought into an expanding network of economic exchanges with the core of the world system. A new sense of responsibility for distant human suffering also first emerged during this time as the societies of Europe and North America became entwined within global networks of exchange and exploitation in the late eighteenth and early nineteenth centuries (Haskell 1985a, 1985b). Thus the origins of a humanitarian concern to come to the aid of 'distant others' lay partly in response to the practices of slavery in the transatlantic world (see Case study 8.4) and to the expansion of colonial settlement in the 'age of empire':

> Not only did colonisation carry a metropolitan sense of responsibility into new Asian, North American, African and Australasian terrains, it also prompted humanitarians to formulate new antidotes, new 'cures' for the ills of the world.
>
> (Lester 2002: 278).

These new antidotes, cures and remedies were to have enduring significance for the shaping of twentieth-century global development theory and practice, which also often carried an implicit 'metropolitan sense of responsibility'. Colonial development was also associated with an unconditional belief in the concept of progress and the 'makeability' of society, being heavily conditioned by the dominance of the evolutionary

Case study 8.4

Race, native lands and the origins of US capitalism and development

When US President Thomas Jefferson acquired the Louisiana Territory of 828,000 square miles of land from France in 1803 he envisioned an 'empire for liberty' populated by self-sufficient white farmers. The plantation economy, however, that emerged in the Mississippi Valley in the years that followed can tell us a great deal about the development of capitalism in the United States and about the indigenous lands, African bodies and global trade networks that this depended upon. As Walter Johnson (2013) has shown, in many ways there was no nineteenth-century US capitalism without slavery. Beginning with the violent expropriation and 'ethnic cleansing' of the land that indigenous agriculturalists (the Muskogee, Cherokee, Chickasaw and Choctaw nations) had farmed for millennia before the arrival of Europeans, the area was quickly transformed into a frontier of accumulation by selling off the collective Native land base to individual capitalist planters. Using enslaved Africans, slaveholders then transformed the Mississippi Valley into the Cotton Kingdom that formed the basis for US capitalism and world trade (Johnson 2013). In 1800, there were around 100,000 slaves living within the boundaries of the present-day states of Mississippi and Louisiana but by 1860 there were more than 750,000 (Johnson 2013: 32). Although there were already some enslaved Africans in the area before the boom, approximately a million slaves were brought to the Mississippi Valley between 1820 and 1840. Thus the slaveholding economy of the American South, which played a foundational role in the wider development of US capitalism, depended in large part on coerced African labour and the dispossession of indigenous lands. Britain was at the time the main industrial giant and imperialist power, and its primary industry was fuelled by US cotton. Most Mississippi Valley cotton went to Liverpool for sale, making up 80 per cent of the cotton that British manufacturers imported (Johnson 2013). Thus the fortunes of cotton planters in Louisiana and cotton brokers in Liverpool,

of the plantations of the Mississippi Valley and the textile mills of Manchester 'were tied together through the cotton trade-the largest single sector of the global economy in the first half of the nineteenth century' (Johnson 2013: 10). The slaveocracy that emerged around the Cotton Kingdom also laid the groundwork for wider continental expansion (America's 'manifest destiny') and US overseas imperialism through attempts to annex Nicaragua and Cuba in order to accumulate more land to distribute to the non-slave holders along with the US obsession with control of the Caribbean and Central America and other military/imperialist ventures (Johnson 2013).

Similarly, Domosh (2015) has shown how some of the key elements of US international development practices in the post-war era can be traced back to the US South, a region considered 'undeveloped' in the first decades of the twentieth century, and the agricultural extension practices that targeted the rural farm home and farm women. This is one of a number of recent studies that trace US development practices to the first decades of the twentieth century, if not earlier, and to events that occurred as much within the USA as outside of it (Ekbladh 2002, 2010a, 2010b; Sneddon and Fox 2011). Domosh (2015) examines the ways in which the Extension Service of the US Department of Agriculture (USDA) targeted rural women and the home as sites of modernization and development through a series of heavily gendered and racially segregated interventions. The US government then drew on its experiences with what was called Home Demonstration Work (HDW) in the American South in order to conduct 'home work' overseas, linking early US interventions into other countries under the guise of agricultural modernization with the USA's own domestic agricultural extension service. Domosh (2015) argues that international development – a form of hegemony different from but related to colonialism – thus needs to be understood not only as a geopolitical tool of the Cold War, but also as 'a technique of governance that took shape within the realm of the domestic and through a racialized gaze developed in the US South' (Domosh 2015: 3).

thinking that was popular in Europe at the time. Imperialism was viewed as a cultural and economic necessity where colonies were regarded as the national 'property' of the metropolitan countries and thus needed to be 'developed' using the latest methods and ideas. With

this came a missionary zeal to 'civilize' and modernize the colonized and their ways of life. An important contention here then is that colonialism 'conditioned' the meanings and practices of development in a number of important ways.

After 1945 and under US President Truman, 'under-development' became the incomplete and 'embryonic' form of development and the gap was seen as bridgeable only through an acceleration of growth (Rist 1997). Globally, development would have its 'trustees', guiding 'civilized' nations that had the 'capacity' and the knowledge or expertise to organize land, labour and capital in the South on behalf of others. Quite a paternal and parental style of relationship was therefore established through the imperial encounter between colonizer and colonized in ways which have continued to have a bearing on the definition of North–South partnerships in the 'post-colonial' world. Additionally, what is also relevant here is that many 'post-colonial' states continue to maintain important political, cultural and economic ties with their former colonial rulers (see Figure 8.1).

Colonialism put in place important political and economic relations but the cultural legacies of colonialism bequeathed deep social and cultural divisions in many societies. In the process of decolonization, 'development' became an overarching objective for many nationalist movements and the independent states they tried to form. Although experiments with development were tried in many colonies, the idea of development

was invested with the hopes and dreams of many newly emerging states who wanted to address these inequalities and divisions in their societies (Rahnema 1997). Decolonization was thus simultaneously an ideological, material and spatial process, just as complicated as colonization (Pieterse and Parekh 1995). An important issue here concerns the extent to which colonial state machineries were reworked and transformed after independence (Power 2003). The colonial state had rested on force for its **legitimacy**, a legitimacy that was thus highly superficial. Colonial states also had a role in creating political and economic communities, defining the rules of the game and the boundaries of community whilst creating power structures to dominate them. The colonial state was also the dominant economic actor, creating a currency, levying taxes, introducing crops, developing markets, controlling labour and production. Above all, colonial state administrations sought the integration of the colonial economy into the wider economies of empire, to make linkages with the metropole and to establish flows of peoples and resources. After the formal end of colonialism, new states have had to formulate alternative methods of garnering legitimacy for their authority (i.e. other than the use of force preferred by the colonists).

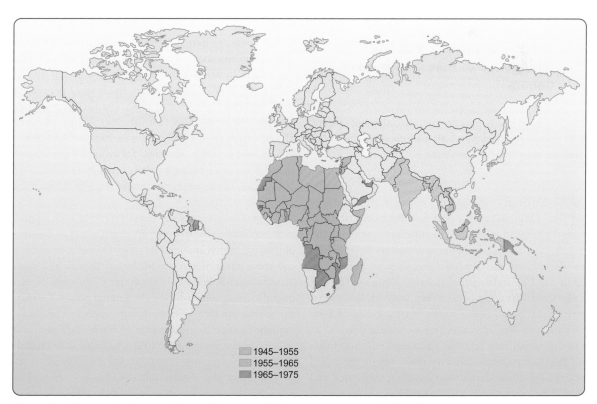

1945–1955
1955–1965
1965–1975

Figure 8.1 Decolonization and the proliferation of independent states, 1945–75.

It is worth remembering that indigenous peoples in Africa, the Americas, Asia and Australasia had highly developed and sophisticated cultures and technologies prior to colonization (Dickenson *et al.* 1996). As the European capitalist system expanded and became ever more global in its reach however, the structures of economic, social and political life that existed in colonies before colonialism were often radically remade. The historical process by which 'gaps' began to emerge between 'North' and 'South' has been interpreted in a variety of ways, but a key question has been: to what extent did European expansion and colonialism 'underdevelop' (Frank 1966) large areas of the world? The impact of imperial expansion was not uniform; the geographical patterns of expansion varied, as did the motivations for it. Hall (1992) argues that an important divide was put in place between 'the West' and 'the rest' as a direct result of this imperial expansion, reminding us that 'the West' is much more of an idea than a geographical reality. By accelerating contact between cultures and economies 'the West' was presented as 'the best' and most advanced or 'civilized' of all humanity. Many accounts of the history of European expansion are thus dominated by the presumed supremacy of 'Europe' and 'the West' with only limited references to the complex histories and cultures of the areas that were colonized.

8.4 The 'rising powers' and the emergence of new 'Southern' donors

[T]he rapid and steady intrusion and recognition of a set of major emerging economies is challenging the established order, wrenching global relations into flux.

(Shaw *et al.* 2009: 27)

The United States emerged pre-eminent after the Second World War and built a post-war international order around a range of governance institutions, including the United Nations, the International Monetary Fund (IMF), the World Bank, the General Agreement on Tariffs and Trade (GATT) and regional security alliances. The end of the Cold War consolidated this American-led global institutional order, but in recent years a group of fast-growing non-Western countries or 'rising powers' as they are sometimes referred to (namely China, India and Brazil) have been rising up the ranks of the world system as the boundaries used to differentiate rich and poor, 'first' and 'third' world countries are becoming

more fluid. In some ways, however, it would be more appropriate to refer to some of these countries as 're-emerging economies' as, until the nineteenth century, China and India were the world's largest economies and dominated global output until the onset of Britain's industrial revolution.

First coined in 2001 by an economist at the multinational global investment firm Goldman Sachs, the 'BRICs' acronym (referring to Brazil, Russia, India and China) identified a group of four countries in particular that were, due to their scale, population size and growing share of global GDP, regarded as the leading non-Western economies and as future motors of global economic change. The 'BRICs' acronym has since come into widespread use as a symbol of the apparently epochal shift in global economic power away from the developed economies towards the 'developing world' and the wider realignment of world economic and ultimately political power that would be engendered by the collective influence of these four countries. South Africa began efforts to join the grouping in 2010 and the process for its formal admission began in August of that year with South African President Jacob Zuma attending the 2011 BRICS summit as a full member.

With the inclusion of South Africa, the five BRICS countries now represent almost three billion people with a combined nominal GDP of US$16.039 trillion and an estimated US$4 trillion in combined foreign reserves (IMF 2013). Over the past decade, FDI inflows to the BRICS countries have more than tripled to an estimated US$322 billion in 2013 (UNCTAD 2014). As a result their share in world FDI flows kept rising even during the recent global economic crisis, reaching 22 per cent in 2013, up from 6 per cent in 2000. The BRICS countries have also become important investors – their outward FDI has risen from US$7 billion in 2000 to US$126 billion in 2012 and now accounts for around 9 per cent of global flows, up from only 1 per cent in 2002 (UNCTAD 2013). As a result, some countries of the global South are beginning to exert more influence on the 'advanced' and 'developed' economies of western nations with significant implications in terms of inflation, wages and unemployment, profits and interest rates. Globally, increasing economic integration has made labour cheaper and more abundant with workers in developing countries consequently losing some of their bargaining power. Further, the monopoly that western donors once had on development finance (and the power to frame the terms and content of development debates) is being steadily eroded. (Power 2015).

The recent global economic crisis has also opened up space for the emerging economies of the global South to play an increasingly active role in the reform of global economic and political governance, to the extent that a 'regime change' in global governance is now at least a distinct possibility (Gray and Murphy 2013). This has been characterized by some as the beginning of a transition from a unipolar US hegemony to one of 'emancipatory multipolarity' (Pieterse 2011), in which the countries that represent the majority of the world's peoples now have a position at the head table, or even as a broader underlying 'global centre shift' or 'hegemonic transition' (Gills 2011). Reforming the governance of the IMF and the World Bank has been a central component in the strategy of 'global power diffusion' pursued by the BRICS. They have argued that the West is overrepresented in the IMF at the expense of developing countries and have called for a greater share of votes and a change in what they see as the organization's obsolete governance. As they are becoming growing net contributors to the IMF, the BRICS are thus pressing for a greater voice within the institution, even threatening to hold back the additional financing requested by the IMF to fight the European debt crisis unless they gained greater IMF voting power.

There have also been discussions about the creation of a parallel mechanism to the World Bank including proposals for a 'BRICS development bank' that would lend to infrastructure projects and the facilitation of sustainable development in the countries of the grouping themselves as well as other developing countries. More generally, the BRICS have also focused on the need for national policy autonomy and have been critical of the global economic governance frameworks that introduce rules and norms corresponding to dominant country interests. The BRICS have also been instrumental in establishing regional development banks that have eroded the primacy of the IMF and World Bank as lenders in Asia and Latin America and have agreed to use their own currencies when trading among themselves, effectively reducing their dependence on the US dollar as the main currency of trade.

There is no doubt then that in recent years both the architecture of international governance and the established modes of development cooperation have been increasingly transformed by the (re)emergence of the rising powers as development donors with important implications for global geographies of investment, production and trade (Power and Mohan 2010). Twenty years ago, it would have been difficult to imagine Brazil as the main regional leader in Latin America, India as a major player in the WTO, or China as the second largest economy in the world (Vom Hau *et al* 2012), but what

is becoming clear is that the rapid and steady intrusion and recognition of a set of major emerging economies is challenging the established global order, 'wrenching global relations into flux' (Shaw *et al.* 2009: 27). As a result Western modernity is 'no longer uncritically viewed as the future of developing countries' (Humphrey 2007: 16). These (re)emerging powers have economies that will rival the USA and Europe in the years ahead and they are already becoming an international economic force. Additionally these (re)emerging powers hold most of the world's financial reserves and are placing significant new demands on energy and raw materials (many of which are being sourced from countries of the global South) with important implications for the environment and the prospects for addressing climate change and sustainable development goals.

The rise of countries like China, India and Brazil thus has potentially far-reaching implications for global geographies of development and the international landscape of development cooperation but also for the post-war institutions of governance in world politics. Further, many of these 'rising powers' are (re)emerging as aid donors themselves, providing development assistance to a range of other non-Western partners and often heralding this as 'South–South cooperation'. These 'Southern' donors are also questioning the very idea of development cooperation as a Western concept but also the development paradigm as a whole (Six 2009). Brazil, China, India and South Africa not only espouse the cause of 'developing countries' but are also vociferous in their assertions that they themselves belong to this group in ways that are reminiscent of older Third Worldist coalitions that some of these countries led at different points in the past such as Bandung (Narlikar 2013). Part of their appeal as 'development donors' (Mawdsley 2012) is that they don't have the same imperial histories of colonizing large parts of the global South that many existing Western donors do. Paradoxically, these 'new' donors represent models of economic success, yet they have been, or are still, recipients of international aid. Although India, for example, is a donor (aid expenditures reached US$1.3 billion in 2014–15, more than double New Delhi's anticipated net foreign aid receipts of US$655 million that financial year) it was the world's eighth-largest recipient of official development assistance as recently as 2008 (to the value of US$2.1 billion) and was fourth overall from 1995 to 2009. Further, considerable levels of poverty and inequality remain within each of the BRICS despite the many claims that have been made about their 'miraculous growth'.

8.5 Conclusions: geography, unevenness and inequality

The idea of development stands like a ruin in the intellectual landscape. Delusion and disappointment, failures and crimes have been the steady companions of development and they tell a common story: it did not work. Moreover, the historical conditions which catapulted the idea into prominence have vanished: development has become outdated.

(Sachs 1992: 1).

Development is nearly always seen as something that is possible, if only people or countries follow through a series of stages or prescribed instructions. Many theories, strategies and ideologies have thus sought to prescribe how development could or should proceed and 'development thinking' has long been caught in a 'Western' perception of reality and been based around 'Western' philosophies, knowledges, experiences and histories. There is a sense, however, that despite the wide variety of interventions that have been made in its name the 'project' of Development has been accompanied by a common story: that it 'did not work' and that its 'steady companions' have been 'delusion and disappointment, failures and crimes' (Sachs 1992: 1).

Some critics have even argued that historically Development is in many ways a dubious solution in search of a problem (Escobar 2011) and has thus 'created abnormalities' such as poverty, underdevelopment, backwardness and landlessness before proceeding to address them in ways that deny value or initiative to local cultures and that prevent individuals from making their own histories and geographies under conditions of their own choosing. More importantly, there is also a sense in which the historical conditions that gave rise to the idea of D/development have fundamentally changed and a sense that the idea lies 'in ruins' or has become 'outdated'. Some of the prior meta-geographical demarcations that have shaped development theory and practice, the categories such as 'Developed' and 'Third World' which emerged after 1945, and which have 'long provided key points of reference, commitment, analysis and mobilisation' (Sidaway 2012), have shattered and are breaking down in part because of the emergence of the BRICS and the rising economies of the South.

Many recent critiques of development thus appear disillusioned with the future of the development industry and its capacity to understand and alleviate world poverty. Further, many politicians in Western countries are only gradually beginning to wake up to the realities of these contemporary global inequalities. A number of them see these concerns as those of distant geographies, a world of problems pushed and 'worlded' beyond the universe of immediate moral concern even though the lines that have historically divided 'North' and 'South', 'First World' and 'Third World' are now present within every nation-state. The effects of poverty and inequality (a bit like those of climate change) are thus regarded as diffuse and long-term (Wade 2001). Additionally, rather than thinking of a single, interconnected and interdependent global economic system, this impoverishment and inequity is constructed as somehow unique or exclusive to the peoples of particular spaces of global Development such as the 'Third World'. If our concern is to build a more radical development geography then it needs to be understood that poverty also occurs in 'developed' countries and that the aid and 'development' policies of such countries, far from being a part of the solution, may actually be considered a part of the problem. Marginality and deprivation (or for that matter, excessive consumption amongst the affluent) in Europe, North America or Russia and other post-communist 'transition economies' should also be seen foremost as issues of 'development'.

The rapid economic growth experienced by (re)emerging powers in the South like Brazil, India and China, and their increasingly significant roles in development cooperation and aid disbursement, requires us to adopt a framework for analysis that is liberated from the tyranny of dualism and that allows for changes in the world economy and variation within and between states. Their collective size and impact on trade, finance, energy, and the environment will make them important players in the years to come. This also means moving beyond the tragic stereotypes of a single condition of 'Third World poverty' and a single 'geography of the Third World'. This could make a world of difference.

Learning outcomes

Having read this chapter, you should understand:

- D/development is both a continuous intellectual and ideological project as well as an ongoing material process
- The value of historical and geographical perspectives on D/development
- The power and politics of 'labelling' and categorizing poor peoples, places and the spaces of development.
- The changing geographies of north-south and south-south interactions and development cooperation and the rise of emerging economies from the global South like China, India and Brazil.

Further reading

Chant, S. and McIlwaine, S. (2009) *Geographies of Development in the 21st Century,* Edward Elgar, Cheltenham. Explores the immense social, cultural, political and economic variations among countries and in different places in the global South, providing an engaging introduction to development.

Desai, V. and Potter, R. (eds) (2014) *The Arnold Companion to Development Studies,* 3rd edition, Arnold, London. Contains short and accessible chapters on a wide variety of development themes. A useful companion text in studying development, with suggestions for further reading on each topic.

Mawdsley, E. (2012) *From Recipients to Donors: Emerging Powers and the Changing Development Landscape,* Zed, London. An accessible introduction to the emergence of new development donors such as China, India, Brazil and South Korea and the implications of their rise for the institutions, practices and modalities of development cooperation.

Potter, R., Binns, T., Elliott, J.A. and Smith, D. (2008) *Geographies of Development,* 3rd edition, Longman, London. Updated and revised in a third edition, this book offers a wide-ranging discussion of theories of development, urban/rural spaces and the important institutions of global development.

Power, M. (2003) *Rethinking Development Geographies,* Routledge, London. Draws out the spatial dimensions of development and outlines how the discipline of geography has been implicated and involved in the theory and practice of 'development'. The book offers a critical and stimulating introduction to the imperial and geopolitical dimensions of development, looking at Cold War and colonial constructions of 'The Tropics' and the 'Third World'.

Rigg, J. (2007) *An Everyday Geography of the Global South,* Routledge, London. Draws on more than 90 case studies from 36 countries across Asia, Africa and Latin America, starting with the lived and 'everyday' experiences of 'ordinary' people as they encounter development.

Sidaway, J.D. (2012) Geographies of development: new maps, new visions?, *The Professional Geographer,* 64(1), 49–62. This paper reconsiders what remains of the 'Third World'.

Williams, G., Meth, P. and Willis, K. (2014) *Geographies of Developing Areas: The Global South in a Changing World,* 2nd edition, Routledge, London. Another rewarding survey that focuses on the diversity of life in the South, and looks at the role the South plays in shaping and responding to current global change.

Willis, K. (2005) *Theories and Practices of Development,* Routledge, London. Explores the development theories behind contemporary debates such as globalization and transnationalism and traces the main definitions of 'development' and 'development theory' over time. It contains student-friendly features, including case studies, with examples, definitions, summary sections, suggestions for further reading, discussion questions and website information.

Useful websites

www.eldis.org   The ELDIS Development information research gateway site with a useful country search facility and good web links.

www.guardian.co.uk/global-development   A site focusing on global development and tracking progress towards the MDGs.

www.peopleandplanet.org   UK students campaigning on world poverty, human rights and the environment.

www.brettonwoodsproject.org   The website of the Bretton Woods Project, an organization seeking to monitor and challenge the power of the World Bank and IMF and to seek alternatives.

SOCIETY, SETTLEMENT AND CULTURE

Edited by Tim Hall

Geographers are interested in difference, the ways places differ, and also in the similarities and interconnections between places. But the changes that human societies have experienced since the late twentieth century render the geographer's task of making sense of the world increasingly difficult. Old dichotomies, like that between 'urban' and 'rural', and the lines which geographers have customarily drawn on their maps to divide country from country, region from region and culture from culture, seem to make less sense in a dynamic globalizing environment. Even so the results of such processes seem not to be a world that is more uniform. While distant places interconnect and interact with increasing intimacy, new spaces appear where people are excluded from such developments, and almost everywhere some individuals who share spaces with others are denied the rights and advantages that the latter enjoy.

It is such complexities, making themselves felt in urban and rural spaces and in the spheres of culture and nature, that form the subject of this section.

The world has become more urban. But the experience of urbanization differs radically between cities, spaces within cities, and for different individuals. The corollary is that the world has become less rural, but again those spaces, and the individuals within them, are affected in very different ways by such processes. Further, culture seems to be assuming ever greater importance in the world. Issues like identity and the meanings and ways of life that are shared by, or that divide, individuals and groups become matters of concern, contestation and even conflict. These processes are interacting though with an increasingly vulnerable and contested global ecology.

Chapter 9 looks at cities, the roles cities now play in global and regional economic and power networks is addressed before the chapter turns to examine urban problems like poverty, cultural diversity and environmental sustainability and how these might best be understood and addressed. Chapter 10 on urban segregation and social inequalities argues that all modern societies are riddled with inequalities. It demonstrates that one of the clearest ways in which social disadvantage is reflected is through its geographical expression, particularly in the existence of spaces described as being 'on the margins'. Chapter 11, 'Rural worlds', analyzes the alternative consequences for both rural spaces and individuals of the processes of urbanization and globalization. Chapter 12 on social constructions of nature argues that nature is not some pre-given physical reality, existing totally outside ourselves, but is in fact an idea which is constructed by society. It is never easy to draw a line between things that are deemed 'natural' and things that are 'social', and different ways of conceiving of what is 'natural' can be used to advance particular political agendas. Chapter 13, which looks at culture, defines it as a process and as a system of shared meanings. The argument is that globalization is not producing a single global culture although the idea of a global culture is becoming important. It debunks the myth that globalization equates with cultural homogenization. Global cultural processes interact with processes occurring at national and regional levels to produce a complex world in which it is necessary to foster approaches that will welcome and celebrate cultural differences rather than shun and fear them.

This section makes clear the fact that the geography of a globalizing world is as much a geography of exclusion and difference as it is one of interconnection and interlinkage.

CITIES: URBAN WORLDS

Chapter 9

Tim Hall and Heather Barrett

Topics covered

- Sociological and administrative definitions of cities
- Edge cities
- The rural–urban fringe
- Levels of urbanization by world region
- Impacts of economic change on urbanization patterns
- Networks and connectivity between cities
- Connectivity and power
- Researching urban connectivity
- The internal structures of cities
- Postmodern urbanization
- Influences of the state and the planning system on urban form
- Global urban poverty and inequality
- Cultural diversity in cities
- Cities and sustainability

There is a tendency, certainly within the media but also at times within the academic **discourse** of urban geography, to talk about cities in very unequivocal terms. Talking about cities in this way tends to perpetuate certain **urban myths**. Pro-urban myths include seeing the city as civilized, modern, liberating, exciting or perhaps romantic, while anti-urban myths see the city as ugly, alienating, corrupting, dirty or dangerous, amongst other things. The tendency to talk about cities in this way is not new. A number of commentators have recognized the existence of urban myths throughout history, tracing the earliest to Ancient Greece and Rome (Williams 1973; Gold and Revill 2004; Short 2006). Urban myths are significant in that they reflect widely held cultural attitudes towards the urban. They tell us what societies think about cities at different times. These urban myths are also significant because they are still constantly reproduced. This is not to suggest that these impressions are untrue, rather that there is a tendency when we talk about the city to focus on these eye-catching aspects and to exaggerate them at the expense of the subtleties and complexities that exist in cities. However, it is important not to dismiss this way of thinking about cities entirely. Such myths emphasize the sheer diversity of the urban world and begin to provide a framework for understanding and working through this diversity. Yet relying entirely on them as a guide carries with it the danger that much of the detail that makes up the daily 'stuff' of urban life eludes analysis. A review of almost any local newspaper, for example, tells of a range of more mundane concerns that typically constitute the daily life of cities. Gloucester is a small city in the south-west of England. Its newspaper, *The Citizen*, for example, regularly runs stories on issues such as the problems caused by an infestation of seagulls in the city centre, recurrent minor incidents of anti-social behaviour and vandalism, deaths and injuries caused by traffic accidents, financial problems affecting independent retailers, educational successes of local schools, and reports from the city's sports clubs. This daily diet of local news is typical of cities the world over. Such mundane issues though are rarely the substantive concerns of urban geographers who tend to focus on the 'big issues' rather than the minutiae of life in the city:

> Urban geography and urban studies is a discipline populated by Big Things. Cities for a start. They are by definition big. Motorways and mass transportation systems, urban redevelopment projects, and suburban shopping malls are pretty big too. Then there are skyscrapers, mega-projects, new-towns, edge cities, again all large, obvious, written across the landscape and close to the heart of urban geography's sense of itself . . . Given its attraction to the Big, it is perhaps

of little surprise that urban geography has not been particularly good at, or indeed often has not been interested in, making sense of many of the smaller elements that make up a city.

(Latham 2008: 215–15)

A corollary of this tendency within urban geography to see the city in unequivocal terms has been the tendency to focus on a narrow range of big cities, such as Los Angeles, London, Mexico City and Tokyo, where the processes of urbanization are manifested most clearly and spectacularly. However, it would be wrong to dismiss both the mundane concerns outlined above and smaller, seemingly less interesting cities. These concerns make up the fabric of everyday life for the majority of urban dwellers and, despite their large population sizes, the majority of the world's urban population do not live in large cities but in smaller urban settlements (Bell and Jayne 2006):

> 52 per cent of the world's urban population resides in cities and towns of less than 500,000 people. A similar picture is painted for developed and developing countries, as 54 and 51 per cent of their urban population, respectively, live in such cities. Despite the attention they command, megacities – cities with over 10 million people – are home to only 9 per cent of the world's urban population.

(UN HABITAT 2009: 27)

Further, although the issues above may seem trivial or of only limited interest in themselves, they constitute part of much bigger, broader, more significant and wide-ranging urban issues and for this reason deserve our attention. Thus, we need to try to appreciate the fine grain of daily urban life, the big issues and the relations between these. This chapter, then, aims to outline ways to think through the complexity and diversity of the urban world and to talk about the ways that geographers have tried to reconcile both big issues and more mundane concerns in their work. It will do this first by focusing on three aspects of cities that form enduring themes in urban geography, which can be thought of as the multiple geographies of the urban world, as follows:

- The macro-geography of the urban world: the ways in which processes of contemporary urbanization are changing the distribution of the urban population around the world.
- The host of networks and connections that exist between cities and the effects that these webs of connections have on cities.
- The diversity of the internal worlds of individual cities.

Although these will be considered separately here, it should be remembered that they are interrelated issues. Each of these aspects affects the others. These can be thought of as some of the basic or fundamental questions of urban geography. Geographers have sought to explore these in a variety of ways over time devising often radically different theoretical perspectives on them. As Paddison argues:

> Historically then, the study of cities is identifiable with continuities and discontinuities – continuities in terms of the basic questions cities pose, discontinuities in terms of how they have been studied and theorised.

> (Paddison 2001: 4)

The discussion of these basic questions is situated within a reflection on some key recent theoretical debates and challenges within urban geography. The chapter concludes by a looking at a number of contemporary issues. While some of these have echoes in earlier phases of urban geography, others have emerged more recently.

9.1 Defining the urban world

Trying to define the urban world is fraught with difficulty. One does not need to be a student of urban geography to recognize characteristics of urban settlements and the differences between cities, towns and villages. However, organizing this understanding systematically and using it to define what and where is urban has proven more problematic. Fundamentally we need to ask if we can recognize any qualities that are uniquely or distinctly urban. Although there are undoubtedly differences between rural and urban, the question here becomes: are these differences of type or of degree? This question formed the basis of a significant strand of sociological debate during the twentieth century.

The search for qualities or processes that are uniquely urban has long been at the heart of sociological enquiry into the city. This originated in the work of Ferdinand Toennies (1887) who distinguished between **Gemeinschaft** (traditional communities) and **Gesellschaft** (modern societies characterized by more instrumental social relations). This spawned a tradition of sociological enquiry that explored the supposed differences between rural and urban societies and the ways of life that characterized them (Savage *et al.* 2003: 109). The most influential of these were the work of Georg Simmel, particularly his essay 'The metropolis and mental life' (1903/2004) and the longer treatment of his ideas in *The Philosophy of Money*

(1907/1978), and Louis Wirth's essay 'Urbanism as a way of life' (1938). Influential in their time, they have been the subject of much debate across a number of disciplines concerned with questions of the urban. Broadly speaking, Simmel's perspective was temporal, arguing that the culture of the modern period (roughly from 1850 onwards) has been urban, while Wirth's was spatial, seeking to recognize distinctly urban qualities that differed from those of the rural. Simmel's concern was primarily with the effects of the development of the money economy in the modern period on social relations. He argued that it produced blazé, reserved, instrumental relations between people that are found at their most developed in cities, the centres of the money economy. This he contrasted with the social relations of earlier historical periods. Simmel's work has often been misinterpreted as attributing causality to cities. However, it was money rather than cities per se which, he argued, produced the distinctive social relations that he observed (Byrne 2001; Savage *et al.* 2003; Hubbard 2006). Wirth, by contrast, attempted to show that the characteristics of cities, notably their size, density and heterogeneity, produced social relations of a different type to rural areas:

> Wirth's basic argument was that city life was characterized by isolation and social disorganization, and that this was due to the fact that all cities were large, dense and heterogeneous.

> (Savage et al. 2003: 108)

Although undoubtedly pioneering and influential, these works have failed subsequently to sustain the notion that distinctly urban qualities, processes and ways of life exist. Criticisms, particularly of Wirth's arguments, have included the recognition of many cultural groups within cities, a plethora of subcultures rather than the singular urban culture that Wirth proposed, and the identification of close-knit communities in cities, though ones frequently undergoing profound change (Hoggart 1957; Young and Wilmot 1962), which runs counter to Wirth's assertions of isolation and social disorganization as the key characteristics of urban society (Byrne 2001; Savage *et al.* 2003).

Defining the urban for administrative purposes, the measurement, management and planning of cities, has proven equally problematic as attempts to define it sociologically. Amongst administrative definitions of the urban, population size is perhaps the most basic criterion used to define the nature of settlements. Internationally though there are huge variations in the ways in which this criterion is applied. While in parts of Scandinavia a settlement of 300 can be classed as urban, in Japan only settlements whose population size exceeds 30,000 qualify. Higher population densities are often cited as a characteristic of urban areas but here again there is no natural or universally agreed cut-off point that separates urban from non-urban settlements. Indeed, the extensive depopulation that has recently been observed in some old de-industrialized cities such as Detroit in the USA and across parts of Eastern and Central Europe (Hall and Pfeiffer 2000; Oswalt 2004) has meant that large parts of these long-established urban areas now have very low population densities.

The task of drawing boundaries around cities, suggesting a neat separation from rural areas beyond, is further complicated by the ambiguous nature of the **rural–urban fringe** or **peri-urban** zone. Here is a zone where rural and urban functions intermingle and where often substantial components of the hidden infrastructure of the city, such as sewage works, power plants and server farms, along with major transport and distribution functions such as airports and motorways sit in otherwise rural surroundings. Many rapidly growing cities in the Global South have extensive peri-urban areas containing a mosaic of urban and rural-agricultural land uses and activities, these zones providing a home for many of the new migrants to these cities (Simon 2008). Commentators have long argued over whether these zones should be more accurately defined as rural, urban, transitional zones, or as something altogether quite different and distinct (Gallent 2006; Gallent and Anderson 2007). A walk around these areas soon demolishes the impression that there is a neat break between urban and rural.

While the landscapes of the rural–urban fringes of many cities are regarded as somewhat prosaic outcomes of urbanization, the edges of some, particularly American, cities are regarded as more spectacular manifestations of these processes. The processes operating here and their outcomes reveal the inability of a relatively static administrative framework to contain the dynamic and unruly processes of late capitalist urbanization. **Edge cities**, as they are generally referred to, are settlements that contain many of the traditional functions of cities but which have grown rapidly through private development during the last 30 years. They owe their name to their location on the edges of, or at times beyond, existing cities. They seem to be producing new geographies of the urban world, prompting some commentators to suggest that they represent a new **postmodern** phase of urban history very different from that of the nineteenth and twentieth centuries (Dear and Flusty 1998; Soja 1989, 1996, 2000; Dear 2000). We look at some of these new geographies of the urban world in the following section. Edge cities, though, can be thought of as alternatives to the city rather than extensions to it, as in the case of suburbs which constitute the archetypal landscape of earlier

rounds of urbanization in many parts of the developed world. Often edge cities straddle administrative boundaries, fragmenting their true form and extent within official statistical returns. The rapidity with which edge cities have colonized rural land in some areas means that where these processes are at their most prevalent, the administrative framework of regions is more a reflection of historical rather than contemporary processes and patterns of urbanization. The amorphous nature of postmodern urbanization has led some to question whether edge cities and associated settlement forms should be thought of as cities at all (Pile 1999: 30). This neatly returns us to the difficult sociological questions of the urban discussed above.

While acknowledging that it is difficult to define exactly what and where is urban, it should not be assumed from this that urban questions are unimportant. 'Cityness', namely the density, not only of people but also of institutions and built forms (Pile 1999), and the intense heterogeneity and juxtapositions of cities, clearly matter (Amin and Thrift 2002: 2). The nature and quality of urban life are different in different places and this is influenced in large part by the surroundings within which urban lives are lived. Living in a suburb of a small European town, for example, is very different to living in the heart of Tokyo. While we should not fall into the trap of fetishising the city, of attaching uniqueness and causality to its qualities, we should not dismiss the differences within and across the urban world. Indeed geography is all about acknowledging these differences and this has emerged as a key aspect of recent theoretical debates in urban geography. Differences in the nature of places matter and have effects on the creative possibilities open to urban dwellers (Florida 2002) and to the fears and problems they face (Valentine 1989; Patel 2000; Hayward 2004; Aas 2007).

9.2 Multiple geographies of the urban world

9.2.1 Global patterns of urbanization

Current trends in urbanization are changing the macro-geographies of the urban world. By macro-geographies we mean broad patterns in the distribution of the global urban population (see Pacione 2009: Chapter 5). The extent to which different regions of the world are urbanized varies hugely. This is a long-standing historical feature in which, generally, levels of urbanization correlate with those of economic development. The most highly urbanized nations, then, have tended to be the most economically developed. Consequently, until the mid twentieth century, significant urban development was largely concentrated in Europe, North America and Latin America. However, since then, urban growth in these regions has been slow with only modest growth in the proportion of their populations living in towns and cities. In addition, within these regions there has been uneven growth by city size, with the largest growth occurring in smaller urban areas. This reflects the changing economic geographies of key sectors in these regions and the choices of mature urban populations for suburban living and relocation to smaller urban areas and the countryside (Champion 1999).

The fate of large cities in these regions has been mixed. A small number of global or major capital cities, such as London, Paris and New York, have maintained their position or grown in population and influence during this period. This has occurred mainly on the back of the growth of their financial sectors and their primacy within international, national and regional economic systems (Short 2004; Kim 2008). These cities have not been without their problems though. Many have seen significant shrinkage in their manufacturing sectors coupled with problems related to their failure to adequately accommodate, manage and plan for large immigrant populations (Sandercock 1998, 2003; Saunders 2010). The problems of Paris' North African immigrant populations that culminated in civil disturbances in a number of suburban *banlieues* typify this (Wacquant 2007). Whereas bald population statistics suggest overall buoyancy in these cities there has been widespread redrawing of their internal social geographies and this has not been without cost (see Chapter 10).

Second-tier, regional cities, particularly those with a large manufacturing economy, have tended to struggle in the latter half of the twentieth century. While this is the result of a general global shift of manufacturing away from its traditional heartlands (see Chapter 14) the outcomes of this are mediated locally. Since the 1950s many of these cities have suffered significant population loss as their manufacturing economies have contracted. Liverpool, in the north-west of England, for example, lost an average of 10,000 people per year during the 1970s. Attempts to regenerate many cities of this type through ambitious property-led, city centre developments seemed to be stemming this decline as, by the late 1990s, many cities such as Liverpool, which had experienced long-term decline, were seeing their populations stabilize and even in some cases grow slightly. These optimistic signs have been tempered somewhat in recent years, however, as the global recession has impacted on the financial, business, travel and property sectors around which these urban renaissances have typically been constructed (Martin 2010). The fortunes of many of these cities seem to be a reflection of broad trends in national or international economics. For some cities, however, there are signs that the process of decline might be more terminal. These include manufacturing cities in the north-eastern United States, such as Detroit, and many in Eastern and Central Europe. Here an almost total reliance on industries that have now declined or relocated globally, a failure to stimulate significant economic growth in Eastern Europe since 1989, and stark inequalities within the deeply racially divided populations of the North American rustbelt, appear to be keys in understanding the problem.

The most significant growth in the urban world in the last 30 years has taken place in those regions with traditionally low percentages of urban populations, namely Africa and Asia. Asia has witnessed particularly rapid urban growth during this period, headed by China and India, something that is predicted to continue into the foreseeable future. Despite both continents experiencing significant urban growth, the nature of growth in Africa and Asia has been quite different. While China, for example, has seen growth in its urban populations concentrated largely in major urban centres, Africa's has predominantly taken place in small and intermediate cities. Yet, concerns have been raised about the volatility and longer-term **sustainability** of much of this rapid urban growth. In China, a number of under-occupied 'ghost cities' have emerged fuelled by unstable economic conditions and volatility in local property markets (see Case study 9.1).

These broad changes in the macro-geographies of the urban world are captured clearly in shifts in the number and location of the world's **mega-cities** (cities with more than 10 million inhabitants) (Figure 9.1). The United Nations predicts that the number of these cities will increase to 41 in 2030 and that the majority of them will be located outside the developed world. The rapid recent urban growth and its concentration in large settlements

Plate 9.1 Kangbashi. China's 'Ghost city'.
(Mark Ralston/AFP/Getty Images)

Case study 9.1

China's 'Ghost City'

The rapid pace of urbanization in China has been a key feature of global urbanization trends in the early twenty-first century. In 1990, 26 per cent of people in China lived in cities; in 2014 this was 54 per cent and is expected to rise to 76 per cent by 2050. Presently, 16 of the world's 71 urban agglomerations containing over 5 million people are in China (United Nations 2014d). However, for all the spectacular urban growth of major cities such as Beijing, Shanghai and Shenzhen other cities in China have experienced more mixed fortunes, with new urban development plans falling foul of overheated property market speculation and a slow-down in economic growth. This has spawned the curious presence of a number of over-built and under-populated 'ghost cities', where new urban development lies empty awaiting the arrival of people.

Perhaps the most well known of these is the new city development of Kangbashi, in the Ordos District of Inner Mongolia. Traditionally a sparsely populated poor rural region, the Ordos District has boomed economically in recent years as a result of the exploitation of its coal reserves. This resource boom and its resulting wealth provided the impetus for the local leadership to embark on an ambitious urbanization plan with the goal of building a 'one million person metropolis'. The plan was to develop an urban district with a new city, Kangbashi, linked to the old urban core of Dongsheng. When development of Kangbashi began in 2004, Ordos seemed set to become a spectacular jewel in China's crown of city states. Kangbashi's role was to be the administrative, cultural and economic centre of the municipality, with a full range of urban functions, infrastructure, and abundant cultural and leisure amenities. The scale of the development has been huge, with large squares, wide roads and the building of an immense square footage of municipal and residential buildings, with dozens of high-rise apartment towers and hotels. The new city is also packed with monuments and cultural references that evoke the Mongolian heritage of the area. Images of the city's spectacular architectural excesses have captured the imagination of the outside world.

To boost settlement in the new city the municipal government moved its administrative offices, key medical facilities and top-ranking schools to Kangbashi. However, despite this the pace of settlement has been slow, due to a number of overlapping causes. First, despite incentives, commercial businesses have been slow to open up, citing lack of customers, and this lack of basic conveniences has discouraged households from relocating. Second, many native Ordos residents have purchased homes in Kangbashi primarily as second homes or investment properties. This fuelled a vibrant speculative real estate market between 2006 and 2011, with high prices stimulating further building but constraining residential settlement. More recently the development of the new city has slowed with the bursting of the local credit and real estate bubble in 2011, linked to a fall in coal prices related to the wider slow-down in China's economic growth rate. The resulting proliferation of unoccupied residential and commercial buildings in the new city, many abandoned mid-construction, has captured media attention around the world and led to its labelling as China's largest 'ghost city'. Commentators have subsequently seized on Ordos as a metaphor for the arrogance and recklessness of China's rampant urbanization.

It is clear that the pace and scale of urban growth during the boom years was unsustainable, and the key concerns now are dealing with the accumulation of vacant property and continuing to attract people, mainly local famers, to relocate to Kangbashi. However, here challenges remain. Simply pushing unskilled farmers into urban labour has not translated into disposable incomes high enough to maintain a life in the city for many as government compensation packages have been reduced. Educating the farmers is now a key goal for the Ordos government, ensuring new residents have the skills necessary to obtain jobs and live a purposeful urban life.

The situation in Ordos has informed broader debates on urban development in China. It can be seen as a 'test run' for the Chinese government's plans to urbanize the rural interior of the country over the next two decades. In 2014, the Chinese government released the 'National New-Type Urbanization Plan', which announced the intention to increase the proportion of the nation's population living in cities to 60 per cent by 2020, which would mean bringing 100 million new residents to cities. The proliferation of similar failed projects in cities around China has raised questions about this model of urban development and how to temper excessive speculative development in real estate and balance housing supply and demand. The longer-term success of Kangbashi is far from certain, and in the meantime it has become something of a tourist spectacle and a curiosity for urban scholars around the world.

Sources: The Land of Many Palaces (2015), dir. Smith, A.J. and Song. T. [film], Pulan Films; United Nations (2014d); Woodward (2015)

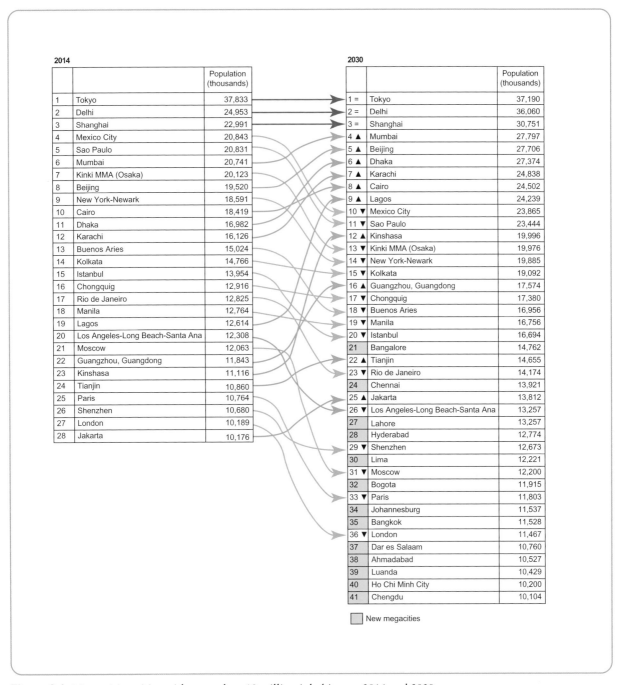

2014		Population (thousands)
1	Tokyo	37,833
2	Delhi	24,953
3	Shanghai	22,991
4	Mexico City	20,843
5	Sao Paulo	20,831
6	Mumbai	20,741
7	Kinki MMA (Osaka)	20,123
8	Beijing	19,520
9	New York-Newark	18,591
10	Cairo	18,419
11	Dhaka	16,982
12	Karachi	16,126
13	Buenos Aries	15,024
14	Kolkata	14,766
15	Istanbul	13,954
16	Chongquig	12,916
17	Rio de Janeiro	12,825
18	Manila	12,764
19	Lagos	12,614
20	Los Angeles-Long Beach-Santa Ana	12,308
21	Moscow	12,063
22	Guangzhou, Guangdong	11,843
23	Kinshasa	11,116
24	Tianjin	10,860
25	Paris	10,764
26	Shenzhen	10,680
27	London	10,189
28	Jakarta	10,176

2030		Population (thousands)
1 =	Tokyo	37,190
2 =	Delhi	36,060
3 =	Shanghai	30,751
4 ▲	Mumbai	27,797
5 ▲	Beijing	27,706
6 ▲	Dhaka	27,374
7 ▲	Karachi	24,838
8 ▲	Cairo	24,502
9 ▲	Lagos	24,239
10 ▼	Mexico City	23,865
11 ▼	Sao Paulo	23,444
12 ▲	Kinshasa	19,996
13 ▼	Kinki MMA (Osaka)	19,976
14 ▼	New York-Newark	19,885
15 ▼	Kolkata	19,092
16 ▲	Guangzhou, Guangdong	17,574
17 ▼	Chongquig	17,380
18 ▼	Buenos Aries	16,956
19 ▼	Manila	16,756
20 ▼	Istanbul	16,694
21	Bangalore	14,762
22 ▲	Tianjin	14,655
23 ▼	Rio de Janeiro	14,174
24	Chennai	13,921
25 ▲	Jakarta	13,812
26 ▼	Los Angeles-Long Beach-Santa Ana	13,257
27	Lahore	13,257
28	Hyderabad	12,774
29 ▼	Shenzhen	12,673
30	Lima	12,221
31 ▼	Moscow	12,200
32	Bogota	11,915
33 ▼	Paris	11,803
34	Johannesburg	11,537
35	Bangkok	11,528
36 ▼	London	11,467
37	Dar es Salaam	10,760
38	Ahmadabad	10,527
39	Luanda	10,429
40	Ho Chi Minh City	10,200
41	Chengdu	10,104

☐ New megacities

Figure 9.1 Mega-cities, cities with more than 10 million inhabitants, 2014 and 2030.

are particularly apparent here. Cities from this region are predicted increasingly to dominate the mega-city league table, whereas longer-standing mega-cities in the West and Latin America, such as New York–Newark and Mexico City, will slip down the rankings. A key issue related to this that has attracted the attention of urban analysts has been that of power in the urban world. Namely, does this changing geography of mega-cities represent a shift

in the distribution of the world's most powerful cities? The issue of power highlights the importance of connectivity in the contemporary urban world.

9.2.2 Global urban connectivity

It is perhaps not surprising that in a global age the issue of connectivity has gained significance within the analysis of cities. Connectivity simply refers to the connections that exist between places, although in actuality the nature of these connections is often highly complex. Commonly places are connected through the movement of goods, people, information, ideas and money. The current age is often represented as one of connection and cities act as vital hubs in global or regional networks of various kinds. Connectivity between cities is not a characteristic of the recent past. Networks of trade, politics, empire and travel, for example, are observable back to ancient history. However, recent technological changes that have led to the development of truly global communications systems have wrought both qualitative and quantitative discontinuities in the nature of these networks. The speed, capacity, intensity, quantity and quality of the connections between cities has grown significantly since the 1980s (Harvey 1989; Dodge and Kitchen 2000; Hubbard 2006). While not dismissing the importance of historical connections and networks stretching around the world (see Sheppard 2002) the ubiquity and intensity of connection in the current age is unparalleled. Social scientists have been quick to pick up on the significance of this. For example, they have adopted various forms of network or *relational approach* (Dicken *et al*. 2001; Sheppard 2002; Bosco 2006; Murdoch 2006) that have sought to problematize the sedentary tendencies of much traditional social theory. Both have been influential in reshaping urban geography in recent years (see Spotlight box 9.1).

The example of London in Spotlight box 9.1 reminds us that, if the contemporary world is a networked one, then the major nodes in these networks are cities. It is here that all major networks coalesce, be they networks of travel and migration, trade, communication, finance or politics. These networks do not coalesce evenly across the urban world, however. Inevitably there is a geography to these networks within which some cities are significantly more important nodes than others. It is here that an important relationship between connectivity and power begins to emerge that destabilizes earlier notions of power associated with cities that were, in large part, related to the size of those cities. For many years it has been taken for granted that the largest cities were the most important. The relational view of cities, though, raises some questions about the validity of this assumption. Rather than simply reading off the power or importance of cities as some function of population size it is now clear that a more accurate and relevant analysis of power in a connected age takes account of the nature and extent of the connections flowing in and out of cities. Attempts to quantify the significance and connectivity of cities in the current age have been a major focus of **global cities** research since the mid-1990s. Analysts have employed a variety of sources of data including the distribution of

financial and producer service offices, air travel, financial flows and electronic communications data to map the networks and connections that flow between the world's cities. Using these methods it is possible to rank cities according to their connectivity and apparent influence within the global economy.

Using these measures, it is possible, for example, for some relatively large cities to be poorly connected, and hence marginal, in the current age despite their size. John Rennie Short (2004; see also Hubbard 2006: 180) cites cities such as Teheran (Iran), Dhaka (Banglagesh), Chongqing (China) and Khartoum (Sudan) as examples of such cities. Dhaka was actually the eleventh largest city in the world in 2014 with a population of 16,982,000 and is estimated to become the world's sixth largest city by 2030 (United Nations 2014d). However, despite this it is relatively little connected into global financial networks, nor is it a major global trade hub or centre of global media networks, except those serving the Bangladeshi **diaspora**. In all the attempts to quantify the significance and levels of connectivity of the world's major cities (see Sassen 1994; Smith and Timberlake 1995; Taylor 2004; Derudder and Wilcox 2005) it occupies a very lowly position, if it is present at all. This relational analysis provides a glimpse of the nature, distribution and operation of power in a global age. However, it has drawn some criticism for its focus on data that reflect the processes of Western economic globalization, thus ignoring other potentially important dimensions of contemporary globalization (Short *et al*. 1996; Robinson 2006). Hierarchies of global cities of culture, religion or politics, for example, might look quite different from those economic rankings that have prevailed in analysis to date. This is not to dismiss the importance of this global cities research, rather, to argue that it represents only one take on globalization, albeit arguably the most significant, amongst many.

9.2.3 The internal structure of cities

The trajectories of urban development vary a great deal around the globe. They reflect the particular combinations of local and general factors that come together in different times and at different places. Consequently the internal worlds of cities are similarly complex and heterogeneous. Despite this, geographers have expended a great deal of effort attempting to find patterns and regularities within this complexity and devise models of the internal structure of cities. Some of the most influential work in the subject is reflective of this tradition within urban geography (see Burgess *et al*. 1925; Hoyt 1939; Harris and Ullman 1945; Shevky and Bell 1955; Mann 1965; Soja 1989, 1996, 2000; Dear and Flusty 1998; Dear 2000). Work

Spotlight box 9.1

Relational approaches and global cities

Relational approaches have encouraged scholars of the city not to regard cities as bounded, isolated entities. Rather they have viewed cities as nodes within a variety of networks, many of which are global in their extent. When thinking about the hinterland of cities, for example, relational approaches have not referred to the contiguous spaces surrounding cities, as was the case in the earlier models of Christaller and von Thünen. Rather they have argued that cities' hinterlands potentially encompass spaces that are spatially distant but which are nonetheless closely bound together within networks. This has led some to question the assumption that we can identify a small subset of 'global' cities – cities such as New York, London and Tokyo commonly painted as the control centres of the global economy – and to argue that all cities are global to a greater or lesser extent (Taylor 2004). London may be a more significant node within global networks than cities such as Gloucester (England), Oaxaca (Mexico) or Hobart (Australia), but these cities are certainly not, somehow, 'non-global' (Hubbard 2006: 185).

Relational approaches represent a fundamental rethinking of prevailing conceptions of space. They potentially profoundly affect the ways in which we conceive of cities. Ash Amin discusses this in the context of the representation of London in maps:

it will take a lot to displace the A–Z or concentric circle image of London by a relational map that incorporates the network of sites around the world that pump fresh food into a distribution centre called Covent Garden, that draws neighbourhood boundaries around settlements in postcolonial countries with which social and kinship ties remain strong, that makes us see sites such as Heathrow airport or Kings Cross station as radiations of trails shooting out across the land and far beyond.

(Amin 2004: 34; cited in Hubbard 2006: 204)

While many, if not most, cities have hinterlands that are potentially global in their extent, there are significant differences between the specific connections that flow in and out of different cities and hence in the nature of these hinterlands. This reminds us that it is important not to be seduced by the global rhetoric that infuses much of this discourse. It is the materiality of the city, the internal mixes of people, firms and institutions and the interactions that take place within cities that affect the ways in which cities articulate with the outside world (and visa-versa of course) (Thrift 1996). The internal worlds of different cities are highly diverse and it is important to appreciate that this is a component of, and a context within which, the geographies of global networks are formed.

exploring the internal structure of cities has tended to be characterized by a focus on either the physical morphology of cities, their buildings, streets and spaces, or the complex and dynamic economic and social geographies that overlie this morphology and that are both reflective of it and active in its transformation. The two-way relationship between the city's physical form and its social and economic geographies is one key to understanding the nature of cities' internal worlds. The focus is on the former here but with a cautionary note not to attribute to it too great a deterministic quality.

While a variety of processes have shaped the geographies of cities it is possible to recognize some broad historical and geographical distinctions within which certain processes have been dominant. The very earliest cities that appeared in places such as Mesopotamia between 5000–6000 BP and later the Indus Valley, Egypt, China and the Mediterranean tended to reflect a combination of local physical and environmental conditions

and the religious and cultural beliefs of societies. Later the emergence of mercantile and subsequently industrial capitalism and processes of colonization became both determining influences on the evolving structures of cities and systems through which ideas about urban form were transmitted around the world. More recently many commentators have argued that globalization and post-industrial or postmodern capitalism has become the dominant influence on urban form across the globe. Some have argued that this most recent phase is one of global urban convergence where difference between the internal worlds of cities is being reduced (Plate 9.2), although other authors have recorded evidence of diversity as well as similarity within postmodern cities (Poulsen *et al.* 2002). These forces, certainly since the medieval period, have also been mediated through the state, which has demonstrated differing degrees of centralization historically and geographically. For example, the cities of communist Eastern Europe and China demonstrated a

Plate 9.2 Global urban convergence? Auckland, New Zealand.

(Mike Deaton)

distinctive 'camel-back' urban form, with a high-density centre surrounded respectively by low-density industrial and high-density residential zones, a form resulting from centralist state-control of land markets and planning and not seen in cities of the capitalist world (Pacione 2009: 184). Further, observable differences between the forms of British and American cities during the twentieth century were attributed largely to the history of UK government state intervention in the housing market (Mann 1965; Ward 2004).

Broad categorizations such as these, or typologies that suggest distinctive epochs or categories either in the evolution of urban form or in types of cities, are undoubtedly helpful in that they begin to work through the complexity and variety of cities. However, they do carry with them the risk of overemphasizing either the pervasiveness of processes such as postmodern urbanization, or the distinctiveness of urban epochs. For example, the extent to which it can be said we are currently witnessing a new phase of urbanization producing cities under conditions of postmodern globalization that are distinctively different from those produced under industrial capitalism has been the subject of considerable debate (Harvey 1989). Similarly, too ready a recourse to models of urban form carries with it the risk of masking a patina of local distinctiveness in the internal worlds of cities. It is important to remember that, eye-catching as the epochal processes of urbanization may be, their imprint on cities is always uneven and their effects are mediated locally. Some cities, perhaps smaller cities in particular (Bell and Jayne 2006), might be relatively lightly touched by these processes while elsewhere processes of contemporary urbanization might be transforming the architectural landscape of cities while leaving the underlying structure or plan relatively unaffected. Cities' internal worlds, then, are often palimpsests within which it is possible to discern many phases of partial urban transformations. The universalizing tendencies within urban theory and its masking or disregard of urban cosmopolitanism has recently been the subject of some significant critiques (Hubbard 2006; Robinson 2006).

9.2.4 Postmodern urbanization

The main process of contemporary urbanization that has caught the attention of urban theorists is that of postmodern urbanization. Some have argued that we are witnessing a new phase of postmodern urbanization that is producing cities that are distinctly different in their form and their social and economic characteristics from earlier waves of urban development. This claim actually rests on empirical investigation of only a small number of cities, of which Los Angeles has assumed a primacy (Plate 9.3). A key motif of postmodern urbanization is an apparent fragmentation of both urban form and the social and economic geographies of the city. The postmodern city is said to demonstrate a chaotic urban form characterized by the juxtaposition of spectacular 'fragments' of commercial and residential development and redevelopment set within extensive areas of environmentally and economically degraded and ethnically segregated space (Soja 1989, 1996, 2000; Davis 1990; Dear and Flusty 1998; Dear 2000). These urban geographies, it has been argued, reflect profound changes in the processes that shape cities and their urban landscapes. Rather than the relatively stable phase of industrial capitalism, mediated by an engaged but not centralized planning system in much of the global North during the twentieth century, we now have a phase of chaotic capitalism and more emasculated planning systems driven primarily by economic rather than social imperatives (Hall and Hubbard 1996, 1998).

Some of the most detailed explorations of the landscapes of the postmodern city include Mike Davis's and Ed Soja's readings of Los Angeles, a city constructed within urban theory as the archetypal postmodern metropolis (Davis 1995; Scott and Soja 1996). Soja has highlighted a number of economic, social and cultural processes that have underpinned Los Angeles' development. Economically he cites the growing significance of new sectors such as producer services, high-technology, cultural entertainment and knowledge-based industries, each of which show distinctive clustering patterns around which new urban forms have emerged. These developments have disrupted the more mono-centric, regular patterns of urban form characteristic of industrial capitalism. Los Angeles is characterized by a number of edge city, or post-suburban, developments, such as those spread across Orange County, which have emerged around these and other new or growing economic sectors. In addition the global connectivity of cities discussed above has seen Los Angeles' functions as a key hub, particularly with links to the Pacific region, underpin growth through an influx of global capital to the city.

Socially Los Angeles has been characterized by heightened levels of, particularly ethnic, segregation and polarization and increasing levels of tension and unrest across its culturally and economically diverse landscapes. Perceptions of Los Angeles as a dystopian realm, while a staple of films such as *Bladerunner* (1982), *Falling Down* (1993), *Escape from LA* (1996) and *Lakeview Terrace* (2008), appear to reflect widely held views of the city by its residents. Increasingly, residential, leisure and commercial landscapes are characterized by 'paranoid' or 'carceral' architecture based on protection, surveillance and the exclusion of perceived threats (Plate 9.4). Evidence would suggest that, rather than making residents feel safer, such 'fortress landscapes' merely exacerbate levels of segregation between communities and, because they preclude the possibility of cross-cultural mixture and dialogue, heighten perceptions of threat associated with unknown or demonized urban populations (Sandercock 2006). A counterpoint to this dystopianism, and perhaps a response to it, has been the pervasiveness of fantasy and simulation throughout the city's landscape. Originally deriving from the fantasy worlds of expositions, world's fairs and theme parks such as Disneyland (Ley and Olds 1999), they now permeate the city more widely and are found in examples such as themed shopping malls and residential districts (Crawford 2004).

While Los Angeles offers a convincing narrative of postmodern urban development, the question remains, as with all urban models, to what extent does this one case represent a more widespread process or a harbinger

Plate 9.3 Los Angeles, constructed as the archetype of postmodern urbanization.
(Tim Hall)

of future urbanization? Although scholars have traced the imprint of postmodernity across urban landscapes and forms well beyond Los Angeles (Watson and Gibson 1995; Poulsen *et al.* 2002), there has yet to emerge

Plate 9.4 Sign warning of private security force in the residential neighborhood of Venice Los Angeles.
(Tim Hall)

a consensus around the extent to which it represents an epochal break in the history of urbanization. Tracing its imprint across the urban world remains an ongoing project for urban geographers. Certainly though, the discourse of a uniform postmodernism as an inevitable form and type for cities around the world would appear to be an oversimplification. There is evidence, for example, of significant differences, as well as similarities, between postmodern cities (Poulsen *et al.* 2002), while the interactions of postmodernism with post-colonial urbanization across the global South are as likely to lead to complex patterns of locally mediated outcomes as they are to the emergence of a uniform global postmodern 'blandscape'.

9.3 Contemporary urban issues

The definition and identification of contemporary urban issues varies with scale. The example, mentioned at the start of this chapter, of the issues highlighted by a local newspaper within a single city, points to a range of issues that are primarily reflective of the local urban context. However, the specific minutiae of these issues should not distract us from the fact that they are also reflective of more broadly conceived urban concerns. Examples of minor incidents of anti-social behaviour are constitutive of broader issues of crime, safety and conflict within the city (Valentine 2001). This in turn might speak of the relationships between different groups of people, for example, distinguished on the basis of age, ethnicity or lifestyle. The problems caused by seagulls in the city centre, for example, speak to broader concerns about the relationships between society and nature, the human and the non-human, in cities (Wolch 2002; Hinchcliffe 2007) and perhaps of cities and sustainability. It is to these broadly conceived contemporary urban issues that we now turn. Although different authors might highlight different sets of concerns, we wish to highlight three pressing issues facing the urban world in the early twenty-first century. These are issues of global urban poverty and inequality, cultural diversity within cities, and the relationship between cities and sustainability.

9.3.1 Urban poverty and inequality

There is nothing inherently urban about poverty and inequality (see Chapter 10). However, the urban world is the context within which they are seen at their most intense and perhaps intractable. While poverty here is understood primarily as an economic phenomenon reflecting levels of wealth, development and income its impacts are much wider, with both social and public health implications, for example. Levels of poverty and inequality are both an issue within cities and between cities and are fundamental to many of the problems that they experience.

There are huge global disparities in the equality of income distribution between countries. While the average income of the top 20 per cent in Sierra Leone is roughly 58 times greater than that of the bottom 20 per cent, in Slovakia this figure is only around four times greater (UN Development Programme 2009). Cities tend to reflect these national and regional patterns of wealth and development but it tends to be within cities that the juxtapositions of wealth and poverty are at their most intense and visible. The effects of this inequality are compounded by the failure of governments in countries within which it is at its greatest to intervene effectively and to support their poorest residents. Put simply, where the wealthiest in a country command so much of the money available there is neither sufficient left over to support the poorest, nor often the political will, given the connections that frequently exist between the economic and political elites. This inequality, and the processes that underpin it, produce fractured cities that are very difficult to plan and manage in any meaningful way. They are not good cities.

Manifestations of urban poverty and inequality differ in the cities of the global North and South. In the global South the most archetypal landscapes of poverty are the, often extensive and now long-standing, **informal settlements** (shanty towns or favelas) that ring many cities (Potter and Lloyd-Evans 1998; Davis 2006). These are a product of the high levels of rural to urban migration and rapid urbanization in these regions and the inability of formal housing channels to provide enough affordable housing for rapidly urbanizing and largely impoverished populations. The provision of basic services such as clean water and sanitation are often impossible in these settings. While these are typically portrayed through reference to poverty and exclusion, some have seen them as sites of hope that provide self-help solutions or alternative futures where the state, the market and international development policy are not able to provide adequate housing (Keivani and Werna 2001). The modernization of some cities such as Dubai has created huge visual contrasts within their landscapes between the monuments to modernization that have been constructed recently and the camps of the construction workers employed to build them (Plate 9.5). The persistence of poverty within many countries of the global South, alongside the embrace of modernization, has produced cities in places such as India whose landscapes, and economic and social geographies can be read as manifestations of ongoing inequality in these countries (see also Case Study 9.1).

Plate 9.5 Landscapes of urban inequality. High rise developments and construction worker in Dubai, UAE.
(Laborant/Shutterstock)

In the global North, postmodern urbanization has been interpreted by many as an urbanization of inequality. The commentaries on Los Angeles discussed above, for example, all highlight the juxtapositions of spectacular wealth and grinding poverty found within it. Inequality lies at the heart of the fear that has been said to permeate residents of postmodern cities which has seen them retreat behind **gated communities** and apparently become so reliant on other fortress landscapes. Of widespread concern within debates about contemporary urbanism has been the apparent emergence of an international urban **underclass**, not only in postmodern cities but also those associated with high levels of immigration and deindustrialization, who have become cut off from routes into the formal economy and who have as a consequence turned to precarious informal and illegal economies, most notably drug dealing, as rational-choice alternatives. The appeal to such evocative labels, which bear the weight of hundreds of years of demonizing the urban poor, carries with it the danger of universalizing conditions that might be particular to only some cities. While groups whose poverty is long-standing and whose ties to the formal economy have been effectively severed do exist, their experience is not typical of all of the urban poor. Poverty for the majority in the global North is much more mundane than evocations of the underclass would suggest, and involves struggles to make ends meet and struggles over inadequate housing, healthy food,

precarious employment and restricted mobility. Certainly the majority would resist having the underclass tag attached to describe themselves and their experiences.

However they may be manifest, poverty and inequality remain some of the most significant and long-standing urban issues. Indeed, many commentators argue that poverty and inequality are increasing as a result of the adoption of a range of neoliberal urban policies in cities around the world (Cochrane 2007), which have seen reductions in state support for local populations in the form of cuts to welfare services, and which it is argued have intensified following the Wall Street Crash of 2008 as part of a politics of 'austerity urbanism' (Peck 2012).

9.3.2 Cultural diversity in cities

The sociologist Sharon Zukin has argued that urban 'publics have become more mobile and diverse' (Zukin 1995: 3). This has resulted in increasing levels of cultural diversity becoming a defining characteristic of contemporary cities. Leonie Sandercock coined the phrase 'mongrel cities' to describe cities in which 'difference, otherness, multiplicity, heterogeneity, diversity and plurality prevail' (2006: 38). This brings with it the potential for innovation, mixing, intercultural dialogue and the emergence of new, hybrid cultural forms. However, it can also pose challenges and give rise to more negative outcomes. Sandercock's work starts from the premise that mongrel cities are an undeniable reality and that it is an obligation of both the city-building professionals and citizens to respond to the challenges those cities present.

Many myths and images of multicultural cities are promoted through the marketing campaigns of cities keen to stress the contributions of different groups to their public cultures. By contrast, Richard Sennett (1994) has argued that mongrel cities tend to lack civic culture (Plate 9.6). He argues that these cities are overwhelmingly characterized by tolerance, rather than hostility, between different cultural groups. However, this is a tolerance characterized by indifference towards other cultural groups rather than an active engagement with diversity. It constitutes a form of indifference across which very little inter-cultural dialogue takes place and a form of stasis in which cultural groups are predominantly inward looking. The result is that little common ground emerges between groups, few meaningful cross-cultural institutions develop and little cross-cultural political capacity emerges through which cities can be shaped in desirable ways. The challenge of cultural diversity in cities, then, is how to develop this missing engagement and solidarity between different cultural groups (Calhoun 2002: 108; cited in Sandercock 2006: 39). Sandercock, drawing on the work of Sennett, argues that this involves 'the challenge of living together

Plate 9.6 Mongrel cities: The Dominican Day Parade New York City August 2010. Whilst parades like this affirm the cultural diversity of the contemporary city, they do so primarily through celebrations of national identity rather than through inter-cultural dialogue.

(Tim Hall)

not simply in tolerant indifference to each other, but in active engagement' (Sandercock 2006: 40).

Leonie Sandercock, in reviewing the work of social theorists in this area, highlights the contributions of the geographer Ash Amin in seeking to explore routes to more convivial futures for mongrel cities (2002). Amin is particularly critical of several popular policy approaches to developing multiculturalism. Many of these are design-led and revolve around the supposed potentials of the public realm as a resource, shared between cultural groups, through which, with appropriate design, inter-cultural encounter can be fostered (Rogers 1999). Sandercock though, drawing on Amin's findings, offers a sceptical assessment of the utopian potentials of public space.

> The depressing reality, Amin counters, is that far from being spaces where diversity is being negotiated, these spaces tend either to be territorialized by particular groups (whites, youths, skateboarders, Asian families) or they are spaces of transit, with very little contact between strangers.
>
> (Sandercock 2006: 44)

Rather than pursuing conventional design-led policies, Amin argued for an alternative focus on the potentials of 'micro-publics', spaces such as workplaces, schools, community centres and sports clubs that provide contexts in which inter-cultural dialogues, although often mundane or 'prosaic negotiations' (Sandercock 2006: 44), can take place. Micro-publics, Amin argues, offer contexts within

which cultural differences can be bridged around a recognition of shared interests, presences and common goals.

Whilst keen not to idealize these micro-publics, Amin recognizes that inter-cultural dialogues will not just happen in these spaces. Indeed within many existing micro-publics such dialogues are not typical. Rather these potentials are something that often need to be shaped and fostered. It is easy to be sceptical of the potentials of micro-publics in this regard. Multiculturalism is not necessarily a characteristic of many sports clubs, for example. It is common in many cities globally to see sport organized formally or informally, to some extent, along ethnic and national lines, as with the case of soccer associations for Latin Americans in US cities (Hamilton and Chincilla 2001: 169) and Asian cricket teams and leagues running in parallel to the official league structure in British cities such as London and Birmingham (Dutta 2014). This is not to say that there is no integration of these communities within mainstream leagues and teams, rather that they are formed as a result of perceptions by some players of exclusion from mainstream clubs, along with the costs of membership. They may also serve as ways of fostering social contact and cultural and national solidarity amongst members. However, given the failure of conventional policy routes towards multiculturalism these settings offer potential alternatives through which to incubate future policy. It would be naïve, though, to pretend that they are any more immune to the politics of indifference, hostility and nationalism than any of the city's other spaces and settings. The challenge, then, is both how desirable dialogues and encounters might be fostered within these micro-publics, and how they might feed into macro-public civic and political movements shaping more convivial futures in mongrel cities.

9.3.3 Cities, sustainability and resilience

The ecological crises of the current age are well known. They are discussed elsewhere in this volume in some detail (Chapters 5, 6 and 7). The challenges posed by dwindling global supplies of accessible oil and climatic chaos are global in their extent and fundamental in their significance to the planet (Atkinson 2007a, 2007b, 2008; Newman *et al.* 2009). The relationships between cities and these ongoing crises are becoming an ever greater concern of urban scholars, as witnessed by the growth of literature on cities and sustainability since early key publications from the mid 1990s (Haughton and Hunter 1994). Concern here is two-way involving both the ways in which cities pose a threat to the environment and the ways in which the environment poses a threat to cities. The latter is evidenced by the recent growth in the urban resilience literature (Coafee *et al.* 2009; Newman *et al.* 2009). The former concern involves both the mapping of the contributions of cities to these crises and outlining possible solutions to them while the latter is concerned primarily with the ways in which cities might build resilience to crisis into their infrastructures and social and economic structures and practices. There is overlap between these literatures as the latter is concerned both with reactive measures to mitigate the impacts of crises but also the development of long-term practices and processes that may contribute to the resolution of ecological crises, or at least their reduction and management.

Without doubt, given that over half of the world's population now lives in cities, the rates of future growth of the world's urban population and the ecological demands made by cities and their populations, the urban world will be the key site across which the impacts of these ecological crises are felt and the key site in any possible resolution of them. It should be remembered that when scholars of the city discuss sustainability, crisis and resilience, their discussions are not restricted to matters of environmental science. Human geographers have key contributions to make to these debates, since inequality as highlighted above, for example, is an inherently unsustainable condition. It compromises resilience as the impacts of ecological crises are felt unevenly across social groups, the poor being less able to insulate themselves from them. Further, it undermines attempts at collective solutions to ongoing problems of environment and sustainability. The debates around the relationships between cities and ecological crises have

encompassed many dimensions including consumption patterns and resource use amongst urban populations (Rees and Wackernagel 2008), sustainable urban size and form (Breheny 1995), the roles of neighbourhoods and green spaces in promoting sustainable development (Carley 1999; Chiesura 2003), transport and mobility (Hall 2003) and encounters with nature in the city (Hinchliffe *et al.* 2005; Benton-Short and Short 2008). Just as many sub-disciplines of human geography have been reshaped as they have undergone a cultural turn in recent years, it is increasingly likely that urban geography will be reshaped as it undergoes an ecological turn in the near future. The imperatives for this could not be greater. Atkinson, in a series of essays (2007a, 2007b, 2008), argues that the current crisis will lead to no less than the collapse of modern civilization as we now know it. Ultimately, he predicts:

> It is not at all clear how fast and through what stages the collapse will unfold because there are many variables which will interact differentially and depend crucially on political decisions taken – and possibly major conflicts – along the way; however, we can be sure that in general the decline will be inexorable. By the latter decades of this century, a radically altered world will have emerged, with a greatly reduced population living surrounded by the defunct debris of modernity, comprised of fragmented and largely self-reliant political entities. Our complex, 'globalized' world of megastates and technological hubris will be but a fading memory. The impacts of global warming and other environmental legacies of our age will reduce the options for reconstruction, possibly fatally.

(Atkinson 2008: 79)

The challenge facing urban dwellers, urban managers and urban geographers in the future is to try to ensure that Atkinson's and other gloomy prognoses for the future of the urban world are not realized.

9.4 Conclusion

The urban world, as we have seen, is big, dynamic, diverse and complex: a potentially intimidating topic of study. However, it is also a fascinating, rewarding and important topic for which there are economic, social and ecological imperatives that demand it is better understood and managed.

This chapter has attempted to provide a broad framework through which to approach cities. This involves, at its heart, the resolution of the small and immediate concerns of the urban here and now with the broader trends, patterns and issues of which they are part.

Urban geography and urban geographers at all levels have important contributions to make to the future resolution of the urban issues identified at the end of this chapter and many more besides. The twenty-first century will certainly be an urban century, but how urban systems and cities will change, and what these will look like at the end of the century, will continue to pose intriguing questions for urban geographers to address.

Learning outcomes

Having read this chapter, you should be able to:

- Appreciate the nature and diversity of the urban world. You should be able to recognize the characteristics of cities, the nature of urbanization, the diversity of global urban forms and their characteristics.

- Recognize the difficulties inherent in trying to define and represent the urban, either within scholarly discourses or through systems of administration, planning and management.

- Think geographically about cities as socio-spatial entities. Cities are the products of social relations. This is reflected both in the relationships within cities, for example between different groups of people, and between cities. Understanding the nature and effects of these relationships is an important aspect of differentiating cities.

- Appreciate the range of issues that face cities in the present era and the ways in which these can vary between different parts of the world and between different types of city. In addition it is important to critically evaluate the different routes to the resolution of these problems that have been advocated.

- Understand the different ways in which cities have been conceptualized in geographical and socio-logical thought. Scholars of cities have developed many different takes on the city, approaching it from different angles and studying different aspects of it. Evaluating the strengths and weaknesses of these different approaches is a key skill for the urban geographer.

Further reading

Amin, A. and Thrift, N. (2002) *Cities: Reimagining the Urban,* Polity, Cambridge. An important contribution to recent debates about the city. Challenges the tendencies within urban geography to see the city as a bounded entity and to focus on the apparently 'big' issues at the expense of the everyday experience. Offers fresh ways of looking at the contemporary urban world.

Hall, T. and Barrett, H. (2012) *Urban Geography,* 4th edition, Routledge, Abingdon. An accessible guide to the subject that focuses particularly on the recent history of cities. Contains a number of student-friendly case studies, examples and exercises.

Hubbard, P. (2006) *City,* Routledge, Abingdon. A panoramic sweep over the contemporary urban world viewed through the lens of urban theory from geography and beyond. An important critical synthesis of ways of thinking about and looking at the city. Combines a historical sensitivity with a keen eye on the city as it is today.

Latham, A., McCormack, D., McNamara, K. and McNeill, D. (2009) *Key Concepts in Urban Geography,* Sage, London. A series of engaging, concise essays on a range of key issues and concepts. Critical, occasionally quirky and contemporary in its organization, approach and outlook. Acts as both a key starting point for the novice urban geographer and a handy source of reference.

LeGates, R.T. and Stout, F. (eds) (2010) *The City Reader,* 5th edition, Routledge, Abingdon. A landmark collection of key writings on the city from the nineteenth century to the present day. An authoritative collection that presents key articles along with useful biographical essays on the authors and overview of their career and work. An essential resource for the serious urban geographer.

Pacione, M. (2009) *Urban Geography: A Global Perspective,* 3rd edition, Routledge, London. The most comprehensive urban geography textbook currently available. Covers cities from the developed and developing world through a series of well organized chapters filled with a wealth of references, examples and illustrations.

Robinson, J. (2006) *Ordinary Cities: Between Modernity and Development,* Routledge, Abingdon. Offers a serious challenge to the tendency of traditional urban theory to universalize the experiences of a small number of cities and fail to engage with the complex diversity of the global urban world. Argues from a post-colonial standpoint for a cosmopolitan urban theory that is able to embrace and include global urban diversity. An important critical intervention in thinking about the city.

Browse the journals *Cities, City,* the *International Journal of Urban and Regional Research, Urban Geography,* or *Urban Studies* for many urban case studies.

Useful websites

www.unhabitat.org   The site of the UN Habitat programme concerned with shaping better futures for cities.

www.lboro.ac.uk/gawc   The home of the Global and World Cities Network at the University of Loughborough. A wealth of data and reports on the networks of global cities.

www.city-data.com   Rich data archive for US cities.

www.architecture.com/RIBA/Aboutus/SustainabilityHub Royal Institute of British Architects – UK. Site containing a collection of materials about sustainable architecture and design.

www.centreforcities.org/   Centre for Cities – excellent resource containing interactive data tools with reports and policy briefs looking at contemporary and recent urban change.

http://maps.google.com   Zoomable maps, satellite imagery and street-level panoramas.

www.thisisgloucestershire.co.uk   The home of Gloucester's *Citizen* local newspaper mentioned in the chapter. Check out the latest on the seagull infestation and other stories concerning Gloucester's citizens. Most other towns and cities will have their equivalent newspaper/site.

URBAN SEGREGATION AND SOCIAL INEQUALITY

Chapter 10

Phil Hubbard

Topics covered

- The city as socially divided

- The connections between social exclusion, poverty and urban segregation

- Stereotyping, urban representation and the exclusionary urge

- Racial segregation: places and spaces of ethnicity

- Regeneration, gentrification and the social 'cleansing' of the city

All societies are riddled by inequalities, some of which are more fundamental than others (for example, a person's skin colour, age, or religion typically plays a critical role in shaping their status in contemporary society, whereas their hair colour or shoe size tends to be less significant). Quite why some social differences matter more than others is a key debate in the social sciences – one to which geographers have contributed in a variety of ways. One contribution involves forms of 'mapping' that show that different social groups are differently distributed in space. Such mappings typically demonstrate that particular social groups, defined by age, **sexuality**, class, gender, religion or ethnicity, dominate in particular areas, often to the exclusion of other groups. Arguably, such mapping of social space began not in geography, but sociology, with members of the Chicago School of Sociology including Ernest Burgess and Robert Park in the 1920s. Burgess in particular was a keen proponent of mapping and expected his students to become proficient in mapping, and able to combine their own observations on the quality of different residential neighbourhoods with extensive use of Census and other sources.

The most famous outcome of this type of social mapping was the concentric zone model of Chicago that represented the city as a set of successive zones typified by rising wealth and prosperity as distance from the centre or CBD increased. Over subsequent years, geographers have developed this initial model to provide other schematic mappings of the city showing its divisions into distinctive social spaces or neighbourhoods. And though the rigid divisions of the industrial city have given way to a more complex post-industrial geography (see Chapter 9), it is clear that the city remains a far from undifferentiated social space: rather, it is a complex 'patchwork' in which different social groups take their allotted place. Many neighbourhoods and streets are of course mixed and, conversely, few residential streets or neighbourhoods are homogeneous in their social make-up. This said, there appears to be strong tendencies towards clustering, segregation and socio-spatial sorting, meaning we can still associate specific neighbourhoods with specific types of residents, whether classified by class, age, ethnicity, sexuality, religion, gender, disability and so on. The underlying logic is simple: those with privileged social identities tend to be found in more valued locations (something reflected in the property prices in different areas. While geographers now deploy different theories to explain this patterning than was the case in the time of Burgess, the same type of conclusions about the city as a 'sorting machine' can be drawn. If anything, these tendencies are becoming more clear-cut over time: in the UK, for example, it is now easier to typify some inner urban areas as

non-white than any time in the recent past, despite general evidence that the nation is becoming more 'multicultural' (Sturgis *et al.* 2014; Johnston *et al.* 2015).

Through such mappings of the city, geographers have demonstrated that the city continues to be divided on social lines. As we will see in this chapter, however, this is merely a starting point for *urban social geography,* that part of the discipline most preoccupied with identifying patterns of segregation and documenting their consequence for different groups. This chapter explores some of the key concepts in this sub-discipline, particularly those revolving around segregation and exclusion. Rather than focusing solely on the idea that neighbourhoods are formed via the clustering of like-minded individuals who want to live alongside one another, it explores the ways that segregation creates clusters or areas associated with social stigma and disadvantage, and proposes that this is, in part, a sign that some groups do not want to live alongside social groups who they identify as Other or inferior in some way. As this chapter will demonstrate, one of the clearest ways that the social disadvantage of such neighbourhoods is expressed is through their labelling as being 'on the margins' – e.g. 'slums', 'problem estates' or '**ghettos**'. For those who do not live in such spaces, these areas can often be spaces of fear and fascination because they represent spatial concentrations of those who fail to match mainstream ideas of how people should live and work. The **stigma** surrounding these places compounds their poverty and isolation, as once a place is labelled as degraded and deprived, its residents may find it hard to be accepted by mainstream society. Underlining the fact that space plays an *active* role in shaping people's standard of living, this chapter's focus on urban geographies of segregation and exclusion demonstrates why a sensitivity to place matters, and illustrates some of the ways urban social geographers contribute to pressing debates on social inequality.

10.1 Poverty and urban segregation

While geography has always had a strong interest in mapping social groups and their location in space, for many urban social geographers this is a means to an end: namely, highlighting the importance of spatial processes in perpetuating social inequality. Urban social geography hence circles around questions of the **quality of life** that people experience in different spaces. In simple terms, quality of life can be defined as the extent to which our needs and desires (be they social, psychological or physiological) are fulfilled. Though this can only truly be measured through subjective assessments of the extent to which individuals are satisfied with their own life, many studies by geographers have reached consensus that it is easier to attain an acceptable or good quality of life in areas that offer ample economic opportunities, good social facilities, and a quality environment. Given this, we can see that our life chances are closely related to our place of residence. One well-known aspect of this is the so-called 'postcode lottery' around health services in the UK: depending on where you live, you will enjoy very different levels of medical provision through the National Health Service (White *et al.* 2012). Likewise, in the USA there are known patterns of health provisioning which mean that poorer people live in areas where health risks are highest and access to good health services lowest (Kwan 2013). Where you are born, and where you live, thus has a major bearing on where (and how) you die.

The same is true of prosperity (or lack of it). Geographical studies of wealth and income suggest that we should not just think about neighbourhoods with concentrations of rich people, but should recognize the existence of *rich neighbourhoods*. This distinction is subtle but significant, for it suggests that wealth is amplified in some places. To elaborate: people who are born in places characterized by high concentrations of affluence are more likely to be wealthy themselves because the concentration of money in the area means standards of education, health care and employment are relatively good. While house prices are high, housing standards are good, and may be an important source of inherited wealth. As Dorling (2004) explains, there is a circularity here whereby affluence breeds affluence.

Surprisingly, geographers have said little about urban geographies of affluence, despite the obvious relationship that exists between income and quality of life (Beaverstock *et al.* 2004; Hay and Muller 2012). In contrast, much has been said about geographies of poverty, with social geographers often drawn towards this topic because they feel their relatively privileged position might allow them to draw attention to – and perhaps improve – the life chances of those living in poorer urban areas. Poverty can be defined as the condition where individuals or households are unable to afford what might be perceived to be the normal necessities of life. Inevitably, judgments of what we need to consume to survive vary across time and space, meaning geographers are generally more interested in *relative* rather than *absolute* poverty. On a worldwide scale, for example, it is evident that indicators such as average income per capita provide only a very superficial insight into experiences of poverty in different nation-states (see Chapter 8). Relative income measures – e.g. the definition of poverty as being 60 per cent of median equivalent income – are somewhat more meaningful, but fail to take into account what that income can secure in

terms of goods, services and the necessities of life. Consequently, recent attempts to measure poverty have generally defined people as being in poverty if they lack the financial resources needed to obtain the living conditions that are customary and 'normal' in the society to which they belong. Identifying such thresholds does not suggest that everyone's needs are the same, but does suggest an income level that is socially unacceptable for any individual to live below. For example, the Poverty and Social Exclusion project suggested that 33 per cent of the British population were living in poverty in 2012 on the basis that their income would not secure at least three of the 35 items considered by at least 50 per cent of the British population as necessary for maintaining an acceptable standard of living (see Table 10.1). While some of these items may not have been considered a necessity in previous decades (and others remain luxuries that many in the global South can only dream of), comparison of these figures with previous studies suggests the incidence of poverty has actually risen sharply. In 1983, 14 per cent of British households lacked three or more necessities because they could not afford them, a figure that increased to 21 per cent in 1990, 26 per cent in 1999 before accounting for a third of the population in 2013 (see Pantazis *et al.* 2006; Gordon *et al.* 2013).

Increases in costs of living clearly have an impact here, with decreases in poverty in the early 2000s seen to be reversing in more recent years as disposable incomes failed to keep pace with rises in fuel costs, food costs and (especially) housing costs. In 2010, the required income for a single person of working age to be able to afford a minimum standard of living was suggested to be around £16,200 per annum, rising to £40,400 for a couple with two dependent children (Davis *et al.* 2014). Roughly translated, such figures suggest that nearly 14 million people in the UK cannot afford what are considered acceptable standards of living. While such deprivation is particularly pronounced among those who are out of work, many of those in the lower strata of the labour market are also living in poverty (the persistence of low-paid, part-time or precarious forms of employment being significant here, alongside the restructuring of welfare provision for those on low incomes). Coupled with the rapidly rising incomes characteristic of managerial and professional occupations (particularly in 'knowledge-rich' sectors such as law and finance), the consequence is an increasingly polarized society. For example, between 1979 and 1991, the average British income grew by 36 per cent, yet for the bottom tenth of the population it dropped by 14 per cent. While the rate of income polarization slowed in the 1990s – partly because of welfare reform – the gap between the 'haves' and 'have-nots' accelerated in the twenty-first century (Dorling and Rees 2003, 2004). By

Table 10.1 Perception of adult necessities and how many people lack them (all figures show % of UK adult population)

Item	Percentage of respondents considering items necessary	Percentage of population unable to afford item
Heating to keep home adequately warm	96	9
Damp-free home	94	10
Two meals a day	91	8
Visiting friends or family in hospital or other institutions	90	3
Replace or repair broken electrical goods such as refrigerator or washing machine	86	26
Fresh fruit and vegetables every day	83	8
Washing machine	82	1
Dental work/treatment	82	17
Celebrations on special occasions such as Christmas	80	3
Attending weddings, funerals and other such occasions	79	3
A warm waterproof coat	79	4
Telephone at home (landline or mobile)	77	2
Meat, fish or vegetarian equivalent every other day	76	4
Curtains or window blinds	71	19
A hobby or leisure activity	70	8
Household contents insurance	70	12
Enough money to keep your home in a decent state of decoration	69	20
Appropriate clothes to wear for job interviews	69	8
Taking part in sport/exercise activities or classes	56	8
To be able to pay an unexpected expense of £500	55	33
Two pairs of all-weather shoes	54	7
Regular savings (of at least £20 a month) for rainy days	52	31
Television	51	0

2010/11, the average income of the top fifth of households was around 15 times greater than for those in the bottom fifth (£73,800 per year compared with £5,000) (see Figure 10.1) and most measures of income inequality suggest the UK is more unequal than at any previous time in the last 30 years.

While some nations do not exhibit the levels of social polarization apparent in the UK, it is important to note that levels of social inequality evident in many other nations are far in excess of this (see Spicker 2006). Yet in each and every case this social inequality is spatially expressed, whether as a division between rich and poor regions, an urban–rural divide or differences in wealth between cities. However, it is clear that the sharpest contrasts between wealth and poverty are found *within* cities, and one of the major contributions urban social geographers have made to debates surrounding poverty is to draw attention to areas of acute urban need. According to the United Nations (2001), over one billion of the world's population lives in 'slum' urban environments without access to safe water, acceptable sanitation and secure, tenured housing of an acceptable standard. Ninety-five per

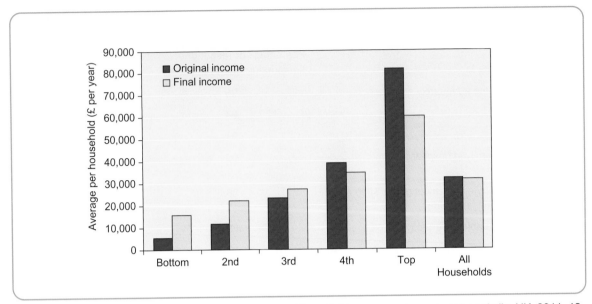

Figure 10.1 Average original and final (i.e. after taxes and benefits) income per household by quintile, UK, 2011–12.

Source: National Statistics Online (2014), www.ons.gov.uk/ons/dcp171778_367431.pdf

cent of these concentrated slum environments are found in the 'Third World', and it has accordingly become something of a geographical cliché to juxtapose the assuredly affluent 'Westernized' city centres now typical of many of the world's rapidly expanding cities with the 'slum' dwellings that are often just a stone's throw away. For instance, profiling Jakarta in Indonesia (population 9 million), Cybriwsky and Ford (2001) contrast the city's Golden Triangle of prestigious residential districts (e.g. Cikini, Kuningan and Menteng) with the *rumah liar* ('wild houses') characteristic of its sprawling, chaotic *kampungs*. They thus conclude that Jakarta 'has extraordinary contrasts between the worlds of prosperity and poverty, and significant challenges ahead for continued development as a global metropolis' (Cybriwsky and Ford 2001: 209).

Yet such 'extraordinary' contrasts between landscapes of wealth and poverty are not just restricted to megacities or those cities living with the legacy of colonial rule: for example, while London remains the most deeply divided city in Britain in terms of income disparities, most British cities display obvious contrasts between the affluent landscapes of the central city and the 'pockets' of deprivation that surround it. Notable here are those areas of 1960s local authority housing, which came to be characterized by high rates of economic inactivity. While these are not 'slums' according to the UN's definitions, evidence from 20 of these 'unpopular' housing estates in the 1990s suggested they possessed unemployment rates, on average, two and a half times higher than the surrounding urban area (Power and Tunstall 1997), representing pernicious spatial concentrations of relative poverty (Table 10.2). In

2010, more than half of those living in the socially rented housing typical of such estates had less than 60 per cent of median income, and could thus be defined as living in poverty (Department of Work and Pensions 2011).

The particular combination of problems encountered in deprived local authority estates created national headlines in the 1990s as confrontations between police and local youths (especially joyriders accused of stealing cars) escalated into fully fledged riots. The spatial concentration of unemployment on these estates, especially among young men, was hypothesized as the most important underlying cause of these disturbances. Figures for the 13 estates affected by serious disorder between 1991 and 1992 suggest that nearly 80 per cent of their occupants were either economically inactive or unemployed (Table 10.2). A simultaneous withdrawal of economic infrastructure – including businesses, shops and banks (Case study 10.1) – meant that there was little money circulating locally, and this had negative impacts on mental and physical health. The mythical black market (an **informal economy** based on petty theft, drug dealing or cash-in-hand trading) did not offer any sort of escape for the majority of residents, given that black markets rarely flourish when there are few people who can afford to buy stolen goods, let alone legitimate ones (Green 1997).

While geographers stressed that uncivil urban actions are also connected to processes of economic restructuring and institutional disinvestment, the media largely ignored such arguments in favour of a rhetoric depicting Britain's local authority and social housing estates as breeding grounds of immorality, characterized by high rates of

Table 10.2 Social characteristics of 12 'riot' estates and 20 'unpopular' estates from 1991 UK Census of Population

	British average (%)	20 'unpopular' housing estates (%)	12 'riot' housing estates (%)
Unemployment	10	34	31
Economic inactivity	36	44	45
Population under-16	19	31	31
Population under-24	33	46	48
Lone parents	4	18	15
Ethnic minority population	6	26	11
Pupils aged 15+ gaining 5+GCSEs (grade A–E)	43	20	20

Source: A. Power and R. Tunstall, *Dangerous Disorder: Riots and Violent Disturbances in Thirteen Areas of Britain, 1991–92,* Joseph Rowntree Foundation, 1997. Reproduced by permission of the Joseph Rowntree Foundation

Case study 10.1

Geographies of retail disinvestment

During the late 1990s, debates on poverty began to focus on the role institutional disinvestment played in exacerbating the problems encountered by those living in 'poor places'. One dimension of this was the withdrawal of financial services from poorer areas, with as many as 15 per cent of bank branches in the United Kingdom closed down in the early 1990s, the majority in low-income, inner-city areas (Leyshon and Thrift 1994). Another was the closure of once-vibrant neighbourhood shops as retail chains concentrated on the development of large superstores catering to mobile and affluent consumers (Williams and Hubbard 2001). Given that many of these were located in out-of-town and edge-of-town locations, this left many neighbourhoods described as food 'deserts', where a range of affordable and varied food was available only to those who had private transport:

> Food deserts . . . are those areas of cities where cheap, nutritious food is virtually unobtainable. Carless residents, unable to reach out-of-town supermarkets, depend on the corner shop where prices are high,

products are processed and fresh fruit and vegetables are poor or non-existent.

> (Laurence 1997)

This has raised serious concerns about the health of those in poor places, with the lack of fresh fruit and vegetables and a reliance on fatty, fast foods implicated in the making of significant health inequalities. Confirming the intensity of food-access problems in some of the large local authority housing estates in British cities, Wrigley *et al.* (2003) noted significant improvements in diet following the construction of a new superstore in the Seacroft district of Leeds, an area that had previously suffered considerable retail disinvestment. Against this, there remains a noted correlation between deprivation and the quality of local high streets in Britain, with the Royal Society for Public Health (2015) suggesting 'unhealthy' high streets remain typified by bookmakers, payday loan shops, fast food outlets and tanning salons, whereas pharmacies, leisure centres, and health services are found on the healthiest and wealthiest High Streets, often alongside a diverse range of independent food retailers (see also Maguire *et al.* 2015; Cox *et al.* 2010).

teenage pregnancy, widespread drug abuse, alcoholism and antisocial behaviour:

> The sense of decline and neglect in many of these areas is palpable: the built environment in many of these areas has now taken on all the classic, ominous characteristics (boarded-up windows, barbed wire

surrounds) of the enclaves of high crime and violence associated with Los Angeles and its ghettos in the months leading up to the 1992 riots. Public space is often colonized by young men in baseball caps and cheap khaki.

> (Taylor 1997: 6 © Guardian News & Media Ltd 1997)

While there were as many as 2,000 local authority housing estates in Britain, accounting for nearly two million people in total (Goodwin 1995), the term 'no-go' estate became a convenient way for the media and public alike to label a wide variety of social environments in the 1990s (even though only a small number of which experienced unrest). Such labelling exacerbated neighbourhood decline: those who could, moved out, leaving behind only the most vulnerable (Hastings and Dean 2003). In the words of Hanley (2011), many large estates appeared 'ringed by an invisible forcefield that asks outsiders why they might want to enter, and insiders why they might want to leave'.

Such factors also appeared to be present in the 'English Riots' of 2011, which involved several nights of looting and public disorder in the largest cities. Although politicians were quick to denounce the riots as the work of 'feral' gangs, and argued for a swift law and order response to quell an 'epidemic' of criminality, other commentators drew attention to the inequalities between those living in the poorer areas of cities and the growing affluence of the richest. Dorling and Lee (2014), for example, describe the disturbances as both symptomatic of a divided nation, but more specifically of dividing cities. In their analysis they quote Ministry of Justice data to conclude that 41 per cent of suspects lived in the 10 per cent most deprived places in England and that the majority of areas where suspects lived were categorized as deprived, with 66 per cent of those areas becoming poorer between 2007 and 2010. For esteemed social theorist, Zygmunt Bauman (2011, np) these riots were seen to be the outcome of the combination of rising consumerism and rising inequality. As he put it, 'this was not a rebellion or an uprising of famished and impoverished people or an oppressed ethnic or religious minority – but a mutiny of defective and disqualified consumers, people offended and humiliated by the display of riches to which they had been denied access . . . city riots in Britain are best understood as a revolt of frustrated consumers' (Bauman 2011). The implication here is that the parallel lives led by residents living in different areas of the city – some privileged, others associated with an 'underclass' – resulted in a moment of collapse when those living in deprived areas, often adjacent to areas of wealth, seized the consumer goods they felt they were denied by the accident of geography.

As we will subsequently see, in recent times British local authority estates have been subject to forms of regeneration that mean that the overt concentration of poverty in such neighbourhoods is being mitigated by processes where more affluent residents are encouraged to move in. However, in other instances, 'problem' estates appear to have been abandoned by both state and market, blighted by a debilitating cycle of labelling and marginalization. An example here is provided by the *banlieues* (suburbs) of social housing surrounding Paris and other major French cities. In October 2005, three young men in one of these *banlieues* – Clichy-sous-Bois (NE Paris) – sought to evade a police check (a regular occurrence in the *banlieues*) by hiding in an electricity substation. Two were electrocuted, prompting an anti-police protest that rapidly spread across the country. In over a week of riots, 10,000 cars were torched and 3,000 people arrested. Video footage of burning cars was screened nightly by the world's media, prompting commentators to speculate why such scenes were happening. Whilst some sections of the press suggested these were simply copycat protests in which young men wanted to appear on television, more trenchant critiques suggested that at their source were structural inequalities that needed to be understood in geographical and historical context. For, as Dikeç (2006) argues, the *banlieues* are not all deprived (and some are reasonably affluent). Yet they have always had negative connotations, identified as '*les quartiers difficiles*' which contain the social problems that have, by and large, been cast out of the central city. At the turn of the millennium, these areas of social housing possessed unemployment rates twice the national average, with 40 per cent of young people unemployed. The fact that some of these areas of social housing were explicitly designed to house North African immigrants in the 1960s is also highly significant here, given that the *banlieue* has always been understood as a 'problem area' (i.e. designed to solve the problem of housing new migrant labour).

Writing before the riots, Tissot and Poupeau (2005: 5) argued that 'when one talks of poverty in France, one can talk of the "socially excluded", the "immigrants", or even of "the young", but it is easier for reports to dwell on the places where it is found: "*les banlieues*"'. Post-millennium, and in a context of considerable Islamaphobia in the West, the problem of the *banlieue* was transformed from one where inhabitants of the *banlieue* were a problem for one another to one where they were imagined as threat to the city (and the nation) as a whole. By way of example, Garbin and Millington (2012: 2071) argue that stigma and shame were attached to La Courneuve's *Citédes 4000* zone that excluded the mainly North African inhabitants from the 'Republican project' in a symbolic defamation that chained residents to this specific space, and denied them wider participation in society. As they write, 'relegated spaces such as La Courneuve enclose individuals and families already deprived of capital and exacerbate their exclusion by reducing the likelihood that they may gain access to capital in the future'.

Plate 10.1 *Banlieue* **riots.**

(AP/Remy de la Mauviniere/Press Association Images)

The connections made here between ethnicity and space are significant, and we will return to these subsequently. At this point, it suffices to say that the white-dominated media in France could not accept that the protest was one in which French citizens were justifiably declaring their anger at the deteriorating housing, lack of transport and poor schooling that characterized their *banlieue*. Rather, this was depicted as a riot in which 'outsiders' from the colonial margins sought to attack the centre (Dikeç 2006). Such arguments support Shields' (1991: 5) view that marginal places 'carry the image and stigma of their marginality which becomes indistinguishable from any empirical identity they might have had'. In this sense, it is clear that media stereotypes play a crucial role in creating and perpetuating social and spatial inequalities.

10.2 Urban segregation and cultural stereotypes

The fact that the media exacerbated the deprivation experienced in the *banlieue* and outer city estates by drawing broad-brushed stereotypes of place suggests that when we explore social inequality, we need to think carefully about the way representations of people and place entwine. This involves consideration of **cultural** issues (see Chapter 13), and shifts attention from the economic manifestations of inequality to questions of why some groups become identified as threats or problems for mainstream society. No matter how widespread the rhetoric that we are all created equal has been, historically it is difficult to identify a

society that has not made distinctions between the social mainstream (or norm) and those Others who seemingly threaten the coherence of society. The notion of a scapegoat is certainly an ancient one, and history can tell of many groups – e.g. Jews, prostitutes, homosexuals – whose lives have been made intolerable because they are seen to pollute the body politic (Sennett 1994). Such groups have often been cast out, physically, as well as metaphorically, socially excluded on the basis that they disturb social and spatial order. In situations where they have been allowed to remain, their occupation of space has often been fiercely contested: in many contexts, the socially excluded have been unable or unwilling to occupy the spaces associated with mainstream society, carving out their own geographies on the margins.

Writing in the context of the urban West, Winchester and White (1988) suggest that socially excluded groups include the unemployed, the impoverished elderly, lone-parent families, ethnic minorities, refugees and asylum seekers, the disabled, illegal immigrants, the homeless, sexual minorities, prostitutes, criminals, drug users and students. If you are reading this book, the chances are that you are a student. If so, the identification of students as an excluded group may be causing you some puzzlement. Even though some students are highly indebted, may come from poor backgrounds or have to take part-time jobs to fund their (supposedly) full-time studies, few live in the conditions of poverty described above. In fact, in the UK the average student is from the South-east (the most affluent part of the United Kingdom) and has parents who are part of the professional or managerial class (Dorling 2004). This means most students are able to afford most of the adult necessities identified in Table 10.1 (and even when they are unable, they may be assisted through hardship grants or student loans). Some now live in privately managed halls boasting state-of-the-art wifi, plasma TVs, integrated gymnasia and security (Smith and Hubbard 2014). So why is it appropriate to describe students as an excluded group?

The answer is that students are identified as a distinctive and different group because their lifestyles are often perceived to lie outside the norms of society, making them infrequent or unwelcome visitors in many of the spaces that are the loci of mainstream social life. Historically, this is related to popular understandings of students as politically radical, embracing alternative fashion and music in a way that marks them out as part of the 'counter-culture'. In the contemporary context, it is also associated with stereotypes of students that suggest they transgress the established social boundaries between work and play (and day and night) by holding late-night parties (at times when other people are sleeping) and sleeping all day (when other people are working). Now, as you read this you will no doubt argue that the reality of the situation is a good deal more complex: not all students enjoy drinking, clubbing and partying to all hours – and those that do are often able to do so while devoting considerable time to their studies. Further, while some students remain deeply committed to issues such as environmentalism, animal rights or the restructuring of Third World debt, stereotypes of student radicalism, drug-taking and 'free love' which were consolidated in the late 1960s are now woefully inaccurate as descriptors of contemporary student cultures.

That said, it is possible that you may have experienced exclusion in your own life as a student. No doubt there are parts of the town or city where you study where you are told students are not welcome and where you may have felt 'out of place'. For example, some pubs or clubs let students know, in subtle or not-so-subtle ways, that they are not welcome. You may even know of instances where students have been verbally abused (or even attacked) just for being students. Thankfully, such instances are rare. In contrast, opposition to *studentification* – the increased student occupation of the local housing market – is becoming very common. This phenomenon is mainly limited to university towns in the UK where on-campus accommodation is not sufficient to house burgeoning numbers of students and where particular areas become associated with high levels of rental accommodation targeting students (Smith and Holt 2007). Though student occupation can increase house prices (with the buy-to-let market proving extremely lucrative), student housing is often opposed by long-term residents who blame it for neighbourhood decline. In some areas, the consequences of studentification have been reported to be nothing short of catastrophic, with lobby groups arguing for stronger controls on the licensing of student housing to prevent neighbourhoods becoming 'over-run' by young, transient populations, displacing longer-term residents (UK Universities 2005). Highly dramatized media stories evoke the environmental and social transformation occurring in districts undergoing student expansion, illustrated with images of overgrown gardens, rubbish left out and sheets used as makeshift curtains. Additionally, campaign groups opposing student occupation allege students cause noise and nuisance, displace local long-term residents and fail to contribute to community life (Hubbard 2008, 2009).

Plate 10.2 A 'studentified' landscape of rented housing in multiple occupation, Loughborough

(Phil Hubbard)

We can see here that media stereotypes of students and student housing are mutually reinforcing in a variety of ways, and certainly many opponents of student housing allege that students do not look after their house because they are too busy socializing. A counter argument here is that the deleterious state of many student houses is down to the absentee landlords who fail to look after them, and, in any case, not all student households are noisy and disregarding of their neighbours. No matter, all it takes is one or two instances of antisocial behaviour to reinforce popular stereotypes and instigate campaigns aiming to reduce student occupation in particular areas (such as Storer in Loughborough, Headingley in Leeds, Elvet in Durham and Selly Oak in Birmingham). In some cases, long-term residents even adopt the metaphor of 'studenticide', arguing that studentification needs to be reversed lest it destroys the urban social fabric: surveys suggest homeowners in UK cities now fear student neighbours more than squatters. And this is not merely a UK phenomenon: studies of studentification suggest the proliferation of student housing is regularly opposed in the USA (Powell 2014), Europe (Boersma *et al.* 2013), China (He 2014) and beyond.

This discussion of studentification is highly relevant to our discussion of **social exclusion**, given it demonstrates that some groups may experience stigmatization irrespective of their income or class. Yet talking about students as a marginal group remains problematic given students occupy their ambivalent social position for a short time only, and typically move from a marginalized and indebted position to one of relative affluence within a few years as they convert their education and **cultural capital** into financial rewards. However, in other instances socially excluded groups suffer social stigmatization that is more likely to be associated with long-term **financial exclusion** or deprivation. For example, Gleeson (1998) suggests that people with a physical impairment or mobility problem typically find themselves excluded from workplaces designed around an able-bodied ideal. Here, the portrayal of the disabled as representing what Shakespeare (1994) describes as the 'imperfect physicality' of human existence is a major factor, with the able-bodied remaining anxious about those who are visibly different. This found acute expression in the USA 'ugly laws' of the nineteenth century, which witnessed several cities forbidding anyone from entering public space who was 'diseased, maimed or mutilated or anyway deformed to be an unsightly or disgusting object' (taken from Ordinance passed in Chicago, 1881, cited in Schwiek, 2009). These acts were used to exclude the disabled from participation in mainstream urban life, compounding fears and fantasies about those who appeared 'different', and collapsing a huge range of identities (and bodies) into a particular emergent category (the 'disabled').

As we have already seen, visceral metaphors also occur in the language used to describe those who live in poorer or deprived areas. For example, Ken Clarke, Conservative Home Secretary at the time, described the participants in the 2011 English riots as 'feral', invoking ideas that this group is less than human. Owen Jones (2012) – author of the book *Chavs* on the demonization of the British working class – also highlighted the ways in which the media rounded on the 'rabble' living in more deprived places, and used the label of 'chav' to reduce the complex causes of the rioting to the level of individual failings. Tyler (2013: 21) also describes the way that the poor in Britain have been described as 'revolting' subjects, known through a language which emphasizes their non-human and even animalistic characteristics. For Tyler, the brutalizing language of Otherness creates 'abject' figures who are required to do 'the dirty work' required by modern societies (e.g. work in the servicing economy in precarious and poorly paid roles), but who are denied full inclusion in that society because of their seeming vulgarity and lack of distinction. This invocation of the notion of *social* **abjection** betrays Tyler's interest in the notion of disgust, a concept more associated with psychology than geography. This concept is significant for work on urban segregation in at least two senses. First, it emphasizes the way that fears of contamination, pollution and despoilment fuels the policing of boundaries which may be boundaries of class, but may also be boundaries between different neighbourhoods. Second, it allows us to think about segregation as a socially lived process, which makes particular subjects the object of a violent, objectifying disgust and subjects then to control, stigma and censure.

In making such arguments, Tyler enriches the theoretical materials available to us for thinking about the ways that the projection of negative values onto Others produces social segregation, extending recent analyses of class relations in contemporary Britain (e.g. Skeggs 1997; Haylett 2001; Lawler 2005; Nayak 2006) by revealing a continuing devaluation of working class cultures created through repeated disgust reactions. This type of analysis suggests that highly diverse groups can become known through narrow social stereotypes, with these stereotypes shaping the relationship between them and dominant social groups. This suggests that while social exclusion has an important symbolic dimension, being created in the realms of *representation*. Here, the term representation is taken to encompass the wide range of media – such as films, TV, internet sites and newspapers – through which we come to understand the world and our place within it (Woodward 1997). Inevitably, such media provide a partial and simplified view of the lifestyles of heterogeneous social groups. Although most people do not necessarily accept these stereotypes uncritically, they inevitably find themselves drawing on them in their everyday life. What is especially significant about these stereotypes is that they are ideological in nature, in the sense they are generally created by (and in the interests of) dominant social groups – typically white, able-bodied, heterosexual, middle-class men. It is those who do not conform to their view of the world who are defined as society's Others.

A vivid example of how such stereotyped images contribute to social and spatial exclusion was provided by the media reporting of HIV/AIDS that occurred in the mid-1980s. In the ensuing **moral panic** that followed diagnosis of the virus and its mode of transmission, a sometimes hysterical media began to focus on the groups most readily identified as at risk – non-white ethnic minorities, intravenous-drug users and gay men (Watney 1987). The presence of HIV infection in these groups was generally perceived to be no accident, but portrayed as a condition affecting those whose 'inner essence' diverged from that of normal society (and whose lifestyles were judged to be incompatible with the maintenance of 'family values'). Hence, sensationalist stories of sexual immorality, irresponsibility and wilful hedonism among those groups most affected by the virus were used to create social barriers between the 'healthy' and those regarded as sexually promiscuous, socially irresponsible and unclean. Consequently, this symbolic marking of HIV-infected groups as deviant informed their social exclusion, encouraging widespread discrimination, prejudice and neglect. As Wilton (1996) has shown, this had clear spatial effects, with those infected with HIV exhibiting 'diminishing geographies' as their access to the workplace, the home and the street was subject to increasing constraint. In his analysis, Wilton stresses that these constraints were not a product of the physical onset of AIDS but of the social stigma surrounding it. Symptoms of this stigma have included employers refusing to take on those with HIV, dentists refusing to treat them and, as Wilton relates, community groups opposing the construction of AIDS hospices in their neighbourhood.

Such neighbourhood opposition to community facilities and welfare services is so widespread in Western society, particularly in suburban landscapes, that few stop to question why people might object to such developments in their neighbourhood. Certainly, many NIMBY (Not In My Back Yard) campaigns are fought with reference to detrimental environmental impacts (such as noise or air pollution during construction). Such impacts are, to an extent, quantifiable; what is less measurable is the concern that homeowners have about the arrival of stigmatized populations. However, for Takahashi and Dear (1997), community opposition to facilities for those living with AIDS/HIV is indicative of the more general antipathy displayed towards Other populations. Their survey of

homeowners in US cities reveals a 'continuum' of acceptance, where facilities for populations depicted as 'different' (such as homes for the elderly) are regarded more favourably than those for populations stereotyped as 'dangerous' or 'deviant' (such as those living with HIV) (Table 10.3). This frequently results in the concentration of facilities in inner-city areas where home-ownership rates are low and community opposition is least vocal (Case study 10.2). As DeVerteuil (2013) writes, NIMBY remains an important concept in urban social geography because it places attention precisely on how the forms of opposition to particular social groups takes spatial expression – and how, in turn, this maintains socio-spatial segregations based on fears of Otherness.

NIMBY opposition to facilities for those living with HIV, those without homes, asylum seekers, people with disabilities and populations dependent on welfare hence demonstrates that the geographies of marginal groups are, to a lesser or greater extent, the product of dominant **imaginary geographies** casting minorities as 'folk devils' who need to be located elsewhere. As Sibley

Table 10.3 Relative acceptability of human service facilities, based on a US survey of 1,326 respondents

Facility type	Mean acceptability, 1 = low, 6 = high
School	4.75
Day care centre	4.69
Nursing home for elderly	4.65
Medical clinic for allergies	4.40
Hospital	4.32
Group home for mentally retarded	3.98
Alcohol rehabilitation centre	3.80
Homeless shelter	3.73
Drug treatment centre	3.61
Group home for mentally disabled	3.51
Group home for people with depression	3.47
Mental health outpatient facility	3.45
Independent apartment for mentally disabled	3.30
Group home for people living with AIDS	3.20

Source: Takahashi and Dear (1997: 83)

Case study 10.2

Community opposition to asylum seekers

In accordance with the United Nations' protocol on refugees, the United Kingdom is obliged to offer asylum to those in fear of persecution on the basis of their race, religion or culture. However, in the late 1990s, a mounting backlog of asylum applications, together with media stories of 'bogus' asylum seekers, combined to demonize this group in the public imagination. One strategy adopted by the government as it sought to diffuse concern about the 'wave' of asylum seekers 'flooding' Britain was the dispersal of asylum seekers away from the Channel ports where their visibility had been exploited by right-wing groups intent on exploiting racist fears of difference. As part of this process of planned dispersal, the Home Office proposed the construction of accommodation centres for asylum seekers in a number of rural locales. However, this policy often met with considerable local opposition. For example, in February 2002, residents of Newton in Nottinghamshire learnt that the Home Office was planning to convert nearby RAF Newton into an accommodation centre for asylum seekers. A series of protests organized by the Newton Action

Group expressed vehement opposition to the proposal, with campaigners arguing that the development would cause increases in crime, vandalism and social disorder, and that property prices would fall. One resident claimed that parents would be 'terrified of letting their children play out', while another asked 'Can we be assured there are no child abusers, drug addicts or convicted rapists among them?'. The fact that this is by no means an isolated example demonstrates how effective the media have been at exploiting public anxieties about the threat that asylum seekers pose to the sanctity and purity of the nation. As an extremely vulnerable group, asylum seekers have been less able than some to oppose these racist myths, and many have reported harrowing experiences of discrimination. For example, in the Sighthill area of Glasgow, the arrival of 1,200 Kurdish and Kosovan refugees in 2001 prompted a number of vicious assaults by local white youths who claimed the asylum seekers were being shown favouritism by the local council. Following a series of attacks, it took the murder of 22-year-old Kurdish asylum-seeker Firsat Dag to draw attention to the everyday racism fuelled by a media rhetoric that depicted asylum seekers as 'social security scroungers'.

(1995: 49) contends, this elsewhere might be nowhere, as when the genocide of gypsies and Jews was undertaken by the Nazis, or it might simply be a space 'out of sight' of mainstream populations (such as the red-light districts that are the focus of sex work in many British cities – see Hubbard 1999). Predating the work of Tyler (2013), in *Geographies of Exclusion*, Sibley (1995) offered a theoretically informed account of how these imaginary geographies fuelled exclusionary practices. Drawing particularly on psychoanalytical ideas about the importance of maintaining self-identity (literally, maintaining the boundaries of the Self), Sibley argued that the urge to exclude threatening Others from one's proximity is connected to ideas about the importance of bodily cleanliness, many of which may be inculcated in early infancy. Sibley detailed how fears of the Self being defiled are consequently projected (or mapped) on to those individuals and groups depicted as polluting or dirty. In turn, Sibley argued that individuals adopt a series of exclusionary strategies designed to retain 'psychic distance' between themselves and Other groups, building symbolic, psychological and physical boundaries in the process.

10.3 Racial segregation in the city

The discussion above suggests that while society is highly diverse, some social differences are 'amplified' into significance through practices of representation. An prominent example here is the division of society on racial lines. Like class, age, or religion, race is a **social construct**, an invention of the many discourses and images that suggest that our skin colour matters, with cultural difference following biological differentiation. Race, therefore, is intimately linked to racism. Unpacking the imaginary geographies that cast minorities to the margins, research in social geography has exposed the way that media negativity identifies ethnic minority groups as the source of social problems such as criminality, poor health and environmental decline (see Smith 1989a; Anderson 1991; Dunn 2001). Sibley (1999) accordingly argues that the equation of whiteness with purity, order and cleanliness in northern European cultures has been responsible for the creation of negative stereotypes of (for example) Africans, Afro-Caribbeans, people from the Indian subcontinent and Roma gypsies. He contends that each of these groups has consequently been allocated only a marginal role in national cultures because of their 'threatening' nature. In turn, such marginalization fuels spatial segregation, with the creation of ethnic-minority enclaves in the poorest neighbourhoods of many European cities being a product of personal prejudice in the job and housing markets that is fuelled by negative media stereotypes (Wacquant 2010). For example, in the UK there remains talk of white and non-white groups leading 'parallel lives', despite efforts at partnership designed to instil 'community cohesion': evidence suggests that the often-convivial everyday encounters that occur in public and workspaces between non-white and white individuals are not necessarily mirrored in the creation of residentially-mixed neighbourhoods (Swanton 2010). In this context, some have suggested ethic segregation in the UK is largely 'voluntary' – and hence self-segregation by both white and non-white groups. While this conclusion is disputed in some quarters (see Peach 1996; Phillips 2006), it suggests that cultural racism and processes of fear, resentment and prejudice maybe more significant than institutional or state-sponsored attempts at segregation

and bordering (Anderson 2010). In other contexts, this segregation has been institutional and via 'tighter' forms of control: for example, under **apartheid** in South Africa, the Group Areas Act prevented black people from straying into residential areas declared 'white', leaving a legacy of cities that are sharply divided on ethnic lines (see Case study 10.3).

While segregationist policies have long been illegal in the USA, whiteness remains profoundly encoded in the city–suburb distinction that exists there, with the suburbs seen to provide a refuge for the white middle classes from the dirt, disorder, and, above all, criminality of the coloured inner city (Valentine 2001). Indeed, the imagined association between areas of predominantly black residence and the welfare-dependent 'ghetto' has become so pernicious in the USA that it dominates white assumptions about Afro-American lifestyles, creating stereotypes that often bear little resemblance to black people's urban experiences. Events such as the Rodney King riots of 1992 (prompted by the acquittal of a white police officer for the filmed beating of a black Los Angeles resident) consolidated the reputation of the US ghetto as a crime-ridden environment;

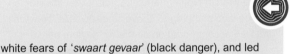

Case study 10.3

Ethnic division in apartheid cities

Apartheid-era South Africa is often cited as representing an extreme example of socio-spatial segregation, with a white minority population passing a series of Acts in the mid-twentieth century designed to circumscribe the mobility of coloured, Indian and African people. Under apartheid laws, non-whites were denied access to major cities except if in possession of a pass that indicated they were gainfully employed in the city. As such, while the ruling white minority depicted non-whites as racially inferior, they recognized their importance as a source of unskilled and semi-skilled labour. Initially, non-white workers were housed in barracks or municipal hostels where they were subject to regimentation designed to curb the 'animal instincts' of natives and instil the importance of 'the proper habits of work and life' (Popke 2001: 740). The understanding that non-whites possessed useful and productive bodies, yet were prone to indolence and incivility, was clearly connected to colonial representations that associated non-whiteness with savagery, animality and nature, characteristics that were repressed in 'civilized' Western cultures (Anderson 2000).

However, the continued growth of non-white 'shanty towns' around the periphery of major cities fuelled

white fears of 'swaart gevaar' (black danger), and led to national legislation designed to construct buffer zones between the white city and non-white townships. Both physically and symbolically on the margins of South African cities, the townships thus became abject landscapes, depicted by the white media as spaces of vice, disease and lawlessness. Repeated attempts at creating racially sanitized, planned townships were thus part of an explicit attempt to modernize South African society while maintaining the distance between poorer non-white groups and the affluent white city.

Rather than suggesting that the apartheid city represents a racist distortion of the processes of segregation evident elsewhere in the world, more recent commentaries on the apartheid era suggest it illustrates the racist conceits that underpinned twentieth-century modernism (Robinson 1997; Popke 2001). As such, it is possible to identify planning and 'improvement' schemes as underpinned by racist imaginaries throughout the world (and not just in those nations with a colonial history). Indeed, despite the abolition of apartheid Group Area Acts, racist fears of difference continue to fuel socio-spatial exclusions in South Africa, with the growth in gated communities being merely one manifestation of this (Jurgens and Gnad 2002).

although the areas of unrest were typically those with the poorest income levels, high population densities and high school-dropout rates, it was the 'racial character' of these areas that was highlighted in the subsequent reporting (Smith 1995).

This association between US minority populations and specific criminalized places has been cemented over the years in those media that have used 'ghetto' as a coded term for the imagined deviance of black people (especially black men). As McCarthy *et al.* (1997) argue, the American middle classes tend to learn more about black inner cities through 'long-distanced' media images than through personal everyday interactions. Stories of 'black-on-black' violence abound in the media, with black urban males depicted as the main criminal threat in the USA (Wilson 2005). The cultural responses – in the form of black media practices – have been ambivalent in their outcomes, with the gangsta rap that emerged in the 1990s accused of banalizing everyday violence and gun crime. Even 'new wave' black cinema such as *Menace II Society, Boyz 'n the Hood, Jungle Fever* and *Straight Outta Brooklyn,* which sought to show something of the reality of everyday life for Afro-Americans, ultimately served to stereotype such places as landscapes of endemic violence and drug dependence (Benton 1995). In this context, 'urban' cinema, film and literature can be seen as a corroboration of dominant white myths that imagine drugs, guns and criminality to be part of everyday ghetto life. Such white fears and fantasies about the black inner city are acidly invoked in Wolfe's (1988) fictional account of the Wall Street trader, Sherman McCoy, who one night takes the wrong turning on his drive home only to be confronted with a side of New York that he remains cosseted from in his 'yuppie' housing development:

> At the next corner, he turned – west, he figured – and followed that street a few blocks. There were more low buildings. They might have been garages, they might have been sheds. There were fences with spirals of razor wire on top. But the streets were deserted, which was okay, he told himself. Yet he could feel his heart beating with a nervous twang. Then he turned again. A narrow street with seven or eight storey apartment buildings; no sign of people, not a light in a window. The next block, the same. He turned again, and as he rounded the corner – astonishing. Utterly empty, a vast open terrain . . . here and there were traces of rubble and slag. The earth looked like concrete, except it rolled down this way, and up that . . . the hills and dales of the Bronx . . . reduced to asphalt, concrete and cinders.

(Wolfe 1988: 65)

Though nearly 30 years old, Wolfe's depiction remains revealing of white anxieties. This depiction of the Bronx as a wasteland inhabited by 'lots of dark faces' again reminds us of the ways in which fears of difference (in this example, based on skin colour) can provoke anxiety and feed the urge to exclude. From the perspective of the white narrator in Wolfe's book, the urban decay of the Bronx mirrors his perceived view of the city's black population as Other: they are street people rather than the 'air people' who inhabit his social world (adopting Raban's, 1990, memorable description of those who can afford to distance themselves from marginal places).

For many Afro-Americans, ghetto life is similarly typified by anxiety, but an anxiety originating from problems of poverty (in 2012, 25 per cent of black families were living below the US poverty line, and 42 per cent of black single parent families, a figure which has increased since 2000). As the renowned feminist and cultural theorist bell hooks relates, the experience of living in the black ghetto is one that consistently reinforces feelings of subordination and inferiority:

> To be in the margin is to be part of the whole but outside the main body. As black Americans living in a small Kentucky town, the railroad tracks were a daily reminder of our marginality. Across those tracks were paved streets, stores we could not enter and restaurants we could not eat in, and people we could not look directly in the face. Across these tracks was a world we could work in as maids, as janitors, as prostitutes, as long as it was in a service capacity. We could enter that world, but we could not live there. We always had to return to the margin, to cross the tracks, to shacks and abandoned houses on the edge of town.

(hooks 1984: 9)

Until the 1960s it was not uncommon to find specific planning ordinances and zoning laws controlling the development of black neighbourhoods. Although such laws have long since been overturned, the legacy of these remain in the racist practices of mortgage financiers, banks and estate agents, who may seek to maintain the blackness or whiteness of particular neighbourhoods in the interests of maintaining house prices (Short 1996). It is thus unsurprising that the Otherness of the Afro-American population is mirrored in what has been termed **hypersegregation**, with black people remaining more spatially concentrated than any other US ethnic minority. The average black citizen lives in a neighbourhood that is 45 per cent black, even though blacks only make up 13 per cent of the overall US population (Logan 2013). However, Dissimilarity

Table 10.4 The ten most segregated cities in the USA, measured by white/Afro-American Dissimilarity Index, 1980–2010

2010 Rank	Area Name	2010 Segregation	2000 Segregation	1990 Segregation	1980 Segregation
1	Detroit-Livonia-Dearbom, MI	79.6	85.9	85.6	83.0
2	Milwaukee-Waukesha-West Allis, WI	79.6	82.2	82.8	83.9
3	New York-White Plains-Wayne, NY-NJ	79.1	81.3	82.0	81.7
4	Newark-Union, NJ-PA	78.0	80.4	82.7	82.8
5	Chicago-Joliet-Naperville, IL	75.9	80.8	84.6	88.6
6	Philadelphia, PA	73.7	76.5	81.4	82.6
7	Miami-Miami Beach-Kendall, FL	73.0	72.4	71.8	79.3
8	Cleveland-Elyria-Mentor, OH	72.6	77.2	82.8	85.8
9	St. Louis, MO-IL	70.6	73.4	77.2	81.6
10	Nassau-Suffolk, NY	69.2	73.6	76.4	76.9

1 = complete segregation, 0 = complete integration

Source: Logan and Stuits (2011)

Indexes exploring how the Afro-American population is distributed relative to the white population suggest that their segregation has actually declined over the past 30 years (see Table 10.4). Yet the declines remain modest, and some metropolitan areas actually experienced an *increase* in **residential segregation** over the period 1980–2010 (the seven highest increases all in the southern USA, including Columbus, GA; Goldsboro, NC; Athens, GA; and Danville, VA). Wilson (2005) also notes a deepening of poverty within the most ghettoized neighbourhoods, measured through the ratio of high- to low-income residents, with the ratio of rich to poor in Chicago's Englewood and Woodlawn neighbourhoods increasing by 40 per cent between 1990 and 2000, and 80 per cent in Cleveland Hough and Fairfax in the same period. Workfare programmes fail to alleviate the situation, with the poorest forced into dead-end and demeaning employment for minimal wages.

While the disappearance of well-paid work from US inner cities (and the associated out-migration of the black middle class) has been postulated as the major cause of such concentrated black poverty in the USA, Mohan (2000) argues that such factors alone cannot explain the continuing segregation of Afro-Americans. Instead, he suggests it is necessary to consider the wholesale institutional abandonment that has accompanied the economic stigmatization of Afro-American communities. Coining the phrase 'desertification' to describe the planned shrinkage of essential health, welfare and emergency services in the Bronx in the 1970s and 1980s, Wallace and Wallace (1998, 2000) suggested that such disinvestment was part of a deliberate attempt to cut back on public spending by withdrawing services from the very districts most in need. As they detail them, the long-term consequences have often been catastrophic (including increases in infant mortality rates, low birth weights, cirrhosis, TB and AIDS-related deaths). At the same time, many areas stigmatized as pockets of black poverty have become insurance no-go zones where small businesses find it impossible to get insurance because premiums are so high, and large percentages of the population are denied car insurance because of excessive costs. Moreover, the intensification of the activities of police, courts and prison is recognized to have disproportionately affected such 'imploding ghettos', with the mass incarceration of young, working class African American men seen by many as a state strategy designed to 'discipline' and manage the socially dispossessed (Waquant 2010). It is for such reasons that some commentators still feel justified in speaking of the 'apartheid' of American cities (Wallace and Wallace 1998).

10.4 Gentrification: reclaiming the margins?

As already noted, all cities possess less affluent areas, whether these are described as 'problem' estates, welfare-dependent neighbourhoods or racialised ghettos. Often, the boundaries of such places have remained stubbornly recalcitrant over time, even if the individuals and groups they contain have changed (an example here might be the persistence of the inner city as a disordered or transient urban zone given the earliest mappings of the Chicago School identified it as such). This is clearly connected to questions of power, with dominant social groups able to physically and symbolically claim the centres, marginalizing the less powerful:

> Centre/periphery distinctions tend frequently to be associated with endurance in time. Those who occupy centres establish themselves as having control over resources which allow them to maintain differentials between themselves and those in peripheral regions. The established may employ a variety of forms of social closure to sustain distance from others who are effectively treated as outsiders.
>
> (Giddens 1991: 131)

In this chapter we have already examined numerous processes which tend to spatially isolate and exclude less powerful groups in urban space – e.g. social prejudice, institutional racism, NIMBY politics and so on. Yet there are significant policy processes which also effect such spaces, with urban policy in particular often prefigured on the idea that marginal places need to be bought back into the 'mainstream' in the interests of economic development as well as social cohesion. In many nations, such policies are underpinned by an increasingly complex diversity of agencies and partnerships, blurring the distinction between public and private sectors as property developers and policy-actors work in tandem to regenerate deprived areas and engineer urban regeneration. Here, a notable trend has been to achieve this through policies promoting social mix. For example, in many local authority housing estates and 'projects' in the USA and UK, there has been an attempt to redevelop and diversify housing with an eye to ending the status of such areas as homogeneously working class or 'poor' places. The key assumption here has been that mixing different types of housing tenure would lead to greater social mix and to positive effects for (poor) urban residents and for deprived neighbourhoods at large.

The impact of such urban regeneration is decidedly mixed. Suffice to say, many policies of regeneration appear to be 'taking back' the margins from marginal people, rather than empowering them, effectively transforming landscapes of poverty and decay into prestigious (and *ordered*) space through selective investment and redevelopment aiming at attracting more affluent residents. For example, some have argued that the public–private partnerships which are being undertaken by the majority of London boroughs in order to regenerate council estates, are merely leading to the displacement of long-established residents (e.g. see Lees 2014 on London's Aylesbury estate). This is a process being resisted by some residents, albeit it has required emphasis on the right of families to remain in place to secure notable press coverage (see Plate 10.3). Hence, the net result of such improvement policy is often the onset of **gentrification**. A much-debated phenomenon in urban social geography, gentrification is the process by which poor neighbourhoods are transformed by an influx of affluent homebuyers and renters. In some instances, this involves individual gentrifiers buying existing properties and transforming them (often with governmental subsidy); in others, it involves the wholesale replacement of low-income housing with prestigious apartments by corporate developers (Davidson and Lees 2010). Either way, the net result is often one of displacement, with former residents frequently unable to afford to live in gentrified areas which become characterised by shops and cultural facilities which cater exclusively for incoming populations (an

Plate 10.3 Resisting gentrification: E15 Mothers protest, Carpenter's Estate London, 2014.

(Archant Norwich)

issue highlighted by the protests against 'hipster' cafes in the East End of London in 2015) (Hubbard 2016).

Marginalized populations may see their neighbourhoods enjoy a spectacular renaissance, but often do not share in its subsequent prosperity (Lees 2008). While little is known about displacement and its consequences, Dutch research (Kleinhans 2003) suggests personality can be important in shaping experiences of displacement, with more resilient individuals most able to take a positive view of the 'relocation' process. In a UK context, longitudinal research in Glasgow by Kearns and Mason (2013) also suggests that there might be a difference in the 'psychosocial' impacts of displacement between those willing to move and those who are reluctant movers. Their conclusion was that 'most of those who moved considered that they had "bettered" their residential conditions, though again less so in neighbourhood than in dwelling terms' (Kearns and Mason 2013: 195). This suggests that the displaced might end up with better housing conditions, but not necessarily in neighbourhoods that provide them with a satisfactory quality of life or 'sense of belonging'.

For such reasons, most Western cities appear to be seeing changes in patterns of segregation, with the emergent of affluent enclaves and gentrified developments displacing and scattering the urban poor, with the latter sometimes forced to relocate to different towns and cities. Hence, while gentrification might instigate processes of improvement that have long-term benefits for marginal groups (and the jury is still out on 'trickle-down' urban theory), most geographers remain sanguine about their impacts. Gentrification, it seems, can be conceptualized as yet another form of profit-generation for the wealthy, representing a property wager rather than an investment in people. Indeed, one of the leading neo-Marxist urban commentators, Neil Smith (1996), famously argued that gentrification ultimately only occurs if the gap between actual and potential land value is such that property development becomes lucrative. In such circumstances, the processes of disinvestment associated with marginalization become the precursor to a subsequent wave of reinvestment. But for profits to be realized, the marginalized groups and land-uses which occupy these devalued spaces must be driven out, so that potential developers can view them as safe investment opportunities. It is here that the role of the local state is crucial. Smith (2002: 442) pointed to this when he detailed how squatters, the homeless, squeegee merchants and 'street people' were ruthlessly dealt with in New York following the election of Mayor Rudolph Giuliani and appointment of Police Commissioner William Bratton. Espousing a rhetoric of Zero Tolerance for miscreants, these individuals were pivotal in identifying the urban disadvantaged as a disorderly population. This urge to tame urban disorder was to trigger notorious police brutality against minorities, justified with reference to the need for improved quality of life, but actually intended, Smith argues, to make particular areas of the city safe for corporate gentrification (and the associated invasion of upper-income groups). One notable example of this process was the wholesale removal of the homeless and their supporters from Tompkins Square Park at a time when developers were seeking to sell the Lower East Side as a space for 'family' residence. The seizure and subsequent 'purification' of the park (and surrounding areas) serves to underline how exclusionary urges may turn a genuinely public space into a space reserved for those who accord with mainstream ideas of living and working (see also Mitchell 1996).

Case study 10.4

Gated communities in Uruguay

One of the most obvious symptoms of social division in our cities is the presence of gated communities (Kenna and Dunn 2009). These communities currently enjoy a widespread popularity because their design promises security as well as a sense of belonging: residents typically sign up to a legally binding code of conduct that ensures all residents understand their rights and responsibilities as members of a community. Physically separated from the wider city, and often offering a privatized form of social life through the provision of enclosed gardens, gymnasia, shops and facilities, gated communities have been postulated as offering a new form of urbanism that may rekindle sociality and encourage diverse peoples to live together. In most cases, however, gated communities have been found to promote social dissociation and sharpen social segregation, being woven into processes of gentrification and urban revanchism by catering to middle-class tastes (and incomes) (Atkinson and Flint 2004).

In the case of Montevideo (Uruguay), there are still only a handful of gated communities (certainly if compared to its Latin American neighbours). Alvarez-Rivadulla (2007: 51) points out that the majority of these are peripheral to the city centre in the Carrasco suburb, and offer a semi-rural setting in which the urban threats of downtown Montevideo are far removed: 'bird song replaces traffic noise, the grey of the city gives way to shades of green'. As is the case in most gated communities, however, the residents are remarkably homogeneous in terms of age, family status and class, as well as sharing certain cultural dispositions (such as their enthusiasm for golf). Their social life tends to be strongly family-oriented, and inward- rather than outward-looking. The occupants are manifestly not part of any global elite, but are significantly more affluent than the average for the city. Significantly, as Alvarez-Rivadulla (2007) notes, this is not a group that had ever mixed with less affluent groups (even if it shares the same urban public spaces and neighbourhoods with them). As such, gated communities reinforce already-existing social tendencies, feeding on fears of difference and myths of urban danger.

Alvarez-Rivadulla (2007) concludes that the reasons that the occupants of Montevideo's gated communities move to them are not so different from the motivations listed by suburban dwellers in studies in the UK and the USA: a desire to escape the unpredictability of the city, seek stability and put down roots. Located on the periphery of the city – an area traditionally associated with Montevideo's urban poor – these gated communities have effectively displaced working class and marginal populations in shanty dwellings, and raised land values in the vicinity, exacerbating contrasts between the traditionally affluent neighbourhoods and the neighbourhoods belonging to the urban poor. In a reversal of the trends we noted earlier in the chapter, an archipelago of affluent gated communities can be seen to be emerging within a sea of poverty (as opposed to cities in the USA and UK, where we noted the existence of islands of deprivation increasingly dissociated from an otherwise mobile and affluent city).

The vicious **urban revanchism** that Smith documents is a symptom of the deep-rooted fear amongst white middle- and upper-class citizens of Other populations, be they the unemployed, sex workers, the homeless and immigrants. It is very common for mainstream middle-class groups to wax lyrical about urban living, and celebrate the diversity of the city, but all too few seem prepared to leave the suburbs unless it is for a similarly homogeneous gentrified inner-city district (Atkinson and Flint 2004). Moreover, these tendencies are not merely confined to the urban West, and it is easy to find instances of marginalized populations being displaced throughout the global South as shanty towns or informal settlements are bulldozed to make way for new middle-class developments, gated communities, shopping centres and highway developments (see Case study 10.4). Though often resisted, the net result is the corporate gentrification of city centres worldwide, to the extent that the CBD of Manila now looks very much the same as the CBD of Sydney (Winchester *et al.* 2003). While such processes of corporate gentrification may ultimately attract mobile consumer capital, and tie Third World cities into a network of world cities, the consequence is of course the production of new landscapes of exclusion and segregation.

The prognosis here for marginal groups is not good, as some of the main policies advocated in their name seem destined to serve interests other than their own. But while such practices of regeneration tend to carve up space in favour of powerful middle-class elites, it is dangerous to suggest that poorer groups are unable to resist these processes. For example, some excluded groups may well resist forms of social closure by **transgressing** into the spaces of the powerful, challenging taken-for-granted expectations about where they should locate (Cresswell 1996). Such transgressions may trigger a moral panic (such as that which surrounded asylum seekers in the late 1990s or people living with HIV in the 1980s), encouraging new forms of social and spatial control. This control is often underpinned by the use of police power, as was the case with the French *banlieue* riots, where curfews were rigorously enforced in affected areas. In such cases, practices of spatial ordering and surveillance quickly reassert the social order, and remind people of their place. However, transgressions may also set in motion social changes by challenging assumptions about who or what belongs where. Parades, sit-ins, strikes, squats: all enact an opposition that, however fleeting, may bring about a change in social attitudes. For instance, gay pride marches in Western cities have often drawn attention to homophobia in society, and over time have encouraged the repeal of discriminatory legislation; perhaps less successfully, Muslim-identifying populations have pursued a variety of public actions designed to topple the **Islamophobia** that is rampant in the Western nations.

Developing these ideas on transgression and resistance, geographers have hence conceptualized places on the margin as sites where the relatively powerless can organize themselves into self-supporting cultures of resistance and cooperation. For example, so-called 'gay ghetto' areas in the USA (e.g. Castro in San Francisco, or West Hollywood in Los Angeles), France (e.g. the Marais, Paris) and South Africa (e.g. De Waterkant, Cape Town) have been transformed from marginal spaces of persecution to relatively affluent centres of gay male cultural life through political organization, creativity and activism, creating new gay identities in the process (see Forest 1995; Visser 2003; Sibalis 2004; Hubbard 2012). Likewise, alternative economies thrive in many racialized areas (particularly in the cultural industries – food, music, fashion, arts and media), allowing 'ethnic entrepreneurs' to bring different values and ideas to the attention of wider audiences, making them more mainstream in the process. This gradual **demarginalization** process may, over time, bring excluded populations into the mainstream – though the debate on the possibilities of this remains heated. Indeed, there remains considerable debate about the degree to which the physical characteristics of a neighbourhood have an impact on the lives of its inhabitants, and whether moving poor people into more affluent areas actually improves their quality of life.

10.5 Conclusion

Segregation is just one of many issues explored by urban social geographers. It is also something of a timeless issue, threatening to drift into abeyance until events like the English riots of 2011 or the French suburban riots of 2007 thrust it back into the limelight. But beyond the headlines, we must acknowledge it remains one of the most important issues facing society in the twenty-first century. As we have seen, many societies possess 'wild' and 'untamed' urban zones – ghettos, slums, *banlieues, favelas* – as well as more mundane sites of marginalization, poverty and stigma. While we need to be wary of suggesting these sites share common characteristics (e.g. the multi-ethnic make up of the French *banlieue* or many British inner cities stands in stark contrast to the ethnic homogeneity of the US 'ghetto'), there are a number of key themes that geographers routinely invoke when analysing their geographies: namely, exclusion, marginalization and segregation. Taken together, these themes emphasize the fact that space is never an abstract surface on which social life is played out, but is socially produced. As such, research on urban geographies of residential segregation does not just provide valuable insights into the particular combination of problems that beset our most vulnerable urban populations; it also makes a key contribution to *theoretical* debates about the role of urban space in constructing socially significant categories of identity and difference (such as class, gender, sexuality and race). In the final analysis, the concept of urban segregation is not solely of relevance to the issues of social inequality discussed in this chapter: it is fundamental to making sense of the diversity that characterizes the contemporary world.

Learning outcomes

Having read this chapter, you should be able to:

- Understand that cities are divided in ways that often segregate stigmatized 'Other' groups.
- Appreciate the complexity of the processes encouraging this segregation, including people's desire to distance themselves from populations represented by the media as threatening or polluting.
- Identify the characteristics of urban spaces of exclusion, which tend to lack economic, social or political infrastructure, and are typified by health problems and a poor quality of life for those who live there.
- Recognize the importance of spatial stigmatization in exacerbating social divides; once a neighbourhood has obtained a reputation as a space of exclusion, it is unlikely to attract investment of a type that will benefit its inhabitants.

- Understand that efforts to reclaim spaces of exclusion in the name of improvement and 'urban regeneration' often instigate urban gentrification – a process that often triggers new forms of spatial purification and exclusion rather than social mixing.

Further reading

DeVerteuil, G. (2015) *Resilience in the Post-welfare Inner City: Voluntary Sector Geographies in London, Los Angeles and Sydney,* London, Policy Press. Focusing on homeless lives and facilities, this timely book provides an overview of changing provisioning for the poor and welfare-users in ten different inner-city neighbourhoods in three global city-regions (London, Los Angeles and Sydney).

Dikeç, M. (2007) *Badlands of the Republic: Space, Politics, and French Urban Policy,* Blackwell, RGS/IBG Book Series, Oxford. Develops ideas about the social and political imaginations that have marginalized French immigrant populations in the banlieues (the 'badlands' of his title), offering significant insight into the 2005 urban unrest in French cities.

Lees, L., Slater, T. and Wyly, E. (2013) *Gentrification,* Routledge, London. Perhaps the most exhaustive and comprehensive account of the causes and consequences of gentrification. International in scope, this is an accessible and critical overview.

Musterd, S. and Ostendorf, W. (eds) (2013) *Urban Segregation and the Welfare State: Inequality and Exclusion in Western Cities,* Routledge, London. This is a very valuable collection for those seeking comparative analysis of patterns of urban segregation in different cities, with a specific focus on comparative welfare regimes and the legacies of governmental initiatives in European cities.

Nightingale, C.H. (2012) *Segregation: A Global History of Divided Cities,* University of Chicago Press, Chicago, IL. Provides a more historic account of segregation than has been possible in this chapter, and considers urban division in the wider context of colonial and post-colonial tensions, especially religious and cultural ones.

Sibley, D. (1995) *Geographies of Exclusion: Society and Difference in the West,* Routledge, London. Remains a landmark theoretical statement on geographies of exclusion, bringing geographical ideas into dialogue with psychoanalytical literatures. The book is illustrated throughout with examples ranging from the marginalization of gypsies to the exclusion of non-white voices from the spaces of the academy.

Wacquant, L. (2009) *Punishing the Poor: The Neoliberal Government of Social Insecurity,* Duke University Press, Durham, NC. A powerfully argued book that suggests contemporary penal strategies in the USA (and beyond) are responding not so much to fears of crime but social resentments underpinned by racial – and racist – imaginaries. The focus on the 'hyperincarceration' of young, black men from 'ghetto' environments suggests neoliberal policy continues to gain its legitimacy from spatial ordering.

CHANGING RURAL WORLDS – A GLOBAL VIEW

Chapter 11

Warwick E. Murray

Topics covered

- Definitions and meanings of 'rural'

- Trajectories and gaps in rural geography as a sub-discipline

- The interlinking of rural change in the global North and South

- Demographic change in rural worlds: depopulation, counterurbanization and rural–urban drift

- Political change in rural worlds: countryside movements and rural resistance

- Cultural change in rural worlds: social constructions of the country, commodification of rural areas, social change

- Economic change in rural worlds: productivist vs. post-productivist agriculture, multifunctional rural areas, ethical value chains (fair trade, organic networks and geographical indicators (GIs))

What do you think of when you use the term 'rural'? Your response will be influenced heavily by where you 'come from' in both a territorial and sociocultural sense. It is an assumption, but if you are from Britain you might imagine black and white cottages, beautiful tidy villages, welcoming pubs, neat hedge rows, and charming village fêtes. I am from such a place and despite doing rural geography research across the globe in order to experience and try to understand multiple rural worlds, this is still what comes to my mind. Yet, perceptions of the 'rural' will be far less pleasant in Tonga, for example. There it might be suggested that poor infrastructure, absence of electricity, grinding poverty, patriarchal governance systems, vulnerable housing, environmental deterioration, and marginal and precarious livelihoods characterize such places (see Plates 11.1 and 11.2 for example). This is not to suggest that all is well with the countryside in the global North and ill in the global South; marginalization and poverty are increasingly recognized to be part of rich-world rural areas, just as there are pockets of privilege in rural areas in poorer countries. Furthermore, within and between the global South and global North there are widely different rural geographical imaginations: in Australia the concept of 'rural' tends to be associated with wilderness, whereas in Western Europe notions of the rural tend to be more idyllic. In the Americas, for example, Argentinian notions of the rural – of unkempt green fields, horseback riders, unpaved roads, and vineyards set against the snowy Andes – are very different to what might be imagined in the US West, where de-populated settlements, iconic landforms, drought and desert might be pictured (see Plates 11.3 and 11.4). The point being made here is that imaginaries and indeed realities of the 'rural' are not homogenous across the globe either within or between regions and territories, varying across time and space in ways that alter how the rural is defined, interacted with, inhabited, interpreted and socially constructed.

Much recent work in rural geography, in both the Anglo/North American/Australasian (**ANAA**) tradition and increasingly in other geographical communities across the world such as those of Latin America, South-east Asia and the Pacific Islands, has sought to show that there are in fact rural worlds within worlds and that peoples' identity and social position play a role in the way rural spaces are conceptualized and experienced. Furthermore, as already suggested, the experience of the rural varies widely between the global North and global South, though much more geographical research

Plate 11.1 A 'typical' English rural setting, conserved and commercialized for tourists. Stokesay, Shropshire, United Kingdom.

(Warwick E. Murray)

Plate 11.2 Rural women make a tapa cloth for ceremonial use and sale, Tongatapu Island, Tonga.

(Warwick E. Murray)

Plate 11.3 Rural Argentina, A hacienda-like vineyard with a view of the Andes, Mendoza, Argentina.

(John Overton and Warwick E Murray)

Plate 11.4 Iconic Wild West Wilderness, Arizona, USA.
(Warwick E. Murray)

on the latter is required (Murray 2008). Although rural spaces differ vastly across the world, arguably they form interlinked parts of one global complex. As such, as globalization unfolds, the social, economic and environmental shifts that are occurring in rural worlds everywhere do not occur in isolation (Murray and Overton 2014). This chapter investigates a range of perspectives on rural worlds from different geographical viewpoints. In doing so, it purposefully draws on my own fieldwork-based examples from around the globe to paint a picture of the highly dynamic and increasingly interwoven spaces we term 'rural'.

From the vantage point of highly urbanized societies that tend to characterize the global North (and Latin America in the global South), it is easy to forget that just under half (46 per cent in 2014) of the world's population lives in rural areas, representing a total of 3.36 billion people. In both absolute and relative senses the global South is more rural with 3.09 billion inhabitants representing 52 per cent of the total population of the South in 2014. Africa and Asia accounted for close to 90 per cent of the global rural population in 2014 with close to 1.5 billion rural inhabitants in India and China alone. The vast majority of the rural world then is Southern. In the global North in 2014 there were just under 276 million rural inhabitants, representing 22 per cent of total population there (UN 2014c). As such, it could be argued that rural geography, at the global scale, should be principally concerned with issues of social, economic, environmental and cultural change in poorer countries. This is why this chapter seeks balance in this respect, building on examples from both the global North and South. The issues at stake in rural worlds across the world are serious and pressing, and concern billions of people. In the rural global South, poverty and deprivation are high, cultural loss and environmental degradation is advancing rapidly. In the rural global North social justice concerns

and local environmental issues, though arguably less pressing than those in the South, are also considerable and the use of the rural idyll as a marketing tool to commodify 'countryside' means that the rural is important across the urban/rural divide. Far from being stagnant or in decline, as it is sometimes portrayed as for example in British sit-com *The Last of the Summer Wine*, the 'rural' is shifting rapidly – and these changes are existent in and have implications for global society as a whole. This chapter looks first at how we might define the term 'rural'; it then turns to how geographers have approached and theorized change in such places. We then move on to consider changing global rural geographies in terms of demographic, political, cultural and economic shifts.

11.1 Words and worlds: what is 'rural'?

What is meant by the term 'rural'? As already discussed above, meanings and definitions vary across cultures and places. At the general level, there are two ways we can approach defining the rural. The first set of approaches might be termed *empirical*, and includes functional approaches including measuring land-use characteristics as well as demographic approaches that involve such things as population density measures. The second set of definitions can be termed *conceptual* and does not use directly quantifiable measures of **rurality**, drawing instead on **social constructs**, which have to do with how we *imagine* the countryside.

Governments have their own methodologies for delimiting what is meant by rural, which are generally empirical and are important for planning and development purposes. Using a functional definition assumes that there is a rural/urban dichotomy and that the rural is defined by what it is not – that is, not urban. But this rural/urban dichotomy will vary between places greatly, as both the rural and the urban are variously understood. In the Pacific Island territories, such as Fiji, Samoa or Rapa Nui (a.k.a Easter Island), many of the areas that are defined as urban in official statistics would likely be seen as rural areas to people from the North; such areas often have lush vegetation, informal communal gardens and relatively low-density populations. Rapa Nui is defined as 100 per cent urbanized in official statistics, for example, as all of its approximately 3,800 inhabitants are located in the capital Hanga Roa (see Plate 11.5). This low-density settlement would most likely not be considered 'urban' by Western standards, however. In this sense, using functional as well as demographic and other empirical measures leads to complexities when intended to allow comparison across societies.

Human geographers realize that the rural and urban overlap in many ways. It is common to refer to peri-urban, rurban and semi-urban areas. In this regard, some have argued that rural and the urban are best thought of as lying on a rural–urban continuum. Overall, it is now recognized that seeking to define the rural and the urban in opposition to each other (what are sometimes called binaries) is not the most useful approach. Both **political economy** and more recent cultural approaches to rural geography emphasize, in various ways, that rural and urban spaces are constructed by processes that cut across both, and that whilst the impacts of these processes on the ground will not be equal they are responding to common stimuli (see Chapter 9).

Conceptual definitions of rural are important, and not as obscure as they may appear at first. As we will see, economic opportunities, planning, infrastructure development and many other 'concrete' outcomes are predicated on how individuals, collectives and governments imagine the rural. Under such definitions rural is something in the mind – and thus rural 'social' space need not correspond with rural 'geographic' space. More will be said on this issue when we consider how rural geography has itself changed over recent years.

Cloke (2000: 718) defines the 'rural' as:

> Areas which are dominated by extensive land uses such as agriculture or forestry, or by large open spaces of underdeveloped land, which contain small, lower order settlements demonstrating a strong relationship between buildings and extensive landscape, and which are *perceived as rural by most residents.* (Emphasis added)

The emphasis is added above in order to highlight the fact that rural geographers have come to think of 'rurality' as much as a state of mind as one based on a specific configuration of functions. Cloke goes on to argue that while some rural areas are still defined functionally, in those closer to urban centres 'rural is more of a socially constructed and culturally constructed and therefore contested category' (Cloke 2000: 718). This latter point is most relevant to the global North where the blurring between urban and rural is increasingly pronounced and where cultural commodification of the countryside and the construction of the rural idyll are widespread. As we will see, although these processes are evident in some cases, rurality in the global South generally has very different connotations.

11.2 Changing rural geographies

In order to understand the geographies of rural space, it is useful to review the evolution of rural geography as a sub-discipline. Rural geography is the study of the relationship between humans and the environment in rural areas, the nature of rural localities, economies, societies, cultures and environments and how this varies across space. Trajectories within the sub-discipline vary markedly across the world, but in the ANAA tradition there has been a relatively common path. Within the context of geography in general, rural geography has, until recently, been somewhat neglected. This may be because in richer countries the rural population is a minority. Also, it could be argued that much Western scholarship carries an urban bias, based on the assumption that it is in such areas that social progress is designed and experienced. The past 25 years has seen a rise in interest in rural geography in the ANAA tradition and rural areas in the global North are seen as spaces where *general* cultural and economic processes can be researched, understood and interpreted.

Plate 11.5 The wharf at Hanga Roa, the urban centre and capital of Rapa Nui (Easter Island), South Pacific.

(Warwick E. Murray)

Indeed, rural studies are increasingly interdisciplinary (see, for example, the leading academic journal in this area, *Journal of Rural Studies*). Rural geographies of the poor world have been treated very differently and have tended to be conflated with development studies: thus, notwithstanding research in Latin America on the *Nueva Ruralidad* there is relatively little cultural geography of the rural global South (see Kay 2008; Murray 2008).

Early geography paid some attention to rural areas but this declined with the quantitative revolution and the rise of spatial science in the 1960s. Rural geography at this time was essentially agricultural geography, as 'rural' and 'agricultural' were – for good empirical reasons – more explicitly interchangeable at the time. Rural geography made something of a comeback in the 1970s and early 1980s, and during this period the sub-discipline could be described as 'functionalist', concerned with such issues as rural planning, land use change and urban encroachment. In hindsight, this approach can be seen as 'uncritical' and theory-free. The relevance of such rural geography was questioned in terms of its contribution to broader society in the late 1980s. Some also argued that by focusing on the distinctiveness of the countryside it ignored processes that cut across the increasingly blurred rural–urban divide (Woods 2010).

By the early 1990s, in the ANAA tradition, there was resurgence in rural geography based on concepts from political economy. This focused in particular on a critique of the role of the 'restructuring' impacts of **globalization** and – although not referred to as such then – **neoliberalism**. This approach saw the application of concepts from neo-**Marxist** and **world systems** perspectives and was focused on how circuits of capital across the world conditioned, and were conditioned by, the nature of rural space in different locations and how the state intervened in such flows. Some such concepts have been applied to agriculture in the South, particularly commodity and value chain analysis, although not always under the title of rural 'geography'. Themes considered during this period included diversification, environmental change, international food chains and deregulation, as well as attempts, in later forms at least, to bring together social and political issues with economic concerns (Cloke 2005a). The latter included work on commodification, **gentrification**, accessibility and **counterurbanization**. Much of the work in this area, particularly in **agri-food systems**, has continued until the present. Indeed one might argue that in New Zealand and Australia emphasis has remained on the political economy of agriculture and on the impacts of globalization, and has not shifted to cultural interpretations to the extent that it has in the UK (Argent 2002). Furthermore, across the world traditional land use studies remain popular; Chilean, Peruvian and

Argentinian rural geography has long been dominated by land use analysis, functional definitions, and quantification oriented towards planning and poverty alleviation, for example, although there are signs this is changing in the fieldwork of a new generation of researchers. In this sense, as Roche (2002) argues in a classic review article, it is more meaningful to talk of rural 'geographies' rather than a singular geography.

The most recent turn in rural geography has been profoundly influenced by the general cultural turn in human geography which itself was stimulated by the shift to **postmodern** ideas in the social sciences. This shift has by no means been homogenous and there are commentators who have argued that this has made our rural geographies less rather than more relevant (see Wilson and Rigg 2003). In the global South new rural cultural geographies have been eclipsed by the study of what is perceived as more pressing socio-economic and environmental concerns. As a consequence the exploration of important cultural themes has been woeful. Only recently have we seen the emergence of more 'holistic' approaches, for example such as *Desarollo rural con identidad* (rural development with identity) in countries including Peru, Mexico and Ecuador. The cultural approach, then, seeks to break down old binaries and structures, interrogating rurality as an environmental as well as social construct, which is participated in by persons of shared cultural, social and moral values. Crucially, the social space of the rural (which can be imagined and thus be located anywhere) need not necessarily overlap with the territorial space of the rural. Thus the new rural geography engages with ideas that have to do with the social construction of categories, and the way they are then represented and reproduced.

Partly in response to the cultural turn, political economy approaches have broadened to include, among other things, studies of those who are 'marginalized', including geographies of rural women, the young, the old and those in poverty, for example. There have also been a number of more contemporary geographies exploring, among other things, rural sexuality, feminism, **travellers** and those who, because of dominant cultural constructions of the countryside (in the United Kingdom at least), have been severely 'othered' (Little and Leyshon 2003; Woods 2010, 2012). Finally, there has been a shift in the ANAA tradition towards the exploration and promotion of 'alternative' and 'ethical' rural and agricultural production networks and sustainable rural livelihoods in both the global North and South, including fair trade, organic projects and geographical indications, for example (see Spotlight box 11.2).

Linking the new cultural rural geography and political economy rural studies is an important challenge (Argent

2002; Philips 2002). Furthermore, building in empirical and theoretical input from geographers in areas other than the United Kingdom and the United States is also very important. Most rural dwellers live outside the countries where the global rural geography agenda is set, and in conditions that are very different to those found there. In this regard, more research on the rural geography of poorer territories and regions is required (Murray 2008). Overall, the important thing to remember is that numerous traditions in rural geography coexist and that 'paradigms' or perspectives never neatly succeed one another; communicating across and between these rural world-views is a central challenge for human geographers in general.

11.3 Shifting rural worlds

In what follows we will consider geographical change in rural demographies, polities, cultures and economies. Relative weight is placed on the latter two categories, although this does not mean that they are more significant than other areas. Processes that operate in any one of these spheres interact in various ways with processes in others, just as rural areas are bound together as one global network.

Rather than considering the global North and South separately, examples from each and the links between them are emphasized within this framework. The forces that cut across these boundaries can be summarized as modernization (see **modernity** in the glossary) (including increased **urbanization** and industrialization), and its latest incarnates, neoliberalism, **retroliberalism** and globalization (see Murray and Overton 2015). These processes fall unevenly in different places, given local histories and respective positions in the global system. As global divisions of labour spread further across the planet and borders become increasingly permeable, rural and agricultural spaces in very different places form constituent parts of an evolving global network of rural spaces. As such, land use and identity and all other aspects of rural change in the North must be seen as intimately tied to changing socio-economic, environmental and cultural ruralities in the South.

11.3.1 Dynamic rural demographies

Rural demographies across the world are highly dynamic. This demographic change has been conditioned, to varying extents, by generally increasing levels of urbanization, the diversification of the economic base of the countryside away from agriculture combined with the rolling

out of neoliberalism, and shifting cultures in rural areas. These shifts have been configured in very different ways across space but, in general terms, **depopulation** in the countryside has been an almost universal trend since the industrial revolution in the global North, and since the export of industrial-led growth models after the Second World War in the global South. Table 11.1 shows that whilst absolute world rural population rose from 1.7 billion to over 3.36 billion between 1950 and 2014, in relative terms it declined, falling from 71 per cent to 46 per cent of the total global population.

Table 11.1 also shows the breakdown of rural population by region, illustrating that in a proportional sense Africa is the most 'rural' – with levels of over 60 per cent – followed by Asia with 52 per cent. Looking at regional data at this scale often hides important variations – for example, Oceania includes the highly urbanized countries of Australia and New Zealand, as well as relatively rural Pacific Island countries such as Vanuatu, Solomon Islands, Fiji, Papua New Guinea and Tonga. Overall, however, it is clear that there is a significant North/South divide in terms of the demographic rural/urban dichotomy; in the richer countries there are just over 275 million rural inhabitants, representing approximately 22 per cent of the total population, whilst in the South there are over 3 billion rural inhabitants, accounting for just over 52 per cent of the total population at the present time.

Since the Industrial Revolution the relative loss of population in the countryside in the global North has proceeded as national economies became based first on industry and then services, both of which are generally, though not exclusively, concentrated in urban areas. This population loss has commonly been highly selective, often taking the young and sometimes the skilled, leaving depleted labour markets and service provision (see Plate 11.6). Indeed, as noted above, rural populations across the world are both ageing and in relative decline. Rates of urbanization are most rapid by far in the global South, while the level of urbanization remains low compared to the West. The most rapid rates of relative rural population decline, then, are found in poorer regions of the planet, which has significant and generally deleterious consequences for the rural society left behind as well as to the swelling urban populations which they are augmenting.

There have been some exceptions to the rule of relative rural depopulation and one of the most studied demographic processes in the global North has been counterurbanization. In the 1970s in the USA, for example, fuelled by rising net in-migration, smaller towns grew at a more rapid pace than larger ones, reversing the historical trend in urbanization towards large agglomerations. In the 1980s and early 1990s in the United Kingdom

Table 11.1 Rural population by region and development grouping, 1950–2050

	1950 Population (million)	%	1975 Population (million)	%	1990 Population (million)	%	2014 Population (million)	%	2050(*) Population (million)	%
Africa	191	85.3	310	74.6	518	63.6	611	60.4	729	49.3
Asia	1162	83.2	1820	76	2313	62.9	2402	58.3	2236	45.9
Europe	271	49.5	232	34.4	206	28.3	201	27.5	152	21.7
Latin America	97	58	125	38.8	129	24.6	121	20.7	113	15.7
North America	62	36.1	64	26.2	66	20.9	63	18.1	53	13.3
Oceania	5	38	6	28.5	9	29.5	11	29.8	11	26.2
Global North	*390*	*47.9*	*350*	*33.1*	*320*	*26.8*	*310*	*25.1*	*240*	*19.2*
Global South	*1400*	*81.9*	*2210*	*73.1*	*2920*	*59.7*	*3059*	*55.4*	*3050*	*43.9*
World Rural	**1790**	**71**	**2560**	**62.8**	**3240**	**53.3**	**3406**	**49.9**	**3290**	**40.1**
World Total	**2520**		**4070**		**6090**		**6829**		**8200**	

* = projected

Source: author's calculations on data from UN (2010 and 2014c)

Plate 11.6 The monthly market in Chile Chico, a small isolated settlement high in the Chilean Andes on the border of Argentina and Chile.

(Warwick E. Murray)

smaller settlements and some rural areas experienced growth whilst inner cities recorded net losses. Hereford, an agricultural centre in the west of England located on the Welsh border, became the fastest growing settlement in the country in the late 1980s, for example. There were, and still are, visible manifestations of urban to rural migration in Herefordshire as a whole, including 'barn-conversions' and small rural housing estates as working populations from cities such as Birmingham, Bristol and

Cardiff re-located to villages and small towns across the county. The real and perceived diseconomies of scale of large cities as well as changes in the nature of work and private mobility led to this outcome. Cultural shifts also influence this demographic change. As people have tired of the costs inherent in urban living, such as congestion, pollution and social distance, some have sought out the idyll of rural life, closer community, and many other stereotypes that abound regarding the countryside in the global North. In New Zealand and Australia the rise of the 'lifestyle block', an acre or two of land in the countryside where the 'good life' can be practiced, within commuting distance of a large city, is a growing phenomenon. In the United Kingdom 'barn conversions' are the outcome of similar processes albeit in a more densely populated context (see Plate 11.7).

The universality of counterurbanization in the global North has been called into question and some see it as very time- and place-specific: related to a period of manufacturing and service decentralization in Europe and USA that took place in the 1970s and early 1980s especially. Countries that have experienced periods of growth in the proportion of the total population living in rural areas include Germany (1970–85), United Kingdom (1950–70), Finland (marginally from 1980 onwards) and Australia (1975–90) (United Nations 2006). There has been a clustering of relative rural population gain in Central and Eastern Europe since 1990 in places including Latvia, Estonia, Slovakia, Romania, Czech Republic and

Plate 11.7 A 'barn conversion' in Herefordshire, England.

(Warwick E. Murray)

also Russia, for example. However, in many countries – including Spain, Holland, Belgium, Canada, Sweden and New Zealand, for example – net counterurbanization has not occurred at all at a national scale, although there are many examples of urban to rural migration, they have not outweighed the reverse. Outside of Europe there are virtually no examples of relative rural population gain over the past 60 years, except in some very small countries or small island nations. However, the rural–urban drift has slowed in the global North; the rate of decline in rural population slowed from rates of 1.35 per cent per annum in the period 1950–55 to 0.66 per cent between the years 2005 and 2010, and declined further by 2014 (United Nations 2009 and 2014c). Rural depopulation is undoubtedly the dominant pattern in richer countries, albeit at lower rates than previously, particularly as inner cities are rejuvenated and people appear to be seeking settlement closer to their place of work (see Chapter 9). Recently, the rise of Internet communications has led some to suggest that a new process of counterurbanization could well be imminent, as people can increasingly locate at a distance from their place of employment. Whilst possible in theory, such technology does not obviate the essential human need to meet face to face and such a process relates to only certain kinds of tertiary and quaternary activities and is therefore socially-selective; to date there is no evidence that cyber-technology is reversing rural depopulation anywhere on the planet.

Although counterurbanization is not a worldwide phenomenon, representing a fascinating yet ultimately unimportant diversion from the principal trend of rural depopulation, there is no doubt that the social structure of the rural population in the global North is shifting because of demographic change. When one looks below the scale of the whole nation-state, it has often been possible to detect smaller regional units of buoyant rural population growth based on migration patterns. This shift is influenced by urban-to-rural migration among certain groups and changes the nature of rural areas in a variety of ways. Some rural areas, particularly those close to larger urban settlements, have become effectively dormitory zones. When in-migrant populations in the rural United Kingdom – characterized inherently by high mobility – bypass local services such as small shops, local pubs, health clinics and small hospitals, post-offices and railway stations, the impact on the socio-cultural nature and economic base of rural areas can be dramatic. The influx of urban migrants in some areas has occasionally led to tensions between the existent and in-migrant population, in terms of how rural settlements are governed and managed. Through the 1970s and 1980s, Welsh nationalists, in response to the perceived 'invasion', burnt a number of holiday homes purchased by non-Welsh newcomers, for example. Interestingly, however, studies in the United Kingdom have shown that social collectives, such as playgroups, village football teams, local fitness groups and creative activities such as orchestras (as in the case of my own home village of Tarrington in Herefordshire) have been characterized by high participation by in-migrants, clearly keen to illustrate their commitment to their new home and live out the imagined community spirit that some might seek. Cloke (2005b) argues that differing densities of population and territorial size lead to different impacts with respect to the processes outlined above. In the United Kingdom, for example, rural areas that are subject to immigration effectively become suburbs. This is contrasted to the situation in the USA, Australia and, to an extent, New Zealand, where the migratory 'footprint' of any given city will be relatively dispersed. Again what should be clear from this discussion is that there are variable outcomes across global rural space.

The demographic processes at work and outcomes in the rural areas of the global South are, generally speaking, very different to those outlined in the preceding discussion, although the theme of rural depopulation in terms of the proportion of total population living in rural areas is a common one. As already noted, this process is generally much more rapid in poorer countries in terms of absolute rates of migration. Although rural–urban drift has ebbed and flowed in different places at different times, this shift has become one of the defining features of social change in the South over the past decades, leading to the abandonment of rural areas in extreme cases (Plate 11.8) and the explosion of urban populations in receiving areas. Latin America has seen a particularly marked rural depopulation over the past 50 years in proportional terms, for example, as has the Pacific Island region, which in many cases has seen the rise of international rural to urban migration (see Case study 11.1).

Plate 11.8 Inca de Oro, which translates as Gold Inca, was formerly an important mining centre in the Atacama region of Chile. The concentration and modernization of mining has seen it decline and suffer depopulation and service decline.

(Warwick E. Murray)

Case study 11.1

Rural depopulation in the Pacific Islands: Niue

Niue provides a good example of rural depopulation in the global South. Niue is a very small island nation with a population of close to 1,500. Although Alofi, its capital, is defined as an urban area, functionally and demographically it is rural, being low-density and dominated by subsistence agricultural production. From a peak of 5,000, this rural island has been losing population since the 1960s, a process which accelerated when the colonial power from 1901, New Zealand, offered dual citizenship for Niueans on independence in 1974. Owing to a mixture of cyclones, environmental degradation, and misguided economic development policy, the islanders have moved consistently and in very high relative numbers to the cities of New Zealand, especially Auckland, and to a lesser extent to Australia. This loss has its positive side – remittances sent back from Niuean migrants, often second and third generation, form part of the backbone of the country's economy, with over 50 per cent of GDP accounted for by such flows, with much of the rest of national income accounted for by aid flows (Murray and Overton 2014).

Unlike remittance-based migration from some rural areas to urban areas in the South, this case is not circular in its nature: it is largely permanent. However, this loss of population means that Niue is the most rapidly depopulating rural zone and country in the world. The consequences of this demographic shift have been devastating: services in retail and transport have declined as they become uneconomic; whole settlements have been abandoned leaving empty shells where once were houses; and the country's agriculture suffers from severe labour shortages (Plate 11.9). After the devastating cyclone Heta in late 2004, some on the right-wing of New Zealand politics asked whether the country could survive and at what point it should be declared unviable. The disappearance of the rural society on the island of Niue would deny the world a unique and fascinating culture that contributes to the world's human diversity. A similar story is true across many of the Pacific Islands such as Rapa Nui, Samoa, Wallis and Futuna, Tuvalu and Tokelau, as rural population is lost to the process of both intra- and transnational urbanization (Murray and Terry 2004; Connell 2008; Overton and Murray 2014).

Plate 11.9 Abandoned housing in Niue, Central Pacific. International rural to urban migration has seen numerous villages in the country struggle to remain viable.

(Warwick E. Murray)

A number of factors explain this rural–urban drift in the South, with the weight of each varying from place to place. Generally speaking, the move abroad of transnational corporations (TNCs) beginning in the 1960s, the increasing mobility of capital from the 1980s onwards, and the concomitant rise in industrial employment, together with development theory and policy that promotes modernization (i.e. industrial urban development) as beneficial and desirable, have combined to precipitate this outcome (Potter *et al*. 2008). The process has been aggravated by the legacy of unequal landholding structures in rural areas, where peasant farmers often exist side by side with large landowners sometimes directly descended from colonial elites. The simultaneous commercialization of agriculture and de-agrarianization of national economies has often led to fewer opportunities for small-scale producers, as larger producers have access to the credit and collateral required to purchase the technology in order to compete. Thus smaller producers have either lost their land to become temporary labourers on large farms or have migrated to the city – leading to what is known as proletarianization in the case of the former, and de-peasantization in the case of the latter (Murray 2006). There are instances when this rural population decline has been stopped or even reversed, as is the case in the Monte Patria *comuna* (district) of northern Chile during the peak years of the grape export boom in the early 1990s and is now the case in the rapidly expanding wine export regions of the Central Valley (Overton and Murray 2011). In some cases in places as diverse as Peru, Fiji and Sarawak, Malaysia the rise of rural tourism has led to localized rural population growth, but overall this is not common.

In short, rural areas in poorer countries have become increasingly less attractive economically and socially and a large-scale drift to the cities has occurred. In some cases this has been coupled with severe environmental decline because of over-exploitation, rapid commercialization or climate change. Severe drought has increased over recent years in the sub-Saharan rural zones, for example, leading to a rise in rural–urban drift. Under such conditions, political circumstances, including wars, and neoliberal and retroliberal economic policies such as export orientation, have often aggravated environmental tensions leading to full-scale food shortages and famine. Problems in rural areas in the South are made all the more significant when one considers that despite rapid relative population loss, the largest *absolute* rural populations are found in poor countries and this is set to be the case in the foreseeable future. Table 11.2 shows the largest ten rural populations by country in 2014, projected into 2050, with the USA being the only country in the global North featuring on the list.

11.3.2 Dynamic rural polities

Political power in the countryside in both the global North and South is shifting considerably in terms of how it is gained and exercised. As such, the governance of rural spaces is increasingly complex and contested. In Northern countries, rural areas have traditionally been over-represented in parliamentary politics, owing in part to the inherited importance of the landed elite in national affairs of state as well as the desire of some democratic governments to escape accusations of urban bias. Within the countryside itself this created space for various countryside interest groups, alliances, political parties and **social movements** that draw on particular imaginaries of the countryside to make their case. In New Zealand, for example, a small political party – the Outdoor Recreation Party NZ – won 1.3 per cent (approximately

Table 11.2 Ten largest rural populations by country, 2014 and 2050 (millions)

Country	Rural population 2014	Country	Rural population 2050 (projected)
India	857	India	805
China	635	China	335
Indonesia	119	Nigeria	144
Pakistan	114	Ethiopia	117
Bangladesh	106	Pakistan	115
Nigeria	95	Indonesia	94
Ethiopia	78	Bangladesh	90
Vietnam	62	Uganda	71
USA	60	Philippines	69
Philippines	56	Dem. Rep. of Congo	61.4

Source: author's calculations from UN (2014c)

25,000) votes in the 2002 general election on a platform of 'preserving' rural areas for hunting and fishing as well as broader rural-first policies and as a consequence of this success was integrated into a larger party – the United Future – in subsequent elections. The Countryside Alliance in the United Kingdom is another case. With the motto 'love the countryside', the movement was formed in 1997 and grew rapidly in reaction to the single issue of the proposed ban on fox-hunting contained in the Labour Party 2001 election manifesto. The movement soon mushroomed to include a range of disgruntled rural groups who argued that central government was increasingly over-interventionist in rural affairs. The Alliance argues that over 100,000 individuals are members. The movement culminated in a massive march on UK Parliament in October 2002 involving approximately 400,000 people. The imagined conflict between city and country – traditional and modern, and 'authentic' and 'fake' – was invoked in speeches during the march. Many groups that are truly marginalized in the countryside, such as travellers for example, were not represented to the same extent as the 'sport' of fox-hunting. This has led some to argue that the Alliance was a smokescreen erected by the elite, utilizing stereotypical interpretations of the countryside, to push a single issue pertinent to them, whilst drawing in support from the rural masses (see Woods 2005 for a discussion). Casting the particularities of the situation to one side, what is interesting is the way the Alliance used 'imaginaries' of the countryside in order to pursue a specific political point. It is also clear that these imaginaries – of fox-hunting and hounds and red suits on horses – are not necessarily shared, or even considered desirable, by the majority in the countryside in the United Kingdom.

But representations of the rural for political gain are not just made from within the countryside itself: arguments about rural identity are sometimes invoked in order to make broader political gains. Countries in the European Union, especially France, have used arguments concerning the importance of 'rurality' to make the case for the maintenance of subsidies for agriculture, organized broadly under the **Common Agricultural Policy (CAP)** since 1962, claiming that such funds help sustain the lifestyles and landscapes that make a broader contribution to the character of the European countryside. More recently, European governments have couched this argument in terms of the protection of the 'multifunctionality' (see also later discussion) of the countryside; that is to say, sustaining agriculture has positive knock-on effects in other areas (such as environmental preservation, for example) that others in broader society also value. Governments of the South, articulated through the G77 and the **World Trade Organization (WTO)** as well as various regional groupings such as the *Union de Naciones Suramericanos*

(UNASUR) and the Southern African Development Community (SADEC), have historically seen this as a form of protectionism, allowing the continuance of subsidized agriculture in richer countries. At the same time that such support persists, global financial institutions insist on the adoption of free-market, non-subsidized, neoliberal policies in poorer countries, a situation that discriminates against millions of rural inhabitants.

In the global South the practice of modernist development has often been described as 'urban biased' (Kay 2001). The persistent neglect of rural development initiatives in favour of industrial urban policy has been written about widely and consistently, most notably in Africa and Latin America. In the latter, rural zones have been neglected by administrations that have been over-centralized, partly a consequence of a legacy of urban-based Hispanic society, and partly the result of the opening of economies to foreign capital which exploits cheap labour pools in urban areas during the recent phase of neoliberalism and subsequent retroliberalism. There are numerous examples of rural resistance to the neoliberalization of rural areas and its associated urban bias in places as diverse as Thailand, Fiji and Brazil. One of the most notable examples is that of the Zapatistas in Chiapas, Southern Mexico (Murray and Overton 2014). This movement was very influential in terms of the rise of the anti-globalization groups that characterized the early 2000s and the group remains powerful in popular culture today, evidenced in Mexican singer/musician Lila Downs' recent song 'Zapata sigue' which celebrates the dynamic and complex rural Mexican culture linked to the figure of Zapata and the uprising in Southern Mexico. Despite rises in commodity agro-exports, effective control of resources still remains in urban areas, resulting in a process of what could be called internal colonialism. Rural dwellers in the South have to endure the double impact of over-centralized and urban-biased governments, and the economic control of large corporations based in capital cities or, often, outside of the borders of the country itself.

There are also examples of resistance to 'modernist' rural production methods in the South by populations in the global North. Participation in alternative food networks, organic supply chains, local economic trading schemes, **slow food** networks, localized farmer markets/**food miles** movements and fair trade linkages as forms of opposition have become significant, on the fringes of the modernist production and consumption networks of the North. Some, however, have conceptualized alternative projects as just part of neoliberalism, controlled by powerful multinational retail conglomerates or bodies that serve their interests, where 'alternatives' are mainstreamed quickly in order to protect the capitalist *status quo*. However, fair trade NGOs and the Fairtrade labelling bodies themselves maintain that consumers can play an important role in terms of caring at distance that can make a difference to rural spaces in poorer countries. McCarthy (2006), however, argued that to date alternative ethical networks had done little to alter existing North–South dynamics and power remains largely concentrated in the former. Research efforts are being undertaken in this area and will reveal more clues as to the impact of such networks in the coming years (see Spotlight box 11.2).

11.3.3 Dynamic rural cultures

Traditional rural cultures are being altered profoundly by the shifting relationship between the urban and the rural, although what is meant by 'traditional' is contested. As noted previously, the increasing intermingling of urban and rural processes and populations raises questions as to what is meant by 'rural' at all. Indeed some have argued that the concept of rurality exists only in the mind and that the 'binary' of rural and urban is a false one. Thus, as noted previously, rural *social* space and rural *territorial* space are not necessarily the same thing and therefore 'rurality' is something that has to be deconstructed. Some have even argued that we have reached a 'post-rural' condition in that pure rurality no longer exists, if it ever did. Cultural geographers have been hard at work trying to tease out the way that meanings of rurality are perceived by different actors in the global North (but relatively little in the South) and how this affects socio-cultural and economic behavior and patterns.

Postmodernists argue that much of the contemporary world is **simulacrum** where symbols or signifiers of an event replace direct experience. Reality is thus experienced through representations of it, creating a 'hyper-reality' that is disembedded from territorial space. It has been argued, based largely on evidence from the UK, that this has occurred in the case of the perception of the rural by some urban dwellers who wish to experience the 'rustic' and the relatively 'untouched', which they imagine to be associated with the countryside. This might include: wearing country clothes, driving large four-wheel-drive all-terrain vehicles around city streets, designing the interior of their homes like country cottages, and so on. It could be argued that many people who live in the rural–urban fringe extend this hyper-reality to their everyday existence. The idea that we are in a post-rural condition takes the argument too far, however, and certainly does in the case of the global South where such notions are at best irrelevant and, at worst, fanciful, elitist and damaging. As such and in general, the cultural meanings associated with the rural have caused a shift in the relationship between society and geographical space, and between culture and nature (see Chapter 12).

The foregoing trends have influenced the cultural consumption of the countryside and the allied commodification of the rural experience. In the global North, rural imaginaries are used to sell things. When objects, traits and ideas of a particular culture are brought into capitalist circuits, or when new traits are invented in order to stimulate economic gain, 'cultural commodification' can be said to be occurring. Increasingly, 'cosmopolitan consumers' seek out 'authentic' experiences that will help them differentiate themselves from the masses. There are further examples across the 'cultural' economy – 'world' music, poverty tourism, 'ethnic' food aisles in supermarkets, cultural quarters: Chinatown, Little India and the like – established in cities as diverse as San Francisco, Singapore, London, Cape Town, Rio de Janeiro and Auckland (see Chapter 13). Although the flow of cultural items from the periphery to the core was initiated during Western imperial times, there can be little doubt that there is a growing tendency towards the consumption of 'the Other' in richer markets facilitated by globalization (see Chapter 19).

In the case of rural areas, cultural commodification has been especially important. This is most obvious in the advertising world, which uses rural references in order to sell products that have little or nothing to do with the countryside. For example, the advertising campaign for Speights Beer in New Zealand involves images of typical rural South Island men who are tough in outlook and pioneering in spirit. As heroes they are spurred on by the taste of Speights beer, which allegedly gives them energy, and which they prefer above all 'urban' temptations (such as a box at Eden Park rugby ground, the main stadium home of the All Blacks, in one advert). The good-humoured rivalry between North and South Islands of New Zealand, which is a proxy for urban and rural in some ways, is used to sell a product that 'real men' drink. In reality, most Speights beers are brewed in Auckland, located in the northern part of the country – a large urban conglomeration much like any other, far away both territorially and culturally from much of the South Island.

There is also a trend towards 'place-making' in rural areas across the global North, for the purposes of creating niche products, including tourism. This involves taking a trait, or inventing one, which is characteristic of a locality and using this for economic gain – another term for this is *fictive place* (see Overton and Murray 2016). Ludlow, in the English county of Shropshire, for example, has reinvented itself as one of the principal gourmet destinations in the country based on the coincidental location there of a number of top restaurateurs in the 1990s. This has created a hub of restaurants, cafés, wine bars and tea shops, which bears little relevance to the 'authentic' history of this small medieval rural town which grew up based around its castle built to defend from and further penetrate that part of the British Celtic fringe now known as Wales. In New Zealand, Taihape has pronounced itself 'gumboot' (wellington boot) capital of the world, has an annual world gumboot throwing competition, and has erected statues and opened tearooms to celebrate this (Plate 11.10)! Towns that have been bypassed by the establishment of large highways turn this to their advantage by advertising the 'best of rural life' on large highway billboards to attract weary travellers, as in the case of Marton, New Zealand. Alexandra in Central Otago, New Zealand, has recreated the original settlers' rural township in order to stimulate the tourist demand for authentic rural experiences, and there are many similar examples across Anglo settler societies such as the USA, Canada and Australia. These examples illustrate attempts to use rural imaginaries to create diversified livelihoods in areas where traditional agricultural production patterns are rapidly restructuring. In such efforts culture, invented or otherwise, plays an important economic role.

A phenomenon linked to cultural consumption is the creation of rural spectacle in order to market place (Cloke 2005b). The construction of 'fresh' and 'natural' experiences is important in this respect. Adventure tourism in New Zealand and Australia – including white water rafting, bungee jumping and zorbing, for example – is an interesting example of how rural areas have reconfigured their economic bases. At Kiwi 360 near to Tauranga, New Zealand, it is possible to visit orchards, take part in activities and tour a museum to kiwi fruit production. The multiple connotations of the word 'kiwi' – which refers to a native flightless bird, a fruit, and often used to describe a New Zealander – are clearly used in marketing such rural spectacles. Related to the concept of rural spectacle is the evolution of cultural visits to

rural areas. In New Zealand, in the area around Rotorua (central North Island), there are numerous 'authentic' Maori villages that have been developed for tourists to visit and experience indigenous culture. In New Zealand's leading tourist destination, Queenstown, in an area not intensively settled by Maori historically, there is a strong tourist-based 'Maori experience' on offer at various performances locations throughout the town. Today, most Maori live in urban areas and their lifestyle is far removed from the hyper-reality and fictive place depicted in such locations, but such businesses provide an important source of income for those involved, including many Maori who lead the groups that perform *haka* (dance) and *waiata* (song). Cultural commodification has the potential to bring economic gains but it can also straightjacket places into fossilized cultural representations, leading to the creation of damaging stereotypes. Notwithstanding this, some have argued that such ventures help maintain traits of Maori culture that might otherwise die out, thereby rejuvenating rural indigenous culture.

In the rural global South cultural issues are very different. Rural cultures are, of course, vibrant and enormously varied. Given that the vast majority of rural dwellers on earth live in the global South this variety is kaleidoscopic. In some cases 'national' culture is rooted in traditional and conservative imaginaries of the rural (see Plate 11.1), although this culture is sometimes fossilized and invented. Notwithstanding this, very little is known of the rural cultural geography of the South, and human geography in the North has tended to ignore it. There is a rich tradition of anthropology of rural areas in the Third World, but this tends to focus on the unusual rather the everyday cultures of the rural poor. In some post-colonial territories rural areas are often home to 'indigenous' cultures, or

Plate 11.10 Taihape, Central North Island, New Zealand – gumboot capital of the world!

(Warwick E. Murray)

Plate 11.11 The annual horse sprint tournament high in the Limarí Valley, Norte Chico, Chile.

(Warwick E. Murray)

at least they were so before the onset of rural–urban drift. This raises particular issues with respect to rural development planning in poorer countries. In Chile, for example, many Mapuche – once one of the only unconquered indigenous group in Latin America – live in the south of the country in a marginalized economic and social environment. Those Mapuche that have moved to the capital city have often fared no better in the urban context and have become, until very recently, almost invisible in the nation's consciousness. Far from the buzzing and primate metropolis of Santiago, the rural Mapuche have, until recently at least, been left behind by the economic and political progress made in the country over the past 25 years. In contrast to the global North, the experience of 'rurality' can be painful and poverty-stricken for such groups (see Spotlight box 11.1).

Across the Third World the **peasantry** is declining and this is leading to rapid change in the cultural life of rural dwellers. As neoliberalism unfolds, peasant farmers and other small-scale producers are forced from their land and, as discussed previously, leave for the cities. In Fiji, despite leaving their homes, urban migrants from the countryside still retain much of their rural culture – although it is metamorphosing. Through the concept of *Vanua* indigenous Fijians are linked to the land; indeed they see themselves as indivisible from the land, and in particular the rural places they come from. Second- and third-generation urban Fijians who live in the urban agglomeration based in and around Suva (population

circa 400,000) might well still consider themselves as 'being of' Taveuni, Ovalau, Tailevu or some other rural area and they will make this known very early on during both formal ceremonial and informal conversational exchanges. Notwithstanding some continuity, there are also significant changes; the influence of urban Fijians that return to the village, temporarily or otherwise, is contested and often bemoaned by those who stay behind, as they bring with them concepts, such as property rights, individualism and capitalism, which hitherto were alien in such societies.

The marketization of the countryside in ways that increase tourism and niche products are relatively rarely practised in the global South, although it is possible to find increasing examples of exceptions to this rule. Wine tourism in rural Chile, for example, is growing in popularity with the urban middle and upper classes who travel to the countryside locations such as the Colchagua and Casablanca Valleys to taste and buy wine on estates that recreate the colonial hacienda period as a rural idyll and fictive place (Overton and Murray 2011). Similarly, there are small rural towns across Africa, Asia and Latin America that specialize in handicrafts for tourists. In Fiji resorts will often re-create a version of traditional rural life, including *meke* (dance) and *kava* ceremonies, in the thatched roofed *bures* that characterize rural settlement for visiting tourists. In rural Tonga, as across Polynesia, women make tapa, a beautifully decorated bark cloth which is traditionally used for ornate and ceremonial purposes,

Spotlight box 11.1

The hidden others of the countryside

As mentioned previously, researching the 'hidden others' of the countryside in the West has now become more important in the ANAA geographical tradition. This research has revealed a darker underside to the rural idyll where people are excluded because of various identity traits or socio-economic characteristics. Work has been undertaken on travellers, marginalized sexualities, the unemployed, the elderly and the poverty-stricken, for example. Poverty in the countryside in the West can be disturbingly high, and this has been particularly the case as the economic base has rapidly restructured over the past two decades under neoliberalism. In New Zealand, for example, the neoliberal restructuring of the 1980s and 1990s led to the closure of many small- and medium-scale dairy reception plants, as the New Zealand Dairy Board (later Fonterra) rationalized

its operation geographically. This, together with other rural economic shifts, led to very high levels of poverty in some rural regions such as Taranaki and the East Coast, rural decline and depopulation, and some unintended consequences such as the closure of rural rugby clubs, further undoing the social and cultural fabric of the countryside (Willis 2001). Despite limited state intervention it has proven impossible for many such areas to regain dynamism, and pockets of poverty, crime and work-poor cultures in small rural towns such as Patea and Waverley remain stubbornly present to this day.

One of the ironies is that many recent countryside movements and alliances, such as those discussed in a preceding section, represent anything but such disadvantaged groups in the case of the global North, although the involvement of all classes in often elitist causes is frequently solicited in order to create the impression of a 'rural consensus'.

for sale at tourist markets in the capital Nuku'alofa. In rural Sarawak (Malaysian Borneo) it is possible for foreign tourists to undertake longhouse (traditional communal dwellings) visits. However, in general, agricultural production, combined with other diversified and off-farm – often precarious – livelihood forms, are the mainstay of such localities, and culture as a commodity usually plays a minor role unless it is invoked to make profit for large companies who might trade on such fictional notions. Notwithstanding, there has been a partial shift – at this stage minimal in impact – towards models of development that seek economic and cultural identity based progress simultaneously such as the *Desarollo rural con identidad* approaches favoured by some rural NGOs previously mentioned in Latin America. Geographical research is currently on-going as to whether such approaches deliver the holistic outcomes they might aspire to.

11.3.4 Dynamic rural economies

In the past the economy of rural localities was essentially agricultural. The terms 'rural' economy and 'agricultural' economy are no longer interchangeable, however. In this section we look at how the rural and the agricultural have decoupled and what has replaced agricultural livelihoods, at least in part. This shift has arisen as the world economy has 'de-agrarianized', involving a large-scale shift away from agricultural to industrial and service activities. Increasingly, and particularly in the North, there is a tendency towards pluriactivity (diversified livelihoods) in rural areas (see Plate 11.12). However, diversification away from agriculture, viewed at the global scale, has been uneven, leading to the creation of very different rural economic landscapes across the world. In order to understand this transition, below we consider 'productivist' agriculture, as well as newer concepts of 'post-productive' and 'multifunctional' rural spaces.

The contemporary agri-food system can be conceptualized as a complex that stretches across continents, linking producers, consumers, supermarket retailers, and government policy makers among other agents, all of which represent nodes within commodity networks. Driving the agri-food system is agribusiness, which is associated with the industrialization and globalization of agriculture (Le Heron 1993). This has led to a shift in the nature of farming in many parts of the world involving a delocalization of activity and the creation of *long networks,* which see production oriented away from local and national markets and towards the global economy. The global agri-food network has not led to the homogenization of rural space. At the same time as we witness the industrialization of agriculture, especially in parts of the global South, we are also seeing the rise of niche, organic and alternative agriculture particularly in the North. Furthermore, in places such as Latin America and South-east Asia where large-scale commercial and export-oriented agriculture is increasingly evident, we see the continued importance of full and semi-subsistence farming.

Productivist rural economies

Productivist agriculture can be defined as the highly intensive production of a limited collection of primary commodities (McCarthy 2005). The agricultural sector has industrialized and commercialized, eclipsing non-capitalist agriculture. Agribusiness has expanded through vertical and horizontal integration, forming

Plate 11.12 Pluriactivity in rural New Zealand – off this stretch of State Highway 1, north of Levin, you can buy petrol, book a river paddle tour and have a cup of tea in an aeroplane!

(Warwick E. Murray)

conglomerates that link the field to the supermarket. This has allowed companies to reduce the costs of transacting, and internalize the risk of the inherently vulnerable business of farming. Consequently, agricultural sectors have increased in terms of ownership, and a new political economy of agriculture based largely on monopoly capitalism and mass production has emerged. Some have referred to this as **Fordist** agriculture. Companies such as Monsanto, Nestlé, Fonterra, Cadbury's and Bulmer's are major players in this new economy.

Given the liberalization of the world economy from the 1970s onwards, agribusiness TNCs have increasingly invested abroad. Cheap labour and land as well as less strictly enforced environmental regulations provide incentives for agribusiness TNCs to diffuse the production component of their operations to poorer countries. This is especially the case in fresh fruit, horticultural and floricultural sectors, resulting in a proliferation of counter-seasonal exports to the Northern markets. As a network, for example, floriculture now generates over US$50 billion in sales per annum, and involves fresh-bloom supply from over 80 countries, as far flung as Ecuador and Kenya, most of which is channelled through the Netherlands to third countries in the rich world. Globalization has drawn Third World rural spaces into global capitalist circuits, yielding profound impacts. Export-oriented agriculture destined for the North has, in the case of Latin America, led to the evolution of monocultural localities which are extremely vulnerable economically, socially and environmentally (Murray and Overton 2014).

Spotlight box 11.2

Researching ethical value chains – resistance to or perpetuation of global networks?

It is in response to the ill-effects of the globalized productivist system that 'ethical' global value chains have evolved. The chains seek to link the South with the North in ways that do not undermine the social-economic viability of small-scale farmers, threaten environmental sustainability, and protect local cultures and identity. Fair trade, organic networks and geographical indications are three – often overlapping – value chains that have evolved in order to address these concerns respectively and in reaction to broader process of agricultural globalization. Northern consumers and some of the elite in Southern territories are increasingly concerned with issues of justice, environment and identity related to the products they consume.

Geographical indicators (GIs) originate from Europe and were developed through the use of *terroir* in the French wine industry – that is, production that is distinct in a physical and cultural sense to the locality from which it emanates. Increasingly such strategies are being adopted and legalized in the South in a range of rural sectors including fruit, wine and fisheries. In Chile, for example, there are now over 20 products registered with an increasingly sophisticated GI system. There is often an element of fictive place in GIs as histories and cultures are moulded to fit marketing purposes. Notwithstanding, the potential to protect local identities is clear. Organic networks are those which are certified as being environmentally sustainable by the proliferation of agencies that has evolved to serve this function. The marketing of this concept also evolves in the North, although farming has been largely 'organic' for millennia, until the rise of Fordist agriculture to feed growing urban populations and to fuel export markets.

Of the three overlapping ethical value chain (EVC) types, fair trade has perhaps captured the imagination the most as a potential way of delivering socio-economic and cultural benefits to small-scale producers in the long networks that bring together the North and South. The system has evolved over the last 50 years, bringing to fruition a much longer heritage of charitable interactions led initially by church groups and building on the concept first proposed at the 1968 UNCTAD (United Nations Commission on Trade and Development) that development required 'trade not aid'. Over the last two decades it has grown considerably to now account for over €5.5 billion of trade. Although this is a minute proportion of the total agricultural commodity trade it does involve hundreds of countries in dozens of products. The largest traded product is coffee, followed by sugar and fruit. Suppliers from across Asia, Africa, but in particular Latin America, supply markets in the North – with the largest single ones being the UK, USA and Germany. A number of agencies have evolved to certify fair trade networks, the largest being Fairtrade international, which was established in 1997 with the amalgamation of a number of labelling systems. In essence, and across the various certifying bodies, to qualify collectives must be established that guarantee a price for growers over the medium term, offer access to credit, information and technological extension, and invest a proportion of the profits on social projects in the localities involved. Producers must have a say in the structure and direction of the collectives and the allocation of the premium. There are many success stories and a visit to the website Fairtrade International (www.fairtrade.net) provides ample evidence of this. Recent work by the author in Chile uncovered a nascent yet very promising fair trade sector evolving in wine production, led by some of the industry's established players but bringing in small-producers. A number of groups has evolved to stimulate this with collectives such as *Ruta de Vino* incorporating economic as well as cultural goals, drawing not only on fair trade principles but also concepts related to GIs, and utilizing organic production.

There can be little doubt that fair trade has helped the lives of millions of farmers across the world and their families. However, the system is not perfect. It remains to be seen whether very marginal producers, the smallest and poorest, can hope to enter the system. Little work has been done on the impacts on labour and only ongoing research will reveal the outcome. Recent unpublished research supervised by the author,

by Heather Walker, Kelle Howson and Kellie Agazziz, has showed that in some communities in East Timor and Indonesia, small growers had little concept of the fair trade system and saw it much as any other commodity market (unpublished research). Furthermore, in the worst cases social premiums did not find their way to the farmers. The literature has identified problems, including eclipsing of justice issues by environmental issues, in-fighting between various labelling bodies, the problems surrounding the correct use of the social premium, discrimination against the least viable farmers, and regressive monopsony dominance by a single buyer (Murray and Overton 2014). Some economists argue that by artificially raising prices, fair trade is actually unfair to others not in the system and locks producers into commodity systems thereby perpetuating the initial rationale for intervention. These latter analyses go too far, fair trade and the EVC networks that they are part of are arguably a move in the right direction; however, they require careful monitoring and regulation in order to serve the purpose for which they were designed and to prevent them from being co-opted by powerful agro-capitalist interests.

The evolution of agribusiness has profound implications for local rural socio-economies in the global North as well. It has, for example, led to the relative decline of the family farm (Whatmore 1995) (see Case study 11.2). Furthermore, agribusiness has altered the rural landscape, removing hedges and practising other policies intended to capture economies of scale. Rural choices have also been impacted by the consolidation of agribusiness.

Post-productive agriculture and rural worlds

We are witnessing the return, in some places, of smaller-scale agriculture, sometimes as a direct resistance to the globalization of agriculture. Simultaneously we can also observe the various uses of rural spaces intended to diversify livelihoods and add 'off farm' components. These can be termed '**post-productive**' rural landscapes where the goals, aside from maximizing agricultural yields,

Case study 11.2

Productivist agriculture in the Hereford cider industry

In the 1980s rapid growth in the UK cider industry led to a fundamental restructuring of the Herefordshire economy as the largest global producer of cider – HP Bulmer's – began an aggressive campaign to dominate local supply networks and to secure the lucrative national market. The company purchased land from small-scale farmers and consolidated orchards in a way that allowed it to take full advantage of mechanized harvesting. At the same time it employed hundreds of medium-sized farmers on two-yearly contracts in order to shore up supply. Bulmer's also took over a number

of competing medium-sized cider producers including Symond's (producer of Scrumpy Jack). This granted Bulmer's a regional bilateral monopsony position (single buyer and seller simultaneously) in the county (and for many country miles beyond). Small-scale cider producers were out-competed, and the grubbing up of many old varieties of cider apples in place of the new mass-production bush-stock varieties accelerated the decline of small-scale farmhouse cider producers, thereby eroding diversity and choice.

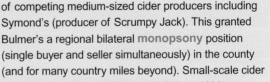

include cultural commodification, optimizing ecological value, and stimulating niche-based agriculture.

The transition to post-productive agriculture is linked to the perceived costs and falling productivity of the globalized model and the regulatory crisis it is facing. Government intervention is being rolled back, and large-scale production operating at a loss can no longer be tolerated. There is some evidence to suggest that the main bastion of productivist protectionism, the European Union's Common Agricultural Policy, may be dismantled over the next decade or so. In this sense the transition to post-productive agriculture is consistent with neoliberalism and cannot be seen as resistance to it. Indeed, if we view the evolution of this part of the system as the consequence of the farming-out of the labour- and land-intensive parts of the agri-food production complex to the periphery, then the rise of post-productivism forms part of the broader evolution of global capitalism.

In contrast to the above, some commentators see the rise of post-productive agriculture as indicative of resistance to globalization, greater concern for the environment and the search for smaller scale, *short network,* sustainable and alternative food networks. Consumer demand has transformed Northern consumption patterns, and food safety and quality issues also motivate elites in the South. This has led to a worldwide boom in organic farming as noted in Spotlight box 11.2 for example, that has impacted agricultural landscapes in the North and South. The *short network* approach can be seen as resistance to commodity production, with all of its inherent injustice and non-sustainability and as such is a further aspect of the ethical value chain system. Yet, arguably it undermines *long network* fair trade systems – does replacing imports, and thus putting out of work producers, from the South lead to an unethical and unjust outcome viewed from the vantage point of the global society as whole? Are *short networks* moral alternatives or just localized protectionism?

In reality, we face a situation in rural worlds where a mixture of productivist and post-productivist functions exist. At the global scale there is, of course, a division of labour that sees much productivist agriculture located in poorer countries because of favourable locational **comparative advantages**, such as cheap land and labour, counterseasonality, and lax environmental regulations. Niche agriculture is undoubtedly becoming more common in Northern countries. However, this dichotomy blurs a complex reality. In the United Kingdom post-productive activities in the countryside are advanced, but in places such as New Zealand, Australia and the USA there is only limited evidence of a post-productive shift. New Zealand is considered one of the most cutting-edge of the agricultural economies

but it is still heavily productivist, and because of a boom in demand from China large-scale dairy farming is in fact on the rise as more and more land is converted to dairy farming. In the global South the evidence for post-productivism is even scarcer. There are some examples, such as the rise of wine tourism in Chile as noted, but in general we are seeing a shift *towards* productivism as neoliberalism is allowed to penetrate localities in the periphery. The rise of **GM** and its diffusion is likely to accentuate this trend. We thus have a significant North–South divide in agriculture, and rural geography might do well to revisit older ideas including **dependency** and **structuralism**, in order to interpret these differentiated outcomes in the context of one global system.

Multifunctional rural worlds?

Post-productivism has been heavily criticized; use of the term is problematic because it makes assumptions about what is meant by 'productivist'. The nature of productivist agriculture has varied, and still does vary across the world; it persists in some localities whilst in others it has never arrived, and probably never will. In places such as the Pacific Islands, subsistence agriculture plays a very important role in agricultural production and rural lives, and commercial networks bypass millions of rural dwellers. Although modernist discourses might portray this as backward, the socio-cultural and nutritional role of subsistence and semi-subsistence is critical. Yet agriculture of this nature is being squeezed by globalization.

In recognizing the problems associated with the concept of post-productivism, the term 'multifunctional' has become employed in Northern rural studies. Wilson argues that the productivist debate has been 'conceptualized from a UK-centric perspective that has largely failed to discuss whether the concept has applicability in Europe or beyond' (2001: 77). Instead he suggests that the use of 'multifunctional agricultural regimes' is a better way to characterize the shifts that are occurring in European rural space. Multifunctionalism refers to the notion that 'rural landscapes typically produce a range of commodity and non-commodity use values simultaneously and that policy ought to try and recognize and protect the entire range of values' (McCarthy 2005: 774). It is argued that this concept is more useful than post-productivism as it offers a positive characterization: it recognizes the continued importance of commodity production and is sensitive to geographical difference.

Multifunctionalism implies that the countryside across the world is used for both productive and post-productive purposes and that the combination of uses, including commodification and conservation, varies from place to place. Whilst this formulation reflects complex rural worlds much more accurately than previous constructions, it is also vulnerable to criticism. In some ways the concept says everything and nothing at the same time. Furthermore, commentators from the South have argued that its use in policy formation in the European Union, for example, is a disguised form of protectionism. As already noted, governments, particularly in France, have argued that subsidies to agriculture create positive social externalities by supporting other, often less tangible, functions of the countryside which help maintain 'rurality'. Meanwhile, poorer countries are expected to open their markets and perform the productivist element of the global agri-food complex. Indeed, it could be argued that there is a move away from multifunctionalism in the South, as monocultural neoliberalized sectors replace formerly diversified livelihoods.

11.4 Conclusion

'Rural' is a relative term; it shifts across time and space. It is also an enormously diverse category and therefore difficult to make generalizations about. It is increasingly difficult to define rural spaces, be they social or geographical. In both the South and North rural spaces are increasingly politicized, often in ways that move beyond 'normal' electoral politics as new political movements abound. Rural identities have conditioned this political change and have themselves shifted in response to new social, economic and cultural configurations. Environments are threatened in all worlds because of neoliberalism and the rapid shift in the economic exploitation of rural areas. Certain constructions of rural culture and fictive places are used to sell the countryside and to represent its interests while 'other' cultures remain marginalized or are disappearing. In short, rural spaces are increasingly dynamic demographically, politically, culturally, environmentally and economically. Rural geography has had to move swiftly in an attempt to capture the complex changes and in the case of change in the South it has not kept pace.

This general shift, at the global level, has been influenced by the unfolding of neoliberalism and globalization. At the world scale, whilst it is true that rural spaces in the global North are becoming increasingly multifunctional and are shifting away from 'Fordist' agriculture, in the South we are seeing an erosion of multifunctionality and pluriactivity overall. This is certainly the case where neoliberal agriculture penetrates and the diversified livelihood-sustaining activities that have often been built up over decades and centuries are eroded. These are dynamic times for rural spaces and populations all across the world, as the insecurities, socio-economic and environmental, associated with the acceleration of globalization abound. This is especially the case in the South where neoliberal governance continues to run unrestrained despite some policy shifts to the contrary. Although rapid advances have been made in rural geography in and of the West, it is imperative that geographers turn attention to rural spaces of the South, which have so often borne the brunt of the evolution of global capitalism. Furthermore, by shifting focus in this way geographers can contribute to a more balanced and democratic human geography that is relevant to rural society as a whole and reflective of truly global change.

Learning outcomes

Having read this chapter you should be able to:

- Discuss the contested definitions of 'rural' from both a functional and conceptual point of view.
- Account for the evolution of dominant trends in rural geography in the ANAA (Anglo/North American/Australasian) tradition and how these have influenced interpretations of rural processes.
- Appreciate the impact of neoliberalism and globalization on rural spaces and how change in the global South and global North is linked.
- Consider the evidence for rural depopulation across the world and outline the arguments for counterurbanization in richer countries.
- Understand shifting rural polities and the nature of the alliances and resistance movements that have evolved over the recent past across the world.
- Interpret the commodification of the 'rural' in richer countries and the contribution of culture to the economic dynamism of the countryside in the global North through fictive place.
- Appreciate the debate concerning the positive and negative aspects of fair trade and other attempts to make value chains ethical.
- Comprehend the concepts of 'productivist', 'post-productivist' and 'multifunctional' rural economies, and debate the shifts between the three in various parts of the world.
- Recognize that more research on issues in the rural global South is required if a more democratic and globalized rural geography is to be written.

Further reading

Cloke, P.J., Marsden, T. and Mooney, P. (eds) (2006) *Handbook of Rural Studies,* Sage, London. This is a very broad-ranging and complete edited collection of viewpoints from some of the top writers in the field of rural studies that is particularly strong on cultural perspectives.

McCarthy, J. (2007) Rural geography – globalizing the countryside, *Progress in Human Geography,* 31(1), 1–6. An excellent stock-take of work in rural geography that seeks to explore the 'globalized' nature of rural areas across the world.

Munton, R.M. (ed.) (2008) *The Rural: Critical Essays in Human Geography,* Wiley-Blackwell, London. A useful way to follow up arguments here through a collection of rural geography essays from the AAA perspective, focusing mainly on the British case.

Murray, W.E. (2008) Neoliberalism, rural geography and the global South, *Human Geography,* 1(1), 33–8. This paper presents an argument for taking the rural geographies of the global South more seriously and highlights the importance of viewing rural change in any location as part of a global whole.

Roche, M. (2002) Rural geography: searching rural geographies, *Progress in Human Geography,* 26(6), 823–9. This review article provides an excellent stock-take and discussion of the main trends and major scholarly articles in rural geography through the 1980s and 1990s.

Woods, M. (2010) *Rural,* Routledge, London. This is an excellent and relatively advanced survey of contemporary debates in rural geography.

Woods, M. (2012) *Rural Geography,* 2nd edition, Sage, London. Although focused on western cases, this is a landmark text and a first rate entrance point into the rural geography literature.

The *Journal of Rural Studies* (Elsevier), is the leading scholarly journal of rural studies. Encompassing work from human geography and across the social sciences it provides the most recent state-of-the-art research in this area. Attempts to 'globalize' the scope of articles in order to include more in the rural global South are underway.

SOCIAL CONSTRUCTIONS OF NATURE

Chapter 12

James Evans

Topics covered

- The concept that nature is not a pre-given physical reality, but an idea that is constructed by society

- The political implications of representing things, behaviours and landscapes as natural

- Environmental myths

- Science and the construction of human nature

- How ideas about nature influence media coverage of environmental change

12.1 Questioning nature

The one thing that is not natural is nature.

(Soper 1995: 7)

What is nature? There is an easy answer. It is the birds and the bees, the plants and the landscapes around us – from the familiar things in our lives, like pet cats and dogs and the park at the end of the road, to more distant things that we see on television, like Amazonian rainforests and Giant Pandas. Nature is the set of things that are *separate* from humans. We have the social world on the one side, with its politics, injustices and cultural achievements, and on the other we have the natural world, a pre-given set of biological entities – the domain of natural scientists – that have no politics and no culture . . . things that simply *are*.

Albert Einstein once quipped that 'the environment is everything that isn't me'. But is it really this simple? Can we draw lines between ourselves and the surrounding world so easily? The microbes that occupy our gut to the food like fruit and vegetables that we eat every day to sustain and reproduce ourselves suggest that it is hard to draw clear lines between our own bodies and the surrounding environment. Food itself is far from natural. We use fertilizers, pesticides and mechanized agriculture to give nature a helping hand. Biologically, food represents the culmination of thousands of years of selective breeding to create more productive plants and animals. In more recent times humans have created new organisms using genetic modification in laboratories. Bruce McKibben (1999) has taken this argument to its logical conclusion, arguing that it is impossible to find a part of the planet that has not been affected by humans in some way – even the remotest inland Antarctic ice sheets have trapped CO_2 in them from industrial emissions. This observation leads him to argue that 'nature', in its traditional sense as something separate from and untouched by human society, has now *ended*. Scientists are in agreement suggesting that the earth has entered a new geological time period called the Anthropocene (from the Greek word *anthropos* meaning humankind), in which humans are now the main drivers of environmental change (Zalasiewicz *et al.* 2011).

It is similarly hard to draw a line between human society and nature at larger scales. Since our ancestor *Homo erectus* began using primitive tools some 1.9 million years ago, the history of human society has been one of environmental transformation, culminating in the massive levels of urbanization that characterize the world today (see Chapters 1–3). With every technological advance, human society has learnt to adapt its surroundings to its own use. Over a hundred years ago Karl Marx tried to understand this process, suggesting that *production* is the critical force driving human interaction with nature:

> Not only do the objective conditions change in the act of reproduction, e.g. the village becomes a town, the wilderness a cleared field etc., but the producers change, too, in that they bring out new qualities in themselves, develop themselves in production, transform themselves, develop new powers and ideas, new modes of intercourse, new needs and new language.

(Karl Marx 1973, originally 1861, *Notebook V*)

This quote captures one of the fundamental arguments of Marxist thought – that social development unfolds through the transformation of nature. From the basic work of a peasant clearing a field to the industrial exploitation of oil resources, economic production simultaneously transforms nature and society.

Perhaps nature existed *before* modern humans arrived on the scene then? Conservationists talk about 'restoring' landscapes that have been spoilt by human activities to their natural condition. Environmentalists hark back to the natural conditions that existed before humans altered the levels of CO_2 in the atmosphere and biologists talk about how many more species there would be in the absence of humans. But *when* was this pre-human condition? For example, the dominant vegetation in pre-industrial Britain was temperate forest, and what is generally considered to be Britain's 'natural' landscape is constituted by the species that typified this landscape, like oak trees. But if one goes back to the last glaciation some ten thousand years ago (when human impact was even less apparent, and thus the landscape it could be argued was even more 'natural') there was no forest, and no temperate species existed in Britain (Birks 1997). Quintessentially British species like oaks did not arrive until the end of the last ice age. Depending on what timescale is used they can be seen as either native to Britain, or as an invasive species. When we go back in time no historical cut-off is more valid than any other as the supposed point at which the environment was in a *natural* state.

12.1.1 The social construction of nature

So, if nature does not exist as something separate, and never really did, then what is it? Many academics have argued that instead of being a pre-given reality, nature is actually an idea, or a *social construct*, which varies for different people in different times and places. The phrase 'social construction' was coined by sociologists Peter Berger and Thomas Luckmann (1966), who argued that humans establish meanings and truths through habits and institutions. So, for example, things like laws are social constructions because they have no essential existence outside of the society in which people have decided to agree and act as if they exist – they are 'social facts'.

Social constructionism recognizes that individuals and groups participate in the creation of their realities through the way in which they perceive things and events. Critically, it follows from this idea that various groups of people will interpret things and events differently, because their perception is coloured by their previous experiences and differing social norms. David Harvey gives a classic example of how this problem of perception can work in relation to nature:

> What's nature? What if I give you a chemical formula and say, how do you feel about your relationship to

that? If I then take that chemical formula and represent it to you as a tree, then you relate to it in a different way. Now, what's nature? Is it all the molecules that make up the tree, or is it the tree? The point is that if you see a tree, you'll react to it differently than you would if you saw a bunch of molecules, and if you see a tree in a habitat in a forest with a spotted owl sitting in it you would react very differently than if you just saw a tree.

(Harvey, in Banrffalo, 1996)

Plate 12.1 shows four representations of the same 'thing'. It is easy to argue that all are natural, and yet

Plate 12.1 Carbon, tree, forest, wood.

(Photdisc Inc (tl); Paul Lunnon (tr, bl, br))

each prompts very different reactions and will be interpreted variously by different types of people. For example, a trained chemist will recognize the carbon molecule as constitutive of wood, while a conservationist will recognize that the forest depicted is not just any forest, but a rainforest – the most biodiverse habitat on the planet. Indigenous inhabitants of that rainforest will react with a whole different set of emotions, although they may not recognize their home from an aerial photo. The pile of timber is a resource to be burned, while the solitary tree is not. The way in which each representation is perceived depends on the experience and knowledge that the viewer has, which in turn depends on the society and culture in which he or she lives. Viewing nature as a social construct helps us to understand why people from different places and times behave so differently towards the environment. To return to the example of trees, early US settlers were fearful of the impenetrable dark forests that dominated the Eastern seaboard, and believed that clearing trees for agriculture was 'God's work'. In stark contrast to the attitudes of today, chopping trees down was actually seen as morally good. The idea of nature is subjective – it means something slightly different to you than it does to me. This matters because it helps us to understand why conflicts occur over the environment and how they might be averted.

That said nature is often presented as if it *is* something fixed and objective, because it provides a powerful basis for how society should behave. As the American environmental historian William Cronon puts it, people tend to 'appeal to nature as a stable external source of non-human values against which human actions can be judged' (1996: 26). Constructions of nature are thus highly political, because specific versions of what is 'natural' can be used to privilege certain social behaviours and actions over others.

Perhaps the most influential idea that has shaped debates concerning the environment and our relationship to it is that of the *limits to growth*. The idea that there are natural limits to population growth comes from the writings of Thomas Malthus in the late eighteenth century. Malthus was a churchman who deplored the overcrowding and unsavoury conditions in which the newly-created working classes of the British industrial revolution lived. In his *Principle of Population* he attributed this problem to a disjuncture between the geometric rate of population increase (1,2,4,8,16) and the arithmetic rate of food supply (1,2,3,4,5). Overstepping the limits of natural resources (most notably at that time, food) would inevitably result in famine and death. Malthus deplored the moral depravity of the working classes and sought to control their behaviour by invoking the idea of *natural limits*. Of course Malthus has been proved wrong. With

the advent of mechanized production and better-yielding crop varieties, food supply has far outstripped population growth. Despite an almost ten-fold increase in the number of people living on our planet since Malthus's time, a greater proportion enjoy clean water today than ever before.

Debates today over food, climate change and oil often fall back on the idea of natural limits. But are these resources really 'natural'? For example, in what way is it 'natural' to burn oil? Oil did not become a resource until the invention of the internal combustion engine, and with the proliferation of electric cars and bio-fuels it will cease to be the most fought-over global resource. Oil is only important to human existence in the relatively recent era of industrialization, and, even then, only if you are one of the few who either buys it or owns it. Far from being a 'natural' resource, the demand for oil depends entirely on the existence of a socio-economic system that values and uses it.

David Harvey (1974) argues that the real cause of scarcity is the unequal distribution of resources. For example, the richest 1 per cent of the world's adult population owned 40 per cent of global assets in the year 2000. By contrast, the poorest half of the world adult population owned only 1 per cent of global wealth (Davies *et al.* 2006). As Harvey notes, the earth could not support the current population if everyone enjoyed a Western lifestyle. The idea that resource shortages are due to overstepping 'natural' limits conceals these grotesque imbalances. When we look at famines on a global scale, the problem is not food production, but the distribution of the food that we produce. Geographers have sought to understand who benefits and who suffers from different social constructions of nature and blaming problems on overpopulation shifts the blame to the poorest people, while protecting the monopoly rich nations enjoy over resources. Radical geographers are interested in how constructions of nature serve different political interests. The notion of natural limits clearly serves the interests of those who control the lion's share of the world's wealth.

Social constructionists seek to understand how ideas of nature reproduce the cultural, political and spiritual beliefs of a society, and the ways in which ideas of nature are used to support specific political viewpoints. If certain types of behaviour or ways of organizing society can be shown to be 'natural', then it makes it hard to justify any other way of acting. The authority to speak for nature becomes the authority to speak for society. Geography has traditionally tried to understand the interface between society and the environment, and the ways in which nature has been constructed and contested have particular relevance to this task.

12.2 Cultural constructions of nature

The great enemy of truth is very often not the lie – deliberate, contrived and dishonest – but the myth – persistent, persuasive and unrealistic.

(J.F. Kennedy)

David Demeritt (1998) identifies the main use of social constructionism within geography as *refuting* established claims about nature. This is perhaps not surprising as social constructions can be understood as a form of 'myth' that may become widely accepted in the absence of any counter evidence. The majority of work in geography on the construction of nature has sought to reveal myths concerning nature.

12.2.1 Wilderness

One of the most cherished notions of nature in Western societies is that of *wilderness*. Images of wilderness are used widely, to sell holidays, relax us and inspire us. Motivational posters showing 'man conquering the great outdoors', with captions like 'Success' and 'Risk', will be familiar to you if you have ever set foot in a gym. The idea of wilderness as a form of nature untouched by humans has a long history. In the USA it has been argued that the idea of wilderness appealed to settlers, who, as they moved west across the country, preferred to believe that the lands they were claiming were devoid of humans and waiting to be inhabited. Exploding what he calls the 'Pristine Myth', Bill Denevan (1992) uses extensive archaeological and historical research to argue that native Amerindians actually managed their landscapes through cutting, burning, terracing and building. These forms of management created landscapes that European settlers assumed were untouched because they were unable to recognize forms of management that they were unfamiliar with. America was only a 'discovery' for the white European and, similarly, the plains of the USA only appeared to be uninhabited wildernesses to white European settlers. While the idea of wilderness is obviously related to the inability of the settler to 'see' the human impacts upon unfamiliar landscapes, it had drastic effects. When indigenous people inconveniently did appear in these landscapes, they were often exterminated.

The idea of wilderness was fundamental to the birth of the modern environmental movement in North America. The first National Park was created by Congress in 1864 in Yosemite Valley, quickly becoming a national symbol of the spiritual home of the modern United States in the aftermath of the Civil War. In 1892 the so-called 'wilderness prophet' John Muir founded the Sierra Club in California, which went on to establish a national wilderness preservation system. Of course, national parks are exactly that – parks – and great effort was required to preserve these areas as wildernesses. People had to be kept out, animals had to be kept in. Vistas had to be opened up for tourists while simultaneously not compromising the appearance of the area as untouched. So painstaking were the efforts to create wilderness that Muir actually praised Yosemite for its resemblance to an artificial landscape garden (Schama 1995: 191).

The artificiality of wilderness is taken to its extreme in the landscapes of Frederick Olmsted, who is perhaps most famous for designing New York's Central Park. In 1887 Olmsted became involved in the preservation of another symbolic American landmark of natural vigour, Niagara Falls. As William Irwin notes (1996: 77), Olmsted 'believed that parks and nature retreats relieved the festering distress of the poor and working classes'. The area had become overrun with disorganized tourist developments and industry, and Olmsted sought to transform the area into a pure pastoral park in which the visitor might enjoy the splendour of nature in peace. In its return to nature, however, the minutest details were planned, including widespread landscaping and the installation of viewing points to maximize the vistas over the falls. The landscape that now surrounds the falls represents an idealized version of how Olmsted thought the Falls *should* look, rather than a reproduction of the original landscape, which was renowned for hindering the efforts of visitors to see the falls.

Wilderness appeals to the American psyche because it is reminiscent of the birth of their country through settlement, and it remains a powerful and emotive cultural construction of nature in contemporary North America. However, while the idea of wilderness is aesthetic on one level today, the politics involved in valuing landscapes that are free of humans are still influential (see Case study 12.1).

In Britain the excesses of industrialization and urbanization in the eighteenth and nineteenth centuries generated a cultural backlash that began to value environments that were seen as more natural. The **Romantic movement** which emerged at this time was typified by Wordsworth's love of the Lake District and an increasingly negative attitude towards cities. This was in part an aesthetic reaction to the physical degradation of the environment associated with the Industrial Revolution, but it was also a moral reaction to the squalor and poverty of the cities. In contrast, the countryside became seen as the repository of moral purity. Interestingly, this represented a U-turn in British attitudes to wild landscapes. In the sixteenth and seventeenth centuries mountainous and uninhabited regions were actually regarded with fear and disregard. We have reports of travellers drawing the curtains of their carriages to block out the 'Satanic' view as they travelled through mountainous regions. Less than one hundred years before Wordsworth claimed of the Lake District 'Who comes not hither ne'er shall know how beautiful the world below', the great diarist Daniel Defoe called the area a 'barren and frightful place'. So if you hate hiking up mountains, simply tell people you have an early Georgian attitude to nature!

As with the US environmental movement, the British Romantic movement established the idea that nature has *spiritual* value. In the United Kingdom this happened primarily as a reaction to industrialization, while in the United States it emerged from the pioneer/settler mentality. In each case the idea of nature has been carefully constructed by societies seeking to preserve a world free of human development.

12.2.2 Landscape

This new relation to nature was expressed through the genre of landscape painting, which emerged in the seventeenth and eighteenth centuries. As a way of seeing, landscape takes a three-dimensional world and represents a single view of it in two dimensions. In doing so it establishes a highly *visual* relation between the viewer and nature that emphasizes aesthetic detachment and mastery over nature.

A classic example of how a landscape painting conveys social power is found in John Berger's (1990) analysis of Gainsborough's *Mr and Mrs Andrews,* which was completed *c.* 1750 (Plate 12.2). The painting depicts an upper-class land-owning couple in the foreground, with their estate stretching into the distance behind them. While the painting shows a highly cultivated patchwork of fields, there are no workers in this rural landscape. Their effacement represents the new balance of power in the countryside after the Enclosures Acts seized common land from peasants and parcelled it up to landowners. The landscape is familiar to us as an archetypically *English* landscape, Constable Country if you like, and the nature in it is archetypically English. There are other things going on in this representation too, such as the dominance of the male figure standing over his seated wife, and the phallic symbol of the gun. The symbolism of masculine control over nature could not be more obvious. Landscape painting invented an English aesthetic of

Case study 12.1

Contesting wilderness

Clayoquot Sound is a small ocean inlet on Vancouver Island in British Columbia. The surrounding area contains 'old growth' temperate rainforest, one of the rarest habitats in the world. While such forests once covered large parts of Europe and Asia they now comprise just 0.01 per cent of the earth's land area. In the early 1990s the logging firm MacMillan Bloedel applied for a logging licence in the area, but was vigorously opposed by the Western Canada Wilderness Society. The geographer Bruce Braun (2002) explored how the resulting dispute played out through a series of representations and counter-representations of the area.

MacMillan Bloedel produced a brochure titled *Beyond the Cut,* which represented Clayoquot Sound as a natural resource that was needed by the Canadian people. Constructing the forest as a resource, they presented their credentials as responsible and experienced managers who would use scientific techniques to create a sustainable industry and create much-needed jobs.

By contrast, the Western Canada Wilderness Society produced a popular and glossily illustrated coffee-table book called *On the Wild Side.* In it they championed Clayoquot Sound as a pristine wilderness, evoking emotive spiritual ideas of the forest as a paradise unspoilt by humans.

On one level, the representations of the forest as economic resource and ecological wilderness reproduced familiar opposing Western constructions of nature. But Braun's real insight is that both the representations of the logging company and the environmental group fail to include the indigenous Indians who live in the forest. He argues that this erasure of the indigenous population is a common feature of both the wilderness and resource constructions of nature, and can be traced back to the tendency of settlers to appropriate nature from the indigenous peoples. The importance of constructing nature as separate from humans (in this case as uninhabited) allows powerful (if opposing) claims to be made over the area by both the logging company *and* the environmental group. The real political import of this process is that the people who live there are excluded from their own home.

Q How does the idea of wilderness exert an influence over global conservation priorities?

Plate 12.2 *Mr and Mrs Andrews* by Thomas Gainsborough.

(*Mr and Mrs Andrews,* c.1748–9 (oil on canvas), Gainsborough, Thomas (1727–88)/National Gallery, London, UK/The Bridgeman Art Library)

landscape, but it also established a new era of control, both of humans over nature and of the landed upper classes over the countryside in Britain.

Representations of landscape are central to national identities. Indeed, the word 'nature' derives from the Latin *natura,* which comes in turn from *nasci* – to be born. Thus *nature* is linked to other words from the same root, such as nascent, innate, native and nation. Just as wilderness plays an important symbolic role in the pioneer mentality of the USA, so the 'countryside' landscape is quintessentially English. Authors have explored the importance of the oak tree to British culture, as a sign of strength derived from their use to build the ships that allowed the British navy to rule the seas for 200 years.

These constructions of nature also have profound political effects. The historical geographer David Lowenthal (1994) argues that in France the legacy of peasant agriculture has left a national landscape of diverse smallholdings, which is cherished for the variety of cheese, wines and foods that it produces. Staunch French opposition to proposed reforms to the European Common Agricultural Policy, which would increase the exposure of its small producers to market forces, suddenly becomes intelligible as an attempt to preserve the French landscape and culture rather than simply blunt economic protectionism (see Chapter 11). The relationship between landscape and national identity was carried to its ideological extreme by the Nazis, who were probably the most ecologically aware government ever to exist.

Fond of being photographed in forest settings, they viewed the Black Forest of southern Germany as their spiritual home. Non-native plants were eradicated in exactly the same way as the non-Aryan human population. As Anne Whiston Spirn notes (1997: 253–4) 'the use of "native" plants and "natural" gardens to represent the Nazi political

agenda should dispel forever the illusion of innocence surrounding the words nature, natural, and native . . .'.

The British association of nature with idealized rural landscapes has impacts that are felt beyond the art gallery. One is to divide the affairs of the city from the affairs of the country. The graffiti artist Banksy produced a series of works exploring the politics of this division, in which he placed typically 'urban' objects such as parking tickets and graffiti into traditional landscape paintings (see Plate 12.3). This juxtaposition disturbs constructions of the countryside as a somehow 'natural' place untroubled by the problems of cities, and in doing so highlights how exclusive this vision of the countryside actually is. As rural geographers have noted, the idea of the rural idyll is not particularly helpful as it conceals real problems of poverty, drug-use and deprivation in rural areas (see

Plate 12.3 Banksy, *Bombed Village,* 2006

(Banksy)

Chapter 11). Conversely, urban areas are assumed to be bereft of nature, despite often being more biodiverse than massive swathes of agricultural land, and supporting vast infrastructures to control elements such as water and waste (Gandy 2002). In many ways elements of nature are *more* important in the city, but have simply been ignored until recently, as they do not correspond with unspoken cultural constructions of what nature should look like.

12.3 Environmental myths

12.3.1 The power of science

What we observe is not nature itself, but nature exposed to our method of questioning.

(Heisenberg 1958)

Science adheres to a very detailed and rigorous set of rules for building knowledge that accurately reflects the natural world, but in practice science is not immune to social constructions of nature. As the biologist Richard Lewontin says (1993: 3), 'Scientists do not begin life as scientists, after all, but as social beings immersed in a family, a state, a productive structure, and they view nature through a

lens that has been moulded by their social experience'. However sanitized lab work is made to appear, experiments require human interaction and judgements to work. Science is a particularly influential realm in which nature is constructed and contested, because it has the capacity to make very strong truth claims about reality, and hence how we should live and behave. But its findings and models remain influenced by cultural factors.

12.3.2 Ecology and politics

In the past 30 years, geographers have become increasingly interested in how dominant models of ecology rely on social constructions of nature. The field of political ecology recognizes that ecological knowledge is not always neutral, but reflects the specific aims of those involved in producing it. This can have profound political consequences upon how different landscapes are managed, and for whom. In the words of Paul Robbins (2004: 12), the goal of political ecology is to 'take the hatchet' to environmental myths, using both scientific and social scientific studies to expose the false assumptions and unsuitability of certain ecological models. Bill Deneven's work on the 'Pristine Myth' described in the previous section is an example of this, but the hatchet has been taken to other scientific myths too (see Case study 12.2).

Case study 12.2

Desertification

Desertification became an important international issue in the 1970s when successive years of drought in the Sahel (the area bordering the southern edge of the Sahara) caused widespread famine. The United Nations (UN) responded with the 1977 conference on desertification, and a subsequent Convention to Combat Desertification, which focused on land degradation in arid, semi-arid and dry sub-humid areas. This conference popularized and publicized the term, but was based on little actual science. David Thomas and Nick Middleton (1994) have identified four 'myths' of desertification in dryland areas:

1 That it is a 'voracious process' affecting one-third of the world's land area.
2 That drylands are fragile ecosystems.
3 That desertification is the primary cause of human suffering and misery.
4 That the UN is central to its understanding and solution.

They argue that the idea of desertification forms part of a longer history of reports from Westerners in the Sahara concerning advancing deserts. For example, early accounts of desertification originated in the eighteenth and nineteenth centuries when scholars believed the Sahara to have been created by the Romans and Phoenicians through deforestation, overgrazing and over-cultivation. In the twentieth century, colonial land managers took on this idea that deserts advance because of the mismanagement and over-exploitation of land. In 1935 E.P. Stebbing, a forester, published his views widely on the causes of the 'encroaching Sahara' in British West Africa, blaming shortened agricultural fallow periods, shifting agriculture and overgrazing. It was concluded that the Sahara had grown, and was still growing, owing to poor land management, which had worsened under the colonial regime. The spectre of sand dunes encroaching upon fertile land remained an enthralling one, and a report in 1975 suggested that the Sahara was advancing at the astonishing rate of 5.5 km per year.

Thomas and Middleton question both the supposed pace and causes of this process. They suggest that biophysical processes have been the primary cause of Saharan advance over the twentieth century, because of the progressive desiccation (drying out) of North Africa since the end of the Pleistocene ice-age 10,000 years ago. Advances and retreats within this overall pattern reflect climatic variations in rainfall over tens of years. They also attack the idea that humans are to blame for desertification, arguing that policies to reduce the grazing of dryland areas are ineffective. 'Expert' knowledges about dryland fragility, they argue, actually undermine adaptive strategies that have evolved over centuries. For example, lowering livestock densities damages the ability of local farmers to resist drought. The focus on mismanagement obscures both the biophysical causes of dryland degradation and specific social problems, such as firewood scarcity. As Batterbury and Warren note (2001), degradation is usually localized and ephemeral, and it is very hard to overgraze in a dynamic non-equilibrium system dominated by annual grasses, such as rangelands, where external forces like drought far outweigh human factors like over-stocking.

The myth of desertification is bound up with the failure of Western scientists to understand the dynamics of dryland areas, simply falling back on received colonial stereotypes of overgrazing and advancing deserts. As Paul Robbins states (2004: 109), the notion of soil erosion was 'a social construction that helped to secure colonial power', and while the term is generally considered unhelpful amongst scientists today, it perseveres within the policies of international agencies such as the UN and NGOs.

Once specific constructions of nature become established, they assume a life of their own. Funding streams for research, policies and the vested interests of those that work within the field act to keep the concern alive. As they circulate through networks of scientists, institutions, funding bodies, the media and policies, such constructions of nature become established as seemingly incontrovertible facts.

Q Why is it hard to produce definite scientific answers to large-scale environmental questions?

These myths have real influence over the way in which environmental problems are tackled. For example, the assumption that degradation is caused by mismanagement generally leads to the imposition of solutions upon people, rather than developing solutions that use their local knowledge and understanding (see Robbins 2004, Chapter 8, for a wealth of examples). This resonates with Bruce Braun's work on Clayoquot Sound discussed in the previous section, where both economic and environmental representations of the forest actively excluded the indigenous population living there.

There are aspects of ecological science that clearly reflect the places and periods in which they developed. Directly parroting the language of US settlement, ecologists in the early twentieth century talked about the succession of plant 'communities' from *pioneers,* who come in first and settle an area, through to the stable 'climax' forest. There is some circularity to this process. Models of ecology reflect the social context in which they are produced, but then, having become established as scientific 'facts', become models for human society. Some authors have argued that the appeal of nature as a stable community goes back to the Judaeo-Christian myth of the Garden of Eden, when humans supposedly lived in perfect harmony with nature before their fall from grace. This yearning for a return to innocence often finds expression in the kinds of stories that are told about indigenous peoples, such as Amazonian Indians, who are romantically depicted living at one with nature, almost as part of nature rather than humanity (Slater 1995). The exclusion of humans from ecological models distorts conservation practices, which lack the ability to capture the value of landscapes influenced by humans. These oversights are unfortunate; not only do humans influence almost all habitats today, but, in order to live more sustainably, we require ecological models that can understand humans as part of ecosystems rather than just undesirable disturbances to them.

12.4 Constructing human nature

There is a long tradition of looking directly to the animal world in order to establish how humans should behave, and science has been integral to such attempts. If science can show certain behaviours or modes of social organization to be 'natural', then it is assumed that they are unquestionably 'right'. As evolutionary biologist and social commentator Richard Lewontin (1993: 87) suggests, 'the problem for political philosophers has always been to try to justify their particular view of human nature'. This is a game of high stakes; think about how often you hear political commentators talk about things like war being 'a part of human nature', or capitalists justifying the free market on the grounds that competition and the need to own things are 'in our nature'. It does not take much to spot the flaws in this logic. Animals do not cook, but no one would say cooking food is wrong because it is unnatural (apart from Raw Food advocates, of course). Putting it another way, James Weinrich says, 'when animals do something that we like, we say it is natural. When they do something that we don't like, we call it animalistic' (1982: in Bagemihl 1999: 77).

The attempt to draw parallels between animal and human behaviour is one of the most obvious ways in which nature acts as a mirror for the values of society. Donna Haraway's (1989) work on primatology (the study of apes) re-examines evidence from major research projects on ape behaviour to show that they are biased by the gender of the researchers conducting the study. Male research teams demonstrate a tendency to explain ape behaviour in terms of sexual competition between aggressive males to impregnate passive females. By contrast, female primatologists focus on communication and basic survival activities of the apes, generating very different interpretations of their social behaviour. Depending on who is doing the research, different aspects of behaviour will be measured and different inferences drawn from them. Gender and politics become tangled up in the process of scientific enquiry, so that the ape becomes the site of legitimization for what is and is not 'natural'. This in turn provides a proxy moral framework for the social behaviour of humans. A more recent debate to hit the media involves the naturalness of homosexuality (see Case study 12.3).

Case study 12.3

Gay animals

WHAT DOES A DOG HAVE TO DO ROUND HERE TO PROVE HE'S GAY????!!!!!

(Ingilby 2002)

In 1999 a biologist called Bruce Bagemihl published a book called *Biological Exuberance: Animal Homosexuality and Natural Diversity* (Bagemihl 1999). Drawing upon a lifetime of research, Bagemihl works his way through the animal world, from mammals to birds to cockroaches, describing a profusion of homosexuality, bisexuality, orgies, transvestism and transgenderism. The book includes field sketches of female bonobos engaging in cunnilingus and photographs of male whales entwining their penises in sexual communion, all of which provoked a considerable degree of outrage. Being gay is seen as an exclusively human behaviour, something that by definition is *not* natural. This is a longstanding Christian idea (although there is very little about it in the bible). The Church Council of Nablus in AD 1120 wrote the first law condemning homosexuality, which was subsequently preserved in the Vatican library. By the time of the Renaissance this idea had found its way into the laws of many countries, and today many groups in society claim that homosexuality is wrong because it is 'unnatural'.

Bruce Bagemihl's book threw this myth into doubt. In some penguin colonies, as many as one in ten pairs of penguins may be same-sex, while in bonobo chimpanzees the whole species is bisexual. If homosexuality is found throughout the animal kingdom then how can it possibly be unnatural? As Bagemihl (1999:

78) says, 'what is remarkable about the entire debate about the naturalness of homosexuality is the frequent absence of any reference to concrete facts or accurate, comprehensive information about animal homosexuality'. Bagemihl also asks a more fundamental question: how has science overlooked this considerable subset of animal behaviour? His answer is that zoology is essentially a conservative profession, dominated by white male heterosexuals who impose social assumptions about homosexuality as perverse and unnatural on to the things they study. He gives examples of how the term 'homosexual' is avoided in favour of terms like 'male-only social interactions', 'multi-female associations', unisexuality, isosexuality or intrasexuality. As one newspaper reported at the time,

> A female ape wraps her legs around another female, rubbing her own clitoris against her partner's while emitting screams of enjoyment. The researcher explains: It's a form of greeting behavior. Or reconciliation. Possibly food-exchange behavior. It's certainly not sex. Not lesbian sex. Not hot lesbian sex . . .

> (McCarthy 1999)

It is not only science that is to blame either. How common is it for parents to tell small children who enquire why two male dogs are mounting each other that they are just 'confused'? In the USA pet owners have been acquitted for shooting their dogs on the grounds that they were exhibiting 'gay' behaviour. The topic of gay animals is laced with contradiction, which may explain why it is a topic so beloved of comedians, from Ricky Gervais to South Park's 'Big Gay Al's Big Gay Animal Sanctuary'

and Sparky the Gay Dog (famously played by George Clooney).

Prudishness is only half the story though. Bagemihl's work is scientifically controversial because it suggests that sex is not solely practised for reproduction. This seems to contradict the most important theory in biology – that of evolution. Researching animal homosexuality is not the road to a successful career: applications for research grants that appear ignorant of the theory of evolution do not tend to stand a good chance of receiving funding. However, sex between animals – as between humans – is often a matter of enjoyment, rather than procreation, and this applies to animals of the same sex as well as opposite sexes. Non-heterosexual practices can also be beneficial. For example, pairs of male birds may rear eggs 'donated' by a female, and two males can command a larger territory than a heterosexual pair, improving the chances of survival for chicks.

In 2006 the Oslo Natural History Museum ran an exhibition on gay animals, tellingly called 'Against nature' (BBC 2006). There was considerable hostility to the exhibition, with organisers reporting criticism and of being told by one opponent they would 'burn in hell'. An American commentator said it was an example of 'propaganda invading science'. More recently still, scientists in America have claimed that they can 'cure' gay sheep by manipulating hormone levels in their brains to make them attracted to ewes (Oakeshott and Gourlay 2006). The implication that gayness might be 'curable' in humans has caused outrage. Competing constructions of nature are not only highly charged politically, but cut across science and religion, parts of modern society that are often seen as unrelated.

Q Do you think there is any such thing as human nature?

12.4.1 Our place in nature

The biological sciences have also attempted to interrogate our genes to find out what makes humans distinctive from other organisms. Attempting to place humans *in* nature, while simultaneously maintaining their position *above* nature, is an old trick. The 'great chain of being' devised by medieval cosmologists represents a clear ordering of different things and beings in the world, with humans second only to God. Maintaining a scientific basis for human superiority has become progressively harder since Darwin placed us squarely among the apes, but has generally been based upon the argument that, while made of the same stuff, humans are much more complex than other animals.

While our attempts to benchmark human behaviour against 'natural' standards have tended to fail, even our own biology is not quite what we were hoping. The Human Genome Project (HGP) was a major international scientific collaboration to map the entire human genome (the entire set of human genes that determines the sequence of our DNA), begun in 1990 and completed in 2003. The project aimed to advance our understanding of human genes in order to support **biotechnology** research. Tori Holmberg (2005) has argued that the HGP represented a modern attempt to discover some inherent physical basis for what makes 'human-ness' distinct from nature. By counting the number of genes of other organisms as well, the HGP promised a potential verification of human superiority.

As the HGP progressed the issue of how many genes human beings possessed became increasingly vexed. Estimates varied wildly from 40,000 and 200,000. When the preliminary results were published in 2001 it turned out that humans only have about 32,000 genes, far fewer than expected. The most disturbing element of this discovery was how close other organisms were, with the popular press jumping on the fact that the weed thale cress has 25,000 gene pairs, worms 19,000 and banana flies 13,600. Suddenly we were not as special as we had thought.

Within the scientific world the idea of human uniqueness, although momentarily shaken, was rescued by the explanation that our genes interact in complex ways that allow them to produce greater numbers of proteins than in other organisms. It appeared that individual genes did not control individual elements of an organism's phenotype (appearance and behaviour) after all. The idea of natural human superiority was transposed from gene numbers to protein numbers, and the things being compared shifted from genes to base pairs. So while reporters could write that we share 99 per cent of our genes with apes, they could simultaneously state that we do not share 3.5 million base pairs, thus upholding the distinction between human and animal. While science places us firmly in nature, our cultural beliefs require reaffirmation of our uniqueness.

12.4.2 Natural disasters

Today, these versions of nature come together in media descriptions of natural disasters, which hold both a fascination with the frailty of human life, and highlight the potential for future ecological destruction. In the environmental era, the spectre of global catastrophe is constantly invoked, from the impending ice age predicted in the 1970s, to the threat of global warming that emerged in the 1990s. In *The Ecology of Fear,* Mike Davis (1998) explores this fascination with disaster through the city of Los Angeles, which he claims has been destroyed 145 times on film and in books by everything ranging from earthquakes and nuclear weapons to Bermuda grass and the Devil. Crisis fascinates humans; it sells papers and makes people watch TV and films.

The film *The Day After Tomorrow* suggests what may happen if the Gulf Stream shuts down because of the melting of the Canadian and Greenland ice caps due to climate change. While there is evidence from Quaternary studies that this has possibly happened in the past, the film suggests that it could freeze the North Atlantic overnight. In reality the process would take at least 50 (and probably more like 500) years. As the poster for the film shows (Plate 12.4), nature's capacity for destruction is used to sensationalize the film. Representations of crisis can also be politically useful, for example to international aid agencies seeking to attract funding.

The irony here of course it that there is little 'natural' about a natural disaster – humans are required

too. The Cambridge dictionary defines a disaster as 'an event causing great damage, injury or loss of life', which means that it cannot be a disaster unless there are people involved. Yet equally a *natural* disaster would be a massive event not harming humans in any way. But the things commonly described as natural disasters do harm humans. Increasingly disasters are seen as events that exacerbate pre-existing social and economic problems. The flooding of New Orleans in 2005 in the wake of Hurricane Katrina demonstrates this point well – the people who were harmed most were the poorest because they were unable to leave. Media representations of the disaster tended to fall back on the traditional construction of nature as a destructive force. A *New York Times* editorial on 30 August 2005 led with the headline 'Nature's Revenge', even though it went on to criticize the government policies that exacerbated the disaster (notably the loss of protective coastal wetlands to development and the disrepair of the levees due to federal budget cuts).

The idea that nature can do things to us often results in its personification as a subjective force (in this case harbouring a whim for revenge). While *The Day After Tomorrow* reflects our fears about upsetting nature through the inadvertent effects of burning fossil fuels,

Plate 12.4 Film poster for *The Day After Tomorrow.*

(20th Century/Lionsgate Film/Ronald Grant Archive)

a similar understanding holds concerning the potential impact of intended responses as well. The potential to 'geo-engineer' our climate by injecting particles into the atmosphere that would reduce the amount of the sun's energy reaching the surface sounds like science fiction, but is being seriously explored as a potential palliative to global warming. Given that this is a fairly unusual and unknown option the UK government commissioned research to investigate public opinion on it, which revealed a strongly held general concern about the dangers of 'meddling with mother nature' (Corner *et al.* 2013). The idea of nature as something that exists separately to us in a state of equilibrium, but which is liable to exert its wrath upon us if we 'meddle' too much in its affairs is clearly alive and well.

12.5 Nature and the media

Did the planet betray us? Or did we betray the planet?

(Trailer for the film *An Inconvenient Truth*)

In each of the examples discussed so far, the idea of what is and is not natural forms a critical bone of contention. The way in which different positions are represented is important in understanding how certain ideas become dominant. For example, the idea of wilderness is inseparable from its representation in landscape painting and, more recently, photography. But how does this process work out in the mainstream media?

It is possible to identify two dominant constructions of nature that animate media discussions of environmental change: fragility and violence. The first is closely related to the emergence of environmentalism, which is concerned with the health of the planet that humankind depends upon for its survival. While the idea of caring for the planet seems quite normal to us now, this idea only emerged in the 1960s and 1970s. Denis Cosgrove (1994) argues that the environmental mindset was shaped by the release of photographs of the earth taken during the Apollo Space missions in 1968 and 1972 (see Introduction, Plate 1). Splashed across newspapers and television, pictures of the earth from space had a huge cultural impact. Never before had the planet upon which we live been viewed as a single object, and the image of an orb hanging in space seemed to show the planet at its most vulnerable, as a finite, isolated island in a sea of nothingness. Books were written likening the earth to a 'spaceship', replete with life-support systems that require managing and conserving. The image of the earth became the leitmotif for Western

environmentalism, a fragile blue image that transcends national borders and political divisions, and on which human features are invisible.

The second construction of nature beloved of the media is that of an uncontrollable, violent force. This version of nature is older, speaking to a pre-modern period in which human fortunes were largely determined by climate, natural disasters and disease. Press reports of floods and hurricanes often speak of nature's wrath, and the unstoppable forces of nature. While the constructions of fragility and violence appear to be contradictory, they both reveal insecurities in society's relation to the environment. Our original fear of nature's capricious power to destroy drove us to strive to control and dominate our surroundings, but our technological mastery has now made us the potential authors of our own destruction. The quote from the trailer for Al Gore's documentary, which opens this section, asks whether we betrayed the planet, or the planet betrayed us. While one can ask whether it is possible for a lump of rock to betray anything, let alone 'us', the personification of nature he uses evokes both our power over nature (the capacity for us to betray the planet) and fear of nature (the possibility that it is going to betray us).

Parallels with religious stories of God punishing humans are hard to ignore. But before we laugh too much at the polytheistic beliefs of ancient civilizations that saw nature as a world inhabited by gods, we should remember that the US National Hurricane Center continues an old tradition of giving *names* to hurricanes. Such disasters are also commonly referred to as 'acts of God' by politicians and insurance companies. The BBC website offers some clues as to what nature may have been taking revenge for, claiming that the levees surrounding New Orleans were a 'snub to nature'. Statements like this beg the question of whether it is actually possible to offend water and wind, and if so, how water and wind would be able to seek revenge. Representations of these disasters as somehow being the 'fault' of nature distract attention from the political, economic and social causes of human loss.

12.5.1 Environmental knowledge and the media

Climate change and natural disasters are pervasive, invading our TV screens and monopolizing newspaper column inches. And everyone seems concerned, from movie stars like Angelina Jolie to politicians like David Cameron. Never has nature been so hot a topic.

The media is a critical sphere in which knowledges about nature are produced and consumed. The wildlife documentaries that are broadcast into our homes reproduce notions of Africa as a great wilderness, going to great lengths to capture scenes in which people and evidence of people are absent (Davies 2000). This is an increasingly difficult task given the level of tourist traffic and numbers of indigenous peoples that are found across many African savannah areas. Wildlife films have been edited for years to present only heterosexual animals, and TV shows like 'Meercat Manor' go out of their way to liken animal behavior to that found in typical human families. The Internet represents a huge source of scientific knowledge but is largely unregulated, producing a range of conflicting claims about the state of nature. For example, popular environmental websites vary wildly in their estimates of biodiversity loss (Ashlin and Ladle 2006 provide a salutary tale concerning the unreliability of information from the Internet).

The media has assumed increased importance in shaping how people understand environmental issues. This is nowhere felt more strongly than in relation to climate change, which has generated a huge amount of media coverage (Boykoff 2007) concerning whether or not we are to blame and if so what should be done about it. While scientists have become increasingly certain that changes to the earth's atmosphere are being caused by humans (IPCC 2013), action has been slow to follow. An Institute for Public Policy Research report has claimed that the representations of climate change in the media are unhelpfully alarmist, focusing on thrilling headlines that prevent the public from understanding what they can do about the problem (Ereaut and Segnit 2006). Based on research that analyzed more than 600 newspaper articles, and 90 TV and radio excerpts, the report identified the dominant construction of nature driving the climate change debate as 'alarmist'. Such articles focus on the overwhelming size of the problem, and its potentially disastrous effects. By focusing on the terrible, unstoppable forces of nature, alarmist constructions represent a form of 'climate pornography' that seeks to thrill rather than increase understanding or engender action. This construction distracts us from what we can actually *do* to tackle environmental change. It is particularly destructive to the campaign of 'small actions', which emphasizes how small changes to behaviour can help combat climate change (and save money in the process). The report suggests that the small actions campaign is rendered impotent by the sheer scale of the alarmist claims. As the primary interface between the majority of the population and environmental issues, the way in which ideas of nature are communicated has a decisive impact on how people understand and respond to environmental challenges.

12.6 Conclusions

12.6.1 Nature: a dangerous idea?

This chapter started by asking what nature is. Geographers have sought to answer this question in a range of ways, suggesting that nature is a social construction that varies between places and periods. Rather than lessen its importance, the idea that nature is an idea reveals its power to dictate how we should behave, how we should live and how we should value and use the environment. It justifies the exploitation of certain people while validating the luxuries of others. It has been used to persecute homosexuals and legitimize genocide. Nature is indeed a dangerous idea.

At the beginning of the chapter it was argued that social constructionists seek to demonstrate two aspects of nature: first how ideas of nature do not represent some external 'truth' but, rather, come to reflect the cultural, political and spiritual beliefs of a society; and second, the ways in which ideas of nature are used to advance specific political viewpoints. In light of the case studies, this picture has become more complex. As dominant cultural norms and preferences influence ideas about nature, so these arguments about nature are then used to support dominant cultural norms. Geographers seek to reveal the circularity of this process in order to expose repressive ideologies and open up new political possibilities for society and our relationship to the environment.

12.6.2 The challenge

The idea of nature remains central to the challenges facing society in the twenty-first century. The growing priority attached to climate change by leading political figures means that debates concerning how we should live, who should make sacrifices and how change should be managed are becoming ever more pressing. The increasing influence of biotechnology as a major global industry raises questions concerning how far we should manipulate biology to our benefit, and whether or not knowledge about our genes will reveal some essential truths of human existence. The idea of nature looms large in all these debates, and will continue to do so. You will see people talking about nature every day on the TV, in newspapers and around you in everyday life. Think about what people mean when they use the word. What characteristics are they attributing to nature? What are they excluding? What political and social arguments are they supporting through their appeal to nature? Be critical of how nature is used; the power to refute dominant presentations of the world and our place in it is the power to create a different world.

Learning outcomes

Having read this chapter, you should be able to:

- Understand nature as a social construction.
- Recognize that perceptions of nature vary across time and space.
- Identify basic constructions of nature in cultural representations.
- Understand the political power of different representations of nature.
- Critique ideas and concepts such as the 'limits to growth' and desertification.
- Appreciate how science is used to make arguments about human 'nature'.
- Understand how the media uses ideas of nature to report environmental issues.

Further reading

Castree, N. (2005) *Nature,* Routledge, London. This book covers the major theoretical approaches to nature that geographers have used through time.

Castree, N. (2011) *Making Sense of Nature,* Routledge, London. This book focuses on the ways in which nature is represented and the implications of these representations for how we act towards the environment.

Demeritt, D. (2002) What is the social construction of nature?, *Progress in Human Geography,* **26,** 767–90. This paper reviews the literature on the social construction of nature in human geography.

Hinchliffe, S. (2007) *Space for Nature,* Sage, London. This book explicitly tries to go beyond ideas of representation and social construction to outline other approaches to understanding and engaging with nature.

Hulme, M. (2010) *Why We Disagree About Climate Change,* Cambridge University Press, Cambridge. This book suggests that climate change is not a simple problem waiting for a solution, but that it is an environmental, cultural and political phenomenon which is understood in different ways by different people. The book develops this argument to show that climate change requires us to re-shape the way we think about ourselves, our societies and our relationship to the environment and planet on which we depend.

Macnaghten, P. and Urry, J. (1998) *Contested Natures,* Sage, London. This book covers a range of social science approaches to nature, focusing on the ways in which representations and social constructions of nature underpin broader debates.

Robbins, P. (2004) *Political Ecology,* Blackwell, Oxford. This is an accessible introduction to the major work on the politics of environmental science, showing how various scientific fields have unwittingly reflected the cultural assumptions of those doing the science.

Useful websites

www.sierraclub.org/john_muir_exhibit   Interesting website containing information and quotes concerning how wilderness became a valued idea in the USA, focusing on John Muir, the 'grandfather' of the wilderness movement.

www.nhm.uio.no/besok-oss/utstillinger/skiftende/against-nature/index-eng.html   The website of the Natural History Museum of Norway for the 'Against nature?' exhibition, which was the first ever to focus on this subject and explore its cultural and scientific significance.

www.youtube.com/watch?v=xwCHAhMu0Fg   Documentary film titled *The Truth about Gay Animals.* The comments posted below present insights on how we construct nature as a mirror for our own beliefs.

www.nytimes.com/2012/05/23/world/asia/fed-by-indians-monkeys-overwhelm-delhi.html?_r=0   This article from the New York Times reports on the scourge of monkeys invading Indian cities. Note the dispute over which agency should be dealing with them that revolves around whether they can still be classified as 'wild animals' or not. The monkeys here are disrupting our received categories of nature.

www.earthobservatory.nasa.gov/Study/Desertification   NASA website with an interesting take on the desertification myth in the era of GIS. The attempts to identify whether desertification is or is not occurring confound our understandings of nature that are based upon the idea of equilibrium.

www.genome.gov/10001772   Information on the Human Genome Project. Lots of outlandish rhetoric about how the HGP will reveal the secrets of our inner universe and 'nature's complete genetic blueprint for building a human being', revealing a view of nature as something mechanical that can be simply 'built'.

www.youtube.com/watch?v=wnjx6KETmi4   The trailer for *An Inconvenient Truth.* Climate porn at its best! Notice the images and wording. Does it 'shake you to your core'?

GEOGRAPHY, CULTURE AND GLOBAL CHANGE

Chapter 13

Cheryl McEwan and Shari Daya

Topics covered

- A definition of culture

- The 'cultural' and 'spatial turns' in the social sciences

- An evaluation of the extent of cultural globalization

- The relationships between place and cultural identity

- Cultural production and consumption

- Progressive ways for geographers to think about culture

13.1 What is culture?

This chapter explores some of the challenges posed by and for culture in the twenty-first century. First, however, it is necessary to define what is meant by **culture**. This is a complex and difficult task. By the 1950s, for example, there were over 150 different academic definitions of culture. As Mike Crang (1998: 1) argues, despite sounding like the most airy of concepts, culture 'can only be approached as embedded in real-life situations, in temporally and spatially specific ways'. Cultures are part of everyday life. They are systems of shared meanings that people who belong to the same community, group or nation use to help them interpret and make sense of the world, and to reproduce themselves. These systems of meanings are often based around such things as religion, language, ethnicity, custom and tradition, and ideas about 'place', which can exist on a number of different spatial scales (local, regional, national, global, among communities, groups or nations). Cultures are one of the principal means by which identities are constructed. They give us a sense of 'who we are', 'where we belong' – a sense of our own identity and identity with others. Cultures are embodied in the material and social world and are dynamic rather than static, shifting and changing historically through processes of cultural mixing, diffusion and transculturation (discussed below).

Cultures are also socially determined and defined and, therefore, not divorced from power relations. Dominant groups in society attempt to impose their ideas about culture and these are challenged by other groups, or **subcultures**. The latter might include various types of youth culture, gang culture, and different ethnicities or sexualities, where identities are organized around different sets of practices and operate in different spaces from dominant cultures (Crang 1998). Culture makes the world meaningful and significant. Geographers suggest that we should think of culture 'not as a thing, but as a relationship' (Mitchell 2000: xviii) or as a process in which we are all involved. Cultures include those social practices that produce meaning, as well as those practices that are shaped by those shared meanings.

13.1.1 The 'cultural turn'

Culture has generated a great deal of interest in recent years, for academics, policy makers, and at the popular level. Geographers have turned their attention towards cultural explanations of global, national and local phenomena, exploring issues such as the cultural embeddedness of economic processes (e.g. James 2007), the relationship between cultures, identities and consumption (see Chapter 19), and cultural constructions of social relations of gender, ethnicity and class that shape people's lives (e.g. Nelson and Seager 2004). However, the current popularity of culture is not simply a trend in academe, but is reflective of a broader cultural turn in (Western) society as a whole.

The world has changed fundamentally in the past three decades and these changes are deeply cultural in character. For example, enormous changes have occurred in 'advanced' economies since the early 1980s (the decline in manufacturing, the growth of services, the feminization of the workforce, increased flexibility – all characteristic of 'post-Fordism', as discussed in Chapter 3). However, as cultural theorist Stuart Hall (1996: 233) argued, if 'post-Fordism' exists, it is as much a description of cultural as of economic change. Florida (2002) characterizes this as a shift from an industrial to a creative age, with 40 per cent of people in the US and UK economies now working in 'creative' sectors of science, technology, culture, arts and entertainment, and creative economies burgeoning in cities as diverse as New York, Shanghai and Bangalore. Culture has increasingly been brought into governmental and economic spheres, with creative economy initiatives developed for a number of years for small towns and small- and medium-sized cities as well as rural regions in the UK, Australia, New Zealand and Canada (Christopherson and Clark 2007; Christopherson 2008). These initiatives hinge on the arts and community cultural activities, including festivals and special events, which are believed to contribute to community identity, increase community pride and foster participation in local economies. Creative industries, it is argued, boost the local economy by attracting tourists, employers and a workforce who appreciate the sense of community that they generate.

Cultural and creative industries have also recently become a policy priority in international development. Global trade of creative goods and services reached a record of US$624 billion in 2011, more than doubling from 2002 to 2011 (UNCTAD), with a 12.1 per cent annual growth in export of cultural products from countries in the global South. Cultural industries (audiovisual products, design, new media, performing arts, publishing and visual arts) are thus one of the most rapidly growing sectors of the world economy and a highly transformative one in terms of income generation, job creation, and export earnings. A recent report (UNESCO 2013) argues that unlocking the potential of the creative economy is a means for promoting the overall creativity of societies, affirming the distinctive identity of the places where it flourishes and clusters, improving quality of life, and enhancing local image and prestige. Culture is increasingly viewed as core to local creative economies in the global South and vital to forging new development pathways. This is illustrated by cities such as Cape Town, designated World Design Capital 2014; Johannesburg, actively promoted as a world-class African city of culture through arts festivals and city-wide cultural events; Rabat, labelled Moroccan Capital of Culture; Gwangju (South Korea), Yokohama (Japan) and Quanzhou (China), each designated an East Asian City of Culture in 2013; and Hue (Vietnam) nominated ASEAN City of Culture in 2014. In all these cities, culture is seen as a major lever for increasing tourism and investment, as well as, often, achieving social development, urban regeneration and economic growth at both the urban and national scales. This is clearly an instrumental view of culture, which many in the arts might wish to resist, and brings with it the danger of the commodification of culture while leaving structural inequalities untouched (discussed in Section 13.5.3), but as we shall see culture is also seen as a route through which to foster inclusive social development, and to create dialogue, understanding and respect between peoples (UNESCO 2013). Culture is thus a terrain in which politics, culture and the economic form an inseparable dynamic (Radcliffe 2007).

Modern consumption is also a cultural process and also depends overwhelmingly on image (for example, the marketing of food and drink products and fashion clothing) (see Plate 13.1). Movements around the world of images, symbols, modes of thought and communications are unparalleled in terms of their volume, speed and complexity. As computer technology, video imagery and electronic music demonstrate, the material world of commodities and technologies is profoundly cultural. In addition, culture has become increasingly commodified; in other words culture is being translated into material goods that can be marketed and sold. We can see this in

Plate 13.1 Image marketing is central to popular consumption: the world of commodities is profoundly cultural.

(Luciano Mortula/Shutterstock)

the rise of 'cultural tourism' (Gibson 2009). In southern Africa, for example, many 'cultural villages' have sprung up in rural areas to showcase local traditions and sell crafts. These villages are intended to change the relationship between consumers in the global North and peoples in global South, being less exploitative of the latter in economic terms and supposedly fostering greater cultural exchange. However, as Saarinen (2007) points out, these cultural villages have developed largely in response to what tourists want; communities package and sell a version of their culture that fits with Western ideas of what African culture should be.

13.1.2 The 'spatial turn'

There has also been a 'spatial turn' in explanations in cultural and social theory. The world is changing fast, and the rate of change is probably greater than ever before. Fast-developing technologies such as the Internet and satellite communications mean that the world is becoming more global and more interconnected. The increased speed of transport and communications, the increasing intersections between economies and cultures, the growth of international migration and the power of global financial markets are among the factors that have changed everyday lives in recent decades. There is no historical equivalent of the global reach and volume of 'cultural traffic' (Held *et al.* 1999) through contemporary telecommunications, broadcasting and transport technologies. The challenge for geographers is to find ways of understanding and interpreting these changes.

Culture can be said to operate at three spatial scales: local, national and global. Two main interpretations have dominated discussion. The first highlights the global aspects of change. At its simplest, this approach suggests that it is possible to identify processes of cultural homogenization – the idea that everywhere is becoming the same – dominated by the USA and most easily recognized in terms such as 'Coca-Colonization', 'McDonaldization' and 'Hollywoodization' (Jackson 2004) (see Chapter 19). This *cultural globalization* involves the movement of people, objects and images around the world through telecommunications, language, the media industries, radio and music, cinema, television and tourism. The second interpretation places emphasis on the local and the localization of people's everyday lives and experiences. Instead of homogenization, emphasis is placed on the diversity of culture, on the ways in which global brands such as Coca-Cola or McDonald's are reinterpreted locally so that they take on different meanings in different places. The emphasis here is on the *interconnectedness* of global and local processes. For example, although the same event can be witnessed simultaneously around the world (e.g. an incident broadcast in a CNN news report, or an international sporting event), this event will be interpreted differently in different places. Furthermore, locality does not necessarily refer to the opposite of globality. For example, some environmentalists imagine the world as a locality, a 'global village'. Cultural theorists have a growing interest in how increasing globalization, especially of cultural production and consumption, affects people's sense of identity and place at both local and national levels (Goss 2006). Thus a geographic or spatial perspective has become central to studies of culture more widely. These are some of the concerns that form the focus of this chapter. Subsequent sections explore in more detail ideas about a global culture, examine ways of rethinking local cultures, and explore progressive ways of thinking about cultures in contemporary contexts.

13.2 Towards a global culture?

13.2.1 Imagining a global culture

Processes of cultural globalization have a very long history and are not peculiar to contemporary times. Through global patterns of trade and migrations, and through the spread of religions and empires, people, objects and ideas have been circulating for centuries (see Chapters 1–3). However, contemporary globalization is distinctive in extent, form, rapidity of change, intensity and impact. Some commentators suggest that the idea of a global culture is becoming as meaningful as the idea of national or local cultures, with different places and cultural practices around the world converging and becoming ever similar. As Shurmer-Smith and Hannam (1994: 76) argue, a global culture might be the product of two very different processes:

1. The export or diffusion of supposedly 'superior' cultural traits (e.g. Western time-frames – the 24-hour day and the Gregorian calendar) and products (e.g. the motor car, television) from advanced countries, and their worldwide adoption ('Westernization', 'Americanization', 'modernization'). This is believed to create global cultural convergence – people around the world are becoming increasingly similar in terms of consumption, lifestyle, behaviour and aspirations (see Case study 13.1). It can be perceived positively (as 'modernization' or 'development') or negatively (as 'cultural imperialism', where 'we' assume that others in the world should aspire to be like 'us').

2. The mixing, or hybridization, of cultures through greater interconnections and time–space compression (the shrinking of the world through transport links and technological innovation), leading to a new universal cultural practice. This challenges the notion of unidirectional 'Westernization' and allows us to consider how Western cultures have influenced and are also being influenced by this mixing of cultures. Flows of music, food, ideas, beliefs and literature continue to percolate from around the world into the cultures of the West. Consider, for example, cultural influences from the East: the global phenomenon of Korean K-Pop (Psy's 'Gangnam Style' was a global hit in 2012); Japanese sushi being sold in North American and European supermarkets; the popularity of traditional Chinese medicines (such as acupuncture) and martial arts (such as karate, aikido and judo), which originate in East Asian spiritual traditions; the increasing popularity of the thirteenth century Persian poet Rumi or the teachings of Jewish Kabbalah.

In reality, both these processes are flawed explanations for what is happening today. If a global culture exists, it is far from a product of unidirectional 'Westernization'. However, alternative ideas about cultures mixing to produce a universal global culture are also problematic. Cultures are mixing, but this does not necessarily mean we are all becoming the same.

Case study 13.1

The globalization of culture: some examples

Fashion
Clothing is globalized both in terms of the cultural identities to which different items appeal ('African' prints, 'Indian' embroidery) and in terms of the global

commodity chains through which they are produced and sold. Through multiple media including magazines, television, blogs and websites, trends travel rapidly across the world. The production, distribution and consumption of clothing have a particular geography. Fashion design happens mainly in 'global cities' in the West, while the labour of cutting and sewing is concentrated in the developing world. These divisions of labour illustrate the uneven distribution of the benefits of global cultural industries: while Western designers and models are glamorized and often handsomely rewarded, factory workers in Asia and Africa typically work long hours under harsh conditions for meagre pay (Crewe 2008). This unevenness manifests not only along geographical lines but also along lines of gender. While men dominate the design industry, women are the main targets and consumers of fashion and also make up the majority of clothing factory workers (see Dwyer 2006). This unevenness was exposed most dramatically by the collapse of the Rana Plaza building in Dhaka, Bangladesh in April 2013, killing over a thousand people, mainly women garment workers. The disaster exposed the appalling pay and working conditions of Bangladeshi women making clothes for brands such as Benetton, Mango, Primark and Walmart, and prompted protests at flagship stores in Europe and North America.

Food

Food has perhaps the longest history of globalization of any cultural artefact. Spices, tea, and sugar are just three of the commodities whose trade have shaped our modern global economies. The globalization of food cultures is exemplified in the idea, famously put forward by the British Foreign Secretary, Robin Cook, in 2001 that chicken tikka masala was now the British national dish (*The Guardian* 19/04/01). Equally, as India's own economy has boomed since the 1990s, that country's rapidly growing middle classes increasingly demand the local availability of ingredients and dishes that they have sampled elsewhere. Fast food and convenience food corporations are only too willing to fill this gap, and in the last five years chains including McDonalds, Krispy Kreme, Taco Bell and Burger King have all expanded or announced their plans to do so within the Indian market. Even as demand increases for exotic and more convenient foods, the environmental and political geographies of what we eat have increasingly come under discussion. Growing consumer awareness of the environmental impacts of food production and travel (food miles), and the potential health risks of mass agriculture and genetic modification have in many societies contributed what Jackson (2010a) calls 'an age of anxiety'. In response, movements promoting locally produced, organic food and 'slow' food have emerged in many places. Similarly, consumer recognition of the often exploitative nature of food production in developing countries has boosted sales of fair trade and other 'ethical' products in Western supermarkets. While these movements aim to break down unjust social divisions, we should also pay attention to the ways in which they may reinforce or re-shape identities of class (organic, 'slow' and fairly traded foods typically cost more) and understandings of 'Third World' producers as 'other' (Cook *et al.* 2010).

Tourism

Tourism is one of the most obvious forms of globalization. Until relatively recently, the geography of tourism has been skewed, dominated by people of all classes from developed countries (North America, Western Europe, Japan and Australia). However, domestic and outbound tourism is now burgeoning in emerging economies with rapidly expanding middle classes. For example, in the past decade, Chinese domestic tourism had a continuous increase of around 10 per cent each year, and outbound tourism increased by 18 per cent from 2012 to 2013 (www.travelchinaguide.com/tourism/ [accessed 15 January 2015]). Domestic tourism in Brazil has more than doubled since 2004 (http://riotimesonline.com/brazil-news/rio-business/domestic-tourism-rises-with-middle-class/ [accessed 15 January 2015]). Tourism can be exploitative, particularly through the growth of international sex tourism and the dependency of some developing economies on the exploitation of women. However, it is a form of international cultural exchange that allows vast numbers of people to experience other cultures and places. It also locks specific places (tourist destinations) into wider international cultural patterns. For example, the English Lake District 'only really became part of England when many visitors, especially artists and writers, travelled to it from the metropolitan centre at the end of the eighteenth century onwards' (Urry 2005: 80). Many key English writers became known as 'Lake poets' even when they were not from the area, and poets such as Wordsworth and Coleridge became tourist attractions, 'locking' the Lake District into a relationship with broader ideas of landscape, literature and romance, which persists today as people from all over the world travel to the area on literary tours.

13.2.2 Debunking global culture?

A different departure point for discussing global culture is that there is no such thing. Ideas about a singular global economy, politics and culture imply some sort of world-wide commonality that does not exist. First, the image of rampant cultural imperialism by the West, and especially the USA, is flawed since apparent cultural sameness is limited in scope, located only in the consumption of certain products and media images. The possibilities of 'Westernization' eroding centuries of local histories, languages, traditions and religions are far-fetched and people in different parts of the world respond to these images and products in different ways. On the one hand, many millions of people are not able even to access the Internet. For example, in 2009, there were on average only about 4 Internet users per 1,000 people in Bangladesh and about 40 per 1,000 people in Malawi, compared with 770 per 1,000 in the USA and 905 per 1,000 in the Netherlands (*CIA World Factbook* 2014). There is no single global culture in part because of the unevenness of globalization. On the other hand, it is also important to acknowledge the cultural dynamism and assertiveness of countries and peoples around the world.

The enormous Indian film industry is very different to the global film industry (dominated by Hollywood) in terms of its level of informality, fragmentation and patterns of investment, reflecting contingent structural, cultural and geographic conditions (Mukherjee 2008), but it too has a global audience, particularly among the Indian diaspora. Similarly, there is a mosaic of urban and national scenes across Asia involving the production and consumption of putatively Asian cultural products, such as the Hong Kong and Korean film industries, Cantopop and Mandarin pop, Japanese manga and anime productions, and animation and digital media industries. The Nigerian movie industry (Nollywood) is increasingly popular with audiences across Africa, to the extent that some film-makers and intellectuals elsewhere across the continent are critical of what they see as the 'dumping' of these rough-and-ready videos in their national markets and the 'pollution' of their own cultural spaces (UNESCO 2013). Paradoxically, the circulation of these diverse cultural products is often enabled by apparently homogenizing technological platforms such as YouTube and Facebook (see Case study 13.2). What is certainly clear, however, is that given the significant growth of the middle classes in countries such

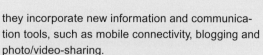

Case study 13.2

Culture and social networking

Since their introduction in the early twenty-first century, social network sites (SNSs) such as MySpace, Facebook, Bebo and Cyworld have attracted millions of users, many of whom have integrated these sites into their daily practices. At one level, we might think of the globalization of SNSs as evidence of an emerging global culture. However, while the technological phenomenon has a global reach (with the caveat outlined previously that millions of people still do not have access to the Internet), the ways in which people around the world make cultural responses to SNSs are complex and multiple. As Boyd and Ellison (2007) argue (see also Miller 2011), while their key technological features are fairly consistent, the cultures that emerge around SNSs are varied. For example, most sites help maintain pre-existing social networks, but others enable strangers to connect with each other based on shared interests, political views or activities. Some sites deliberately cater to diverse and heterogeneous audiences, while others attract people based on common language or shared identities, such as ethnic, sexual, religious or nationality-based identities. Sites also vary in the extent to which

they incorporate new information and communication tools, such as mobile connectivity, blogging and photo/video-sharing.

The question of whether and how much cultural differences impact upon the way people respond to and interact with social networks is an important one. It could be argued, for example, that networks such as Facebook mainly reflect and accommodate values and norms prevalent in Western cultures, which explains why they were at first more successful in countries such as the UK, USA and Canada than elsewhere. However, the design and use of SNSs also varies in different locations and are often adapted to local cultural norms, tastes and preferences. For example, the page design of SNSs varies from place to place, with greater use of pastel or muted colours and emoticons on South-east Asian sites, in contrast to the bolder, darker colours used by sites in Europe and North America. Different cultural expectations around privacy and personal modesty also shape the use of SNSs. For example, some users are often uncomfortable with posting pictures of themselves, preferring to use avatars. Therefore, while technologies such as SNSs become increasingly global, local and national cultural norms continue to shape how people use social networking.

as Brazil, Nigeria, India and China, the notion of Western global cultural dominance is becoming increasingly anachronistic.

Second, some theorists would argue that national cultures remain stronger than global cultures. This is borne out when we consider the many conflicts occurring throughout the world along the geopolitical fault-lines of national cultures (the ongoing conflict between Pakistan and India is but one example of this). For the past 200 years, nation-states and national cultures have monopolized cultural power (state television is one example of a national institution influencing national cultures within national territorial boundaries). At the end of the twentieth century, this balance began to change, with international telecommunications and media corporations challenging the centrality and importance of national cultures. However, it could be argued that despite these changes a great deal of cultural life is still organized along national and territorial lines.

Third, if culture is a system of shared meanings, then looking at the world today there are clearly many systems of shared meanings and many different cultures. People in different places use different techniques and technologies to reproduce culture, such as oral histories, literature or television and cinema. These techniques have different patterns of dispersion, penetration and scale. Therefore, some cultures are more likely to become globalized than others – those reproduced through television, cinema and increasingly through digital media platforms have a greater range and speed of dispersion than those reproduced through oral histories. However, this does not mean that globalized cultures completely erode localized cultures; the ways in which these different cultures intersect is important. Those 'things' (products, symbols, corporate entities) that have become global signifiers are clearly globalized (they are recognized the world over), but the ways in which people around the world make cultural responses to them are complex and multiple (see Case study 13.2). Globalization of products and symbols does not necessarily equal Westernization. For example, Japanese consumer goods do not sell on the back of exporting Japanese culture but on a market strategy based around the concept of *dochaku* ('glocalism'). This involves a global strategy not of imposing standardized products but of tailoring Japanese consumer products to specific local markets. These goods are, therefore, both globalized and localized. Consequently, how intersections between cultures are played out at local levels is of significance, and this suggests that imagining a universal global culture is quite problematic.

13.2.3 Rethinking global culture

Instead of imagining a global culture that is erasing local and national cultures, we can think of local, national and global as three important, interconnected spatial scales at which culture operates. Those aspects of culture that operate at the global level are 'third cultures' (Featherstone 1995: 114). National institutions are no longer in complete control of cultural globalization and 'third cultures' (sets of practices, bodies of knowledge, conventions and lifestyles) have developed in ways that have become increasingly global and independent of nation-states. Phenomena such as patterns of consumption, technological diffusion and media empires are part of these third cultures, and transnational and multinational corporations are the institutions that make them global. In this sense, global cultures exist but only as third cultures, outside national and local cultures, yet intersecting on both these scales in different ways around the world.

Acknowledging that 'our' global view might be very different from that of people elsewhere, living in very different contexts, is also important. It is clear that multiple global cultural networks exist, such as those connecting the overseas Chinese with their homeland, or those linking Islamic groups around the world. These networks disrupt any notion of a singular global culture. Power and inequality bring into question the idea of global cultures. As Massey (2009) argues, a **power geometry** exists, which gives people with different access to power different notions of what global means. New institutions (like global media corporations) for the production, transmission and reception of cultural products are creating infrastructures supporting cultural globalization, including electronic infrastructure (radio, television, music, telecommunications, digital platforms), linguistic infrastructure (the spread of bi- and multi-lingualism, particularly the dominance of English), and corporate infrastructure (producers and distribution networks). As we have seen, these new institutions often operate at scales beyond the nation-state, and they are sites of power in the production of culture. The ownership, control and use of these institutions remain uneven across and within countries (Held and McGrew 2007), thus creating 'power geometries' that are centred overwhelmingly on the West. People have very different experiences of culture because of their different locations in the world and their relationship to these sites of power. Mapping this power geometry, identifying sites of power and revealing the marginalization of some peoples around the world by cultural globalization are increasingly significant. Of equal significance are forms of resistance, such as **culture jamming** (Dery 2010) by anti-consumerist social movements. This involves tactics such as media hacking, information warfare, satire, 'terror-art' and graffiti to invest advertisements, newscasts and other media artefacts with subversive meaning, or to refigure logos and product images in order to challenge what is considered as 'cool'. Another form of resistance is exemplified in 'buycotts', the purchasing of oppositional products aiming to provide a socially acceptable alternative to a more powerful brand. A good example of this is Mecca Cola, marketed in the Middle East, Europe, Asia and Africa as providing a means of expressing solidarity with Muslims worldwide (Littler 2008). Promoted as an alternative to the archetypal American product Coca-Cola, Mecca Cola purports to offer consumers a way to subvert what the company sees as American imperialism, especially as displayed in the support offered by the USA to the Israeli occupation of Palestine and the US invasion of Iraq in 2007. It is also important, therefore, to take account of the ways in which marginalized peoples might be empowered by engaging with, and perhaps transforming, the new institutions driving cultural globalization.

In summary, global processes are occurring, but they do not produce a universal global culture, they are not distributed evenly around the world and are not uncontested. Global cultural processes are not simply a result of a unidirectional 'Westernization', since culture flows transnationally. A number of different global cultures exist as 'third cultures' – in patterns of consumption, flows of knowledge, the diffusion of technologies and media empires that operate beyond, but connecting with, the local and national scales.

13.3 Reinventing local cultures?

13.3.1 Locality and culture

It has often been assumed that there is a simple relationship between local place and local culture. Places were thought of as having a distinct physical, economic and cultural character; they were unique, with their own traditions and local cultures that made them different from other places. It is clear, however, that processes of globalization are also posing serious challenges to the meaning of place. Places and cultures are being restructured. According to Massey and Jess (1995a: 1), 'on the one hand, previous coherences are being disrupted, old notions of the local place are being interrupted by new connections with a world beyond'. The appearance of 7–11 stores in the rainforests of northern Thailand is one example of how even the remotest of places are becoming increasingly internationalized, in this case through tourism. 'On the other hand', Massey and Jess continue,

'new claims to the – usually exclusive – character of places, and who belongs there, are being made.' We see this in contemporary Western Europe, North America and Australia, where 'asylum seekers, migrants, Muslims, militant youths, pan-handlers, carriers of transmissible diseases' (Amin 2010: 10) are increasingly racialized and viewed as threats to established value systems and ways of life. Similar problems have also emerged in countries such as South Africa, which experienced a dramatic rise in xenophobic violence in 2008 that persists today (Dodson 2010). Therefore, modern life is characterized both by decentralization and globalization of culture *and* by the resurgence of place-bound traditions. Following this, the impact of the new global context on local cultures has two, possibly contradictory, outcomes.

13.3.2 Negative sense of culture

Where global processes are perceived to pose a threat to local culture, there might be an attempt to return to some notion of the exclusivity of culture. At the extreme, this might take the form of exclusivist nationalism or even 'ethnic cleansing'. Reactions to the perceived threat to local cultures include nationalistic, ethnic and fundamentalist responses, which also entail a strong assertion of local cultures, such as reviving or inventing local traditions and ceremonies. These can create a level of local fragmentation, with a parochial, nostalgic, inward-looking sense of local attachment and cultural identity. In this sense, cultures are thought of as **bounded**, with very clear definitions of 'insiders' and 'outsiders' in the creation of a sense of belonging, and producing **geographies of exclusion** (Sibley 1995).

For example, English rural areas are often conceptualized as the preserve of culture and identity (see Chapters 11 and 12). This idea is mobilized through the myth of the 'rural idyll', in which rural village communities are portrayed as neighbourly and close-knit, with villagers perceived as having a deep-seated sense of local identity complemented by strong feelings of belonging (Garland and Chakraborti 2006), and in which rural cultures are thought of as timeless, unchanging and unaffected by global processes. This cosy vision of a peaceful countryside excludes many people who live in rural areas, but do not fit this stereotype. Different notions of rural idyll create similar exclusions in other countries; for example, Canada's rural idyll is embedded within the colonial legacy of a white settler society (Cairns 2013). The myth of the English rural idyll deems travellers, environmental protesters, hunt saboteurs, people with alternative lifestyles and people from minority ethnic communities to be 'outsiders' and a threat to local cultures (Garland

and Chakraborti 2004). The pervasiveness of this myth of the white rural idyll made headlines in the UK in a recent controversy over the cast of popular TV drama *Midsomer Murders,* set in a fictional Cotswolds village. When questioned about the all-white cast, the producer described the programme as the 'last bastion of Englishness' and stated 'We just don't have ethnic minorities involved. Because it wouldn't be the English village with them' (in Pool 2011). As Garland and Chakraborti (2006, 2009) argue, the perpetuation of this myth obscures and marginalizes the experiences of minority ethnic residents who often feel excluded from village life. Moreover, their research suggests that conflation of rurality with notions of Englishness and 'whiteness' serves to reinforce this marginalization and can also lead to racist victimization. The 'rural idyll' is thus a selective representation, exclusive in its class, race and status connotations, is profoundly conservative and demands conformity. It is based on a very inward-looking **sense of place** and culture (see Plate 13.2).

Conservative reactions to change can be thought of as a kind of cultural fundamentalism through which the process of cultural change is often bitterly contested. Gender plays an important role in this. Women are often considered as guardians of the borders of culture (Yuval-Davis 1997). They not only bear children for the collective, but also reproduce it culturally. In closed cultures, the control of women's sexuality is seen as imperative to the maintenance of the purity of the cultural unit; women are discouraged from marrying outside their cultural and ethnic group. Ethnicity and culture, therefore, are seen to be one and the same. In addition, symbols of gender play an important role in articulating difference between cultural groups. Women's distinctive ways of dressing and behaving very often come to symbolize the group's cultural identity and its boundaries. Women are often the intergenerational transmitters of cultural traditions, customs, songs, cuisine and the 'mother' tongue, primarily through their role as mothers. This is especially true in minority situations where the school and the public sphere present different and dominant cultural models from that of the home. Recent controversies over the Islamic veil, for example, have seen countries across Europe wrestling with issues of religious freedom, civil rights, women's equality, secular traditions and escalating fears of terrorism. France banned Muslim headscarves and other 'conspicuous' religious symbols at state schools in 2004, and in 2010 made it illegal in public places to wear any clothes designed to hide the face. Belgium passed a similar law in 2010, banning any clothing that hides the wearer's identity in public places. Turkey, a secular Islamic country, banned the wearing of head-scarves in all civic spaces in 2005 but amended the ruling in 2008 to allow women at universities to wear scarves tied under the chin. The Italian parliament approved anti-terrorist laws in July 2005, which make covering one's features in public – including through wearing the burqa – an offence. The Dutch cabinet backed a proposal in 2006 to ban the few dozen Muslim women who choose to wear the burqa from doing so in public places on grounds that it disturbs public order, citizens and safety. In the United Kingdom in 2010, the Conservative MP Philip Hollobone proposed a law to regulate wearing in public garments that cover the face, calling the burqa offensive. The debates over Islamic dress reveal some of the issues that can arise when marginal, minority cultures are seen to clash with the norms and expectations of the majority population, which in turn raises questions about the possibilities and challenges of multiculturalism as opposed to integration and/or assimilation (discussed below in Section 13.4).

Plate 13.2 Exclusion in the countryside: travellers and other minority groups are often excluded from shops and public houses, marking their position as 'outsiders'.

(Boston Globe/Getty Images)

Societies do not evolve smoothly from closed, bounded perceptions of culture to more open, dynamic notions. The question of cultural power, identity and resistance also needs to be considered. For many groups, cultural survival is seen to depend on a closed idea of culture, with strongly marked boundaries separating it from 'others'. The controversies over Islamic dress, and the continuing sectarianism and possible threats of terrorism that still exist in Northern Ireland despite recent progress, are examples of different cultures, religions and national identities colliding with each other. Elsewhere the mixing of cultures under the impact of globalization is often seen as threatening and as weakening the sense of cultural identity. Immigration is seen as a particular threat, creating a revival of ethnicity that cuts across the political spectrum. Examples include the 'little England' reaction to closer European integration, encapsulated by the rise of the UK Independence Party, which campaigns on a platform of UK withdrawal from the European Union and imposing strict controls on immigration. Migrants to Britain have become scapegoats for almost every contemporary problem, from the squeeze on public finances and services, the declining economy, and the increasing numbers of working poor. Similar attitudes are evident in post-apartheid South Africa, where since 1994 African immigrants have been associated with illegality, criminality and a struggling welfare system, in both political and public discourse. According to one commentator, 'The poor and the vulnerable – especially those who do not share the same language or customs or religion – have always been a politically convenient scapegoat for a society's various ills. It's the oldest trick in the book' (Fraser 2014). It is also a means of turning those most affected by economic downturns and government austerity measures (e.g. working and lower middle classes) against other increasingly marginalised groups. This trend can be observed in the rise of neo-fascism across Europe, also characterized by anti-immigration and racism. Perceived threats to religious identities have also witnessed the strengthening of Islamic and Christian fundamentalism around the world. These phenomena are not all the same, but they do share a response to globalization that involves a closed, fixed, bounded and often place-specific definition of culture, and a strong resistance to changes heralded by cultural globalization.

13.3.3 Positive sense of culture

A more positive response to global processes would be to imagine cultures as fluid, ever-changing, unbounded, overlapping and outward-looking – akin to Massey's (1994: 151) 'progressive sense of place'. This involves people being more cosmopolitan (free of prejudice and

tolerant of difference). Increasing interconnectedness means the boundaries of local cultures are seen to be more permeable, susceptible to change, and difficult to maintain than in the past. Rather than everywhere becoming the same, some nation-states have reconstituted their collective identities along pluralistic and multicultural lines, which take into account regional and ethnic differences and diversity. In Europe, this involves re-creation and invention of local, regional and substate or new 'national' cultures (for example, the cultural renaissance of the Basques and Catalans, or the cultural assertiveness of minority ethnic communities in cities such as London, Paris and Berlin). The 2014 Scottish independence referendum saw Scots vote narrowly to stay within the United Kingdom, but also saw the emergence of a powerful civic nationalism – generally a non-xenophobic nationalism (although paradoxically not without occasional anti-English sentiment) that purports to be based in values of freedom, tolerance, equality and rights – as opposed to ethnic nationalism based in notions of cultural sameness. Thus, what can be perceived as destruction of local cultures by globalization might in fact be the means of creating new senses of locality and nation. This still involves notions of local and national identity, but recognizes both the differences between cultures and their interconnectedness, taking account of the positive aspects of cultural mixing and increased cosmopolitanism. This new sense of identity is based on notions of inclusion rather than exclusion.

This is not to say, of course, that all people within the same place will share the same culture and the same sense of locality. Within these more culturally pluralistic and cosmopolitan locales, different class factions, ages, genders, ethnicities and religious groupings mingle together in the same sites, consuming the same television programmes and products, but in highly uneven ways. These groups often possess different senses of affiliation to places and localities, possess different cultural identities and belong to different cultural groupings (Featherstone 1995: 97). A progressive sense of culture does not foresee the locale as a 'melting-pot', where everything becomes the same, but rather recognizes the different experiences of people, and that increasing interconnections might create new, dynamic and exciting cultural forms. An understanding of this is crucial to the creation of a progressive notion of place and culture, which recognizes cultures as fluid, dynamic, open and interconnected, and accepts that older local cultures might decline as new ones emerge.

In summary, localities are important in maintaining cultural difference, but can also be sites of cultural mixing and transformation. Ideas about culture can be negative (bounded, fixed, inward-looking) or positive (progressive, dynamic, outward-looking). Bounded, fixed notions of culture can lead to localized resistance, racism, nationalism, and even 'ethnic cleansing'. Progressive ideas about culture involve the recognition of differences between cultures, the interconnectedness of cultures and their constant evolution.

13.4 Multi- and hybrid cultures?

13.4.1 Hybridity

One of the major contemporary challenges concerns what we do with the concept of culture in the changing global scene, where nation-states are forced to tolerate greater diversity within their boundaries. Some want to see national identity as homogeneous and assimilatory – in other words, different cultures are subsumed into the dominant culture (the 'melting pot' idea) (see Case study 13.3). Denmark, for example, is highly assimilationist and has one of the toughest policies on immigration in Europe. Others call for the acceptance of ethnic pluralism and the preservation of minority ethnic cultures as a legitimate part of the national project. This is the politics of **multiculturalism**, which instead of thinking of different cultures as being absorbed by dominant cultures, relies more on a notion of a cultural mosaic, or a 'patchwork quilt' of cultures. Each culture is recognized as different and distinct, but these differences are understood and valued. Sweden, for example, rejects Denmark's assimilationist model in favour of multiculturalism.

Multiculturalism might seem more progressive, but it can sometimes reinforce difference because culture is seen as essentially connected to **race**, and racial difference as rooted in biological difference. (These ideas are no longer considered acceptable; anti-racists have demonstrated that 'race' is socially constructed and has little basis in biology (Price 2010). We could just as easily have 'races' of blue-eyed and brown-eyed people.) Multiculturalism, therefore, still relies on a negative notion of bounded cultures. It might suggest tolerance, but often results in segregation and ghettoization. The United Kingdom and Netherlands, for example, have tended towards multiculturalism but have increasingly witnessed tensions surrounding the lack of integration of some Muslim communities. The murder of Dutch film-maker Theo Van Gogh in 2004, the London bombings in July 2005 and the attacks on satirical magazine *Charlie Hebdo* in Paris in 2015 – all by apparent 'home-grown radical Islamists' – are seen by some to represent the failures of multiculturalism. Similarly, the 2006 riots in the suburbs of Paris were seen as a product of the deep alienation of poor, largely immigrant communities facing high levels of unemployment, discrimination in housing and jobs markets, and police harassment (see Chapter 10); the 2011 London riots have been blamed on racism, classism and economic inequality that are seen as linked to criminality, breakdown of social morality and gang culture.

In contrast, a more progressive idea of culture (and its manifestations in ethnicity, gender and sexuality) might be developed through the concept of **hybridity**. Hybridity breaks down barriers, adhering to neither the 'melting pot' nor 'mosaic' idea of cultural mixing, but rather seeing different cultures coming together and informing each other in different ways to produce something entirely new. This process has a long historical trajectory. Indeed, some argue that cultures have always been hybrid forms and processes – they have never existed in isolation from other cultures, and thus have always been subject to change and influences from elsewhere (Werbner 1997: 15).

One of the most obvious places we can observe hybridity is in popular mass culture, an immediate example being popular music. Innovations in music have always involved the fusion of different styles to create new sounds and rhythms. Rock-and-roll, rhythm-and-blues and Latin jazz are obvious examples. We might also think of recent and contemporary forms of music that fuse different styles, such as 'trip hop', which emerged in the 1990s; 'post-trip hop', which has since integrated trip hop with other genres, such as ambient, R&B, breakbeat, drum 'n' bass, acid jazz and new age; 'nu metal', which from the late 1990s until around 2005 combined heavy metal with other genres such as grunge and hip hop; and electro house, which fuses house music with several other electronic dance music subgenres and came into prominence between 2000 and the present. Theorists such as Barthes (1972), Bourdieu (1984) and Bakhtin (1984) see popular hybridity as an exciting challenge to, or subversion of, dominant cultures and the exclusive lifestyles of dominant elites. Such popular mixings and inversions, like the subversive elements of youth cultures (Hebdige 1979; see also Hammett 2009; Carr 2010), are hybrid in the sense that they bring together and mix languages and practices from different and normally separated domains. They have the potential to disrupt dominant cultures by their 'out-of-placeness'.

In many ways hybridity is related to the notion of **transculturation**. Transculturation describes one of the key cultural processes that operate between hitherto sharply differentiated cultures and peoples who are forced (usually by the processes of imperialism or globalization, and primarily through migration) to interact. This interaction often takes place in profoundly asymmetrical ways in terms of relative power between different groups. However, communication technologies that enable simultaneous connections and transactions between people in

Case study 13.3

Bounded or hybrid national culture?

Nationalists around the world cling to a notion of bounded cultures that make them distinct from others. One effect of globalization has been resistance in the form of increased nationalism to what is perceived to be the erosion of national cultures. Increased mixing of cultures is seen to pose a threat to the survival of national cultures. Nationalists seek to preserve the symbols of nationhood, such as language, lifestyles and cultural forms, in the face of what are perceived to be sweeping changes. However, cultures are not unchanging; a fundamental flaw in nationalist ideology (especially ethnic nationalism) is the adherence to a notion of static culture, and its reliance on a mythical history of the origin of the nation. For example, English nationalists define Englishness as distinct, which is used to justify anti-immigrationist ideas, anti-Europeanism and, in some cases, racism. But who are 'the English'? After the last ice age many communities settled Britain and Ireland from all over Europe. They lived and fought with each other and in a short space of time produced a mixed group of people who eventually called themselves English. The islands have been subject to waves of invasion and settlement (e.g. Celts, Romans, Anglo-Saxons, Vikings, Normans). England has always been hybrid; peoples and cultures have mixed and evolved together. Some English nationalists avoid thinking about this point by arguing that the final invasion (by William the Conqueror in 1066) marks the origin of England and Englishness (Anderson 1983). This myth is also flawed. William the Conqueror spoke no English. Whom did he conquer? He conquered 'the English'. For many nationalists the founding father of England is French! It is also no small irony that one of the symbols of Englishness, the monarchy, changed its official name to Windsor in 1917 from Saxe-Coburg-Gotha, thus hiding its German origins.

Even protectionist policies towards language are flawed; as with culture more generally, language is always hybridised and evolving. Most sentences in 'English' contain words that derive from German, French, Spanish, Latin, Nordic and Celtic languages. One legacy of British imperialism has been the incorporation of elements of the languages of the colonized into everyday English. Words from Indian languages, for example, punctuate English, including Hindi (bangle, bazaar, caravan, cot, jungle, juggernaut, pajama, pundit, shampoo, thug), Sanskrit (atoll, aubergine, avatar, bandana, candy, cash, dinghy, karma, sugar), Tamil (catamaran, curry, mantra, pariah), and Urdu (bungalow, khaki). Technological innovation introduces not only new words, but has the capacity to alter grammar: verbalising nouns (adding endings to nouns that turn them into verbs, such as 'texting', 'emailing', 'googling', 'interfacing') is now commonplace in British English. Such hybridity within national languages provides evidence for the ways in which cultures have always been dynamic and mutually influential. Similar myths of origin and notions of bounded cultures exist elsewhere in the world. In some places protectionist policies emanate from deeply contradictory ideas (anti-immigrationist views in the USA and Australia, for example). In other places notions of bounded culture have led to conflict (for example, between Georgia and South Ossetia in 2008, between the Tamil separatists and the Sri Lankan state in 2009, and the continuing struggle by Kurdish nationalist organizations, some of whom seek to create an independent nation-state of Kurdistan, consisting of some or all of the Kurdish areas in eastern Turkey, northern Iraq, north-western Iran and northern Syria, while others campaign for greater Kurdish autonomy within these existing national boundaries). The idea of nationhood, based on fixed, bounded and unchanging cultures, is an ideological creation that masks profound cultural divisions of gender, race, class and religion within a nation-state (see also Chapter 22), and ignores the fact that, in reality, all cultures are hybrid and dynamic.

even remote parts of the world are creating the possibility for more democratic forms of intercultural exchange. For example, intercultural exchange between schools and universities in different parts of the world is increasingly popular, facilitated by digital technologies. This has enabled such things as intercultural music-making, which promotes knowledge of and respect for cultural diversity, as well as stimulating creativity of hybrid musical forms. One example of an intercultural exchange between

Tswana university students in South Africa and students in an Australian university (Klopper 2010) promoted a better understanding of their own and other musical traditions – the centrality in African cultures of music to tradition and oral histories, its inseparability from other performance arts and its links to joy and shared experience, in contrast to the technical training and individual mastery of classical music by Western students (which classical musicians might point out also becomes joyful and shared when played in an orchestra). Digital and communication technologies (video, on-line chat rooms and web-cams) also allowed the students to collaborate in making music together. As Klopper (2010: 48) argues, such technologies ensure that 'cultural boundaries are no longer geographically dictated'.

Despite the illusion of boundedness, cultures have always evolved historically through borrowings, appropriations, exchanges and inventions. Cross-fertilization of cultures is endemic to all movements of people throughout history (see Case study 13.3) and it may be that new technologies simply speed up the process and enhance the possibilities. However, for those who aspire to bounded notions of culture and refuse this idea of perpetual hybridity, cultural mixing is felt to be threatening and a deliberate challenge to social order. In reality there are no fixed cultures in modern nation-states, but some people cling to ideas of pure or impure cultures. For others, however, hybridity remains the site of revitalization, resistance and fun (see Case study 13.4).

Case study 13.4

Hybridity/diaspora – some examples

Samba-taiko in São Paulo, Brazil

Samba-taiko is a hybrid form of music, combining the percussion styles of Japanese taiko (meaning 'big drum') and Brazilian samba, and a recent style of music emerging out of the Japanese diaspora in Brazil. Taiko performances are highly visual, visceral, and energetic in dynamics, rhythm, and movement, with dramatic full-body choreography and highly stylized strokes and arm movements. Solo taiko has its origins in ancient rituals, linked to Buddhism and everyday life. Taiko ensemble drumming is a relatively recent development in Japanese musical culture, which has allowed it to be appropriated and developed independently in Japanese migrant communities in both North and Latin America. São Paulo, home to the largest Japanese diaspora, has become the site of an emerging hybridization of Brazilian and Japanese percussion instrumentation and styles, which is also changing function of this music as cultural identity. Samba is a central part of Brazilian national identity (*brasilidade*), referring to both the musical style and the place or circle in which the music is placed, either in the home (*casa*) or in the street (*rua*). A popular idiom used to refer to 'playing badly' is 'the Japanese in the samba', which is symbolic of a wider exclusion of the Japanese diaspora from the notion of *brasilidade*. After a century of immigration, people of Japanese descent in Brazil are not considered 'Brazilian' in popular discourse, and are regularly referred to as 'Japanese'. Samba-taiko originated in São Paolo with Setsuo Kinoshita, the first taiko professor in Brazil, who began teaching both taiko and samba in an effort to help Brazilian-Japanese students deal with exclusion and internalized racism, and to become more comfortable with their dual identities. In 2003, Kinoshota and his students began performing their innovations in hybrid samba-taiko styles (see, for example, Kinoshita's video clip at www.youtube.com/watch?v=nuVSB67IDgg), sparking a craze in Brazil, and inspiring the formation of over 150 taiko groups in which young Japanese and non-Japanese Brazilians come together through music. Through a shared tradition of percussion, it appears that a truly Japanese-Brazilian cultural rapport, particularly among young people, is emerging after a century of cultural disconnect.

Source: adapted from Sybert (2014)

Cuban Santería

Santería is an example of a syncretic (hybrid, mixed) religion. It is based on West African religions brought by slaves imported from what are now Nigeria and Benin to the Caribbean to work the sugar plantations. These religions were suppressed by the European plantation owners and in Cuba slaves were forced to convert to Catholicism. However, they were able to preserve some of their traditions by fusing together various West African beliefs and rituals and syncretizing these with elements from Catholicism. One factor enabling this process was that many of the *orishas* (primary gods) shared many of the same characteristics of Catholic saints. This enabled slaves to appear to be practising Catholicism while practising their own religions. This has evolved into what we know today as Santería, the Way of the Saints, whose traditions are transmitted orally from generation to generation. Despite suppression by Fidel Castro's Socialist Revolution since 1961, its influence is pervasive in Cuban life. Devotees are found in most households, Yoruba proverbs litter Cuban Spanish, and high priests (*babalawos*) offer guidance based on ancient systems of lore. Today, with less religious persecution, Santería is experiencing a rise in popularity and is part of an emerging Cuban youth culture. Similar syncretic religions are found in Haiti, Puerto Rico and other Caribbean and Latin American countries.

Source: adapted from Betts (2002)

13.4.2 Diaspora

Related to the idea of hybridity is the notion of **diaspora**. This term was originally used to refer to the dispersal of Jewish peoples, but is now used in reference to the long-term settlement of peoples in 'foreign' places that follows their scattering or dispersal from their original homeland. It refers to a modern condition where a sense of belonging is not derived from attachment to territory, and where different peoples mix together through the processes of migration (forced or free). European imperialism and associated processes of globalization have set many of these migrations in motion. Diasporas are classic **contact zones** – spaces in which two cultures come together and influence each other – where transculturation or hybridization takes place. Diasporic identities are at once local and global and based on transnational identifications encompassing both 'imagined' and 'encountered' communities (e.g. Irish-Americans belong to an imagined international community of people who have 'Irishness' in common, but whose identities are also informed by the communities in which they live in the USA). In other words, diasporas are a direct challenge to the idea that there is a simple relationship between place and culture. They transgress the boundaries of the nation-state and provide alternative resources for constructing identity and fashioning culture.

The concept of **diaspora space** allows us to think of 'culture as a site of travel' (Clifford 1992), which seriously problematizes the idea of a person being a 'native' or an 'insider'. Diaspora space is the point at which boundaries of inclusion and exclusion, of belonging and otherness, of 'us' and 'them' are contested. As Brah (1996: 209) argues, diaspora space is 'inhabited' not only by those who have migrated and their descendants, but equally by those who are constructed and represented as indigenous or 'native'. In the diaspora space called 'England', for example, African-Caribbean, Irish, Asian, Jewish and other diasporas intersect among themselves as well as with the entity constructed as 'Englishness', thoroughly reinscribing it in the process. Like notions of hybridity, the concept of diaspora is important since it allows for the recognition of new political and cultural formations that continually challenge the marginalizing impulses of dominant cultures.

13.4.3 Selling hybridity and the commodification of culture

In today's world, culture sells. Hybrid cultures, in particular, sell. Cities are now constructing themselves as cosmopolitan, and hybridity has become a form of 'boosterism' – where city authorities create marketing images to attract investment in the form of business and tourism. Hybrid culture is perceived as creating economic advantage. With increasing deindustrialization in Europe and North America, and many countries in the global South by-passing an industrial age to fast-forward to a knowledge- and service-driven economy, cultural strategies have become key to the survival of cities. Examples include the international marketing of cultural/religious festivals such as Mardi Gras in Sydney or New Orleans, Gay Pride Festivals in Toronto, Cape Town or London, or the importance of 'Chinatowns' and other 'ethnic' districts to tourism in cities throughout the world (see Plate 13.3). Ironically, hybridity is in danger of becoming just another marketable commodity. For example, treating the political work of some British-Asian bands as marketable, hybridity trivializes black political activity and leaves problems of class exploitation and racial oppression unresolved. As Hutnyk (1997: 134) suggests, to focus on hybridity while ignoring (or as an excuse for ignoring) the conditions in which this phenomenon exists (the commodity system, global economic inequality, inequitable political relations) is problematic in that it maintains the status quo. Hybridity and difference sell, but in the meantime the market remains intact, power relations remain unequal, and marginalized peoples remain marginalized. Moreover, as culture is subsumed into capitalism, those marginalized peoples who might be capable of oppositional politics are also subsumed under the rubric of hybridity.

The notion of hybridity, therefore, can be problematic. In some Latin American countries, cultural elites and nation-states have appropriated the hybrid mestizo (mixed) identity, making it dominant. This has been seen to be oppressive of 'Indian' populations, who have in turn been accused of ethnic essentialism (or emphasizing their racial difference) because of their desire to

Plate 13.3 Chinatown in San Francisco: 'ethnic' districts are promoted as major tourist attractions in many 'global' cities.

(Jeff Whyte/Shutterstock)

protect their cultures (Radcliffe and Westwood 1996). In the West, ideas of hybridity are currently popular with highly educated cultural elites, but ideas about culture, ethnicity and identity that develop in poverty-stricken underclass neighbourhoods are likely to be of a different nature (Friedman 1997: 83–4). Evidence of racial tensions in many North American and European cities points to the fact that class and local ghetto identities tend to prevail, with little room for the mixing pleaded for by cultural elites. Such fixed notions of identity are produced and perpetuated in wealthy areas too. In Cape Town, where urban segregation persists 20 years after the end of apartheid, several violent, racist incidents in public spaces in predominantly white neighbourhoods made newspaper headlines in 2014. The global, cultural hybrid, elite sphere is occupied by individuals who share a very different kind of experience of the world, connected to international politics, academia, the media and the arts. In the meantime, the world becomes more polarized in terms of wealth, and heads towards increasing **balkanization** where regional, national and ethnic identities are perceived as bounded, threatened, and in need of protection. As Bhabha (1994) reminds us, hybridity is an insufficient means through which to create new forms of collective identity that can overcome ethnic, racial, religious and class-based antagonisms – it sounds nice in theory, but does not necessarily exist outside the realms of the privileged.

As Stuart Hall (1996: 233) argued, we should not view the current fashionability of hybridity in a wholly negative light. Even as cultures are increasingly commodified, we should not forget the potential for the democratization of culture in this process, the increased recognition of difference and the diversification of the social worlds in which people now operate – the case of samba-taiko in Brazil (Case study 13.4) is but one example. This pluralization of social and cultural life expands the identities available to ordinary people (at least in the advanced economies) in their everyday working, social, familial and sexual lives. For Bhabha (1994: 9), the interconnections of different cultural spaces and the overlapping of different cultural forms create vitality and hold out the possibility of a progressive notion of culture.

We thus need to think about the place and meaning of cultural hybridity in the context of growing global uncertainty, xenophobia (fear of foreigners) and racism. Why is cultural hybridity still experienced as an empowering, dangerous or transformative force? Why, on the one hand, is difference celebrated through a consumer market that offers a seemingly endless choice of identities, sub-cultures and styles yet, on the other hand, hybridity continues to threaten and shock? Conversely, why do borders, boundaries and 'pure' identities remain important,

producing defensive and exclusionary actions and attitudes, and why are the latter so difficult to transcend? Is the sheer pace of change in cultural globalization producing these reactions?

To summarize, hybridity and diaspora are examples of more progressive ways of thinking about culture. It could be argued that all cultures are always already hybrid; they are never pure, have always evolved and changed through time and through contact with other cultures, and they continue to evolve. In today's world, hybridity is being commodified, which might make it less radical. However, despite this, it has the potential to democratize culture and to allow us to rethink culture in ways that are more tolerant of difference. Finally, cultural hybridity needs to be understood in the context of growing global uncertainty, xenophobia and racism.

13.5 Conclusion

In this chapter it is suggested that there are two apparently contradictory tendencies in thinking about cultures – the attempt to secure the purity of a culture by conceptualizing it as strong, fixed, bounded, permanent and homogeneous, and the hybridity of most cultures. Culture is thus a contested concept. A progressive way of thinking about culture is to reject the idea of boundedness and internal cohesion. In the modern world especially, culture is a meeting point where different influences, traditions and forces intersect. There is, therefore, a continual process of change in cultural practices and meanings. Globalization is undermining closed, fixed ideas of culture and leading to new ways of conceptualizing cultures (transculturation, contact zones, hybridity and diaspora). However, the fact that cultures are not fixed or homogeneous does not mean that we will stop thinking of them in this way. As Hall (1995: 188–9) argues, this is because some people need 'belongingness' and the security that closed conceptions of culture provide.

Despite this, recent years have witnessed a decentring of culture, with nation-states increasingly superseded by transnational institutions that are producing cultural globalization and greater cultural diversity. There has also been a shift in the awareness of the cultural capital of the West, and an understanding of the cultural dominance of developed countries. At the same time, there are now more voices talking back, reflecting the cultural assertiveness of marginalized groups and making us aware of new levels of diversity. Even though most people remain physically, ideologically and spiritually attached to a local or a national culture and a local place, complex cultural flows and networks ensure that it is becoming increasingly impossible for people to live in places that are completely isolated and disconnected culturally from the wider world. Thus,

> if there is a global culture it would be better to conceive of it not as a common culture, but as a field in which differences, power struggles and cultural prestige contests are played out . . . Hence globalization makes us aware of the sheer volume, diversity and many-sidedness of culture.
>
> (Featherstone 1995: 14)

This points to a 'more positive evaluation by the West of otherness and differences' (Featherstone 1995: 89). For Massey and Jess (1995b: 134), globalization is not simply a threat to existing notions of culture, but a 'stimulus to a positive new response'.

People around the world have different cultures and systems of meaning, but we cannot avoid reading the world from within our own cultures and interpreting it through our own systems of meaning. Understandings of global culture for the majority of the readers of this book are filtered through the logic of the West (Spivak 1985). Western ideas and cultural forms are still considered superior and have become hegemonic, or dominant. Similarly, one's own cultural positioning (on the basis of gender, ethnicity, class, location, sexuality, stage in life cycle, ability) also influences understandings of local cultures. The same processes operate at local levels; dominant cultures marginalize others on the basis of ethnicity, sexuality, gender and religion. However, as we have seen, those dominant cultures also produce resistances that have the potential to create new ways of thinking about culture.

The challenge is to confront the limits of 'our' knowledge, to recognize other worlds, to acknowledge the legitimacy of other cultures, other identities and other ways of life. Accepting 'cultural translation' (Bhabha 1994) involves understanding the hybrid nature of culture, the influence of marginal cultures on dominant cultures, and that people in marginal cultural systems at local, national and international levels are also active in creating their own systems of meaning. They do not simply absorb ideas from, or become absorbed into, more dominant cultures. It is possible to develop cosmopolitanism in the twenty-first century that is global, sensitive to cultural difference, and dynamic.

Learning outcomes

Having read this chapter, you should be able to:

- Understand the complexities of culture; it is a process, rather than a thing, and subject to change over time.

- Demonstrate ways in which cultures operate at local, national and global levels.

- Discuss examples of global cultural processes and how these are filtered through localities to contest notions of a singular global culture.

- Discuss examples of negative (closed, bounded), or positive (progressive, hybridized) local cultures.

- Critique and utilize concepts such as hybridity and diaspora as a progressive way of thinking about culture.

- Reflect on your own cultures of knowledge, and the ways in which these condition your ideas about global, national and local cultures.

Further reading

Anderson, J. (2010) *Understanding Cultural Geography: Places and Traces,* Routledge, London. This book provides a broad-based overview of cultural geography, arguing that its essential focus is *place.* The book presents specific chapters outlining the history of cultural geography, as well as the methods and techniques of doing cultural geography and focuses on topics such as corporate capitalism, nationalism, ethnicity, youth culture and the place of the body.

Anderson, K., Domosh, M., Pile, S. and Thrift, N. (eds) (2003) *Handbook of Cultural Geography,* Sage, London. This book offers an assessment of the key questions informing cultural geography and contains over 30 essays. It is an invaluable resource for students looking for an assessment of major issues and debates and the breadth, scope and vitality of contemporary cultural geography.

Atkinson, D., Jackson, P., Sibley, D. and Washbourne, N. (eds.) (2005) *Cultural Geography: A Critical Dictionary of Key Ideas,* London: I.B. Tauris. A broad-ranging collection of mini-essays on topics germane to the themes of this chapter, including globalization/globality, travel/tourism, diaspora, hybridity, colonialism/postcolonialism.

Duncan, J.S., Johnson, N.C. and Schein, R. (eds) (2004) *A Companion to Cultural Geography,* Blackwell, London. A comprehensive introduction to cultural geography, with 32 chapters written by leading authorities in the field and covering debates about cultural theories, nature/culture, culture and identity, landscapes and colonial/post-colonial geographies.

Nayak, A. and Jeffrey, A. (2011) *Geographical Thought: An Introduction to Ideas in Human Geography,* Routledge, London. This book is not labelled as cultural geography, but it develops many of the themes identified in this chapter. Students of cultural geography will find the chapters on the 'Cultural Turn', 'Geographies of Sexuality', 'Ethnicity and Racialisation', 'Postmodern Geographies', 'Postcolonial Geographies' and 'Emotions, Embodiment and Lived Geographies' of interest.

Shurmer-Smith, P. (ed.) (2002) *Doing Cultural Geography,* Sage, London. This is a good book for those students thinking of undertaking projects or writing dissertations in cultural geography. It explains the theory informing cultural geography and encourages students to engage directly with theory in practice.

Murray, W.E. and Overton, J. (2015) *Geographies of Globalization,* 2nd edition, London, Routledge. A lively textbook providing a useful introduction to geographies, theories and histories of globalization. The chapters on globalizing cultural geographies and progressive globalization are pertinent to readers with interests in cultural geographies of globalization.

Useful websites

www.culture.gov.uk   The official website of the UK government's Department for Culture, Media and Sport (DCMS). An animated site that includes information about the role of the DCMS, and government policy towards media and arts, heritage, libraries and museums, sport, the National Lottery and tourism. Also has links to other useful sites in each category.

www.unesco.org/culture/pdf/creative-economy-report-2013.pdf   The latest report and web-documentary from the United Nations Educational, Scientific and Cultural Organisation (with the United Nations Development Programme) on the creative economy and its relationship to economic and social development.

http://unctad.org/en/Pages/DITC/CreativeEconomy/Statistics-on-world-trade-in-creative-products.aspx   UNCTAD Global Database on Creative Economy, including lots of useful statistics.

www.adbusters.org/home   An example of 'culture jamming'.

www.un.org/womenwatch   The official United Nations Internet Gateway on the Advancement and Empowerment of Women, and part of the global phenomenon of cyberfeminism, which might be considered an example of a 'third culture'. Has useful links to other sites advancing women's rights through new technologies.

For an introduction to Cuba's hybrid cultures see www.afrocubaweb.com.

PRODUCTION, EXCHANGE AND CONSUMPTION

Edited by Peter Daniels

The idea of going 'global' is often associated with the economic aspects of human geography. The geographical outcomes are increasingly a function of links and dependencies that extend far beyond the local or national; reflecting diverse and dynamic interactions between places and people distributed worldwide. The recent shift in the global economic centre of gravity towards China or India is a good example. Many of the symptoms of 'globalization' are most obvious in the sphere of consumption (Chapter 19); Apple (USA) or BMW (Germany) are universal brands, although not equally accessible everywhere. This is also the case, although perhaps less obvious, in the context of global food production and consumption (Chapter 15).

Consumption is both a consequence, and a driver, of the globalization of production. The shift from production systems largely focused on national markets to those organized as sophisticated global production chains and networks has accelerated (see Chapter 16); including food chains or networks (Chapter 15) that vary in complexity and geographical coverage for different products. The search for new suppliers or markets as national opportunities become saturated adds to network complexity. Improved access to information via the Internet, cable and satellite services has also, metaphorically, made the world smaller.

During the first quarter of the twentieth century Fordist methods of production fulfilled demand for high-volume, low-cost, standardized products, followed by a shift towards post-Fordist production systems based on greater flexibility, specialization, customization, strategic alliances (see Chapter 16), even more fragmented divisions of labour and expertise (Chapter 17) and horizontal rather than vertical integration of production. The trend was led first by manufacturing and then by the rise of service industries (see Chapter 17). Localities have reasserted their role as a focus for production (Chapter 14) although an increasing disconnection between, for example, food producers and consumers also creates food security challenges (Chapter 15). Symbols of the Fordist era, such as massive production plants, have been replaced by industrial districts made up of networks of firms, small and large, that form distinctive nodes of production such as the Third Italy or the City of London.

Yet, large firms are as influential as ever in shaping the geographies of production and consumption (see Chapters 14, 16 and 17). Transnational corporations (TNCs) often command more financial resources than many national governments and exercise significant influence on economic decisions, investments in infrastructure, or regulation by nation-states as well as international organizations such as the World Trade Organization (WTO).

Consumption and production are mediated by the circulation of finance capital (Chapter 18). National governments, companies, or individuals require finance to execute investment strategies (companies) or purchasing decisions (households). Advances in information technology have greatly increased the global circulation of finance, and also enable innovation in the financial instruments traded on stock, commodity, or currency exchanges in London, New York, Shanghai or Singapore. Yet again, however, the flows of finance capital mediated by such financial centres are spatially uneven, to the significant disadvantage of marginalized nations, regions and groups.

This section demonstrates how the geography of the economy simultaneously incorporates global and local economic perspectives. They are inseparable even though there have been some important shifts in modes of production and mechanisms of consumption over time and across space. Some of the causes and the consequences of the uneven economic development that results are highlighted. An overview of the contributions suggests that there are many important issues, questions and challenges that economic geographers can usefully address as the twenty-first century unfolds.

GEOGRAPHIES OF THE ECONOMY

Chapter 14

Peter Daniels and Andrew Jones

Topics covered

- The changing nature of economic geography
- The rise of the global economy
- A geographical approach to economic processes
- Places and localities in the global economy
- A new global informational economy?

The economy is everywhere. It is a set of human activities and institutions linked together in the production, distribution, exchange and consumption of goods and services. Wherever we happen to live, work or play our daily existence requires us to make decisions that have an economic basis. Yet, we tend to take for granted the ways in which society determines how the scarce resources at its disposal are used to provide for its material needs and to produce wealth. The news media regularly cover the economy: the balance of trade, the unemployment rate, consumer spending, trends in house prices, the relocation of jobs to other countries, or the prospects for the global economy. Sections on business and the economy in the 'quality' daily newspapers, specialist weekly business publications, or 24-hour satellite television channels are exclusively devoted to news and information about economic affairs.

You may have noticed that 'economies' or 'economy' are often preceded by adjectives such as: global, local, market, command (or redistributive), capitalist, informal, subsistence, mixed, Internet, information, new, or space economy. There are clearly many different kinds of 'economy' depending on the starting point for analysis; for example, an informal economy signifies how it is organized while a digital economy signifies something about the medium used to undertake economic transactions. Economic geographers are interested in the space economy; the way in which the organization of geographical space reflects the behaviour, values, and actions of actors (individuals, firms, institutions) that comprise the economy. Each actor operates from or occupies some unit of space: a field for a crop, a room used by a self-employed person working from home, a building of several thousand square metres for a corporate call centre, a site of several hundred hectares used for vehicle production in Korea or Japan, or an area of hundreds of square kilometres occupied by a sheep station in the Australian outback. The households providing the labour required for producing goods and services also require space in which to live and are, in turn, a major source for consumption of the outputs from production that are accessed via informal and formal transactions and trading. The challenge for economic geographers is how to analyse and explain the geographical patterns of economic activity at different scales, how they change over time and the relationships between them.

14.1 The changing nature of economic geography

The uneven distribution of economic activities is plain enough to see. It can be explained by the fact that different parts of our planet are, for example, endowed with different resources, climates, or levels of accessibility. Thus the major sub-discipline of economic geography 'is concerned with the spatial organization and distribution of economic activity, the use of the world's resources, and the distribution and expansion of the world economy' (Stutz and de Souza 1998: 41). While the geographical distribution of economic activities is influenced by historical, political, social, and environmental factors the outcomes arise from **spatial interaction** in that it is not possible for all the actors in the economy to be located at one point in geographical space. During the early twentieth century economic geography was termed 'commercial geography': a largely factual compilation of the way in which different commodities were produced and exchanged around the world. Commercial geography sought, for example, to analyze the factors that affected where particular commodities such as coal or iron ore were produced. Gradually the emphasis shifted towards explaining observed variations in the location patterns of commodity production and trade with the transformation from commercial to economic geography consolidated when explanations for the location of economic activity were derived from neoclassical economics (Spotlight box 14.1). This is an early example of how economic geography has used ways of thinking and modes of analysis used by other disciplines, in this case economics, to inform its own agenda. Neoclassical economics is the study of the allocation of scarce resources amongst alternative ends when there are several alternative outcomes. Interestingly, one of these is the maximization of social welfare that is based on the idea that the economic basis of society determines the form of its social institutions. We will see later that the social basis of the economy is very much part of contemporary analyses of geographies of the economy.

In the meantime, economic geography as a sub-discipline has undergone various transformations since the mid twentieth century (see Scott 2004). During the 1950s and 1960s economic geographers led the way in the testing of theories and ideas, using numerically-based quantitative methods and modelling that were seen to be rigorous. However, by the 1970s a different political economy approach emerged within the sub-discipline that made extensive use of Marxist-based interpretations of economic change and its socio-economic consequences (Harvey 1982; Swyngedouw 1982). Analysis of economic crises such as the global oil shortage of 1973 or the debt crisis of the early 1980s focused on issues of regional inequality, manufacturing decline and social justice (Bluestone and Harrison 1982). In the 1980s the growth of political economic interests was also accompanied by empirical and theoretical analysis of some new and surprising economic growth in places previously regarded as peripheral or outside the mainstream. In Europe, for

Spotlight box 14.1

Models of economic location

There has been much interest in economic geography in theories or models that help to explain the development of economic activities within a spatial context. *Neoclassical economic theory* was first used by Von Thünen in 1826 (Hall 1966) to model patterns of agricultural land use and later applied to industrial location (Weber 1929) and for explaining the distribution of services and of settlements (Christaller 1966). In these and numerous other cases the objective is to generalize about patterns of economic activity. However, such is the complexity of the real world that it is necessary to make some assumptions: decision makers behave in a sensible (or rational) fashion; they possess complete and correct knowledge (often referred to as perfect knowledge); everyone is attempting to maximize profits; competition is unconstrained; economic activity takes place on a uniform land surface. The key assumption is that distance is the main influence on decision-making by households and businesses with the resulting spatial patterns of economic activity explained by examining the relationship between distance and transport costs. The outcome of this approach is an ideal or optimal pattern of land use or industrial location.

The main criticisms are the unrealistic nature of the assumptions and the oversight of many other factors that have an impact on the geography of economic activity such as changes in the technology of production and consumption or the variety of ways in which businesses are organized.

The limitations of neoclassical models encouraged the development of alternatives. The *behavioural model* also attempts to arrive at generalizations but the focus is shifted to the role of the individual as the principal explanation for spatial patterns. The motives, opinions, preferences and perceptions of the individuals making location decisions are incorporated

However, behavioural models have been criticized for being overly descriptive. In response, a *structuralist approach* makes use of a more holistic way to explain the location of economic activity and how it changes. It is based on the premise that behaviour is shaped or constrained by wider processes in the social, political and economic spheres. Notions of culture and of class rather than individual ideas determine the spatial structure of economic activity. It is not enough to explain patterns of economic activity; rather, it is necessary to examine the 'hidden' mechanisms or processes (e.g. social, political) that underpin economic patterns.

example, these included the proliferation of small-scale, skilled production units to form **new industrial districts** in north-east Italy, Emilia and central Italy collectively known as the Third Italy (Brusco 1990). Economic geographers also began to analyze the changing nature of manufacturing production in the world economy, particularly the rise of new flexible kinds of post-Fordist production systems (Amin 1994) in North America and Japan (Gertler 1992). This period witnessed a marked increase in the international division of labour, led by multinational corporations (Fröbel *et al.* 1980), which became but one of the trends symbolic of globalization and international economic interconnectedness. The way in which production processes, labour and transnational corporations were becoming increasingly caught up in complex **global production networks (GPNs)** became an increasingly central concern for economic geographers (Dicken 2015) and we will return to this theme later.

The 1990s saw two parallel developments that have diversified both the nature and disciplinary reach of economic geography. The first is the dramatic revival of quantitative and modelling approaches to economic

geography within another social science discipline – namely, economics. The Nobel Prize winning economist Paul Krugman advocated what became known as 'the **new economic geography**' (NEG) (Krugman 2000; Fujita and Krugman 2004). This provoked a response from geographers who have argued that NEG is really economic geography as opposed to 'geographical economics' (Martin 1999a). Economists claim that, methodologically, NEG belongs to them but economic geographers claim that economists have finally acknowledged the role of space (geography) and moved it from the edges of their discipline into the mainstream of economic theory; away from the 'wonderland of no dimensions' (Sheppard and Barnes 2000: 3). To avoid confusion, the rest of this chapter will use 'geographical economics' to refer to this strand within economics.

The second development is the impact on economic geography of the 'cultural turn' within human geography (Barnett 1998; Cook *et al.* 2000c). This 'new economic geography' as practised by human geographers increasingly recognized the importance of 'social' and 'cultural' factors when interpreting the 'economic world' (see Chapter 19 for a discussion of the links between culture and the consumption of goods and services). It is argued that lifestyles, beliefs, languages, ideas, imaginations and representations interact with the economic to produce culturalization of the economy rather than the economization of culture. For example, goods and services incorporate cultural attributes into their design, marketing, packaging and potential benefits to users. Material possession of a good (car, camera, smartphone) or consumption of a service (tourism, fast food, financial transaction) is only part of the experience (a real as well as an imagined event) of using or being seen to use or to consume. Consumption of goods and services involves beliefs about what it says about us as individuals or groups: social or job status, image or wealth (see Chapter 19). Economic geographers have previously recognized cultural factors when using terms such as 'socialist economy', 'Chinese family production networks', or the various 'corporate cultures' encountered in transnational corporations (TNCs); but only recently have they considered the economic and the cultural to be intertwined rather than worthy only of separate study.

We could conclude the overview of NEG here but it is worth loitering a little longer to consider some further issues. For example, is it too simplistic to talk of 'economic geography' rather than 'economic geographies'? If the economy is shaped, at least in part, by social relations (that are by their very nature complex) and exchanges that reflect multiple variations in the value associated with the production, consumption, or circulation of a good or service, then 'are the geographies constituted through peoples' struggle to construct circuits of value sustainable across space and time'? (Lee 2006: 417) As Lee points out, if societies cannot do this in ways that allow them to make a living they can only materially reproduce themselves with great difficulty. In this sense, there is more than one economic geography.

Another important issue is the way that the NEG has spawned new strands of work around a range of different concepts for understanding the spatial nature of the economy and economic activity. In the 1990s, for example, economic geographers developed an increasing interest in the (spatial) nature of relations between different economic actors (Bathelt and Glückler 2003). Yeung suggests that economic geography underwent something of a 'relational turn' that is 'concerned primarily with the ways in which socio-spatial relations of actors are intertwined with broader structures and processes of economic change at various geographical scales' (Yeung 2005: 37). Central to this shift is a realization that economic geographers need to better understand how power shapes economic action. Global production networks (GPNs) encapsulate many of these features (see Chapter 16 for a detailed discussion of their geographies). A second thread to the NEG has followed on from this, focusing broadly on the nature of economic practices and how their spatiality affects economies (Jones 2014). This sociological perspective in economic geography has also been concerned with the significance of power in relation, for example, to how transnational firms are managed or how knowledge practices spread innovations through firms and industries (Amin and Cohendet 2004). This is also related to a third strand of NEG that has looked beyond the boundaries of geography to work in economic sociology, cultural and technology studies as a way to develop what has been termed a 'cultural economy' approach (Amin and Thrift 2004). Economic geographers in this area have ranged into new industries and areas of the economy that have been previously ignored – notably creative sectors such as fashion design, music, or computer games software. The cultural economy approach has also brought a fresh perspective to the traditional concerns of the economic geographer, such as the growing body of work on financial and other kinds of markets that seeks to understand them as produced through the interactions between networks of social actors, their performances, power relations and technological devices (Berndt and Boeckler 2009).

Spotlight box 14.2

Perfect competition

The intensity of competition among firms encourages efficiency and helps to keep prices low. The ultimate expression of this is *perfect competition*. In these purely theoretical circumstances the actions of any one individual buyer or seller have a very limited impact on market prices. This is because everybody has access to all the information they need, all products are the same, and firms earn only the base minimum profit. If firms earn excess profits (more than the base minimum) other firms will enter the market. This will continue to happen until profits are driven down so that only normal profits are made.

NEG is therefore also about how to theorize economies, economic actors and their geographies. The scope that this provides for a healthy, on-going debate can be illustrated using a set of basic propositions that are assumed to be true when we conceptualize a capitalist economy (Hudson 2004). First, there should be a variety of concepts of a capitalist economy that reflect the diversity of the flows of people or knowledge, for example, in space and time that make up economies. Second, the concepts used should not be constructed on the basis that there are separate economies; rather, they should necessarily be treated as interrelated. Third, economic behaviour and practice is undertaken by individuals or subjects possessing knowledge and skills, although not in the sense that everyone has complete knowledge and skills, as in perfect competition (see Spotlight box 14.2). Therefore, and fourth, economies are a social construct incorporating the full range from the informal habits of individuals to the formal institutions of the state. Fifth, individual and collective behaviour in a capitalist economy is influenced by, and its structures and institutions based on, long-term social relationships. Finally, capitalist economies are reproduced using various governance institutions that exist because capitalist economies are formed via social relations and practices that are competitive and not natural.

You may recall from the beginning of this chapter that there are many different kinds of economy; the capitalist economy is but one among many and you should consider whether conceptualizations such as the one above are likely to be the same, or different, to those applied to an informal, alternative, digital, or knowledge economy?

14.2 What is the economic problem?

Each of us has a variety of needs and wants that, when they are combined, comprise demand for goods and services. The resources available to fulfil this demand are finite. The economic problem (Heilbronner 1972) is how to devise a system that combines the physical and human resources needed to produce and distribute the output of goods and services to attain given ends, such as the maximization of social welfare. Possible solutions are numerous but they can be distilled to just three mechanisms (Dicken and Lloyd 1990). The first of these is **tradition** in which the allocation of resources to production relies on a set of 'rules' based on convention or past practice, such as the handing down of land from father to eldest son. Given the contemporary interest in the relationship between the economic and the social, it is notable that traditional solutions to the economic problem incorporate socially determined norms.

A second mechanism for resolving the economic problem is a **command economy** in which a key objective is redistribution of wealth based on public ownership of the factors of production. Prior to its demise during the late 1980s countries such as the former Soviet Union, Poland, Hungary and East Germany used central political authority to prepare directives setting production targets for a defined period (say three or five years) for the types, and quantities of goods and services to be produced. In order to achieve the targets and to distribute the output the centralized direction of national economic development is combined with control over the allocation of human and physical resources. Some countries such as Cuba and North Korea continue to use this approach for solving the economic problem. Capitalist countries may use this mechanism during national emergencies (e.g. wartime) in order to mobilize resources quickly.

The market is the third approach to solving the economic problem. In contrast to command economies, market economies rely on decentralized decisions by consumers and by firms about the quantities of goods to produce, the prices to charge, and how, when and where exchange transactions take place. Generalizations about the modern market system and its outcomes are actually quite difficult because decentralized decision-making creates complexity; for example, professional economists can rarely agree about the significance of the latest unemployment figures, the impact of a change in bank interest rates, or the likely impact of a steep rise in crude oil prices on the stability of the global economy.

Economies that operate by voluntary exchange in a free market that is not in some way managed or controlled by a central authority do not in practice exist. Most developed nations are mixed economies in that they allow markets to drive most of their economic activities, using regulations and government intervention to ensure stability and efficient economic operation. Market/mixed economies are now in the majority, with fast emerging economies such as China making big strides in the same direction.

Within such **capitalist** economies most of the resources and the means of production are controlled by a relatively small proportion of individuals and firms who are seeking to improve their economic well being through competition (see Spotlight box 14.2). If we assume that there is more than one producer of a given good or service, each is seeking to create the most favourable value (such as lower price, better quality, superior design, or efficient after-sales support) so as to retain or enhance its share of the market.

The principle of freedom of action may be paramount but, in practice, market economies incorporate regulation by national governments and/or international

Spotlight box 14.3

Transnational corporations (TNCs)

The definition of a TNC is that it:

- controls establishments/economic activities in at least one other country apart from its home country;
- possesses an ability as a result of its size or the ownership of particular knowledge or skills to move its operations and its resources quickly between international locations, i.e. it is relatively footloose;
- can exploit or take advantage of differences between countries, regions or cities around the globe in factor (land, labour, capital) and non-factor (information, knowledge, regulation) endowments;
- owns and controls overseas activities, although this is not a prerequisite for TNC status since there are

many other ways, such as franchising, licensing or joint ventures, of achieving a presence in markets outside the home country;

- organizes aspects of its operation across national borders at the global-scale, rather than duplicating its activities in each national economy where it is present.

You may well encounter a related term: multinational corporation (MNC). This suggests a firm that has premises or production plants in several countries. TNC is therefore a much more all-embracing term than MNC; there are many more TNCs than there are MNCs and they provide the basis for a more realistic assessment of the scale of international investment.

institutions. In the interests of equity, society needs to control the behaviour of those who own the means of production; the market is not necessarily the most effective and equitable way to allocate its rewards. Thus, most countries have a national organization that monitors and adjudicates company acquisitions and **mergers** in an attempt to avoid the development of monopolies, i.e. a market situation in which there is only one provider of a particular product or service. The absence of economic competition will allow a monopoly to sell a lower quantity of a product at a higher price than firms in a purely competitive market, leading to monopolistic profits. Because of the increasing integration of national economies and firms (see later in this chapter), the actions of individual national governments are complemented by groupings of nation-states such as the North American Free Trade Area (NAFTA), Asia-Pacific Economic Cooperation (APEC) or international institutions such as the World Trade Organization (WTO) that regulate and facilitate trade flows of goods and services and the movement of labour.

One of the key targets for cross-border control and regulation are **transnational corporations** (TNCs) which serve markets and operate production plants or distribution facilities that extend well beyond their home countries (see Spotlight box 14.3) (see also Chapters 16 and 17). The distribution of TNCs varies by industry sector and by country; most are small relative to a limited number of very large global TNCs. But they generate significant flows of capital, knowledge, information, expertise, products, raw materials and components

amongst their own establishments and between countries. There are few parts of the world that are not in some way affected by the activities and decisions of TNCs and, for some countries, it makes the difference between inclusion as opposed to exclusion from the economic mainstream.

14.3 What are economies?

So far we have considered the economy in more or less abstract terms, although we have made reference to various 'actors' such as individuals, households, companies, government departments, national governments, and so on. In order to help economic geographers to measure and interpret the processes and interactions that help to shape spatial patterns of economic activity, it is necessary to simplify the complexities of real economies into manageable categories or groupings.

One of the most common approaches to generalizing the structure of economies is to divide them into four broad economic sectors:

1. Activities engaged in the exploitation of natural resources, such as agriculture, fishing, mining and oil extraction, form the **primary sector**. Although still a significant share of activity in the less developed economies, this sector is declining overall. Some of the output from the primary sector has limited use and value until it has been transformed in some way to become part of usable goods.

2. Whether the transformation takes place near the source of the primary commodity or after transfer to a location some distance away it requires a **secondary sector** (or manufacturing). This sector is still expanding in some less developed economies and the emerging economies but contracting (share of employment or **gross domestic product, GDP**) in most developed countries. The outputs from the manufacturing sector may be immediately suitable for final use by consumers, or they may be components for incorporation in other final products.

3. The outputs of the secondary sector require distribution to the places and markets where they can be assembled, consumed, or purchased (Plate 14.1). The **tertiary sector**, which includes wholesale and retail trade, transportation, entertainment and personal services, fulfils this role. Improvements in transport and telecommunications and their integration following major advances in computing technology since the early 1980s have transformed the operation and reach of firms in both the secondary and tertiary sector. The growth of international purchasing by firms and individuals via the Internet is symbolic of these changes.

4. A fourth, **quaternary**, sector has increasingly been identified as a separate grouping which includes banking, finance, business and professional services, the media, insurance, administration, education, and research and development. These intellectual services assemble, transmit and process the information, knowledge and expertise used by activities in the other three sectors to enable them to adjust effectively and efficiently to the changing geographic, economic, social and cultural parameters of doing business in

the twenty-first century. The share of the tertiary and quaternary sectors in the total economy has expanded steadily for at least a hundred years and they now account for four out five jobs in countries such as the USA, Canada, Britain, Hong Kong or Australia.

Another useful way for tracking change in economic structures is the distinction between white-collar and blue-collar occupations. The former are salaried professionals (such as doctors, lawyers or airline pilots) and employees engaged in clerical or administrative occupations performing tasks that are mentally rather than physically demanding. Blue-collar workers, on the other hand, tend to earn hourly wages for performing skilled or unskilled tasks in factories, construction, or technical installation work. An intermediate category, the pink-collar worker, is also sometimes used to distinguish women mainly engaged in white-collar occupations that do not require as much professional training or who perform tasks to which lower prestige is attached. In line with the increasing share of the tertiary and quaternary sectors, the proportion of white-collar workers has continued to grow in advanced Western economies and this shift has become increasingly evident in emerging economies during the twenty-first century.

14.4 A geographical approach to economic processes

One of the benefits of analyzing the structure of economies is that it enables economic geographers to measure the dynamics of change and whether, and how, it has impacts at different spatial scales. These dynamics occur at all levels of analysis: from small rural localities to the largest metropolitan areas, from peripheral to core regions, from least developed to most developed economies. This is not new or surprising but during the closing decades of the twentieth century it was dominated by changes that will shape the economic agenda well into the present century (such as more flexible production systems, see Chapter 16; or the changing nature of work, see Chapter 17).

As we have already noted, the share of country employment in the secondary sector has been declining steadily; by 2007 it directly supported only one in four jobs in the OECD countries (Table 14.1). The primary sector, already a very small part of the economy in developed countries, is contracting further as improved crop disease resistance and better fertilizers enhance farm productivity. Meanwhile, the tertiary and quaternary sectors have expanded and diversified as rising standards of living and disposable incomes have boosted demand

Plate 14.1 Global flows of goods rely heavily on containers shipped through specialized ports, such as Oakland in California, before being transferred to trucks for region- or nation-wide distribution.

(cdrin/Shutterstock)

Table 14.1 Distribution of employment, by sector (%), selected OECD countries, 2002 and 2012

Country	Agriculture 2012	2002	Change	Industry 2012	2002	Change	Tertiary 2012	2002	Change
Australia	3[1]	4	−1	21	21	0	761	75	1
Czech Republic	3	5	−2	38	40	−2	59	56	3
Germany	2	3	−1	28	32	−4	70	65	5
Greece	13	16	−3	17	23	−6	70	62	8
Japan	4[2]	5	−1	25[2]	30	−5	70[2]	62	8
Korea	7[2]	9	−2	17[2]	27	−6	76[2]	63	9
Poland	13	19	−6	30	29	1	57	52	5
Sweden	2	2	0	20	23	−3	78	75	3
United Kingdom	1	1	0	19	24	−5	79	75	4
United States	2[2]	3	−1	17[2]	22	−5	81[2]	76	5

Notes: Agriculture = hunting; forestry; fishing.

Industry = mining and quarrying; manufacturing; construction; and public utilities.

Tertiary = wholesale and retail trade and restaurants and hotels; transport, storage and communications; financing; insurance, real estate and business services; community, social and personnel services.

[1] 2009

[2] 2010

Source: World Bank, World Development Indicators at *http://data.worldbank.org/data-catalog/world-development-indicators* [accessed 4 January 2015]

for tourism, travel or private health services. The production of goods and services also now incorporates more knowledge-intensive services that are heavily weighted towards the employment of engineers and scientists (see Chapter 17). These activities are growing most rapidly in the newly industrialized countries such as China or Brazil that are 'catching up' with economies where services already provide more than 70 per cent of total employment (see Table 14.1).

There are numerous historical, political, social and institutional explanations for structural and functional changes in economies. However, from an economic geographers' perspective it is useful to think about the geographical nature of the processes of change that are occurring in the contemporary global space economy. At least five interconnected and overlapping processes are worth identifying when exploring how the world economy (and within that, individual national economies) is evolving in the twenty-first century:

- *Globalization* refers (in economic terms at least) to the integration across national boundaries of markets, finance, technologies and nation-states in a way not witnessed in the past. It has enabled nation-states, TNCs, as well as individuals, to extend their reach (markets, travel) across the globe faster, further, deeper and at lower cost than could ever have been imagined,

even ten years ago (Plate 14.2). Economic globalization, however, cannot be separated from the social, political and cultural context in which it is embedded which means it is not really 'a unified phenomenon', more a 'syndrome of processes and activities' (Dicken 2007: 8). We shall return to consider this in more depth shortly.

- *Informationalization* denotes the increasingly central role of information in production and consumption in the world economy. The sociologist Manuel Castells (2009) argues that we now live in an era of a global informational economy, where information (or knowledge) is the key input to economic activity whatever the industry. The rise of a whole range of new information and communications technologies (ICT) and the development of the Internet are, of course, key enablers of this process.

- *Neoliberalization* is used as a shorthand term to describe the spread of a complex set of political and policy trajectories that lead to greater liberalization of international trade and financial markets, reductions in government spending and a greater role in the economy for the private sector.

- *Tertiarization/quaternerization* is used to describe the on-going development of the global service economy. The proportion of GDP and employment in advanced economies in service-sector activities continues to rise,

Plate 14.2 Globalization has been accompanied by increasing geographical concentration of corporate control as symbolized by the density of office development and the skyline of Manhattan, New York City.
(T. Paul Daniels, Bromsgrove)

and this is now also happening in less developed economies (see Chapter 17).

- *Financialization* refers to the growing importance and centrality of financial capital in all geographical regions and industry sectors in the global economy; it is also used to describe the growing power of finance and financial logics (see Chapter 18).

These processes impact and affect different parts of the world economy in different ways, and with different consequences. They form, however, the basis for developing an understanding of why economic development is uneven at the global scale, and how it is likely to evolve. We now turn to consider in more depth how these processes have led to the emergence of an increasingly globalized world economy that requires analysis as an entity rather than as a collection of many smaller economies restricted to nation-states or regions.

14.5 The rise of a global economy

Earlier conceptions of globalization suggested a convergence of economic, social and cultural values across the localities, regions and nations that come together as the 'global economy'. However, as Dicken (2015) argues, whilst 'there are undoubtedly globalizing forces at work, we do not have a fully globalized world economy'. Globalization is 'reflected in' and 'influenced by multiple geographies, rather than a single global geography' (Dicken 2015: 7). As all the other chapters in this section of the book show, we should beware of regarding globalization as producing convergence or uniformity. Rather, 'globalization' is convenient shorthand for capturing ideas about an integrating global economy, but it should

not divert us from the reality that there are persistent variations in the levels of participation of different parts of the world (Figure 14.1).

Globalization may be far from smoothing economic inequalities but if we assume for the moment that 'every country may not feel part of the global[ization] system, but every country is being globalized and shaped by it' (see Friedman 1999, 2005), then what are the symptoms? The first is the pivotal role of *knowledge*. The informationalization of economies (Castells 2009) means that production processes themselves are dependent on knowledge as the key input that creates value. For manufactured goods, for example, it is the design, marketing and customer support experience that makes products successful and makes firms' profits. And because the creation and exchange of knowledge tends to be embodied in people (see also Chapter 17) rather than machines, national economic health relies more than ever on 'producing' an educated and skilled workforce.

Second, *technology has become transnationalized*, especially amongst knowledge-intensive economic activities such as financial services or information and communications technologies (ICT). This does not necessarily mean better access to the factors of production; the increased complexity of the opportunities created by advanced technology means that only those individuals, companies and institutions with the resources to manage high technology can really take advantage.

Third, *there has been a marked increase in the power and influence of finance* through a range of financialization processes. Finance capital now takes many forms and moves almost seamlessly and with great speed, especially between the world's stock, currency, commodity and futures exchanges located in 'global cities' such as Tokyo, New York, London and Hong Kong (see Chapter 18).

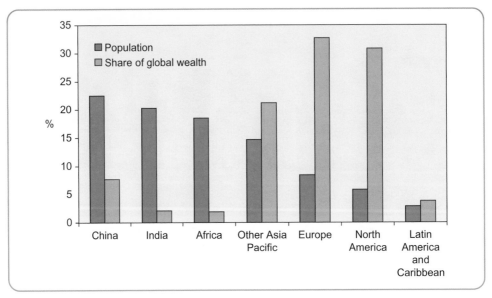

Figure 14.1 World population and wealth, by region (%), 2010.

Source: Extracted from World Bank Development Indicators data, *http://data.worldbank.org/indicator* [accessed 17 December 2014]

Electronic trading has ensured volatile and fast-changing financial markets that can transform the economic prospects of companies and, more importantly, of national or regional economies very quickly indeed. Equally, over the last couple of decades many new kinds of financial capital and financial firms have appeared replacing older and more traditional forms of finance for economic activity. This has not always been regarded as a positive development, however, with financialization processes seen by many within and beyond economic geography as creating greater instability and risk in an increasingly interdependent global economy (c.f. Harvey 2009).

The most recent example of this is, of course, the global financial crisis and economic downturn that began in 2007 and has led to an on-going period of low growth and global economic uncertainty. The recent recession was the deepest economic downturn in the world economy since the Second World War, and was transmitted initially through increasingly globalized financial markets. It began in the United States where banks and other financial firms got into trouble after developing new forms of finance around the housing industry. The financial industry sold on household mortgages as new kinds of financial 'debt' products (known as mortgage-backed securities) that were sold on in global financial markets. Banks across the globe bought these new products, and banks in other countries (the UK, for example) also sold their mortgage debt on in a similar fashion. This had had the effect of making mortgages cheap in countries like the USA and the UK, but when their economies began to slow, it became clear that

many of the original mortgage borrowers were unable to repay the loans. This triggered a financial crisis with many banks suddenly being exposed to huge losses, or even going bankrupt in the case of Lehman Brothers and Bear Stearns in the USA. In Europe, governments had to intervene to prevent even large banks like Halifax Bank of Scotland (HBOS) and former building societies like Northern Rock from going bust. The 'contagion' that this financial crisis triggered, and the subsequent economic recession, penetrated every corner of the world economy and demonstrates how finance has bound the world economy ever more closely together.

A fourth symptom of globalization is the emergence of *global oligopolies,* that is, markets dominated by a small number of suppliers of a product or service (Case study 14.1). For a market sector in which there are very few buyers the term *oligopsony* has been coined. This is the converse of an oligopoly; for example, just six companies in the USA own the majority of movie theatres so that a film distribution company has very few negotiating alternatives. A similar story exists in many industries; the majority of drugs are increasingly made by a diminishing number of very large pharmaceutical companies like GlaxoSmithKline and Pfizer, and in the airline industry, mergers continue apace with even large airlines like British Airways, American Airlines and Iberia seeking to merge. There is now a sense in which corporate and economic survival requires 'going global'. The fifth symptom of globalization is that the power of individual nations to regulate their own economic development or to exercise a strong influence on the outcome, for example, of trade

Case study 14.1

An oligopoly: Nestlé

Nestlé is a Swiss-based company founded in 1866 that is now the top-ranking food and beverage producer in the world with sales of over US$100 billion in 2007. It employs 265,000 and has factories and operations in almost every country in the world. Nestlé has achieved this position by acquiring other related companies and brands; in 2001 it purchased Ralston Purina, making it the leading pet food manufacturer in the world; it purchased the leading French bottled water producer (Perrier) in the late 1990s to become number one for that product, the UK chocolate maker Joseph Rowntree in 1998 (Kit Kat) and Novartis Pharmaceutical in 2007 (Ovaltine). It now owns eight further French waters including Vittel, as well as regional brands like Buxton in the UK, that are sold in 37 different countries in 2010. Nestlé is the leading producer of instant coffee (Nescafé was the first instant coffee on the market), and a major

manufacturer of sweets and chocolates, and has increased its dominance of the ice-cream sector by merging the Nestlé Ice Cream Company with the leading US company (Dreyers) in 2003. In addition to food products, Nestlé is involved in cosmetics (it has a large stake in L'Oréal), nutritional supplements and eye care. Its long-term strategy is to continue expanding worldwide, especially into emerging markets such as China, India, Latin America and Russia where, for example, in 2007 it invested US$120 million in a new coffee-processing plant.

Other oligopolies include Coca-Cola, Pepsico, Pearson, Interbrew and Gillette. For these leading oligopolies the key objective is to protect or to acquire world-class brands. There are currently some 40 consumer brands worldwide with sales in excess of one billion dollars annually (Coke, for example, sells over US$15 billion). The companies with these exceptional products are growing and expanding internationally at more than 10 per cent per annum.

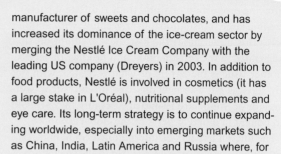

agreements has been diluted by *the rise of transnational institutions* such as the International Monetary Fund (IMF) or the World Trade Organization (WTO) that coordinate, steer and even regulate aspects of the world economy. Nation-states have also increasingly organized themselves into regional trading blocs to facilitate easier and greater volumes of trade. The **European Union (EU)** is one, but such regional economic arrangements have grown in importance in the last 20 years elsewhere. Examples include the North American Free Trade Agreement Area (NAFTA) and the Association of Southeast Asian Nations (ASEAN).

14.6 Global uneven development: the examples of trade and foreign direct investment

In light of the many processes of integration and interconnectedness in the world economy, it thus makes sense to talk of a 'global economy'. However, it is also important to realize that economic globalization has been and continues to be highly uneven. It produces a range of *global economic geographies* whether you are considering the complex spatial form of the global city networks that are key in controlling global economic operations, or new kinds of global labour markets that shape patterns

of employment and migration. In order to understand better the uneven consequences of the emergence of an increasingly globalized world economy, we consider, in this section, two aspects to this unevenness: trade and foreign direct investment.

14.6.1 Uneven trade

Trade in the world economy refers simply to the buying and selling of goods and services between actors in different localities. As the world economy has globalized, total trade has grown enormously but trade benefits some localities and not others depending on the nature of their economies. Whilst growth in total world trade stalled during the 2007–9 economic downturn, the long-term trend has been one of expansion. In 2013, world trade measured in terms of goods exports amounted to US$18.3 trillion, while exports of commercial services were worth US$4.7 trillion (WTO 2014b). Much of this trade at the level of nations is concentrated between the wealthier countries in the global economy, although in the last decade developing countries like China and India have experienced huge trade growth, with China's trade surplus becoming an increasing source of tension in international politics (see Section 14.9).

Globalization processes have made understanding the idea of trade increasingly difficult, however. Conventionally, trade was measured at the national level with nation-states counting how many goods and services they exported and imported. However, globalization processes have complicated this in a number of ways. For one thing, a growing proportion of world trade is different parts of the same large transnational firm 'trading' with another part – this undermines the historical assumption that trade ended in the consumption of a product or service. Another issue is the nature of what is traded, with not only services but also new digitized products (e.g. software, music, film) hard to measure because they are sold and bought in different parts of the global economy.

The uneven impacts of international trade in certain markets have over several decades led to the emergence of a growing civil society movement to promote 'fair trade' amongst, in particular, the rich countries of the global North and developing countries of the global South. The argument is that the power of oligopolies in the global economy has forced down prices for basic commodities such as tea, coffee, sugar, cocoa and cotton that are often produced in poorer countries with the result that the producers (often small farmers) are penalized by low prices. Fair trade initiatives and campaigns for 'trade justice' thus seek to create a range of market-based mechanism to deliver better terms of trade to producers in low-income countries (see Spotlight box 14.4) (see also Chapter 16).

We can illustrate the growth and development of world trade in the contemporary global economy with the example of the worlds' largest industry – namely, tourism. The United Nations World Tourism Organization (UNWTO) divided country arrivals in 2013 into leisure, recreation holidays (568 million), business travel (152 million), and visiting friends and relatives, religious purposes, health treatment and so on (367 million). Apart from demand for land, air and sea transport services, such large-scale flows also represent tourism receipts at a large number of destinations. Whether travelling on business or for leisure, visitors spend on accommodation, food and drink, local transport, shopping, entertainment and so on. In many cases this trade in tourism creates much-needed employment and other economic development opportunities, often in those less developed regions that have been largely bypassed by some of the other symbols of participation in the global space of flows (Table 14.2). Tourist destinations such as the Caribbean islands, Thailand, Bali, the Maldives or Fiji are benefiting from **comparative advantage** (Spotlight box 14.5) as well as the concept of **competitive advantage**, which is the advantage that a country or a business has over its competitors because of the quality or superiority of its products or services which will persuade other countries or customers to buy from it rather than from competitors (Porter 1990). The latter is a more useful way of explaining how individual nations participate in the international tourist market in that it incorporates differences in values, cultures, histories and institutions as well as variations in endowments of the factors of production that make some tourist destinations more appealing than others.

Spotlight box 14.4

Fair trade?

The idea of fair trade has its root in the 1940s and 1950s, but it was in the 1960s that a number of non-governmental organizations based in developed countries began to argue that the rise of large multinational firms and free market capitalism was not necessarily beneficial for the poorest people in the world, most of whom lived in the global South and worked in agriculture. MNCs (now TNCs), along with the tendency for oligopolies to form in many industries, meant that small farmers and commodity producers in poor countries received a very low price for their goods. The fair trade movement thus developed with the goal of rebalancing these trading relations and giving poor producers in developing countries a fair price for their products and produce. The fair trade movement started with fairly priced 'handicraft goods' in the 1960s, but by the 1980s the emphasis had shifted to commodities like coffee, cocoa, sugar and cotton.

In 1998, four organizations (Fair Trade Labelling International, the International World Fair Trade Association, the Network of European Workshops and the European Fair Trade Association) that had all been set up to achieve a more equitable trading system for producers in developing countries formed an organization called 'FINE' with the aim of together promoting fair trade in a coherent way. FINE produced a common definition of fair trade as 'a trading partnership, based on dialogue, transparency and respect, that seeks greater equity in international trade' and also which contributes 'to sustainable development'.

Fair trade products have now achieved more market penetration in richer countries than at any point previously with, for example, major supermarket chains like Tesco and coffee retailers like Starbucks selling fair trade products.

Table 14.2 International tourist arrivals and receipts, world regions 1990 and 2013

Region	International tourist arrivals (million)			Tourist receipts (US$ billion)	
	1990	2013	Share (%)	2013	Share (%)
Europe	266	563	51.8	489	42.2
Asia and the Pacific	56	248	22.8	359	31
Americas	93	168	15.5	229	19.8
Africa	15	56	5.1	34	3
Middle East	10	52	4.7	47	4.1
World	439	1,087	100.0	1,159	100.0

Source: United Nations World Tourism Organization (2014) *World Tourism Highlights, 2014 Edition,* UNWTO, Madrid

Spotlight box 14.5

Comparative advantage

Comparative advantage explains the tendency for countries (or regions/localities within countries) to specialize in certain goods and/or services even if they have the ability to fulfil their needs from domestic production. As long as countries or regions specialize in those products and/or services in which they have comparative advantage, they will gain from trade. Advantages can stem from spatial variations in, for example, mineral or land resource endowments, from variations in the educational levels of the labour force, in access to markets, or differences in levels of technology. For comparative advantage to work effectively it is necessary to assume a system of free trade, hence the significance of the trade liberalization that has been high on the agenda

of many countries since the 1980s. There is a nagging concern, however, that comparative advantage is not reflected in actual patterns of world trade. We would expect the biggest flows to be between the countries with the largest cost differences. It seems that consumer tastes and geographical proximity are actually more important than cost differences. This explains the fact that the vast majority of trade is between countries with relatively small cost differences, often involves similar rather than different goods (such as cars, electrical goods of all kinds, certain kinds of business services such as management consulting),and occurs on a 'nearest neighbour' basis. Well over half of EU goods and services trade takes place between the member states while Canada and Mexico are the major trading partners of the USA.

14.6.2 Foreign direct investment

Another indicator of the integration of the global economy is *foreign direct investment* (FDI). In the context of our example of tourism, the development of many international tourist destinations relies on FDI, which is defined as the acquisition by an individual or enterprise resident in one country of assets (such as hotels, restaurants and clubs) located in another. World FDI inflows and outflows for developed and developing economies fluctuate from year to year in line with the performance of world, regional or individual national economies (Table 14.3). Overall, flows have been increasing in real terms since 1990, with the developed economies generating outflows of FDI in excess of US$935 billion in 2010, or just over 75 per cent of the world total. FDI fluctuates year on year and is particularly vulnerable to economic

shocks such as the global economic crisis between 2007 and 2010; outflows from the developed economies exceeded US$1.1 trillion a year prior to 2007 but had fallen back by 2010. An earlier slowdown of the world economy in 2000–1 caused a decline in corporate cross-border mergers and acquisitions (M&As) which make up a large part of FDI activity, but by 2006 M&A activity once again reached a record high with deals worth US$4 billion before a significant decline again in the 2008–10 period (OECD 2009). FDI between developed countries is more important than FDI into developing countries. However, some of the biggest inflows in recent years, although still a relatively small proportion of the total, have been recorded by the newly emerging economies of Central and Eastern Europe and by the BRICS (Brazil, Russia, India, China and South Africa).

Table 14.3 FDI inflows and outflows, developed and developing economies, 1990–2010

$US (million)		1990	2000	2010
Developed economies	Inflows	172,516	1,138,040	601,906
	Outflows	229,584	1,094,728	935,190
	Balance (I-O)	−57,068	43,312	−333,284
Developing economies	Inflows	34,868	257,617	573,568
	Outflows	11,914	134,914	327,564
	Balance (I-O)	23,054	122,703	246,004
World	Inflows	207,455	1,402,680	1,243,671
	Outflows	241,498	1,232,117	1,323,337

Note: FDI inflows and outflows comprise capital provided (either directly or through other related enterprises) by a foreign direct investor to an FDI enterprise, or capital received by a foreign direct investor from an FDI enterprise. FDI includes the following components: equity capital, reinvested earnings and intra-company loans.

Source: United Nations Conference on Trade and Development (UNCTAD) Major FDI Indicators (extract from table at http://unctad.org/sections/dite.dir/docs/WIR11_web%20tab%202.pdf [accessed 8 January 2015])

TNCs contribute significantly to FDI activity. Although the number and size of developing country TNCs is now increasing, most FDI inflows result from the activities of developed country TNCs and over 60 per cent of their investments are made in other developed economies. Outflows from developing and transition economies (particularly BRICS) are now increasing as TNCs from these countries evolve into major regional and even global players. For those countries able to attract it, FDI helps to secure access to capital, technologies and organizational expertise. The net effect is modernization of infrastructure, an increase in industrial capability and an improvement in the quality and breadth of much-needed financial, business and professional services. China, a vast potential market comprising more than one-fifth of the world's population, was closed to FDI until the mid-1980s but is now one of the leading recipients. Prior to an economic downturn during the late 1990s, almost two-thirds of the FDI flows to developing countries went to Asia (excluding Japan). These flows to Asia have subsequently recovered, but whilst there has been some increase in the last decade, much of the African continent continues to be bypassed for any form of FDI, even though many of its countries are resource-rich. With the exception of South Africa and a few West African countries such as Nigeria which have seen some growth (UNCTAD 2009), consumer-purchasing power is low and average incomes per capita are at best growing slowly and not in a way that will raise the consumption of major consumer goods to a level that justifies the investment attention of most TNCs.

To summarize, the globalization of economies has strengthened the role of market forces while, as a result of advances in telecommunications and transportation technology, it has eased some of the constraints on interaction imposed by space and time. With the real cost of international telecommunications declining steadily over the past 25 years, global financial integration has strengthened and has been accompanied by diversified opportunities for new kinds of international trade, especially in services, and enabled easier transfer of the technology and innovation that encourages economic development and participation. The importance of non-government organizations, TNCs, and regional trading blocs such as the European Union, ASEAN and NAFTA for shaping the economic geography of globalization has also been greatly enhanced and will continue to increase.

14.7 Places and localities in an uneven global economy

While the geography of economies accommodates a global dimension, this is not at the expense of individual localities. Indeed 'it is the combination of national and intensely local conditions that fosters competitive advantage' (Porter 1990: 158). Localities are subdivisions within nations, such as cities or regions or places that often have a particular economic identity because of the kinds of activities that take place there. Rural districts or subdivisions that specialize in the production of very particular kinds of wine (Bordeaux region, France), dairy products (Jutland region, Denmark) or woollen goods (Wales), for example, are also included. Many are identified as named territorial units while others are industrial districts or agglomerations whose identities are derived from specific economic activities, such as Motorsport Valley (Pinch and Henry 1999) in southern England, Silicon Valley in California or the light industrial districts of the Third Italy. Although these are often highly specialized and self-contained localities with systems of governance and regulation that fit their particular needs, they are inextricably linked with the wider national and global economic system.

These local economies and 'industrial clusters' thrive on the dynamism, innovation and 'untraded interdependencies' (knowledge and information that circulates through the transfer of key workers between firms or via social and other networks) that are made possible by proximity. Even TNCs, that are now often portrayed as being 'placeless' because their operations are so extensive and relatively mobile, started from businesses that were nurtured in a particular locality with its own economic and other characteristics to such an extent that the locally shaped attributes of such firms are carried through into their organization and transformation into TNCs (Dicken 2015). Economic geographers have, for example, sought to understand how the proximity of firms in clusters produces 'regional innovation systems' where the concentration of firms or sectors into one locality is argued to be instrumental in producing competitive success through innovation in the global economy (Asheim *et al.* 2007).

An outstanding example of the synergy between local and global processes is the City of London. This one-square-mile (259 hectares) district and the areas that fringe it in central London provided employment for 392,000 workers in 2013 (Department of the Built Environment 2014). The special characteristic of the City in particular is that the majority of its business activities are knowledge-intensive services. These include commercial banks and insurance companies, international banks, sophisticated private and corporate banking, firms operating in the foreign exchange, securities, commodities, shipping and derivatives markets, fund management, corporate finance, professional advisory services (legal, accountancy) that are associated with the City's financial-services complex, as well as advertising firms and other highly specialized activities. Furthermore, a large proportion of these activities are owned or managed by non-UK enterprises to such an extent that it is sometimes said that the City has stronger links with Europe and the rest of the world than it has with the rest of the United Kingdom. In 2013 more than 41 per cent of all global foreign exchange trading was undertaken in London; it was the second largest global centre for legal services, and in 2009 it handled 45 per cent of the total global market turnover in company equities (shares) that took place in exchanges other than the companies' domestic (or home market) exchanges.

These are just a few of the indicators of the unique localization of highly dynamic entrepreneurial, innovative and international economic activities in one very small space. There is clearly something about the environment in such localities that facilitates their competitiveness. For the City of London local factors such as high quality professional and support services, a skilled and diversified labour force, a focus on leading soft and hard infrastructure, and a consistent, politically neutral legal system that is widely used and understood globally help to place the City ahead of its global competitors (Tokyo, New York, Frankfurt) (TheCityUK 2014) (see also Table 14.4). It is not just about economic advantages; quality of life, cosmopolitan cultures, linguistic diversity, and a fair and just business environment are some of the social/cultural factors that also help us to understand how such localities work. On the basis of its prominent international status, firms operating from the City of London are able to attract the most skilled foreign workers who meet its needs both for highly educated staff offering very specialized knowledge as well as for more routine occupations in hotels and catering, transport services, or office servicing.

It has been argued that increased localization and agglomeration effects are thus a crucial converse outcome of wider globalization. Whilst London (and not just the City of London) is a leading example, research on global cities more widely suggests that to some extent all of them are experiencing similar trends and that economic success in localities is increasingly affected by the complex mixture of place-based factors. National governments have responded to these ideas with policies aimed at giving localities greater autonomy over the institutions and instruments that they put in place, using the insights gained from detailed knowledge of local networks, to capitalize on their economic advantages or to create economic and social environments that will attract new investment. One very influential idea is that the economic success of cities and other localities is increasingly dependent on skilled knowledge workers who undertake (in a broad way) the creative aspects of economic activity in the global information economy (Florida 2002). Attracting this new 'creative class' has been argued to be a crucial component of any policies introduced by local government or other institutions that are seeking to develop strategies for strengthening regional economic development (see Spotlight box 14.6).

Table 14.4 Rank of top ten financial centres by factors of competitiveness, 2013

Rank	Human capital	Business environment	Financial sector development	Infrastructure	Reputational factors
1	London (–)	London (–)	London (–)	London (–)	London (–)
2	New York (–)	New York (–)	New York (–)	New York (–)	New York (–)
3	Hong Kong (–)	Hong Kong (–)	Hong Kong (–)	Hong Kong (–)	Hong Kong (–)
4	Singapore (–)	Singapore (–)	Singapore (–)	Singapore (–)	Singapore (–)
5	Tokyo (+1)	Zurich (–)	Tokyo (+3)	Tokyo (+1)	Tokyo (+2)
6	Zurich (–1)	Tokyo (+2)	Zurich (–1)	Zurich (–1)	Zurich (–1)
7	Boston (–)	Geneva (–1)	Boston (–)	Boston (–1)	Boston (–1)
8	Geneva (–)	Boston (–1)	Seoul (+7)	Geneva (–)	Geneva (–)
9	Frankfurt (–)	Chicago (+1)	Geneva (–3)	Washington DC (+5)	Toronto (+4)
10	Chicago (+2)	Frankfurt (–1)	Chicago (+1)	Chicago (+1)	Chicago (+1)

Note: () denotes change in rank since GFC13; (–) denotes 'no change'.

Source: Yeandle and Davies (2013), Table 11, p. 35.

Spotlight box 14.6

The importance of a 'new creative class' in today's global economy

The American social scientist, Richard Florida, suggested the idea of a new creative class in his book *The Rise of the Creative Class* published in 2002. Florida's initial concern is the role in the US economy of what he identifies as a new class of creative workers that comprises some 40 million people (about a third of the workforce). Using the standard occupational classification, Florida divides this creative class into three groups, the two major ones are the 'super-creative core', which covers a wide range of occupations (science, engineering, education, computer programmers, research, arts, design) that creates products and consumer goods, and the 'creative professionals', who are essentially more conventional knowledge-based workers in finance, legal services, healthcare and education. A third, much smaller, group comprises the bohemians, including artists, writers and

dramatists. The key argument Florida makes is that it is these segments of the workforce that are the major drivers of growth in today's global economy, and American (and hence other) cities and regions need to focus on attracting and supporting these groups.

The concept of the creative class has had enormous influence amongst policy practitioners beyond the USA since it was proposed, but it is not uncontroversial. Economic geographers (amongst others) have been critical of the idea in a range of ways, including the view that the concept has no causal mechanism (it is more about description than about any process) (Peck 2005) or that empirical research has found little sense of identity amongst those people supposedly in these groups, with membership being based more on educational achievement than any measure of creativity (Markusen 2006). However, workers that could be classified in this way are an increasing feature worldwide, including in emerging economies across Asia and South America in particular.

14.8 The rise of a new global digital economy?

In many respects the interaction between localities and the global economy is shaped by the so-called digital economy. It is estimated that there were three billion Internet users worldwide (almost 43 per cent of the total

population) at the end of 2014 (ITU 2014), up from two billion in 2010 (Table 14.5). E-commerce was already expanding at the end of the 1990s but it is now growing and diversifying even more rapidly, led by business-to-business (B2B) and business-to-customer (B2C) transactions by service sector activities such as telecommunications, information technology, publishing and the media, travel and tourism, retailing, transportation and professional services like management consultancy, industrial design and engineering. Although consumer sales attract the publicity (such as the phenomenal growth of eBay or Amazon), much of the expansion of e-commerce is between and within businesses. Global B2C sales topped US$1 trillion for the first time in 2012 with the USA alone accounting for US$365 billion but are dwarfed by B2B transactions estimated at US$.7 trillion by 2020, led by Chinese firm Alibaba accounting for twice the combined ecommerce transactions of Amazon and eBay. The potential for growth in direct cross-border sales to consumers is substantial as Internet access (see Table 14.5), user confidence, payment systems, Internet/Web security, and mechanisms for tracking transactions for levying taxes and duties, continue to improve. Furthermore, the development of new so-called 'Web 2.0' technologies have again transformed the nature of Internet usage itself, with the rise of 'real-time' streamed data and increased storage capacity online. Social networking businesses such as Facebook offer new but still underdeveloped e-commerce opportunities, and the rapid proliferation of mobile web devices (Apple's iPhone, for example) means that online commerce is a rapidly changing sector both in terms of hardware and software (see Case study 14.2).

Apart from the numerous legal, regulatory, security and other challenges it presents, the global digital economy is likely to be accompanied by new geographies of the economy. Just as the Industrial Revolution generated significant economic and social changes (both positive and negative) in the form of new jobs, new industries and new industrial regions, so will the digital economy stimulate its own revolution. Perhaps the Internet will finally

eliminate the effects of friction of distance on economic interactions. But this will require a truly global network of telecommunications and computer infrastructure that is accessible to all, and increasingly it seems likely that the unevenness persistent in the material economy will be a feature of the digital one too. As the data in Table 14.5 show, some national economies are yet to be 'plugged in' to the Internet. To be excluded is to widen the gap that already exists between those countries 'inside' and those 'outside' the global digital economy. A networked readiness index (Figure 14.2) reveals wide differences in the geographical distribution (number, density and processing power, for example) of the computers, telecommunications networks and software required to participate in the global economy. However, Africa's digital economy deficit may be rectified much more rapidly than expected with the expansion of cellular (mobile) telephony. Cell phones not only offer voice services but also technologies that bypass the need for a computer to access the World Wide Web so that as early as 2001 Africa was the first world region where the number of mobile subscribers exceeded the number of fixed-line subscribers. Access to mobile phones opens up all kinds of economic and social benefits such as better access to information about crop prices, guidance and support from government institutions on how to run small businesses, accessing bank services without the need to travel (including money transfers), or keeping in touch with family and friends.

A second challenge posed by the digital economy is the demand for human resources. More jobs will be created by the digital economy than will be lost but they are generally in higher-skilled and better-paid occupations. In order to fill new digital-economy jobs, economies

Table 14.5 Internet usage, by world region, 2014

Region	Internet usage (000s)[1]	Penetration (% of total population)	Usage (% of world)	Population 2014 (% of world)	Usage growth 2000–14 (%)
Africa	297,886	26.5	9.8	15.6	6,499
Asia	1,386,188	34.7	45.7	55.6	1,113
Europe	582,441	70.5	19.2	11.5	454
Middle East	111,180	48.3	3.7	3.2	3,304
North America	310,322	87.7	10.2	4.9	187
Latin America/Caribbean	320,313	52.3	10.5	8.5	1,673
Oceania/Australia	26,790	72.9	0.9	0.5	252
World total	3,035,749	42.3	100.0	100.0	741

[1] 6 June 2014

Source: International Telecommunications Union (2014), *www.internetworldstats.com/stats.htm* [accessed 12 December 2014]

Case study 14.2

Facebook versus Google?

One of the most dramatic developments in the global economy since the turn of the century is the continued rise of new media and web industries. During the late 1990s, the so-called 'tech boom' led to the rapid rise (and equally rapid demise) of many new firms in web-based software whose success was built on the emergence of e-commerce and new software for the World Wide Web that had increasing technical capacity. However, since the turn of the century, this new era of 'Web 2.0' has produced another phase comprising a mixture of new and existing firms enjoying meteoric success. No companies exemplify this more than California-based rivals Facebook and Google.

Founded in 1998 by two Stanford PhD students, Larry Page and Sergey Brin, Google is a software company that has become the dominant web search engine. Now based in California's Silicon Valley, and at more than a decade old in today's digital economy, it is a long-standing player. Google has developed its business beyond web-search into online advertising, and perhaps most importantly a range of software products that include the Android operating system for third-generation cellphones. In this latter area it competes with Apple, but it is in the lucrative area of online web advertising where Google makes most of its money, it also competes with a relative newcomer, Facebook. Famously founded by Mark Zuckerburg in his Harvard dormitory in 2004, Facebook has grown spectacularly and had overtaken Google in terms of visitors to its website by mid-2010. Facebook's product is of course its social networking software that is based on Web 2.0 technology, giving users a personal profile they manage themselves. In May 2012, Facebook listed on the stock exchange at a value of US$104 billion, still the largest recorded value of any public listed company. By June 2014 it had 1.3 billion active users worldwide.

The very rapid growth of companies like Google and Facebook reflects the global penetration of the Internet in the contemporary global economy, and the potentially vast commercial revenues that new forms of web advertising and product sales may generate. The ongoing challenge for both companies is how to generate commercially viable business models in a digital world where technology moves at break-neck speed, and new competitors seek to break-in with new innovations almost continuously.

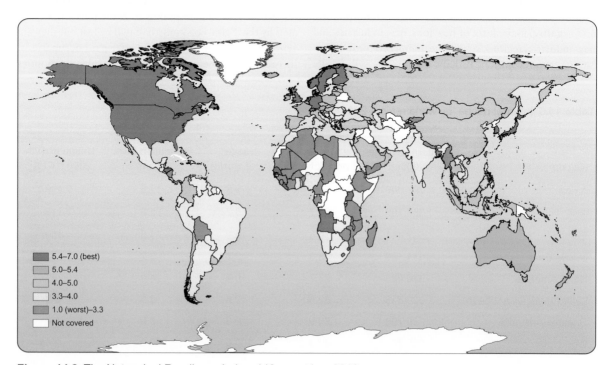

Figure 14.2 The Networked Readiness Index, 148 countries, 2013.

Source: compiled from data at: *www3.weforum.org/docs/GITR/2014/GITR_OverallRanking_2014.pdf* [accessed 12 December 2014]

everywhere need to retrain existing workforces and to train future workers. History suggests that the response to this challenge will be uneven; comparative advantage will enable some economies and some localities to respond more quickly and effectively than others. Perhaps less certain is how this will modify existing spatial patterns of economic development. A digital economy, for example, enables a wide range of purchasing and banking transactions to be undertaken from home via the telephone, laptop computers, televisions, or on the move using mobile phones that provide access to Internet services. An international door-to-door delivery time of 24 hours or much less is now commonplace, depending on the type of good or service, whether it is required just in time, or the location of the supplier. Moreover, cross-border transactions and payments are as easy as those made to the local supermarket or bookstore. With shopping sites on the Internet presenting themselves as 'virtual malls' and encouraging users to place their selections in 'baskets' or 'carts', they are attempting to replicate offline retail outlets. More than 75 per cent of Internet users shopped online for books, travel, banking and a wide range of goods in the USA and 85 per cent in Australia and New Zealand in 2013. This, combined with trends such as increased working from home or teleworking, whether self-employed or as an employee of a TNC, points to the potential for significant changes.

The challenge for economic geographers is how to understand the ways in which the digital economy impacts on the structure and pattern of economic activities at different scales, on the structure of localities and their relationship with the global economy, or on the relative importance of nations and TNCs in regulating or influencing the outcome.

14.9 Global re-balancing: the eastward shift

We end our overview of the geographies of economy with a consideration of probably the most pressing question that economic geographers can address in the first half of the twenty-first century: the re-balancing of the geography of the global economy away from the historical pattern of economic activity that has long been dominated by North America and Europe. In short, the key issue is the progressive 'shift eastwards' in terms of the centre of gravity for growth and output in the global economy.

Whilst there has been a longstanding trend since the 1980s for significant growth in the formerly 'less developed' economies of Asia, since the turn of the century

this has become much more pronounced. China's rate of economic growth since 1995 has rarely fallen below 5 per cent per annum. Despite the economic crisis during the late 1990s other Asian economies have also enjoyed sustained growth during the first 15 years, surpassing the growth rates of the traditional developed countries in Europe and North America. Equally important to the 're-balancing' of the global economy towards the East, is the geographically uneven impact of the global economic downturn of 2007–10. Whilst the formerly wealthiest industrialized economies of the G7 (USA, UK, Canada, France, Germany, Japan and Italy) in the global North suffered declines in GDP of up to 9 per cent from their 2006/7 peaks, economies in Asia suffered far less with a much more short-lived recession (and in some cases continued positive growth).

The result is a dramatic transformation that by 2010 had reached a critical turning point whereby the G7 no longer account for the lion's share of global GDP. In the period between 2000 and 2010, the share of global GDP accounted for by the G7 countries declined from 72 per cent to 53 per cent (IMF estimate for 2011). In 2013, the economy of countries like the UK struggled to breach 0.5 per cent. Compare this to the Chinese government's attempts to manage a much higher growth rate of 7.7 per cent in 2013 that continues a trend that makes it the globe's second-largest economy after the USA. China's economic power has thus not only increased over the last decade, but has even eclipsed almost all the formerly 'rich' countries of the G7. Whilst, because of its enormous population, GDP per capita still places it as an upper middle-income

Plate 14.3 The demolition of older dwellings to makes way for numerous new high-rise residential areas is a major feature of the rapid economic transformation of cities across China such as Chongqing, Guangzhou or Shanghai.

(Pyty/Shutterstock)

rather than a high-income country, China is no longer accurately described as a developing economy; many parts of its coastal regions are highly developed even if large areas of its inland provinces remain poor and agricultural. To a lesser extent, as there remains considerable poverty in many areas, a similar transformation has also been occurring in India around the key metropolitan centres of Delhi, Mumbai and Bangalore. With annual GDP growth ranging between 3.5–7 per cent between 2004 and 2014, India's rapid economic growth has also led to the emergence of a new middle class (some 24 per cent of the population in 2010) with rising incomes and increasingly employed in the tertiary sector.

Furthermore, annual growth rates across the globe seem set to continue this re-balancing beyond just Asia. Increasingly economic geographers have become interested in other growth nodes in the former south. A new focus has been the so-called BRICS (Brazil, Russia, India, China, South Africa) economies, but transformations are also evident in other parts of the global South – in Tanzania (east Africa), or in small but increasingly prosperous Costa Rica and Panama in Central America. While it may not be pertinent at present to refer to an eastward shift in terms of GDP, there are signs that the general rebalancing away from the global North comprises a complex pattern of haves and have-nots.

The implications of this shift in economic power for understanding the economic geography of the global economy are enormous. It seems likely that Asian economies will continue to grow more strongly than many economies of the global North over the next decade, and political unrest notwithstanding in central Asia and Russia, the trajectory of the BRICS economies appears one of continued significant growth in the coming decades. Moreover, historic divisions between the nature of the economies in the global north and south are also eroding as tertiary and quaternary industries take hold to at least some extent in many economies of the global South. The questions that face economic geographers are no longer therefore so much about the impact of developing economies that become more developed, but rather about the effects of a fundamental further geographical shift in the centre of gravity of the global economy away from the advanced industrial economies of the West.

Learning outcomes

Having read this chapter, you should be aware of:

- The nature and changing concerns of economic geography as a sub-discipline.
- The importance of economic restructuring and the shift from manufacturing to services in the contemporary economy.
- The significance of globalization processes in the structure and spatial development of the world economy.
- The major role performed by transnational corporations in trade, foreign direct investment and other indices of globalization.
- The challenges posed to economic geographers by the rapid growth of the global informational economy and its potential for changing established patterns of economic activity.

Further reading

Dicken, P. (2015) *Global Shift: Mapping the Changing Contours of the World Economy,* 7th edition, Sage, London. A broad-ranging overview of the evolution of internationalization and the globalization of economic activities. Focuses on the complex interaction between transnational corporations, global production networks (GPNs), nation-states and the rapid developments in information and communications technology, drawing on fields outside geography such as political science and economics.

Knox, P., Agnew, J. and McCarthy, L. (2014) *The Geography of the World Economy: An Introduction to Economic Geography,* 6th edition, Taylor and Francis, London. A synthesis of the factors shaping the development of contemporary economic patterns in market-oriented and centrally planned economies. Strong emphasis on interdependence of economic development at different spatial scales, from local through national to international.

Mackinnon, D. and Cumbers, A. (2011) *Introduction to Economic Geography: Uneven Development, Globalization and Place,* 2nd edition Pearson, London. Explores the wide range of approaches and models that are debated about and used by economic geographers. Focuses on globalization, uneven development and place. Covers more conventional topics such as regional development and labour markets alongside an introduction to economic topics that are subject to rapid change such as consumption, information and communications technologies and tourist geographies.

Murray, W.E. and Overton, J. (2014) *Geographies of Globalization,* 2nd edition, Routledge, London. An eminently readable exploration of the idea that as globalization marches on, geography and its core principles matter more than ever for understanding the process, its challenges, and its impacts on places from the local to the global scale.

Useful websites

www.ilo.org/global/lang-en/index.htm   International Labour Organization. Provides documents and statistics on a wide variety of employment and labour market issues for individual countries and on a comparative basis for countries around the world.

www.un.org   United Nations. Reflects the wide-ranging responsibilities of the United Nations but includes a useful section on global economic and social development, including an annual report on trends and issues in the world economy. Links to other websites.

www.wto.org   World Trade Organization. Offers a wide range of documentation and statistical material about global trends in trade in goods and services, regional aspects of trade, electronic commerce and background research and analysis on all aspects of world trade. Links to related websites.

www.ec.europa.eu/index_en.htm   The European Commission. Readers of this chapter will find the links to the various Directorates-General (DGs) sites within the Commission (Industry, Transport, etc.) useful starting points for monitoring economic development patterns, problems and policies across the European Union.

www.oecd.org   Organization for Economic Cooperation and Development. Represents mainly the developed economies and provides free documents, summaries of OECD economic surveys and statistics.

www.unctad.org/en/Pages/Home.aspx   United Nations Conference on Trade and Development. Focuses in particular on the interests of less developed countries in relation to international trade and foreign direct investment. Publications, statistics and links to related websites.

www.weforum.org   World Economic Forum. Brings together political, business, academic and other leaders in collaborative activities to shape global, regional and industry agendas. Identifies challenges, solutions and actions, supported with reports and statistics that are a valuable resource for economic geographers.

GEOGRAPHIES OF FOOD PRODUCTION

Chapter 15

Damian Maye

Topics covered

- Thinking about food

- Geographies of food production and global supply

- Alternative geographies of food

- Food security

- The ethical foodscape

15.1 Thinking about food

This chapter introduces some debates about the changing nature of food provision and presents ideas and case studies to prompt critical reflection. Food has become a topic of great interest to human geographers in the last decade or so (see, for example, Cook *et al.* 2006, 2008, 2011; Morgan *et al.* 2006; Maye *et al.* 2007; Goodman *et al.* 2010; Sage 2012; Maye and Kirwan 2013; Hopma and Woods 2014; Friedberg 2014) and the chapter begins by identifying its value as a tool for geographical analysis. The chapter examines the changing nature of agri-food production systems and shows how the way food provisioning is conceptualized, framed and debated changes over time. Analysis of past debates about industrial agriculture and more recent calls for the 'sustainable intensification of global agriculture' (Beddington 2010) reveals important differences in terms of external pressures that in part shape restructuring processes, even if the mainstream mantra remains essentially productivist. This more recent period of agri-food restructuring is characterized by the need for an effective rather than exploitative use of resources, in response to growing concerns about the depletion and rising costs of energy supplies, population growth and climate change.

Such a 'mode of thinking' is significantly influenced by past events and a realization that energy-greedy production systems that propelled food systems in the 1980s and 1990s are no longer workable or sustainable (Jarosz 2009; Harding 2010). Food has thus become a touchstone for wider environmental discourses. As Harding (2010: 4) puts it, 'feelings about eating and not eating are more immediate than thoughts about rainforests; like the energy or water embedded in the produce we buy, many fears, including fundamental ones about life and death, destruction and incorporation, are already embedded in food'. As we shall see later in this chapter, these feelings, fears and anxieties (Jackson 2010a) have been compounded by recent global price increases and the trends that food analysts suggest they reflect.

First though, it is useful to think about food more generally and to consider why we – as humans – relate to it in the ways Harding and others (e.g. Belasco 2008) suggest that we do. The first point to note is that food extends well beyond its obvious biological significance as the protein for sustaining life. It is something that one relates to on a very human scale – it reflects who we are. According to Atkinson (1991) food is a 'liminal substance' that links humans and nature. It also reveals important social, cultural and economic geographies. On the social side, there are inequalities in terms of food access, good nutrition and the reported problems with obesity and diet, often tied to socio-spatial inequalities in terms of wealth and education (for a critical review of these issues, see Guthman 2011). Food also has cultural significance. Thus, 'food shapes us and expresses us even more definitively than our furniture or houses or utensils do' (Visser 1986: 12). Think, for example, about the different places associated with eating food (e.g. roadside café, Burger King, a Michelin-starred restaurant) and the different behaviours associated with them. There are also cultural associations between different cultural groups and ethnic or national cuisines (e.g. the favourite dish in the UK is Tikka Masala – this curry dish originated in the first Indian restaurants in Soho, London in the 1970s and exemplifies the cross-cultural origin of some foods), as well as a range of cultural images used to market and sell food. Finally, the economic significance of food is enormous: for instance, one only has to think about the investment and the number of people involved in the production, processing and retailing of food. In the USA, for example, almost 10 per cent of US Gross Domestic Product is food-related.

Thus it is quite easy to make a case as to why food matters as an object of study in human geography. However, tracing material and metaphorical associations with food is less obvious because they are connected together in complex ways and often 'hidden' as incidental parts of everyday life. For example, drinking a cup of coffee has numerous social and geographic connotations (Giddens 2001): it has symbolic value (as part of day-to-day life); it is a drug (caffeine provides 'extra lift', but coffee drinkers would not be seen as 'drug users'); it represents past social and economic relationships (e.g. in terms of colonization, mass consumption); and it is a symbol of globalization and world trade links (e.g. global brands like Nescafé and Starbucks). Geographers argue that one cannot separate these localized, mundane acts from larger social settings that extend around the world. This realization about the need to trace '*connections*' between food production and consumption, sparked in part by on-going public debates about obesity, food risks and so on, has become central to agri-food studies and has been given further impetus more recently by debates about food security and the interdependence of food systems with wider environmental and socio-economic systems (Maye and Kirwan 2013; Hinrichs 2014).

A key feature of geographical research in this area involves thinking about where and how food is produced, how it is retailed and how and where it is consumed. The routes traced by particular foodstuffs from 'farm to fork' are often referred to as a '**food chain**' (or 'network') and geographers have attempted to 'map' the system of connections for different products, which may vary both in complexity and geographical coverage. Hartwick (1998: 425) defines food chains as 'significant production, distribution and consumption nodes, and the connecting links between them, together with social, cultural and natural conditions involved in commodity movements'. Geographers have thus adopted the supply chain metaphor to literally trace and follow the nature of 'connections' for particular commodities (Cook *et al.* 2006). The food chain is not a new concept but it has been re-cast as a 'food system', 'food circuit', 'food network' or 'food convention' (see, for example, Maye and Ilbery 2006; Morris and Kirwan 2010). Despite the varied terminologies, the food chain continues to have symbolic and applied values.

Food, therefore, is a geographical topic. This includes its role in society and economy, and the food chain can be used as an overall organizing framework to explore geographies of food production. The rest of the chapter is divided into four parts: first, past and present modes of global food supply are examined, including the changing nature of global food chains; second, some of the ways in which producers and consumers are beginning to establish alternative systems of food provision are outlined; third, debates about food security are examined, including its definition and interpretations about how food should be produced now and in the future; and finally, the chapter summarizes some recent food chain trends and discussions about the ethics of food production, recognizing the need for geographers to continue to critically interrogate the conceptual foundations of food production and supply.

15.2 Geographies of food production and global supply

This section examines farming, food production and global food supply. It outlines some of the ways geographers and other food analysts have framed global food production until relatively recently. Two processes are significant: the industrialization of farming and the **globalization** of food supply. After introducing some concepts, case studies of global food commodity chains in different parts of the world are explored and then some questions are raised, particularly about the relationship between agricultural productivity, food governance and trade. Globalization is often defined in terms of the integration of systems among geographically dispersed places (see Dicken 2015). Crucially, this process of global integration has been guided by powerful **transnational corporations** (TNCs), institutions and actors, which in this context led to a new **political economy** of agriculture, epitomized by the mass production of manufactured food. Despite inequalities, developed and developing

countries are reportedly linked together in 'highly industrialised and increasingly globalised networks of institutions and products, constituting an agri-food system' (Whatmore 1995: 37).

The global food economy is not new. For example, Friedmann and McMichael (1989) argued that relations between agriculture and industry have historically been more global than generally thought. Using the concept of **food regimes**, they linked international patterns of food production and consumption to the development of the capitalist system since the 1870s. They identified three food regimes, each one representing the modern food system of its time (see Spotlight box 15.1). Thus, there has been a global dimension to the geography of food supply for some time and, as we will see later in the chapter, the food regime concept is now being reapplied in the context of the 'new food crisis' (McMichael 2009; Sage 2013).

The main criticism of this conceptualisation is its view of the globalization of agriculture as a logical progression (similar in this respect to modernisation theory). In reality, it is much more unstable. Take the fast food chain McDonalds for example, often heralded as symbolic of global mass food consumption. Its global presence is in fact atypical of the complex and highly uneven process of globalization that has reshaped food production since the post-war period. Much less contentious in these debates is identifying the key agents involved. FitzSimmons (1997), among others, identifies TNCs as the primary agents of globalization in the agri-food sector; to her mind, they sit at the centre of webs of relations that link farming, processing and marketing. Food retailing in Europe and America is concentrated in the hands of a few supermarkets and these agents also play an important role in developing regulatory systems that ensure their dominance over the supply of key food products. It is also agreed that TNCs and corporate retailers played significant roles in the 'industrialization' of farming and food production activities, which, initially at least, were mostly concentrated in the developed world.

15.2.1 Industrialized agriculture in the developed world

Encouraged by governments as a response to food shortages and the need to raise productivity after the Second World War, 'industrial farming has dominated . . . agriculture in the EU and North America since the 1950s' (Millstone and Lang 2008: 38). This system of farming is particularly prominent in livestock (i.e. meat, dairy, and eggs production) and is designed to maximize productivity in the shortest timeframe (Sage 2012). Key features of the industrial model of farming include a specialization of labour, product specialization and intensification, and assembly-line type production. It has led to three

Spotlight box 15.1

Global food regimes since the 1870s

First regime: pre-industrial (1870s–1920s)
This involved settler colonies supplying unprocessed and semi-processed foods and materials to the metropolitan core of North America and Western Europe. Characterized by *extensive* forms of capital accumulation, the main products were grains and meat. The regime slowly disintegrated when agricultural production in developed countries competed with cheap imports and trade barriers were erected.

Second regime: industrial (1920s–1970s)
This regime relates to the productivist phase of agricultural change, focused on North America and the development of agri-industrial complexes based around grain-fed livestock production. Characterized

by *intensive* forms of capital accumulation, the second regime incorporated developed and developing nations into commodity production systems. Agricultural surpluses and environmental disbenefits undermined this phase of production in the 1970s.

Third regime: post-industrial (1980s onwards)
This regime refers to the crisis surrounding industrialized farming systems and involves the production of fresh fruit and vegetables for the global market, the continued reconstitution of food, and the supply of inputs for 'elite' consumption in developed countries. Characterized by a *flexible* form of capital accumulation, this regime is dominated by the restructuring activities of agribusiness TNCs and corporate retailers.

Source: based on Robinson (2004), as derived from Friedmann and McMichael (1989)

important food production trends in the developed world: first, the concentration of agricultural production on a limited number of large-scale farms; second, an increase in capital expenditure on major agricultural inputs like chemicals; and third, a growth in the processing and manufacturing of food. These developments explain why it is now vital to view farming in the wider context of an **agri-food system**, where the production sector itself is inextricably linked to various 'upstream' (input supplies) and 'downstream' (processing, distribution and marketing) industries. In many cases, the food supply system is also dominated by large **agribusinesses** which, according to Davis and Goldberg's (1957) seminal work, are the sum of all operations involved in the manufacture and distribution of farm supplies, the production operation of the farm, storage, processing and distribution of farm commodities and items made from them. These agribusinesses often develop commodity chains beyond national boundaries (Wallace 1985; McMichael 2009).

A number of studies have charted the **industrialization of agriculture**, especially in the United States. Two brief examples are presented here. The first is the Salinas Valley in California where lettuce production was transformed between 1950 and 1980 by two key things: *intensification*, as a result of a shift to more investment in intensive crops, increased labour productivity and intensified planting; and *restructuring*, whereby large farms dominated sales (FitzSimmons 1986). By 1978, the ten largest grower-shippers in the region sold 65 per cent of all lettuce. Over time, therefore, power and control

shifted towards the largest firms. FitzSimmons also identified a process of **vertical disintegration**, whereby segments of the production process were subcontracted out to smaller scale growers. The second example is poultry, a key product when it comes to integrated production systems and the first livestock sector to industrialize. Constance *et al.* (2013) provide a historical analysis of poultry production and processing in the United States. They show how the locus of production activity shifted from the North-east, where it started in the 1930s, to the South by the 1950s. Underemployed farm labour, a favourable climate, lower wages and less unionization, cotton-crop failures, and the stabilization of feed prices were key factors that made the South an attractive place to locate. A model of vertically-integrated production, based on contract production and non-union labour, was developed. In a bid to increase market share, a number of mergers and acquisitions took place in the 1980s and 1990s, leading to a process of **horizontal integration** and industry consolidation that created regional monopsonies. This model of a few very large vertically integrated poultry farms anchoring agro-industrial districts is efficient in that it produces low-priced chicken for consumers, but it has also been criticized as a system of asymmetrical power relationships that marginalizes contract producers, workers in processing plants, and rural communities.

In these and other examples, it is often the non-farm sectors of the agri-food system that have become most industrialized and dominated by TNCs. This has occurred through two processes (Goodman *et al.* 1987): **appropriationism**, where certain agricultural inputs are replaced by 'industrial' alternatives (e.g. synthetic chemicals replacing manure); and **substitutionism**, which focuses on outputs rather than inputs and is concerned with the increased utilization of non-agricultural raw materials and the creation of industrial substitutes for food and fibre (e.g. sweeteners for sugar). Agri-food systems are different from other production systems because agriculture is bound by biological processes and cycles, and the essential aim of appropriationism and substitutionism is to 'replace' nature. Agribusiness TNCs also attempt to increase their influence over farming indirectly through a process of formal **subsumption**, where arrangements or contracts are made with farmers to provide 'raw materials' for their value-adding food manufacturing activities. Agricultural industrialization is also increasingly global in scale, where food commodity chains lengthen and producers become 'distanced' from consumers.

The overall key pattern of agricultural industrialization is *concentration* in particular sectors, regions and individual countries characterized by large farm businesses that have adopted intensive farming methods and become integrated into global food networks. In the European Union, for instance, 80 per cent of agricultural production is concentrated on less than 20 per cent of farms in particular 'hot spots', including East Anglia, the Paris Basin, southern Netherlands, and Emilia Romagna in north-east Italy. In response to various issues in the developed world market, a key feature of TNCs and major retailers has been their attempt to relocate the production function of the agri-food system to new agricultural spaces, often in **less developed countries** (LDCs). This shift was associated with the intensive production of high-quality, high-value food commodities.

15.2.2 Developing world agriculture

Goodman and Watts (1997) argue that the classic export commodities (e.g. coffee, tea, sugar, cocoa) associated with the LDCs have been complemented by high-value foods, including fruits, vegetables and shellfish. By the 1990s, 24 low-middle income countries annually exported over US$500 million of **high-value foods**; just five countries (Brazil, Mexico, China, Argentina and Kenya) accounted for 40 per cent of such exports from the LDCs. The growth in high-value food exports reflects various things, including: technical changes in the food industry, the liberalization of world trade, and dietary changes in the developed world, with high-value foods produced to satisfy consumer tastes. Agribusiness TNCs are also attracted to high-value food production

in newly agriculturalizing countries because of low-cost labour, government support (via **structural adjustment programmes**), good global communication links and the ability to produce high quality/value products for the developed world market. There are a number of detailed accounts of the export trade in high-value foods (see, for example, Freidberg 2004; van der Ploeg 2010).

The example used here is salmon farming in Chile. It is mostly located in Chiloe, a large island that runs along the southern third of the Chilean coast and is characterized by a mild, rainy climate and protected inlets. Since the 1990s, the salmon farming industry has been growing rapidly; in 1987 Chile produced 2,000 tonnes of Pacific salmon, but did not produce any Atlantic salmon (Phyne and Mansilla 2003). By 2000 Chile produced 17 per cent of the world's Atlantic salmon and also dominated the global production of Pacific salmon. At its peak, in 2006, Chile contributed 38 per cent of the world's salmon trade and was the leading exporter of farmed salmon after Norway (Iizuka and Katz 2015). However, the sector suffered decline in 2007 as a result of a salmon disease crisis, which decimated stocks (Atlantic salmon stocks dropped from 400,000 tonnes in 2005 to 100,000 tonnes in 2010). Figure 15.1 shows a simplified model for the salmon aquaculture supply chain which starts when eggs are hatched and the fingerlings raised near the hatchery; once fingerlings become smolts, they are raised in smolt-rearing facilities in fresh-water cages; after a period of 12 months they are shipped to sea-water cages and raised for a further 12–18 months (thanks to new feeds, this grow-out stage is reducing rapidly); harvested salmon enter processing plants (with automated feeding systems and where labour is most concentrated) and are prepared by standards set in Japan and America. Over 80 per cent of the product is sold to Japanese and American retail markets.

This case study shows how the Chilean salmon farming industry is inserted into a **'buyer-driven' commodity chain**, where major distributors and retailers in export markets shape the nature of production. Power is at the retail end of the chain rather than the production end. Essentially, the industry is characterized by governance from lead firms and external authorities (Iizuka and Katz 2015; cf. van der Ploeg 2010). In the middle part of the salmon supply chain there is also clear evidence of concentration and squeezing, with forward integration by feed giants and increasing concentration of production by foreign and domestic firms. At the production end of the chain, benefits are skewed in favour of those in management positions. Grow-out sites and processing plants are where most local people work. Wages are low and the working conditions poor, with 80 per cent of plant workers being female. Analysts of the sanitary

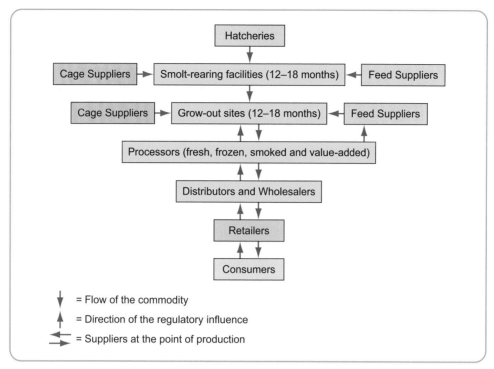

Figure 15.1 A simplified model of the salmon aquaculture supply chain.
Source: Phyne and Mansilla (2003); Iizuka and Katz (2015).

crisis that severely damaged the sector in 2007 argue it was the result of overexploitation and overconcentration of fish farms (Iizuka and Katz 2015). In this example, and in others cited, global food production raises significant questions, especially in terms of who truly benefits.

15.2.3 Global food production hubs and the diffusion of governance innovations

Recent studies of global agriculture (e.g. Gardner 2013) reveal sustained and increasing regional spatial concentration for certain food/crop types. North America and Europe are now important areas for maize and wheat production. China and India collectively grow a quarter of the world's wheat and over half the global production of rice. A large proportion of the world's animal feed is produced in South America, North America and Eastern Europe. Not all of these systems will be highly industrialized but most are, or will be, moving rapidly in that direction.

A key trend in food production concentration is the rise of **newly agriculturalizing countries** (NACs). This idea is not new (Friedman 1993), but Spotlight box 15.2 introduces a case study of Brazil to show how some NACs are attempting to become new *global food production hubs*. NACs were originally associated with world trade in high value foods. This process has continued

apace (Gardner 2013) and is criticised because countries focus on growing for the global market at the expense of staple products required for the domestic market. The Brazil case shows a continued focus on global demand, but in this instance the emphasis is on growing bulk food commodities like soybeans, as well as expanding its beef markets, with increasing reliance on GMO technology from abroad to develop resistant beans, an innovation which farmers want but environmentalists reject on the grounds that these forms of bioeconomy 'lock in' Brazil to certain, technology-reliant, ways of farming.

Certain types of productivist, intensive farming systems have relocated to 'peripheral' regions to take advantage of local conditions (for example, cheaper labour, land). Also significant is the diffusion of the **vertical integration** food governance model to other countries around the world. Processes of agricultural industrialization and globalization are therefore more complex than a shift from core to periphery. The model of poultry production developed in the US South, for example, around agro-industrial districts, has since been adopted and applied elsewhere as a low-cost production system. The outcome of this diffusion process is the creation, by transnational agribusinesses, of a global poultry agrifood complex that targets the best production areas and the most profitable consumer markets. These complex governance arrangements include powerful US companies

Spotlight box 15.2

The rise of Brazil as a 'global farm'

Brazil is rapidly overtaking other countries in food pro-duction and exports. In particular, Brazil is emerging as the world's lead producer of beef, a commodity that is being consumed in growing quantities globally every year. In the past decade, Brazil quadrupled beef exports, overtaking Australia as the world's largest exporter. The rise of Brazil as a 'global farm' is also about a second commodity: soya beans – it's the country's largest food crop, with an estimated value of US$17 billion in 2008.

Soya was mostly grown in the south of Brazil until the 1960s. Since then plant breeders and agricultural scientists have developed varieties that can grow across most of the country. It is now competing with the USA to be the world's largest soya exporter. Transgenic crops are also important. The first GM soya plant – a herbi-cide-resistant bean, developed and sold by Monsanto (a US-based company) – was approved for cultivation in 1998. A judge later issued a moratorium to block the use of the seed but Brazilian farmers ignored the legislation and started to import it (illegally!) from Argen-tina. Its use became so widespread that the Brazilian president signed a law in 2003 to legalize it. The law was designed to better control imports and to protect Brazilian seed companies. Brazil now has 21 types of GM plant approved for use in the field. GM soya makes up 70 per cent of the Brazilian soya market.

Brazil currently relies on GM products developed abroad, although in 2010 its biosafety commission approved the first transgenic seed to be developed by Brazilian scientists. At the moment transgenic crops used in Brazil help farmers to fight against weeds and insects – they do not increase the amount of food pro-duced by individual plants. Pro-GM scientists argue more productive varieties could eventually take pressure off the Amazon rainforest, which has been extensively cleared to make way for agriculture. Producing for a global market thus offers economic benefits but it can also come at a significant cost.

Sources: *Tollefson (2010); Sage (2012)*

like Tyson, who have joint-venture poultry operations all over the world, but also companies like JBS, which is Brazilian-owned and is now the largest multi-protein processor in the world.

15.2.4 Trade patterns, food policy and global governance

Agricultural industrialization is thus extending its global reach; it is also clear that large-scale agribusinesses and corporate retailers have successfully linked regional economies and food sectors to a global system of food production and consumption. However, these systems of provision also raise questions about, for example, their suitability for LDCs, especially their contribution to sharp inequalities in income, productivity and tech-nology compared to the sector producing staple foods (i.e. foods that are eaten regularly and provide a large proportion of a population's energy and nutrients, such as cereals or tubers) and the unsustainable nature of agri-cultural practices often favoured by agribusiness TNCs. Questions also abound about the logic and impacts of industrialized farming, particularly in relation to food production, fair trade and environmental responsibil-ity. We turn now to look in more detail at the role and influence of food policy in shaping patterns of global food production and supply. This is an area that has also faced significant criticism.

International trade in food has expanded dramati-cally in recent decades. Between 1961 and 1999, there was a four-fold increase in the amount of food exported (Millstone and Lang 2008). In 2012, the USA and the EU dominated agricultural exports (16 per cent and 14 per cent respectively) and imports (12 per cent and 17 per cent respectively) (Gardner 2013). However, the pat-tern of world food trade is changing. The simple two way north–south world trade exchange has now become much more complex. In recent years, for example, devel-oping countries have increased production of staples (e.g. wheat, maize) and now export to each other, as well as exporting high value fruit, vegetables and meat to Europe and North America. As noted earlier, trade in high value foods has increased rapidly. China and other BRICS countries (Brazil, Russia, India and South Africa) are increasingly involved in world food trade.

One of the drivers of this process has been the World Trade Organization (WTO). The WTO's Agreement on Agriculture promoted trade liberalization through reductions in agricultural subsidies, tariffs and import quotas. More than 150 countries are signatories of the General Agreement on Tariffs and Trade (GATT) (Carolan 2011). However, concerns have been voiced about the unfairness of global trade because of the continued use of national subsidies and tariffs. For example, a number of trading blocs exist that have significant power when it comes to how food is traded. These regional trading blocs sit below the GATT/WTO governance structure and include the North American Free Trade Agreement (an agreement between the USA, Canada and Mexico) and the European Union (which comprises 28 countries). Effectively these arrangements promote patterns of bilateral food trade and also influence how food is grown and traded, because they distort markets. Developed nations use direct or, as is now more common, indirect or **de-coupled payments** (i.e. the payment is deemed non-trade distorting because it is independent of production levels) to support their farmers. As Carolan (2011: 20) remarks, 'these payments still shield producers from low prices . . . they make farmers deaf to market signals, allowing them to continue to (over)produce and profit even when the costs of production exceed what the market is willing to bear'.

What this tells us is that free trade is rarely fair. At the time of writing the latest debate in this area concerns the development of the **Transatlantic Trade and Investment Partnership (TTIP)** deal. This is still being negotiated, and hotly debated, but if it goes ahead it will effectively create a trading area that would stretch as far as Alaska to the Black Sea. It is proposed that standards between the United States and the EU will be harmonized across a plethora of issues, including animal welfare, food safety and public services. Lobbyists argue the process is undemocratic and designed by and for big corporations. Many argue it will also inevitably lead to a reduction in standards on both sides. If approved, TTIP is likely to significantly influence how and where food is produced and traded globally in the future.

15.3 Alternative geographies of food: concepts and case studies

One important way to respond to some of the above criticisms is to establish **alternative food networks** (AFNs). There has been a huge resurgence of interest within many developed market economies in foods of local and regional provenance (Watts *et al.* 2005; Maye and Kirwan 2010; Tregear 2011; Goodman *et al.* 2012; Rippon 2014). These include consumer initiatives like the Slow Food movement and fair trade, as well as a growth in food purchases from 'alternative' supply chains rather than supermarket outlets, including farmers' markets

(FMs), box schemes, community supported agriculture, buying-groups and food cooperatives, and home deliveries (Renting *et al.* 2003; Kneafsey *et al.* 2008; Little *et al.* 2010). In 2012, 7.8 per cent of US farms were marketing foods locally, for example (USDA 2015). This interest is often seen as a response to the environmental and socioeconomic disbenefits associated with agricultural industrialization and global food supply.

Many authors have referred to the distinctions drawn between 'conventional' and 'alternative' agri-food systems (see Table 15.1). Binary opposites such as 'quality', 'embedded', 'sustainable', 'traditional' and 'natural' characterize alternative food production systems (Ilbery and Maye 2005). In reality, these binary opposites are not as simple and clear-cut as this. For example, while organic food may be regarded as 'alternative', most organic sales still occur through 'conventional' supermarkets. Interest in the alternative food economy has also led some geographers to proclaim the emergence of 'alternative geographies of food', which revolve around changing production and consumption relations that give rise to new regional and local food 'complexes'. It has been argued, for example, that alternative geographies

Table 15.1 Distinctions between 'conventional' and 'alternative' food supply systems

Conventional	Alternative
Modern	Post-modern
Manufactured/processed	Natural/fresh
Mass (large-scale) production	Craft/artisanal (small-scale) production
Long food supply chains	Short food supply chains
Costs externalized	Costs internalized
Rationalized	Traditional
Standardized	Difference/diversity
Intensification	Extensification
Monoculture	Biodiversity
Homogenization of foods	Regional palates
Hypermarkets	Local markets
Agrochemicals	Organic/sustainable farming
Non-renewable energy	Reusable energy
Fast food	Slow food
Quantity	Quality
Disembedded	Embedded

Source: based on Ilbery and Maye (2005)

of food may be associated with agriculturally peripheral regions because such regions have, '. . . for a variety of reasons, failed to fully engage with the productivist conventions that have predominated in the agri-food system in the second half of the twentieth century' (Parrott *et al.* 2002: 243). Goodman (2003) draws a comparison between American and European alternative food practices, conceptualizing US alternatives more as social and oppositional movements, in contrast to the EU's more endogenous interventions, linked to historical and cultural traditions of product and place.

One can equally talk about alternative geographies of food in a global sense, notably through the international **fair trade** and organic food movements that challenge exploitative relations in agri-food systems. These networks offer ethical and ecological possibilities that counter some of the negative externalities associated with conventional food supply (Maye *et al.* 2007). International trade often appears as a remote concern, but when commodity prices fall it has devastating impacts on the livelihoods of millions of small producers. The prices paid for coffee, for example, have not increased in real terms in the last 40 years, whereas the costs of inputs like fertilizers and machinery have. Low coffee prices in the early 1990s had catastrophic impacts on the lives of millions of small farmers, mostly in LDCs, who were producing coffee at a loss. However, despite the positive benefits of fair trade and organic foods, both sectors have been subjected to recent debates about 'mainstreaming' and 'conventionalisation'.

Fair trade offers an alternative to overcome the injustices of free trade, guaranteeing producers a fair price. It was started some 50 years ago by development agencies and charities like Oxfam and Traidcraft who realized the important role consumers could play in improving the lives of impoverished producers. Fair trade is now available in most European supermarket chains, with some products achieving 15 per cent of the national market share. It is, quite rightly, a global success story and fair trade consumerism is celebrated as enabling better everyday ethical practice. The success of these networks depends upon the ability and willingness of Northern consumers to pay redistributive premiums for such commodities. Some fair trade organizations have started to compete on price, lowering premiums paid to producers and aggressively pursuing 'mainstreaming' strategies. This parallels developments in organic farming where some have argued that organic supply chains have become 'conventionalised' (especially in terms of rent structures, the size of businesses controlling production, conventional patterns of marketing and distribution), suggesting that it is often very difficult for alternative economies to maintain their differences from the global capitalist economy (Guthman 2004; Goodman *et al.* 2012).

Spotlight box 15.3 provides a summary of two concepts central to an understanding of the development of 'alternative geographies of food'. These and related concepts will be examined further below, via some empirical case studies; hopefully, they will also help you to think critically about the blurring between 'conventional' and 'alternative' systems of food provision. A simple 'alternative geography of food' does not exist. The processes affecting 'alternative' food chains are complex. We explore some of these issues using three case studies that attempt to 'reconnect' food production and consumption and make a statement about the alternative food economy, especially in terms of the nature of the food chain.

Spotlight box 15.3

Conceptualizing AFNs: key concepts

Short food supply chains (SFSCs)
The key characteristic of SFSCs is that foods reach the final consumer having been transmitted through a supply chain 'embedded' with value-laden information concerning the mode of production, provenance and distinctive quality assets of the product. In many cases, the number of nodes between the primary producer and the final consumer will also be minimized (Renting *et al.* 2003). While this 're-connection process' is best demonstrated through forms of direct marketing and thus face-to-face contact between producer and consumer, Marsden *et al.* (2000) identified two further types of SFSC: spatial proximity and spatially extended. The former is where products are sold through local outlets in the region, locality or place of production, so that the consumer is immediately aware of the locally embedded nature of the product at the point of retail. In contrast, the latter occur when products are sold to consumers (e.g. via the Internet) who are located outside the region of production and/ or have no personal knowledge of the area.

Social embeddedness
This propagates the idea that economic behaviour is embedded in, and mediated by, a complex and extensive

web of local social relations. In the case of local ('alternative') foods, both economic (e.g. price, markets) and social (e.g. local ties, trust) relations are vital for success (for details see Hinrichs 2000). By stressing the role of social relations in generating the trust necessary for economic transactions, it is easy to make the false assumption that social embeddedness relates just to alternative food systems. In reality, all economic relations are socially embedded in a range of contrasting ways and so there are different degrees of embeddedness in all food supply systems (Winter 2003). Nevertheless, social interaction between producer and consumer can make the difference between success and failure for local food businesses. This can take the form of acknowledgement, attention, respect, friendship and sociability, often subsumed within the concept of 'regard' (Sage 2003; Kirwan 2006).

15.3.1 Quality food

One of the dominant features of AFNs, particularly in Europe, has been the attempt to link 'product and place' in order to add value to agricultural products (Watts *et al.* 2005; Ilbery and Maye 2010). This is often defined as a process of relocalization, in which locally distinctive quality food products (see Plate 15.1, for example) are transferred to regional and national markets as a

Plate 15.1 Speciality cheese from Italy.

(MARKA/Alamy)

mechanism to provide a valuable economic stimulant and reduce the deleterious impact of national and EU subsidy reforms and increasing trade liberalization. In other words, quality and locality are inextricably linked. In particular, regional speciality food products have been linked to particular places in this way, especially via a formal system of quality food labels and the establishment of regional speciality food groups. The most notable example of this is the Protected Designation of Origin (PDO) and the Protected Geographical Indication (PGI) quality labels introduced by the European Union in the early 1990s to 'protect' and 'promote' food and drink products with a recognizable geographical origin (Rippon 2014). Groups of producers in Europe can thus apply for either a PDO label (product originates from a specific place and is linked to its natural environment) or PGI label (linked to place, but not necessarily in terms of raw materials). These labels protect producers from attempted copies and act as a marketing device. These changes have been interpreted as symbolizing a **quality turn** (Goodman 2003), with particular emphasis on specialist food production, especially in 'marginal economies'.

In terms of geography, the UK already has 60 PDO/PGI labels. Specialist cheeses dominate the PDOs, indicating that these are made exclusively from local raw materials (e.g. Stilton cheeses). In contrast, drinks dominate the PGIs. The sales value of British Geographical Indications in 2010 was €5.506 billion and food and agricultural products comprised €1.059 billion (Rippon 2014). There are now more than 595 PDOs and 601 PGI designations in the EU, with a southern concentration in places like France and Italy (over 150 each, including cheeses, wines and meats, such as Parmigiano-Reggiano, Roquefort and Champagne) and Greece and Portugal (over 80 each), compared with limited numbers in northern member countries (e.g. Finland, Denmark and Ireland). This implies that regional/speciality food has more cultural significance in some European societies than in others (Parrott *et al.* 2002). Protected status thus provides cultural benefits by preserving place-based identities. They also provide exclusive control over geographical names, allowing businesses to exploit the positive ideas that consumers have about particular territorial names (Rippon 2014). Some countries have developed this form of market premium more than others.

15.3.2 Direct food

Studies of the local food sector in the USA, UK and other parts of Europe typically include some of the archetypal examples noted earlier, especially farmers' markets, box schemes, farm shops and on-farm butchers (Watts *et al.* 2005; Maye and Kirwan 2010; USDA 2015). Significant

in all these examples is the direct nature of the supply chain and the important social and economic benefits that accrue from these types of food transaction. This is illustrated in Plate 15.2, which shows the *direct interaction* between producers and consumers at a farmers' market. To help explore some of these processes in more detail, the second case focuses on an organic meat producer business (Ilbery and Maye 2005).

The organic farm and on-farm butchery is located in the Northumberland uplands. Established in 1998, the business produces and retails a range of organically reared meat products, using local branding and **traceability**. The business supply chain is reproduced in Figure 15.2 and records both the upstream inputs coming into the business and the downstream links in terms of how and where final products are sold. This '*whole chain*' approach extends previous conceptualisations of SFSCs which focused only on downstream elements of the supply chain (cf. Marsden *et al.* 2000).

Most of the inputs coming into the farm are from local suppliers. Constructed to add and retain value from primary production, the business sources some cattle, sheep, pigs and poultry from other organic farms in the region. All livestock are slaughtered at the (organically accredited) abattoir at Whitley Bay in North Tyneside, Tyne and Wear (about 20 miles from the farm), and then delivered to the on-farm butchery to be processed and packaged for retail. Businesses like this have to 'dip in' and 'dip out' of 'conventional' supply chains because of the ways in which the dominant agri-food system is currently structured. The meat products are sold through various SFSCs, for example direct sales, local/regional specialist food shops and caterers, and mail order. Meat sales over the Internet are minimal. Over time, the business reduced sales output at farmers' markets and stopped supplying (specialist) butchers in the region in favour of more

Plate 15.2 Selling food direct via a farmers' market.
(Daniel Korzeniewski/Shutterstock)

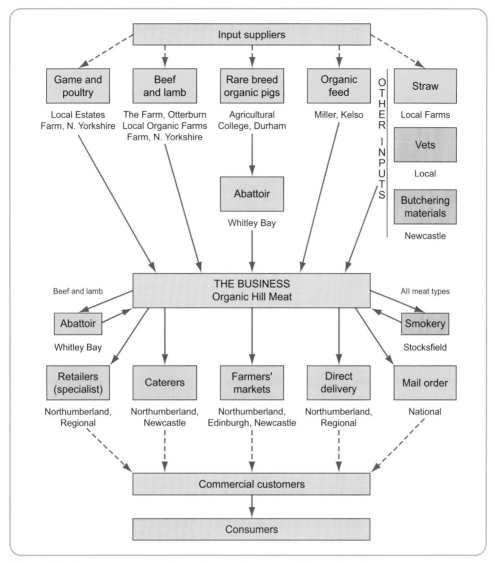

Figure 15.2 Business supply chain diagram for organic hill meat producer.

'stable' alternatives (e.g. independent retail and catering). Thus the producer adjusts the supply chain in a bid to establish as much control of it as possible.

15.3.3 Community food

Attempts to relocalize food production and establish 'alternative' supply chains also extend beyond farm-based production. This is an important point. The final case study of the Kansas City Food Circle (KCFC) is an example of a **community food scheme** (Hendrickson and Heffernan 2002). KCFC is presented as a (local) site of resistance within an industrialized food system dominated by global corporations like Con Agra, Cargill, and Monsanto whose food chain arrangements are typified by joint ventures and strategic alliances. The KCFC

organization began in November 1994, seeking to educate the public about the consequences of the industrial agricultural system and to persuade more people to participate in local, sustainable alternatives. It argued that industrial agriculture had eroded soils, made water unfit to drink, and increased pesticide resistance in insects; the food system had become so centralized that citizens lacked control over their food choices. For KCFC, the industrialized food system was unhealthy, unjust, unethical and economically unviable.

The explicit political alternative that emerged from this critique was an attempt to create a local, organic food system where consumers can get seasonal, fresh food at a price that supports farmers who use sustainable practices. The KCFC thus connects all actors in the food system in a way that sustains and returns control to local communities. Effectively, the KCFC is about creating a new kind of community that recognizes the interconnectedness of people through the production and consumption of food. The Circle continued to grow, with 30 organic growers in the region surrounding Kansas City signing up to supply food, and roughly 600 consumers. The trust-based relationships that the KCFC is trying to cultivate between farmers and consumers mirror those reported in other similar studies (see, for example, Kneafsey et al. 2008; Little et al. 2010).

15.3.4 Critiquing and redefining AFNs

Given the range and diversity of work on 'alternative geographies of food', these mechanisms of food supply can also be critiqued, especially in terms of the privilege assigned to terms like 'local' and 'alternative'. Geographers and other agri-food researchers are thus asking what is 'alternative' about the alternative food economy (see Whatmore et al. 2003; Maye et al. 2007; Goodman et al. 2012). This critique is evident in the critical tone of the 'conventionalisation thesis' introduced earlier, which raises important questions about the alternative status of some fair trade and organic food chains. Watts et al. (2005) distinguish between 'weaker' and 'stronger' alternative systems of food provision. The former place emphasis on quality and the labelling features of locality *food* networks (i.e. the product is key), whereas the latter focus on the revalorized and embedded characteristics of local food *networks* (i.e. the supply chain/network and nature of relations are key). In the three examples of AFNs, the first case study falls within this weaker classification, whereas the other two are stronger because of their emphasis on establishing alternative production-consumption networks. It is beyond the scope of this chapter to enter into debates surrounding the definition of terms such as 'local', 'locality' and 'regional' (see Maye and Kirwan 2010, Goodman et al. 2012); nevertheless, it is important to also note that the literature is divided about whether 'quality' or 'local' is more important in local food production. Winter (2003) used the concept of **defensive localism** to suggest that the turn to local is more important than a turn to quality based on, for example, organic or ecological principles. The turn to local is not just about alternative food systems; instead, it can cover different forms of agriculture and a range of consumer motivations.

Goodman et al. (2012) suggest that '*first-generation*' AFNs (regional PDO/PGI locality foods, organic agriculture, local food networks that involve farmers' markets, CSAs and box schemes) are now being renewed and complemented by a '*second generation*' of *relocalization initiatives,* many of which involve collective, non-market

and community-based forms of innovation and alterity (otherness). There is certainly evidence to support the need for a broader range of AFNs. Kirwan et al.'s (2013) analysis of the Local Food programme in England, for example, looked at the types of organization responsible for running local food projects and found that by far the most common were registered charities, followed by a range of community groups and schools. Renting et al. (2012) introduce '**civic food networks**' (CFNs) as a useful way to conceptualize new modes of food governance and contemporary sources of innovation within agri-food networks. It is an attempt to conceptualize new types of consumer-producer cooperation in food networks (i.e. 'second-generation AFNs') where consumers play an active role. These networks are often organized by civic groups (NGOs, charities, etc.) and the concept is intended to complement rather than replace previous conceptualisations of AFNs and SFSCs. Examples include consumer co-ops, solidarity buying groups of local and organic foods, CSAs and collective urban gardening initiatives. The key argument is that the role of civil society as a governance mechanism for agri-food networks has increased in significance compared to market and state actors. As we will see in Section 15.4, these debates about AFNs have been further unsettled by recent increases in, and volatility of, global food prices alongside concerns about food availability. The scale of the discussion has therefore shifted from the regional and the local back to the global.

15.4 Food security: questions of scale, definition and interpretation

Some of the challenges associated with food security have been usefully discussed earlier in this book (see Chapter 7). It merits attention here too because it is significantly re-shaping how we think about global food production. Food security has commonly been associated with developing countries in recent decades. Given the choice and daily availability of foods in supermarkets and restaurants, it is easy to see why the thought of food shortages or supply chain disruptions might not be uppermost in peoples' minds in most developed market economies. However, there is now recognition that the food system and issues associated with securing food supplies need urgent attention (Maye and Kirwan 2013).

The reason why political interest in food worldwide has suddenly arisen is easy to explain: global food prices have increased significantly in recent years (House of Commons 2009). The significant price spike was in late 2007, when the price for basic food staples rose sharply on international commodity markets (the price for wheat rose by 50 per cent and for rice by 20 per cent, for example). The price spike was unusual in one important way in that '[it] applies to almost all major food and feed commodities, rather than just a few of them' (Chatham House 2008: 2). High prices in agricultural markets are not uncommon, but increases across such a range of food commodities are.

The escalation in food prices had some well-documented impacts, notably a series of violent protests and demonstrations that were witnessed in different parts of the developing world, including the 'tortilla riots' in Mexico. Some countries (e.g. Argentina) also imposed trade restrictions to limit the amount of food being exported to protect national food supply. The price spike affected households in developed nations such as the UK in less dramatic ways, via food inflation. Prices for oils and fats in the UK rose by 29 per cent in the year to July 2008, meat by 16.3 per cent, bread and cereals by 16 per cent, vegetables by 11.1 per cent and fruit by 10.7 per cent (Barling *et al*. 2008, quoted in House of Commons 2009). Although less dramatic, these impacts served to underline 'our global interdependency and demonstrated the political and social importance of affordable food' (Chatham House 2009: 5).

The factors that contributed to the increase in food prices at this time are widely reported and include poor harvests, the use of food crops for biofuels, especially maize in the USA, rising energy prices, which led to high prices for fertilizers and fuel, changes in demand for certain foods (e.g. growing demand for more meat in China), export bans and speculation (Jarosz 2009). There is still on-going debate about whether food price rises will be sustained longer term, or whether what was experienced in 2007 was merely a blip (see Gardner 2013). Food prices have fallen again in international commodity markets, but they remain volatile. Industry analysts suggest higher and more volatile food prices are set to stay (von Braun 2009).

Addressing the consequences of higher food prices is only part of the challenge. Constraints on global food supply are also influenced by longer-term trends, notably changing global patterns in diet and world population pressures. Population expansion is a particularly significant driver of the long-term increase in food demand, with predictions that the world may need to feed over nine billion people from 2050. Projections suggest that 95 per cent of this growth will occur in the developing world. At the World Food Security Conference in Rome in June 2008, it was estimated that food production needed to increase by 50 per cent by 2030 and to double by 2050.

Undercutting all of this discussion is an increased awareness of the risks posed by climate change and increasingly scarce natural resources. Various environmental and resource challenges require urgent consideration, notably the need to reduce greenhouse gas emissions produced by the food system, the need to reduce dependency on fossil fuels, and the need to reduce the depletion of natural resources and ecosystem services on which food depends (especially soil and water) (House of Commons 2009: 13; Sage 2013). Any response to the above crisis is not simply about producing more food; it is about doing it in a way that is sustainable and uses resources less exploitatively. Increases in food production will thus need to be achieved, making an effective, rather than exploitative, use of resources (Ilbery and Maye 2010). This has been described elsewhere as 'an unprecedented double challenge' (House of Commons 2009: 13). The following sub-sections consider two aspects of this debate: first, how the term food security is defined and for whom; and secondly, some ways food analysts suggest we respond to the challenge.

15.4.1 Food security for whom?

The emphasis in much of the discussion on the current, perceived 'global food security crisis' is about the need to produce more food (i.e. food availability). There is recognition that increases in production must be consistent with systems that are sustainable and that we produce food that consumers want. However, this policy places too little emphasis on broader understandings of food security, which include questions about access and utilization as well as availability (Maye and Kirwan 2013). The standard definition of food security is that given by the United Nations Food and Agriculture Organization in its 1996 World Food Summit Plan of Action:

> Food security exists when all people, at all times, have physical and economic access to sufficient, safe and nutritious food to meet their dietary needs and food preferences for an active and healthy life.

> (quoted in Ericksen 2008: 234)

Food security has multiple meanings for different people and organizations and varied scales of interpretation (global, national, regional, local, the household). It can be viewed as a 'master frame' with several distinct claims to ownership or, in other words, there is 'contested ownership behind the apparent consensus on food security' (Mooney and Hunt 2009: 470; see also Maye and Kirwan 2013; Hopma and Woods 2014). Three collective action frames that encompass food security as a master frame have been suggested by Mooney and Hunt (2009) and these are:

- Food security associated with hunger and malnutrition;
- Food security as a component of a community's developmental whole; and

- Food security as minimizing risks in industrialized agricultural production in terms of the risk of 'normal accidents' and 'intentional accidents' associated with agri-terrorism.

These collective action frames are grounded in the US experience and identify the different perspectives and interests on one seemingly consensual social problem. It also distinguishes between relatively tame institutional responses and much more critical viewpoints and positions. This resonates with earlier material in this chapter in which weaker and stronger variants of alternative food networks are identified as part of a critique of neoliberalism (Watts *et al*. 2005). Crucially, Mooney and Hunt (2009: 493) do more than simply identify a plurality of framings by locating 'this process within an ordered, yet contentious, multi-organizational political field of differential power wielded by various insiders and outsiders'.

15.4.2 Three food security 'action frames'

This sub-section outlines three illustrative action frames that are emerging outwith the US experience:

1. **Sustainable intensification.** There has been a strong science-oriented or techno-centric discourse underpinning the response to the current 'global food security crisis'. This is described by Godfray *et al*. (2010) as 'sustainable intensification'. The essence of this idea is that we need to achieve higher yields from the same acreage without damaging the environment. In a similar vein, the UK Government's Chief Scientist, John Beddington (2010: 61), argues that we need 'a new, "green*er* revolution"' (original emphasis). Advocates of this approach claim that science and technology have time and again provided huge increases in yield growth when required. Important areas to focus upon in this context include, for example, crop improvement, smarter use of water and fertilizers, the introduction of novel non-chemical approaches to crop protection, the reduction of post-harvest losses and more sustainable livestock and marine production. Projects and initiatives are also emerging to meet the challenge to produce more food (or they are at least marketed in this food crisis context). One example is the development of modern hydroponic schemes. A state-of-the-art version now exists in the UK, called Thanet Earth (see Spotlight box 15.4), and such schemes are well known in The Netherlands and California. Another highly controversial example is the proposal to build the UK's first 'super dairy'. Plans were originally submitted for an

---

Spotlight box 15.4

Is the future hydroponic? Thanet Earth

Hydroponic schemes are a well-established feature of the California and the Netherlands agro-foodscape. A state-of-the-art version also now exists in Kent, called 'Thanet Earth'. It is owned by a consortium of Dutch growers and Fresca, a fresh-produce agglomerate. The consortium bought 90 hectares of land and has assembled three gigantic glasshouses, with planning permission for another four.

In 2009, Thanet Earth's first year in production, 2.5 million tomatoes left the glasshouses for the sorting area in an average week and the cucumber and pepper harvests peaked at half a million and three-quarters of a million a week (Harding 2010). This amounts to about 2 per cent of UK demand and the target is to supply 4 per cent of all tomatoes, cucumbers and peppers consumed in the UK.

Thanet Earth is heralded as an example of low-carbon horticulture on a grand scale. As Hardy notes, it scores well in terms of certain facets of sustainability. In

terms of water, for example, produce is grown on blocks of rock wool about a meter off the ground and surplus water drains into long trays underneath the blocks and from there to lagoons, along with rainwater off the roofs, to be pumped around again. Thanet Earth is also clever in terms of its energy strategy, using a system called combined heat and power. On other issues it is also virtuous – minimal pesticide use and preserving biodiversity – but it scores less well in terms of labour, with very few indigenous British workers among the workforce who harvest the crop, although such labour issues are not uncommon in other, smaller-scale, horticultural enterprises.

So could Thanet Earth-like growing models potentially bring Britain to self-sufficiency in 'salad'? The paradox is that it is not just about growing more food; it is also about getting people to eat the right type and balance of foods. As Harding (2010: 7) puts it: 'A larger query hanging over hydroponic growing in the UK is quite what it solves until we all start eating many more tomatoes, cucumbers and peppers.'

8,100 cow dairy herd on a single farm in Lincolnshire. The scheme, including a revised proposal (for a 3,770-cow herd), was eventually withdrawn in response to continued opposition from the Environment Agency (the regulator managing UK freshwater systems), as well as animal welfare groups and local residents.

2. *Waste*. This example is about making better use of what we already have (i.e. we need to be less wasteful). There is growing realization that we are eating beyond our means and that food chain dependency on imports creates vulnerability. This approach is captured well in Stuart's (2009: xxii) text, *Waste*, where he argues 'industrialized nations need to learn what it means to live in scarcity – because the appearance of infinite abundance is an illusion'. The essence of his argument is that we can increase food supply and reduce environmental consequences by reducing waste within the food supply chain. In the USA, for example, around 50 per cent of all food is wasted. In Britain, we create up to 20 million tonnes of food waste per year. The Japanese dispose of food worth ¥11 trillion [US$101.6 billion] annually. Food is treated as a 'disposable commodity' throughout the developed world (Stuart 2009: xvi). We waste food at all stages of the food chain, from production and harvesting through to post-purchase by the consumer. Waste may arise due to poor handling, poor storage, cultural perceptions, retailer demands, consumer ignorance or sheer laziness. Stuart (2009: xix) argues that we can turn this wastefulness to our advantage in that 'the world's mountain of surplus food is currently an environmental liability – but it is also a great opportunity'. Efficiency measures could create savings and help the fight against hunger. Salvaging food would also help tackle global warming. In Europe, for example, more than 30 per cent of Europe's greenhouse gas emissions come from food. If food waste was halved, emissions would be reduced by 5 per cent or more. There are now a number of social movements, national and global campaigns and food chain initiatives emerging to promote awareness about reducing different forms of food waste, including Feeding The 5000.

3. *The urban foodscape*. Burgeoning prices for basic foodstuffs and concerns about the security and sustainability of the agri-food system are also raising awareness of the pressures facing urban areas and their need to grow as well as consume food. For example, in a study of the evolution of food strategies in London and New York it is argued that both of these world cities are being forced to think anew about food security so that 'despite being highly developed sites of global capitalism, [they] have not managed to banish the spectre of hunger from their streets' (Morgan and Sonnino 2010: 222). Urban food security policy in both cities is focusing on two key dimensions of the problem: food production and food access. For the former, new planning dispensation for urban agriculture allows the city to feed itself from within (as in London) or from neighbouring areas (as in New York). For the latter, both cities have used the school meal service as the main food access scheme for children, with New York actively promoting the consumption of fresh food in poor districts via schemes like *Green Cart*.

The last of these three indicative examples articulates a wider definition and framing of food security beyond that conceived in the pages of agricultural trade journals and the sustainable intensification mantra (i.e. not just about availability of food but also concerned with access and utilization). As Mooney and Hunt (2009) suggest, these framings exist side-by-side as part of a multi-organizational political field of differential power networks that constitutes food security.

15.5 Conclusion: the ethical foodscape

This chapter has reviewed the changing nature of food production, especially in the context of developed market economies. The important contributions that geographers have made to debates concerning the long-term sustainability of agri-food systems have been highlighted. Such a broad assessment is always partial in its coverage, but it shows how geographers have examined different systems of food production in different spatial and temporal contexts. Different types of production system have attracted particular research attention at certain times. A good deal of the research in the late 1970s, 1980s and early 1990s examined industrial agriculture and the industrialization of the food system. The capitalist mode of production still prevails and large agri-food companies and corporate retailers have developed considerable power and effectively exert control over the entire food supply system. Geographers and others are continuing to provide valuable insights into these processes, as evidenced through the salmon farming studies in Chile and Friedberg's (2014) recent work on the *technopolitics* of Life Cycle Assessment footprints. Techniques like footprinting are increasingly used by food corporations as new forms of governance that demonstrate and at the same time construct how sustainability is defined.

Despite these efforts, there is dissatisfaction with the performance of the food system. Since the late-1990s, much attention has been placed on alternative and local food systems. Farmers and other producers have developed 'alternative' forms of agriculture, based on territorial association and direct consumer contact, and geographers continue to actively examine these modes of production. In some cases, these systems of provision directly challenge 'mainstream' forms of food provision. They represent ways of growing and procuring food that are different in terms of scale and operation. Debates about food security are also attracting renewed attention from food policy analysts, geographers and other agri-food researchers. This threat to 'global food security' is not new and many food analysts have in fact predicted it for some time. Crucially, the new emphasis is forcing a re-think about the way we produce food, where and how we produce food, and how we value food. Much of this is still to be worked out, but we are already seeing how the 'crisis' is forcing different actors in the foodscape to reposition their alliances (Maye and Kirwan 2013).

This debate is also forcing us to re-conceptualize food systems and the way in which we assess whether they are a sustainable and ethical way of food provisioning. As Hinrichs (2014: 143) argues, the present context of intertwined and intensifying economic, environmental and climate change challenges and crises means we must enlarge our thinking about food systems change and sustainability transitions. McMichael (2009) argues that the food regime concept is a useful way to do this because it not only reveals the structured moments and transitions in the history of capitalist food relations, but also of capitalism itself (see also Sage 2013). In these terms the 'world food crisis' is thus a consequence of industrial capitalism's long-term over-dependence on fossil fuel, combined with the inflation-producing effects of biofuels offsets, financial speculation activities, and the concentration and centralization practices of agribusiness capital.

Another example relates to 'ethical foodscapes', where 'morality is a key and growing currency in the provisioning of food in much of the post-industrial North and beyond' (Goodman et al. 2010: 1783). While all food has ethical implications, some food has taken on the connotation of being, often in quite particular ways, more

ethical. This applies particularly to foods labelled as alternative. Many of these more ethical foods are equally a part of conventional food systems and many foods that we label 'conventional' or 'ordinary' have their own implicit moralities and ethical relationships and meanings so that 'the ethics of ethical foodscapes can thus be ambiguous, slippery and consist of a number of interwoven layers' (Goodman et al. 2010: 1783). This means that we need to break down dualistic characterizations of 'alternative' foods as uniquely ethical and conventional foods as unethical. We also need greater critical analysis of our assessments of 'goodness' and 'badness', whether in terms of practical indicators, material practices or acceptable food politics. The current 'food crisis' offers an excellent opportunity to carry out closer food system examinations of what constitutes 'goodness' and 'badness'. How and where should we grow food? Do we want our cities to be places where we grow (more) food? Should we challenge methods of growing food that promote so-called 'sustainable intensification'? What about the role of local food systems in the future?

Finally, new debates about '*sustainable diets*' (i.e. how diets impact and could be changed to improve the sustainability of the planet) and the emergence of 'less meat initiatives' (Morris et al. 2014) raise significant socio-economic and ethical questions, including their potential to contribute to a transition towards more sustainable forms of meat production, provisioning and eating. As a more general concluding point, it is suggested that an emphasis on food ethics in a context of growing uncertainty about food supplies is a highly fruitful means by which to examine food production geographies. A better understanding of food production geographies and capacities will also help to ameliorate social and ecological inequalities. The material presented in this chapter suggests the era of endless food may be winding down. Our habits will have to change because, as the food writer Felicity Lawrence (2008; quoted in Harding 2010: 3) puts it, 'they simply cannot go on. We are now entering a period of rapid transition'. Human geographers are well placed to provide analytical insight into transitions to food sustainability.

Learning outcomes

After reading this chapter, you should have:

- An understanding of the importance of food to modern economies and societies and what is meant by a food chain and its application in different contexts.

- An awareness of how and why the agri-food system has become globalized – especially the dominance and spatially uneven penetration by transnational agribusinesses.

- An awareness of the emergence of quality-based commodity food production in some parts of the developing world and the reasons why this has happened.

- An understanding of 'alternative food networks', including some of the main reasons why they have arisen, how they are conceptualized and case study examples to explain their diverse character.

- An appreciation of recent debates about food security and ethics and a sense of how these issues disturb and unsettle notions of 'goodness' and 'badness' in relation to food production and provisioning more generally.

- An ability to begin to think critically about geographies of food production.

Further reading

Friedberg, S. (2004) *French Beans and Food Scares: Culture and Commerce in an Anxious Age,* Oxford University Press, Oxford. A comparative case study of global food commodity networks, tracing the supply of green beans for two culturally specific trade links – France/Burkina Faso and England/Zambia.

Gardner, B. (2013) *Global Food Futures,* Bloomsbury, London. This book provides a very useful account of the 'new food crisis' from an economic perspective, including detailed overviews of world agricultural trade and production.

Maye, D., Holloway, L. and Kneafsey, M. (eds.) (2007) *Alternative Food Geographies: Representation and Practice,* Elsevier, Oxford. This book examines debates and practices surrounding efforts to establish 'alternative' systems of food provision, with studies from Europe, North and South America, Australia and Africa.

Morgan, K., Marsden, T. and Murdoch, J. (2006) *Worlds of Food: Place, Power and Provenance in the Food Chain,* Oxford University Press, Oxford. This book provides a review of agri-food networks, including so-called 'conventional' and 'alternative' food networks, with case studies from Italy, the UK and the USA.

Millstone, E. and Lang, T. (2008) *The Atlas of Food,* 2nd edition, Earthscan, London. A good introductory text that reveals the often surprising ways we make, process, ship, trade and eat foods.

Sage, C. (2012) *Environment and Food.* Routledge, London. This book provides a very good introduction to food and environment relations, including ecological impacts of different agri-food systems.

Stuart, T. (2009) *Waste: Uncovering the Global Food Scandal.* Penguin Books, London. An excellent text on the way we treat food as a disposable commodity and have, in effect, created our own global food crisis. It also offers solutions to fix it.

Useful websites

http://ec.europa.eu/agriculture/index_en.htm This web link is the Directorate General (DG) responsible for Agriculture and Rural Development, and is part of the official (and much bigger) website of the European Union. This DG site contains information on the EU's Common Agricultural Policy, key speeches and policy papers, statistics and links to member state sites.

www.defra.gov.uk The site of the UK government's Department of Environment, Food and Rural Affairs. The site contains information on UK agricultural policy (including the most recent round of mid-term reforms), statistics and links to other government departments, non-ministerial departments and NGOs. Similar sites exist for other national governments (see, for example, www.usda.gov, home of the US Department of Agriculture, including useful details about the US farm bill).

www.sustainweb.org The site for Sustain – the alliance for better food and farming, an NGO umbrella organization which campaigns for more sustainable food chain practices. Contains information about various projects Sustain are working on and a raft of challenging position papers and responses to various food-related topics.

www.soilassociation.org This site is home to the UK organization dedicated to promoting organic food and farming. The site contains an online library with useful papers on various topics, including local/regional food schemes, food and farming policy, GMs and animals and food security, as well as a 'links' page which lists other useful websites related to food and farming. You can also visit their consumer website, http://why.organic.org, which contains useful information about the nutritional benefits of organic food.

www.fairtrade.org.uk Site for the Fairtrade Foundation. Contains information about the fair trade movement, products sold, suppliers, etc.; it also has a useful resources section with links to downloadable position papers and case studies. For those interested in ethical consumerism more broadly, see also www.ethicalconsumer.org, which examines the ethical credentials of individual products/organizations.

www.fcrn.org.uk/ Site for the Food Climate Research Network. Its aim is to better understand how the food system contributes to greenhouse gas emissions, which includes researching and promoting ways of reducing emissions. It is a fantastic resource for those interested in questions about food security and sustainability, with resources, case studies, interviews and a link to an email list.

www.bis.gov.uk/foresight/our-work/projects/current-projects/global-food-and-farming-futures Site for the Global Food and Farming Foresight study and contains various reviews and outputs from the study, which reported in 2011. It also contains a link to other relevant Foresight studies, including one about the future of land use in the UK.

www.feedbackglobal.org/ Site dedicated to campaigning against the global food waste scandal. It contains links to on-going campaigns, including Feed the 5000, and a section about 'food waste facts', which includes a video link to Tristram Stuart's excellent TED talk.

THE GEOGRAPHIES OF GLOBAL PRODUCTION NETWORKS

Chapter 16

Neil M. Coe

Topics covered

- Defining and identifying production networks

- Spatial divisions of labour

- The governance of production networks

- Production networks in their institutional contexts

- Reshaping production networks through 'standards' and 'codes'

16.1 Engaging with global production networks

Imagine the scene. We could be in San Francisco, Shanghai, Sheffield, Singapore or Sydney, or many other places besides. A student – having just been to a lecture and en route to her evening job in a restaurant – stops for a drink in a café. After choosing from the extensive menu of coffee options, she takes a window seat and boots up her laptop computer, instantly connecting to the free wifi the café offers for its customers. Essay assignment in hand, the student starts surfing the Internet, looking for the reading materials and background information she will need. Every so often, she pauses, takes a sip of coffee – an iced caffè mocha or some such like – and gazes out at the street . . .

On the one hand, what is being described here is a unique consumption event, an individual lost in her thoughts as she consumes her coffee and uses her laptop at a particular time and in a particular place (see Chapter 19). And yet, on the other hand, the two central non-human artefacts in this particular story – the coffee and the laptop – may have remarkably similar economic geographies and histories, wherever the event is taking place.

For example, the coffee bar in question might be a branch of Starbucks, with annual revenues of US$16.4 billion making it the world's largest coffeehouse chain, serving millions of customers every day in some 20,500 cafés across more than 60 countries (as of January 2015). It is one of many other similar chains offering their own standardized take on the continental European coffee house experience: for example, Caffè Nero, Costa Coffee or Coffee Republic in the United Kingdom; Caribou Coffee or Coffee Bean and Tea Leaf in the United States; Barista

or Café Coffee Day in India; and Gloria Jean's or Dome in Australia. There is a strong chance that the coffee beans were roasted and processed by one of just ten American and European firms – a mixture of large transnational corporations such as Nestlé, Mondelez and D.E. Master Blenders 1753, and a few big coffee roasters such as Smucker's, Strauss, Starbucks and Tchibo – which handle some 40 per cent of the world's coffee each year. Equally, the laptop used by our student may well be made by either Hewlett Packard (HP) or Lenovo, which between them, at the end of 2014, accounted for 39 per cent of the global market share. Indeed, just five companies – HP, Dell, and Apple (US), Lenovo (China), and Acer (Taiwan) – account for almost 70 per cent of laptop sales worldwide.

Why are these observations interesting? In short, because both the cup of coffee being consumed and the laptop being used are the end result of far-reaching global production networks, which are in turn dominated by powerful corporate interests of various kinds. Almost all the commodities that we consume have complicated histories and geographies and yet, as a system, capitalism seems to conceal these. The purchase of commodities such as coffee or computers with money serves to *disconnect* producers and consumers, meaning many consumers are unaware of the nature of the production system that has enabled those commodities to be available to them. This poses profound challenges to both conscientious consumers actively curious about the history of the commodities they consume (see Chapter 19), and economic geographers who want to understand connections and interdependencies within the global economy. In reality, even drinking just one cup of coffee links the consumer – albeit unknowingly in most cases – to hundreds of thousands of workers involved directly or indirectly in its production through complex global webs of connections.

Plate 16.1 A common scene – but what stories lie behind these everyday products?

(KieferPix/Shutterstock)

This chapter is therefore about how we, as economic geographers, can explore and understand the inherent variability of global production networks. In what follows, we will look in turn at four generic dimensions of all global production networks, namely their organization, geography, power relations or 'governance', and institutional context. We will use the contrasting examples of the coffee and laptop global production networks as illustrations of these various dimensions. In the final section of the chapter we will look at ongoing attempts to reshape production networks through the implementation of different kinds of standards and codes of conduct.

16.2 Production chains, production networks . . .

Every economic activity can be thought of as a production chain – a linked series of **value-adding activities** (see Figure 16.1). In very simple terms, material and non-material inputs are combined and transformed through some kind of production process, leading to a new good or service that needs to be delivered to the customer who then consumes it. Consumption, in turn, is not just a single act of purchase, but an ongoing process that may include maintenance, repair, waste disposal, recycling and the like. This basic model holds whether it is a physical good – such as a television or bicycle – being produced, or a service such as a haircut or insurance policy, with the difference coming in the relative balance of tangible and intangible elements in the production chain (see Chapter 17). While simple chains can be thought of in linear terms, in reality (as Figure 16.1 shows) they are enmeshed within much wider *networks* of relationships involving a broad range of other functions that are necessary for economic activities to take place: for example, research and development, market research, technological inputs, logistics services, advertising, legal services, accounting, personnel management, software, security and so on. In turn, these inter-firm relations are embedded in broader financial and regulatory systems that may bring non-firm entities such as the state and its many institutions into view. In this chapter we use the term *production network* to refer to the full mesh of relationships that lies behind any economic activity.

Production networks vary greatly in their complexity. At one end of the scale is the single farmer who grows

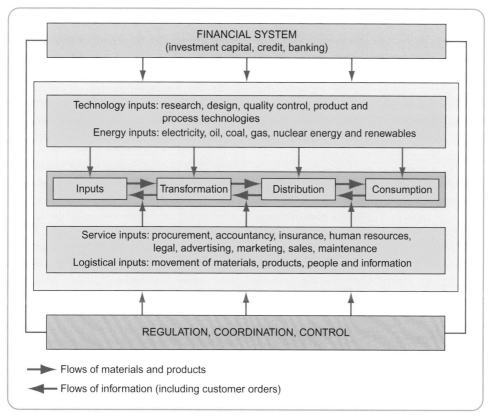

Figure 16.1 A generic production network.
Source: Dicken (2015), Figure 3.3c

one particular kind of vegetable and transports it to a local market for sale at harvest time. Conversely, a complicated manufactured product such as a car mobilizes a wide range of skills and technologies to bring together the thousands of components that comprise the finished product. The next step is to think about *who* undertakes the different activities in a given production network. Hypothetically, every single function might be carried out by one huge firm, which would coordinate the production network through its internal management hierarchy (a vertically integrated system). Equally, every single function might be undertaken by separate firms, meaning that the production network would take the form of a series of external, inter-firm relationships (a vertically disintegrated system). In reality, all production networks fall somewhere between these extremes. In a context of increased global competition, however, the dominant trend has been for firms in many sectors to focus on their core activity or 'competency', while seeking non-core inputs via external relationships. For some commentators, this trend is part of a broader shift from *Fordist* to more flexible *post-Fordist* production systems.

These increasingly important external networks can take on many forms:

- *Markets:* some inputs – usually of low value and standardized – will simply be purchased by firms on the open market. In this case, there is no long-term relationship between the two parties and firms can readily switch between suppliers.
- *Subcontracting:* this involves firms buying inputs that have been made, under contract, to meet their own specific requirements. The stability of the relationship will vary according to the formality and length of the contract. Subcontracting may involve the entire manufacture of a particular good or service, known as *commercial* subcontracting, or it may take the form of a firm buying in particular inputs that it does not have the skills or capacity to produce cost-effectively 'in-house'– *industrial* subcontracting.
- *Strategic alliances/joint ventures:* this is where firms come together to create a new corporate entity in order to undertake a particular task, for example costly joint research. In many other respects the participating firms may still remain competitors.
- *Franchising and licensing:* here, firms allow a company (the franchisee or licensee) to sell their product or service in a particular territory under given terms and conditions, and in return for a set fee. Franchising is very common in the service sector (including fast food, retailing, coffee shops, etc.), allowing rapid geographical expansion.

In sum, every production network constitutes a unique constellation of activities performed via complex combinations of internal and external network connections. The first step in understanding any production system, therefore, is to map out the key participants and the *nature* of the relationships that connect them.

The coffee production network is relatively straightforward and is represented schematically in Figure 16.2. Even so, coffee travels a long way and changes hands several times on the journey from bean to cup. The major participants in the network are depicted by boxes, and the transactions that move coffee in its different forms between participants are shown by arrows. Coffee flows through the network from the growers, who in effect begin the system, to the consumers who represent the end point. Coffee – which comes in two main types, Arabica and Robusta – is generally grown on small farms or estates in the tropical countries. Once basic processing has extracted the 'green' coffee beans from picked coffee cherries, they will pass in 60-kg bags from an exporter to a consuming country importer, trader or broker, then on to a roaster or instant coffee manufacturer, and then finally to a consumer via either a supermarket shelf or café of some kind. These relationships are essentially 'arms-length' *market* connections, with prices being set by international commodity markets such as the New York Board of Trade (Arabica) and the London International Financial Futures and Options Exchange (Robusta). We will see later, however, how the roles of these various participants have evolved over time.

In contrast, laptop computers are the outcome of a much more complicated production network that brings together hundreds of different components into the finished product. It is estimated, for example, that a laptop may contain around 2,200 separate parts (Dedrick *et al.* 2010). The personal computer (PC) industry is therefore a complex network of firms involved in a wide range of different industry segments – from microprocessors and other electronic components to applications and systems software providers – and covering a wide range of activities: R&D and design, manufacturing, assembly, logistics, distribution, sales, marketing, service and support. How these various functions are split between different companies has changed over time. Historically in the computer industry, vertically integrated giants such as IBM, HP and Siemens operated in all the industry segments and carried out the key functions of product innovation, manufacturing and customer relations internally.

Since the advent of the PC, however, a much more complex 'tiered' network has evolved in which most companies concentrate on one particular market segment, for example, assembling PCs, or making circuit

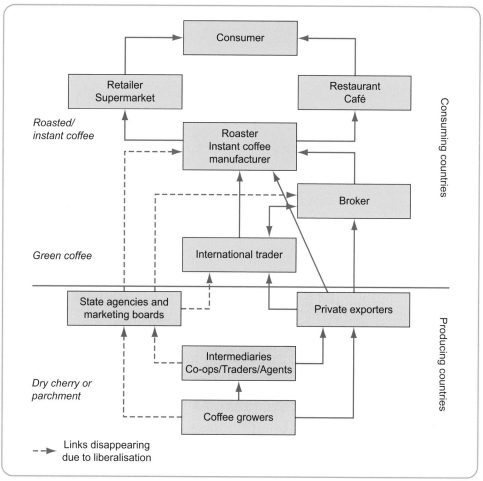

Figure 16.2 The coffee production network.

Source: adapted from Ponte (2002), Figure 1 and Talbot (2004), Figure 2.1

boards or disk drives (see Figure 16.3). The PC can now be described as a *modular* product, whereby 10 to 15 relatively self-contained sub-components (e.g. keyboard, monitor, hard drive, etc.) are brought together and assembled, an attribute that facilitates the disintegration of the production network across separate firms. Branded PC companies now focus primarily on design and customer relations, 'outsourcing' the remainder of the production process to other firms. This system reflects the nature of the PC as a standardized product assembled from components that can be produced in a wide variety of locations by a broad range of firms. Only limited value is added by assembling a PC: in most cases PC firms add value through customer relationships, either directly through their own direct sales and service relationships (e.g. help desks, repairs, etc.) or indirectly through their branding, marketing and quality assurance practices. They also extract value from the network through coordinating the

logistics operations that turn components into finished products on customer doorsteps. As Curry and Kenney (2004: 114) suggest, 'a PC assembler is, in many ways, more a logistics coordinator than a manufacturer'.

Most laptop assembly operations, therefore, are subcontracted to contract manufacturers (CM), and increasingly, to a particular form of subcontractor known as the original design manufacturer (ODM) who will also contribute to the design process. In the case of contract manufacturers, a branded PC firm is likely to employ its own, on-the-ground design and development teams throughout the production process to supervise subcontractors: this is the model preferred by Toshiba and Lenovo (the leading Chinese manufacturer), for example. With an ODM, however, the PC maker may take primary responsibility for design, but it will then pass a product specification on to the ODM for final development and manufacturing; HP and Apple operate in this way and

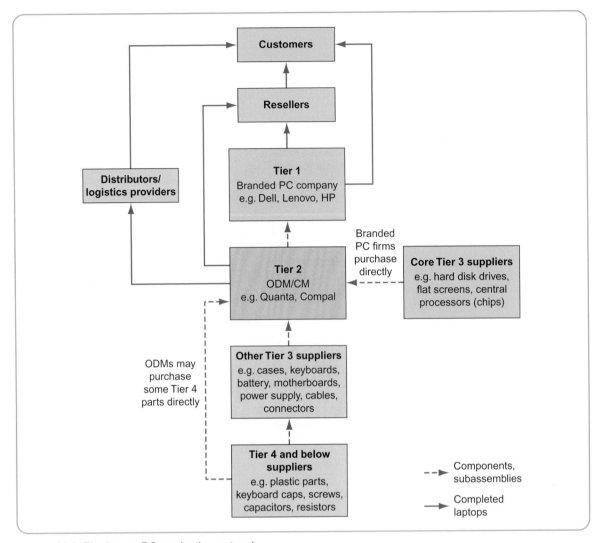

Figure 16.3 The laptop PC production network.

Source: adapted from Foster *et al.* (2006), Figure 2

this is currently the most common model in the industry. In yet another model, smaller PC vendors without the scale to undertake their own design activity may simply purchase generic 'off-the-shelf' products from ODMs to be labelled and sold under their own name. Backwards relationships from branded PC firms to ODMs may also extend forwards to the customer through the delivery and servicing of laptops on behalf of PC vendors. Overall, the result is a highly responsive and efficient production system in which an order via a branded PC company's website can be dispatched by an ODM within 48 hours.

It is important to bear in mind that Figure 16.3 only provides a limited window on what is, in reality, a highly complex network connecting together hundreds of firms and tens of thousands of workers. For example, the hard disk drive industry (see 'Core Tier 3 suppliers' box in

Figure 16.3) is itself a significant sector involving several tiers of firms and assemblers spread across East and South-east Asia. It is to these complex, on-the-ground geographies of production networks that we now turn.

16.3 Geographies of production networks: spatial divisions of labour

It goes without saying, of course, that the production networks described above do not exist on the head of a pin, but rather connect together, and indeed partly constitute, real places within the global economy. Every production network requires a **spatial division of labour**, which refers to the way in which certain elements of the production process are concentrated in particular places. The concept of the spatial division of labour is elucidated particularly well by Massey (1984) who explored how these spatial variations are both *created* and *exploited* by the ongoing restructuring of capitalist firms in their pursuit of profit. After examining the spatial restructuring of the UK economy in the 1960s and 1970s, her key argument was that under conditions of increased global competition, corporations were increasingly looking to separate spatially the *control* functions performed by managerial workers from the *execution* functions undertaken by manual workers. In its most simple form, low-skilled manual tasks were tending to locate in peripheral areas, while managerial and R&D tasks were concentrating in core cities and their surrounding regions. Massey argued that, over time, different *layers* of investment fan out across the economic landscape, redefining the nature of relationships between places as they gain or lose different kinds of activities.

Different spatial divisions of labour arise from variations in corporate structures which, at a simple level, can be divided into *cloning* and *part-process* structures. In the cloning structure, the production apparatus is simply replicated in different localities, with ultimate control residing at a headquarters, usually sited in the firm's initial place of origin. In the part-process format, there is a technical division of labour between branch plants, with components being made in one location and passed on to another for final assembly. The different stages of the production process will have varying requirements, and hence tend towards different kinds of location.

Massey's conceptual apparatus is still extremely powerful today, although her study – which was primarily about *intra-firm* and *intra-national* divisions of labour – needs to be extended in two important ways. First, as we have already noted, spatial divisions of labour can be constructed through combinations of intra-firm (internal), and increasingly, inter-firm (external) networks. Second, we need to apply these ideas at the *international* scale. One of the defining characteristics of the world economy over the past two to three decades has been the dramatic increase in the number of transnational corporations (TNCs) organizing their spatial divisions of labour at the international scale. It is now difficult to think of a production network that does not have at least some international elements, even if it is just seen in the sourcing of one or two inputs, or a limited export market for the final good/service. *Global* production networks, as we will call them here, have become one of the most important organizational features of the contemporary global economy. Spotlight box 16.1 considers different attempts to conceptualize the nature of international divisions of labour at different points in the global economy's evolution.

We can make three further arguments about the geographies of global production networks:

- First, their *geographical complexity* is increasing, enabled by a range of developments in transport, communication and process technologies. As we shall see shortly, the assembly of a laptop requires components manufactured at places all across East Asia.

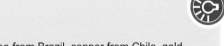

Spotlight box 16.1

Conceptualizing global divisions of labour?

It is helpful to distinguish between three separate attempts to conceptualize international spatial divisions of labour, which broadly coincide with different phases of development of the global economy.

- First, it is possible to identify the traditional **international division of labour** (IDL) that took shape by the nineteenth century and prevailed largely unaltered until the 1950s. The IDL essentially depicted a *trading* system – shaped initially by global trading empires, and later by the rise of the USA as an economic power – in which the developing world or 'periphery' was largely relegated to providing raw materials and agricultural plantation products

(e.g. coffee from Brazil, copper from Chile, gold and diamonds from South Africa) for the industrialized economies of the 'core' (Western Europe and the USA). High-value manufactured goods were exchanged between the industrialized countries, and some were exported back to developing countries.

- Second, from the 1960s onwards, a **new international division of labour** (NIDL) started to emerge in which European, North American and Japanese TNCs created labour-intensive export platforms in so-called 'newly industrializing economies' (NIEs) (especially in East Asia and, to a lesser extent, Latin America) in response to falling profit rates in the core countries. Crucially, the system depended on new technologies that allowed production fragmentation, thereby creating tasks that could use, often young and female, semi-skilled or unskilled workers in the periphery. Two kinds of technology were important: *process* technologies that allowed the subdivision of the manufacturing process into simple and self-contained tasks, and *transportation* technologies such as jet aircraft and containerized shipping that allowed the efficient shipment of both components and finished goods.

- Third, it has become clear that in recent decades a *new global division of labour* has emerged that is far more complex than the system depicted in the NIDL model, which does not capture, for example: how the range of NIE economies has broadened and deepened considerably, particularly in Asia; increasing investment into NIEs, such as China and India, to access their domestic markets; significant outward investment by NIE transnational corporations, e.g. from South Korean giants such as LG and Samsung; continued high levels of investment between developed economies and the emergence of complex international divisions of labour in the service sector. The contemporary global economy is clearly not characterized by one single type of IDL but rather many different forms. Rather than disappearing, the traditional IDL and the NIDL remain important in a range of industries (e.g. natural resources and clothing/toys, respectively) and have subsequently been overlain by, and have interacted with, newer and more complex international divisions of labour. For more on these debates, see Coe (2011).

- Second, the geographic configurations of global production networks are becoming *more dynamic* and liable to rapid change. This flexibility arises, first, from the use of certain 'space-shrinking' information and communication technologies and, second, from organizational forms that enable the fast spatial switching of productive capacity (Dicken 2015). In particular, the increased use of subcontracting and strategic alliance relationships (noted above) allows firms to switch contracts between different firms and places without incurring the costs of moving production themselves.

- Third, we need to connect these ideas about the geographical extensiveness and complexity of global production networks with notions concerning the geographical *clustering* of economic activity. Not all the connections within the system can be 'stretched out' across the global economy; some interactions will need to take place within the same locality because of the sheer intensity of transactions or because of the importance of place-specific knowledge to the activity concerned. From this perspective, global production networks need to be seen as the organizational forms that connect clusters together.

Let us now move on to apply these ideas to our two products. The global map of coffee production and consumption is not very complicated. Growing coffee involves several million farmers, who ultimately support the consumption of an estimated 2 billion cups of coffee every day. The vast majority of coffee production takes place in tropical countries while most of the consumption occurs in the wealthy markets of North America, Western Europe and East Asia. Some 8.5 million tonnes of coffee were produced in 2014, of which 6.7 million tonnes, or nearly 80 per cent, were exported. Although over 50 countries currently produce coffee, the top 12 exporters account for more than 90 per cent of the global trade (Figure 16.4). The geography of production is shaped by the ecology of the coffee plant which requires a consistently warm and wet climate, making it most suitable for growing in tropical highland areas. The production geography is not static, however. Most notably, exports of Robusta coffee grown in the central highlands of Vietnam have expanded dramatically over the last two decades – rising from just 100,000 tonnes in 1990 to 1.3 million tonnes by 2012 and remaining at or around that level ever since – creating an over-supply in the global market and putting severe downward pressure on prices. As a result, coffee growing is an increasingly marginal practice for growers across Central and Latin America and Africa. The consumption of coffee has a long history linked to colonial expansion by Europeans, which served to both spread the taste for coffee, particularly from the sixteenth century onwards, and spread coffee cultivation from its supposed origins in present-day Ethiopia to the band of tropical countries shown in Figure 16.4 (Topik 2009). The key commodity markets and international traders and roasters are, however, all based in the USA and Europe (see Figure 16.2).

Turning to the geography of the laptop production network, the majority of the world's laptops are produced by Taiwanese firms. All branded manufacturers – such as HP, Acer, Apple and Toshiba – rely on Taiwanese ODM firms for manufacturing and product development. In 1998, Taiwanese companies accounted for 40 per cent of a world market of 15 million units; this rose to 72 per cent of the 46 million laptops produced in 2004, and 94 per cent of the 195 million laptops produced in 2011. By the end of 2014, the top five Taiwanese manufacturers (see Table 16.1) alone produced 34.6 million (or 75 per cent) of the 46 million laptops shipped worldwide that quarter. Production is also growing faster than the PC market as a whole; in

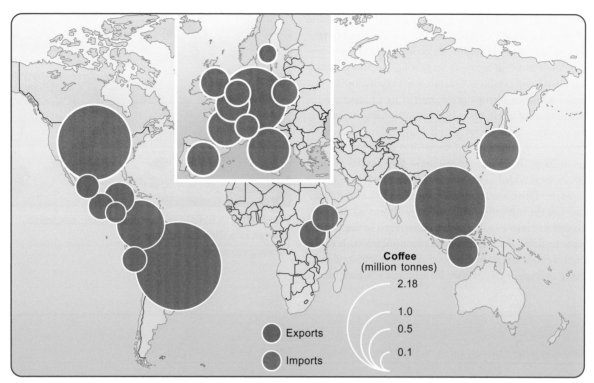

Figure 16.4 The top twelve coffee producing (exports) and consuming (imports) countries, 2014.

Source: data from www.ico.org [accessed 8 February 2015]

2005, one in three PCs sold globally was a laptop, while by 2014 nearly six in ten PCs were laptops. The industry can change incredibly rapidly, however, with both desktop and laptop PC shipment levels under threat of being overtaken by tablet devices by 2015, the production of which has mushroomed since the release of the first iPad in 2010. As Table 16.1 suggests, each leading laptop vendor tends to contract with two or three Taiwanese firms, arrangements which in the cases of HP and Apple account for upwards of 90 per cent of their total global laptop production; for Japanese companies such as Sony, Sharp and Toshiba, the proportion tends to be somewhat lower (50–70 per cent). Taipei – and the nearby region of Hsinchu where many Taiwanese high-tech firms are based – is therefore a critical node in the laptop production network.

However, these geographies are also far from static. Taiwanese electronics firms have been moving production 'offshore' – to South-east Asia, Europe and, most importantly, China – since the early 1990s. There are now two key PC clusters in China: the Shenzhen area of Guangdong province (in the south of the country), specializing in desktop machines, and the Shanghai/Suzhou/Yangtze River delta area, home to the laptop PC industry (see Figure 16.5). Before 2001, the Taiwanese government prohibited its laptop manufacturers from undertaking final assembly in China. When this restriction was lifted, the ODMs moved collectively, and incredibly rapidly, to the Shanghai area: in 2001 only 5 per cent of Taiwanese laptops were produced in China but by 2004 the figure had shot up to 80 per cent, and it is now almost 100 per cent. The

Table 16.1 Top five Taiwanese laptop PC manufacturers, 2014

Company	2014 shipment (millions)	Largest client	Second largest client	Third largest client
Quanta Computer	48.5	HP	Apple Inc	Asustec
Compal Electronics	43.1	Lenovo	HP	Dell
Wistron Corp	21.0	Dell	Lenovo	Hewlett-Packard
Inventec Corp	18.5	HP	Dell	Lenovo
Pegatron Corp	9.8	Asustec	Toshiba	Acer

Source: http://world.einnews.com/article/212643959/YtHuloncE0J-bEKD [accessed 18 February 2015].

lower costs of land, labour and facilities on the mainland allowed the firms to build giant factories, expand output and reduce costs through scale economies. The production levels involved are quite staggering: in 2014 the leading Taiwanese producer Quanta was manufacturing just under 4 million laptops per month at its Chinese plants. The offices of these firms in Taiwan remain responsible for product development, technology research, materials procurement, financial management and marketing (Saxenian 2006). In this way, a new *intra-firm* spatial division of labour is added to the system depicted in Figure 16.3.

Many Taiwanese component suppliers had already relocated to the region by 2001, and now almost all the parts needed to make a laptop are manufactured in the Suzhou area. Initially, the highest-value components such as the central processor, hard drive and displays continued to be made overseas by Japanese, Korean and US companies,

Plate 16.2 A female worker assembling electronic devices in a Chinese factory.

(ArtWell/Shutterstock)

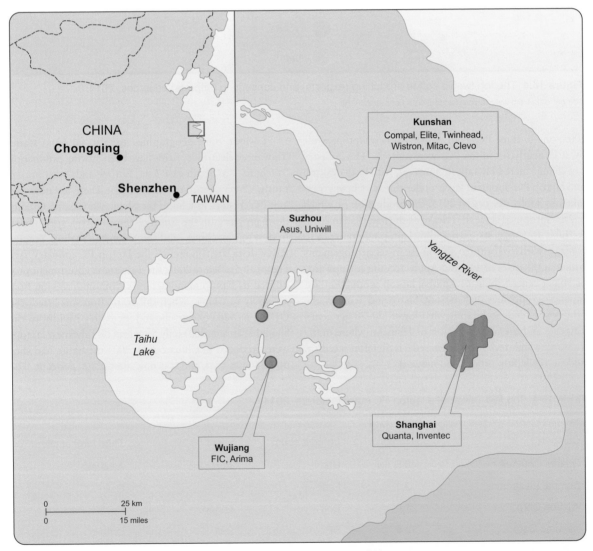

Figure 16.5 The laptop manufacturing cluster, Yangtze delta region, China.

Source: based on Yang (2006), Appendix 2

but over time many firms such as the US hard disk drive manufacturer Seagate and chip firm AMD have themselves established production facilities in the Shanghai region. Moving the entire supply chain to the Shanghai region in this way allowed the Taiwanese firms to overcome deficiencies in the Chinese logistics and distribution sectors. The scale of the undertaking should not be underestimated: by 2005 some 3,300 Taiwanese firms had already invested US$26 billion in Suzhou alone. Several of the transnational computer brand manufacturers (e.g. Toshiba, Samsung and Sony) also have bases in the region.

More recent developments suggest that these geographies are once again in flux, driven both by rising costs in the coastal provinces and strong growth in the Chinese domestic market for IT products and services of all kinds. In line with many other kinds of manufacturing activities in China, since 2010 significant levels of PC production have started to move to inland provinces. In particular, the massive inland city of Chongqing in Sichuan province (see Figure 16.5) has rapidly become an important site of PC manufacturing involving both branded PC firms and Taiwanese ODMs. In 2010, for instance, HP and the Taiwanese motherboard company Foxconn jointly opened two facilities in the city capable of manufacturing 20 million laptops a year. The companies were attracted by the low labour, land and logistics costs as well as the city's free trade zone. They were also able to benefit from a discounted corporate tax rate of 15 per cent (down from the usual 25 per cent), while the city authorities also promised to extend the second runway of the local airport to

meet HP's logistical requirements. Quanta and Inventec have likewise established manufacturing bases in the city. As these trends continue, the geography of global laptop construction is once again being reworked.

While the laptop global production network has a relatively concentrated geography around the key nodes of Taipei/Hsinchu and Shanghai-Suzhou, the PC industry generally has a somewhat more disparate geography. We can use the case of Dell as an example. There are three distinctive elements to Dell's business model. First, the company only sells direct to its customers, bypassing almost entirely distributors, resellers, and retailers (see Figure 16.3). Second, unlike some PC manufacturers, Dell chooses to undertake a significant proportion of the final assembly of both desktop and laptop computers itself, allowing customers to specify the components included in a particular product line (a process that can be thought of as 'mass customization'). The proportion of final assembly has been declining over time due to competitive pressures, however, with some laptops now made entirely by ODMs and some arriving in Dell's factories semi-assembled (the so-called 'two-touch' approach). Third, it has aggressively used the Internet to establish not only its system of direct sales, but also the procurement and assembly operations, thereby dramatically reducing its inventory of components. Figure 16.6 illustrates how Dell services its global market by using a series of regional production and service clusters (Fields 2004). Such clusters are an integral part of the global space economy (see Spotlight box 16.2).

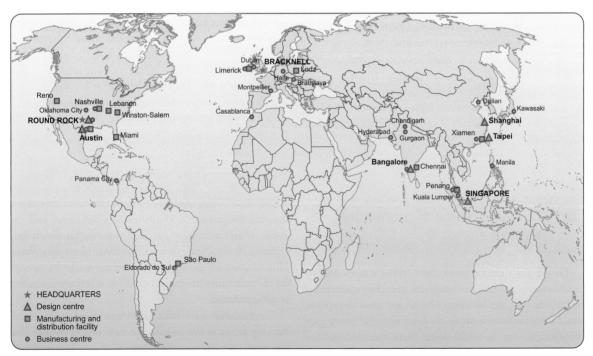

Figure 16.6 Dell's global production network, mid-2009.

Source: data from www.dell.com [accessed 22 June 2009]

Spotlight box 16.2

Types of clusters in the global economy

There is a wide variety of different kinds of clusters in the global economy, created through different historical processes, and bound together by varying combinations of both *traded* and *untraded* interdependencies. Traded interdependencies are created by firms co-locating in a cluster alongside suppliers, partners and customers with which they have formal trading relationships. Untraded interdependencies are the less tangible benefits of being located in the same place, for example the emergence of a particular pool of specialized workers. In particular, clusters can facilitate patterns of intense and ongoing face-to-face communication – and thereby transfers of important forms of intangible knowledge – between people working in the same or closely related industries.

We can think of at least eight significant types, each performing different roles within the global system:

1. *Labour intensive craft production clusters.* These are often found in industries such as clothing where firms are involved in tight subcontracting networks and often use high levels of immigrant labour and homeworkers. Examples include the garment production districts of Los Angeles, New York and Paris.

2. *Design intensive craft production clusters.* These refer to dense agglomerations of small- and medium-sized firms specializing in a particular aspect of the high-quality production of a good or service. Examples include the renowned towns and districts of the Third Italy including Prato (textiles), Santa Croce (leather goods) and Sassuolo (ceramics).

3. *High-technology innovative clusters.* These clusters tend to have a large base of innovative small- and medium-sized firms and flexible, highly skilled labour markets in sectors such as computer software and biotechnology. Examples include Silicon Valley in the USA and Cambridge, United Kingdom.

4. *Flexible production hub-and-spoke clusters.* In these clusters, a single large firm, or small group of large firms, buys components from an extensive range of local suppliers to make products for markets external to the cluster. Examples include Boeing in Seattle, USA, and Toyota in Toyota City, Japan.

5. *Production satellite clusters.* These clusters represent congregations of externally owned production facilities. These range from relatively basic assembly activity, through to more advanced plants with research capacity. Examples are to be found across the export processing zones (ePZs) of the developing world – the Shanghai laptop cluster would also fall into this category.

6. *Business service clusters.* Business services activities such as financial services, advertising, law, accountancy are concentrated in leading cities – such as New York, London and Tokyo – and their hinterlands.

7. *State-anchored clusters.* Some clusters have developed because of the location of government facilities such as universities, defence industry research establishments, prisons, or government offices. Examples include agglomerations that have developed because of government research investment (Colorado Springs, USA; Taejon, South Korea) and universities (Oxford/Cambridge, United Kingdom).

8. *Consumption clusters.* There are also strong propensities to cluster – often in central urban areas – in a wide variety of consumer service activities including retailers, bars and restaurants, and cultural, leisure and tourism facilities.

16.4 The governance of production networks

So far we have exemplified the various actors within production networks, the functions that they undertake, and where they are located. The next step is to explain how such production networks function, and more specifically, the way in which some firms use their power over other firms to control or 'drive' the overall system.

These 'lead' firms are able to define which other firms can join the network, the roles they perform, and the financial and technological conditions under which they perform those roles – despite not directly owning them. This shaping of global production networks by powerful corporations through inter-firm relations is known as governance.

Governance can take different forms. A useful starting point is the distinction between networks that are *producer-driven* and those that are *buyer-driven*

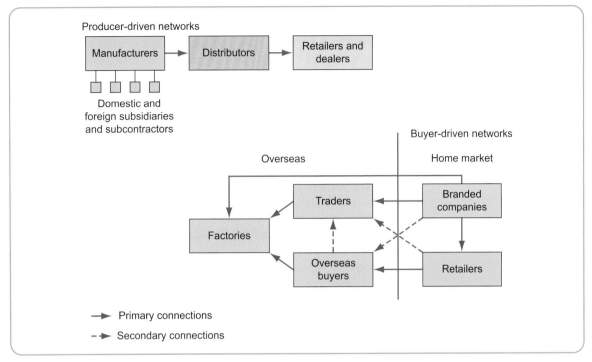

Figure 16.7 Producer- and buyer-driven production systems.

(Gereffi 1994; see Figure 16.7 and Table 16.2). Producer-driven networks tend to be found in sectors where large industrial corporations play the central role in controlling the production system, for example in capital- and technology-intensive industries such as aircraft, automobile and semiconductor manufacturing. Power in these networks is exercised through the headquarters operations of leading TNCs, and manifests itself in the ability to exert control over 'backward' linkages to raw material and component suppliers, and 'forward' linkages with distributors and retailers. High levels of profits are secured through the scale and volume of production in combination with the ability to drive technological developments within the production system. The automobile

Table 16.2 Producer-driven and buyer-driven production networks compared

	Form of economic governance	
	Producer-driven	**Buyer-driven**
Controlling type of capital	Industrial	Commercial
Capital/technology intensity	High	Low
Labour characteristics	Skilled/high wage	Unskilled/low wage
Controlling firm	Manufacturer	Retailer
Production integration	Vertical/bureaucratic	Horizontal/networked
Control	Internalized/hierarchical	Externalized/market
Contracting/outsourcing	Moderate and increasing	High
Suppliers provide	Components	Finished goods
Examples	Automobiles, computers, aircraft, electrical machinery	Clothing, footwear, toys, consumer electronics

Source: adapted from Kessler and Appelbaum (1998)

industry provides an excellent example of producer-driven networks. Leading assemblers such as Toyota and Ford coordinate production systems involving literally thousands of subsidiaries and tiers of subcontractor firms around the world, as well as extensive global networks of distributors and dealers.

Buyer-driven networks, by comparison, are characteristic of industries where large retailers (e.g. Wal-Mart or Tesco) and brand-name merchandisers (e.g. Nike or Reebok) play the central role in establishing and shaping the network, with production activity itself often located in developing countries (see Figure 16.7). This form of global production network is common in labour-intensive consumer goods sectors, such as clothing, footwear, toys and handicrafts. Production is usually undertaken using tiered networks of subcontractors that supply finished goods subject to the specifications of the powerful buyers. These buyers in turn extract substantial profits from bringing together their design, sales, marketing and financial expertise with strong brand names and access to large consumer markets.

The notions of producer- and buyer-driven networks are ideal types that allow us to get an overall impression of how a particular system functions, and in turn, who benefits most from the way it functions. In reality, however, the governance of global production networks is highly complex and variable both within, and between, different economic sectors. We can think about this complexity in three ways. First, there may be other forms of governance that seem to better characterize the overall nature of a particular production network. For example, in some contexts it might be useful to think of *relational* forms of governance that fall in between the producer- and buyer-driven models (Gereffi *et al.* 2005). These can be thought of as close inter-firm relationships that develop on a more even footing. In others, it might be trading firms – such as the Japanese giant trading firms, the so-called *soga shosha* – or intermediaries that drive the network. In the Internet era, for example, there is evidence that new forms of 'infomediaries' with extensive access to online consumer information (e.g. Google, AOL, etc.) may play increasingly important roles in production networks (Gereffi 2001). Second, when we look at the detail of a particular production network, it is important to recognize that there may be a variety of governance types in operation between the various actors within the overall system. A study comparing the PC production networks in the Yangtze and Pearl River delta regions of China, for example, found that in reality governance relations are extremely complicated and, indeed, varied significantly within the same industry (Yang and Coe 2009). Third, governance regimes are not static, but need to be seen in *dynamic* terms. The nature of a production

network – and indeed the constituent relationships within it – may change over time because of a wide range of factors, both internal and external to the system. In particular, firms and/or particular regions may seek to improve their position within the global production network through pursuing *upgrading* strategies.

At first glance, comparing coffee and laptops would seem to provide a nice contrast between buyer- and producer-driven networks. The coffee network is 'clearly buyer-driven and coffee roasters play the lead role in determining the functional division of labour along the chain. In other words, roasters define the key terms of participation directly for their immediate suppliers and indirectly for other actors further upstream' (Gibbon and Ponte 2005: 83). Roasters capture about 30 per cent of the value that is added in the coffee production network, but retailers (22 per cent) and international traders – such as Neumann and Volcafe – also do well (8 per cent). The result is that at least 60 per cent of the economic value derived from coffee goes to developed country firms, although some estimates put the figure as high as 80 per cent (Fitter and Kaplinsky 2001). The domination by these actors is in large part a simple story of concentrated market power and economies of scale: the top four international coffee traders account for 40 per cent of the global trade; as noted in the introduction to this chapter, the top ten roasters handle about 40 per cent of the world's coffee; and the top 30 global grocery retailers account for about one-third of global coffee sales. Roasters, for example, reap the economic benefits of buying the beans in bulk and having captive suppliers that depend on their purchases. Even so, the coffee network is not *as* buyer-driven as networks driven directly by supermarket chains (e.g. fresh fruit and vegetables) or by retailers and branded marketers (e.g. clothing and footwear). To a degree, the strong coffee roasters/brands are able to counteract the huge buying power of the retailers, meaning that influence is shared. Ideal-type buyer- and producer-driven chains, then, should perhaps be seen as the ends of a spectrum rather than discrete categories.

Typically, as noted in Table 16.2, the computer industry has been seen as a capital-intensive producer-driven network dominated by vertically integrated giants such as IBM. However, the computer industry has changed beyond recognition over the past 25 years as the PC has increasingly become a mass-market standardized product. The branded PC companies continue to drive the global production network, taking the decisions that drive the whole system and coordinating the activities of the other main players. But their role has changed over time. Leading manufacturers like HP and Apple have increasingly focused on final assembly, design and branding, with the vast majority of production outsourced to Asian subcontractors, thereby sharing the characteristics of the lead firms in buyer-driven systems such as clothing and shoe production. Over time, there has clearly been a shift in the governance characteristics of the PC industry.

However, it is possible to make another argument relevant to the PC sector. The branded PC marketplace has become increasingly competitive over recent years as the standardization process has progressively reduced profit margins for even the leading firms. The result has being ongoing consolidation and rationalization, with several large brands being swallowed up by competitors (e.g. Compaq by HP, IBM by Lenovo). O'Riain (2004) has suggested that we might think of the PC network (and others like it) as falling into another governance category – the technology-driven network, in which it is control over technical standards which is critical for exercising power over the system. In that sense, it is the firms that set the dominant architectural standards for PCs in terms of software (Microsoft's operating systems) and hardware (Intel's computer chips) that benefit most from the production network and secure profits

rates significantly higher than any other participants in the industry. 'Power . . . resides, therefore, in what is getting made and mobilizing networks of support for those products rather than in how that product is itself produced – emphasizing the place of intellectual property holders in securing the rewards . . . within the system' (O'Riain 2004: 645). These arguments are supported by detailed research into the gains associated with manufacturing a HP laptop computer (Dedrick *et al*. 2010). The study found that while Microsoft and Intel secured net profits of 36 and 31 per cent respectively, and key component manufacturers in the range of 4 to 12 per cent, HP themselves only made a profit of 4 per cent, with the assembler (i.e. ODM) making an even lower profit rate of 2.4 per cent. These pressures are forcing the Taiwanese ODMs to branch out from laptop manufacturing into other segments, for instance Pegatron is moving into tablet production while Inventec and Quanta are expanding production of data servers. In Case study 16.1 we use the case of the iPhone to consider more broadly the issue of who gains from electronics global production networks.

Case study 16.1

Who gains from electronics global production networks? The case of the iPhone 3

As with laptop computers, the final assembly of many leading smartphones also takes place in the coastal provinces in China. The Apple iPhone 3 (available from 2009 to 2012) provides an interesting case in point (Xing and Detert 2010). It was primarily assembled by Taiwanese manufacturer Foxconn at its huge production complex in Shenzhen, China. Trade data records that, in 2009, 11.3 million iPhones were shipped to the USA from China at an average cost US$178.96 each, a trade flow of US$2.02 billion worth of goods. However, that presents a somewhat misleading picture. If you were to disassemble the iPhone 3, you would find that eight other companies, none of which are based in China, supplied the key manufactured components assembled by Foxconn. The most important, by value, were provided by Toshiba (Japan), Samsung (Korea) and Infineon (Germany); the other five main suppliers were in the USA, Germany and Japan. Toshiba, for instance, contributed the touchscreen and the flash memory, while Samsung manufactured the all-important microprocessor. Unpacking the

US$178.96 that Apple paid for an assembled iPhone 3 to see where the money ultimately went shows that U$172.46 went to component manufacturers, leaving just US$6.50 to be accrued in China by Foxconn for product assembly (see chart below). For example, the

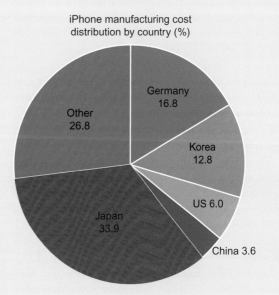

iPhone manufacturing cost distribution by country (%)

flash memory provided by Toshiba alone accounted for US$24.00 of the total, with this firm accruing around one-third of the total manufacturing costs of the iPhone. The US–China trade deficit created by iPhone shipments is therefore much smaller than it first appears, and a more realistic assessment of China's contribution to the manufacturing process of iPhone becomes possible – essentially it is operating as a low-wage assembly location for components created elsewhere. Ultimately, of course, the biggest share of the value from an iPhone is captured by Apple itself; the 'mark up' on the iPhone creating a US retail price of US$300+. The wider lesson here is that assessing who gains most from global production networks – either in terms of firms or places – is not a simple process but requires a detailed understanding of the configuration of such networks and how they touch down in particular places.

Returning to coffee, we can start to appreciate the complexity and dynamism of global production networks. The coffee production network is not static in organizational and governance terms. It can no longer simply be understood as a sequence of market transactions. Three changes illustrate this point. First, the roasters are increasingly concentrating on their roasting, blending and branding activities, employing coffee traders to source coffee and manage their supply networks for them, along with undertaking the steaming of certain kinds of beans. These are particularly important roles in a coffee network which is increasingly concerned with coffee quality testing and assurance, and reflect the establishment of more long-standing, relational connections between roasters and traders. Second, international traders are vertically integrating their operations by buying export firms in producing countries in order to ensure secure and high-quality supplies. This serves to consolidate the position of traders within the system and potentially increase further the value captured by developed-country firms. In turn, the potential for developing countries' producers and processors to upgrade their activity is restricted by the fact that roasting and final processing ideally needs to be undertaken near final markets. Third, growing consumer demand for new kinds of specialty, organic and fair-trade coffees has opened up some direct connections between producers and smaller roasting houses, potentially at least improving the financial returns for the coffee farmers connected to these new networks. We shall return to this issue in the last section of the chapter.

In terms of the laptop production network, at the same time as branded PC firms have retreated from manufacturing activity, Taiwanese manufacturers have evolved or upgraded to take on new roles and, as a result, now occupy much more significant positions within the production network. Many Taiwanese firms started out as simple assemblers of components for PCs. Over time, they moved – through what is known as *process* upgrading – into the manufacture and assembly of PCs sold under the brand names of other firms (i.e. they became OEMs – original equipment manufacturers).

The next step was to develop design capacity, as we have already noted, becoming ODMs (original design manufacturers) through a step known as *product* upgrading. Next, some firms have taken things further and started to manufacture and sell PCs under their own brand, thereby becoming OBMs (original brand manufacturers) through *functional* upgrading. Acer, for example, started out as one of Taiwan's main electronics suppliers, producing various computer products for international buyers. Over time, it separated off its OEM activity, leaving it to focus on the marketing and R&D activities of its own brand laptops. Acer's rise to the very top of the industry was confirmed by the purchase of two large US PC brands, Gateway and Packard Bell, in 2007 and 2008 respectively. Asus followed a similar path, spinning off much of its manufacturing activity into the now independent Pegatron. In reality, however, these categories may not map neatly onto individual firms, many of which will combine both OEM/ODM and OBM activities. In some cases, firms may be able to use their expertise to shift into entirely new production networks (e.g. from laptops to smartphones) in a shift termed *chain* upgrading (Kaplinsky 2005).

Two further points should be noted here. First, there is no automatic or simple progression along this upgrading path. These shifts reflect changing *strategies* on the part of Taiwanese firms in response to changing market conditions. As PCs have become ever more standardized commodities, however, OEM and ODM producers have increasingly been squeezed for cost savings by branded PC firms. They have tended to respond in one or more of four different ways: moving into original brand manufacturing themselves; making more components themselves as a way of cutting costs (i.e. vertically integrating their activity); trying to cut costs through production relocation within China; or by expanding in new but related product segments such as tablet computers. Second, the successful ongoing upgrading of Taiwanese electronics firms is not only due to firm strategies and inter-firm networks. It also reflects a range of deliberate strategies pursued by the Taiwanese state to develop the industry since the early 1970s, for example: the establishment of the Hsinchu Science Park; direct investment in early key players in the sector including UMC (United Microelectronics Corporation) and TSMC (Taiwan Semiconductor Manufacturing Corporation); and steering developments in the industry through its agencies such as ERSO (Electronics Research Service Organization), ITRI (Industrial Technology Research Institute) and CETRA (China External Trade Development Council). These reveal the importance of also considering the institutional context of production networks, a topic to which we now turn.

16.5 The institutional context of production networks

So far we have focused almost entirely on the production network as a mesh of intra- and inter-firm connections. Production networks are also shaped by a wide range of *extra*-firm relationships that (as we saw in Figure 16.1) are an integral part of the system and may incorporate a wide range of non-firm entities (e.g. supranational organizations, the state, labour unions, business associations, etc.). Expressed slightly differently, every relationship in a production network is shaped by its *institutional context*.

We can unpack the complexity of these institutional contexts in two ways. First, institutional context is significant at various spatial *scales*. At the sub-national scale, local governments may seek to stimulate particular kinds of economic activity in their locality, for example by providing low-rent premises for small high-tech businesses. At the national scale, nation-states still wield a huge range of policy measures to try to promote, and steer, economic growth within their boundaries (Dicken 2015). Increasingly important in an era of globalization are measures designed to promote (or restrict) movements of traded products, investment and migrants across national boundaries. At the macro-regional scale, regional blocs such as the European Union or the North American Free Trade Agreement (NAFTA) have considerable influence on trade and investment flows within their jurisdiction. At the global scale, supra-national institutions like the World Trade Organization (WTO) and the International Monetary Fund (IMF) increasingly determine the regulatory frameworks for global trading and financial relationships. Even a relatively simple global production network will, therefore, cross-cut and connect a wide range of institutional contexts. Second, it is important to distinguish between *formal* and *informal* institutional frameworks. The former relates to the rules and regulations that determine how economic activity is undertaken

in particular places (e.g. trade policy, tax policy, environmental regulations and so on), while the latter refers to the rather less tangible, and often place-specific, ways of doing business that relate to the social, economic and political *cultures* of particular places.

Again, we can use the examples of coffee and laptop production to illustrate these arguments. First, the coffee production network demonstrates the importance of *formal* institutional frameworks at the national and global scales. From 1962 to 1989, the international trading of coffee was governed by a series of International Coffee Agreements (ICAs) managed by the International Coffee Organization (ICO), a supra-national organization made up of representatives of a wide range of coffee importing and exporting countries. The ICAs combined price bands and export quotas to provide a coffee trading system that was widely credited with both raising and stabilizing coffee prices. During this period, many exporting countries established coffee marketing boards: government institutions that controlled markets, monitored quality and acted as a link to exporters and international traders (see Figure 16.2). Such boards provided an important protection for farmers and growers from the vagaries of the international coffee market. In 1989, however, the ICA was not renewed in the face of rising production levels and low-cost competition from non-member exporting countries.

The ending of the ICA regime has dramatically altered the balance of power in the coffee chain, as the now market-based coffee trading system has led to lower and more volatile coffee prices. Its demise has served to concentrate power in the hands of consuming-country firms, and in particular the small group of roasters introduced earlier. The collapse of the ICA has meant that coffee-producing countries are no longer cooperating, but are in fact competing with each other, resulting in overproduction and a drop in prices which the roasters have been able to benefit massively from, a process exacerbated by the fact that consumer coffee prices have not dropped in a similar way, but have in fact risen significantly. At the same time, the national coffee marketing boards in the exporting countries either have been eliminated, or have retreated into a restricted overseeing role that has left them marginalized within the production network (see dotted lines in Figure 16.2). As a result of these changes to the interlinked international and national institutional contexts, millions of coffee farmers worldwide are exposed to price fluctuations on the global coffee market. On occasion, this can result in farmers receiving less for their coffee beans that it costs to grow them.

What this story shows is how changing institutional frameworks can impact on all the other dimensions of a global production network. In terms of its basic structure, the demise of the ICA has led to the bypassing of a previously important actor, namely the coffee marketing boards. In terms of changing geographies, the rapid growth of exports from Vietnam was both a cause of the ICA's demise and at the heart of the subsequent overproduction. The expansion of production in Vietnam – strongly supported and marshalled by the government – also shows the significance of national institutional factors. Overall, in governance terms, the post-ICA regime has enabled a further concentration of power in the hands of roasting firms.

The laptop industry is similarly affected by multi-scalar regimes of formal institutional relationships. For example, as we have seen, rules governing outward investment from Taiwan to China were crucial in determining the timing of shifts in laptop production, and the fact that, for geopolitical reasons, direct flights between Taipei and China only restarted in 2008 had a significant impact on the practicalities of investment. Moreover, the role played by municipalities such as Kunshan, Suzhou and Wujiang in setting up industrial parks and actively courting investments from Taiwanese ODMs was crucial in helping the Shanghai region steal leadership in the Chinese PC industry from the longer-established Guangdong cluster (Yang 2009). Similar mechanisms underpin the more recent production shifts to Chongqing. Here, however, we will use the laptop industry to open a window on a range of other less formal connections that are integral to the success of Taiwan's electronics industries. More specifically, there is now increasing recognition of the significance of migration flows of skilled engineers between Taiwan and California for driving the economic success of both high-tech regions. Hsu and Saxenian (2000) describe the development of a *transnational technical community* linking Hsinchu and Silicon Valley. For several decades now, Taiwanese migrants to Silicon Valley – in combination with those from India, China and other parts of Asia – have played an important part in the continued dynamism of the Californian region through their entrepreneurial activity and links back to Asian markets and supplier firms.

However, the more recent reversal of this standard 'brain drain' phenomenon has seen thousands of US-educated engineers returning to Taiwan – reaching a peak of 5,000 per year in the mid-1990s – and playing a pivotal role in transforming it into a high wage and skill economy. 'These returnees to Taiwan, many of whom had worked for at least a decade in the United States, brought with them not only technical skill but also organizational and managerial know-how, intimate knowledge of leading-edge IT markets, and networks of contacts in the United States technology sector' (Saxenian 2006: 149). Return migrants have taken on leading roles in Taiwan's technology sector: they are highly represented in the management cadre of leading firms,

appear to be more entrepreneurial than non-migrants, and are active players in Taiwan's burgeoning venture capital markets. Not all are permanent returnees, however: some have instead become the 'new argonauts' of the global economy (Saxenian 2006), criss-crossing the Pacific on a weekly or monthly basis and facilitating connections between firms, suppliers, clients and investors in the two high-tech clusters. What these migrant flows serve to demonstrate is that global production networks in industries such as the PC sector are more than just formally regulated firm-to-firm connections – they are also constituted by broader personal and knowledge flows.

16.6 Reshaping global production networks?

We now have an appreciation of how to identify, analyze and explain global production networks. But what if various actors – and in particular, we as consumers – want to try to change how a production network is structured and operates? In an increasingly media-saturated and interconnected world, awareness has grown in consuming countries of the social, economic and environmental conditions under which commodities are produced. This has seen a rise of so-called *ethical* consumption, whereby interventions surrounding the consumption stage are designed to improve conditions at points 'upstream' in the production network (see also Chapter 19). There are a number of forms such intervention may take. Perhaps the simplest form of consumer campaign is to *boycott* – that is, not purchase – the products of a particular company. We can also think of *corporate campaigns* that seek to target highly visible corporations by mobilizing information regarding violations against workers or the environment, such as were targeted at the sweatshop operations of sportswear giants like Nike and Reebok in the late 1990s. Increasingly, however, the development of various kinds of *benchmarks* or *standards* – against which various end products and their production processes can be measured – are an increasingly important part of production network regulation within the global economy (see Figure 16.8).

The world of standards and codes has very rapidly become a broad and varied one. There are seven dimensions to this complexity:

1. They may be applied to different facets of the production system, for example environmental, social or labour conditions or rates of economic return.
2. They may take a variety of forms: a code of conduct, a label on a finished product, a tightly specified technical standard, a set of voluntary initiatives or a combination of some, or all, of these forms.

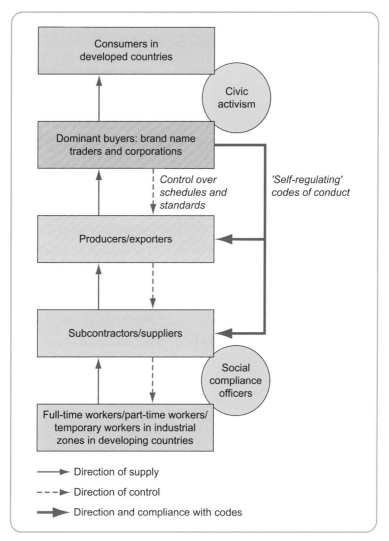

Figure 16.8 New modes of regulating production networks.

Source: adapted from Sum and Ngai (2005), Figure 1

3. They may apply to a particular chain (e.g. beef), a sector (e.g. fresh meat), or be generic (e.g. all fresh foods).
4. They may be developed by firms, NGOs, trade unions or international organizations, and usually by a combination of some, or all, of these institutions.
5. The certification or accreditation of the standards – that is, judging whether they have been met – may be undertaken by public or private, and profit or not-for-profit organizations.
6. They will range from the voluntary (e.g. seeking 'Fair Trade' status for a product) to the mandatory (e.g. safety standards for plastic toys).
7. They are inherently geographical, in terms of both the territory in which they apply (often the place of consumption) and the places in which the effects are felt (usually places of production).

In terms of our two case studies in this chapter, we will focus exclusively on coffee, as these kinds of initiatives are more prevalent and developed in buyer-driven sectors characterized by labour-intensive production – e.g. shoes, garments, food stuffs, etc. A wide range of schemes seeking to promote sustainable coffee production currently exist (Table 16.3). The eight listed schemes clearly illustrate the degrees of variation just described. For example, they may apply primarily to environmental or economic conditions (Bird-friendly vs. Fair Trade, respectively); involve a label or be primarily a code of conduct (Fair Trade vs. Utz Kapeh); and be global or regional in their coverage (Organic vs. Bird-friendly). Moreover, schemes may be initiated by companies (e.g. Starbuck's CAFE – Coffee and Farmers Equity – Practices), civil society organizations (e.g. Fair Trade) or

Table 16.3 Certification schemes for sustainable coffee

Name	Year established	Actors or organizations setting the standards	Characteristics	Geographic coverage
Organic	1972	The International Federation of Organic Agriculture Movements (IFOAM)	Advocates for the principles of organic agriculture across the four pillars of health, fairness, ecology and care	Global (800 affiliates in 117 countries)
Fair Trade	1988 (in Netherlands)	Fair Trade Labelling Organizations International (FLO)	Minimum guaranteed price paid to registered small farmers' organizations that match standards on socio-economic development	Global
Rainforest Alliance certified (shade-grown)	1996	Rainforest Alliance	Certifies farms on the basis of sustainability standards; covers environmental protection, shade, basic labour and living conditions, and community relations	Primarily Latin America
Utz Certified	1997	UTZ Certified (The Netherlands)	Includes standards on environmental protection and management, and labour and living conditions	Global
Bird-friendly coffee (shade-grown)	2000	Smithsonian Migratory Bird Center (SMBC)	Minimum standards on vegetation cover and species diversity needed to obtain use of label; also covers soil management	Latin America
Nespresso AAA Sustainable Quality Programme	2003	Nestlé Corporation	Designed to help farmers adopt best practices in relation to coffee quality, sustainability and productivity	Global
Starbucks CAFÉ (Coffee and Farmer Equity) Practices	2004 (guidelines established in 2001)	Starbucks Corporation	Designed to ensure high-quality coffee, protect the environment, and promote fair relationships between farmers, workers and communities	Global
Common Code for the Coffee Community (4C)	2005	4C Association (Germany)	To achieve baseline levels of social, ecological and economic sustainability for all types of coffee production systems	Global

Source: adapted and updated from Daviron and Ponte (2005), Table 5.11, and Neilson and Pritchard (2009), Table 6.1

multi-stakeholders organizations (e.g. 4C) encompassing a range of domains. A growing proportion of global coffee falls under these schemes which are rapidly becoming mainstream: while the overall level was estimated at just 1 per cent of total production in 2003, by 2013 the various schemes accounted for 40 per cent of global coffee production. Interestingly, however, certified coffee accounted for only 15 per cent of the coffee purchased (e.g. between 28–35 per cent of coffee certified as Fair Trade, Rainforest Alliance and Utz Kapeh at the point of production was sold as such). This discrepancy suggests two things: first that there is a ceiling to market demand for generally more expensive certified coffee, and second that the schemes overlap, with the same coffee having multiple

Plate 16.3 A shade-grown organic coffee plantation on the western slopes of the Andes in Ecuador.
(Dr Morley Read/Shutterstock)

certifications (e.g. there is significant overlap between Organic and Fair Trade coffee).

Such schemes have certainly initiated improvements in the social, economic and environmental conditions of the coffee growers that are enrolled in them. Growers of certified Fair Trade coffee, for example, are guaranteed a premium above the market price, and their product may fetch significantly more in certain market conditions. And yet we need to add some significant notes of caution, such as the fact that the majority of the world's coffee farmers are still labouring outside the jurisdiction of these schemes which are voluntary in terms of participation. Additionally, as we just saw, producing certified coffee does not necessarily mean the coffee will be sold as such. And we need to ask who pays for, and who benefits from, the certification process? The rise of standards-based schemes has fuelled the emergence of a new category of commodity chain participant, the independent auditor – such as Scientific Certification Systems (SCS), for example, who audit the Starbucks scheme – many of whom themselves are profit-seeking firms. The costs of auditing long and complicated production networks are significant, and firms will vary in their ability and willingness to meet these costs. In many instances, buying firms will expect suppliers to meet the extra production costs. Farmers involved in certified organic coffee production in Oaxaca State, Mexico, for example, may pay between 10 and 30 per cent of their gross receipts to certify their produce. This serves as a significant barrier to entry and only the best organized and most well-funded farmers can turn organic production into a profitable enterprise (Mutersbaugh 2005). Together, these points suggest that we need to look carefully and critically at initiatives to alter the nature of global production networks; there is always the risk that, in certain contexts, they will serve to enhance the very injustices and inequalities they seek to diminish.

16.7 Conclusion

Returning to where we began, we now understand far more about the global economic interconnections and exchanges that enable the student in the café to drink a coffee and surf the Internet on her laptop computer. We could tell similar, yet at the same time profoundly different, stories about the smartphone in her jacket pocket, about the jeans she is wearing, about the machine that brewed the coffee, the furniture in the café and so on. Whether the student in question is aware of the complex 'back stories' of the commodities around her is uncertain: as economic geographers, however, it is beholden on us to unravel those stories and their implications for the people and places across the globe that they connect.

This chapter has provided us with a framework and a language for exploring and understanding these economic geographies. Sophisticated global production networks lie behind nearly all of the products and services that we consume on a daily basis. These can be understood as the meshes of intra-, inter- and extra-firm relationships through which material and non-tangible inputs are transformed into consumable outputs of many kinds. They provide the organizational glue that connects together the disparate local clusters of economic activity that constitute the 'on the ground' reality of the global economy. As a result of recent shifts associated with increased competition, technological change, and trade and foreign investment deregulation – for which globalization is often used as shorthand – global production networks in general have arguably become more geographically extensive, disintegrated and dominated by developed-country buyers. Ultimately, however, each global production network has its own unique organizational structure, geographical configuration, governance regime and institutional context. In this chapter we have used just two examples, namely the coffee and laptop computer production networks, to explore some of this inherent variability in the configuration of global production networks.

What this chapter has also demonstrated is the futility of seeking to understand the contemporary global economy and its workings without adopting a geographical perspective. Lead firms in global production networks *use* uneven geographies – taking advantages in differences in labour costs and skill levels, for example – and in turn *reshape* those uneven geographies through their investment and disinvestment decisions. Today's global economy is undoubtedly more complicated and interdependent than ever before: it is the task of the economic geographer to unravel and explain this complexity.

Learning outcomes

After reading this chapter, you should understand:

- How all economic activities can be conceptualized as a form of global production network.
- That global production networks have distinctive, yet changeable, geographical forms.
- That global production networks exhibit a range of governance regimes according to the types of firms involved.
- That the range, complexity and efficiency of global production networks is heavily shaped by multi-scalar institutional contexts of different types.
- How attempts can be made to reconfigure production networks by introducing various kinds of standards and codes of conduct.
- The importance of a geographical perspective for understanding the organization of the contemporary global economy.

Further reading

Coe, N.M. (2012) Geographies of production II: a global production networks A-Z, *Progress in Human Geography*, 36, 389–402. Provides a useful overview of the current state of, and challenges facing, geographical research into global production networks.

Coe, N.M., Kelly, P.F. and Yeung, H. (2013) *Economic Geography: A Contemporary Introduction*, 2nd edition, Wiley, New Jersey. A clear, engaging and student-friendly introduction to contemporary economic geography.

Dicken, P. (2015) *Global Shift: Mapping the Changing Contours of the World Economy*, 7th edition, Sage, London. Now in its seventh edition, this remains far and away the best textbook on the structure, evolution and geography of the global economy.

Massey, D. (1984) *Spatial Divisions of Labour*, Macmillan, London. This landmark book theorizes, and exemplifies, the concept of spatial divisions of labour. A second edition was published in 1995 with a new concluding chapter.

Neilson, J. and Pritchard, B. (2009) *Value Chain Struggles: Institutions and Governance in the Plantation Districts of*

South India, Wiley-Blackwell, Oxford. A fascinating account of changes within the South Indian coffee and tea industries. Particularly strong at revealing the institutional dimensions of the production networks.

Yang, C. (2009) Strategic coupling of regional development in global production networks: redistribution of Taiwanese personal computer investment from the Pearl River Delta to the Yangtze River Delta, China, *Regional Studies*, 43, 385–407. A detailed study of the development of the Taiwanese laptop industry in and around Shanghai.

Useful websites

www.globalvaluechains.org This site contains a wealth of conceptual and empirical material on global value chains.

gpn.nus.edu.sg/index.html The website for the recently created Global Production Networks Research Centre at the National University of Singapore.

unctad.org/en/Pages/DIAE/World%20Investment%20 Report/World_Investment_Report.aspx The United Nations Conference on Trade and Development (UNCTAD) website provides free access to the annual World Investment Report on foreign investment trends. The 2013 edition focused on specifically on global value chains.

www.unido.org The United Nations Industrial Development Organization (UNIDO) website offers a wide range of data and reports on different commodity chains and the potential they offer for economic development in different localities.

www.oecd.org/sti/ind/global-value-chains.htm The Organisation for Economic Co-operation and Development (OECD) has a range of useful information on global value chains across different industries and countries.

www.goodelectronics.org/about Excellent website about labour conditions in the electronics industry.

www.ico.org/index.asp The website of the International Coffee Organization provides a range of information on the coffee industry and, in particular, its evolving regulatory structures.

www.fairtrade.org.uk The UK's Fairtrade Foundation is one of the most well-known attempts to improve the economic returns offered to commodity producers.

SERVICE ECONOMIES, SPATIAL DIVISIONS OF EXPERTISE AND THE SECOND GLOBAL SHIFT

Chapter 17

John R. Bryson

Topics covered

- Defining services
- Services capitalism
- Service employment versus output
- The body, the personality market and emotional labour
- The division of labour
- Spatial and gender divisions of labour
- Spatial divisions of expertise
- The second global shift

Other chapters in this book explore the environmental implications and inequalities of wealth creation at a variety of spatial scales. This chapter is about the large and complex capitalist economic system and, in particular, the ongoing shift from manufacturing to **services** that is being experienced by a range of economies (Plate 17.1). Put another way, it is a shift towards various forms of expertise- or knowledge-intensive employment in economies that are increasingly structured around experiences (Sundbo 2015). Services support all aspects of everyday living – logistics, communications, dining, entertainment, education – and have become an important component of international trade. In 2013 the value of world exports of commercial services was US$4.6 trillion, or 20 per cent of total trade (WTO 2014: 24–5). The export of commercial services had increased from US$1439 billion in 2000.

The focus here is on understanding some of the dynamics of expertise-intensive service work, with the important caveat that the complexity of the modern economy makes it problematical to view service activities as a distinct and separate category from manufacturing. One consequence is that the other chapters in this section that cover aspects of manufacturing, finance, knowledge-intensive services, and even consumption, should be seen as part of an integrated whole. Isolating finance, manufacturing or food production processes from a range of service functions overlooks the multiple interconnections between them to form a complex and integrated production system. The flows of money and finance that take place around the world in the twinkling of an eye are manipulated and coordinated by service workers, or more specifically knowledge workers. They convert information into knowledge that then informs investment

decisions of all kinds; this is enabled by manufactured technologies such as computers. Many manufacturing firms now produce hybrid products that blend service and manufacturing tasks (Bryson and Rusten 2011), for example smartphones combine a good, the phone, with a service, an advanced operating system that links the phone to a complex array of web-based services (Bryson and Rusten 2011). This implies that a post-industrial society is not inevitably a post-manufacturing society; it thrives on the relationship between production, manufacturing and services in which the latter are just part of a much more complex production process. Economic geographers should explore production in the round rather than exploring aspects of manufacturing and service activities in relative isolation.

This chapter begins by defining services and placing them within the context of the overall production system. The continued development of this system over time (and space) reflects the ongoing process of economic specialization that has in turn driven the continuous extension of the division of labour, which is 'one of the foundational features of what capital is about' (Harvey 2014: 112) and the development of a new **spatial division of expertise**. The division of labour refers to the disaggregation of complex activities into discrete tasks that comprise a continuous extension of the **division of labour** and the development of a new spatial division of expertise. The latter is a key concept that will be examined in more detail in the second part of this chapter where the ways in which service expertise is integrated into complex production systems are explored. The chapter concludes with an introduction to some of the characteristics of services offshoring/reshoring, global sourcing or the rise of the **second global shift** (Bryson 2007).

17.1 Defining services

A walk through a supermarket highlights the role that marketing, advertising and packaging design services play in our society. Simple products incorporate quantities of visible and often invisible service expertise; the former as advertising campaigns and the latter as the logistics services that ensure that raw materials and completed manufactured goods are transported and distributed efficiently to producers and consumers. Much of the service expertise hidden within products arises from the constant search for product differentiation. In the economically developed market economies, the vast majority, often more than 75 per cent, of all jobs involve some form of service work (Bryson *et al.* 2004; Bryson and Daniels 2015a, 2015b). Furthermore, in Europe,

Plate 17.1 An open plan office typical of the kind of space used by many service industries.

(Monkey Business/fotolia)

North America, Japan, Australia, New Zealand, as well as parts of the developing world, some 90 per cent of new jobs are created in services (Table 17.1). As a result, the economies and societies of these countries appear to revolve predominantly around service activities and the experience of service work. Indeed, scholars and policy makers generally accept that developed market economies are now dominated by various forms of service work, ranging from extremely well-paid lawyers and merchant bankers to less well-paid hotel and retail workers. Services contribute to economic growth in a variety of ways; for example, they are traded locally, regionally, nationally and internationally. They are also heavily wrapped within and around the production processes of manufactured goods as well as other services; they add value by smoothing the relationship between production and consumption, for example via market research, product design, development and testing and advertising (Bryson and Rusten 2011) (Spotlight box 17.1). Services can be exported either directly via transfer across borders or direct representation of the provider in another country or indirectly through the incorporation of a service into a product or another service which is then exported.

Table 17.1 Employment in manufacturing and service, 2012 and 2013 (all persons)

	Service employment		Manufacturing employment	
	2012	2013	2012	2013
Australia	8,685,688	8,819,650(+)	948,107	921,999(−)
Austria	2,884,525	2,896,000((+)	660,075	651,125(−)
Canada	13,635,730	13,847,730(+)	1,785,517	1,734,217(−)
Chile	5,047,329	5,189,401(+)	881,428	882,185(+)
Czech Republic	2,876,650	2,935,525(+)	1,299,075	1,285,275(−)
Denmark	2,089,800	2,097,375(+)	333,825	325,000(−)
Finland	1,817,000	1,796,775(−)	356,725	350,300(−)
Germany	28,145,600	28,613,100(+)	7,917,050	7,839,925(−)
Hungary	2,520,425	2,567,350(+)	803,100	823,175(+)
Ireland	1,416,250	1,431,950(+)	208,775	213,125(+)
Italy	15,687,580	15,496,130(−)	4,207,650	4,128,775(−)
Japan	44,771,670	45,230,830(+)	10,317,500	10,390,000(+)
Korea	17,184,430	17,502,510(+)	4,104,900	4,184,017(+)
Netherlands	6,917,800	6,941,775(+)	771,700	768,225(−)
New Zealand	1,624,250	1,667,150(+)	245,875	247,675(+)
Norway	2,005,625	2,017,400(+)	239,125	228,775(−)
Poland	8,890,500	8,949,050(+)	2,905,800	2,968,675(+)
Slovak Republic	1,379,500	1,417,825(+)	570,325	539,475(−)
Slovenia	562,100	549,550(−)	206,475	203,200(−)
Spain	13,244,230	13,017,480(−)	2,223,900	2 118 675(−)
Sweden	3,651,500	3,712,900(+)	537,925	524,900(−)
Switzerland	3,360,250	3,402,425(+)	576,275	581,325(+)
United Kingdom	23,511,900	23,917,420(+)	2,886,775	2,913,900(+)
United States	115,675,200	116,593,800(+)	14,686,420	14,869,080(+)

Source: OECD (2014b)

Spotlight box 17.1

Services and the production process

The creation of any product or service requires service expertise to be embedded in different parts of the production process – pre-production, during production and post-production or consumption (Figure 17.1) (Bryson and Daniels 2015b). Pre-production involves understanding the design process, including market research and the ability to innovate; it may be applied to the design of a production process as well as to an actual product or service (Bryson and Rusten 2011). The development of services may require the creation or modification of a process, for example the systems that support a financial services transaction or the check-in process at an airport. Services incorporated into the production process are concerned with achieving its efficient management, for example performance management of a manufacturing process, queue management at leisure parks or call monitoring in call centres. Post-production incorporates marketing and related services or supporting services, for example finance packages linked to the purchases of goods (cars, furniture).

The production process can be divided into five parts with each part requiring different forms of service knowledge and expertise:

1. *Pre-manufacturing* – product development, research & development, design, product testing, market research, finance.
2. *During manufacturing* – finance, quality control, stock control, purchasing, safety, management, continuity/contingency planning, testing, etc.
3. *Selling* – logistics, distribution networks, marketing, finance.
4. *During product and system utilization* – maintenance, leasing, finance, etc.
5. *After product and system utilization* – waste management, recycling, etc.

Source: Bryson *et al.* (2004)

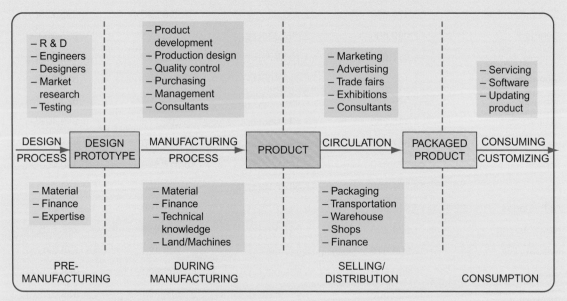

Figure 17.1 The production process.
Source: Bryson *et al.* (2004), p. 52

During the 1970s economists tended to consider services as 'immaterial goods or simply as goods' (Hill 1977: 315). But services are not goods; they exhibit a range of characteristics that fundamentally distinguish them from goods. Hill (1977) identified some of the primary differences between goods and services beginning with the observation that a diverse selection of services, the shipment of goods by a transport firm, vehicle repair, painting and decorating, the cleaning of a house by servants, hairdressing and dentistry, actually share a common set of characteristics. For Hill the two defining characteristics were the way in which services brought about:

1. A change or transformation in the condition of a good or person.
2. A change that is the result of the activity of another individual or firm.

Hill used these principles to construct what is considered to be the classic service definition: 'A service is defined as a change in the condition of a person, or of a good belonging to some economic unit, which is brought about as the result of the activity of some other economic unit, with the prior agreement of the former person or economic unit' (Hill 1977: 318). While very useful, this definition also highlights one of the primary problems with the category of services, namely that in many instances the consumer often only observes or experiences the production or performance of the service (Sundbo 2015). This simultaneous production and consumption, and even co-production of a service, creates confusion between the process of producing it and the final end process of consumption. This added complexity may be confusing but fundamental to the distinction between goods and services should be the realization that the delivery of the latter does not result in the exchange of ownership of a material product. The output of many services is ephemeral or non-material, for example attendance at a lecture or viewing/experiencing a live theatrical performance. It is often suggested that software could be considered as a material service since it is can be stored on a computer device, but this overlooks the fact that the software provider does not transfer complete ownership of the software to the user: most of us own the software under licence from the service provider. This is different from the way in which ownership of a laptop computer or a mobile phone is physically transferred from the seller to the purchaser.

It is important not to become too distracted by attempts to arrive at a precise definition of service activities. Nevertheless, their classification is an important activity for those engaged in measuring the economy, for example national statistical agencies. It is far too easy to become preoccupied with systems of classification at the expense of understanding the changing dynamics of capitalism. In any event, such is the pace of economic change that classifications have to be continually modified to incorporate the development of new types of work or the on-going 'extended division of labour' (Sayer and Walker 1992; Bryson 2009).

All attempts to classify services must accommodate the complexity and diversity of the business activities involved (Illeris 2007). For our purposes a simple classification of service activities incorporates six different types:

1. Consumer services that provide services for final end-users, for example retailers, opticians, hotels and retail banks.
2. Producer and business services that provide intermediate inputs into the activities of private- and public-sector organizations.
3. Services incorporated in to manufactured goods. This includes goods that are leased to provide services, for example, Rolls-Royce, the British engine manufacturer, leases engines to provide 'power-by-the-hour' (Bryson 2010: 698).
4. Public services provided directly by the state or indirectly by the private sector and not-for-profit organizations.
5. Not-for-profit organizations working beyond the confines of the state (Bryson *et al.* 2002).
6. Informal services or unpaid service work, which is usually predominantly undertaken by women, and which is a vital element of peoples' daily lives.

Each of these categories includes a heterogeneous collection of service functions. It is not proposed to cover them all in this chapter. Rather, the focus here is predominantly on knowledge-intensive services (second in the list above). This reflects the increasing importance of a group of distinctive activities that have exhibited dramatic growth rates in both the numbers of firms established and their contribution to employment creation. It incorporates key sectors such as legal services, accountancy, market research, management consultancy, design and technical consultancy. All these services make an important contribution to economic development. They contribute directly to the creation of added value; they contribute to a national economy's **balance of payments** through exports; and they have also experienced dramatic growth rates in employment as well as new firm formation.

17.2 Two common misconceptions about service economies

It is far too easy to assume that manufacturing no longer matters in economies that are dominated by service employment. Many service jobs are highly visible within the economy, as a visit to a local shopping centre saturated with service experiences shows. In contrast, manufacturing employment remains largely invisible since the production process is almost always isolated from the consumption of the product (Bryson *et al.* 2008; Bryson *et al.* 2015). This separation of the production process from the moment of consumption is atypical of many service-based economic relationships. The dominance of the latter and the apparent recent shift from manufacturing has led to two common misconceptions about service employment and it is to these that we now turn our attention.

17.2.1 Services as old as the Industrial Revolution

It is a common mistake to assume that the transformation of economies towards services is a phenomenon of the twentieth century. The social sciences have paid too little attention to the role services played during the Industrial Revolution or earlier. A good example is the development of London in the nineteenth century as the command and control centre of the British Empire. A detailed analysis of London's fire office registers between the years 1775 and 1825 concluded by noting that the

> service industries made no less contribution to the British economy during the Industrial Revolution than manufacturing, and that nowhere was this more true than in London. Its service economy was on a very large scale, serving the nation as a whole as well as the capital . . . London's service industries underpinned both its own and the national manufacturing and commercial infrastructure and at the same time contributed to the new 'commercialisation of leisure'.
>
> (Barnett 1998: 183)

During the late eighteenth century London was already being transformed into an important world city; a process that has continued to the present and which has further enhanced its status as a global city (see Chapter 14). Deane and Cole (1962: 166, 175) calculated that in 1851 some 45.3 per cent of the United Kingdom's national income was derived from service activities (trade, transport, housing, the professions and the civil service) as the structure of employment changed dramatically as a result of technological innovation and the increasing maturity and extension of the capitalist system. Growth occurred in occupations that facilitated the exchange of goods and services between producers and consumers (Plate 17.2). Between 1881 and 1901 the number of business clerks increased from 175,000 to 308,000; bank officials from 16,000 to 30,000; and insurance officials and clerks from 15,000 to 55,000 (Marsh 1977: 124). During the nineteenth century the expansion of international trade was restricted by financial problems until it was enabled and supported by the introduction of bill markets and banking facilities of the kind associated with the flow of tea and silk from China to Europe between 1860 and 1890

Plate 17.2 Clerks at work in a US Government office, *c.* 1915.

(Everett Historical/Shutterstock)

(Hyde 1973). As the United Kingdom and the United States were becoming industrialized societies they were simultaneously being transformed into service economies; the growth of manufacturing employment went hand in hand with the growth of service employment.

17.2.2 Productivity and services and the myth of service economies

Since the nineteenth century the employment structure of many countries has steadily shifted away from manufacturing to service employment. This shift should not be equated with the demise of manufacturing or the complete displacement of manufacturing with service work. Many national economies (Germany, Italy; see Table 17.1) are still dominated by the development, design, manufacture and sale of goods; the absence of manufacturing within a national economy would present serious problems since everyday life as well as service work is supported by a complex array of manufactured products – clothes, toasters, cars, clocks, toothpaste, tissues, deodorant, laptops and toys (Bryson and Rusten 2011). Some of these products can of course be traded between countries but many need to be manufactured or customized locally, for example products that are difficult or impossible to transport (perishable foods, commercial air-conditioning systems) or production processes that require close contact between producers and consumers, for example, customized alterations to machine tools or the co-innovation of new products (Bryson *et al.* 2008).

Since products can be traded for services, it is possible to argue that manufacturing no longer needs to be undertaken in service-dominated economies. Nevertheless, many services support and are supported by manufacturing activities, for example the complete removal of manufacturing from the West Midlands (United Kingdom) would reduce the client base of local service companies by 25 per cent (Daniels and Bryson 2005: 3). It has also become apparent that a national economy that is over-reliant on products that are manufactured elsewhere is increasingly exposed to many different types of risk. First, since the 2008 financial crisis and global recession manufacturing firms in Germany and the UK have proved to be more resilient than many service firms with increases in employment, output and exports (Markit 2011). Over-reliance on products manufactured abroad also has implications for health and safety. In August 2007, for example, Mattel, the world's largest toy company, issued a product recall for 436,000 toys made in China that were painted with lead-based paint and 18.2 million toys that were designed with small magnets that could become detached. This type of product recall provides American toy manufacturers with a competitive advantage as they are able to market their toys as 'Made in America' (Rusten et al. 2007) and as '100 per cent kid-safe' (Martin 2007).

After the Second World War, manufacturing employment encountered gales of creative destruction (Schumpeter 1942) that eventually culminated in, what some commentators have termed, the crisis of Fordism (Gaffikin and Nickson 1984). This led to an ongoing reduction in manufacturing employment and a shift towards a diverse collection of service jobs. The difficulty is that scholars and policy makers tend to equate such a decline of (often) high-profile manufacturing firms with a contraction in manufacturing overall. In practice it does not mean that countries in Europe and North America, for example, have been transformed into service economies; it is essential that a distinction is made between adjustments to the employment composition of an economy and changes in economic output (productivity). These two indicators of economic change are not necessarily related, or they are related in unexpected ways.

Especially important is that the types of productivity improvements that have been achieved by manufacturers through automation and process improvements are not necessarily achievable by service providers. The category 'services' includes an extremely diverse group of business activities: from very highly paid professional occupations (lawyers, surgeons, bankers) to very poorly paid occupations (janitors, waiters). The common denominator is that, unlike manufacturing, many of these occupations rely on people-based skills or what is commonly termed 'embodied labour' (Bryson et al. 2004; Bryson and Daniels 2015a). In these circumstances the challenge of improving productivity is considerable. It is at its highest and still increasing where there is interaction

between work practices and new technologies (such as the introduction of people-facilitated, as well as automated, call centres) but is either non-existent or extremely low in, for example, medical services, teaching and the creative industries. It is very difficult for a dance company to achieve productivity improvements; it involves putting on more performances, using fewer dancers, or increasing the speed of delivery to enable two performances to be given during the time previously devoted to a single performance. This is a good illustration of the fact that many service occupations are labour-intensive (Moretti 2013: 63) and often involve face-to-face interactions between service providers and clients for which productivity improvements are difficult to achieve. As a result, overall productivity improvements in the service side of the economy have, as a general rule, lagged behind manufacturing with the implication that this differential partly explains the shift from manufacturing to service work.

The significance of this reasoning can be demonstrated with reference to UK manufacturing exports, which amounted to £230 billion or 46 per cent of total exports in 2013 (Rhodes 2014). Yet manufacturing directly employed only 2.62 million workers, with a further 3 million jobs dependent on the sector. A major problem is that official definitions of manufacturing employment do not include jobs and activities that depend on, or are closely allied to, manufacturing such as design or marketing activities undertaken by specialist 'service' providers. Recent research has identified that some of the highest paid services are tied to manufacturing, for example research and development, design and finance (Sisson 2011). One difficulty with analyzing the shift towards service-dominated economies is that activities that were once undertaken in vertically-organized manufacturing firms have been outsourced and are now purchased on the market (Levinson 2013).

On average, UK manufacturing output has grown by 1.4 per cent a year since 1948, but it contracted during the economic downturns of the early 1970s, 1990s and following the 2008 economic downturn. The overall rate of output growth has been at a much slower rate than other sectors of the British economy (Hardie and Banks 2014). Thus, although the gross added value (GVA) created by manufacturing increased by 26 per cent over the period 1992 and 2003 (Figure 17.2), it was actually lower than the rate achieved in other sectors of the economy. Service sectors were growing at a much faster rate even though in absolute, rather than relative, terms manufacturing's contribution to the overall economy increased over this time period. It is important to recognize that a restructuring of economic activity is taking place; new types of economic activity such as information management or digital services (e.g. website design) are flourishing

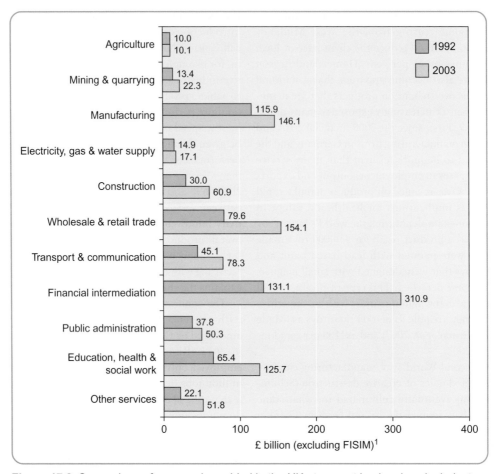

Figure 17.2 Comparison of gross value added in the UK at current basic prices by industry between 1992 and 2003.

[1]FISIM = Financial Intermediation Services Indirectly Measured

Source: from Mahajan, S. (2005) *Input-Output Analysis: 2005,* p. 23, Office for National Statistics, London. Office for National Statistics licensed under the Open Government Licence v.1.0

alongside the development of innovations in well-established services such as insurance, banking and retailing. Such restructuring arises from, first, the externalization of previously in-house services to independent providers and, second, the continuation of an extended division of labour based upon the development of new services, technologies and business models. The latter arises from the growing complexity that accompanies many service innovations as service providers seek to refine product differentiation in the marketplace.

While most of the key manufacturing sectors have therefore declined in relative terms, and some in absolute terms (for example, footwear, knitted goods, leather goods, man-made fibres, wearing apparel), the service sector has expanded, whether measured by employment or GVA. In the United Kingdom between 1992 and 2004 GVA increased by 381.5 per cent in computer services, 252.2 per cent in other business services and 266.2 per

cent in market research and management consultancy (Figure 17.2 and Table 17.1). In 2004, computer services alone accounted for 2.9 per cent of total GVA (£30.0 billion). It is clear then that the recent growth of the UK economy has been led by service industries; they comprise all of the top ten fastest growing industries between 1992 and 2004, for example. An inexorable decline in manufacturing employment has therefore been offset by employment gains in services.

While the shift towards services is ongoing the economy continues to be integrated in complex ways and it is important to identify and explore some of the interactions between manufacturing and service activities. The question is 'How does this perspective affect our interpretation of employment gains in services at the expense of manufacturing?' After all, the employment roster of a manufacturing company can be largely made up of individuals working on activities such as marketing, advertising, management, accounting and purchasing. This returns the analysis to the definition of manufacturing and services. On the one hand, we can suggest that part of the shift towards service employment reflects a transfer of service tasks that were previously undertaken within manufacturing firms to external service providers. On the other hand, we can suggest that 'although the objective of manufacturing industry is the production of commodities many people employed in manufacturing are not directly employed in the actual production process' (Crum and Gudgin 1977: 3). Questions then follow about the wisdom of dividing the economy into service and manufacturing activities (Daniels and Bryson 2002; Bryson and Rusten 2011). In 1971 every two production workers needed to be supported by rather more than one non-production worker (Crum and Gudgin 1977: 5); the term non-production is used to identify people within a manufacturing firm who are not directly involved in the actual production process (managers, designers, sales team, research scientists).

Since Crum and Gudgin's research, there have been two major organizational changes to production processes. First, knowledge has become more important as well as being increasingly combined or embedded within products and services. Second, the production of goods and services has increasingly required the blending of different types of expertise that include processes involving shop-floor workers (manufacturing as well as services) and a complex array of service and management expertise. All these different types of expertise can be organized within a manufacturing company or, alternatively, by buying in the activities provided by many separate and independently owned service firms. These relationships between manufacturing and services can be measured as 'multiplier' effects whereby jobs in one sector create jobs in other sectors. For example, Bivens (2003) has estimated that in the United States business services have an employment multiplier of 1.63: that is, every business service job creates 1.63 jobs elsewhere in the economy. Manufacturing jobs have an employment multiplier of 2.91 and jobs in transportation a multiplier of 1.66. The high multiplier for manufacturing highlights that the production of goods creates jobs in other manufacturing firms, as well as in transportation, business services and retailing.

17.3 The body, services and emotional labour

The classic definition of services developed by Hill (1977) highlights the importance of people-based expertise in the creation of services. This implies that many service experiences must be co-created as part of an interaction between service producers and consumers delivered by people rather than by machines. Unlike manufacturing, it is difficult, and in many instances impossible, to replace service workers with machines and this means that productivity improvements are difficult for those services that rely on people-based expertise. This is an important point given that some service activities can certainly be codified and replaced with relatively simple computer programs. A good example is an application for a mortgage that can be processed by a computer using simple rule-based logic such as a simple 'yes' or 'no' answer, for example, related to the value of the property or the income of the applicant(s) (Levy and Murnane 2004: 16–17). Yet it is very much the case that such simple rule-based software cannot replace many service jobs because they require complex pattern recognition such as reading body language in service encounters.

The importance of face-to-face contact in the simultaneous production and consumption of a range of services plays an important role in differentiating the new world of service work from that of manufacturing (McDowell 2009). At the centre of interactive service relationships are three important elements: client interaction, an individual's reputation, and embodied knowledge. In this service age, the workplace is increasingly conceptualized as a stage upon which employees must execute an aesthetically pleasing performance. Service employment is not simply about the exchange of goods or services but is a complex skill in which presentation, communication and display are integral to success (Bryson and Wellington 2003: 60). It follows that for some service jobs, appearance, the body and accent matter (McDowell 2007) and this implies that service economies have within them cohorts of people who do not possess the desired bodily attributes to meet the expectations of employers and perhaps customers (Bryson and Wellington 2003). McDowell argues that in the United Kingdom this group includes white working-class males who find it difficult to obtain well-paid service work.

The academic literature on service work is heavily influenced by Arlie Hochschild's (1983) important work on the commercialization of emotions in face-to-face service encounters. Hochschild was inspired by C. Wright Mills's (1959 [1951]) classic work, *White Collar*. Mills was the first sociologist to explore the complexity and diversity of service work in his analysis of the new American middle class. Mills developed the concept of the 'personality market' to describe the 'shift from skills with things to skills with people' (1959: 182); central to this shift is the enhanced importance of the psychological dimensions of service work. In this account of the new world of work, men and women 'are to be shaped'

(1959: 183) and their personalities managed, by themselves and by others.

Horchschild developed Mills's work by undertaking theoretically grounded research into the commercialization of the body and the feelings of male and female flight attendants and debt collectors. Central to this analysis is '**emotional labour**', a concept that describes the management of employees' feelings during social interaction in the work process (Hochschild 1983: 137). The best example is the emphasis placed on providing a 'service with a smile' to show customers that they are valued. Hochschild reveals that much face-to-face interactive service work (flight attendants, debt collectors, waitresses, secretaries, fast-food operations) involves having to present the 'right', managerially prescribed, emotional appearance or mask to the customer or client, and that this involves real labour. In these occupations workers are faced with the dilemma of how to identify with their work role without it becoming part of their identity.

Service employees have to depersonalize the work by 'surface acting' and 'deep acting'. In surface acting 'we deceive others about what we really feel, but we do not deceive ourselves' (Hochschild 1983: 33); the body not the soul is the main tool of the trade; the smile on the face of the worker is a false smile, but it is still a smile. In emotional labour a smile becomes attached to the feelings that a company wishes to project rather than being attached to its usual function – to show a personal feeling (Hochschild 1983: 127). In deep acting the 'act' is no longer an act but becomes part of the individual's persona. It is about persuading employees to be sincere, 'to go well beyond the smile that's just "painted on"' (Hochschild 1983: 33). Unprecedented efforts are being made by employers to control employees not simply in terms of what they say and do at work, but also how they feel and view themselves. In deep acting the disjunction between displayed emotions and private feeling is severe and potentially psychologically damaging. The danger is that deep acting becomes part of the worker's personality and is used beyond the workplace. If this occurs then the new 'emotional proletariat' (Macdonald and Sirianni 1996) might find it difficult to 'interpret and take appropriate action in response to bodily signals' (Shilling 1993: 119). Hochschild's account of male debt collectors highlights how the display of aggression required by debt collectors can spill over into personal relationships with wives and children. According to Bryson and Wellington (2003: 62), 'active involvement in "emotional labour" renders employees' appearance and personality a form of "adjudicated cultural capital" that can be recruited, managed, manipulated and utilized to buy the hearts and minds of consumers'. The commodification of image, not surprisingly, is highly visible in interactive business service occupations and, in particular, the 'professional managerial classes'.

The importance of the body and image in service economies has led to a new occupation, that of image consultancy or impression management. Image consultants are employed by individuals and firms to alter the surface appearance of the body. Image consultants provide seminars and one-to-one consultations directly related to the restructuring of professional employees' bodies. According to Wellington and Bryson (2001: 940):

> KPMG [the accountancy firm] employs image consultants on a monthly basis primarily to provide employees with a 'confidence boost', and also to provide staff with a 'bonding experience'. The accountants Coopers and Lybrand as well as Ernst and Young hire image consultants to provide seminars in personal presentation for their audit teams. These seminars examine ways of increasing credibility and projecting the right image when undertaking client audits and when pitching for new business. Price Waterhouse employed image consultants to instruct potential partners in dining etiquette and in the art of looking, acting and sounding like a partner of a major global accountancy company. Note the use of the terms act and art and the link to the literature on flight attendants.
>
> (Taylor and Tyler 2000)

The literature on emotional labour suggests that in the service economy employees have to develop skills in dealing directly with people. The implication is that extrovert personalities may have little difficulty in fitting into this new world of service work, but that introverts may experience some challenges. It is important to remember that in many instances facing-based work that is heavily involved in emotional labour will be supported by back office or out-of-client-sight supporting labour. This suggests that a new division of labour is developing that links front and back office workers together. The concept of emotional labour also highlights the importance of proximity in the co-creation of services (Bryson 2007). Developments in information and communications technology continue to transform the relationship between geography and economic activity. In 1970, Tobler famously identified what he termed 'the first law of geography; everything is related to everything else, but near things are more related than distant things' (1970: 236). This 'law' draws attention to the importance of the localization of relationships of all types – social, economic, financial, service, etc. Tobler's first law is important for understanding services: all expertise, knowledge and emotional labour is determined by its geographical context.

17.4 Services and the spatial division of expertise

The division of labour is a key concept for understanding the organization of work under capitalism and the shift towards service activities. In 1776 Adam Smith published *The Wealth of Nations*, in which he established the foundations of economic theory. For Smith,

> the greatest improvement in the productive powers of labour, and the greatest part of the skill, dexterity, and judgement with which it is anywhere directed, or applied, seem to have been the effects of the division of labour.

(Smith 1977: 109)

To illustrate the importance of the division of labour, Smith explores pin-making, suggesting that an individual without knowledge of the production process would be unable to make even one pin in a day. The production process of pin-making can be divided into 18 distinct operations: from the drawing out of the wire to the making of the pin head. If one person performs all of these tasks, then they might make 20 pins in a day. If, however, individuals specialize in particular tasks, by introducing a division of labour, Smith shows how ten people could make 48,000 pins in a day (Bryson and Henry 2005).

Adam Smith's division of labour is based on his observations of specialization within factories. There is no reason, however, why its principles should not be applied to the services production process, not least to the ways in which new service activities are identified and firms developed to create a market for the provision of new forms of services. It is worth noting that the division of labour was extremely well known prior to Adam Smith's work. In 1678 Sir William Petty published an essay on political arithmetic in which he noted that one of the greatest English clockmakers of the seventeenth century, Thomas Tompion (1639–1713), produced watches via a complex division of labour in which 'one man [sic] shall make the *Wheels,* another the *Spring,* another shall engrave the *Dial-place,* and another shall make the *Cases,* then the *Watch* will be better and cheaper, than if the whole work be put upon one man' (Petty 2004[1678]: 16).

Adam Smith's theory makes no explicit reference to geography. The obvious extension of the division of labour is to incorporate geography into the process, and this leads to a spatial division of labour (Massey 1984). Once a production process had been subdivided into its component parts it is a comparatively simple step to construct warehouses or offices dedicated to a particular part of the production process, such as consignment assembly and packing for despatch or a marketing function. The spatial division of labour began with manufacturers establishing specialist units that were contiguously located, but soon developed into a more dispersed spatial division of labour. Different parts of the production process were located close to sources of raw materials, the market, or cheap or skilled labour. Very quickly, some regions and countries came to specialize in particular types of economic activity. For example, a (international) division of labour soon developed between the industrial countries (core) producing manufactured goods and the non-industrialized countries (semi-/periphery) supplying raw materials and agricultural goods as well as a market for manufactured products. This spatial division of labour can occur *within* service or manufacturing firms (Bryson *et al.* 2004) (Case study 17.1). One location (a major city such as London) is used for the headquarters (HQ), another for research and development (R&D), yet another (a peripheral region, South Wales, or a country, China) for the manufacturing branch plant, and sales and service centres will be distributed over the globe (Bryson and Rusten 2008).

Case study 17.1

ICT and business process outsourcing factories in the Philippines and India

Developments in ICT have made the transfer of service jobs to low-cost locations possible (Bryson *et al.* 2004; Bryson 2007). What is occurring is an intriguing ongoing international division of labour, but with a difference; it used to be that branch plants in developing or less developed countries were only associated with the assembly of products designed by and for the developed world: now, many such branch plants process data and/or interact with customers located thousands of miles away.

Data-processing factories, for example, in the Caribbean or Philippines are linked via cable and satellite with service workers in Ireland, the Dominican Republic, Jamaica, Mauritius and the United States. To Freeman this development 'signals an intensification of transnational production and consumption – of labour, capital, goods, services and styles' (2000: 1). In 2013,

Plate 17.3 A call centre where business is outsourced from Western companies in New Delhi, India.

(Sherwin Crasto/Reuters/Corbis)

the Axiem Corporation established a business process outsourcing (BPO) facility in Mandaluyoing City, Philippines. The company employs over 200 providing data entry, call centre services, accountancy and IT services to clients from Australia, New Zealand, Europe, USA and Asia. It is worth emphasizing that this example highlights the shift away from the provision by offshore BPS providers of relatively simple data entry to the provision of more knowledge-based services such as accountancy including taxation.

Call-centre operations are labour-intensive, labour accounting for over 65 per cent of their running costs. In the 1990s, in the United Kingdom, American Express and British Airways (BA) transferred their customer services divisions from the United Kingdom to Delhi and then Bombay. BA was attracted by India's large pool of English-speaking graduates who could be employed on starting salaries of between £1,500 and £2,500. India has dominated the market for the provision of English-speaking call centres, but is being challenged by countries like the Philippines. Every year India produces 2 million graduates, mostly taught through English, and

who are desperate for well-paid employment in a country where the national average wage is £300. It has been estimated that the Philippines has 350,000 call handlers compared to 330,000 in India; Philippine call-centre workers speak English without an accent (Walton 2015) but wage costs are also between 50–80 per cent less than in the USA, UK and Canada. In the United Kingdom, call centres are staffed by students and temporary workers and are considered to be twenty-first century sweatshops with high staff turnover rates and low salaries (£12,000–15,000). In India, they are desirable places, regarded as 'hip and funky places to work, somewhere to hang out with like-minded, outward-looking young people' (Spillius 2003: 44). In the 1990s the call-centre industry did not exist in India, but by 2003, 1,500 Indian call-centre providers employed 102,000 young people in the 'remote services' industry; the industry is growing by 70 per cent a year (Spillius 2003: 41). The increasing maturity of the offshoring market is seeing growth in the Philippines, Poland, Romania and Mexico and the continued existence of small centres (Caribbean, Guatemala). Nevertheless, higher-value service work, for example mobile app development, remains located in developed market economies.

Deciding to offshore a service function is a difficult decision. Cost might be the most important driver, but for some firms this might mean the provision of a less than satisfactory service to clients. There is a continual attempt by companies to reduce costs and the offshoring of services, at the moment, plays an important role in this process and this create disadvantages for clients and staff. In 2011 staff at an Orange call centre located in England were told that they could retain their jobs if they relocated to the Philippines (Walton 2015).

Offshoring is a complex process that involves an on-going reorganization of the relationship between service functions, place and space. The first decade of this century was associated with the rise of service offshoring. The current decade has seen 'onshoring' or the return of previously offshored functions to relatively high cost locations. In July 2011 Santander, UK, announced that it had returned all its call centres in India to the UK because of customer complaints. The banks noted that customers were frustrated in dealing with offshore call centres and that this rapidly turned into dissatisfaction. Quality issues have played an important role in the new process of 'return onshoring'. India has also experienced higher wage inflation whilst high unemployment rates in the UK have increased staff retention and reduced the cost differential related to training and wages.

Within geography, the division of labour concept is traditionally associated with deskilling, branch plants of manufacturing companies, and the ongoing development of an international division of labour, mostly associated with textiles and clothing, automotive, electronics and to a much lesser extent services (Dicken 2015). It has been noted earlier in this chapter that the services literature increasingly emphasizes the importance of emotional labour and embodied expertise in service relationships and production (Hochschild 1983; Fineman 2000; Warhurst *et al*. 2000; McDowell 2007, 2009). The concept of a spatial division of labour therefore needs to accommodate the increasing centrality of embodied expertise in the economy (Wellington and Bryson 2001; Bryson and Wellington 2003). There has also been a shift in the nature of particular forms of work. Some types of high-paid work, for example, are moving away from delivery by labour that is controlled by capital and regulated by company law to a situation in which control, or more correctly power, in the 'employment' relationship is transferred from the employers to the employed experts. These are the most important asset 'owned' or managed by expertise-intensive firms; such walking, highly mobile resources leave their firms' offices each evening and may, or may not, return next morning. This contrasts with manufacturing where owners of capital exercise most of the power in the relationship with their employees. The rise of expertise-intensive occupations has shifted power away from employers to employees. Indicative of this 'new order' are the difficulties experienced by firms trying to manage business service professionals and the controversial role of staggered bonus payments and golden handcuffs for staff retention in, for example, investment banking (Leicht and Fennell 1997; Alvesson 2000).

The *spatial division of labour* has continued to evolve and is increasingly centred on the expertise that is located within or outside client companies. This is not to suggest that the spatial division of 'production' labour is still not important, but it is now conceptually useful to distinguish between corporate strategies that affect production workers and those that involve expertise or forms of creative work. A spatial division of expertise distinguishes between the *spatial organization of expertise* (non-production activities, advanced business and professional services (BPS) and management functions) and the *spatial organization of production* (Bryson and Rusten 2005, 2006, 2008). It reflects the distinction between production and non-production activities within manufacturing (Crum and Gudgin 1977). The concept of a spatial division of expertise shifts the focus of analysis to the places where expertise is produced and consumed; it also exists within and between international business service firms and manufacturing firms. The building blocks of these 'expertise' economic systems are distributed in a complex mosaic that reflects the ways in which all firms (from micro- to large transnational) try to maximize profitability. The spatial division of expertise is informed by the social division of labour, which gives considerable emphasis to relationships between people and to the joint supply and co-production of service knowledge/expertise.

The development of a spatial division of expertise has important implications for the geographies of service as well as manufacturing companies (Case study 17.2). Companies, and even governments, increasingly develop services (as well as products) using production processes designed to exploit differential comparative advantages. This is not an entirely new process; earlier international divisions of labour were based on core countries producing and exporting manufactured goods whilst peripheral countries exported raw materials. This was the first manufacturing division of labour, or the first global shift (Dicken 2015). The evolution into a spatial division of expertise came later. The comparative advantage for services is derived from a different form of raw material, that is, a highly educated and expert labour force and, importantly, language skills. It is to the geographies of the new spatial division of expertise that we now turn our attention.

Case study 17.2

Boeing's new spatial division of expertise

It is becoming increasingly difficult to distinguish between manufacturing and service companies (Daniels and Bryson 2002). Many physical products contain embedded services, for example software, or are supported by service agreements. The increasing symbiosis that is developing between manufacturing and services is changing the geographies of production in complex ways, creating new business models that capitalize on service/manufacturing expertise and repositioning expertise as a key source of competitive advantage. There are many examples, but perhaps one of the most dramatic is found in the aerospace industry. In 2002, Boeing, the American manufacturer, began

→

Plate 17.4 The first Boeing 787 Dreamliner takes shape in the assembly plant in Everett, WA, USA.

(AP Photo/John Froschauer/Press Association Images)

developing the 787 Dreamliner, a new aircraft with a range of 8,500 nautical miles that carries between 200 and 300 passengers (see Bryson and Rusten 2006, 2008, 2011). This was in response to airline's new concern with fuel efficiency rather than extra speed.

For Boeing the Dreamliner manufacturing programme represented a new way of designing and manufacturing a complicated product that requires an extended, complex supply chain. Before the Dreamliner programme, Boeing followed a build-to-print model. Over 1,000 companies in Boeing's supply chain were provided with detailed part specifications and they only became involved with the aircraft programme towards the end of the design and development process. These companies provided parts that Boeing assembled into subsystems and then aircraft. In this production model, Boeing was responsible for the detailed design of the complete plane. For the Dreamliner, Boeing was responsible for the overall design of the plane, for systems integration and final assembly, but detailed design work was transferred to a network of global partners. The result was a new spatial division of expertise that was constructed around

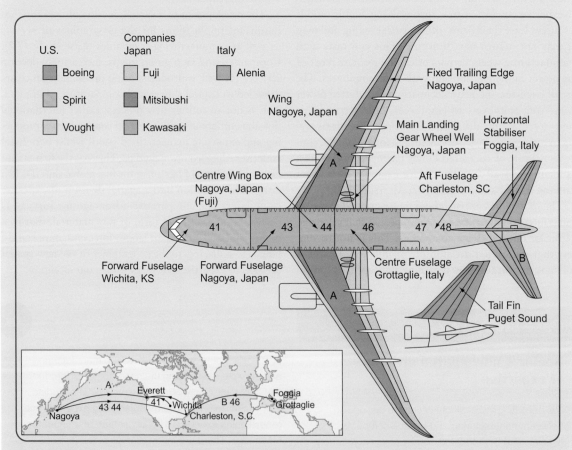

Figure 17.3 Spatial divisions of labour and expertise in the design and fabrication of Boeing's 787 Dreamliner aircraft.

Source: Bryson and Rusten (2008)

capitalizing on Boeing's own internal design and management expertise combined with that of its partners distributed around the globe. This expertise is a combination of research and development with industrial design inputs developed in centres of excellence that support high-tech engineering activities. This new spatial division of expertise was based on the recruitment of around 50 Tier 1 suppliers or partners and these suppliers sourced parts from Tier 2 suppliers that included parts from Tier 3 suppliers.

This new model represented a radical alteration to the way Boeing designed and manufactured aeroplanes; most of the manufacturing was undertaken at factories owned and managed by Boeing's partners; the only major part of the Dreamliner's airframe made by Boeing was the vertical tail. Boeing's key partners include three major Japanese manufacturing companies (Kawasaki Heavy Industries, Mitsubishi Heavy Industries and Fuji Heavy Industries) and Alenia Aeronautica, an Italian company. The Japanese companies were responsible for the design and production of the Dreamliner's wings; the first time Boeing had outsourced the most important part of an aircraft. Initially, the Japanese wing design team worked closely with Boeing's design team and was based at Boeing's Everett facility in Washington State (USA). This team then returned to Japan to concentrate on the development of the detailed designs for the wing while the Boeing design team shifted focus to concentrate on systems integration.

In this way the Dreamliner combined Boeing's 'service' expertise (design, development, system integration, project management) with that of its partners. Once assembled in the Kawasaki plant the completed wing box are transported by barge to Nagoya's new Centrair airport and from there flown to Charleston, South Carolina, in modified 747 cargo freighters (Figure 17.3). Charleston is the main fuselage hub in this spatial division of expertise; sections manufactured in

Japan, Italy and the USA are assembled before being flown to Everett for a final assembly process that normally takes only three days. This is both a conventional spatial division of 'production' labour, with finished parts travelling from one supplier to another down the chain, and a spatial division of 'embodied' expertise. This is an example of an expertise-rich production system in which conventional shop-floor manufacturing workers play a relatively minor role. Some 3,600 engineers were directly employed by Boeing in the design of the Dreamliner, with the majority of these positions based at the company's Everett plant (Washington, USA) (Gates 2005). A further 670 engineers are employed by Spirit Aerosystems, Wichita (Kansas, USA) and 570 in Japan.

The Dreamliner was three years behind schedule when it made its first commercial flight in October 2011. The development programme was delayed due to difficulties with the engineering, supply chain problems and a 58-day labour strike in 2008. The new production process based on global outsourcing (a new global production network) proved to be flawed. Some of the partners in the Dreamliner's supply chain experienced major capacity problems and there were technical and quality difficulties. In 2009, Boeing spent US$1 billion to acquire a plant located in North Charleston, SC, owned by Vought Aircraft Industries that makes parts for the 787's rear fuselage. There had been difficulties with this supplier that was causing a bottleneck in the Dreamliner supply chain. Boeing employed additional staff at Everett to overcome many of the difficulties the company faced as it tried to complete this new aircraft. The production of the Dreamliner highlights the importance of the interplay that occurs between manufacturing and services as companies develop new spatial divisions of labour. The Dreamliner's development programme was delayed due to engineering difficulties and problems coordinating and managing Boeing's new approach to working with suppliers.

17.5 The second global shift

The traditional view of services is that they were produced and consumed locally; they were regarded as having limited export potential. As we noted earlier in this chapter this reflects the way in which services were conceptualized in traditional economic theory. Today, however, services are exported and companies are increasingly adopting business models that involve combining service expertise, activities and functions located in different parts of the world. In other words, companies are developing competitive advantage through the development of

an evolving spatial division of expertise. In the popular media or in political accounts this trend is known as 'service offshoring' (see Case study 17.1), a term developed in the Anglo-American context that should be used with considerable care. Services can indeed be 'offshored' but this is a less than helpful and even misleading term when applied to the transfer of work from, say, France to Eastern Europe. Outsourcing can occur at many different spatial scales – from the local to the international whilst the term 'offshoring' describes the international outsourcing of service functions. Perhaps the best term to use would be 'international outsourcing' rather than offshoring.

The concept of service outsourcing emerged during the 1990s, but only became of major concern during this century. Between January and May 2004, there were 2,634 reports in American newspapers that focused on service outsourcing (Amiti and Wei 2004: 4). Journalists tended to focus on the fear of job losses as service outsourcing had the potential to strip jobs out of the American labour market and relocate them to lower-cost production locations. Service offshoring is based on the concept of outsourcing, a term that describes the process by which a firm procures a material or service input from another organization.

Service offshoring was made possible by developments in ICT. During the late 1980s and early 1990s pioneer companies experimented with offshoring service functions on the basis of opportunistic searches to reduce costs and also in response to sequential learning (Lewin and Peeters 2006). In the early stages, relatively simple business processes related to finance, accounting and information technologies were offshored. As experience of offshoring these functions has accumulated, it has encouraged firms to include more technically complex processes and higher value-added tasks. Offshoring was originally developed by business units within firms interested in cutting costs but it has become a standard business process and another management tool or approach sold by management consultancy firms to their clients and also heavily marketed by providers of offshore services.

Service offshoring occurs when firms shift production to foreign locations. The objective may be to reduce costs, to service a foreign market, to reduce exposure to country risk, or to access skilled labour. An additional factor influencing the location of offshore service centres is the requirement to provide a 24-hour service to customers or an extended service beyond standard working hours. The cost of providing such services can be high as late-shift workers expect higher wages or extended holidays. Advanced call-routing and networking technologies enables companies to mitigate this by implementing a 'follow-the-sun' geographical policy. By locating call centres open 8–12 hours per day in widely separated time zones, companies can use automatic call routing to provide clients with a 24-hour/7-day-a-week service. Country risk is removed when a company is able to shift the provision of a function between facilities located in different countries.

Global data on service offshoring and inshoring is difficult to find (Amiti and Wei 2004); inshoring describes the amount of outsourcing that a country receives. In 2008, estimates of the size of service offshoring ranged from US$101 to US$157 billion (Gereffi and Fernandez-Stark 2010: 6) and in 2008 the OECD estimated that the offshore services market would reach US$252 billion in 2010. This activity is included within commercial services exports; the top five exporters in 2013 were the United States (14.3 per cent of the world total), the UK (6.3 per cent), Germany (6.2 per cent), France (5.1 per cent) and China (4.5 per cent). If the European Union is treated as single entity then it becomes the top exporter of commercial services (US$891 billion, 25 per cent of the world total). The top five importers of commercial services in 2013 were the United States (9.8 per cent of the world total), China (7.5 per cent), Germany (7.2 per cent), France (4.3 per cent) and the UK (4.0 per cent) (WTO 2014: 27).

Service offshoring is not easily analyzed because service tasks can be traded in four ways (United Nations 2002: 1):

Mode 1: cross-border supply occurs when suppliers of services in one country supply services to consumers in another country without either supplier or consumer moving into the territory of the other.

Mode 2: consumption abroad refers to the process by which a consumer resident in one country moves to another country to obtain a service.

Mode 3: commercial presence occurs when enterprises in an economy supply services internationally through the activities of foreign affiliates.

Mode 4: presence of natural persons describes the process by which an individual moves to the consumer's country to provide a service, whether on his or her own behalf or on behalf of his or her employer.

Three of these modes are concerned primarily with service transactions between residents and non-residents. Mode 1 involves the provision of services that require no direct contact with customers but procedures must be developed to overcome cultural barriers that exist between countries. Recently, there has been a particular interest in Mode 3, whereby enterprises supply services internationally through the activities of foreign affiliates (Bryson *et al.* 2004). For services, the Mode 3 'method of serving foreign markets is particularly important because it is often the only method that permits the close and continuing contact between service providers and their customers necessary to compete effectively with indigenous firms' (United Nations 2002a: 54). In this instance the provision of services through foreign direct investment represents a type of *captive offshoring* or offshoring without outsourcing. Captive offshoring enables a firm to retain control over its assets, intellectual property and core business processes. Trade in services must address cultural differences between countries that restrict the ability of service providers to export standardized services. Modes 3 and 4 enable service providers to localize provision to take into consideration local cultures and client expectations. Modes 1, 3 and 4 involve what is commonly termed 'service offshoring' or more correctly 'service global sourcing'. This is encapsulated by the concept of a '**second global shift**' (Bryson 2007). The first global shift involved the relocation of manufacturing employment to low-cost production locations while the second implicates services in this process. There have been three distinct phases to the second global shift. First, during the early 1990s IT programming, testing and network support activities were outsourced and then globally sourced. Second, during the late 1990s global sourcing diversified into the provision of back-office and call-centre functions and also the development of computer applications. Third, during the early years of this century full service centres emerged that provide a wide range of administration, process, contact and support functions.

The second global shift highlights the potential for transferring service work from developed economies to low-cost locations, and it has provoked a major policy debate, or even panic, in the USA and Europe (Parker 2004; Blinder 2006). For example, Forrester (a consultancy company) has estimated that 1.1 million Western European jobs will move offshore during 2005–15 and that two-thirds of these jobs will originate from the United Kingdom (Parker 2004). Perhaps the best estimate comes from an analysis of occupational data for several OECD countries which suggests that around 20 per cent of total service employment has the potential to be geographically footloose as a result of rapid developments in ICT (van Welsum and Reif 2005: 6). Ultimately, the only types of service jobs that will be safe are those for which face-to-face interaction is absolutely essential (Levy and Murnane 2004).

The development of service offshoring represents a new type of international division of labour, but with a difference. It is various forms of service activity, ranging from call-centre-based work to back-office administration that is being relocated to low-cost locations rather than manufacturing or assembly activities. This new form of trade involves low-value call-centre-type activities as well as high-value services such as legal work, accountancy, design, business analysis, and equity research (Table 17.2). Using high-speed fibre-optic cables and undersea telephone lines data scanned in Britain or America is transmitted to a low-cost offshore location to be processed in back offices or used in call centres.

A number of factors influence the decision to send a particular service activity offshore. First, it must be capable of some degree of standardization that does not require face-to-face interaction with consumers or clients. Second, the inputs and outputs required to deliver the service must be capable of being traded or transmitted with the assistance of ICT (OECD 2005: 12). Third, some service activities are not fixed in space and can be provided either as a form of foreign trade or by the temporary relocation of a service worker to a client's premises, for example management consultancy or various forms of auditing. Fourth, specialist services can be provided from central locations with consumers travelling to avail themselves of the service. In many cases such services would be provided within the confines of a nation-state, but some are being consumed by a form of service-based travel, for example education (secondary and tertiary), plastic surgery and a whole range of other surgical procedures.

During the 1980s India began to develop capability and capacity in the provision of offshore services. It was triggered by three events. During the late 1980s some of the key chip designers employed by Texas Instruments in America were Indian and Texas let them return home to work for them from there using early forms of ICT. In 1989, Jack Welch, the then Chairman of the American conglomerate General Electric (GE), visited India and realized that it offered a pool of talented individuals who could be of benefit to GE. A team was sent to India and GE set up a joint development project with an Indian engineering company, Wipro. Second, during the late 1990s the Y2 computer crisis, or the millennium bug, provided India with clients interested in computer remediation. When computers were originally designed, to save memory their clocks used six digits for dates – two for the day, two for the month and two for the year. When the year 2000 arrived there was a risk that computers would not recognize it, but would think that it was the year 1900. The resulting need for Y2 upgrading was tedious work and many American and European companies commissioned Indian companies for the task. This allowed the Indian computer industry to enter the global marketplace for the provision of computer services, an opportunity they would build upon when the Y2 work was replaced by the e-commerce or dot-com boom. The dot-com boom led to investment in undersea fibre-optic cable, but the dot-com bust that followed meant that the cost of using this cable was virtually nil and this vastly increased the number of American companies wanting to outsource service activities to India (Friedman 2005: 106–10).

Outsourcing services to companies located in other countries comes with a number of risks attached to language, culture and the quality of the provided service. Unlike the first 'global shift', the geography of the second global shift is determined by the educational and

Table 17.2 Service jobs that have been sent offshore from the United Kingdom

Customer-facing – constant contact between producer and consumer	Back office – business process outsourcing
Call centres	Business services
Customer services	Accountancy
Out of hours claims (call centre)	Legal services
Back office administration	Finance
Back office processing	Human relations
E-commerce	IT provision
Credit control	Business systems
Internet services	Graphics and architectural services
Internet claims	Document production
IT helpdesk	Underwriting
Rail timetable enquiries	Technical lists
	Equity research
	Business analysts
	Legal secretaries
	Software development
	City analysts
	Transcription services (voice and shorthand)
	Copy-editing
	Management of University programmes
	Computer-based learning
	Website design and management

Source: after Bryson (2007)

language abilities of service workers located in foreign locations that may also perhaps, but not always, be lower-cost locations (Bryson 2007). For the English-speaking world this means that potential suppliers must be able to provide English-speaking employees in other countries, while France, Norway or Sweden, for example, require a pool of staff fluent in French, Norwegian or Swedish. Language and culture plays a much more important part in this global shift than they did during the development of an international division of manufacturing labour. This means that countries with relatively localized languages may be protected from the global sourcing of services whilst countries with more widely spoken 'global' languages (such as English, Spanish or French) will almost certainly participate in the second global shift. Therefore the geography of the second global shift is also different from the first; it is more constrained by language as well as cultural nearness, that is, the ability of foreign

service suppliers to relate to customers located in other countries (Figure 17.4).

An implication is that countries which developed extensive empires during the nineteenth century may have inadvertently laid the foundations for the emergence of foreign competitors who are able to exploit the benefits associated with their acquired or imposed non-native language. This is a form of 'post-colonial twist' in that the various trading and political empires encouraged the use of a common language and, in many cases, common legal and educational systems (Bryson 2007). It is therefore not surprising that countries such as the United Kingdom and the United States that are part of a globalized language grouping may be most at risk from companies choosing to deliver services from lower-cost locations either by establishing their own operations via a process of foreign direct investment or by subcontracting the activities to a third party and often foreign service provider. Whether

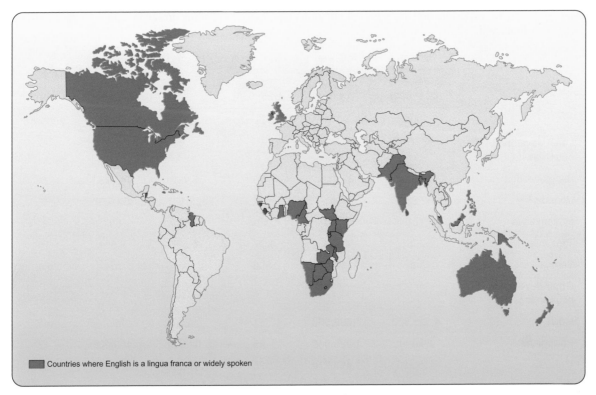

Figure 17.4 Language as a factor in the geography of outsourcing countries where English is a *lingua franca* or relatively widely spoken.

this is a 'real' threat will depend on whether the availability of lower-cost services will actually enhance the competitiveness of other parts of the developed market economies, leading to future innovation and wealth-creation opportunities. It is also important to remember that the second global shift does not just involve the transfer of jobs from high- to low-cost economies but it is also a two-way process in which service providers based in low-cost locations must also establish branch offices in developed market economies. Service offshoring is a complex process involving the development of firms that have the ability to provide service functions from a number of different locations. This type of transnational service firm can develop out of the activities of firms located, for example, in the United States or United Kingdom (developed market economies) or in India or China (developing or transition economies).

The evolving geography of service offshoring is complex as the geography differs by the task that is offshored and by sector. Technological innovations, the Internet, and the language and IT skills of the workforce have facilitated the offshoring of information technology services. The World Trade Organization's (WTO) Information

and Technology Agreement (ITA) was concluded in 1996 and this removed duties on IT products included in the agreement. The ITA facilitated major growth in the export and import of IT services. India has become the predominant location for the offshoring of software services (Table 17.3). In 2009, India exported US$33 billion of computer services and other developing countries (Philippines, Malaysia and Costa Rica) have experienced significant growth in IT exports. The export of IT services in some developing countries has been growing at much greater rates than developed economies so that the Philippines, for example, has experienced dramatic growth with IT exports increasing from US$89 million in 2005 to US$1.9 billion in 2010; an annual growth rate of 85 per cent (WTO 2014: 92)

Service offshoring represents a stage in the evolving global geography of production. It was driven by developments in ICT and also salary differentials. The threat of offshoring service jobs from the US and Europe exerted a downward pressure on salaries rather than leading to major job losses in developed market economies. Developments in computer coding, new algorithms and industrial robots have perhaps displaced many more

Table 17.3 Top five exporters and importers of computer services by economy grouping, 2005–10 (% and US$ thousand)

	Exports		Imports			
	Value (US$ '000)	Growth p.a (%)	Value (US$ '000)	Growth p.a (%)		
	2005	2010	2005–10	2005	2010	2005–10
Least developed countries (LDCs)						
Bangladesh	18,557	37,440	15	3,792	4,873	5
Uganda	32,825	37,407	3	22,191	32,679	8
Mozambique	121	5,237	112	2,659	691	-24
Tanzania	265	4,634	77	4,597	9,561	16
Samoa	n.a.	972	n.a.	n.a.	n.a.	n.a.
Other developing economies						
Israel	4,528,500	7,699,500	11	n.a.	n.a.	n.a.
Philippines	89,000	1,928,000	85	62,000	109,000	12
Malaysia	435,260	1,453,770	35	379,295	1,206,030	34
Costa Rica	254,378	1,216,190	37	10,721	20,844	14
Hong Kong, China	207,000	812,000	31	371,000	488,000	6
Developing country G20 members						
India	n.a.	33,383,179	n.a.	1,048,870	2,175,840	16
Russian Federation	374,570	1,273,280	28	378,620	1,637,450	34
Argentina	235,210	1,237,340	39	190,730	445,356	18
Brazil	80,223	195,100	19	1,656,840	3,414,480	16
Korea, Republic of	n.a.	149,000	n.a.	n.a.	170,600	n.a.
Developed economies						
Ireland	19,369,000	37,196.458	14	378.063	752,273	15
Germany	8,415,411	15,304,988	14	8,587,027	14,066,711	10
United Kingdom	8,476,394	9,952,424	3	3,339,921	5,256,661	10
United States	3,554,000	8,771,000	20	2,000,000	18,394,000	56
Sweden	2,608.025	6,813,995	21	1,384,166	2,341,998	11

Source: after WTO (2014: 92)

call-centre operators in developed market economies that service offshoring. In 1998, Jack Welch, the then chief executive of General Electric, noted that 'ideally, you'd have every plant you own on a barge to move with currencies and changes in the economy' (*The Economist* 2013: 11). The factors that influence the location of a call centre or any business activity are constantly changing. Salary differentials narrow and may be replaced by a concern with the quality of service provided. In 2012, KPMG International noted that there was a revolution underway in business services that might mean 'the death of outsourcing' as we know it (Justice 2012).

Outsourcing is considered as playing an important role in developing new processes and technologies, reducing cost, accessing new sources of talent and transforming business through working with new partners. Nevertheless, KPMG notes that different firms have very different attitudes to the provision of services. Some firms consider sales and general administration as technical necessities that must be managed to reduce costs whilst other firms consider these business functions as part of a differentiation strategy in the marketplace. This is to highlight the important role core services play in building market share and reflects a shift away from a focus just on cost control. Some business activities that used to be outsourced and offshored, such as data management and the analysis of Big Data are increasingly considered to be strategic business processes that are best undertaken in-house.

The global sourcing or offshoring of services does not have to entail the supply of services over large distances. It may occur as 'near-shoring' or the relocation or provision of services over short distances and often between locations on the same continental land mass (Gál 2009), for example the 'near-shoring' of American services to Canada. Services can now be supplied on-shore, near-shore and offshore. Presented in this manner these may appear as simple alternatives but in many instances firms have developed '*blended delivery systems*' that capitalize on the place-based advantages of coupling or blending activities located in a variety of different locations: home country, near, far (Bryson 2007).

17.6 Conclusion

The history of economic development is one of increased economic specialization combined with the development of new and often complex geographies. All this represents and reflects the constant working through of new divisions of labour and new ways of maximizing wealth creation. The development of service-dominated economies represents a working through of the division of labour but it is worth remembering that it is important to differentiate between employment and output. All services must be supported by manufactured products and all manufactured products are supported by services. The implication is that we have an integrated economy in which the worlds of production (services and manufacturing functions), finance and consumption combine to produce local, national and international economies.

The spatial division of expertise and the related second global shift continue to evolve and have the potential to rework the national and global dynamics of the capitalist economic system. Employment that was considered to be safe from foreign competition is suddenly exposed to business models that operate by blending together different forms of expertise related to differential comparative advantage. This may enhance productivity improvements, leading to new innovations, but it also has the potential 'to undermine the service-based solution to the employment crisis that is still being experienced by many developed regional economies' (Bryson 2007).

Learning outcomes

Having read this chapter, you should understand:

- Different ways in which services have been defined and conceptualized by economists and geographers.
- The concept of a 'personality market' or emotional labour highlights the importance of embodied labour, or skills with people, in the world of service work.
- Appreciate that as the United Kingdom and the United States became industrialized societies they were simultaneously transformed into service economies.
- Service economies should not just be identified by measuring employment, but should also take into consideration gross value added (GVA).

- Economic production is a story of economic specialization and the continual reworking of the division of labour.
- A spatial division of labour occurs with the geographical separation of production tasks, for example, writing, printing, binding and distributing a book.
- The development of a concept of a spatial division of expertise draws attention to the development of new corporate strategies that are founded upon exploiting comparative advantage based on expertise.
- Different economic geographies can be explained by distinctive combinations and patterns of spatial divisions of labour and of expertise.
- Services were conventionally conceptualized as local untraded activities. The rise of the second global shift or service offshoring highlights one of the latest developments in the capitalist economic system.

Further reading

Bryson, J.R. (2007) A 'second' global shift? The offshoring or global sourcing of corporate services and the rise of distanciated emotional labour, *Geografiska Annaler,* 89B(1), 31–44.

Bryson, J.R. and Daniels, P.W. (eds) (2015) *The Handbook of Service Business: Management, Marketing, Innovation and Internationalisation Industries,* Edward Elgar, Cheltenham.

Bryson, J.R., Daniels, P.W. and Warf, B. (2004) *Service Worlds: People, Organizations, Technologies,* Routledge, London. The most recent account of the different divisions of labour amongst service activities and occupations as well as the role of ICT in altering the geographies of production systems.

Bryson, J.R. and Rusten, G. (2008) Transnational corporations and spatial divisions of 'service' expertise as a competitive strategy: the example of 3M and Boeing, *The Service Industries Journal,* 28(3), 307–23.

Gál, A. (2009) 'Future Bangalores? The increasing role of Central and Eastern Europe in services offshoring', available at: http://papers.ssrn.com/sol3/papers.cfm?abstract_id=1334165.

GEOGRAPHIES OF MONEY, FINANCE AND CRISIS

Chapter 18

Manuel B. Aalbers and Jane Pollard

Topics covered

- Money and finance in economic geography
- The relation between globalization and financialization
- Geographies of the financial crisis
- Global monies and local monies
- Occupy Wall Street and other responses to crisis

Money is simultaneously everything and nothing, everywhere but
nowhere in particular.
(David Harvey 1985b: 167)

This chapter explores the social, economic, political and geographical attributes of money, finance and crisis. Many accounts of money and 'the global financial crisis' are written by economists or finance specialists, who pay little attention to its geographical anatomy. Is finance something that we should think about geographically? Money can certainly be placed, whether it's in your pocket, your bank account or in the stock market, but only in the first case is your money a physical object. As the Harvey quote suggests, money can be a difficult subject and many contemporary debates about **globalization** stress the increasingly integrated, global machinations of the financial system in which 'virtual' or 'digital' monies can be moved around the globe at the touch of a button. One of the purposes of this chapter is to persuade you of the existence and importance of different geographies of finance that together contribute to an understanding of the so-called 'global financial crisis'.

Novelists, filmmakers and social theorists alike have grappled with money's contradictory characteristics. Money can be everything and nothing, everywhere and nowhere; money can be the root of all evil and a source of independence and freedom. Even simple questions like 'what is money?' present some difficulties. Davies (1994: 29) suggests that money is 'anything that is widely used for making payments and accounting for debts and credits'. Historically, a wide range of items including beads, shells, whales' teeth, cattle, salt, skins, tobacco, beer, gold and silver have been used as money. Such variation suggests that rather than asking what money is, we should perhaps ask what functions does money perform? This question reveals the important economic functions of money and finance and their status as a source of social power. This is illustrated through a geographical reading of the financial crisis that started in 2007 and ended in . . . well, we are not so sure about when the financial crisis ended or will end, as it has mutated from a **subprime mortgage** crisis and a **foreclosure** crisis into a banking crisis, an economic crisis, a political crisis, a sovereign debt crisis and a euro crisis.

We are used to thinking of money and finance 'oiling the wheels' of commerce and also being a measure of worth or value. Yet these two facets of money and finance can be contradictory. As a store of value, it is desirable for money to be a stable, fixed representation of value. As a medium of circulation and as a form of **capital** – money that is thrown into circulation with the intent of generating more money – it is desirable to have money freely available as credit, divorced from its moorings in the 'real economy'. As Davies (2002: 30) argues, the history (and geography) of the evolution of money reveals 'unceasing conflict' between borrowers, keen to expand the *quantity* of money in circulation, and lenders, keen to limit the supply of money and, at all costs, preserve the *quality* of monies in circulation. Managing this conflict or, more accurately, reacting to financial crises resulting from it, has been and still is the mission of various regulatory authorities.

18.1 Money and finance in geography

Although we may be used to thinking of money as primarily an economic phenomenon, geographers and other social scientists are now recognizing that money is saturated with cultural, social and political significance. In this section, we examine some of the social-geographical aspects of money. We focus initially on money and power, before moving on to consider the **financialization** of society and the geographies that connect individuals and groups in different places and times. We also examine some of the arguments concerning the globalization of money and finance, before outlining some of the problems with this view.

Many of the social and cultural aspects of money are related to its role as 'the very incarnation of social power' (Harvey 1982: 245). Again, however, we confront the contradictory qualities of money. As a means of expressing social power money has both desirable and less desirable qualities. Leyshon and Thrift (1997) talk of two discourses about money: one of suspicion and one of liberation.

To understand the discourse of suspicion, we can turn to the work of Georg Simmel (1978: 277), for whom money is 'the most perfect representation' of the tendency to reduce quality to quantity. As a store of value and unit of account money transforms social relations – qualitatively different commodities and experiences – into an abstract quantity, namely their price. In contemporary capitalism, money has become *the* mediator and regulator of economic relations between individuals, a measure of wealth and a means of expressing social power. All manner of social, political and cultural issues – from healthcare, housing, education, leisure and sports, the environment, and so forth – are debated not in terms of what they are worth, but in terms of *how much* they are worth in the sense of what can be afforded. Money 'affects our very ideals of what is good and beautiful and true' (Mitchell 1937: 371). Money, in this sense, has corroded the importance of other meanings and measures of 'value'.

Yet there is also a discourse of liberation that accompanies money. First, money provides a degree of individuality, freedom, security and independence for those that hold it. This is especially true in societies like the UK where laws regarding private property buttress ideologies of liberty, equality and freedom. The idea that money is empowering and liberating is central to the desire to possess money, to work for it, to accept it as payment and to save and invest it. Second, as Simmel (1991: 20) argues, money 'creates an extremely strong bond among members of an economic circle'; people have far more connections to other people in modern, monetized societies than was the case in feudal society. Through the **division of labour** in capitalist societies (see Chapter 2), money links people together in offices, factories, homes and shopping malls in different parts of the world. Money may in some senses be corrosive of social bonds, but it also creates a community that can forge new connections and hold people together.

18.1.1 Global monies?

Many geographers, particularly those working in a **political economy** tradition, have argued that capitalism appears to be speeding up and spreading out (Harvey 1989; Massey 1994). Capitalism is seen to be spreading out in that more people in different countries and regions are becoming bound up with the logics of contemporary capitalism. It is also speeding up in that the pace of life seems to be increasing in different parts of the globe. In Spotlight box 18.1, we noted the ability of money to transform qualitatively different commodities and experiences into an abstract quantity, a price. This has led many theorists to argue that money is a vehicle for the *homogenization of space*, for making different spaces more similar. While there are ongoing debates about the extent to which capitalism is generating a *global culture* (see Chapter 13), it is difficult to argue with the contention that financial markets in different countries have,

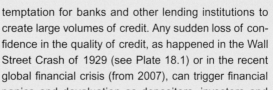

Spotlight box 18.1

The functions of money

- Money is a *unit of account*: it is the base of economic accounting systems.
- Money is a *measure of value*: it is the commodity against which the values of other commodities can be calibrated and compared on the same scale.
- Money is a *store of value,* in that you can sell a good for a certain amount of money and then use that money to buy something else at a later date. Money thus allows for the separation of the sale and purchase of commodities over space and time *if* it is a reliable store of value. Preserving this ability of money to store value is one of the reasons why governments are so concerned about the phenomenon of inflation.
- Money is a *medium of exchange and circulation*.
- Money is a *means of payment and a standard for deferred payments*.

These different functions of money often come into conflict with each other. As a store of value, governments, firms and individuals alike want monies to maintain their value and hence their purchasing power, between different times and spaces. As a medium of circulation, however, it is important for money to be extended as credit.

Banks create credit – and thereby money – by extending loans to individuals, firms, governments and . . . each other. During economic growth, there is

temptation for banks and other lending institutions to create large volumes of credit. Any sudden loss of confidence in the quality of credit, as happened in the Wall Street Crash of 1929 (see Plate 18.1) or in the recent global financial crisis (from 2007), can trigger financial panics and devaluation as depositors, investors and financial institutions flee from credit moneys and seek out safer havens.

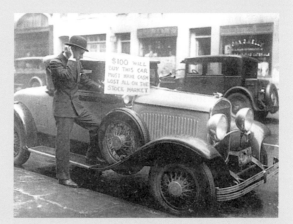

Plate 18.1 The Wall Street Crash 1929: the stock market collapse of October 1929 brought the 1920s boom to an end and led to widespread bank failures, bankruptcies and drastic reduction in the availability of credit.

(Bettmann/Corbis)

since the mid-1970s, become more interconnected (Harvey 1989; Martin 1994) and homogeneous.

When we talk about the *globalization of finance*, however, we are talking about more than just the growth of international financial transactions, or the growing presence of multinational companies in domestic financial markets. Globalization implies:

> a strong degree of integration between the different national and multinational parts . . . the emergence of truly transnational banks and financial companies . . . that integrate their activities and transactions across different national markets. And above all, it [globalization] refers to the increasing freedom of movement, transfer and tradability of monies and finance capital across the globe, in effect integrating national markets into a new supranational system.
>
> (Martin 1994: 256)

The emergence of this *supranational* system coincides with the increasing difficulties faced by *nationally* based regulatory authorities like the Bank of England or the US Federal Reserve. The 'discourse of suspicion' we mentioned earlier rears its head in many popular representations of 'global finance' as a 'global financial casino staffed by faceless bankers and hedge fund speculators who operate with a herd mentality in the shadowy world of global finance (Korten 1998: 4). This kind of discourse was also prevalent in the UK in 2008: Alex Salmond, First Minister of Scotland, argued that 'spivs and speculators' were putting 'the quality of life and jobs of hundreds, thousands and millions of people across the world at risk through "short-trading"' – where investors make money by betting that the price of shares in a company will fall (cited in McIntosh and Maddox 2008). Whether or not you agree with these views, it is true that the degree of integration of the financial system profoundly shapes and connects the lives of people thousands of miles away from each other. In this sense, Leyshon (1995) talks of money being able to 'shrink' space and time, bringing some (but not other) parts of the globe relatively closer together through the working of financial markets. A good example of this is considered in Case study 18.1, which describes how the fates of property developers in Bangkok (Thailand) ultimately affected the fortunes of a bartender, Graham Jones, in Whitley Bay (UK). The fates of individuals and companies in Britain and Thailand are connected through the workings of foreign exchange markets that, in turn, link national currencies to the competitiveness of different nation-states.

This example highlights only some of the interconnections between changes in the value of the Thai baht and how these affected businesses across Asia and Europe.

We could extend the example by thinking through how job losses in any other place would also have been felt by those not in paid work. For those in households dependent on the wages of someone made redundant there would be further belt-tightening or a search for alternative sources of income. For the unemployed, job losses in the area might mean more competition for any new jobs that are created and so forth.

18.1.2 Forces for globalization and financialization

The organization of monies into different financial markets can appear dauntingly complex. In addition to the financial jargon describing different products and markets, the 'global financial system' can sometimes seem like something 'out there', a fast-moving, volatile 'thing', running out of control, increasingly uncoupled from the 'real' economy and operating beyond the regulatory reach of any one nation-state (Langley 2003). This global sense of money and finance can be difficult to grasp and sometimes it is difficult to understand just how its machinations affect us. For example, how did the US housing and subprime mortgage crisis that started in 2007 change the lives of people not only in the United States, but also in other continents (see Section 18.2)?

The global financial crisis is often framed as one caused by unscrupulous financial practices in both the global financial command and control centres (London, New York and so forth) and the daily life of consumer banks and their customers. There is a feeling that finance is now playing a bigger part in both the economy at large (the Economy with a capital 'E', that is measured in 'gross domestic products', stock indices and other statistics) and the economy of daily life (the many economies with a lowercase 'e', i.e. how individuals and households go about in their personal lives) have become more financialized. The burgeoning literature on financialization tries to answer the who, what, how, why, when and where questions of the presumed financialization of the E/economies. Financialization can be defined as 'the increasing dominance of financial actors, markets, practices, measurements and narratives, at various scales, resulting in a structural transformation of economies, firms (including financial institutions), states and households' (Aalbers 2015).

The '-ation' part of financialization suggests that it is not a state or end result but an action, something that is produced. Many financialization scholars situate the beginning of this most recent bout of financialization in the 1970s with the rise of neoliberalism (see Chapter 8), the crisis of Fordist capitalism in the West (see Chapter 3), the breakdown of the Bretton Woods system (see Section 18.1.3) and other developments. Others

Case study 18.1

From Bangkok to Whitley Bay . . .

1 Devaluation in Thailand, July 1997

In 1997, several property companies collapsed in Thailand; property prices and the stock market started to fall. Currency speculators, already nervous about slowing growth in the region, started to sell the baht (Thai currency) as they expected the currency to be devalued. In July, the baht was devalued. As a result, Thai exports became cheaper and, to stay competitive, Indonesia, Malaysia, South Korea and the Philippines allowed their currencies to fall sharply. Some Korean firms who needed foreign currency to pay off loans started dumping cheap microchips, forcing microchip prices down from US$10 a unit to US$1.50.

2 Factory closure in North Tyneside, UK, 31 July 1997

Rapidly falling semiconductor prices meant losses of £350 million for German electronics company Siemens. Siemens semiconductors were produced at plants in Tyneside (UK), Taiwan, Germany, France and the USA. Managers in Munich announced plans to close their £1.1 billion plant in North Tyneside that employed 1,100 people and had opened only in 1994.

3 The cleaning company

The Siemens factory provided 10 per cent of business in the North East for Mitie, a cleaning company. One-third of the workforce of 90 people were facing redundancy and their boss had his salary bonus cut 10 per cent, in line with the loss of work from Siemens.

4 The hotel

Siemens and its contractors, like Mitie, were the single biggest sources of business for the Stakis Hotel. The hotel responded to the closure by switching their market focus. As the flow of German executives and their UK contractors slowed and then ceased, the hotel sought to attract more families.

5 The taxi firm

Foxhunters, a taxi firm, had a contract with Siemens that generated more than a dozen runs a day, usually to the Stakis Hotel, the airport or the university. Since August, Siemens business had dried up and 85 drivers were chasing work for 50. Despite working longer hours, drivers' takings were down by between £100 and £200 a week. Drivers started to economize by bringing in their own lunches and by cutting down their trips to the local pub.

6 The local pub

Takings at Cameron's had fallen by £600 a week since August. The landlord, who blamed the Siemens shut-down for the reduced trade, cut his opening hours. Attempts to drum up more trade by price reductions had little effect. The landlord was hoping for more business around Christmas. He and his partner had less money for spending on their leisure activities, which included visiting places like Whitley Bay.

7 Graham Jones, bartender in Whitley Bay, October 1998

Graham was fired from his job at a pub in Whitley Bay; there was not enough business to occupy two bartenders in the public bar.

Source: adapted from Carroll (1998)

have pointed at financial deregulation and the associated changes on Wall Street and the City of London in the 1980s, including technological developments (see below) and the growing volumes of money that pension funds seek to invest. The decline of communism and the fall of the USSR (see Chapter 3) at the end of that decade are also mentioned as contributing factors, in part because they discredited non-capitalist alternatives and under-wrote how neoliberal and financial discourses became dominant (Aalbers 2015). More generally speaking, financialization is part of and key to structural trans-formations of advanced capitalist economies. According to some scholars, we have been here before, e.g. in the run-up the 1929 Wall Street Crash that was followed by the 1930s depression, and financialization thus should be understood as a recurrent phase in capitalist development (Arrighi 1994).

To illustrate the financialization argument, differ-ent authors cite different statistics to show that a whole range of financial markets have grown rapidly since the 1970s. In the USA finance has become the dominant source of profits since the 1990s (Krippner 2011), but this can be witnessed in most OECD countries. For the EU27, Eurostat (2011) has calculated that the FIRE (finance, insurance and real estate) sectors together contributed 29 per cent to GDP. Even in Germany, which is often said to have a less financialized economy, the FIRE sectors contributed more to GDP than manufacturing (30 per cent and 20 per cent respectively). Financial assets held by institutional investors as a percentage of GDP grew rapidly in all OECD countries and now represent more than 200 per cent in countries like the USA and UK and around 100 per cent in countries like Germany and France, increasing three- (US) to tenfold (France) between 1980 and 2001 (Deutschmann 2011). By contrast, the wage share of national income has fallen across the board, although less so in countries with strong labour unions (Epstein and Jayadev 2005). Geographers have repeatedly stressed that financialization is an inherently spatial phenomenon that should be much more central to economic geographic analysis. Local, national and macro-regional institutions act as filters of how financialization plays out and is perceived.

How has this financialization of the economy and globalization of money come about? There is a range of factors to consider here. First, through the 1980s and 1990s, different governments and international institutions, like the **International Monetary Fund** (IMF), have pursued neoliberal, free market policies and encouraged the deregulation of financial markets (by eliminating exchange and capital controls) and the liberalization of flows of capital across national borders.

Second, there have been advances in telecommunications and computing technologies. Computers have transformed payments systems. For hundreds of years, payments and transfers of money were completed in cash – coins and notes – and written down in ledgers. Coins and notes were superseded by cheques that in turn have been superseded by electronic monies that can be moved around the world at the speed of light. Semiconductor chips in computers mean that consumers in many countries can use credit and debit cards to pay for goods. In some countries, computer chips are now embedded in plastic 'smart' cards to allow the use of '**electronic**' or '**digital money**', or, more accurately, electronic representations of currencies, to pay for groceries, public transport or lunch at the university cafeteria. Finally, there are the systems of communication, using earth-orbiting satellites, that are integral to the operation of computing systems, e-mail, the Internet and other forms of communication that are used by banks, governments and other financial players. These innovations have made 24-hour trading possible as high-speed computers link stock markets in different countries. New communications and software technologies have also spawned the proliferation of financial websites, information providers and intermediaries able to provide financial information

to firms and consumers. Online providers, without the costs of maintaining the bricks and mortar associated with a high street presence, provide insurance, banking, pension and other financial products to firms and consumers with access to Internet technologies.

Third, and closely related to developments in technology, there have been innovations in tradable financial products that have made it easier and faster to move money around the globe. Derivatives are one example of this kind of innovation. **Derivatives** are contracts between two entities that specify rights/obligations based on (hence 'derived' from) the performance of some other currency, commodity or service. They often include swaps, options, futures and mortgage-backed **securities** (see also Section 18.2.2 and Spotlight box 18.4). They can be used to hedge against risk, or to provide leverage. In the 1970s, financial derivatives were created to allow financial managers to deal with currency risk, but since that time they have become increasingly sophisticated and extended to more markets. Since 1997, for example, energy suppliers, transport agencies, construction companies, wine bar owners and other firms exposed to weather risk (the possibility that weather could have an adverse impact on their profits and cash flow) have been able to purchase weather derivatives contracts to protect themselves against this risk (Pollard *et al.* 2008). With this extension, however, there has been the proliferation of purely speculative trading of such financial instruments – and the development of other much more complex contracts. The derivatives' market has grown exponentially between 1990, when the market was almost too small to measure, and 2006 when the number of outstanding contracts added up to US$370 trillion (BIS 2008).

Innovations in computing and software technologies and in financial instruments are fundamental to arguments about the growing financialization of the economy alluded to earlier; this is an argument that asserts that the speculative accumulation of capital has become an end in itself in contemporary capitalism, that the financial system has come to feed on itself, so to speak, rather than supporting firms and industries and other elements of the 'real' economy (Strange 1999). Round the clock trading of financial instruments in different places and time zones opens up opportunities for speculation and arbitrage, which is the ability to profit from small differences in price when the same financial product is being traded on more than one market. One indicator of how growth in the international financial system is outpacing the growth of the 'real' economy is provided by foreign exchange trading data. According to the Bank for International Settlements the daily turnover of foreign exchange trading in 1973 was US$10–20 billion, roughly twice the amount necessitated by world trade. By 2004, daily trade in foreign exchange averaged US$1.9 trillion, roughly *ninety five* times that necessitated by world trade. By April 2010, daily trading volumes had reached US$4 trillion (www.bis.org/publ/rpfx10.htm). For individual consumers with access to the appropriate technology there are now on-line financial bookmakers encouraging clients to enjoy spread betting (and possibly tax-free profits) on price movements of stocks, stock indices, currencies, interest rates, commodities and even house prices.

These, then, are some of the ways in which money has become more global since the 1970s. But what motivates such changes? What motivates the implementation of 'free market' policies, the development of new technologies and financial instruments like derivatives? For those working in a political economy tradition, like David Harvey (1989), the motivation for these changes is the search for profit. Capitalism is fundamentally about the accumulation of surplus. Competition drives capitalists to seek out new markets, new products and to reduce the *turnover time of capital* (see Spotlight box 18.2). In different parts of the globe, finance is the language through which the imperatives of capitalism are being communicated.

So, there is a very strong economic rationale for the globalization of money. And it is difficult to argue with the contention that money has become more globalized since the 1970s, that it has, increasingly, connected people in distant places and homogenized financial space. For Richard O'Brien (1992) the growth of the international financial system is tantamount to 'the end of geography', the notion that geography is becoming relatively less important because money, in its different forms, is able to overcome the friction of distance and link distant places together. Others argue that this view is too simple, that geography remains critical to our understanding of global finance. We now turn to consider these views in more detail.

18.1.3 Debunking global monies

A rather different departure point for talking about the 'globalization of finance' is to argue that the financial system is not really global at all, that it is more like a *web of connections* between different financial systems, some of which are bound together more tightly than others. This argument has developed because the idea of a 'global financial system' is problematic for several reasons.

The first problem stems from the simple observation that 'global finance' is largely the province of North America, Europe and parts of Asia, most notably Japan, Hong Kong, Singapore and, more recently, China; it is an idea centred on the experiences of the West. Many parts of Africa, Asia and Latin America are not only not included in 'the global financial system'; they are being actively excluded as banks refuse to lend money until outstanding debts have been repaid. There is what Massey (1993) describes as *power geometry* at work when some commentators describe the financial system as 'global'. For some financial workers in New York, London, and Tokyo, international finance may be regarded as 'global' in the sense that all countries and regions of the globe deemed creditworthy and capable of producing profits have been included; sub-Saharan Africa, however, ceases to exist in such a conception of 'the global'.

Second, and resulting from this geographical concentration of the management of 'global finance' in North America, Europe and parts of Asia, some currencies circulate more widely and have greater spatial reach than others. The Japanese yen, the euro and most especially the US dollar are very useful in international markets because they are accepted as forms of payment, unlike, for example, Indian rupees. For that reason, the US dollar

Spotlight box 18.2

The circulation of money as capital

In capitalist societies, the circulation of money as capital is as follows. From left to right in the equation, money (M) is invested by producers to purchase commodities (C), namely labour power (LP) and the means of production (MP), say pieces of wood and wood-cutting machinery. Labour power and the means of production are combined in production (P) to make more commodities (C'), in this example, let us say chairs, which are then sold for more money (M') than was originally invested (M).

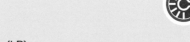

$$M \rightarrow C \rightarrow \frac{\{LP\}}{\{MP\}} \rightarrow P \rightarrow C' \rightarrow M' \rightarrow \ldots$$

The purpose of production in capitalist societies is to produce profit and accumulate capital. The *turnover time of capital* is the amount of time it takes for money to complete this circuit. The shorter the turnover time, the more often money can be lent out and the more profit can be made. Producers therefore have a very strong incentive to, where possible, reduce the turnover time of capital; time *is* money.

is also the most popular as a global reserve currency, that is, as a store of value (see Spotlight box 18.1). Historically, the country that occupies a dominant economic and political position has underwritten the soundness of the international financial system and had its currency accepted internationally as the currency in which commodity prices are quoted and payments made. Before the Second World War, Britain and the pound sterling fulfilled this role; after the Bretton Woods conference in 1944, the US dollar became the key international currency. More recently, as the economic dominance of the USA has declined, the yen, the euro and the Chinese renminbi have become relatively more important in international markets.

So, some currencies, like the US dollar, are truly international while some others are national. There are estimated to be over 4,000 *local currencies* in operation around the globe that facilitate exchange only within very specific spatial and social contexts. For example, Local Exchange Trading Systems (LETS) are associations whose members list their services needed/offered in a directory and trade with each other in a local unit of currency; for example, 'bobbins' in Manchester and 'solents' in Southampton (Williams 1996). Since their establishment in Canada in 1983, LETS schemes have spread to Europe, Australia, New Zealand and North America, allowing members not only access to credit, but also the chance to engage in productive activity to earn such credit. Some local currency schemes are devised in times of hardship to allow local people to trade goods and services when they are unemployed and have little money. Other schemes are motivated by ecological concerns, the desire for community development and social cohesion, and the desire to construct alternative local economic geographies as a form of resistance against the global spread of capitalism (Lee 2000).

Third, as Martin (1999b: 6) argues, for all the talk of 'global finance', there remain different *geographical circuits of money* that form the 'wiring' of an economy, along which 'currents' of wealth, consumption and power are conveyed. He identifies four geographies of money: locational, institutional, regulatory and public. The *locational geography* refers to the location of different financial institutions and markets. Financial institutions and specialized functions (like foreign exchange markets) tend to be agglomerated in large urban centres, with London, New York and Tokyo sitting at the top of the global hierarchy. Different countries also have different *institutional geographies,* in that they organize their financial institutions and markets in distinct ways. In parts of Asia, Latin America and Africa, banks and other community-based financial institutions like Rotating Savings and Credit Associations (ROSCAs) (see Spotlight box 18.3) are important in organizing and funding economic activity. ROSCAs take different forms in different regions and vary with the class, gender and ethnicity of their members (Ardener and Burman 1995). One of the attractions of ROSCAs for men and women in Ghana and elsewhere is the speed with which news of hardship or an emergency can be spread, and the order of rotation of the fund changed, to help out a member in trouble (Ardener 1995).

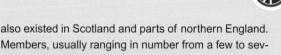

Spotlight box 18.3

Rotating Savings and Credit Associations (ROSCAs)

A ROSCA is 'an association formed upon a core of participants who agree to make regular contributions to a fund which is given, in whole or in part, to each contributor in turn' (Ardener 1995: 1). ROSCAs are known by different names, depending on their form and scale, the social classes of their members and their location. In South India they are known as *kuris, chitties* or *chit funds,* in Cameroon as *njangis* or *tontines,* and in Suriname as *kasmoni,* a word probably derived from 'cash money'.

ROSCAs were well developed in China, India, Vietnam and parts of West Africa and the Caribbean by the end of the nineteenth century. Variants of ROSCAs also existed in Scotland and parts of northern England. Members, usually ranging in number from a few to several hundreds, make regular contributions, in cash or in kind, to a fund. The fund, or part of it, is then given to each member in turn, depending on age, kinship seniority, or by rules established by the organizer.

In addition to encouraging regular savings and providing small-scale capital and credit for their members, many ROSCAs have strong moral and social dimensions. Trust, social solidarity and responsibility are emphasized and members have an interest in ensuring that no member defaults on regular payment. Some ROSCAs are women-only and their potential to empower women, by giving them greater control over income and credit, has attracted the attention of anthropologists, sociologists and feminists (see Ardener and Burman 1995).

These varied institutional geographies are products, in turn, of contrasting *regulatory geographies*. There are a wide range of supranational, national and regional regulatory agencies that govern the workings of financial institutions and markets. As Martin (1999b: 9) observes,

[M]oney has had a habit of seeking out geographical discontinuities and gaps in these regulatory spaces, escaping to places where the movement of financial assets is less constrained, where official scrutiny into financial dealing and affairs is minimal.

Offshore financial centres like the Bahamas, Cayman Islands, Jersey and Guernsey are attractive because of their low tax rates and minimal regulation. But countries like Ireland, Luxembourg, Switzerland and the Netherlands are also key centres in moving money around the world in order to minimize tax payments. Some of that behaviour is legal, but some of it is illegal.

Finally, when Martin (1999b) discusses *public geographies,* he refers to the role of states in distributing monies across regions in the form of goods and services, infrastructure, health, education and so forth, and in transferring monies in the form of various social and welfare programmes.

18.2 The global financial crisis

The financial crisis that started in 2007–8 and continues to drag on and mutate in various ways and places can be characterized as a global crisis since it affects most sectors of the economy and most places around the world (Aalbers 2009). The fact that one can mention sectors or places that are not affected much by the crisis, should not be seen as proof that this is not a global crisis. It is merely proof that some sectors and places have not yet been fully integrated into the global capitalist system or that they are not seen as safe havens to switch investment to. This is 'only' the third global crisis of capitalism; it follows the 1930s Depression (with the Second World War as its aftermath) and the post-1973 crisis that had been building up throughout the 1960s. The current global crisis was the culmination of various economic disruptions throughout the 1990s and early 2000s; these included more localized events such as the first subprime crisis in the late 1990s in the USA, the late 1990s Asian and Russian financial crises, the Argentine crisis at the dawn of the new millennium, and the explosion of the dot-com bubble in the early 2000s.

This section discusses the global financial crisis from a geographical perspective. We look at it not only from an economic but also from urban and political geography

perspective, to arrive at a geographical understanding of the global financial crisis. The concepts of globalization and financialization that were discussed in the previous section are central to such a geographical understanding. We start in the USA where *local* housing problems turned into a *national* crisis, that then became a trigger for the *global* financial, economic and political crisis.

18.2.1 Subprime lending in the United States

Real estate (houses, offices, factories, malls, etc.) is, by definition, local as it is spatially fixed. Mortgage lending, however, has developed from a *local* to a *national* market and is now increasingly a *global* market. An understanding of the financial crisis is ultimately a spatialized understanding of the linkages between local and global. Housing bubbles, faltering economies and regulation together have shaped the geography of the financial crisis on the state and city level in the USA. Subprime and **predatory lending** have affected low-income and minority communities more than others and we therefore not only see a concentration of foreclosures, or property repossessions, in certain cities, but also in certain neighbourhoods (Aalbers 2009; Immergluck 2009).

The default and foreclosure crisis that was at the root of the financial crisis has hit US households across the country, but people in some states and cities are more likely to be in foreclosure (see Case study 18.2). The rise in default rates started some years ago in the American Rustbelt (the North-east and Mid-west of the USA, regions most heavily affected by deindustrialization processes) where housing prices went down and unemployment went up. The combination of lack of employment and falling housing prices is perilous. People who lose their job in an area of high unemployment not only have a smaller chance of finding a new job within a few months, but they also more likely to be unable to pay off their mortgage loan and might then be faced with **negative equity**, a situation that occurs when the amount of the outstanding loan is larger than the market value of the house for which the loan is provided. As a result lenders will see higher foreclosures as a direct result of default, compounded by the fact that homeowners with financial problems in declining housing markets are less likely to sell their house which would have enabled them to pay off their loan.

The rise of subprime lending started in the early 1990s, often in the poorer parts of Rustbelt cities. Increasing default rates led to a first subprime mortgage crisis in 1997–8, ten years before the second subprime crisis (Ashton 2009; Immergluck 2009). Subprime mortgage lending had been growing fast, from about US$35 billion (5 per cent of total mortgage originations) in

Case study 18.2

Foreclosure cities and neighbourhoods in the USA

Up to 2006, the top ten foreclosure cities almost exclusively consisted of Rustbelt cities. In 2007, when the crisis started, the list was a mix of Rustbelt and Sunbelt cities, but since 2008, the top ten foreclosure cities is entirely made up of Sunbelt cities, although Rustbelt city Detroit occasionally makes it back to the top ten. There are several such foreclosure lists and they look slightly different, but generally speaking cities in California made up more than half of them between 2008 and 2010. Since 2011, cities in Florida have increasingly taken the lead. The differences across the USA are huge: in 2008, at the height of the foreclosure crisis, the foreclosure rate in Stockton, CA – the 'foreclosure capital' – was almost 100 times as high as in Richmond, VA (Aalbers 2009). Although some cities in the Sunbelt are now hit harder than those in the Rustbelt, on a neighbourhood level the Rustbelt still tops the foreclosure lists. On the list of most foreclosed zip codes, four are now in Detroit, while the Slavic Village in Cleveland has the most foreclosure filings. From the 1950s onwards, redlining and suburbanization (see Chapter 3) hit this neighbourhood hard. Due to a combined economic and foreclosure crisis, demand for housing has fallen so dramatically that one can now buy many homes in the Slavic Village for under US$30,000; on eBay you could even buy one for less than US$5,000. The Slavic Village, now referred to as foreclosure's ground zero, has also seen a rapid increase in crime (Christie 2007).

Subprime, and in particular predatory, loans frequently result in mortgage foreclosures at the individual level and housing abandonment at the neighbourhood level (Immergluck 2009; Squires 2004). It is not just defaulting borrowers that are hit; in addition, there are severe spillover effects on housing prices, crime and neighbourhood decline. Besides borrowers and neighbourhoods, cities are also hit hard because their tax income goes down in line with property foreclosures and lower real estate prices, while their expenses increase as a result of foreclosures and property crime (Dymski 2010; Immergluck 2009). Local governments around the USA have cut expenditures on education, infrastructure and social services. The public school system in California alone faces a loss of US$4 billion in funding in 2009. Many cities in these states, but also in countless others, are facing lower incoming taxes (in particular real estate taxes) and cuts in funding of schools, social services, garbage collection, infrastructure, etc. One complication in the USA is that local governments as well as many states are not allowed to run a deficit. While the national government tries to stimulate the economy by spending more, municipalities and many states that are faced with decreasing revenues also have to cut back on expenses. This is a significant development. State revenues in New York, a state that in no way presents a worst-case scenario, went down 36 per cent in one year (fiscal year 2007–8).

1994 to US$600 billion (20 per cent) in 2006 (Avery *et al*. 2006), 75 per cent of which was securitized (see Spotlight box 18.4). The growth of subprime lending halted for a few years in the late 1990s as a response to the first subprime crisis, but picked up again after 2000 when **subprime loans** were no longer exclusively targeted at borrowers with low credit scores but re-designed to be sold to middle-class borrowers, in particular in the Sunbelt, i.e. the South and South-west of the USA, regions that had seen above-average economic growth since the 1970s. As a result, the fastest increases in defaults and foreclosures since 2007 were not in the Rustbelt but in the Sunbelt where housing prices had been rising fastest and subprime loans were more common. In Nevada and a few other states subprime loans accounted for more than 30 per cent of the loans originated in 2006.

Subprime lending is often defined as lending to a borrower with poor credit, but this would be a misrepresentation of the essence of subprime lending, which is lending at higher fees and interest rates whether or not the borrower actually has bad credit (Aalbers 2012a). Some estimates suggest that more than half of the subprime loans went to prime borrowers (Brooks and Simon 2007).

Housing prices can go down because of structural stresses in economies such as those of the Rustbelt, but also because they have been growing rapidly in the way typical of many cities in the Sunbelt. Housing prices in the Sunbelt were simply more inflated than elsewhere in the USA: the housing bubble was bigger and more likely to burst. However, some local and regional economies in the Sunbelt also showed signs of a declining economy.

Spotlight box 18.4

Securitization

- **Securitization** is the process of transforming localized, non-standard and opaque assets like mortgages into transparent and liquid securities that people can easily exchange on global markets. Securitization is designed to reduce the uncertainty of buying and selling atypical assets (leases, homes, loans, etc.) by transforming them into marketing investments that have common features and characteristics. Securitization has been used as a tool to obtain funding for lenders by liquefying assets and to reduce regulatory capital holdings. As a mechanism for easing the spreading and trading of risk, securitization seeks to homogenize diverse commodities and weaken the institutional buffers between local, national and global markets. Securitization may also be used to transform mortgage default risk into a range of low-risk notes (that were comparable with the risk rating of sovereign debt) whilst creating a smaller range of high-risk debt.

- **Secondary mortgage market**: The market where investment banks, financial institutions and the two major government-sponsored enterprises – the Federal National Mortgage Association (FNMA, or Fannie Mae) and the Federal Home Loan Mortgage Corporation (FHLMC, nicknamed Freddie Mac) – repackage mortgages as securities to sell to institutional investors in national and global capital markets. While the secondary mortgage market originated during the 1930s, it was not until the 1980s that Congress passed several statutes to encourage the securitization of relatively illiquid assets, such as mortgages, and attract new sources of investment to finance real estate. Unlike the primary mortgage market, where the source of profit is the payment of the mortgage to the bank that originated the loan, the source of profit in the secondary mortgage for securitized mortgages is the sale of mortgage pools that contain hundreds or thousands of individual mortgages. The goal of the secondary mortgage market is to increase the exchangeability and liquidity of mortgages through the rationalization and standardization of mortgage features and characteristics.

- Fannie Mae was founded in 1938 to buy and sell mortgages as an expedient to stimulate capital investment in the residential construction industry that had collapsed because of the Great Depression. A related purpose of Fannie Mae was to stimulate cash flow to enable mortgage banks, savings and loan associations, and commercial banks to make new loans. In 1949, Fannie Mae expanded its activities to include buying and selling mortgages guaranteed by the Veterans Administration (VA). The Housing Act of 1968 removed Fannie Mae from the federal budget and privatized the agency as a shareholder-owned company. In 1981, Fannie Mae issued its first mortgage-backed security. The economic downturn caused by the subprime crisis motivated the federal government to put Fannie Mae under conservatorship on 7 September 2008.

- Freddie Mac is a government sponsored enterprise (GSE) of the US federal government. The US Congress created the FHLMC in 1970 to attract investors to finance housing through an expanded secondary mortgage market. Freddie Mac buys mortgages on the secondary market, pools them, and sells them as a mortgage-backed security to investors to increase the money available for new home purchases. In response to the savings and loan crisis, the Financial Institutions Reform, Recovery and Enforcement Act of 1989 (FIRREA) revised the regulation of Freddie Mac and made the Federal Department of Housing and Urban Development the supervisory agency of the GSE. The economic downturn caused by the subprime crisis motivated the federal government to put Freddie Mac under conservatorship on 7 September 2008.

Source: adapted from Aalbers (2012a)

Furthermore, high economic growth equated with a high rate of new construction and more homeowners who had recently bought a house, thereby increasing the pool of possible victims of falling housing prices. Finally, several states in the USA have tightened their own regulations in an effort to minimize the many excesses of subprime lending. As Wyly *et al.* (2009) have shown, states like North Carolina, New Mexico, Massachusetts and West Virginia regulate a wide range of practices related to foreclosure rules, prepayment penalties and other things. New Mexico, for example, introduced the *Home Loan Protection Act* (2003).

18.2.2 The globalization of the crisis

The current financial crisis originates in local housing and mortgage markets, but it affects financial markets and economic sectors around the world (Aalbers 2009; Engelen and Faulconbridge 2009; French *et al.* 2009). A few decades ago most mortgage lenders were local or regional institutions. Today, most mortgage lenders are national lenders who tap into the global credit market. This is not so much because lenders are global financial institutions – most lenders are national in scope – but because they compete for the same credit in a global market. In the past the idea was that in the wider credit market it would be easy for mortgage lenders to get funding, as mortgages were considered an ideal investment for low-risk investors. Cheaper credit, in return, would result in lower interest rates on mortgage loans. Fannie Mae and Freddie Mac, two government-sponsored enterprises that were meant to spur homeownership rates for low- and middle-income households, had already introduced securitization in the 1960s. Securitization enables mortgage lenders to sell their mortgage portfolio on the secondary mortgage markets to investors (see Spotlight box 18.4).

In 2007, when foreclosure and default rates were rising and housing prices were falling, the credit crisis was inevitable. It was clear that investing in mortgages was not as low risk as people thought. The value of mortgage-backed securities (MBS) fell even more dramatically. This was not only the case because many people had mortgage loans that were granted without down-payments, but also because MBS were sold on the basis that they would provide high returns. These were partly based on high interest rates and not just on the value of the house, and partly on speculation, which increased the value of MBS beyond what they were actually worth. In sum, not only were risks underestimated, returns were also overestimated.

It now becomes easier to understand why the impact of partly local and partly national problems in housing and mortgage markets is global in scope and also affects other credit markets. The crisis does not just hit investment banks on Wall Street, European banks and pension funds that bought MBS, but also individual investors and cities and towns around the globe (Case study 18.3). Cities and towns around the globe have been hit by the financial crisis. There are cities in Greece, Spain, Ireland and Iceland that have all been severely hit, but also cities in countries that seem to have weathered the financial crisis, whether they are located in Germany, Turkey, Brazil, China or Australia. In some way, the crisis is felt in most economic sectors and in most places around the world. The only partial inclusion of, for instance, China in the global capitalist system has meant that production growth was slowed down but not that the country entered a recession. Yet, the rapid increase in the number of vacant luxury apartments in Chinese cities suggests that Chinese capitalism is also feeding local and national real estate bubbles – bubbles that have resulted in a crisis of real estate and may lead to a larger economic crisis in China and likely elsewhere. It is crucial to link the spatial and temporal dimensions of local and global crises alike.

Cities, pensions funds, banks and individuals around the world had invested in MBS or the financial institutions that went down in this crisis such as the US Lehman Brothers or the Icelandic Landsbanki. Narvik (see Case study 18.3) illustrates well how connected the world has become in the twenty-first century. It also illustrates very well that the world is not flat: the old geography of local housing markets has not been replaced by a global housing market, but by a chain that starts with the local (a mortgage loan on a particular property), turns national (through lenders), then global (in the MBS market) and then reverts to the local again (via the effects in places like Narvik). Nearly everyone in North America, Europe and Australia, and many in Asia, are in some way involved in

Case study 18.3

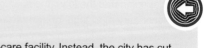

Narvik, Norway

The example of Narvik in the far north of Norway is widely discussed (e.g. Aalbers 2009; Pani and Holman 2013). The city council of Narvik (population: 18,000) and three small, nearby municipalities had invested US$78 million of the revenues of a nearby hydroelectric plant in MBS and other products offered by investment banks – they lost most of it. The city's investments were meant for the construction of a new school, a nursing

home and a child-care facility. Instead, the city has cut the budget and as a result several small rural schools will be closed, budgets for elderly care have been cut, the city is behind payments to civil servants, and the fire department will cease their 24-hour/7-day-a-week service and switch to day-time service (in a city with mostly wooden houses). The Norwegian state has declared it will not help Narvik and other municipalities, as it does not want to set a precedent by which the national state has to bear the losses of local authorities.

Plate 18.2 Occupy Wall Street (2011), a grassroots response to the financial crisis.

(Spencer Platt/Getty Images)

this crisis, often as passive investors, e.g. through pensions funds or investments by local governments. We may not all be capitalists now (as a saying goes), but most of us are investors, whether we want – or know – it or not.

It took surprisingly long before the financial crisis resulted in mass demonstrations. The streets of Dublin remained almost empty after the government had bailed out the banks at the expense of its citizens. Cutbacks in Greece and Spain have resulted in many demonstrations, but it was the Occupy Wall Street (OWS) movement that resulted in something more akin to a global grassroots response to the financial crisis, even though OWS itself was inspired by revolts throughout the North and South Mediterranean region (Aalbers 2012b).

18.3 Conclusion: placing finance

Financial markets have become increasingly globalized since the 1970s, although truly 'global' markets are concentrated in a select number of major financial centres located in global cities (Sassen 1991). There remain distinct regional, national and supranational geographies of money, such that the 'global financial system' can be conceptualized as a web of intersecting networks, some fast, some slow, some long, some short. These financial networks connect different geographies of employment, technology, regulation, government policies, leisure trends and so forth. Such a conceptualization allows us to understand how the fates of property developers in Thailand affected Graham Jones in Whitley Bay. It is important to remember then that when we talk about 'global finance', we are not talking about a machine operating 'out there', but a socially, economically, culturally and politically constructed network of relations with which we engage, in some way, shape or form, on a daily basis.

While in the past a mortgage bubble or a housing bubble would affect construction firms and homeowners, the recent bursting of these bubbles affects the economy not just through homeowners (of which there are also many more these days), but also through financial markets. Because lenders are now national in scope this no longer affects only some housing markets, but all housing markets throughout a country. In addition, secondary mortgage markets are global markets, which means that a crisis of mortgage securitization implies that investors around the globe, and therefore economies around the globe, are affected. Housing bubbles, faltering economies and regulation together have shaped the geography of the financial crisis at the state and city level in the USA. Subprime and predatory lending have affected low-income and minority communities more than others and we therefore not only see a concentration of foreclosures in certain cities but also in certain neighbourhoods, often those places inhabited by low-income and minority groups that have been excluded by earlier rounds of exclusion and exploitation. Yet, the meanings of globalization, not unlike the causes and consequences of this crisis, remain geographically uneven. It is important to understand that cities are an essential element in both, and that the fates of places like Stockton and Narvik are not only related to each other, but also to those of Wall Street and Raffles Place (Singapore's financial district). The space of places is intrinsically linked to the flow of spaces.

Are the geographies of money, finance and crisis merely a specific case of geographies of the economy? As should be clear after reading this chapter, money, finance and crisis are also attached to political geographies. First, financial institutions don't exist outside the political sphere but lobby to get what they want and what they don't want. They do not simply want less regulation, but sometimes more regulation to enable them to innovate/destruct. This is not only something that happened in the decades prior to the financial crisis, but also something that continues and is undermining re-regulatory efforts. Second, states, in particular, though not exclusively in the USA, have failed to protect their citizens. Financial institutions have been able to prey not only on homeowners and pensioners but also on businesses and the people who depend on them for their livelihoods. States are complicit in the crisis because they have facilitated financial innovation/destruction. Years of neoliberal restructuring, albeit in different forms and intensities, have yet to be replaced with more consumer protection and financial regulation. The fundamental question of what state/market relations should be, has hardly been addressed. There is no simple answer and it is of course heavily politicized (as it should be), but the Occupy movement and others, including insiders from the financial sector, have pointed to the under-regulation and under-policing of financial institutions.

Learning outcomes

After reading this chapter, you should be aware that:

- Money has geographical, economic, cultural, social and political significance and mediates our experiences of social relations.
- The 'global financial system' is a socially constructed web of intersecting networks operating at different speeds and over different distances.
- There are distinct urban, national and supranational networks of money and this is reflected in the geographies of the financial crisis.
- There are many causes and consequences of the financialization of the economy and the globalization of money.

Further reading

Aalbers, M.B. (ed.) (2012) *Subprime Cities: The Political Economy of Mortgage Markets,* Oxford: Wiley-Blackwell. This is a collection of essays on the global financial crisis, written by geographers, sociologists, political scientists and economists.

Leyshon, A. and Thrift, N. (1997) *Money Space: Geographies of Monetary Transformation,* Routledge, London. This is a compilation of Leyshon and Thrift's essays on money.

Martin, R.L. (ed.) (1999) *Money and the Space Economy,* Wiley, Chichester. A wide-ranging collection of essays covering geographies of banking, financial centres, money and the local economy, and money and the state.

Sassen, S. (2001) *The Global City: New York, London, Tokyo,* Princeton University Press, Princeton, NJ. This book looks at the growth and internationalization of the financial system and its effects on the economic base and social structure of its three 'command centres', London, New York and Tokyo.

Useful websites

www.ft.com   The *Financial Times* website contains useful links to financial and other firm, sector and country data, as well as breaking news stories.

www.money.cnn.com/   The US-based CNN financial website, like the *Financial Times* site, contains numerous links to business, financial and market news, by country, sector and firm.

www.worldbank.org/   The World Bank website is home to a host of information on World Bank publications, research, data and related organizations.

www.bis.org/statistics   This site, maintained by the Bank for International Settlement, provides sources of banking data and statistics.

www.imf.org/   The home page of the International Monetary Fund. This site provides a wealth of information about the IMF and its mission in addition to country information.

www.occupywallst.org   The home page of Occupy Wall Street.

www.grameen-info.org/   The website of the Bangladesh-based Grameen Bank. It has information on the mission of Grameen Bank and how it works, together with material on other microcredit schemes.

www.ecb.int/home/html/index.en.html   A site dedicated to European central banking issues.

www.creativeinvest.com   The site of Creative Investment Research, a US-based firm specializing in 'socially responsible' investment and providing many links on women and minority-owned financial institutions.

www.cdfa.org.uk/   The site of the CDFA, the trade association for Community Development Finance Institutions (CDFIs) which are designed to be sustainable, independent financial institutions that provide capital and support for individuals/organizations in disadvantaged communities or under-served markets.

http://blog.mint.com/blog/finance-core/a-visual-guide-to-the-financial-crisis/   A visual guide to the recent US/UK subprime financial crisis, illustrating the complex links between consumers, housing markets, credit ratings, financial instruments, banks and crisis.

https://youtu.be/qOP2V_np2c0   Geographer David Harvey explains the *Crisis of Capitalism* with the help of animations created by Cognitive Media.

http://tegenlicht.vpro.nl/backlight/money-and-speed.html   Documentary on the so-called 'flash crash' in 2010, the fastest and deepest US stock market plunge – and recovery – ever.

http://tegenlicht.vpro.nl/backlight/quants.html   Documentary on 'quants', the math wizards and computer programmers who designed some of the financial products that contributed to the global financial crisis.

CONSUMPTION AND ITS GEOGRAPHIES

Chapter 19

Ian Cook and Philip Crang

Topics covered

- Economic geographies of consumption
- Branding and marketing geography
- Local geographies of consumption
- Consumption and geographies of (dis)connection

19.1 Economic geographies of consumption

If production refers to the economic process of making goods and services, then **consumption** refers to their utilization. Consumption is vital to capitalist economies. Without consumption, capitalist ways of organizing economic life simply could not function. Businesses need the sales generated by consumption in order to realize value from their production processes. However, consumption does not just happen as a matter of course. It does not follow production as night follows day. The sales that businesses require involve huge organizational efforts. Those efforts are of crucial importance to capitalist economies; they are not just 'afterthoughts' that try to sell what has been made but key components that shape the wider economy and its geographies. Thus, retailing is a large economic sector devoted to the fostering of consumption and, in many cases, retail capital exercises profound organizational power within the systems of commodity production (Wrigley and Lowe 1996). More generally, marketing, advertising and **branding** are now recognized as strategically central to contemporary economies. This importance reflects their vital mediating role between the worlds of the producer and the consumer (Jackson and Taylor 1996; Nava *et al.* 1997; Nixon 1997; Hackley 2010). In parallel, discourses of consumption – that is, framing thought and action through a focus on 'the consumer' – have come to dominate organizational theory (du Gay 1996), spreading out across not only private enterprise but on to marketized public services. The consumer has become a key figure, perhaps the key figure, in governing political economic life. Research in economic geography has responded to these trends, recognizing consumption

as an important interest, alongside concerns with the geographies of production and finance.

However, even as consumption is economically vital, it is not purely economic. Indeed, this is one of the main reasons why so much effort and expense is devoted to commercial practices of retailing, advertising, marketing and branding. Consumption is not a simple matter and goes well beyond the limited transactional moment of purchase. Any sale has a 'back story', the predispositions that shape our buying of this or that. Any sale also has an 'afterlife', as we use what we have purchased. If we reflect back on our opening definition of consumption – the *utilization* of the products of human labour – then we see how purchase is but the start of an on-going story concerned with the active use of the things we buy. If we think of consumption as being about how we use products then we begin to sense that whilst consumption is central to economics it is not reducible to it. How we use things is implicated in an array of other issues: the way we conduct our daily lives, our management of household and family affairs, our senses of self-identity, our moral senses of how our lives ought to be and of how we ought to relate to others. This is one reason why consumption has been something of an enigma to mainstream economics (Douglas and Isherwood 1996).

Our suggestion, then, is that consumption is a vital economic process, but not limited to a narrowly defined economic realm. In particular, it extends into our wider culture. Consumption is cultural as well as economic; it is 'cultural-economic' (Amin and Thrift 2004). One has to approach consumption not through a narrow economic geography but through a wider 'cultural-economic geography' if one is to understand its causes, characters and consequences. The cultural character to consumption has been pursued in various ways that, in turn, relate to varied emphases on what is meant by culture. For some, this means emphasizing the adoption of goods within existing status structures and patterns of class distinction, so that consumption is regulated by, and reproduces, socially structured and inherited cultural tastes (Bourdieu 1984). What we consume both reflects and creates what sort of class position and cultural identity we have. Others highlight the role of commodities within the private dream worlds of consumers, so that consumption is more about fulfilling our culturally inflected fantasies and desires than conforming to socially structured tastes (Campbell 1987). And still others, focusing on more mundane forms of consumption, like household provisioning and food shopping, attend to how the things we buy enact domestic relations of love and care. From this perspective, consumer culture is about concretizing our relationships to our nearest and dearest and forming domestic 'moral economies' (Miller 1998).

Plate 19.1 'The consumer: at the heart of economic geographies'.

(1000 Words/Shutterstock)

Another way of framing the cultural character to consumption is to emphasize that often what we are consuming is not only material goods but images, meanings, feelings and experiences. A close to hand example may help to illustrate the point. Think a little about the clothes you are currently wearing. Clothes are material goods. In capitalist societies most of our clothes are products of industrialized systems of production and consumption. Notwithstanding the supposed renaissance of crafts like knitting, we rarely make our own clothes. Now, for sure, clothing fulfils some basic material needs such as warmth, but it does much more than that (Miller 2010). Clothing can be a language, through which we say something about who we are. It is likely, for example, that your clothes speak to aspects of your identity such as your gender or your age. They may do this through their material form – what type of clothing they are (blouse or shirt?; skirt or trousers?), what cut and shape they are, what fabric or colour – and through their associations with particular retailers and designers – what brand they are, whether they are new or second-hand or 'vintage', and so on. And clothes do not just convey an image; they help to make us who we are through their role in our embodiment. Clothes do indeed maketh the man and woman. What we wear shapes how we carry ourselves, maybe even how we feel. An old pair of sweatpants for 'slobbing out' at home; high heels to feel glamorous; a suit, to be professional; there are lots of examples that illustrate how what we wear shapes how we comport and feel about ourselves. What about you? What are you wearing right now? What do your clothes say about you? How do they make you feel?

Not all the consumption we undertake is as self-conscious as when we choose what clothes to buy and wear. Another way of thinking about consumption as cultural (as well as economic) is to emphasize its relationship to somewhat taken for granted habits and technologies. This has become known as a 'theories of practice' approach to consumption (Warde 2014). Here, the emphasis is not so much on how we can express our social and cultural identities through consumption, but rather more on how routine practices of consumption come to be and come to be taken for granted.

Another 'close to hand' example can illustrate the approach. While writing and editing this part of the chapter in his study at home this morning, one of us, Philip, got cold, and in response turned on the central heating. He is now buying additional gas. He is also, to a small measure, further depleting the quantity of a non-renewable energy resource. He is doing so because his own sense of comfortable domestic ambient temperature was disturbed, and because he has become used to responding to a feeling of cold by turning the heating on or up. Both that embodied sense of comfort, and his response, are far from innate. Nor are they subject solely to crude economic forces of price. As Elizabeth Shove has demonstrated, our senses of things like comfort are not fixed, but change historically and between cultures (Shove 2003; Shove and Walker 2014). Philip, for example, grew up in a house without central heating; back then, if he was cold during the day he either moved to a room that had a heat source in it (an open fire or the cooking range) or put on more clothes. Now, like most households in the UK, he has got used to a normal domestic environment close to 20°C and the energy consumption that goes along with that. Now when he feels cold he turns on the heating. His habits and embodied senses of comfort have changed in conjunction with transformations in domestic infrastructure such as central heating. This may seem pretty inconsequential, after all Philip only flicked a switch. But, as Shove says, it 'acquires more sinister overtones when we recall the

Plate 19.2 'The iPhone. Do you really need one?'

(urbanbuzz/Shutterstock)

global environmental costs of maintaining what we now think of as comfortable conditions indoors' (Shove 2003: 28). It is quite likely that as you read this chapter you may also be in a centrally heated or air-conditioned building and thus part of a conventionalized consumption practice of ambient temperature and artificial climate control. You too may need to feel comfortable to work well. You too may be undertaking a mundane, habitual act of energy consumption that has wider implications. You too may be embodying how consumption is shaped by taken for granted cultural norms and practices that co-evolve with socio-technical systems like domestic heating and energy supplies.

Our argument, then, is that consumption is: (a) an important topic for economic geography; and (b) one that tends to require approaches that are, in various ways, 'cultural-economic' in character. In turn, this begs the question of the kind of relationships between culture and economy generated through consumption. For some, the predominant trend is for economic, commercial imperatives to dominate and degrade our cultural lives: a so-called 'economization of culture'. Famously, the philosopher Herbert Marcuse argued that in capitalist societies 'false needs' are produced (Marcuse 1964), with consumption promoted by a wanting and requiring of far more than is materially necessary (Plate 19.2). More specifically, numerous studies have debated the role of advertising in stimulating consumption, creating desires for products that would otherwise not exist (for a classic study in this vein, see Packard 1977). According to this portrait, then, it is economic forces that dominate.

Indeed, here consumer culture is cast as a way of life that is brought into being in order to ensure that mass production is accompanied by the appropriate levels of mass consumption. All in all, in such accounts consumers are portrayed as rather sad and pacified figures whose cultural lives are subordinated to the economic priorities of producers (see Spotlight box 19.1).

On the other hand, it is possible to see consumer culture as less passive, as less controlled, as less subordinate. Here the emphasis is not on consumers being made to consume, but on consumers *using* the things they buy for their own ends. In this perspective, consumption is less the death of the commodity, the end point of an economic chain that began with the commodity's production, and more the commodity's resurrection. Here, consumption is seen as involving the 'culturalization of the economy'. In this spirit a range of research has stressed how consumers can creatively rework the products being sold to them, giving them new meanings in the process, and using them as launch pads for their own symbolic and practical creativity (Willis 1990). A classic example is the Italian motor scooter and its histories of consumption in the UK (Hebdige 1987). Having been originally aimed in the post-war years at a market of young, urban women in Italy, in the United Kingdom the Lambretta and Vespa scooters became a central identifier of the 'Mod' subculture. Initially attractive to Mods for its Italianicity and design aesthetics, by the late 1960s the scooter was increasingly symbolically recast and materially customized to act as a subcultural icon opposed to the British, brute masculinity of 'Rockers'

Spotlight box 19.1

Don Slater on consumerism as the end of culture

Consumers are often cast as 'irrational slave[s] to trivial, materialistic desires who can be manipulated into childish mass conformity by calculating mass producers. This consumer is a **cultural dupe** or dope, the mug seduced by advertising, the fashion victim . . . yuppies who would sell their birthright for a mass of designer labels. Ostensibly exercising free choice, this consumer actually offends against all the aspirations of modern Western citizens to be free, rational, autonomous and self-defining.

(Slater 1997: 33)

'Consumer culture', in this perspective, is merely an ersatz, artificial, mass-manufactured and pretty poor substitute for the world we have lost in post-traditional society. In fact, it is the antithesis and enemy of culture. In it individual choice and desire triumph over abiding social values and obligations; the whims of the present take precedence over the truth embodied in history, tradition and continuity; needs, values and goods are manufactured and calculated in relation to profit rather than arising organically from authentic individual or communal life. Above all, consumerism represents the triumph of economic value over all other kinds and sources of social worth. Everything can be bought and sold. Everything has its price. 'Consumer culture', therefore, is a contradiction in terms for much of modern Western Thought.

(Slater 1997: 63)

and their motorbikes (Plate 19.3). The scooter became part of a culture that its original designers had no knowledge of and certainly did not control. Designed as a form of transport for urban women in post-war Italy, the Italian motor scooter actually enabled a novel form of working class culture and youthful masculinity to be created in the UK.

More recently, commentators have placed renewed emphasis on these forms of consumer creativity. In particular, some have argued that consumers are increasingly becoming '**prosumers**', not just using products supplied to them but making them anew or completing them (Ritzer and Jurgenson 2010). Digital culture is often cast as central here, leading to product forms where consumers are also producers. Think of a smartphone. It is made and supplied with a range of capacities but it is the consumer who completes and develops these: downloading apps, creating a music library, and so on. In turn, how consumers use their smartphones becomes central to digital economies. Taking photos, making videos, downloading and using apps like Instagram and Twitter, building up contacts, friends and followers . . . putting these together through the smartphone helps to make a new media economy in which consumer practices (what we do), cultural identities (how we present ourselves) and social networks (who we share this with) become monetized (see Pfaff 2010).

In weighing up these relations between economy and culture in consumption this chapter focuses on three geographies. First, we focus on 'brands' as a crucial component of contemporary economic geographies,

reflecting on the process of branding, the circulation of brands, and the implications of both for cultural and geographical difference. Second, in examples ranging from **shopping** centres to nightclubs, we foreground the local contexts of consumption, reflecting on how they can both represent the strategies of commercial interests, designed to promote and regulate consumption, and stage the remaking of places into forms that accord to different cultural logics than those of commerce and economic rationality. Third, we turn to the connections between consumers and producers forged through consumption. The everyday acts of consumption we undertake in particular places are dependent upon wider networks of provision. The last part of the chapter therefore reflects on these networks and what we consumers know about them. In so doing, it offers a critical consideration of ideas of a (geo)ethical consumption and the kinds of worldly knowledge fostered through our lives as consumers.

19.2 Branding and marketing geography

Today's consumer landscapes are populated with brands (Arvidsson 2006). From renowned exponents of brand development (like Apple or Nike), to globally recognized brands (like Coca-Cola and McDonald's) and more locally specific brand names (like Marks & Spencer, Aldi or Lidl in Western Europe), brands mark out both what and where we consume. Pike defines a brand as an 'identifiable kind or variety of good or service . . . constituted of values or "equity" . . . such as associations, awareness, loyalty, origin and perceived quality' (2009a: 619). In many

Plate 19.3 Originally designed to be a stylish mode of travel for Italian women, the Italian motor scooter became a crucial component of the British Mod subculture. The meaning of things we consume are not simply controlled by those who design them, but are remade through their consumption.

(ermess/Shutterstock)

Plate 19.4 'Nike: Just do it': Nike's advertising helps to establish the Nike brand's sign value, associating the brand with the power of athletics and exercise.

(Joshua Rainey Photography/Shutterstock)

areas of the economy, analysts see a shift in emphasis away from material manufacture and towards the fashioning of branded 'signs and spaces' (Lash and Urry 1994) that are oriented to commercially profitable consumption.

According to Robert Goldman and Stephen Papson (1998), Nike are exemplary here, illustrating a wider shift towards a 'sign-economy' in which brands are central to both production and consumption. For them, Nike do not so much make and sell sportswear as make and sell the Nike brand, constituted through the sign and typography of the Nike name, the logo of the 'swoosh', advertised 'philosophies' such as 'Just do it', and retail spaces like 'Niketown'. Nike adverts work to present the brand and its values. Rather than focusing on specific products and their material qualities, Nike adverts have tended to focus on portraying Nike in relation to wider ideals of empowerment and self-realization ('Just do it'). The now ubiquitous strategy of celebrity brand ambassadors and representatives was pioneered by Nike, as a means to associate the brand with sporting achievement in general, specific impressive figures (from Michael Jordan to Serena Williams) and wider sporting and style cultures (in particular, American black cultures). For Nike, Goldman and Papson suggest, the brand is now supreme; the material good and its production are simply a means to that end. Nike sportswear and its other physical products are the vehicles to mobilize the brand. So, Nike sub-contract manufacture; they do not make Nike stuff themselves. Sure, Nike executives are concerned about the physicality of Nike products, but this is less in terms of them as manufactured goods than in terms of them as outcomes of a 'design' process that materializes brand and sign value within the product. Goldman and Papson document how Nike invest far more in advertising and promotion (around 10 per cent of annual revenues) than in physical infrastructure (around 3 to 5 per cent; and this includes facilities such as the 'Niketown' retail outlets) (Goldman and Papson 1998: 13). Nike's business and its corporate geographies are constructed to be market-led and market-leading. In emphasizing the brand and its brand values, Nike is consumption focused.

19.2.1 Branded geographies of nothingness?

Economic geographers have now begun to pay attention to brands (see in particular Pike 2009a, 2009b, 2011). One key area of interest is the relationship between brands and cultural and geographical differences. For some, brands are powerful forces of **homogenization** in the world. It is hard to miss the worldwide spread of products and brands such as McDonald's, Coca-Cola or Starbucks. Indeed, such brands have entered academic language – in the form of theses on the 'McDonaldization of society' (Ritzer 2000) or of 'Coca-colonization' (for a critique see Flusty

2004) – as bywords for a consumerist homogenization and cultural imperialism (Plate 19.5). In a fascinating analysis, the sociologist George Ritzer (2004) sees brands as part of a new global culture of 'nothingness'. As he puts it: 'The social world, particularly in the realm of consumption, is increasingly characterized by nothing. In this case, "nothing" refers to a social form that is generally centrally conceived, controlled and comparatively devoid of distinctive substantive content . . . we are witnessing the globalization of nothing' (Ritzer 2004: 3, 2). In turn, brands are associated with designed commercial spaces, 'brandscapes' and 'non-places', characterized by a lack of substantive difference, which makes them amenable to global distribution. For Ritzer, consumption tends to produce empty forms and spaces, devoid of ties to particular times and places. McDonald's the brand is delivered through McDonald's outlets that look and feel the same around the world.

Others are less sure that the result of global brands is global homogenization. Indeed Ritzer himself accepts that sometimes branded nothingness is reworked into 'something' through how it is received in particular times and places. Consumer culture does not float above the world in some abstract space of capital or modernity. Global products land and take root in particular places and times. In so doing, such forms of global consumer culture not only impact on their surroundings; they are also shaped by them. Anthropological studies in particular have developed this theme, exploring how globally distributed facets of consumer culture – whether particular goods, styles or cultural orientations – are locally incorporated. Take, for example, one of the exemplars of homogenizing American consumer culture: McDonald's restaurants. They are famed for their uniformity; the same decor, the same basic menu (with very small variations, such as McSpaghetti in the Philippines or the Maharajah Mac in India), and the same service style the world over. And yet, McDonald's may not be just a force for cultural homogenization. This

Plate 19.5 Coca-colonization?
(meunierd/Shutterstock)

was certainly Watson's (1997a) conclusion, based on studies of the consumption of McDonald's in East Asia (see Case study 19.1). These studies found that McDonald's has been localized, indigenized and incorporated into traditional cultural forms and practices, even as it has played a part in the ongoing dynamism of those traditions. As Watson poses the question:

> Does the spread of fast food undermine the integrity of indigenous cuisines? Are food chains helping to create a homogeneous, global culture better suited to the needs of a capitalist world order? . . . But isn't another scenario possible? Have people in East Asia conspired to change McDonald's, modifying this seemingly monolithic institution to fit local conditions? . . . [Perhaps] the interaction process works both ways.

(Watson 1997a: 5–6)

His conclusion is that there is indeed a two-way interaction:

> McDonald's has effected small but influential changes in East Asian dietary patterns. Until the introduction of McDonald's, for example, Japanese consumers rarely, if ever, ate with their hands . . . this is now an acceptable mode of dining . . . [However,] East Asian consumers have quietly, and in some cases stubbornly, transformed their neighborhood McDonald's into local institutions. [For example,] In the United States fast food may indeed imply fast consumption, but this is certainly not the case . . . [in] Beijing, Seoul, and Taipei . . . [where] McDonald's restaurants are treated as leisure centers, where people can retreat from the stresses of urban life.

(Watson 1997a: 6–7)

Case study 19.1

Consuming McDonald's in East Asia

McDonald's outlets have colonized much of East Asia, from their arrival in Hong Kong in the 1970s to their growth in metropolitan mainland China since the 1990s. However, just how McDonald's is consumed varies across the region. In Beijing, for example, McDonald's lost its American role as a place of fast and cheap food. Instead, Yan suggests, it became a middle-class consumption place, somewhere for a special family outing where 'customers linger . . . for hours, relaxing, chatting, reading, enjoying the music' (1997: 72). McDonald's here is seen as American, but Americana means something stylish, exotic and foreign, resulting in the meanings and experiences of McDonald's in Beijing being very un-American. In contrast, in Japan, whilst there is a similar leisurely use of McDonald's, it is not a place of exotic social prestige, but a youth hangout, a place where someone in a business suit would be out of place (Ohnuki-Tierney 1997). In Hong Kong (Watson 1997b), where McDonald's was introduced in the 1970s, its restaurants were initially patronized by adolescents seeking to escape products associated both with China and with Hong Kong's perceived provincialism. However, by the 1990s McDonald's had become routinely local, just another mundane part of the Hong Kong landscape: '[t]oday, McDonald's restaurants in Hong Kong are packed – wall to wall – with people of all ages, few of whom are seeking an American cultural experience. The chain has become a

local institution in the sense that it has blended into the urban landscape . . . McDonald's is not perceived as an exotic or alien institution' (Watson 1997b: 87, 107).

Plate 19.6 McDonald's in Beijing: American fast food becomes exotic, stylish Americana.

(Joseph Sohm/Shutterstock)

Hence the meanings and practices of consuming McDonald's – often cast as an icon of global homogenization – vary from place to place. Melissa Caldwell's work (2004) on McDonald's and consumer culture in post-Soviet Moscow reinforces the argument. In Russia too McDonald's has been indigenized or 'domesticated', and not just at the level of everyday practice. Counterintuitively, McDonald's – which as outsiders we might read as an American export to Russia – has come to be understood by consumers in Moscow as an 'authentically Russian product', to the extent that eating there is seen as responding to 'nationalist-oriented consumer campaigns' (Caldwell 2004: 5). Whilst initially perceived and promoted as an exotic American import, more recently McDonald's has become Russian, explicitly marketed as 'Nash Makdonalds' (which Caldwell translates as 'our McDonald's'). Since the mid-1990s, Russian consumer culture more generally has evidenced a patriotic enthusiasm for goods understood as 'Nash'. This Nash ideology entangles notions of national space with those of everyday familiarity and trust. McDonald's in Moscow has embraced this ideology and has thus been transformed from American exotica to both mundane familiarity and imagined Russianness.

19.2.2 Brands and their geographical entanglements

Not only does the consumption of branded products differ from place to place, but also ideas of cultural and geographical difference – what we might call 'imaginative geographies' (Driver 2014) – are produced and sold within brands themselves. Pike sees this as part of the 'geographical entanglement' of brands, how brand values and equity 'are imbued to varying degrees and in differing ways by spatial connections and connotations' (2009a: 619). Taking the example of Newcastle Brown Ale (a beer brand) (Plate 19.7), Pike (2011) shows how the meanings of the brand are bound up with imaginations of its geographical origin (sometimes framed as Newcastle, sometimes framed as the North, sometimes framed as England). An iconic Newcastle landscape, with the bridge over the Tyne, still adorns Newcastle Brown Ale's logo and packaging. These imaginations are also related to the product's spatial movements around the world; for example, in the American market, where sales now outnumber those for the UK, Newcastle Brown Ale's particular local origins are less important than a looser sense of it as an English and an 'urban' product. Others too have noted how geographical images are a resource to be used in projects of brand making and differentiation. Marianne Lien, for example, narrates a fascinating case study of frozen pizza marketing in Norway, as one company (given the pseudonym Viking Foods) differentiates its product lines through geographical associations (Lien 2000). Some of these are predictable and none too subtle: one pizza line is 'made Italian' and more 'authentic' through packaging that references Il Tricolore's green, white and red, and uses Italian place names and language; another line is 'made American', more 'modern' and more oriented to a youthful market with a packaging that incorporates images of the stars and stripes, American football helmets, cowboys and the Statue of Liberty! But other positionings are more complicated, in particular in the case of a pizza product line that Viking Foods wanted to establish as meaningfully Norwegian to their Norwegian consumers. This meant branding and producing what they term a 'folkepizzaen' (which one might translate as 'the Norwegian people's pizza').

More generally, you are probably familiar with a range of examples of such branded place association. Think, for example, about the bottled waters that appeal to place imagery to differentiate a somewhat generic commodity: Highlands water from Scotland, French mineral water from Evian, Fiji Water ('straight from the isolated and idyllic Fiji Islands without ever being touched by man'), and so on (on water branding see Wilk 2006; for the case of marketing

Plate 19.7 A geographically entangled brand: Newcastle Brown Ale.

(urbanbuzz/Shutterstock)

Fijian water see Connell 2006 and Kaplan 2007). Or consider products that associate themselves in some way with imagined geographical areas such as the tropics or the rainforest, often to claim some 'natural' qualities (for a critical analysis of a 'rainforest' perfume see Slater 2004; on 'tropical fruit' see Cook *et al.* 2004). Or there are the brands that draw upon national identities in framing their brand equities: for example, the likes of Paul Smith and Burberry presenting their Britishness within the fashion economy (Goodrum 2005); or car brands like Alfa Romeo (claiming Italian passion) or MINI (with its fascinating marriage of British quirkiness and Germanic efficiency).

This interest in the 'geographical entanglements' and 'placing' of brands (Pike 2009a) builds on longer standing arguments. Central here is research on 'brandscapes' and themed environments, that focuses on how imaginative geographies shape the making of consumption spaces (Klingmann 2007). In Disneyland and Disney World, for example, the amusements and other consumption opportunities are not just randomly arrayed, but organized into distinct imaginative geographies: Frontierland, themed on the American West; Adventureland, themed on landscapes of European colonialism and imperialism; and so on (see Gottdiener 1982; Wilson 1992; Bryman 1995). This is a pattern to be found in many large shopping centres, most famously the huge West Edmonton Mall in Canada (Crawford 1992; see also Goss 1999a) but also in more recent developments such as the Mercato Mall in Dubai. The promotional text on the Mercato Mall website gives a good sense of the geographically and historically themed experience on offer: 'Mercato is ideally located in the heart of Jumeirah, one of Dubai's most prestigious residential areas. Much more than just a shopping mall, Mercato epitomizes the very best in Italian architecture and transports you back to the Renaissance period. Home to picturesque cobbled streets, charming piazzas and authentic Tuscan and Venetian features, Mercato on Jumeirah Beach Road offers a unique and incomparable ambience, not to mention a thoroughly enjoyable shopping and leisure experience' (http://mercatoshoppingmall.com). Whole urban areas can extend this sort of themed consumption landscape; the Las Vegas strip being perhaps the best known. Indeed, Gottdiener (1997) goes so far as to posit that consumer culture has produced a general 'theming of America', so that theme parks become models for what is happening across the urban landscapes outside them. Sack (1992: 98) agrees that consumer culture is marked by a production of 'pseudo-places'. As part of a wider time–space compression, Harvey (1989) sees a general trend towards highly packaged, and indeed simulated, experiences of cultural and geographical difference, such that microcosms of the whole world are encountered in particular consumption spaces.

There are a number of implications of these associations between consumption and imaginations of cultural and geographic difference. For a start, it means we need to broaden the critique of consumer culture beyond a debate over its tendencies for homogenization (making everything and everywhere the same) to consider capitalist processes of '**heterogenization**' (making things and places 'different' as a marketing process). In Naomi Klein's terms, we need to recognize the emergence of a 'market masala', where differences become part of capitalist consumer culture (Klein 2000). For some commentators, such as Klein herself, it is the politics of incorporation that are key here. Capitalism, via consumer culture, increasingly absorbs forms of difference, whether cultural, geographical or political, that might seem in opposition to it. Oppositional voices need to find ways either to resist or to use this incorporation for their own ends (see also McGuigan 2009; Mukherjee and Banet-Wieser 2012).

For others, capitalist heterogenization is not so much a top-down process of incorporation as it is a diverse range of ways in which difference becomes commodified and consumption acts as a space for cross-cultural encounters and translations (Jackson 1999). In this perspective a range of other issues come to the fore. How, for example, are consumer cultures implicated in present and past circulations of different material cultures, and with what effects on national cultures? What kinds of differences are fostered or discouraged within consumption and what are the implications of this for the wider politics of identity? What options are there for both producers and consumers to express and develop their cultural identities through commercial cultures? Such questions have shaped a set of research projects by Philip Crang and colleagues on the presence of South Asian 'stuff' in British consumption cultures, especially of food and fashion. Drawing on wider conceptual reflections on the relations between commodity cultures and transnationality (Crang *et al.* 2003) these studies have looked at topics such as: how 'Asian' and 'Eastern' difference is presented and commodified in contemporary British food marketing (Jackson 2002) and fashion design and retail (Dwyer and Crang 2002; Dwyer and Jackson 2003; Jackson *et al.* 2007); and how these contemporary fashions for South Asian styled goods relate to past colonial histories in which South Asian materials (such as cotton, or the boteh/Paisley pattern) were central to British cultures of design, fashion and dress (Crang and Ashmore 2009; Breward *et al.* 2010).

More generally, we have long argued that consumer cultures can act as arenas of geographical knowledge, in which understandings of both the origins of what we consume and our own places in the world are played out

Plate 19.8 Eating into Britishness: by what process do these 'Indian' restaurants become 'British'?

(Michaelpuche/Shutterstock)

(Cook and Crang 1996). Think, for instance, of how food marketing presents geographically referenced cuisines (Indian food, Chinese food, Italian food, Mexican food, and so on). Here, a mundane realm of consumption is also a setting in which ideas of cultural difference and mixture are played out, as retailers and restaurants present consumers with 'the world on a plate' (for a sample of work on food geographies see Cook *et al.* 1999, 2000a, 2008; Duruz 2005; Monrreal 2008).

19.3 Local geographies of consumption

Earlier we suggested that consumption involves the extension of the economy into realms of life that we might not usually think of as economic, into our wider 'culture'. This is also true at the more immediate scale of our own everyday economies. When we buy goods we take them home; we 'domesticate' them. In consuming things, we make them part of household relations; we live with them and their lives become shaped by ours (Gregson 2007). They become part of what we might call 'moral economies', insofar as: '[t]he household is a moral economy because the economic activities of its members are defined and informed by a wider set of cognitions, evaluations and aesthetics, which themselves are defined and informed by the biographies of the household and its members' (Silverstone *et al.* 1992: 11). The language here may be unfamiliar, but we all have experiences of how economic goods become part of something else, something more than economic, in their consumption: the toys that become childhood companions and then symbols of our childhood and its end (a narrative powerfully mined by the makers of Pixar's *Toy Story* movie trilogy); the little 'treat', bought by a loved one in a mundane shopping

event, that says they were thinking about you (Miller 1998); the birthday present; and so on.

This entangling of economic and social relations through consumption is not limited to domestic space. It is also true of public spaces of consumption. Here commodity culture is implicated in our forms of public sociality and in how we relate to our immediate environments, our local places. By way of illustration, we start with the places where people go shopping.

19.3.1 Shopping and place

Shopping centres (or malls as they are more commonly termed in North America) are routinely cast as the cathedrals of our consumerist age, symbols of our worship of commodity culture. But what goes on inside a shopping centre, and what does this tell us about the kinds of places being produced in the world of consumption?

One response would be that in shopping centres we are manipulated into behaving in certain ways, and especially into buying things, by the power of the shopping centre as a place. It is certainly the case that shopping centres are in part designed according to a 'merchandise plan' (Maitland 1985: 8) that tries to maximize the exposure of consumers to goods. In older shopping centres and malls this plan tended to be understood in quite mechanical terms. Shopping centres were seen as functional 'machines for shopping'. 'Generator' stores are used to pull us to the shopping centre in the first place, and once we are there 'magnet' stores every 200 metres or so make sure we do not just pop in and out, but explore every part of it. Here, then, 'the public mall [is defined] as essentially the passive outcome of a merchandising plan, a channel for the manipulation of pedestrian flows'

Plate 19.9 The Mall of America, Bloomington Minnesota: 40 million visitors a year experience not just shops but also an aquarium, fun fair and outdoor theme park.

(Jeffrey J Coleman/Shutterstock)

(Maitland 1985: 10). There are well-known tricks to make us behave as the shopping centre management and its shops want: escalators arranged so we have to walk past shop fronts or merchandise when going between floors; hard seats so we do not linger too long without getting up and seeing some more potential purchases; no water fountains so we have to buy expensive drinks (see Goss 1993).

In more recent shopping centres, however, the manipulation may be more subtle. Increasingly, retail planners and developers see their job as providing spectacular places that people will want to spend time in. This is partly because research suggests that the longer people stay the more on average they spend; but it also stems from intensified competition between shopping centres, such that each one needs more than just the usual shops to attract us in the first place – everything from fountains to funfairs (see, for example, Goss 1999b on The Mall of America). Here, then, the manipulation of shoppers is less mechanical and more 'affective'. The hope is to excite, inspire, relax and please. Jacob Miller's (2014) study of the Abasto mall in Buenos Aires, Argentina is an excellent up-to-date exploration of this issue. Of course, as Miller notes, these are promotional intentions rather than shoppers' experiences. As Chaney (1990) puts it in his review of the MetroCentre in Gateshead, north-east England, the designer's utopian impulses to produce a place of perfection often result in rather underwhelming, 'subtopian' forms. Nonetheless, there is much here to be taken seriously. There is the attempt to produce a fabricated space in which the individual consumer can be made to feel like consuming (see Goss 1999a). There is the emphasis on creating an internal, closed-off, privately owned but partially public environment, divorced from the harsh exterior world, not only climatically but also socially, through the operation of security systems that ensure the absence of anyone who might threaten this consumer paradise or disrupt the pleasure of the shopper. There is the emphasis on managing how malls make us feel, their affective qualities and atmospheres, as part of the commercial work of retail capital (Miller 2014).

Such shopping centres recognize that there is much more to going shopping than buying things (Glennie and Thrift 1992). Shopping is in part about experiencing an urban space, seeing and being seen by other shoppers. It is a social activity. Malls seek to manage this social experience. The street gets recast as a purified space of leisurely consumption, cleansed of 'nuisances' that inhabit the 'real' streets, like 'street people'. However, this fashioning of the mall can be disturbed. Retail spaces can be reclaimed by those who use them. Leading the charge are a mixed assortment of senior citizens and adolescents.

Take the case of Bert, 78 years old, and a regular visitor to a shopping mall in New England (USA):

> I come here at quarter to eleven and I leave at twenty minutes past one . . . I do this five days a week, except I missed one day this year . . . And I have my lunch here at noontime . . . I move every half-hour. I go from here down to where the clock is, I go down in front of Woolworth's, then I come back again and go up there and take my bus by the front of JC Penney.

(Quoted in Lewis 1990: 126)

For Bert, the mall is not a place to shop, but somewhere sheltered to go outside his house, a chance to meet up with friends. For the mall management there is the option of evicting these low-spending visitors, but ejecting old people forcibly on to the pavement is hardly good public relations. Instead, and as part of wider moves to see malls as the new civic centres, Bert's mall has actually established its own walking club for the elderly, with over 300 members, for whom the doors open at 6 a.m., rather than 9 a.m. when shops open.

Adolescents also use the mall as a meeting place, somewhere to hang out. They also spend very little. 'Suburban kids come to malls to look around, meet and make friends, and hang out – because there is nowhere else to go' (Lewis 1990: 130). Or as Ed and Tammy, self-confessed 'mall rat' and 'mall bunny' respectively, put it:

> [Gesturing around himself] I met all these people here. I've met lots of other people, too. One place where you can always find someone . . .

(Ed; quoted in Lewis 1990: 130)

> I used to come here every Saturday from 11 am to 9.30 pm and just walk around with my friends, like Gina here, and just walk around and check out the guys.

(Tammy; quoted in Lewis 1990: 130)

Unlike the elderly, the mall is less indulgent of these teenagers. There are constant skirmishes with the security staff over how long ten people can share one Coke at the food court, and some mall rats and bunnies get banned altogether.

So what are we to make of our trip to the mall? What does it tell us about the local geographies of consumption? Well, it certainly tells us that place matters to consumption. But how? Here the answer is more ambivalent. In part what we see is a pseudo-public space symbolizing and enacting claims for consumption to be all there is to civic life, making citizens consumers in a very concrete way. In this light, shopping centres illustrate how place can produce both acts of consumption and people as consumers. Yet in shopping centres one also sees the small-scale, trivial resistances that people enact, their refusal to be just consumers in the sense of purchasers, their determination to use this space for their own ends. And that too has a wider symbolism, signalling the possibility that consumption is rarely just about what we are being sold, but also about fulfilling our own needs for social affiliation, participation and place making.

19.3.2 Economies of experience: skateboarding and dancing

Shopping is not just about buying goods, then; it is a placed experience. More generally, a range of research has framed consumption as experiential. For some, this involves understanding consumption as a resistant act in which we, as consumers, creatively use the places made for us. Writing from the discipline of architecture, Iain Borden (2001) pursues this approach in a study of skateboarding, space and the city. Paying particular attention to 'street skating', he argues that skateboarders remake urban spaces designed for other purposes: sometimes explicitly symbolic monumental space (e.g. town halls, national theatres, historical monuments, tourist attractions); but more often everyday spaces of neglect, the left-overs of rational, economically focused planning (e.g. mini-roundabouts, the spaces under bridges and urban highways, mini-malls). Thus spaces of public, official symbolism and of arid architectural functionality become the stages for energetic practices of place consumption. Handrails become tools for 'ollie nose grinds'; cement banks opportunities for 'shredding'. Skaters consume the city with their boards, recomposing it in the process. Skateboarding enacts a way of consuming the city that precisely emphasizes use over commercial or other values. The city becomes a site of play, of skillful embodied

practices, of memorable performances. For Borden, this contests the commodified logic that underpins contemporary urban space.

However, these sorts of performative engagements with place can also be reclaimed as commodities. The business theorists Joseph Pine and James Gilmore talk more generally about the emergence of an 'experience economy' focused on the production and consumption of memorable experiences (Pine and Gilmore 1999; see also Sundbo and Sorensen 2013). Place is again central here; this is a theatrical economy, in which places are the arenas in which certain kinds of social performances can be developed. Consumption is the undertaking of those performances. Clubs (in the sense of nightclubs) are exemplary.

In London alone there are over 500 club nights on offer every week. In Britain the industry has a turnover of £1.8 billion per annum, and it is estimated that 42 per cent of the population now visit a club once a year, 42 per cent of 15–19-year-olds at least once a month (Mintel 2004, 2006). Although the industry has suffered some decline in the UK (Robinson 2013), urban and regional economies have developed based on thriving club scenes: in Berlin, as clubbers jet in on low-cost carriers from across Europe; in Ibiza, as a youthful tourist market is targeted; in Goa, as international 'trance freak' tourists join Indian youth in sometimes uneasy dancing crowds (Saldanha 2002). But what are such economies actually selling? Ben Malbon (1997, 1999) argues that clubs are spaces of play. This should really not need saying. It is patently obvious that people go to clubs to have fun. It is also patently obvious that this fun is achieved through a variety of means. Through enjoyment of the music; through an enjoyment of being part of a crowd of people with whom, temporarily, one can feel at one; through the feelings of competency and bodily expressiveness that dancing can give you; through the sharing of a special place and time with friends; through behaving in ways one cannot in other social situations, for example at work. Perversely, though, this fun needs to be taken seriously. We need to understand the playfulness of such consumption. We need to analyze the complicated micro-spatial practices through which this play is enacted; the ways in which one gets to feel, and enjoy being, part of the clubbing crowd; the ways in which one dances so as to lose oneself in the music. We need to grasp the importance of place to playful consumption; the ways in which one has to be in the right place, with the right music and the right crowd, to have these feelings of exhilaration, communality and vitality; the way that in such consumption 'the emphasis is placed on the near and the affectual: that which unites one to a place, a place that is experienced among others' (Maffesoli 1996: 128). And we need to appreciate

Plate 19.10 Party People @ Club Amnesia, Ibiza.
(PhotoSmart/Shutterstock)

the wider significance of such playful consumption for our productions of local experience, such that consumer culture is not just made up of atomistic, avaristic individual consumers, but also facilitates temporary, some would say 'neo-tribal', gatherings, through which people come to feel part of something bigger than themselves (see Maffesoli 1996: 72–103).

Clubbing is, then, a place-specific practice of consumption. Whereas in the shopping centre or with street skateboarding senses of communal belonging tend to be forged by those occupying space for purposes other than those for which it was designed, in clubs that communal belonging is the very product that people are buying. Clubs may be distinctive places of consumption, characterized by an exceptional emotional and bodily intensity, but they also point to wider trends within the so-called 'experience economy' towards localized places of theatrical consumption.

19.4 Consumption and geographies of (dis)connection

In this final section of the chapter we discuss the wider implications of our everyday practices of consumption. Our focus in particular is on how consumers are both connected to, but often feel disconnected from, the other people and places involved in providing the things we consume.

Consumption may often feel mundane, or perhaps not serious enough to matter that much, but it has profound political and economic implications. In the words of Danny Miller, the figure of 'the consumer' has become a sort of 'global dictator': 'Today, real power lies unequivocally with us, that is the waged consumers of the First World' (1995: 10). In consequence, opposing the study of consumption because so many in the world are not affluent consumers is profoundly misplaced. Quoting Miller again, 'The acknowledgement of consumption need not detract from the critique of inequality and exploitation, but this critique is foundering precisely because the enormous consequences and attractions of consumption are left out of the analysis' (ibid.: 21). A fundamental challenge for the twenty-first century is to fashion economic forms that fulfil those attractions of consumption, but deal too with its consequences.

19.4.1 Dis-connections

In Robert Sack's view, we consumers are profoundly ignorant of the geographies of provision that bring goods to us: 'A shop that sells Colombian coffee does not reveal the social structure that produces the coffee, the economic impact of coffee production on the Colombian economy, or the way coffee growing affects the Colombian environment' (Sack 1992: 200). Such ignorance, he argues, makes it impossible for consumers to behave responsibly in relation to those involved in commodity production and distribution. Unless we know about the origins of the goods we consume, then we lack the necessary understanding to assess the impacts of our actions as consumers; without such understanding of consequences, responsible action is impossible. Thus, modern consumption's disconnected geographies make it deeply amoral.

One critical response to such ignorance and amorality is to see consumers as blinded by a veil that is draped over the things we consume, through a process of what Marx called '**commodity fetishism**'. In this portrait the true history or biography of a product, and its basis in the productive work of others, is obscured to consumers. Instead, one is confronted by advertising imagery that seeks to associate the product with other fantasy worlds. The critical response to this situation is often to puncture these fantasies with some sharp shafts of reality, to 'de-fetishise' the commodity. Writing in the 1990s, Elaine Hartwick points to the startling incongruities and inequalities that such a puncturing can bring to light:

> Michael Jordan, basketball player extraordinaire, receives US$20 million a year to endorse Nike; Philip Knight, cofounder and chief executive officer of Nike, is worth US$5.4 billion; Indonesian workers are paid US$2.40 a day and Vietnamese workers are paid US$10.00 a week to make the sneakers . . . The Walt Disney Company is publicly criticized for its treatment of Haitian workers making Pocahontas shirts for 28 cents an hour; Disney's chief executive officer makes US$78,000 a day.
>
> (Hartwick 1998: 423)

Hartwick's suggestion is to approach consumption in terms of 'commodity chains'. Here she draws on a much wider body of scholarship (see Hughes and Reimer 2004) to argue for what she terms a 'geoknowledge' of consumption, one that traces back the stuff we consume through the links in a provision chain, eventually connecting consumers to producers. Such knowledge, she argues, allows a 'geoethics' of consumption, attuned to the politics of the economic systems upon which consumption depends.

Smith's account of Starbucks Coffee shops makes a similar 'de-fetishisation' argument. He highlights how unfairly traded coffee sees only 25 per cent of the retail price returning to the producing country, with even less going to those who actually cultivate the crop (the smallholders, waged workers and seasonal pickers). He contrasts the stylish coffee-shop culture that a brand like Starbucks epitomizes with the lives of those who produce coffee. For the women who pick the coffee beans, their working day begins somewhere between three and four in the morning. Getting back home at six in the evening, they still have evening meals to prepare, water to fetch from the river, a family to feed and clear up after. Few live in houses with electricity or running water. They face a major health hazard from the pesticides used on the coffee plants (M.D. Smith 1996: 512–13). Other academic accounts profess a more open reading of the juxtapositions of different moments and places in a commodity's life (see Cook and Woodyer 2012). Cook's 'followings' of foods – particularly the papaya - provide vivid examples of what is possible here (Cook *et al.* 2004, 2006).

It is not just academic accounts that look to make apparent the often hidden relations between the producers and consumers of commodities. The spoof shopping website followthethings.com documents over 60 examples of '**follow the thing**' work by journalists, filmmakers, artists, activists and others. There are a number of serious documentary films here including: Dziga Vertov's (1924) *Kino Eye,* which involves reverse-action sequences following beef steaks back to pasture lands in Russia (Cook 2011a); and Mark Phillips' (1997) *Mange Tout,* which follows a UK supermarket buyer as he visits a farm producing mangetout peas in Zimbabwe and asks packing house workers to trim them differently 'for the consumer' (Cook 2011b). There are bitingly funny activist films, like Amnesty International's (2006) spoof *Teleshopping* advert in which shopping channel demonstrators show how easy it is for children to buy and kill people with AK-47 rifles (Livingston 2011), and Emily James' (2002) film *The Luckiest Nut in the World,* in which an animated American peanut sings country and western songs about the international trade rules which favour him over other nuts grown commercially outside the USA (Cook 2011c).

There are commodities reworked and made afresh by artists and activists. Examples include: the bottles of 'B'eau Pal' mineral water ('bottled at source') produced by the Bhopal Medical Appeal and the YesMen in 2009 for delivery to the UK headquarters of Dow Chemical whom they wanted to pay compensation to the victims of the 1984 Bhopal chemical factory explosion (Parkin 2013); and the labels found in Primark clothing in 2014 saying 'Degrading Sweatshop Conditions' and 'Exhausting Hours' which were believed to have been sewn in to them by an artist/activist who then returned them to the store for re-sale (Kelleher and Cook 2014a). There are the 'real' letters found in commodities that were written by the people who made them to the people who bought them. A recent example is the letter found in a Saks Fifth Avenue shopping bag in New York from Tohnain Emmanuel Njong, a Cameroon national making them in a Chinese prison who wanted a consumer to know about the terrible conditions in which he was forced to work and to help his story to be told (Kelleher and Cook 2014b).

Finally, there are the apparently accidental traces of producers' work that are left in and on commodities for consumers to discover. Perhaps the most famous of these happened in 2009, when photos of a quality control worker in a Chinese electronics factory were found on a new iPhone when it was first turned on by a consumer in the UK. He posted them online with a note asking if anyone else had found photos like this on their phones. The story then went viral with countless people around the world posting their opinions about who she was, why the photos had been taken and left on the phone, and what would happen to her now she could be identified as having left them there (Cook 2011d).

Naomi Klein (2000) notes how the power of global brands, combined with their concern for their sign values, has generated a political response – a '**brand boomerang**' – in which the meanings being promoted in marketing discourses are contested by other stories, often centred on the social relations of production. In recent years, these contestations have increasingly taken place online via websites, blogs and social media-based 'marketing' strategies working in parallel to those used by corporations (Baringhorst *et al.* 2009). Using relatively non-specialist on- and offline tools and networks, journalists and activists have been able quickly and vividly to highlight, hijack and call into question large corporations' neglect of the health, safety and wages of farmers, factory workers and others making their branded goods. This work is said to be responsible for some corporations' apparent turn towards more transparent and ethical business practices. One notable example is what happened after the Hong Kong based NGO Students and Scholars Against Corporate Misbehaviour (SACOM) hijacked Apple's carefully planned launch of the iPad in 2010 (see Case study 19.2).

19.4.2 Ethical Consumption

These academic, journalist, activist and other attempts at reconnecting consumers and producers speak to a wider consumer movement, that of '**ethical consumption**'. Here, consumption is explicitly cast in relation to wider provisioning systems and their human and non-human participants, of which the consumer is a part (for a general introduction, see Lewis and Potter 2011). Green consumerism, fair trade, vegetarianism and other animal welfare concerns would be principal strands.

Case study 19.2

Timeline: the iPad – 'a gadget to die for?'

San Francisco, 27 January 2010: at an invitation-only event, Apple CEO Steve Jobs unveils a thin, light, aluminium and glass 'multi-touch' tablet media player called the iPad. It is, he claims, a 'magical and revolutionary device' which 'creates and defines an entirely new category of devices that will connect users and their apps and content in a much more intimate, intuitive and fun way than ever before' (in Apple 2010a). A video of his presentation is posted on the Apple website, YouTube and elsewhere, and the iPad features in news stories worldwide.

Online, 31 March–1 April 2010: iPads distributed to a small, select 'inner circle' in advance of their sale are reviewed in mainstream North American media outlets – like *Time* magazine – and on specialist blogs – like *boinboing.net.* Readers submit hundreds of online comments in response, and these reviews are read, commented upon, and written about worldwide.

USA, 3 April 2010: the iPad goes on sale. Reports describe people queuing for days to be the first to get one in store. Customer reviews quickly appear online and in the press.

San Francisco, 3 May 2010: Apple announces that one million iPads have been sold. Jobs states that 'Demand continues to exceed supply and we're working hard to get this magical product into the hands of even more customers' (in Apple 2010b).

Hong Kong, 25 May 2010: SACOM publish a report and lead a group of protesters performing traditional Chinese funeral rights at the headquarters of the Fox-conn Corporation. The report details a series of ten suicide attempts (eight 'successful') since the beginning of 2010 by young factory workers employed by

Plate 19.11 'A gadget to die for': *The Independent,* 27 May 2010, when news of the new iPad launch and the suicides of the workers who made them became front page news in the UK.

(The Independent)

Foxconn in Shenzhen City's Longuhua Science and Technology Park. Foxconn is China's biggest exporter and, with 300,000 assembly workers, this is the largest factory in the world. Local press reports attribute the suicide attempts to 'overwork', 'too much pressure' and 'unstable emotions' resulting from the factory regime. TV news bulletins in China show security camera footage of one 24-year-old victim 'walking unsteadily out onto the roof of a Foxconn building on the way to her death' (Moore 2010). An ongoing series of TV news reports about 'Foxconn suicides' – in Chinese, English and with English subtitles – are posted on YouTube. By the time SACOM's report is published, Foxconn workers at Longhua Park have already assembled two million iPads (alongside Nintendo Wiis, Nokia cellphones and other popular consumer electronic devices). The report suggests that Apple's marketing campaign and the enthusiastic take-up of iPads by US consumers contributed to the suicides by sending 'extreme pressure all the way down to [Apple's] Chinese suppliers' (Chan 2010: 5).

UK, 27 May 2010: the front page of a UK national newspaper brings the two strands of this story together in a starkly visual way (Hickman 2010a). Beneath the headline – 'A gadget to die for?' – is a photograph of two objects in a spotlight. They're the same size and shape. One is an iPad. The other is a framed photo of a young Chinese man. The text beneath one reads, 'This is the iPad, the most eagerly awaited consumer product of the year, available in the UK from tomorrow'. The text beneath the other reads, 'This is Ma Xiang-qian, driven to suicide, the latest victim of "inhuman" conditions in Asia's electronics factories'. His suicide is detailed in SACOM's report, and his family takes this framed photograph with them to protest and mourn the Foxconn deaths. Hundreds more mainstream and online media stories link the iPad to the 'Foxconn suicides' over the following days, weeks and months.

Worldwide, 28 May 2010: after delays caused by massive sales in the USA, the iPad goes on sale in Australia, Canada, France, Germany, Italy, Japan, Spain, Switzerland and the UK (Apple 2010c). Similar scenes, stories, reviews, comments and discussions are reported in the press.

San Francisco, 2 June 2010: Jobs claims the Foxconn factory is not a 'sweatshop', that its suicide rate is lower than the USA's, and that Apple is 'on top' of the situation (Beaumont 2010). A worker dies there after working a 34-hour shift.

Shenzhen, 3 June 2010: Foxconn raises basic Shenzhen factory wages by a third.

Hong Kong, 8 June 2010: SACOM declares this day the 'Global Day of Remembrance for Victims of Foxconn', protests outside a Foxconn shareholder meeting, and hands over a petition endorsed by 'more than 5,000 organizations and individuals from over 100 countries' (SACOM 2010 np).

Shenzhen, 9 June 2010: Foxconn is reported to be 'employing psychologists, punchbags for prostrated workers . . . and safety nets around its roofs to stop workers leaping from them' (Harding 2010, np).

Shenzhen, 10 June 2010: Foxconn pay rises encourage workers in other Chinese factories to strike for higher pay.

Shenzhen, 11 June 2010: Foxconn is reported to have recruited monks and social workers to help workers with their problems, and to have compelled workers to sign contracts promising not to sue Foxconn as a result of 'any unexpected death or injury, including suicide or self-torture' (Malone and Jones 2010 np).

USA, 12 June 2010: an Apple fan called Mike Daisey returns from talking to Foxconn workers in preparation for a monologue show about Steve Jobs and concludes, 'It's painful to realize that these things you love so much have blood on them' (in McKeon 2010 np).

China, 6 July 2010: Chinese factory workers are reported to have been following this press coverage online, to be coordinating strike action via social networking websites, and to be gaining pay rises as a result of their actions.

UK, 16 July 2010: journalist Leo Hickman (2010b, np) argues that Apple is no longer the 'creative, edgy innovator that launched the iPod in 2001', and that the reputation of the 'entertainment and information colossus' has crumbled.

Washington DC, 20 July 2010: the premiere of Mike Daisey's *The Agony and the Ecstasy of Steve Jobs* takes place in the Wooly Mammoth Theatre. This becomes a controversial, high-profile critique of Jobs' company. Two years later, one reviewer describes it as 'the play that shook Apple and has compelled labor reforms in China' (Anonymous 2012, np).

China, 22 July 2010: Foxconn workers are reported to have been offered two pay rises in June which could more than double their pay, the company increased its prices to clients to cover increasing wage costs, the wave of strikes in China's coastal industrial cities continued, and Foxconn was said to be increasing automated production and moving low-margin production to new, lower-wage factories inland.

The story continues . . .

Source: edited version of Cook *et al.* (2010)

In ethical consumption, being a consumer is not opposed to being a political actor or a citizen. Rather, consumption is seen as a realm for political agency. However, the motivations, forms and implications of such agency cannot be assumed. Ethical consumption is not as simple as correcting the ignorances and amorality of most consumers through more accurate information about the origins of products. This is so in at least three ways.

First, we have argued that consumption is an arena for the production, circulation and reception of geographical knowledges. It is tempting for Geography academics and students to respond by looking to export the factual knowledge of our subject to this everyday arena, in order to correct the ignorances that we all operate under as consumers. But *that*, we suggest, is both too easy – offering a very simplistic account of both geographical knowledge and the politics of consumption – and impossibly difficult, given the complex histories and geographies of the multitude of things we consume (Cook *et al.* 2007). Just think, for example, about how many component parts your mobile phone has, how many hands those parts and their constituent materials have been through. To detail these would take many thousands of words; to find out about them many hours, days, maybe even months of research. Even the most committed ethical consumers therefore rely on shorthand rationales, whether that be guidance from those judged to be experts on appropriate ethical actions, recognized audits of ethical standards (e.g. through certification schemes such as Fairtrade, organic or animal welfare), or adverts that present ethical products (with their carefully managed, and often romanticized, representations of producers; see Wright 2004 and Zick Varul 2008). Ethical consumption is not about a simple transparency; it still involves the representation of commodity production and its relations to consumers (Goodman 2004).

Second, studies of ethical consumption also suggest that its existent forms stem as much from personal histories and collective organizations of political action as they do from the decisions of better informed consumers (Barnett *et al.* 2005, 2011; Clarke *et al.* 2007; Clarke 2008). In consequence, ethical consumption practice is as much a matter of political organization, and collective regulation, as it is of individual product choices. In turn, those forms of regulation operate within complex political fields where the interests of a range of interest groups have to be negotiated and may compete. Producers may, and do, find ethical regulation an imposition upon them by powerful consumer interests; corporate actors, such as supermarket retailers, may use ethical concerns to reinforce their role of speaking for consumers and dictating terms to producers (Cook *et al.* 2000b; Freidberg 2003). The politics of ethical consumption are complex.

Third, a preoccupation with the dark side of consumption – to put it crudely, with suffering, injustice, and our responsibility for it – is too partial. Rather than articulating worlds of consumption and production, it can end up dismissing worlds of consumption and their positive possibilities altogether. It is not a coincidence that Hartwick's (1998) commodity chain approach pays no attention to consumption per se. The danger of that limited view is that consumption is framed as unequivocally bad. That is neither true, as hopefully the discussions earlier in this chapter have demonstrated, nor terribly attractive in shaping political action. Particularly if one's own worlds of production, as a worker, are thoroughly unrewarding – admittedly not usually the case for academic critics of consumption, but true for many others – then giving up all the pleasures of consumption is pretty hard to stomach. Certainly the last three decades in Western politics suggest that failing to recognize the genuine senses of autonomy and creativity that consumption can facilitate is a sure way to alienate those very same workers in whose name one wishes to re-centre the world of production (Miller 2001).

The pleasures and responsibilities of consumption do not have to be opposed in this way. There are connections to be made. Early empirical research on ethical consumers in London challenged any sense of ethical consumption as joyless moral prescription (Bedford 1999), instead emphasizing the positive pleasures gained through such consumer movements: the feelings of achievement, the senses of empowerment, the forms of sociality fostered (see also Barnett *et al.* 2011: 153–80). What is more, much routine consumption has a moral core, centred on caring for one's nearest and dearest. Ethical consumption looks to extend the reach of such a consuming sensibility. We consumers are both global dictators and local freedom fighters. Understanding and inhabiting those two roles in conjunction remains a significant challenge.

Learning outcomes

After reading this chapter, you should have:

- An understanding of the importance of consumption to modern economies and cultures.
- A sensitivity to the continuing importance of cultural and geographical difference within contemporary consumer cultures.
- An understanding of the character of public space fashioned within the worlds of consumption.
- An understanding of the connections that exist between worlds of consumption and production, and of how ethical and political consumption looks to address these.
- An ability to think about the geographies of your own everyday consumption practices.

Further reading

Barnett, C., Cloke, P., Clarke, N. and Malpass, A. (2011) *Globalizing Responsibility: The Political Rationalities of Ethical Consumption,* Wiley-Blackwell, Oxford. This book argues for understanding ethical consumption as a political phenomenon, based on empirical research in the UK.

Cook, I. *et al.* (2004) Follow the thing: papaya, *Antipode,* 36(4), 642–64. An engaging narration of the lives connected through the travels of this tropical fruit from its Jamaican 'production' to its UK 'consumption'. This article attempts to show the complexity of 'defetishisation' research.

Hartwick, E. (1998) Geographies of consumption: a commodity chain approach, *Environment and Planning D:* *Society and Space,* 16, 423–37. A pithy comparison of the advertising imagery used to sell gold and the ways in which that gold is produced. Argues for a knowledgable and ethical connection of consumers and producers.

Mansvelt, J. (2005) *Geographies of Consumption,* Sage: London. This is an excellent textbook that develops and extends the account of consumption begun in this chapter.

Miller, J.C. (2014) 'Malls without stores (MwS): the affectual spaces of a Buenos Aires shopping mall', *Transactions of the Institute of British Geographers,* NS 39, 14-25. Building on earlier work, this study provides an up to date account of retail space geographies, focusing on how malls are engineered to create atmospheres conducive to consumption and the limits to such commercial ambitions of environmental control.

Useful websites

www.followthethings.com Opened in October 2011. This website is run by Ian Cook and collaborators, and collects, researches and showcases work that seeks to understand consumption and its complex geographies using a 'follow the thing' approach.

www.adbusters.org This website presents examples of 'culture jamming', i.e. re-workings of well known advertising campaigns, as well as magazine and blog materials devoted to contesting the cultural power of corporate promotional culture.

www.exchange-values.org This website presents Shelly Sacks' artwork *Exchange Values* in an online format. The artwork presents audio testimony from banana farmers in St Lucia, who speak to you, a banana consumer, about their hopes and concerns.

POLITICAL GEOGRAPHIES:
GEOPOLITICS, TERRITORY, STATES, CITIZENSHIP AND GOVERNANCE

Edited by James Sidaway

Those who have reached this section after reading other chapters should already be aware that many elements of geography touch on political issues. Such 'politics' may not be confined to those things that are usually designated by the term: governments, elections, referendums (or the lack of them), political parties, revolutions, territorial conflicts and so on. Rather, readers will have noticed that debates about culture, economic change, history, changing gender relations and many other things described in this text are also political. They are political in the sense of being about power, albeit at different levels and in lots of different ways. So, in an important way, all geographies are political geographies. Though focused on geopolitics territory, nation-states and global governance, the chapters that follow aim to bring that home. Chapter 20 examines the meanings of geopolitics. It will explore how geopolitics has been defined in different times and places: including South America in the second half of the twentieth century, Germany, some other European countries and Japan before and during the Second World War as well as through the Cold War confrontation between the Soviet Union and the USA, the 'global war on terror' of the 2000s to contemporary debates about the rise and role of China; all building on the moment when geopolitics was first established as a way of understanding (and indeed seeking to influence) world politics, in early twentieth-century Europe. As the chapter describes, when considering what geopolitics might mean today and in the future, these pasts are mobilized and reworked.

Chapter 21 examines 'territory'; the ways that human individuals and social groups claim or are assigned to particular areas: in short, the human territorial strategies which regulate, demarcate and divide social and political spaces, and their uses. Whilst this is perhaps most clearly expressed in the form of the political geography of nations and states and their boundaries (the focus of Chapter 22), Chapter 21 stresses that territoriality operates in myriad ways and at local scales: for example, in the manner in which particular areas within many cities become associated with different ethnicities (as in the history of urban ghettos and city 'quarters' or other places that are seen as being overwhelmingly white – such as many rural areas in Britain) or, more widely, in the ways that some spaces are seen as public and others private or as male and female. Readers will therefore find many connections with earlier sections of the book here. Chapter 22 introduces the historical and geographical variability of nations and states. It stresses that neither the nation nor the state is to be taken at face value. Or in other words, it examines how nation-states are complex symbolic systems that crucially depend upon particular visions and associations of territory, place and space. Chapter 23 focuses on citizenship: the relationship between individuals and political units (largely, but not only states).

The last chapter in the book should be read in tandem with the others in this section. Its consideration of the geographies of global governance also connects with many others in the book. In particular, it is easy to see how Chapter 24 relates to issues of population, resources, development and the environment that are considered in Section 2. In the relationships with culture, nature and cities, the links to Section 3 are evident, but so too are those with the economic and financial geographies described in Section 4. And it is not hard to appreciate how the present and future of all the issues considered in this section derive from the historical geographies examined in Section 1. Such interconnections are part of what makes a geographical approach so inviting and exciting.

GEOPOLITICAL TRADITIONS

Chapter 20

James Sidaway, Virginie Mamadouh and Chih Yuan Woon

Topics covered

- Origins and history of geopolitics, critical perspectives and 'popular geopolitics'
- Diversity and dissemination of geopolitical discourses
- Changing 'World Orders'

Few modern ideologies are as whimsically all-encompassing, as romantically obscure, as intellectually sloppy, and as likely to start a third world war as the theory of 'geopolitics'. Popularized at the beginning of the twentieth century by an eccentric British geographer, Sir Halford Mackinder, geopolitics posits that the earth will forever be divided into two naturally antagonistic spheres: land and sea. In this model, the natural repository for global land power is the Eurasian 'heartland' – the territory of the former Russian empire. Whoever controls the heartland, wrote Mackinder, will forever seek to dominate the Eurasian landmass and ultimately the world.

(Charles Clover 1999: 9)

20.1 Introducing the idea of a geopolitical tradition

Geopolitical rhetoric is more popular than ever. Writing in the (London-based newspaper) *Financial Times* in May 2015, China's ambassador to Britain began his article on how China's growing power and investments should not be seen as threatening, with a note about how 'A century ago, Sir Halford Mackinder, the British geographer and politician credited as the father of western geopolitics' had coined ideas about power and space in Eurasia that 'captivated generations of geo-strategists who saw Eurasia as the "heartland" of the world's most populous and pivotal region' (Liu 2015: 9).

Ambassador Liu noted that new Chinese proposals for enhanced transport and trade links connecting Europe and Asia were being misinterpreted by some as confirming Mackinder's theories. Instead he stressed the shared benefits of 'development and prosperity' from Chinese initiatives, arguing that 'the Chinese mind is never programmed around geopolitical or geoeconomic theory' (op cit.). Some beg to differ, however, and as the closing section of this chapter details, Chinese actions are frequently interpreted through geopolitical lenses.

But what does **geopolitics** mean? Our answer is that whilst the term can and does refer to many things, and is much in vogue, it is important for students of geography (a subject with which geopolitics has often been associated) to understand that geopolitics is commonly associated with particular ways of writing (and thinking) about space, states and the relations between them. Often this takes the form of mapping, emphasizing the strategic importance of particular places (as in Figures 20.1 or 20.3). Geopolitics in this sense often sees itself as a tradition: that is, something conscious of its unfolding historical development and with a sense of important founders (and certain key texts written by them). Many of those who write about this tradition or see themselves as working within or extending it usually trace its origins to the late-nineteenth-century writings of a conservative Swedish politician Rudolf Kjellén. Kjellén is reputedly the first person to have used the term 'geopolitics' in published writings (see Holdar 1992; Tunander 2001). But beyond this idea of a founding moment when the geopolitical 'tradition' begins with the first use of the term by Kjellén, things start to get complicated. The 'tradition' divides, fractures, multiplies and finds itself translated into many languages and cropping up in everything from the writings and speeches of American politicians to texts written by Brazilian generals and Russian journalists. All these reinvent and rework the 'tradition' as they go along. As the introduction to a critical collection on 'rethinking geopolitics' explained:

> the word 'geopolitics' has had a long and varied history in the twentieth century, moving well beyond its original meaning in Kjellén's work . . . . Coming up with a specific definition of geopolitics is notoriously difficult, for the meaning of concepts like geopolitics tends to change as historical periods and structures of world order change.
>
> (Ó Tuathail 1998: 1)

In other words, exactly what is meant by the term 'geopolitics' has changed in different historical and geographical contexts. However, a good way to begin to understand something about this idea of a tradition of geopolitics is to look at some of the people, places and ideas associated with one of its most significant appearances, in the ideology of the right-wing dictatorships that ruled many South American countries in the 1960s, 1970s and 1980s. In most cases they had come to power through military coups and became more concerned with internal security (patrolling the towns and country as a kind of police force and running the wider government) than with fighting or preparing to fight wars with other countries.

Consider the case of Chile. On 11 September 1973, the elected left-wing government of Chile (headed by the communist President Salvador Allende) was overthrown in a brutally violent coup led by the head of the armed forces General Augusto Pinochet (Plate 20.1). Pinochet and his generals ruled Chile with an iron fist. All opposition was crushed and thousands of people were rounded up by the armed forces. Many 'disappeared' into secret military jails. Hundreds of these prisoners were tortured and murdered. The use of torture became a routine instrument of state. For the next 17 years, Chile was ruled by Pinochet and his cronies who imposed a new 'neoliberal' economic and political model (**of the form that is described in Chapter 8**) and murdered any significant opposition. Pinochet finally stepped down as head of state in 1990, when democracy was restored, but not before he had entrenched himself as a senator (in the parliament) for life; he died from heart failure in 2006, aged 91.

The ideology of the military regime in Chile (like those elsewhere in South America) was intensely nationalist. More importantly it was a particular conservative form of Chilean nationalism. The nation was held to be sacred and the military were rescuing this 'sacred body' from communists, subversives and so on (i.e. anyone who opposed the military vision of ultra-nationalism and order and the neoliberal economic and social model which was now imposed). It is in this nationalism and

Plate 20.1 General Pinochet: geopolitics in action.

(SIPA PRESS/Rex Shutterstock)

conception of the nation as a kind of sacred body that geopolitics enters the picture. A few years before the coup, Pinochet had published an army textbook on geopolitics. Intended mainly for use in Chilean military academies, the 1968 textbook indicated that Chile's future dictator took the subject very seriously. For Pinochet, geopolitics was a science of the state, a set of knowledges and programmes to perfect the art of statecraft, that is to strengthen the state in a continent and wider world in which it was held to be in competition with others. The starting point and the heart of Pinochet's textbook and of the wider bleak tradition of geopolitics that it presents is an organic theory of the state.

20.2 The organic theory of the state

This idea is at the core of most South American geopolitical writings and of the wider geopolitical tradition. In summary, it holds that the state or country (and the sense of nation that goes with it) is best understood as being like a living being. Like any living organism, it therefore needs space to grow and it will be in competition with other living beings. An idea that the state needs 'living

space' (a certain amount of resources and land) for the nation to thrive is particularly evident in South American geopolitics. A certain reading of Charles Darwin's idea of a struggle for the 'survival of the fittest' is therefore transferred to the realm of states. Drawing upon conservative German writings of the nineteenth and early twentieth century and with this organic notion of the state in mind, geopolitics claims to identify certain laws that govern state behaviour and that, once identified, can be a guide for those charged with furthering and protecting the 'national interest' (or at least a certain definition of the latter).

It is not difficult to see how this idea could appeal to South American military dictators, for it gives the military, equipped with the supposedly scientific study of geopolitics, a special mission. In other words it legitimizes their rule. Moreover, the organic idea was extended further to legitimize the extermination of those whom the military defined as enemies of the state. People labelled as communist or subversive, indeed all those who oppose the military dictatorship, can be compared with a disease or cancer which threatens the lifeblood of the state-organism and is best 'cut out', that is, eliminated. The otherwise unthinkable (the murder of thousands of people in the name of the wider welfare of the nation-state) is made to seem natural and a good thing, since it serves the longer-term interest of the health and power of the 'living being' that is the state (see Hepple 1992 for an exploration of this). With the 'cancer' of subversion and disloyalty eliminated, the 'state-body' can go on to grow and thrive.

20.3 Brazilian national integration

Aside from Chile (and neighbour Argentina, of which more will be said in Section 20.4), perhaps the most important expressions of geopolitics in South America were in Brazil. The military in Brazil overthrew the democratic government in 1964 and stayed in power for the next 20 years. Although never as despotic as the regime led by Pinochet (or similar military governments in Argentina and Uruguay), the long years of military rule gave the Brazilian generals a chance to elaborate and impose a geopolitical vision on the country. One of the most evident aspects of Brazilian geopolitics is the idea that state security requires a measure of national integration. The vast scale of Brazil, the difficulty of travel across its Amazon 'heartland' (the world's largest tropical rainforest) and the fact that it shares borders with every other South American country except Chile and Ecuador gave the geopolitics of the Brazilian generals a special sense of its

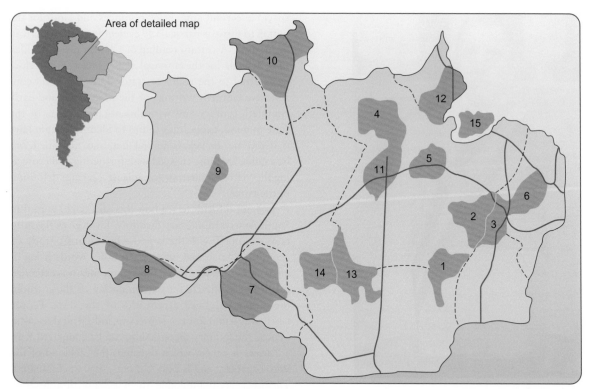

Figure 20.1 National integration in Brazilian geopolitics: Amazon development poles. The shaded areas represent the 15 'development poles' where financial resources would be concentrated and concessions offered to mining, settlement, industrial, lumber and agricultural development resources.

Source: Hecht and Cockburn (1989: 127)

national mission and an obsession with the potential for the country to be a great power (known in Portuguese as *Grandeza*). The associated sense of the urgency of the integration of Brazil required the extension of a network of highways across Amazonia and the settlement of its lands by farmers and ranchers. It is this geopolitically inspired vision, combined with a highly corrupt system of patronage and favours to those close to the regime, that underlies the enclosure and division of Amazonia into private lands (some larger than European countries such as Belgium) and the accompanying transformation or destruction of the tropical rainforest (see Hecht and Cockburn 1989; Foresta 1992) (Figure 20.1).

Although the Brazilian military have been back in the barracks for more than three decades and Brazil is again a lively democracy, the long-term consequences of this geopolitically motivated (and economically profitable) strategy have been disastrous for many of the indigenous peoples of Amazonia. They have found themselves forced off land that was traditionally theirs, sometimes murdered or attacked by ranchers, the state and settlers, and disoriented by the arrival of a frontier culture of violence, destruction and consumption. Poor peasants, particularly from the impoverished north-east of Brazil,

have also moved into the Amazon region in search of land and freedom. They are fleeing from the oppression and landlessness they themselves face in the north-east of Brazil, where the vast majority of the land is still in the hands of an elite class. Of course, in the geopolitical visions of the Brazilian generals, this population movement was seen as overwhelmingly positive, reinforcing the Brazilian population of the Amazon and redistributing what they regard as marginal 'surplus' people in the process (in much the same way that the colonization of the 'wild west' was seen as the advance of civilization and America's 'manifest destiny' in the United States). At the same time this has defused some of the political pressures for land reform in north-east Brazil. In all this we can see how Brazilian geopolitics was implicated in a complex web of social and environmental transformations.

20.4 Antarctic obsessions

An interest, at times an obsession, with the last unexploited continent of Antarctica is evident in much South

American geopolitics. Antarctica is also prominent in geopolitical writings from Argentina, Chile and Uruguay and also appears in Peruvian, Brazilian and Ecuadorian geopolitical texts (see Dodds 1997). To understand what this amounts to and what forms it takes necessitates some understanding of Antarctica's exceptional political geography. Antarctica has a unique territorial status, in so far as it has no recognized state on its territory. Everywhere else in the world forms part of the patchwork of states that we learn to be familiar with and take for granted. Antarctica is a stark reminder that there is nothing natural or inevitable about this. The absence of recognized states in Antarctica reflects the inhospitability and remoteness of the continent, the only one without an indigenous human population. Although the plankton-rich waters around Antarctica were exploited for seal and whale hunting in the nineteenth century, it was not until the twentieth century that exploration of the interior began. Even today, Antarctica has only a non-permanent population (at any time) of a few hundred scientists. This presence, plus the relative proximity of the continent to South America and the possibility of exploitable mineral resources, has led to a series of territorial claims. Although Argentinean writers had already represented Antarctica as an extension of the southern Argentine area of Patagonia, the British made the first formal claim in 1908. In turn, parts of this claim were 'granted' to Australia and New Zealand. France and Norway made claims in the 1930s and 1940s, followed shortly by Argentina and Chile. After 1945, the USSR and the USA also established a wide network of bases, although without staking formal claims to territory. The claims made by Argentina, Chile and the United Kingdom overlapped – and foreshadowing the British–Argentine conflict over the Falklands/Malvinas, British and Argentine forces exchanged fire in Antarctica in the late 1940s and early 1950s. In the context of this potential for conflict and growing possibility of Cold War confrontation (on the Cold War, see Section 20.7), a United Nations Treaty in 1959 agreed that all claims would be (forgive the pun) 'frozen' for at least 30 years, and the continent reserved for scientific (not commercial or military) use. The Treaty was extended in 1991. But prior to then, it was not clear what the future status of the continent would be. Even today, the Treaty merely defers the issue of claims.

Argentina is the South American country with the largest claim (Figure 20.2). The Argentine claim has also become central to geopolitical discourse there. As Child (1985: 140–1) explains in a study of geopolitics and conflict in South America:

> For Argentine geopolitical writers, the subject of Antarctica is not only linked to tricontinental Argentina [a power in the South American continent and the South

Atlantic], but also to. . . national sovereignty, patriotism, and pride. This is a particularly touchy combination after the humiliating defeat of the Malvinas/Falklands conflict. The Argentine National Antarctic Directorate has professors of Antarctic geopolitics on its staff. Through the media, maps, and postage stamps and the centralized educational system, Argentines are constantly taught and reminded that there is an Argentine Antarctic just as much as there are Argentine Malvinas. The need to assert Argentine rights in the Argentine Sea, islands, and Antarctica is linked to dreams and national projects of Argentine greatness.

20.5 Heartland

Although Antarctica and the South Atlantic are significant components of Argentine (along with Brazilian and Chilean) geopolitics, the former also looks beyond other Argentine frontiers. In particular, Argentine geopolitical writers together with some Brazilians and Chileans have taken a particular interest in the security of Bolivia. They have scripted Bolivia (a relatively impoverished land-locked mountainous country, which has borders with Argentina, Brazil, Chile, Paraguay and Peru) and proximate areas of its neighbours as a key strategic continental **heartland** (see Kelly 1997). Control of Bolivia, in this vision, would be a vital key to a relative dominance in the South American continent. That Bolivia has a strong revolutionary tradition and was for many years characterized by chronic political instability has reinforced the tendency of the other South American countries to meddle in Bolivian politics. Indeed, during the years (1976–82) when Argentina was last ruled by a geopolitically obsessed military junta, the Argentine armed forces were actively involved in supporting a Bolivian military government. This activity took the form of the kinds of brutal suppression and frequent murder of those (trade union leaders, dissidents, opposition members and leaders) who opposed the military government and its economic and social strategies. The idea of Bolivia as a 'heartland', control of which would be a kind of magic (geopolitical) key to domination of South America, links back to one of the best-known genres in classical (European) geopolitical thought. For although the South American countries have seen some of the most significant expressions of geopolitical discourse of modern times, geopolitics originates in Europe and it is to some examples of European geopolitics, including the idea of heartland, that we now turn.

The designation of a heartland was first made by that British geographer (and strongly pro-imperialist

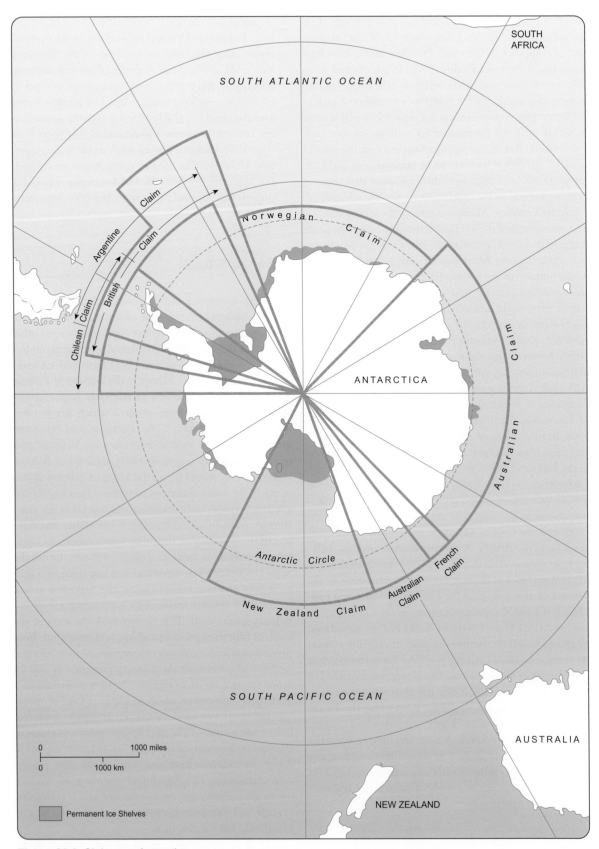

Figure 20.2 Claims on Antarctica.

conservative politician) Halford Mackinder. In what has since become a widely cited article first published in 1904 following its presentation to the Royal Geographical Society (RGS), Mackinder argued that the age of (European) geographical exploration was drawing to a close. This meant that there were hardly any unknown 'blank' spaces left on European maps of the world. According to Mackinder, the consequence of this closing of the map, this end of the centuries-long task of exploration and discovery, was that political events in one part of the world would invariably affect all others, to a much greater extent than hitherto. There would be no more frontiers for Europeans to explore and conquer. Instead, the great powers would now invariably collide with one another. Mackinder called this end of European exploration 'the post-Columbian age' and the closing of frontiers, the emergence of a 'closed political system'.

Given that this was the case, Mackinder claimed to identify the places of greatest world-strategic significance, control of which would give any great power a key to world power. In his 1904 paper, he termed this the 'pivot area'. With Mackinder's address to the RGS and his subsequent article came a series of maps, the most frequently reprinted one of which claims to describe 'The Natural Seats of Power' (Figure 20.3). As Ó Tuathail's (1996a: 25) critical account of Mackinder argues:

> Mackinder's January 25 [1904], address to the Royal Geographical Society, 'The Geographical Pivot of History', is generally considered to be a defining moment in the history of geopolitics, a text to which histories of geopolitics invariably point.

One of the key formulas in Mackinder's notion of geographical determinism is his identification of a 'pivot area' or 'heartland zone' in east-central Europe, control of which would be a kind of magic key to world domination. Reworking the ideas of his 1904 article after the First World War, Mackinder refined this notion and penned a formula that encapsulated it:

Who rules East Europe commands the Heartland.

Who rules the Heartland commands the World-Island.

Who rules the World-Island commands the world.

(Mackinder 1919: 4)

According to this (simplistic) formula, 'rule' of the eastern portion of Europe offered the strategic path to that of the African–Asian–European continents (which together constitute what Mackinder terms the 'World-Island') and hence a dominant position on the world scene.

Mackinder's writings reflect his place and time. Mackinder, writing from the vantage point of imperial Britain, is concerned to identify threats and dangers to British power. At the time when Mackinder presented his paper to the RGS, Britain was the pre-eminent world power. It still seemed that way to Mackinder in 1919 when he wrote about the 'Heartland'. But British imperial politicians, like Mackinder, were aware of the growing power of the United States of America, Germany and Russia. In fact, potential British imperial competition with the latter in Asia provided a key context to Mackinder's work. As Peter Taylor (1994: 404) explained:

> Behind every general model there is a specific case from which it is derived. For the heartland model this is particularly easy to identify. Throughout the second half of the nineteenth century Britain and Russia had been rivals in much of Asia. While Britain was consolidating its hold on India and the route to India, Russia had been expanding eastwards and southwards producing many zones of potential conflict from Turkey through Persia and Afghanistan to Tibet. But instead of war this became an arena of bluff and counter-bluff, known as the 'Great Game'. . . . Mackinder's presentation to an audience at the Royal Geographical Society would not have seemed so original as it appears to us reading this paper today . . . . Put simply, the heartland model is a codification and globalization of the Great Game: it brings a relatively obscure imperial contest on to centre stage.

Not only does this envisage the world in a particular way, as a 'stage', but it sees only select key actors as the significant figures at play. These are the European powers (plus Russia). Other peoples and places are merely the backdrop for action by White Men. The taken-for-granted racism of Mackinder's model, in which only Europeans make history, is also that of European imperialism and that of the bulk of wider European geographical and historical writings of the time (see Chapter 3).

Yet, although Mackinder's 1904 paper is very much a product of its time and Mackinder's own conservative world-view, it has proven durable and has been integrated into rather different contexts, which saved it from the relative obscurity that it deserves as a turn-of-the-century imperialist text. The transfer of the discourse of 'Heartland' to Bolivia by South American codifiers of geopolitics has already been noted. In addition, 'Heartland' was appropriated by German geopolitics in the 1930s and 1940s and formed part of the backdrop to Cold War American strategy from the late 1940s through to the last decade of the twentieth century. Today it is widely read and debated in Russia and other countries of the former Soviet Union, such as Ukraine (Wilson 2002) and

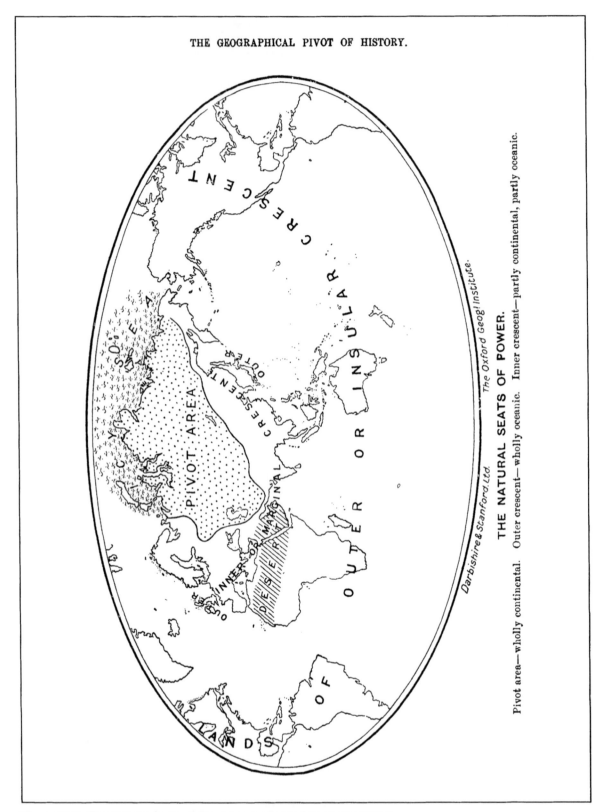

Figure 20.3 'The Natural Seats of Power' according to Mackinder (1904).

Uzbekistan (Megoran and Sharopova 2012). The next two sections of this chapter will examine aspects of Nazi, Fascist and Cold War geopolitics in greater detail.

20.6 Nazi and Fascist geopolitics

The formal tradition of writing about space and power under the title of 'geopolitics' also found fertile contexts in Italy, Portugal, Spain and Japan. Influenced and supported by Nazi Germany, all these countries (together with Hungary and Romania) saw the rise and victory of ultra-nationalist or Fascist governments (often through violent struggle or full-scale civil war with democratic or communist forces) (see Chapter 3). In each case geopolitical debates were crucially negotiated through other cultural and political debates about race, nationalism, the colonial pasts and futures, supposed national 'missions' and destinies and the European and global political contexts. In Portugal, for example, the right-wing dictatorship argued that it was bringing Christianity and civilization to the territories it had acquired in Africa and Asia, even projecting these onto a map of Europe to show that – if the African territories controlled by Portugal were taken into account (Figure 20.4), then Portugal was not a small country (Sidaway and Power 2005)! In similar

terms, in Italy under the fascist dictator Benito Mussolini, geopolitical journals saw themselves as serving and expressing the aspirations of the fascist state to establish a new Roman Empire across the Mediterranean (Figure 20.5) (Antonsich 2009). However, it is the German geopolitics of this epoch that has become the best-known. In Germany, organic notions of the state had already been popularized by conservative nineteenth-century academics. Moreover, Germany was characterized by extreme political and economic turbulence in the decades following its defeat in the 1914–18 World War. This combination provided a fertile environment for the elaboration and circulation of a distinctive geopolitical tradition. In Ó Tuathail's (1996a: 141) words:

> After the shock of military defeat and the humiliation of the dictated peace of Versailles, the Weimar Republic proved to be fertile ground for the growth of a distinct German geopolitics. Geopolitical writings, in the words of one critic, 'shot up like mushrooms after a summer rain'.

The main features of these writings (which they shared with a wider German revanchism, later codified in Nazism) were a critique of the established 'World Order', and of the injustices imposed on Germany by the victors. German claims were often presented graphically in maps

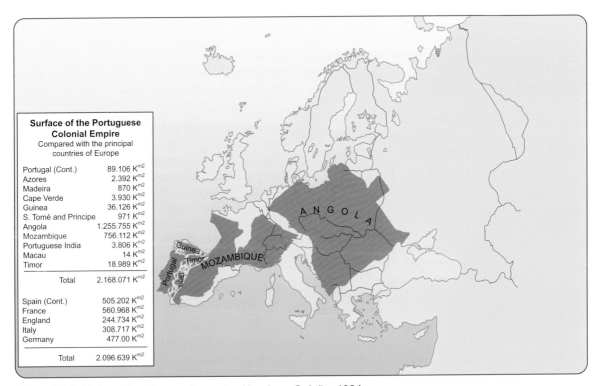

Figure 20.4 Portugal is not a small country. Henrique Galvão, 1934.

Source: adapted from Sidaway and Power (2005)

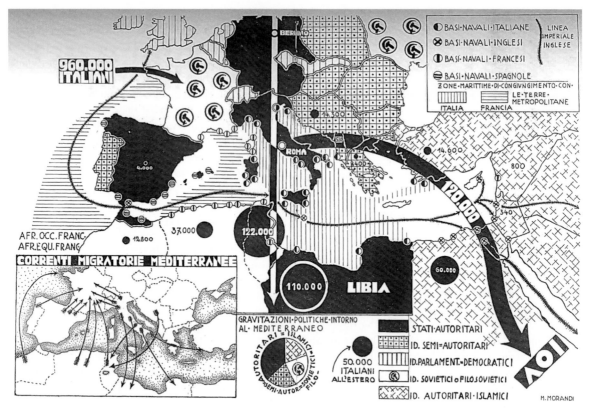

Figure 20.5 Italian living space in the Mediterranean Region.

Source: *Geopolitica*, 3 (1939) p. 161. Reprinted in Antonisch (2009)

that were widely circulated (see Herb 1989: 97). Like the variants of the geopolitical tradition that were developed amongst right-wing and military circles in Italy, Portugal, Spain and Japan, German geopolitics also asserted an imperial destiny. Indeed, as Agnew and Corbridge (1995: 58–9) explain: 'The Nazi geopoliticians of the 1930s came up with formalized schemes for combining imperial and colonized peoples within what they called "Pan-Regions".'

In this vision, notions of racial hierarchy were blended with conceptions of state 'vitality' to justify territorial expansion of the Axis powers (see O'Loughlin and van der Wusten 1990) (Figure 20.6). In Europe, related conceptions of the need for an expanded German living-space were used as justification for the mass murder of occupied peoples and those who did not fit into the grotesque plans of 'racial/territorial' purity. The practical expression of these was the construction of a system of racial 'purification' and mass extermination. At least 6 million Jewish people were murdered in concentration camps together with millions of others: disabled people, gays and lesbians, gypsies and political opponents. Historical debates about the role and relative significance of German geopolitics within the Holocaust and within

broader Nazi ideology and strategy continue (see Heske 1986: 87; Bassin 1987; Ó Tuathail 1996a; Natter 2003). Paul Gilroy (2000: 39), however, reiterates the connections between racial, early ecological and geopolitical thinking:

> connected in profound ways to the notions of Leben-sraum (living-space) that figured in but were not created by the racist population policies and agricultural and scientific planning of the Nazi period . . . [and to] the geo-organic, biopolitical and governmental theories of the German geographers Friedrich Ratzel and Karl Haushofer and the early-twentieth century geopolitican Rudolf Kjellén. These writers supplied important conceptual resources to Nazi racial science, helping it to conceptualize the state as an organism and to specify the necessary connections between the nation and its dwelling area.

In the United States in the 1940s, German geopolitics became the subject of lurid tales and depictions, cropping up in media, military and government 'explanations' of Nazi danger. Popular magazines, such as *Readers Digest*, would inform Americans of the 'scientists behind Hitler' describing German geopolitics as *the* key to Nazi

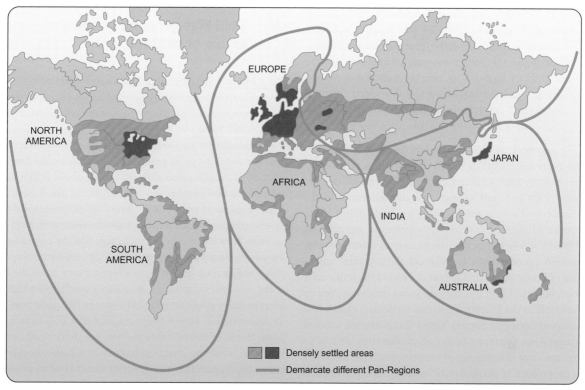

Figure 20.6 'Pan-Regions' as envisaged in Nazi geopolitics.

Source: O'Loughlin and Van der Wusten (1990) 'Political geography and the pan regions', *Geographical Review,* 80, adapted with permission of the American Geographical Society. Copyright © American Geographical Society, 1990

strategy. And whilst the relative significance of the German geopolitical tradition in the wider genocidal ultra-nationalism of German Fascism was certainly overstated in such accounts, we should see geopolitics as a particular expression of *wider* academic and intellectual involvement and complicity in authoritarian state power, war-making and genocide. Much more widely, beyond the geopolitical tradition per se, academic geography was deeply implicated in these activities. Exploring this, Natter (2003: 188) notes how

[T]he work of disciplinary historians of geography has demonstrated the extent to which the demarcation of geography seems inseparable from the history of war, imperialism and quests for national identity. . . . Geopolitics, thus, would mark a particular, but in no way separable (and hence containable) geopolitical deployment of geo-power.

An example of this wider complicity was the way in which the models of 'Central Place Theory' (an abstract model of the ideal spatial distribution of towns), which were developed in Germany by Walter Christaller in the 1930s, were elaborated with the express purpose of providing planners with a model of German settlement to impose on conquered territories of Eastern Europe,

once the minority Jewish and Gypsy populations there had been murdered and the majority Slavic population enslaved (see Rössler 1989 and Barnes and Minca 2013).

The defeat of the Axis powers in 1945 (culminating in the use of American atomic weapons against the civilian populations of Hiroshima and Nagasaki in Japan) and the lurid wartime depictions of Nazi geopolitics in the United States dealt something of a blow to the formal tradition of geopolitics. In the 1990s, however, right-wing geopolitics returned – in Russia and Ukraine for example, where references to Nazi-era concepts (such as *Großraum*, 'larger space') and associated racist and anti-Semitic ideologies have become influential within some contemporary geopolitical thought (Ingram 2001; Wilson 2002; O'Loughlin *et al.* 2005). Moreover, references to geopolitics had continued through the 1950s to the 1970s in both Spain and Portugal (see Sidaway 1999, 2000; Sidaway and Power 2005), where Fascist regimes remained in power to the mid-1970s, as well as in Turkey (especially when it too was under military rule through part of the 1960s, and again in the early 1970s and early 1980s). On the Turkish example, Pinar Bilgin (2007: 753) argues that:

Constructed through texts authored by military geopoliticians, and disseminated through a variety of institutions including compulsory military service (with access to all males 18+ years of age), the National Security Academy (proving in service training to high level civil servants and journalists), and the compulsory high-school course 'National Security', Turkey's geopolitical discourse has allowed the military to play a central role in shaping domestic political processes but also make this role seem 'normal'.

In addition, as this chapter has detailed, geopolitics has been influential in recent decades in a number of South American countries, especially in the 1970s' and early 1980s' epoch of military rule through much of the continent. These regimes (and plenty of others) were integrated into the US-led anti-communist network of allies. In a policy that became known as **containment**, the USA aimed to encircle and block the potential expansion of Soviet power and influence beyond the immediate borders of the USSR and the pro-Soviet states installed by the USSR in the Eastern European territories that it had occupied during its Second World War battle for survival against Nazi Germany. In the allied countries (and as an expression of this strategy of containment), the functions of geopolitics, in particular its 'strategic vision' and claim of 'scientific' objectivity, continued to operate or were displaced into other disciplines and branches of knowledge, including geography and the expanding subject of International Relations. This displacement of strategic knowledge was particularly evident in the United States, which by 1945 was the greatest power that the world had ever seen, constituting over half of the world economy and (until the recovery of the Soviet Union and its own development of atomic weapons in 1949) possessing a virtually unrivalled military capacity.

Plate 20.2 The gateway to the Auschwitz concentration camp. The Nazi regime used concentration camps to execute their policy of racial/territorial 'purification'.

(Caminoel/Shutterstock)

20.7 Cold War geopolitics and the logics of containment

The Cold War is used as a shorthand description of the conflict (which to many seemed to be a conflict for world domination) between the 'communist' East, led by the USSR, and the 'capitalist' West, led by the USA from around 1949 to around 1989. This was not simply a rift between two great powers, but a complex ideological conflict, which often appeared to be about different ways of life and contrasting social systems (the bureaucratic 'command economies' based on predominantly state ownership of the means of production, with a ruling class drawn from the bureaucracy; and the capitalist economies based on predominantly private ownership, with a ruling class drawn from a bureaucracy controlled by the owners of capital). It was also a conflict in which *direct* military confrontation between the two great powers was avoided. Hence the metaphor of Cold, that is, 'poor, frozen or frosty' relationships, but short of all-out 'hot' war, involving direct exchanges of missiles, bombs and so on. In part this avoidance of direct conflict arose because both powers were conscious of the enormous stakes, armed with nuclear, chemical and biological weapons as well as vast arsenals of increasingly high-tech 'conventional' armaments. By the 1960s, they were each capable of destroying virtually all human life several times over. Moreover, neither could attack the other without being sure that the enemy would not still possess enough undamaged nuclear weapons to retaliate, a 'balance' of terror known, appropriately enough, as MAD (Mutually Assured Destruction). Instead, conflict took the form of the continual preparation for war (as in 'civil defense' preparations, see Plate 20.3) plus proxy wars in what became known as the (originally not pro-West, not pro-East, but contested) '**Third World**' and many other political, economic and cultural forms of competition. That is, it was a conflict conducted by *every* means *except* direct military confrontation between the superpowers.

Of course there was no shortage of indirect confrontation and preparation for war. Europe was divided into two armed camps and split down the middle between Soviet and American zones of influence by a fortified military and ideological frontier that became known as the 'Iron Curtain'. Whilst Europe was characterized by an uneasy stability and balance of terror, by the 1970s the term 'geopolitics' had been revived (or rediscovered) by US national security advisers Henry Kissinger and Zbigniew Brzezinski (see Hepple 1986; Sidaway 1998) to refer to the strategic vision deemed necessary to

Plate 20.3 The cold war came to American cities: a nuclear shelter.

(karenfoleyphoto/fotolia)

circumvent the sense of growing Soviet power, particularly in the Third World, where a wave of successful revolutions had brought left-wing, pro-Soviet governments to power. One of these was in Cuba, but by the end of the 1970s, there were also pro-Soviet governments in the countries of Indochina (Vietnam, Laos and Kampuchea) where the United States had been unable to defeat communist insurgencies despite a massive military effort, in the African countries of Angola and Mozambique, in the Arabian country of South Yemen and in Afghanistan as well as in the small Central American state of Nicaragua. Although China had moved away from its close alliance with the Soviets by the early 1960s, communist

China remained a force to be reckoned with and opposed American support for Taiwan. Thousands of American troops stationed in South Korea were just a short distance from a hostile communist North Korea. By the early 1980s, American concern about the security of oil supplies from the Persian Gulf region had escalated to the extent that the then US President Carter declared that it was of vital importance to the USA (see Spotlight box 20.1). In this world of superpower competition, geopolitics again found its moment and expression in the visions of the national security advisers and American generals.

More widely, American leaders and policy makers declared that the Soviet Union had to be *encircled* and *contained*. The metaphor of disease (containment) was mixed with that of 'dominoes' – if one country (say Vietnam or Cuba) had 'fallen' to Soviet control or influence, then it could (like a chain reaction) 'infect' other proximate ones. The irony of this (which is equally present in the formal geopolitical tradition) is that in the name of security and strategy, the real complexity of *human* geographies in the places (such as Vietnam or Chile, or Afghanistan, Nicaragua or the Persian Gulf) that are deemed strategic is sometimes obscured or erased. Forget about the complex details of the people, culture and society. What matters is the 'strategic value' of the place, or the political identity of its government as an ideological and strategic friend or foe. At times this could take quite extreme forms, as with US National Security Advisor Robert McNamara (previously head of Ford, and later head of the World Bank):

Plate 20.4 (left) Containment in action: the aftermath of napalm bombing on a Vietnamese village by US-backed (anti-communist) South Vietnamese forces. (right) 'Containment' explained: US Secretary of State for Defense briefing journalists during the Vietnam war.

(© Bettmann/CORBIS)

Spotlight box 20.1

The Carter Doctrine: contexts and consequences

In late 1979, the USSR invaded Afghanistan. For the Soviets, this meant supporting a communist government in a neighbouring country, who had come to power just a couple of years before (in a coup, after several years of political instability) and were facing rebellion and resistance in the Afghan countryside (already being fostered by the Pakistani and US intelligence agencies). For strategists in Moscow, the invasion would secure the USSR's southern flank, especially from the growing perceived threats from a new Islamic radicalism: the USSR had millions of Muslim citizens in its Central Asian territories, and feared that the Islamic revolution in Iran and the insurgency in Afghanistan might influence them and threaten Soviet power and stability. However, for the USA – at least to those in influential positions, like US National Security Advisor Zbigniew Brzezinski – this marked a new phase of Soviet expansion and a failure of containment. In tandem with the Islamic revolution in Iran which overthrew the Shah (who was an American ally and whose rise to power in the 1950s was orchestrated by the USA and Britain) was the second jump in oil prices in a decade, and American concern over the security of oil supplies from the Persian Gulf region grew. Brzezinski and the American media had already starting talking about the region as 'an arc [or crescent] of crisis' (see Sidaway 1998) (see Plate 20.5, which shows how the influential *Time* magazine represented these 'geopolitical dangers'). And soon after the Soviets invaded Afghanistan the US media started to describe it as the first Soviet step towards the Middle East, and President Carter announced that any threat by an outside force to the Persian Gulf was a matter of direct American strategic interest and would result in a military response. This commitment became known as the Carter Doctrine, taking its place amongst a succession of other US Presidential geopolitical doctrines: such as Truman in 1947, who set out the overall commitment to containment, to (after Carter) the Reagan Doctrine in the 1980s (which

sought to roll back Soviet influence in places like Afghanistan and elsewhere in the Third World where pro-Soviet regimes had come to power, rather than simply contain the USSR and its allies). Under the Reagan Doctrine, vast quantities of weapons were channelled to rebel forces fighting the pro-Soviet government in Afghanistan. Amongst those who took part in the anti-Soviet struggle in Afghanistan and through which the armaments were channelled was Osama Bin Laden – later to turn against the United States, whom he came to regard as intent on dominating the Muslim world (Coll 2004).

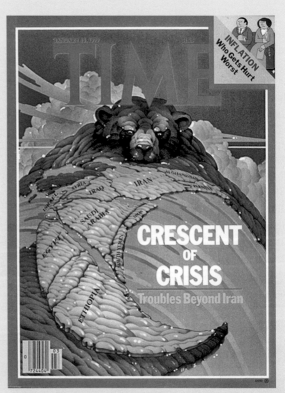

Plate 20.5 'The Crescent of Crisis' as depicted on the front cover of *Time* Magazine,15 January 1979.

(From TIME, 15 January 1979 © 1979 Time Inc. Used under license. TIME and Time Inc. are not affiliated with, and do not endorse products or services of, Licensee.)

Robert McNamara was, of course, the leading specimen of *homo mathematicus* – i.e., men who behave and believe other men [and, we might suppose, women too] behave primarily in response to 'hard data', usually numbers (infiltration rates, 'kill ratios', bomb tonnage). Like the classic private eye on television,

they are always looking for 'the facts', but usually the wrong ones. They miss reality, for they never get close enough or related enough to another society to do more than count things in it. If you relate to a country as a military target you do not need to know anything about it except details as are easily supplied by reconnaissance satellites, spy ships, secret agents, etcetera. You need never know who the victims of your attack were. Your task is merely to assess the results of what you have done and this is done by counting bodies, destroyed factories, enemy soldiers.

(Barnet 1973: 119)

Such logic is seemingly far removed from the prominence of maps in the formal geopolitical tradition. Yet we can see that, in *both* the kind of thought present in McNamara's mind and in classical geopolitics, there are moments when the myriad complexity of the world is reduced to a simple black and white representation, be it numerical or cartographic.

20.8 Cold War geopolitics in art and culture and 'popular geopolitics'

Few works of art explicitly refer to geopolitics. A famous one that does is *Geopoliticus Child Watching the Birth of the New Man* by the Catalan painter Salvador Dalí. It was painted in 1943 in New York, during his stay in the United States from 1940 to 1948 (Plate 20.6). The painting is generally read as representing the rising of the USA as the new world power during the Second World War. The crushing of Europe is seen as a representation of its diminishing role in international politics and the oversize of Africa and South America as a growing importance of the (former and remaining) colonies. More widely, however, the art world and, in particular, the course of

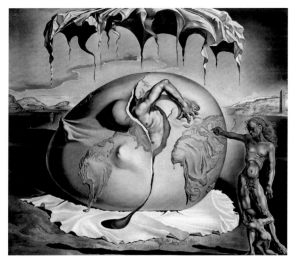

Plate 20.6 *Geopoliticus Child Watching the Birth of the New Man* by Salvador Dalí, 1943.

(Superstock/Getty © Salvador Dali, Fundació Gala-Salvador Dalí, DACS, 2016)

modern art in the second half of the twentieth century became intertwined with Cold War geopolitics. More generally, art and politics have frequently been intertwined. The Nazis (and their leader Adolf Hitler, who was a failed artist of minimal talents) detested modern art, condemning it as decadent. Other dictators, such as Joseph Stalin, the leader of the Soviet Union from the mid-1920s till his death in 1953, were also wary of modern art and favoured a garish realist style, depicting heroic smiling workers and peasants. Meanwhile, and especially in the years between the two World Wars, Paris became the centre of production of modern art. The American Central Intelligence Agency (CIA) stepped in after 1945 to fund and promote American modern art, bankrolling major exhibitions and tours, to demonstrate the creative artistic culture of the United States.

Of course, the Cold War was waged too in everything from science fiction comics and action movies and thrillers (in which good Americans, like Rambo, and the occasional heroic Brit, like James Bond (Plate 20.7), faced and defeated totalitarian, alien and frequently communist enemies) to chess (where 'Soviet Man' could demonstrate intellectual superiority and training) and Olympic sports (in which the Soviet, Chinese, East Germans and Bulgarians invested enormous resources in training and drug-enhanced muscles, to 'prove' the superiority of the communist system in the Olympic stadiums). Heroic men (and sometimes women) were invoked. Each one seeking to outdo the other, rather like men on sports fields or in street fights might (see Spotlight box 20.2). The 'Space Race', to build and launch artificial satellites and then to put men into space and reach the moon became a military, technical and a cultural expression of the Cold War – full of moments of national superpower pride, media spectacles and the basis of tales of heroic and daring American and Soviet men in space (Carter 1988). We might thus write of a 'popular geopolitics' to designate how geopolitical concepts are reflected in and take on meaning through popular culture: from art and literature, through film to comics, sport, computer games (Power 2007) or the Internet (Dodds 2006) and more traditional media like magazines, newspapers, radio and television. Cartoons and comic books have received ample attention in studies of such popular geopolitics – and continued to proliferate after the Cold War (Plate 20.8): see the article by Dittmer (2005) listed in the further reading for this chapter. Even more radically removed from the circles of policy makers are the studies that contest the bird's eye views of classical geopolitics and that firmly refocus the attention upon the impact of geopolitical policies and practices in the everyday life of regular people. Feminist geopolitics have offered the most powerful avenues towards such analyses (see Spotlight box 20.2).

Plate 20.7 Cold War in cinema: James Bond (007) saves the West from communists and criminals.

(© 2005 Topfoto)

Spotlight box 20.2

Feminist geopolitics

As in other academic fields, feminist scholars brought social struggles into academia to question taken-for-granted assumptions in geopolitical research and, more generally, in political geographical scholarship. Bringing issues of emancipation and empowerment, and their counterparts subordination and oppression, to the fore, feminist approaches problematized the state-centric approach of geopolitics, its elitism (as it is concerned with the visions and the behaviour of those in power), and its abstract, disembodied view of politics. They question, for example, the definition of security in terms of state security, undermine the idea of a national interest that would give clear direction for the conduct of foreign policy, and scrutinize by contrast how foreign and military policies affect the everyday life of people on the agenda. After all, if a state is more secure, does it automatically mean that the people it rules are? And whose security? Of ruling elites, or the state? Or security from disease, detention or from violence in the home?

Fiona Smith (2001), for example, showed how the end of the Communist regime in Eastern Germany and German reunification were received with mixed feeling by people whose life was highly disrupted by the institutional changes (disorientation, massive unemployment,

disappearance of many public services, etc). Addressing more acute situations, Jennifer Hyndman (2007, 2010) discusses the politics of body counts in the American intervention in Iraq and the fate of child soldiers in different geopolitical context. Another line of research has been the inquiry into the militarization of the lives of soldiers and their families, not only in wartime but also in military bases, for example as epitomized by the pioneering and prolific work of feminist scholar Cynthia Enloe (1983, 1989, 1993, 2000, 2004, 2007). As such, feminist geopolitics also examines environmental geographies of militarization (such as pollution by weapons in and around the battlefields and test sites – see Woodward 2004, 2005). Rachel Pain (2009, 2014) has addressed the geopolitics of globalized fear. She questions the hegemonic discourse about globalized fear and security that has become pervasive in the West and serves to justify the US led wars in Afghanistan and Iraq and the intensification of surveillance practices. She foregrounds the uneven distribution of the insecurities of everyday life among people, and how much less attention and less means are devoted to the reduction of everyday insecurity and widespread forms of domestic violence that she calls 'everyday terrorism' than to the terrorist attacks that remain exceptional.

Plate 20.8 Captain America: geopolitics in action.

(Everett Collection/Rex Shutterstock)

20.9 New World Order, the Long War, Cold Peace and beyond

The notion of the Cold War faded with the collapse of the USSR and associated communist allies between 1989 and the early 1990s, leaving the United States as the sole effective global military superpower. Yet this Western and American 'victory' quickly produced a certain sense of disorientation. This had been evident before, as the so-called 'bipolar' world of the early years of Cold War confrontation in which Washington and Moscow were the main political, economic and ideological points of orientation became progressively more 'multipolar' from the 1960s onwards. That is, as Western Europe and Japan recovered from wartime devastation and as Communist China split on ideological grounds with the USSR, the sense that the world was divided into just two superpower points of orientation lessened. But the sensation of geopolitical complexity was to grow precipitously once one of the established 'poles' (Soviet communism and pro-Soviet regimes in Central and Eastern Europe) collapsed at the start of the 1990s. Having a clearly demarcated and identifiable enemy – as both sides had in the Cold War – offered contrasting but apparently solid ideas of identity, purpose and common cause that has faded in a post-Cold War world. If the Cold War embodied a relatively coherent geopolitical map (East against West, with the allegiance of the Third World as one of the prizes), the post-Cold War world has been characterized by a diversity of maps and scripts. A variety of interpretations and geopolitical 'models' now attempt to offer explanation and impose meaning on contemporary events.

Amongst the most influential of these was the discourse of **New World Order**, articulated by then US President George Bush (senior) in the early 1990s. In Bush's vision, what is called the 'international community' (the member states of the United Nations, led by the USA, but with financial and military support from key allies such as Germany, the United Kingdom and Japan) would act as a kind of global police force, intervening where and when they felt necessary to maintain or restore 'order'. Both the 1990–1 Gulf War and the 1999 conflict with Yugoslavia were justified and conducted (in part) in the name of building such a 'New World Order'. But it was his son, President George W. Bush, who was left to articulate a new American strategy (which became the Bush Doctrine, of pre-emptive attack on states that may – it was claimed – threaten the United States or harbour terrorists) in the aftermath of 9/11. And even this was, arguably, partially within a long American geopolitical tradition of overthrowing overseas regimes during and before the Cold War, which has its roots in the rise of American power in the Pacific and Americas in the late nineteenth century and has some deeper roots in the colonization of the continent (Kinzer 2006). Even well before 9/11 and the Bush administration's strategic reactions to it, critics had pointed out that, as Booth (1999: 49) put it, the New World Order 'means the New World [gives out the] Orders'. That is, the United States was seeking global military hegemony and with the Soviet resistance out of the way, at first there seemed little, save its own 'public opinion' (or perhaps, economic limits?) to stop it.

Others stressed that such apparent American military superiority and rhetoric counted for less than might appear at first sight, and that what continued to be evident in the post-Cold War world was enhanced economic (and in some ways, cultural) competition between blocs or great powers. In this vision, American power is potentially contested by Russia and more notably China. But the terms of the 'contest' not simply in conventional military and strategic terms (though these continue) than in competition for markets, productivity and profit. A world of 'geopolitical' competition is, it was argued, being partially displaced by 'geoeconomic' competition (for an example, see Luttwak 1990). In the USA (and beyond), this was also sometimes interpreted as an impending 'supposed clash of civilizations' (e.g. Huntington 1993), between that of the 'West' and, for example, societies oriented to alternative belief systems such as (Chinese) 'Confucianism' or 'Islam'. Although superficially quite different, notions of geoeconomic competition and a clash of civilizations both betray a sense that the relative military dominance of the USA at the end of the Cold

War may not in itself be enough to preserve America's sense of leadership, power and world-historical destiny in the context of a complex 'multipolar' world. Certainly it quickly faced multiple challenges, as attempts to implement visions of 'A New American Century [of leadership]' (www.newamericancentury.org) mutated into an open commitment to what the US Department of Defense, in the form of National Security Strategy documents, called (and codified in the February 2006 Defense Review as) 'The Long War' with the 'global war on terror' (GWoT) taking the centre stage once occupied by communism. However, as Buzan (2006: 1102) argued, despite the prominence of the global war on terror in these texts, it could not define contemporary US grand strategy overall:

> US grand strategy is much wider, involving more traditional concerns about rising powers, global energy supply, the spread of military technology and the enlargement of the democratic/capitalist sphere. US military expenditure remains largely aimed at meeting traditional challenges from other states, with only a small part specifically allocated for the GWoT. The significance of the GWoT is much more political . . . the main significance of the GWoT is as a political framing that might justify and legitimize US primacy, leadership and unilateralism, both to Americans and to the rest of the world.

A few years later, Clark (2011: 20) noted how:

> President Obama's 2010 National Security Strategy . . . described 'a dynamic international environment in which different nations are exerting greater influence' and 'emerging powers in every region of the world are increasingly asserting themselves'. . . . Official US projections up to 2025 paint a broadly similar picture. These highlight the trend towards multipolarity, associated with a greater diffusion of power internationally.

Meanwhile, as Sakwa (2015b: 565) describes: 'An extended period of "cold peace" settled over relations between Russia and the West, although punctuated by attempts by both sides to escape the logic of renewed confrontation'. By the mid-2010s, this cold peace was starting to look more like a reproduction of Cold War practices (Sakwa calls this 'mimetic Cold War') but without the deep ideological divide. This, plus fears about cybersecurity, geoeconomic shifts, the assassinations of Bin Laden and other al-Qaeda leaders, the conflict between Russia and Ukraine in the east of the latter, the 2011 war in Libya, and the ensuing wars between factions in that country and in post-revolutionary Egypt, the establishment of the Islamic State in Iraq and the Levant, its ethnic-confessional cleansing policies and the succeeding wars in Northern Iraq and in Syria, have been at the fore of renewed debate about geopolitics in the United States and elsewhere. Who would have predicted these two or three decades ago? And what forms will such debates take in 20–30 years' time?

20.10   Conclusions: shifting hegemonies?

Despite early post-Cold War proclamations about the great prospects for a more peaceful and secure New World Order, the world soon came to appear to American strategists (and many others) as more 'disordered' and unpredictable. So on one level, the apparent simplicity of the great power and Cold War confrontations, let alone demarcated and fixed 'heartlands', have been replaced by the sense of a world of proliferating uncertainty and threats. Indeed, the scares, anxieties and insecurities that revolve around (non-state) terrorism activities in different parts of the world have greatly reinforced this – from the loose and amorphous terrorist networks of Al-Qaeda to the transnational threats posed by Islamic State (IS) in Syria and Iraq.

But this is not to suggest that traditional state-centred powers have fallen under the global geopolitical radar. Contrary to that, there have been widespread debates (especially in the 'West') that the remaining superpower (i.e. the USA) will have to contend with the challenges presented by emerging players on the geopolitical scene. Notwithstanding notions of the European Union (EU) as a distinctive geopolitical actor (Bachmann and Sidaway 2009; see also Spotlight box 20.3) it is, however, the concern over whether China is set to replace America as the next global hegemon that have garnered widespread attention (see Mearsheimer 2010; Luttwak 2012). Indeed, given the proliferating discourses pertaining to China 'on the rise', it is worth reflecting deeper on the geopolitical logic underpinning such claims and the associated reactions within China.

That China is often viewed through the lens of ascendancy is hardly surprising: there is an impressive list of economic growth credentials, not to mention its sheer advantage of size in both area and population. But more crucially, the series of assertive actions that have characterized Chinese foreign policy since 2008 – including China's extensive territorial claims in the South China Sea (see Chapter 24 on global governance) as well as its new doctrine of defending 'core interests' (核心利益) in Taiwan, Xinjiang and Tibet – have come to serve as testaments of a China that is intent on extending and consolidating its growing geopolitical influence (Li

2010; Swaine 2010). However, China has been quick to dismiss such actions as emblematic of its irredentist and expansionist geopolitical ambitions. Chinese leaders have constantly maintained that its contemporary geopolitical engagements are in line with its purported idea/strategy of 'peaceful rise' (和平崛起) and its so-called 'aggressive behaviors' are no more than justified acts (as per global norms) to preserve its 'territorial integrity' (主权领土). According to Hughes (2011), such a reasoning constitutes the Chinese state's 'pragmatic nationalism' which carefully traverses the duality of conveying China's status as a responsible global actor whilst simultaneously attempting to fuel a recognition and respect of the nation's sovereign space. The latter is achieved through a 'cartography of national humiliation' (Callahan 2010) whereby historic and contemporary instances of humiliation (国耻)

at the hands of foreign powers are routinely invoked by Chinese elites through maps (see Figure 20.7) to shape and defend imaginative geographies of China's *geobody* (Wang 2012).

But as Hughes goes on to caution, this seemingly pragmatic approach adopted by China can be easily exploited by variants of what he calls 'geopolitik nationalism' that currently infuse popular Chinese political writings (see also Lei 2005). As opposed to a defensive strategy, these works hinge on a *geopolitik* view of international relations as the struggle for survival to exhort for strong leaders and a militaristic China. For instance, *Wolf Totem* (狼图腾) describes China as an entity with a personality that can only function properly if it strikes the right balance between the 'sheepish qualities' of the Han and the 'wolfish traits' of the northerners, with the latter being

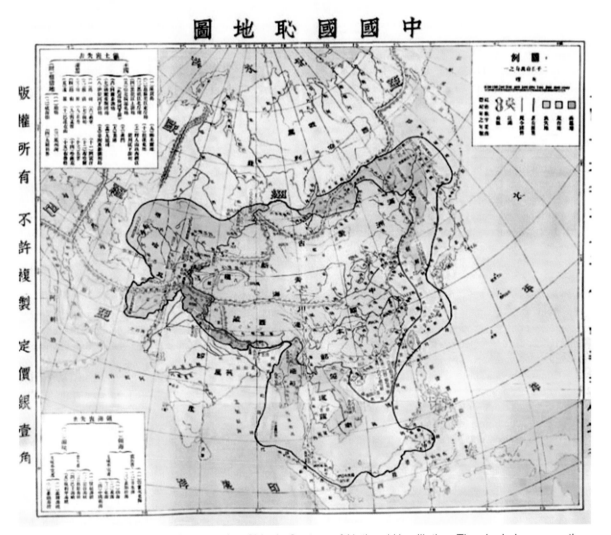

Figure 20.7 One of the maps documenting China's Century of National Humiliation. The shaded areas on the map represent the loss of China's territory between 1895-1945 as a result of Japanese invasion.

'somewhat greater' (Jiang 2004: 375). The strategic implications for China then, is to become a 'sea wolf', emulating models such as Genghis Khan and the Japanese pirates of old, so as to satisfy its need for *lebensraum* (生存空间). The need for China to defend its living space is also addressed in Zhang Wenmu's (2009) *China's Maritime Rights* (中国海权). Zhang (ibid: 109) looks to Alfred Mahan's ideas about sea power to develop a 'naval theory with special Chinese characteristics' in order to uphold China's interests which are threatened by a combination of EU trade

barriers and a US Navy that can block access to imports, as the world's hegemon sucks up the world's resources like a giant leech. It is interesting to note that a sense of moral exceptionalism pervades these Chinese texts, which is reminiscent of arguments used by 1930s and 1940s German *geopolitik* thinkers to claim that their own country's expansion is aimed at restoring equilibrium in an unjust international order. Thus, China's 'rise', as many of these Chinese scholars argue, will be different because it is built on a 'humane power' (王道) rather than the 'hegemonic

Spotlight box 20.3

The EU as a geopolitical actor

The European Union (EU) incrementally developed a new type of geopolitical role. At the beginning of the 1950s, France and West Germany aimed at constructing new collaborative institutions between Western European states in an effort to prevent a fourth major conflict between themselves after the French Prussian war of 1870–1, the Great War of 1914–18 and the Second World War of 1939–45; these collaborative institutions later evolved into the European Union.

The first effort to collaborate more formally was the establishment in 1952 of the European Coal and Steel Community (ECSC) by six member states: France, West Germany, Italy, Belgium, Luxembourg and the Netherlands. This was a limited and technical form of integration, but economically and militarily crucial. Coal was still the major source of energy then and steel was key to manufacturing and weapons industry. The geopolitical idea behind the proposal of the French Minister of Foreign Affairs Robert Schumann was articulated by high-ranked civil servant Jean Monnet who had worked during the world wars and in the postwar reconstruction at collaborative efforts between the allies to improve their war and reconstruction logistics. The idea of a technical and technocratic approach was successful and the role of the Community has spilled over to many other economic and social activities and enlarged to include 28 member states: including many former communist states that had been precluded from joining during the Cold War.

The EU remains, however, an extraordinary geopolitical actor as it does not have its own army and it has to coordinate its diplomatic services, the European External Action Service (EEAS) and its foreign policies with that of its member states.

The content of its geopolitical representations is worth underlining. The EU is primarily conceived as a

civilian power: its weight in regional and global politics is derived from its economic, political and cultural influences, not from its military power (Bachmann and Sidaway 2009). As the largest single market and the largest economy in the world (if the economy of the 28 member states is taken as one), with a large regulatory and normative power, it greatly influenced a wide array of countries with strong ties with it, economic or otherwise.

The civilian power of the EU is projected particularly strongly in the so-called European neighbourhood, the countries bordering the EU, some of them applicants to become EU members at some point, like the Balkan countries and Turkey, with others encouraged to become 'good' neighbours' like North Africa, Ukraine and the Caucasus. These policies more than once reveal the contradictions between the EU's principles and its actions, for example when it implements a restrictive migration policy and externalizes the control of its external border to neighbouring countries who do not respect human rights, let alone the rights of asylum seekers and migrants in transit (see for example Bialasiewicz 2012 for the relation with Gaddafi's Libya).

Although the ENP policy is conceived as benevolent in Brussels, it is perceived as threatening in Moscow, and it has proven particularly divisive in Ukraine where a conflict about signing the Association Agreement with the EU was the catalyst of massive protests that evolved into a civil war and the disintegration of the state, with the Russian annexation of the Crimea and an ongoing war in the Donbas(s), including the shooting-down of a commercial airliner – flight MH17 from Amsterdam to Kuala Lumpur – on 17 July 2014 above Eastern Ukraine. The confrontation between Russia and the EU (and the USA) has brought about a revival of geopolitical narratives both from the Cold War period and from the 1930s and the disastrous appeasement policies towards Hitler's ambitions (Sakwa 2015b).

way' (霸道) of the 'West'. Moreover, as Agnew (2010a), Reid and Zheng (2008) and Zeng *et al.* (2015) have rightly pointed out, China, as with any other country in the world, does not operate in a vacuum and has to negotiate its relations with other states, international organizations and all manner of private actors. There is no easy or predictable end to this uncertain situation and new challenges – climate change – complicate the global scene. New and old challenges and shifting patterns and forms of power, resistance and domination are expressed in space and time.

Learning outcomes

Having read this chapter, you should understand:

- That the term 'geopolitics' has been associated with a wide variety of texts and contexts.
- However, geopolitics is frequently associated with the sense of a self-conscious tradition of writing about and mapping the relations between states, geography and power.
- This is usually traced to the early twentieth-century writings of Rudolf Kjellén and Halford Mackinder.
- One of the key features of this tradition is the idea that the state resembles a living organism which requires living space and will compete with others (the organic theory of the state).
- The oppressive military regimes in South America (notably Argentina, Brazil and Chile) during the 1960s and 1970s elaborated and applied a variety of the geopolitical tradition.
- However, it also proliferated in a number of European countries and Japan, particularly between the two world wars.
- The rise and eclipse of the Cold War have produced wide and deep geopolitical transformations.
- Since this proliferation of geopolitics was most evident in Fascist states, the defeat of the Axis powers in 1945 signified its relative decline as a formal tradition, although it continued in Fascist Spain and Portugal and in South American military circles.
- Beyond the self-conscious tradition of geopolitics, similar forms of thinking about territory, states and power have proliferated in many disciplines and countries. Indeed, we can also think of 'popular geopolitics' – whereby everyday culture (such as cinema) contains and expresses wider geopolitical narratives.
- This has been particularly evident during the Cold War, when broader geopolitical discourses suffused many aspects of art, science, culture and daily life.
- Since the decline of the Cold War, there was a proliferation of geopolitical visions of the 'New World Order', amongst them a more complex cartography

of perceptions of threats and dangers. However, the ability of any new single geopolitical 'big picture' (such as 'the war on terror') to inherit the mantle of the Cold War was limited.

- There is a flourishing debate about the geopolitical impacts of rising Chinese power, Western responses and the geopolitical dynamics and consequences of other conflicts, latterly in Eastern Ukraine, Iraq and Syria.

Further reading

A century after its original publication, Mackinder's (1904) paper was reprinted in *The Geographical Journal* (Volume 170, Number 4, December 2004), along with a set of commentaries and reflections.

Agnew, J., Mamadouh, V., Sharp, J. and Secor, A.J. (eds) (2015) *The Wiley-Blackwell Companion to Political Geography,* Wiley Blackwell, Malden MA and Oxford. The chapter by Sami Moisio on Geopolitics/Critical Geopolitics will deepen your understandings. However, at more than 500 pages, the 37 chapters cover other themes introduced in this section and indicate the vitality and breadth of political geography.

Dittmer, J and Sharp, J. (2014) *Geopolitics: An Introductory Reader,* Routledge, Oxford and New York. Probably the best place to begin to follow-up this chapter.

Dodds, K. (2014) *Geopolitics: A Very Short Introduction,* 2nd edition, Oxford University Press, Oxford. Like other books in this series of very short introductions, the first chapter is free to download.

Dodds, K., Kuus, M. and Sharp J. (2013) *The Ashgate Research Companion to Critical Geopolitics,* Ashgate, Farnham. A good way to go deeper into the histories and present of geopolitics.

Two accounts by historians that offer startling insights into the geopolitics of the Soviet Union and Nazi Germany. Both were enabled by the opening of archives since the decline of the Cold War:

Jersild, A. (2011) The Soviet state as imperial scavenger: 'Catch Up and Surpass' in the transnational socialist bloc, 1950–1960, *The American Historical Review,* 116(1), 109–32.

Snyder, T. (2010) *Bloodlands: Europe between Hitler and Stalin,* Basic Books, New York. An account of millions murdered in the name of geopolitical projects. Snyder's book is not a light read or good bedtime reading: it is the stuff of nightmares.

Good ways into feminist critiques of geopolitics are:

Hyndman, J. (2003) Beyond either/or: a feminist analysis of September 11th, *ACME: An International E-Journal for Critical Geographies,* 2(1), 1–13 (free to download at: www.acme-journal.org). But see too:

Ó Tuathail, G. (1996) An anti-geopolitical eye: Maggie O'Kane in Bosnia, 1992–3, *Gender, Place and Culture,* 3(2), 177–85.

For an introduction to popular geopolitics (and with reflections on geopolitical traditions more widely):

Dittmer, J. (2010) *Popular Culture, Geopolitics and Identity,* Rownman and Littlefield, Lanham.

Finally three papers that take critical scrutiny of geopolitics in different directions:

Larsen, H.G. (2011) 'The need and ability for expansion: conceptions of living space in the small-state geopolitics of Gudmund Hatt', *Political Geography,* 30(1) 38–48. The fascinating case of a Danish geographer who became entangled with Nazi geopolitics.

Sidaway, J.D. (2010) 'One island, one team, one mission: geopolitics, sovereignty, "race" and rendition', *Geopolitics,* 15(4), 667–83. How colonial, Cold War and post-Cold-War geopolitics interact in the Indian Ocean.

Van der Wusten, H. and De Pater, B. (2013) How German geopolitics passed through the Netherlands, 1920–1945: a case study in the geography of one of geography's projects. *Tijdschrift voor Economische en Sociale Geografie,* 104(4), 426–38.

TERRITORY, SPACE AND SOCIETY

Chapter 21

David Storey

Topics covered

- The creation of territories
- Territoriality and territorial strategies
- Social processes and spatial relations
- Territories and class, race, gender, sexuality
- Leisure, work and home space
- Geographies of security and resistance

21.1 Territory and territoriality

We live in a world where we are regularly confronted with signs reminding us of where we can or cannot go, and how to behave when we are there. We may be barred, admonished, instructed or warned through signs telling us 'keep out', 'authorized personnel only', 'no trespassing', 'keep off the grass' and so on. These are everyday reminders of how control of space facilitates various forms of social control (Plate 21.1). The global political map provides us with the most obvious formalized manifestation of this territorialized mode of thinking. However, this macro-scale territorialization is accompanied by a myriad of much more micro-scale, often less formal, variants. In everyday usage, territory is usually taken to refer to a portion of geographic space which is claimed or occupied by a person, a group or an institution. In this way it can be seen as an area of bounded space. Following from this, the ways in which individuals or groups lay claim to such territory can be referred to as '**territoriality**'. Territories and territorial strategies are bound up with attempts by individuals or groups to wield power, or to resist power imposed on them. However, as will be seen, these somewhat simplified definitions mask considerable complexity.

It is sometimes assumed that humans have a natural tendency to behave in a territorial manner: to claim space and to prevent others from encroaching on 'our' territory. Considerable debate has occurred over the extent to which territorialization and territorial behaviour should be seen as a 'natural' or 'social' phenomenon, a debate echoing wider long-standing arguments over the relative influence of nature and nurture, a division that many see as somewhat blurred (see Whatmore 2014). In his landmark book *Human Territoriality: Its Theory and History,*

published in 1986, Robert Sack cautions against determinist views of human territoriality as a basic instinct and emphasizes instead its role as a geographic and political strategy. For Sack, territoriality is 'the attempt by an individual or group to affect, influence, or control people, phenomena, and relationships, by delimiting and asserting control over a geographic area' (Sack 1986: 19). He draws attention to the means through which territorial strategies may be used to achieve particular ends. In essence the control of geographic space can be used to assert or to maintain power, or, importantly, to resist the power of a dominant group:

> Territoriality, as a component of power, is not only a means of creating and maintaining order, but is a device to create and maintain much of the geographic context through which we experience the world and give it meaning.

> (Sack 1986: 219)

In this way territoriality is deeply embedded in social relations and territories, rather than being natural entities, result from social practices and processes and are produced under particular conditions and serve specific ends (Delaney 2005). Sack (1986) argues that territoriality involves a classification by area whereby geographic space is apportioned. However, territories are more than mere spatial containers; they link space and society conveying clear meanings relating to authority, power and rights (Sassen 2006; Delaney 2009). David Delaney has defined a territory as 'a bounded social space that inscribes a certain social meaning onto defined segments of the material world' (2005: 14). These geographic spaces convey messages of political power and control which are communicated through various means, most notably through the creation and maintenance of *boundaries* that divide those 'inside' from those 'outside'; separating 'us' from 'them'. Space is controlled and territory facilitates classification, communication, enforcement and exclusion through boundary-making. This may have important implications, through constraining, restricting or limiting mobility, for example.

While Sack's work focused usefully on territoriality as a political strategy, more recently Stuart Elden has drawn attention to the concept of territory itself. He argues that debates on territoriality have tended to take the idea of territory for granted so that they 'conceptually presuppose the object that they practically produce' (2010: 803). In *The Birth of Territory* (2013) and in other writings, Elden suggests that the concept is bound up with particular ways of thinking about geographic space; ways which reflect notions of power and control. He persuasively argues that territory is contingent and the relationships

Plate 21.1 No trespassing.

(labalajadia/fotolia)

between people, place and land have been understood differently in different historical and geographic contexts so that our ways of thinking about geographic space are more historically and temporally specific than we might otherwise imagine. Within this, Elden argues that our contemporary ideas of territory emerged alongside developments in cartography and spatial calculation. Territories are more than simply land; instead territory can be viewed as what Elden calls a 'political technology', related to the measurement of land and the control of terrain. Territory can be seen as something calculable, mappable and controllable. As such, it is suggested that both territories themselves and their boundaries (concepts which we tend to take for granted) reflect a distinctive mode of social and spatial organization which is dependent on particular ways of thinking about space. The Swiss geographer Claude Raffestin (2012) views territoriality as a process produced by the various relationships between individuals and groups and their wider social environment. While he emphasizes the meanings of space for individuals rather than the functional attainment of particular goals, the ways in which spatial practices become solidified allows for the utilization of territory in strategic ways (Murphy 2012). The features of territoriality identified by Sack (1986), in allowing classification and differentiation, are thus a product of the way in which space is imagined and territories are in effect politicized space; mapped and claimed, ordered and bordered, measured and demarcated.

If territories reflect a particular way of thinking about space, then this points to the importance of maps in solidifying and legitimizing these spatial units. Rather than neutral depictions of supposed geographical realities, a more critical analysis suggests that maps have always been useful weapons in larger political projects associated with territorial claims, and counter-claims (Harley 1988; Black 1998; Crampton 2014). Mapping of territory itself functions so as to enhance power sending out messages signifying control over portions of geographic space. Maps of the British Empire conventionally depicted Britain's overseas territorial possessions in pink, conveying information while simultaneously proclaiming power over roughly one quarter of the planet's land area. Advances in cartography altered the ways in which space was considered and led to attempts to apportion and control it. The military and political underpinnings of cartographic developments and the consequent role of mapping (in both practical and symbolic terms) in the creation of colonial territory was a key element in the imposition and maintenance of political control (Smyth 2006; Hewitt 2010).

While being mindful of the complexity of ideas surrounding territory and territoriality, it is clear they serve useful political functions. Territoriality and the production of territories can be seen as devices that tend to reify power so that it appears to reside in the territory itself rather than in those who control it. Attention is thereby deflected away from the power relationships, ideologies and processes underpinning the maintenance of territories and their boundaries. In this way, as Delaney argues, 'territory does much of our thinking for us and closes off or obscures questions of power and meaning, ideology and legitimacy, authority and obligation' (2005: 18). Once created, territories can become the spatial containers in which people are socialized through various social practices and discourses so that territoriality can be seen as 'a primary geographic expression of social power' (Sack 1986: 5). As Paasi (2003) suggests, a number of important dimensions of social life and social power are brought together in territory. There is a material component such as land, a functional element associated with control of, or attempts to control, space, and a symbolic component associated with people's social identity. The spatial is not simply the outcome of the social but the two are intrinsically bound up together (Delaney 2009). Painter (2010) argues that territory is an effect or an outcome of a set of practices and networks of inter-connections. Such things as the collection and production of regional statistics and the devising of regional economic strategies, reproduces a sense of delimitation, contiguity and coherence to the idea of regional divisions. The social, cultural and political are brought together so that people identify with territories in such a way that they can be seen 'to satisfy both the material requirements of life and the emotional requirements of belonging' (Penrose 2002: 282). Notwithstanding the evolution of a more globally interconnected world, territory continues to retain both an allure in terms of identity as well as a strategic value (Agnew 2010b; Murphy 2013). This is reflected in a variety of ways such as preferential claims to jobs on the basis of nationality (Ince *et al.* 2015).

The creation and imagining of territories and the utilization of territorial strategies can be observed at a variety of spatial scales. The most obvious (and regularly contested) expressions of territoriality are manifested at the level of the state, currently the world's dominant form of political organization (see Chapter 22). Political maps of the world display this territorial configuration of bordered spaces in a way that leads us to view it as 'natural' and this impression of solidity engenders a very state-centred view of the world in which territory is viewed as a mere canvas on which political processes play out (Kadercan 2015). However, the state system is a political and geographic construct that displays considerable dynamism. In recent decades the number of states has risen dramatically, consequent on state collapse (many associated with the fall of communism) and secessionist nationalism. Clearly, secessionist ideologies (Basque, Kurdish or Scottish nationalism for example) are premised on the construction of a territory, politically detached from the state(s) to which it currently belongs. Elsewhere, groups such as 'Islamic State' (in Iraq and Syria) and Boko Haram (in Nigeria) are utilizing the control of space in the pursuit of ideological objectives. The emergence of quasi-states such as South Ossetia (officially part of Georgia) and Transnistria (formally belonging to Moldova) reflect a means of territorial construction through opting out of larger spatial-political entities (Blakkisrud and Kolstø 2011; O'Loughlin *et al.* 2011). Ultimately territorial sovereignty is relative, contingent and never complete. It is useful to think in terms of effective sovereignty wielded by both states and quasi-state actors and deployed across a range of territorial contexts where sovereign power does not necessarily stop at the border (Elden 2009; McConnell 2010; Kadercan 2015). The effective sovereignty of many states is reduced through various processes and global flows, alongside the widening range of non-state actors who might be seen to exert power across networks rather than over rigidly bordered territory (Agnew 2005a). More broadly, some have begun to suggest that jurisdiction and sovereignty are not inextricably dependent on territory and boundaries, suggesting a need to think in terms of broader conceptualizations associated with religious law or ideas of natural law, for example (Miller 2013).

Apart from these state and sub-state examples, territorial configurations exist at a variety of spatial scales. Although these may be less obvious and may often seem more vaguely defined with less clear-cut boundaries, these 'informal' divisions run through a wide range of social, cultural and political issues concerning race, class, gender and sexuality so that what can be termed spatial enclaves of varying degrees of permanence are regularly created and sustained (Sidaway 2007). The remainder of this chapter explores some of these examples, demonstrating how particular social practices are spatialized and the ways in which territories are constructed, contested and used to achieve particular outcomes. While the examples are arranged under distinct headings, it should be abundantly clear that many of the issues raised are interrelated (and also overlap with earlier chapters in the book and others in this section). Identity is a highly complex and contested term. People have more than one single identity: gender, sexuality and ethnicity cross-cut each other in a system of overlapping identities. Ethnic groups and classes are not immutable but are social constructs. In other words, they vary in time and space and are not simply natural categories, but human (or social)

products. Rather than seeing identities as rigidly defined, it is more useful and realistic to regard them as unstable, relational and contingent. Consequently the chapter is concerned with raising questions about who is 'allowed' to be in particular spaces and who is barred or discouraged from being there. In doing so, it sheds light on the ways in which space is conceived, used and organized, and highlights the idea that identity is both a social and spatial phenomenon. The chapter also highlights the use of territorial strategies in both managing and policing specific issues, and also in resisting particular forms of domination.

21.2 Territoriality, race and class

21.2.1 Class and territorial segregation

Societies are seen to be marked by clear inequalities: between rich and poor; between property owners and those who are not; between those who own and control resources; and between those who are paid workers or are unable to obtain a job. These social divisions (together with race, ethnicity, gender and others) not only reflect inequality, they are also deeply spatialized. What have been termed social enclaves emerge and these are frequently manifested spatially. For example, most cities appear to have distinct residential neighbourhoods, colloquially defined as 'rich' or 'poor', 'working class' or 'middle class'. These spatial divisions are reflected in ideas that some people come from 'the wrong side of the tracks' and everyday discourses of 'good' and 'bad' areas within cities. These latter zones are often viewed as separate spaces inhabited by many people who are marginalized not just in social and economic terms, but also spatially. Moreover, discourses of securitization, operationalized through the deployment of various technologies, often leaves many people relatively immobile and spatially confined, reflecting what sociologist Bryan Turner (2007) has referred to as an 'enclave society'. Parts of cities may become synonymous with high unemployment, crime and related negative images. Their residents suffer discrimination and inequality, while being subjected to negative stereotyping and often harsh policing. Such areas may come to be characterized as dangerous neighbourhoods inhabited by people pathologized as an underclass. These feelings of alienation and animosity fuel an intense stigmatization of both residents and the places in which they reside. The stigmatization of place tends to be self-reproducing, serving to further reinforce **class** and ethnic divides.

Forms of segregation arise and are reinforced through various mechanisms, particularly the housing market which effectively determines who can afford to live where. The 'poor' cannot afford to live in 'rich' areas and the rich are generally unlikely to want to reside in close proximity to poorer run-down neighbourhoods. Nevertheless, attempts to regenerate older working class areas tend simply to reshape the geographies of class rather than eliminate them. Gentrification is where parts of the urban area experience regeneration or renewal, resulting in more affluent residents moving in and displacing the original predominantly working-class inhabitants. Driven in part by economic processes and in part through consumer choice, it serves to reinforce economic divisions within society, thereby perpetuating the idea that some households do not belong in particular places. Linked to this, it is argued that the role of urban 'gatekeepers' (such as estate agents) may play a key role here in altering (or endeavouring to maintain) the social composition of particular areas (Shaw 2008). Gentrification reflects broader socio-economic processes and the resultant residential territorializations can be seen as an expression of both demand for housing (from homeowners) and supply of capital (from financial institutions). It serves to highlight how broader global processes play out alongside (and are implicated in) the destruction and reconstruction of local territorialized identities (Butler 2007). The major regeneration schemes undertaken in recent decades in older industrialized and dockland areas in cities throughout Europe and North America reflect this transformation from manufacturing and working-class residential spaces into service sector zones with middle-class residents. Dockland and waterfront areas, like other 'regenerated' urban zones, have been transformed into different places, with quite different uses and symbolic meanings (Plate 21.2). In South Wales, for example, the regenerated Cardiff Bay area has been transformed from a place associated initially with the export of coal and subsequently with industrial decline and decay. Other UK cities like Glasgow, Liverpool and Birmingham continually engage in processes of re-imagination. Such processes are sometimes entwined with attempts to claim a 'prize' that may further enhance the city's profile and boost its image, such as being crowned European Capital of Culture. The scale and extent of contemporary developments in global cities like New York and London, where a super-rich elite engages in intense investment and conspicuous consumption, has led to the coining of the term super-gentrification (Butler and Lees 2006). These attempts to purify urban space have led to the displacement of some urban residents while others are rendered homeless. In cities such as San Francisco fragile lives are lived out on the streets amidst an atmosphere in which the homeless are seen as a blot to be removed rather than a manifestation of a systemic problem. Homeless people are criminalized and medicalized so that urban space can be cleansed and put to more profitable uses (Gowan 2010).

Class-based segregation is rendered even more obvious through the long evident phenomenon of urban gating (Atkinson and Blandy 2006; Glasze et al. 2006; Bagaeen and Uduku 2010). The apparent rise in the numbers and varied forms of gated communities within urban areas in various parts of the world in recent years could be interpreted as a very obvious manifestation of attempts to control and limit access to portions of geographic space. The creation of residential fortresses where security guards patrol the perimeter of walled residential zones in

Plate 21.2 Former Docklands in London.

(Justin Kase/Alamy)

an effort to exclude those seen as 'undesirable' has been repeated and deepened in many other cities in order to exclude those seen as not belonging there, so maintaining the 'undefiled' and 'exclusive' nature of the neighbourhood. The level of 'fortification' of these developments is quite varied ranging from perimeter walls, gates and barriers, through the limiting of non-residential access by intercoms and associated 'screening' devices, to more perceptual barriers or codes deterring access (Plate 21.3). Individual streets, where homes are owned by super-rich global elites, may be subject to private security and monitoring, as in parts of London. The general population is prevented, or at least discouraged, from traversing such spaces (Gentleman 2014).

The idea of gating can be seen as a consequence of two inter-connected factors: security and prestige. Though not strictly the preserve of the better-off, discourses of safety and security serve as a useful rationale for developers to design, build and promote spatially exclusive housing often surrounded by security fences and with highly limited public access regulated by intercoms and other 'screening' technologies which have come to be regular features in contemporary landscapes of power. These territorial strategies work in ways which ensure a particular residential mix and may well serve to link together both racial and class divisions. These tendencies have been facilitated by technological advances in recent decades through geodemographics and the use of postcode data and associated marketing strategies of companies who are keen to identify particular types of consumer, and link these to geographic areas. In this way residential homogeneity is both reflected and reproduced. The social and the spatial are inextricably linked as 'gated minds' are translated into gated places (Landman 2010). While the forms it takes may vary somewhat according to place-specific circumstances,

gating in its various guises touches on vitally important questions of the privatization of previously public space, inclusion, exclusion and the territorialization of social life (Lemanski and Oldfield 2009; Rosen and Razin 2009). Extremely exclusive forms of gating can be recognized in places such as Dubai, Malaysia and Singapore. Pow (2011) points to the creation of microterritories (facilitated by state incentives) inhabited by a global elite who enjoy the specific environment while cocooned and protected from the outside world, though they are intimately connected to it in many other ways via work, travel, media and so on. Paradoxically, such mini-territories, though bordered and separated, function as inherently transnational spaces.

21.2.2 Ethnicity, 'race' and space

In the same way that class is mapped onto space, so too is ethnicity. Ideas of race are firmly embedded in everyday discourses but racial and ethnic categories are social constructions rather than innate biological realities. While race can be questioned as a problematic and dubious form of social classification there is no doubt that racism and 'race thinking' are very real social phenomena (Saldanha 2011). Kobayashi and Peake argue that race is socially constructed but that 'racialization' is 'the process by which racialized groups are identified, given stereotypical characteristics, and coerced into specific living conditions, often involving social/spatial segregation and always constituting racialized places' (2000: 293). While issues linked to 'race' are clearly social phenomena, they are often manifested spatially. Amongst the most rigid examples of **racialized space** was that devised under the apartheid system in South Africa from the late 1940s through to the early 1990s: a territorial system that enhanced and entrenched the political, economic and social power of a minority white population over nonwhite populations. Both nationally and at the more localized level of individual urban areas, space was divided on racial lines. Non-white people were 'placed' in locations not of their own choosing in order to entrench minority white power. In this way, there was a legal transposition of inequality on to geographical space. This spatial arrangement was designed to ensure greater degrees of control over the majority black population and is a classic example of the utilization of a territorial strategy to attain political objectives. At localized levels, there was a racialization of space with buses, public toilets and other amenities reflecting this divide. A racial ideology was mapped on to the South African landscape. Although apartheid ended in the early 1990s, after a long struggle for democratic rights for all in South Africa, its legacy means that a division of space based on the racial and

Plate 21.3 Security gates on gated residential development.

(EyeMark/fotolia)

class lines reinforced during the apartheid era has left enduring marks on the social landscape.

Elsewhere, nationalist conflicts may give rise to attempts to create ethnically pure spaces through the forcible removal of ethnic 'others'. The phenomenon of ethnic cleansing in parts of the former Yugoslavia during the 1990s is a striking example of an attempt to 'purify' territory of those deemed to belong to other ethno-cultural groups in an apparent attempt to justify territorial control in the name of the nation (Case study 21.1). In a not unrelated manner, the generally negative stereotyping of gypsies in much of Europe has led to considerable discrimination, with gypsies seen as an undesirable 'other', as a consequence of which they are effectively de-territorialized; they are seen not to belong anywhere and active attempts are made to exclude them from certain spaces. In recent years there have been attempts to exclude gypsies from France through 'repatriation' of ethnic *Roma* (gypsy) people to Romania and Bulgaria, a flagrant breach of EU policy on freedom of movement between member states. Collective expulsion was justified through a security discourse that portrayed the *Roma* as a threat to French society, culture and identity (Bărbulescu 2012). Broader issues emerge here in relation to groups which pursue nomadic lifestyles and who, consequently, are subject to considerable public opprobrium. Attempts by gypsies and other traveller groups to use particular spaces are often resisted by settled residents. As a group they are partly de-territorialized, simultaneously belonging everywhere and nowhere, their mobility juxtaposed to the settled nature of place-based communities. The mobile lifestyles of some are seen as unnatural and those who practice them are often

depicted as untrustworthy and are subject to a range of discriminatory practices (Shubin 2011). Yet travellers also have nuanced notions of community, territory and belonging amidst movement that may parallel, as well as clash with, those of more 'settled' communities (see Convery and O'Brien 2012).

Leaving aside these overt and coercive examples, it is clear that many cities exhibit high degrees of ethnic segregation. In most US cities and European cities, for example, the elites and middle class are disproportionately white, reflecting the coincidence of class and ethnic segregation (Crump 2004). These patterns of exclusion and inclusion and attendant territorialities reflect the complex intersections of race, class and ideology. In considering these spatial concentrations of ethnic groups in urban areas, it might be argued that individuals choose to locate in such areas for a variety of reasons. In brief there are a combination of 'positive' and 'negative' factors; for some there are attractions such as 'being amongst one's own', while others may feel driven to seek sanctuary from a racist, hostile society. Clustering offers feelings of defence, mutual support and a sense of belonging and community. This in turn may be a useful means through which group cultural norms and heritage may be preserved. Clustering also produces spaces of resistance whereby external threats, whether to cultural norms or of physical attack, may be reduced. However, these arguments should not detract from the fact that residential clustering is often more a function of necessity rather than free and unconstrained choice. The idea that people may choose to cluster is to ignore the fact that quite often no easy alternatives are available. Discriminatory ideologies of race work to exclude people from particular areas through the

Case study 21.1

Ethnic territorial cleansing

Following the disintegration of Yugoslavia in the early 1990s, violent conflicts erupted in Croatia, Bosnia-Herzegovina and, later, Kosovo. These ethno-national conflicts were characterized by attempts by various groups to eradicate other ethnic groups from 'their' territory. This strategy was built on an essentialist version of defining ethno-national identity and, quite literally, clearing the territory of those possessing a supposedly 'different' identity. Armed movements claiming to be representing Serbs, Croats and Bosnians (predominantly Muslims) tried to carve out spaces which they could call their own in the ruins of

the former federal state. Viewed from the outside it is easy to argue that such a strategy is both dangerous and simplistic. However, for those directly involved the control of territory was seen as an essential element in the conflict. Despite the region's complex multicultural history, reductionist interpretations of identity led to attempts to assert territorial control through the elimination of 'others'. Nationalist rhetoric, and the associated desire to control particular portions of territory in the name of a specific group, hardened divisions which were of relatively minor significance only a few years previously when Yugoslavia was a federal (and communist) republic under one-party rule. Once the conflict was underway, however, it became impossible to reverse, as the conflict drew upon and *reinforced* group identities and competing territorial claims underpinned through reference to historical myths and forms of boundary-making, particularly within Bosnia. In order to achieve peace, areas were mapped and information gathered on the various ethno-national groupings living in different localities. In this way territory was designated 'Serb', 'Muslim', 'Croat', and so on, with lines dividing towns and cities into different zones. After a number of failed alternatives, the Dayton Agreement of 1995 divided Bosnia-Herzegovina into two autonomous units: a Muslim-Croat Federation and a Bosnian Serb Republic (*Republika Srpska*). While this solution was

lauded in many circles, critics have argued that it is inherently unstable and that it also reinforces ethnic divisions rather than rising above them (Figure 21.1).

The partition of territories and 'transfer' of populations has occurred in many other situations of territorial, ethno-cultural, national and state conflict. Greece and Turkey in the early 1920s, India and Pakistan in 1947, Palestine and Israel in 1948 and Cyprus (whose northern part was occupied by Turkey in 1974) are all examples. Understanding them requires critical attention not only to the details of each case, but also to the concepts (territoriality, the political geography of nations and states and geopolitics) and background that are considered *both* in this *and* the other chapters in this section.

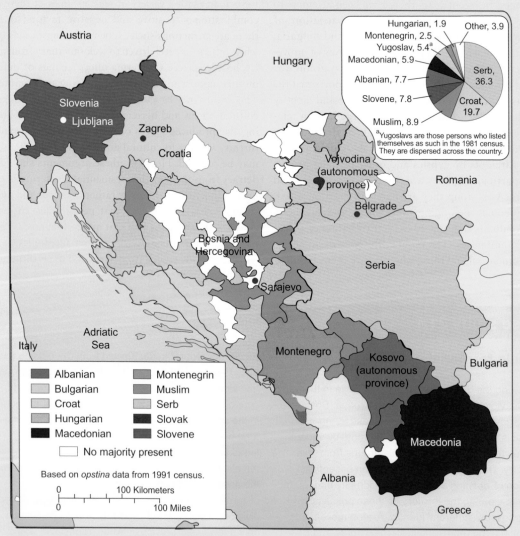

Figure 21.1 Majority ethnic groups within Yugoslavia in 1991.

operations of the housing market and other processes, thereby translating social exclusion into geographical exclusion (see Knox and Pinch 2010).

We should also be mindful of the fact that much discussion surrounding issues of 'race' and ethnicity in Western societies tends to assume 'whiteness' as the norm. As McGuinness (2000) argues, much progressive research itself falls into this trap with a focus on non-white groups, tending to deflect attention away from white ethnicity. One consequence is that relatively little attention is given to 'white spaces'. Ideas of white flight to the suburbs (in response to the evolution of 'black' ghettos) and the creation of 'white' territories are themselves elements in the racialization of space. Similarly the construction of rural Britain as a relatively 'white space' reflects deeply embedded ideas associated with belonging, rurality and with national identity (Holloway 2005; *Journal of Rural Studies*, 25(4), 2009). Such constructions can have serious implications for those who do not (or are seen not to) 'fit in' with the dominant assumptions and ethos. Recent debates over immigration into the UK and other Western European countries, fuelled by populist right-wing politicians, have tended to focus on supposed 'swarms' of asylum seekers and 'illegals', and 'hordes' of Eastern Europeans (Gilmartin 2008; Storey 2013a). While much of this is inaccurate and misleading, the nature of the comments suggests that countries should increasingly seal themselves off from invasions from 'outside' by those who do not 'belong' there. These arguments are often (misleadingly) bound into security discourses emphasizing the need to protect the country and its citizens. Territory, terrorism and identity become inextricably linked in debates calling into question who has the right to be in certain places and who has not. Additionally, countries are seen to extend their border controls well beyond their own territory with immigration personnel screening passports in foreign airports in order to interdict those deemed 'illegal' (Mountz 2009).

21.3 Geographies of security, policing and protest

Given the territorializations noted above it is worth exploring the ways in which space is policed. Fyfe initially drew attention to the geographies of policing in 1991. One elementary version of this is the division into police forces with responsibility for particular regions: West Mercia police in the UK and so on. Linked to this are ideas of particular spaces in which special units operate such as harbours and airports, where specific concerns

linked to immigration, smuggling and security are seen as priorities. The manner in which policing is carried out also reflects ideas of territory and territorial control, ranging from police having particular 'beats' or zones of responsibility to the spatial tactics employed by police, for example funnelling street marches and protests along agreed routes. Policing of space does not just regulate that space, it also plays a role in the social construction of space and shapes the ways in which particular spaces are imagined (Herbert 1997, 2006).

While traditionally policing has been seen as the purview of state forces, in recent years, and in many countries, the nature of policing has become ever more complicated, with an expanding array of agencies with often overlapping geographic and authoritative remits (Yarwood 2007). The increasing array of non-state (private) actors engaged in forms of policing also brings with it a series of additional territorializations, with private security firms patrolling office blocks and shopping malls, or controlling access to pubs and clubs, as well as running security screening at many airports and ports. These sometimes create various tensions over authority and power, including attempts to prevent people taking photographs in certain spaces. The advent of citizen-based groups such as Neighbourhood Watch also rests on notions of local territories, with people encouraged to report suspicious behaviour. Current government strategies in the UK and elsewhere appear designed to deepen trends towards greater community control, the broadening of policing partnership arrangements and a significantly enhanced role for private security providers. Recent years have also seen an increasing range of security measures deployed in various contexts at places such as airports, national monuments and so on, which highlight tensions over the securitization of public space thereby placing constraints on freedom of movement while increasing levels of public surveillance (Benton-Short 2007).

Policing is about more than simple law enforcement, it is also about the regulation and endorsement of specific values and moral codes (Mawby and Yarwood 2011). In addition to territorializations associated with the policing of space, there are those which endeavour to exclude individuals or particular forms of behaviour from certain spaces. In the United Kingdom, Anti-Social Behaviour Orders (ASBOs) and related instruments provide a controversial example of bringing a territorial approach to dealing with particular behaviours that are seen to constitute a nuisance. They can be used to prevent specified individuals from being in particular places, streets, and so on, or to prevent individuals from repeatedly engaging in specified behaviours such as aggressive begging, disturbing neighbours or drunkenness in public places. They have proved controversial, seen by some as the criminalization of certain social behaviours (Squires 2008). What they clearly do is suggest the idea that certain forms of behaviour are not allowed in public space and they can be punished with territorial exclusion. What is also clear is that they tend to be imposed on people in certain types of place, mainly areas of public housing in UK cities (Painter 2006). Similar so-called 'bubble' laws in the USA also function to exclude people behaving in certain ways from specific places (Mitchell 2005). Regardless of our view of the rights and wrongs of such moves, and whether they might be deemed successful even on their own terms, they raise important geographical questions related to what is meant by 'public', who is allowed to be where, and how people are expected to behave (Cameron 2007).

Of course the ultimate spatial sanction for lawbreaking is imprisonment. In all societies, those who are convicted (or even in some cases simply accused) of criminal offences may also be excluded by territorial confinement (this is a key function of prisons) or controls on their movement. Geographers have displayed an emerging interest in what have been termed carceral geographies with explorations of the geographic distribution of systems of incarceration and the experiences of these (Moran 2015). In the USA, the prison population has quadrupled in recent decades, so much so that a new extended geography of prisons and incarceration can be critically mapped (Gilmore 2007; Martin and Mitchelson 2009). In the current geopolitical climate, territory and territorial strategies are deployed in intriguing ways. The US prison camp at Guantánamo Bay (on the island of Cuba) is *outside* the territorial United States and its ambiguous territorial status has proven an effective excuse in allowing the indefinite detention without trial of its inmates who are simultaneously subject to interrogation by US military authorities (see Reid-Henry 2007).

At a more micro-scale, taken alongside the privatization and 'gating' of residential zones, the proliferation of covered shopping malls can be seen as the erosion of shared urban street space and its replacement with privatized, more exclusionary spaces of consumption. Where once streets were open to a broad public, there are now privatized spaces whose owners (invariably resorting to security firms who take on some police powers) can evict those seen to behave inappropriately or who simply look 'out of place'. The shopping mall has become a privatized and highly regulated space in which people may be excluded by virtue of their appearance or behaviour (Staeheli and Mitchell 2006). Shopping complexes are considered private space into which people are 'invited' rather than having any automatic right to be there. These 'secure' shopping centres, office blocks and apartment buildings, complete with gates and intercom systems,

exemplify a trend towards socio-spatial design whereby territorial strategies associated with crime prevention effectively exclude those not wanted. Some people are effectively barred from certain areas – a policy of territorial containment enforced through increased surveillance and architectural design features. In part, these forms of exclusionary policing reflect broader geographies of fear and the perceived risk of crime associated both with specific groups and with specific geographic spaces (Pain and Smith 2008). Increasingly space is patrolled by private security companies whose remit is territorially circumscribed. In cities such as Cape Town in South Africa this produces a patchwork of fragmented spaces patrolled by different companies, leading to displacement of undesirables from certain streets and commercial zones (Paache *et al* 2014).

While space is policed, it is also used to facilitate protest, as marches, demonstrations, sit-ins or rallies happen in specific places. However, state authorities can delimit (or try to) where and when these may take place. Many countries honour the right to use public space to protest and permission to march through the streets is granted, though in most instances there is a requirement that routes must be pre-agreed and these events are generally heavily policed. In the UK in recent decades anti-war protests, as well as demonstrations by student groups opposed to higher fees for university education, have taken place in London and other cities. The Occupy Movement (see Case study 23.4 in Chapter 23) is a good example of a protest organized with a specific spatial dimension. Protests against global social and economic inequality and the wider capitalist system emerged in 2011. Individuals and groups were motivated by opposition to austerity measures seen to affect the more vulnerable within society while ignoring the deep-seated structural issues and the wider global financial architecture that enriched a minority at the expense of the majority. Using slogans such as 'we are the 99%', these protests tapped into a collective feeling of unfairness and injustice. The initially spontaneous happenings saw an occupation of public space, itself a clear political statement, but the spaces themselves were symbolically chosen. Wall Street in New York (where the protests first emerged) is the US financial hub. Protest then spread to many other cities in the USA and other countries. The London version was initially intended for the stock exchange building, but heavy security meant it concentrated in the open space outside the nearby St Paul's Cathedral at the edge of the city's financial heart. Occupy and other social movements were simultaneously globally connected while being grounded in place. These protests, while drawing attention to serious global issues, also highlight the right to protest and the right to do so within particular spaces.

21.4 Territoriality, gender and sexuality

21.4.1 Gendered spaces

As with race and class, issues of gender are mapped on to space in various ways and the implications of gender are seen to be as important as other political, social and economic factors in the structuring of spaces and places. In its most simple form this is reflected in the sexist notion that 'a woman's place is in the home'. The home has tended to be seen as a space of reproduction juxtaposed to the workplace as a space of production (Laurie *et al.* 1999). Underpinning this are ideas that distinguish between sex as a biological fact and sex as gender, which refers to the socially constructed roles of both male and female identities. In emphasizing the role of social conditioning, the argument is that as individuals we are not biologically predetermined to be more suited to some roles rather than to others.

One reason for the relative absence of women in particular places is overt discrimination or active discouragement in the sense of certain activities or pursuits not being deemed suitable for women. Historically, women who transgressed these boundaries were often portrayed in a negative light, an idea reflective of notions of 'good' and 'bad' women. Women out alone at night might be seen as not conforming to what is expected of them. A crucial aspect of the relationship between women and place centres on the perception of some specific places as 'unsafe'. Many women do not feel safe in certain public places, most notably darkened streets. As Valentine (1989) suggested, women transfer a fear of male violence into a fear of certain spaces, which has profound implications for the ways in which men and women negotiate their way through urban areas. Clearly, the various strands of feminist thought and practice have resulted in significant advances with regard to equal rights for women. While this can be seen within the arena of legislation in many countries associated with equal pay and related issues, it is also reflected in terms of spaces. Thus, the heightened visibility of women in public space reflects the changing status of women. Phenomena such as 'reclaim the night' marches demonstrate the overt use of a spatial strategy to make a political and human point. While particular groups may find themselves excluded from certain spaces, those spaces can also be reclaimed (Plate 21.4).

Historically, the **gender division of labour** tended to confine women to the private realm, leaving men to inhabit (much of) the public domain. This view of women as playing a subordinate role has in the past been reflected in discriminatory attitudes and practices, particularly in relation to women in the paid workforce, with active discouragement through lower wages, if not actual exclusion, from many jobs. These views are predicated on the undesirability of women going out to work. It can be argued that this ascribing of women's role, through delimiting the spaces in which women were encouraged to appear, is another spatial expression of power. In other words, the confining of women to domestic space, and their exclusion from male territories, was a key element in male control (see Little 2002). With increasing female participation in the workforce and a raft of equal opportunities legislation in many countries, such a generalization may appear to have lost some of its validity. Nevertheless, the division between a (largely) male public sphere and a (largely) female private sphere still has considerable resonance in many societies (although the extent of this is itself immensely geographically variable across the world).

Where women enter the workforce, they may still encounter territorial divisions in the workplace. Thus,

Plate 21.4 Reclaim the Night march.

(Chris Scott/Getty Images)

Spain (1992) documents the 'closed door' jobs of managers (mainly men) and the 'open floor' jobs of manual workers (who may be predominantly women in certain countries/ regions/sectors). Employers may locate in particular localities (or countries) in order to take advantage of what they see as an available (and exploitable) workforce based on prevailing wage levels or skills and assumptions about gender roles (Hanson and Pratt 1995). The presence of women in the armed forces periodically provokes debate over the supposed appropriateness of women performing such roles. The deaths of female soldiers in recent years in the wars in Afghanistan and Iraq have been depicted in especially poignant terms in the media while the appropriateness of women being engaged in military activity in a war zone, rather than being at 'home' playing the key role in bringing up children is never far below the surface. In Iraq and Syria in 2014–15, Islamic State's recruitment of young women (expected to perform support roles, rather than 'front line' action) has also provoked sets of responses which reflect the perceived 'abnormality' of women participating in violent actions. Social processes reproduce attitudes that tend to 'naturalize' a gendered division of labour in which women perform certain functions which are acted out in specific spaces, for example 'home-making' and child-rearing in domestic space. Socially constructed gendered difference is inherently also spatialized. Within the arena of sport and leisure, gender stereotyping remains prevalent. While there are undoubtedly marked changes, gendered ideas and practices about leisure activities and, hence, separate spaces for men and women, are still common. Such social practices are built upon ideas of *what* is or is not acceptable behaviour for men and women to engage in (built on socially or culturally constructed notions of masculinity and femininity) and *where*. Stereotypes of women spending leisure time shopping while men attend sporting events, or watch them on television at home or in pubs, have a self-perpetuating quality. Within most Western societies, deep-seated ideas about woman's role as homemaker, cook, cleaner, child-rearer, and so on, mean that women have often been historically presumed to 'belong' in some rooms and spaces more than others. While such ideas have been challenged (and in many cases transformed), they sometimes endure. All these reflect territorial expressions of power whereby the designation or apportionment of space within the domestic sphere reflects the relative status or roles of the individuals concerned.

21.4.2 Sexuality and space

The idea of places territorialized by particular groups on the basis of sexual orientation has begun to receive more academic attention in recent years (see *Political*

Geography, 25(8), 2006; Browne *et al.* 2007). At its most elementary level this has seen the mapping of gay and lesbian 'zones' in selected cities. It is fair to point out that such spaces are not as easy to identify as, say, areas inhabited predominantly by a particular ethnic group. It is equally obvious that, in the main, these are not strictly demarcated areas. Rather, they are zones where gay people may feel more at ease through being accepted rather than rejected, scorned or ignored (or worse) by their neighbours. The mapping of 'gay territories' runs the risk of focusing on what some see as deviant behaviour as well as essentializing sexuality and reinforcing a gay/straight dichotomy. Nevertheless, the fact that those who identify themselves as gay and lesbian do, in some instances, become associated with particular (usually urban) spaces, suggests that another form of territorial behaviour may be evident. A concentration of visibly gay restaurants, bars and clubs results in the creation of what Castells calls 'a space of freedom' (1997: 213). Places such as the Castro District of San Francisco (Plate 21.5) and the more spatially confined 'gay village' in Manchester serve as important examples, while the city of Brighton has acquired an image as the 'gay capital' of the UK (Browne and Lim 2010).

Plate 21.5 Rainbow flag: a symbol of gay, lesbian, bisexual and transgender pride flying in the Castro District of San Francisco.

(Oksana Perkins/fotolia)

The construction of such zones may arise for reasons similar to those associated with ghettos and other forms of segregated space. Castells (1997) has argued that there are two key factors: protection and visibility. The first of these is fairly obvious. The idea of 'strength in numbers' may make people feel safer from homophobic 'gaybashers'. Visibility may have an emancipatory effect through which identification as gay or lesbian within a culture that is predominantly straight (heterosexual) and in which a straight discourse dominates, may work to nullify views that see homosexuality as deviant or abnormal. Gay neighbourhoods become a means of asserting identities. The significance of San Francisco's gay area was reflected in that community's ability to gain political representation. In obtaining power over territory they also gained political representation and San Francisco has become recognized as something of a 'gay capital' of the United States with a somewhat more liberal attitude. In this way, the designation of 'gay territories' plays a crucial role in raising awareness of gay people and issues and also provides a means by which some degree of power and self-confidence can be attained. Celebratory events such as 'gay pride' marches can be seen as an assertion of citizenship rights through staking a claim to public space. Conversely, heightened visibility may render people targets for homophobic assault, both verbal and physical. The examples of gay and lesbian spaces suggest another important point, that of the temporality of territory. The longevity of these spaces may be quite brief as the 'scene' moves to somewhere else. Lesbian spaces may be very short-lived in time, whether caused by the transience of lesbian bars/clubs or the even more short-term phenomena of lesbian or gay evenings.

Of course, such places and events may be inextricably bound up with factors that extend well beyond the realm of identity. 'Gay spaces' have often been associated with an economic imperative as the importance of the 'pink pound (dollar, or euro)' in aiding urban regeneration has frequently added a strong commercial angle to these developments. As with 'ethnic' spaces, one consequence may be the 'co-option' of the identity in order to present an 'acceptable' image of the group concerned which feeds into broader strategies of place promotion. Not surprisingly, some activists have expressed disquiet over the appropriation of such events and their dislocation from their original social and cultural roots and from their original territorial base. The fact that Manchester's 'gay village' and San Francisco's Castro District are firmly on the tourist trails of their respective cities may be lauded as an acceptance of identities previously scorned but it can also be seen as a commercialization of that identity which may, to some extent, serve to further ghettoize it. The instrumental use of an identity for wider purposes of urban regeneration or place promotion is problematic. The complex intersections between different identities can create specific tensions which play out in different ways in different places. For example, the ways in which gay and lesbian identities are interconnected with processes of gentrification through which they take on a spatial dimension is apparent in places such as the Marais district in Paris where tensions between 'old' and 'new' residents and within the 'gay community' emerge (Sibalis 2004). Similarly, the intersections of sexualized and racialized identities in post-apartheid Cape Town serve as another useful insight into how issues of identity play out in specific contexts (Tucker 2009). The relations between class, capital, sexual identity and place may be manifested in various complex ways. Sexual citizenship becomes implicated in wider processes of urban transformation while sexualized spaces may continue to be quite highly regulated (Bell and Binnie 2004). The perception of gay spaces as the effective preserve of white gay males may lead to the emergence of different types of 'queer' neighbourhoods. As Nash (2013) highlights, Toronto's gay village is effectively incorporated into the wider image and social, economic and political structures of the city. In this way, it has been argued both gay identities and the spaces associated with them have become increasingly commodified.

It might be argued that it is acceptable to be openly gay in an area so designated but in other spaces and societies the pressure to keep this identity hidden may well persist. While gay spaces may allow for more open expressions of sexual identity, homophobic assaults on sexual minorities reflect contested place meanings (Sumartojo 2004). Openly gay behaviour may be accepted or tolerated in some places but may remain decidedly unacceptable elsewhere. Here of course there are profound links between the small-scale (often neighbourhood or urban) territorialities and the wider policies of the city or state concerned. Many countries still criminalize gay sexuality and almost everywhere sexual mores and regulations are highly territorialized.

21.5 Work, rest and play

We can recognize two important social tendencies that bolster territoriality: the wish by people to have space of their own and the wish by others to exclude people from certain spaces. We have already seen ample evidence of the latter in this chapter. Even in what might appear to be very mundane or innocuous ways, the apparent claim to territory seems to manifest itself. At its most elementary level, the assertion of territoriality is reflected in claims to private property. Thus, people desire to mark their own home, to adorn it in their chosen style (influenced of course by social trends, technologies and fashions) and, in various ways, to mark it out as theirs. Homeowners are generally keen to stamp their personality on their home through the ways in which they choose to decorate it, alterations to layout, choice of colour schemes, furnishings and so on. This personalizing of space is further manifested through such things as the display of paintings, posters or photographs and the collection and arrangement of ornaments. The geographer Jean Gottman suggested that people 'always partitioned the space around them carefully to set themselves apart from their neighbours' (1973: 1). This manifestation is commonly interpreted as being symptomatic of our inherently territorial nature. This emphasis on the centrality of the home also has a broader cultural and political significance. Symbolic connections are often made between the domestic home and the nation whereby images of the former are seen to give material meaning to the latter. The home is seen in some ways to be at the heart of the nation. In times of war, for example, people have been encouraged to fight for the 'homeland' and the defence of 'hearth and home'.

Private property is regarded by many as an outcome of human territorial behaviour and it represents a claim to space that is reinforced by the legal system of many countries. However, as Alland points out, it might well be the case that 'private property is the child of culture and develops into a major preoccupation only with the evolution of complex society' (1972: 64). It follows that we need to be careful to avoid the trap of translating a need for **personal space** into an ideological claim for the sanctity of private property. The centrality of the family home, encapsulated in such phrases as 'home, sweet home', glosses over the fact that the privacy which many of us associate with the home is comparatively recent and is specific to some societies. Where 'domestic' space is limited (or for those who find it constrains them), life may be lived in the street (or perhaps the mall or car), much more evidently than the 'behind four walls' lifestyle many take as 'natural'. We need to be mindful of social, ethnic and geographic differences in the ways in which the home is conceived. In the United Kingdom, the notion of private home space was initially quite a middle-class idea which has since permeated the rest of society (Morley 2000).

Hegemonic ideas of the home within Western societies, exemplified by such notions as the home being an 'Englishman's castle' or associated with 'The American Dream', can be argued to have led to an ignoring of internal tensions and, in particular, a consideration of the different positions, roles and experiences of men, women and younger people within this domestic space, as discussed earlier (McDowell 1999). While the home is commonly depicted as a refuge from the outside world it may also be a site for domestic violence and fear (Squire and Gill 2011). Similarly teenagers may view the home as somewhere to escape from. In any event, the emphasis on the domestic idyll may have highly exclusionary consequences (Delaney 2005).

Even within buildings territorial behaviour can be recognized. As we have seen, the idea of the kitchen as a 'woman's place' is one example of this. The domestic home in many different cultural contexts is often spatially divided, not just in terms of gender but also in terms of age, with certain spaces being designated for women or for children (Spain 1992). The banning of children from some rooms and the proprietorial attitude towards one's own room in a house are other examples of this. In the home, space is even being claimed at the level of 'my chair', 'my place at the table' and so on. There are also distinctions amongst those allowed in, with differential access for close family and friends on the one hand and more casual acquaintances on the other. Even then, friends may be welcomed into the living room but are less likely to be invited into the more 'private' spaces such as bedrooms (Morley 2000). In any consideration of the home, we need to be mindful that it is not a straightforward and unambiguous entity. While for some it conjures up feelings of comfort and security, for others it may be a place of discomfort, alienation and tension (Blunt and Dowling 2006). For some the home may come to feel like a prison – quite literally so for those sentenced to home imprisonment or the many others subject to degrees of curfew, control and house arrest. Home is therefore a social construction in which social identities are (re)produced but which conveys different meanings to different people.

Equally, in workplaces some areas and rooms can only be entered by staff of a certain level and are out of bounds to more junior staff (Case study 21.2). These can be interpreted as managerial strategies designed to ensure a particular outcome; staff know their 'place' and can be more effectively controlled, sometimes through very obvious visual intrusion. Hanson and Pratt (1995) reveal how companies reproduce social segregation through spatial practices within the workplace whereby different sets of workers inhabit different parts of the factory and rarely, if ever, meet. Thus, office staff may be located downstairs in 'cubicles' separated by room dividers, with sales staff and management upstairs in individual or shared offices while production staff are located in an entirely separate part of the building. Socializing between workers often reflects their spatial segregation with limited social contact between them. Work hierarchies are reflected in the spatial arrangements of the workplace. These practices

Case study 21.2

Playgrounds and lecture halls

There has been a growing interest recently in the geographies of younger people (see Holloway and Valentine 2000; Leyshon 2008; Yarwood and Tyrrell 2012) and as an example of micro-scale territoriality it is instructive to consider the space of the school playground. Thomson (2005) suggests that while children's behaviour is clearly spatialized in a wide variety of ways, it might be thought that the playground is 'their' space in which school children can enjoy a degree of freedom to engage in a range of activities as distinct from the constraints imposed in the more formalized and controlled spaces of the classroom or other parts of the school buildings and grounds. However, while play spaces can be seen as emancipatory they are simultaneously regulating. Thomson's research indicates that on closer inspection the playground displays two key criteria associated with territories and territoriality. First, it remains heavily controlled by adults (teaching staff) who delimit the times it can be used and the activities which are permitted there. Second, it often contains internal territorial divisions in the sense of discrete spaces for different types of 'play' activity – sports, etc. What is also obvious of course is that children themselves will often endeavour to claim their own territory within the larger space of the playground with groups 'hanging out' in particular places. In addition it is equally apparent that these spatial practices are open to contestation. Rival groups of children may 'compete' for spaces within the playground. What is also apparent is the manner in which children may try to test or push the spatial boundaries imposed by teachers and supervisors through such actions as encroaching on grass playing pitches and so on. Another important dimension of this (in addition to classification, communication, enforcement and resistance) is the way in which the control of territory is masked through

recourse to other discourses such as that of health and safety – prohibiting access to spaces deemed dangerous or hazardous (Thomson 2005).

In a similar vein we might take the example of the university teaching room. Here a lecturer may exert a strong degree of territorial control; occupying a space at the top of the room while controlling (or trying to) who else may speak and when they may do so. Even in highly interactive and more student-led sessions, a lecturer, by virtue of their status, continues to exert control over the space. She or he can 'command' the room and walk around it in ways which students cannot (or are discouraged from doing). However, such control has very obvious temporal constraints. What the students and lecturer may regard as 'their' room is usually limited to a regular time-tabled slot. Before and after that time, their right to be there is denied as other lecturers and students take over the space and control it. Your geography lecturer is unlikely to walk into a lecture theatre during a biochemistry class and commence to speak to the assembled students. (Well, they might try to do so but they would be met by a bewildered reaction and, more than likely, a phone call to security!) (Plate 21.6).

Plate 21.6 University lecture theatre.
(Matej Kastelic/Shutterstock)

have clear outcomes. They may render it difficult for workers to organize through physically keeping them separate and through engendering a sense of difference between different sections of the workforce.

Taking the idea of territory down to its most elementary level, the desire for personal space can be seen as a form of territorial behaviour. Humans like to have a pocket of space around them that is 'theirs' and they

resent others 'invading' their space (unless invited!). This can be interpreted as a territorial claim to a portion of geographic space. While this might be taken as reflecting a natural tendency, it is worth noting that the amount of space needed appears to vary from one society to another, a fact noted long ago by Hall (1959). For many young people, their own room, apartment, etc., may seem like a 'natural' ambition, but for many of the world's inhabitants

such a desire is completely unobtainable. For those living in overcrowded conditions, the amount of personal
space available is extremely limited. For a homeless person, their 'own' space may be limited to a hostel bed in
central London, a doorway in downtown Manhattan, or
a small patch of pavement in the Tenderloin district in
San Francisco (Gowan 2010). Nurture, culture, power and
politics all need to be considered where the complexities
and diversities of human territorialities are concerned.

Sport provides an example of an activity in which territory and space are of obvious importance. Sport is deeply
connected to questions of place and identity with some
sports intrinsically connected to particular places, Gaelic
games in Ireland being a classic example (Storey 2012a).
Particular spaces are required for sports and these range
from formal arenas and large stadia down to the level of
the street or indeed to a corner of a room, depending on
the sport. Sports grounds and facilities occupy areas of
urban and rural space and we can consider these in relation to wider ideas of inclusion and exclusion. Issues of
gender or ethnicity may be important here and the maintenance of men only rules at some sports facilities results
in a highly gendered division of recreational space. Sports
such as football and rugby thrive on inter-place rivalry and
fans come to closely identify with their sporting 'home'.
In some instances this rivalry may be at a relatively localized, yet highly intense, scale such as that between Arsenal
and Tottenham Hotspur football clubs in north London.
In some cases wider social issues may overlay geographic
rivalry, as with Celtic and Rangers football clubs in Glasgow, Scotland where sectarian division between Protestants
and Catholics is part of the cultural context for the antipathy between supporters. At a still more micro-scale fans
will occupy different sections of a ground, usually related
to security considerations designed to keep 'home' and
'away' supporters apart. In some cases minorities of supporters may try to 'take' the home section of ground while
visiting fans sometimes like to be seen to assert control
over some bars and streets in the 'host' city or town, a version of territoriality of very short duration. In sport itself
territorial strategies of dominating the pitch, or areas of
it, may be a fundamental tactic. In rugby endeavouring to
keep play in the opposition's half is a normal tactic while
tennis players may wish to dominate the court as a means
of dominating their opponent.

21.6 Conclusions

The idea of territory reflects a way of thinking about
geographic space while territorial strategies are utilized
in conflicts concerned with social power and identity.

Territorial thinking, the production of territories and the
employment of territorial strategies are bound up with
maintaining power or with resisting the imposition of
power by a dominant group. While forms of exclusion can
be consolidated and reinforced through territorial practices, they can also be resisted through similar means. The
examples provided in this chapter are evidence of the ways
in which social relations are expressed through spatial
patterns and they highlight how these geographies help
in turn to shape social relations. Social phenomena such
as class, racial or gendered identities invariably embody a
territorial component. Territorial strategies are often used
to control and police those who are defined as 'out of
(their) place'. In this way particular ideologies are transposed on to space. People are confronted with wider practices through their use of space or through the ways in
which they are allowed to use space. Power relationships
take on a spatial dimension, even at the most mundane
and everyday level. Issues of identity, particularly within
multi-cultural societies, have a spatial expression as social
divisions (associated with class, ethnic, religious, gender
or other factors) are given material form through spatial
divisions. The examples used here demonstrate the spa-
tialization of wider ideas and they show how people are
kept 'in their place' whether through overt mechanisms or
more subtle means. Social boundaries are often communicated through space. This can have serious implications
with some groups of people effectively treated as 'second-
class (or indeed as non-) citizens' denied full rights in the
society in which they find themselves, confined to spatial
enclaves which become characterized as dangerous and
threatening spaces. Social and spatial exclusion has the
effect of denying full access to those rights often thought
of as inalienable for all people everywhere. Many territorial strategies have deeply discriminatory and exclusionary outcomes giving rise to social and spatial exclusion.
They can be used to deny people effective participation
in society through restricting choice, mobility and possibilities to participate. However, as indicated earlier,
just as dominant ideologies can be reinforced through
territorial practices, they can also be resisted. Territorial
strategies are useful mechanisms in the assertion of identity. Spatial concentrations within particular geographic
areas make visible people and issues that might otherwise
remain unseen. They can be used to draw attention to
exclusionary practices and to assert the right to be equal
citizens. In doing so, this demonstrates the 'positive' and
'negative' dimensions to territoriality; it can be both a
force for oppression and also one for liberation. Particular
strategies can be used to assert an identity and territorially transgressive acts can be employed to reclaim space
and, hence, to assert basic rights. While many people
do not necessarily freely choose their 'place', they may,

nevertheless, identify with their immediate neighbourhood or locality. This sense of identity can in turn be converted into forms of action aimed at obtaining particular outcomes. The formation of community or residence groups reflects feelings of belonging or attachment to a particular place. It follows that notions of territory are connected with ideas of social power. The claiming of space is a political act whether it occurs in the 'public' or 'private' arena (and the categorization and demarcation of these areas is a key expression of territoriality)

and territories provide a material expression of the fusion of meaning, power and social space (Delaney 2009). In other words, *power* permeates society and this is something which is marked in and expressed through a range of human geographies. As the next chapter details, the nation-state has come to be a key container of power and an expression of human territoriality. As such, nation-states are frequently contested, not only by other states, but also by those acting in the name of other loyalties and other scales and ideologies of belonging.

Learning outcomes

Having read this chapter, you should understand:

- How social issues linked to class, racism, ethnicity, identity, gender and sexuality are mapped on to geographic space and become the basis for territorial strategies.
- Some of the ways in which social inequalities and differences are manifested spatially.
- How territorial practices are used to exert control through the policing of space at macro- and micro-scales.
- How territorial strategies can be useful mechanisms for groups to promote their identities and rights and to resist exclusionary practices.
- The ways in which many aspects of everyday life are reflected in spatial practices and relationships.

Further reading

Sack, R. (1986) *Human Territoriality: Its Theory and History,* Cambridge University Press, Cambridge. As outlined in this chapter, Sack's book has become a classic geographic text on territory and territorial behaviour, setting it firmly within a 'social' rather than 'natural' framework. For commentaries revisiting Sack's book more than two decades after its original publication, see Classics in human geography revisited, *Progress in Human Geography,* 24(1), 2000, 91–9.

Delaney, D. (2005) *Territory: A Short Introduction,* Blackwell, Malden.

Storey, D. (2012b) *Territories: The Claiming of Space,* 2nd edition, Routledge, London.

These both build on Sack's work and deal with territory and territoriality in social and political contexts. Storey's updated book contains many more case studies of territoriality than can be considered here. Delaney's book also offers a good survey (and some critique) of Sack's ideas and lots of case studies.

The work of Stuart Elden extends earlier thinking on the nature of territory and the relationships between territories and geographic space. In particular, he stresses the necessity of thinking historically about how territory has evolved. See, in particular, his history of the concept: *The Birth of Territory* (University of Chicago Press, 2013) and also Elden, S. (2010) Land, terrain, territory, *Progress in Human Geography,* 34(6), 799–817.

Two reader-friendly introductions to the intersections between politics and geography, providing very good examples of some of the themes covered here, which also contain lots of material relevant to other chapters in this section (for example, on the territorial state and geopolitics) are:

Jones, M., Jones, R., Woods, M., Whitehead, M., Dixon, D. and Hannah, M. (2015) *An Introduction to Political Geography: Space, Place and Politics,* 2nd edition, Routledge, London.

Painter, J. and Jeffrey, A. (2009) *Political Geography,* 2nd edition, Sage, London.

There are a range of useful social and cultural geography texts dealing with many of the concerns of this chapter. These can be read with a view to the complex operations and manifestations of territoriality:

Anderson, J. (2015) *Understanding Cultural Geography. Places and Traces,* 2nd edition, Routledge, London.

Del Casino, V.J. (2009) *Social Geography: A Critical Introduction,* Wiley-Blackwell, Chichester.

Horton, J. and Kraftl, P. (2014) *Cultural Geographies: An Introduction,* Routledge, London.

For two contrasting cases (one on territoriality in a school playground, another on parades), both drawing on Sack, see:

Thompson, S. (2005) 'Territorialising' the school playground: deconstructing the geography of playtime, *Children's Geographies,* 3(1), 63–78 and O'Reilly, K. and Crutcher, M.E. (2006) Parallel politics: the spatial power of New Orleans Labor Day parades, *Social and Cultural Geography,* 7(2), 245–65.

On policing and security, see: Yarwood, R. and Paasche, T. (2015) The relational geographies of policing and security, *Geography Compass* 9(6), 362–70.

For a more specific focus on urban gating see: Bagaeen, S. and Uduku, O. (eds) (2010) *Gated Communities. Social Sustainability and Historical Gated Developments,* Earthscan, London.

This is an interesting collection of chapters casting light on sexuality and space:

Browne, K., Lim, J. and Brown, G. (eds) (2007) *Geographies of Sexualities: Theory, Politics and Practice,* Ashgate, Aldershot. See also the book by Andrew Tucker (2009) *Queer Visibilities: Space, Identity and Interaction in Cape Town,* Wiley-Blackwell, Chichester, and the commentaries on it by Ward *et al.* in *Political Geography,* 29(8), 2010, 454–62.

For a useful examination of the complex natures and meanings of home:

Blunt, A. and Dowling, R. (2006) *Home,* Routledge, London.

On social movements, protest and activism see the useful insights provide by the following:

Arenas, I. (2014) Assembling the multitude: material geographies of social movements from Oaxaca to Occupy, *Environment and Planning D: Society and Space,* 32(3), 433–49.

Chatterton, P. and Pickerill, J. (2010) Everyday activism and transitions towards post-capitalist worlds, *Transactions of the Institute of British Geographers,* 35(4), 475–90.

Halvorsen, S. (2015) Encountering Occupy London: boundary making and the territoriality of urban activism, *Environment and Planning D: Society and Space,* 33(2), 314–30.

THE PLACE OF THE NATION-STATE

Chapter 22

James Sidaway and Carl Grundy-Warr

Topics covered

- The ubiquity and geographical diversity of nations and states
- Interpretations of nationalism as a territorial project
- Relationships between nations, states and territory
- Challenges to territorial states
- Transnational identities and borderlands
- Geologic and fluid claims by states

The territory of a nation is not just a profane part of the Earth's surface. It is a constitutive element of nationhood which generates plenty of other concepts and practices directly related to it: for example, the concepts of territorial integrity and political sovereignty; border control, conflict, invasion and war. It defines and has some control over many other national affairs, such as the national economy, products, industry, trade, education, administration, culture and so on. Unarguably, the territory of a nation is the most concrete feature of a nation for the management of nationhood as a whole. For a theoretical geographer, it is the territoriality of a nation . . . For people of a nation; it is a part of SELF, a collective self. It is a nation's geo-body . . . . The geo-body, the territoriality of a nation as well as its attributes such as sovereignty and boundary, are not only political but also cultural constructs.

(Winichakul 1996: 67)

22.1 Historical and geographical variability of states

Although it is also other things, notably a provider of services, a system of regulations, ideologies, legal regulations and police powers ('law and order'), flows of capital (budgets, taxation and government spending) backed up by the threat of discipline and violence (for example, armed forces), the state can be interpreted as a form of community. As earlier chapters (in particular those in Section 1) have shown, forms of human community and their attendant territorialities (see Chapter 21) have been extremely variable historically and geographically.

The contemporary system of states, in which all of the land surface of the earth (with the partial exception of Antarctica as is detailed in Chapter 20) is divided into state units, whose outlines become familiar to us from maps and globes, is after all fairly new. In the early twentieth century, the borders between many of today's states were only vaguely defined, and more recently large areas of the world were ruled by colonial empires or dynastic realms (the Austro-Hungarian in Central Europe, Ottoman in the Balkans and Eastern Mediterranean, and Ch'ing empire in China, for example). Alternatively, the concept of nation-statehood was simply not in the political vocabulary. In the latter cases, ethnically, linguistically or religious specific groups owed allegiance to the imperial order rather than to a defined nation. That is, loyalty would be foremost to the empire and any sense of national or ethnic identity would be a local or 'private' matter.

Such imperial visions are no longer dominant and today few formal colonies and no large-scale dynastic empires remain (see Chapter 3). Therefore the territories that were once ruled as part of, for example, a Japanese, British, French, Ottoman (Turkish), Portuguese or Russian empire are today mostly divided into self-avowed and recognized *sovereign* states. They possess the same apparatus of statehood (leaders, flags, capital cities, administrations, postage stamps, seats at the United Nations and so on) that the former imperial powers have. Moreover, the global map of states continues to change. In recent decades, some have disappeared as separate states (like the former East Germany and South Yemen), whilst others have split into two or sometimes many component parts (like the former USSR, Ethiopia, Sudan and Yugoslavia), and others have been subject to violent fragmentation fuelled by civil unrest, internal and external power plays using coercive force (such as Syria and Somalia). All this reinforces the point that states, like other communities, particularly the 'nations' with which they are associated, are not to be taken at face value. The claims

Plate 22.1 The state as a system of organized violence: armed forces.

(TheStockCube/fotolia)

made for and on behalf of them deserve critical examination. However, this is not an easy task. For, as Benjamin Akzin (1964) pointed out over half a century ago, to discuss nations, states and nationalism is to enter a terminological maze in which one easily and soon becomes lost. Claims to nationhood frequently involve the blending of 'tangibles' and 'intangibles' in a unique brew that may contain such volatile ingredients as 'blood', language, 'race' and religion. A fundamental goal of nationhood is to generate a strong sense of belonging associated with a particular territory. In practice it may prove difficult to distinguish between 'the nation' and other human collectivities, but as Walker Connor (1994: 93) puts it, 'what ultimately matters is not what is but what people believe is'. This chapter will indicate some pathways into the maze of tangibles and intangibles surrounding the term nation-state. It begins with an account of 'nations' and nationalism before returning to the relationship of these to states.

22.2 Nations as 'imagined' political communities

One of the most influential and suggestive critical studies of nations and nationalism was a book by Benedict Anderson (1983) entitled *Imagined Communities: Reflections on the Origin and Spread of Nationalism*. He begins with a reminder of the ubiquity of nations and nationalism:

Almost every year the United Nations admits new members. And many 'old nations' once thought fully consolidated find themselves challenged by 'sub'-nationalisms within their borders – nationalisms which naturally dream of shedding this subness one happy day. The reality is quite plain: the 'end of the era of nationalism', so long prophesied, is not remotely in sight. Indeed, nationness is the most universally legitimate value in the political life of our time.

(Anderson 1983: 3)

Although enormously variable between, say, Nepali, Israeli, Singaporean, Nicaraguan, Vietnamese, Eritrean, American, Greek, Turkish and Irish versions, the ideology of nationalism holds that everyone will have a primary identity with a particular 'nation'. Such communities should be able to express themselves in a state; that is, they should enjoy what is called 'sovereignty' within certain geographical boundaries. 'Sovereignty', which is a term of long vintage and was previously associated with royal dynasties (the sovereign monarch), shifts to the 'people' of a 'nation', and even if a royal figurehead is retained, she or he will have to become in some way a 'national' symbol. However, it is important to remember that territorial sovereignty as depicted on the world political map of today is of relatively recent origin (see Section 22.3), that more differentiated forms of sovereignty and other territorialities have existed in the past, and that sovereignty is continually being challenged in various ways.

Examples of quite different conceptions of sovereignty in the past are abundant in many parts of the world, from medieval Europe to most parts of the pre-colonial world. The labyrinthine world of medieval times in Europe was at some levels intensely 'local', involving much smaller communities and political units than today, although these were usually a 'part of a complex hierarchy of political or cultural entities, such as the Church of Rome, the Hanseatic League, or the dynastic Habsburg Empire' (J. Anderson 1986: 115). Sovereignty was not rigidly territorial as it mostly is with modern nation-states (see Chapters 1 and 2). As James Anderson (1995: 70) explained:

Political sovereignty in medieval Europe was shared between a wide variety of secular and religious institutions and different levels of authority – feudal knights and barons, kings and princes, guilds and cities, bishops, abbots, the papacy – rather than being based on territory per se as in modern times. Indeed the territories of medieval European states were often discontinuous, with ill-defined and fluid frontier zones rather than precise or fixed borders. Then the term 'nation' meant something very different and non-political, generally referring simply to people born in the same locality. Furthermore, the different levels of overlapping sovereignty typically constituted nested hierarchies, for example parish, bishopric, archbishopric for spiritual matters; manor, lordship, barony, duchy, kingdom for secular matters. People were members

of higher-level collectivities not directly but only by virtue of their membership of lower-level bodies.

In many parts of the pre-colonial world, sovereignty was not based upon fixed boundaries and territorial control per se. For instance, much of North Africa and the Middle East had very different forms of political sovereignty in pre-modern times. According to George Joffé (1987: 27):

political authority was expressed through communal links and was of varying intensity, depending on a series of factors involving, inter alia, tradition, geographic location and political relationships. The underlying consideration, however, was common throughout the region and involved a concept of political sovereignty that derived from Islamic practice. The essential condition was that ruler and ruled were bound together through a conditional social contract in which the ruler could expect loyalty in return for enduring the conditions in civil society for the correct practice of Islam.

Not surprisingly, many of the colonially inspired geometrical boundaries that define the modern states of the Middle East and North Africa have limited relation to pre-colonial political landscapes. They have faced post-colonial challenges, by nationalists who argued they did not coincide with where national borders should be and by those who refute them in the name of confessional (religious) identity, most dramatically the leaders of the self-declared Islamic State that emerged in Iraq and Syria in 2014. Similarly, in many pre-colonial Asian states, the emphasis of sovereignty was not on the territorial limits of control 'but on pomp, ceremony and the sacred architecture of the symbolic centre' (Clarke 1996: 217). In the classical Indianized states of South and South-east Asia, sovereignty was often focused on rulers who claimed divinity, and further eastwards, emperors held the 'mandate of Heaven', and the mandarins' right to exercise their authority was derived from their being 'superior men' (Sino-Vietnamese, *quan-tu*; Chinese *chun-tzu*) 'who acted according to Confucian ideals' (Keyes 1995: 195). But it would be too simplistic to think of sovereignty purely in terms of emperors, kings, queens, chiefs and so on, as ruler-ruled/ state-society relations in pre-modern societies were often complex, hierarchical, shifting and not based on strict territoriality. O.W. Wolters (1982: 16–7) described the scheme of power relations in South-east Asia as *mandala* (a Sanskrit word that defies easy translation, but which refers to a political apparatus that was without fixed boundaries, but which rested on the authority of a central court):

[The] mandala represented a particular and often unstable political situation in a vaguely definable geographical area without fixed boundaries and where smaller centers tended to look in all directions for security. Mandalas would expand and contract in concertina-like fashion. Each one contained several tributary rulers, some of whom would repudiate their vassal status when the opportunity arose and try to build up their own networks of vassals.

Territories of pre-modern kingdoms were often discontinuous, with outer tributaries and chiefdoms often paying tribute to more than one authority at the same time, and with areas of sovereign ambiguity, particularly in heavily forested zones, high mountain areas, and remote regions. In a sense, the vast mountain 'frontiers' of the mainland South-east Asian massif, Southwest China, Himalaya, and Afghanistan, have variously retained certain 'frontier' 'resistance' and 'refuge' characteristics well into the era of modern nation-states (refer to Case study 22.2).

This system of tributary relationships carried its own forms of obligations, sanctions and allegiance. Mandalas created complex geographies of power, 'a polycentric landscape-seascape' (Friend 2003: 18), including smaller chiefdoms paying tribute to more than one 'overlord' at the same time. Initially, the multiple sovereignties of the region were very confusing to the European imperial powers in the region who were eagerly trying to carve out their own spheres of unambiguous control. As Theodore Friend (2003: 21) notes in relation to the making of Indonesia:

> The Netherlands required centuries to unify Indonesia in their own fashion: first for mercantilist advancement of trade and then for nineteenth-century motives of geographic empire . . . How could so few succeed over so many? The answer: because only a handful of mandalas had to be overcome, each caring little about the others or knowing nothing of them. The Dutch brought a layer of assiduous modernity to political vacuums strung throughout a vast archipelago. Geographically disconnected and culturally discordant but now administratively centralized, the Netherlands East Indies was for the length of one human generation the first comprehensive empire that region had ever known.

Although significant vestiges of such territorial structures remain, today they have mostly been displaced by nation-states with fixed (though sometimes disputed) boundaries. Sometimes the new geography was imposed by the colonial powers, but indigenous polities were also active in transforming the political map, such as China's long quest to have political control over numerous stubborn non-Han ethnic polities in the vast south-western frontier (Giersch 2001), and in Siam in the late nineteenth century, where the Siamese Court began to employ 'modern' political cartography backed up by military power to determine the sovereign limits of the kingdom (Winichakul

1996). Through the twentieth century, the ideology of nationalism (and the associated idea of nation-states) became one of the dominant and most widespread influences on politics across the world, arguably becoming a key (or the key) manifestation of modern territoriality.

Occasionally nationalisms recognize that the state itself may be multinational (as in British nationalism, which contains English, Scottish, Welsh, northern Irish protestant and catholic, and other affiliations due to generations of migrants and mixed religious, ethnic groups over time becoming part of the United Kingdom), but in so doing, the wish is usually expressed that somehow a more inclusive national identity will evolve or has evolved which coincides with the boundaries of the state. Britain, China, Switzerland, South Africa, Nigeria and the United States of America are all cases where different versions of the claim and goal of an inclusive 'national identity' that supposedly unites disparate 'sub-nations' or communities have been asserted. All have been challenged and contested, sometimes peacefully through political process (referenda, debate and elections), but often violently by those who would wish to secede, eliciting rounds of repression and violent response. Often, the assertion of a particular dominant nationalism in a territory has required the suppression of or conflict with other national claims on the same territory (the emergence of the state of Israel is a clear example of this; and in turn the project of a national home for Jewish people in the land of Palestine is in part a reaction to the genocidal extremes associated with German and other European nationalisms earlier in the twentieth century). As a result many 'national' communities that assert a claim to statehood have been denied this (see Case study 22.1, for example). Others remain contested. Myanmar, for example, has witnessed over five decades of protracted ethno-nationalist struggles, particularly between successive military regimes holding power in the predominantly ethnic-Burman heartlands, and various movements in the provinces that are seeking either greater political autonomy within a federal structure or complete independence. Indeed, for many years, large tracts of northern and eastern Myanmar are patched together by a series of fragile ceasefires and natural resource joint ventures between the ruling military junta and various ethno-political parties, companies and warlords. Specific armed political groups, such as the Wa United State Party, have effective authority over sections of the Burma–China and Burma–Lao border areas, which provide examples of de facto territorial power by 'shadow state' organizations (Grundy-Warr and Dean 2011). Thus, the political-legal integrity of 'the Union of Myanmar' has been contentious. Following the Myanmar national elections in November 2015, in which the National League for Democracy (NLD) party led by Daw Aung San Suu Kyi

Case study 22.1

A nation across states? The Kurdish case

Gerard Chailand (1993: 4) claimed that: 'the Kurd-ish people have the unfortunate distinction of being probably the only community of over 15 mil-lion persons which has not achieved some form of national statehood, despite a struggle extending

back several decades'. The lands predominantly inhabited by Kurds came to be divided between four states (see Figure 22.1): Iran, Iraq, Turkey and Syria (there are also smaller Kurdish communities in the former Soviet Union – Armenia, Azerbaijan and Georgia – and significant Kurdish diaspora popula-tions in Europe, especially in Austria, Germany and Scandinavia).

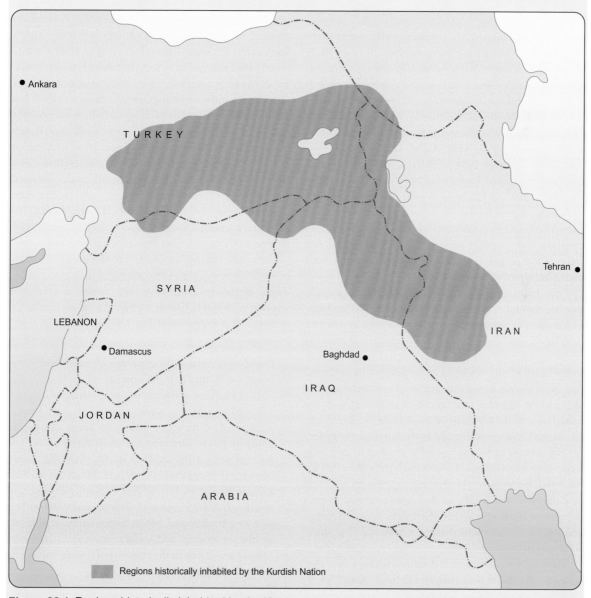

Figure 22.1 Regions historically inhabited by the Kurds.

Source: after Chailand (1993: ix)

Yet frequent attempts on the part of the states in the region to eradicate Kurdish identity and nationalism were not able to quash either the widespread sense of Kurdishness or the often violent struggle in pursuit of a Kurdish nation-state. After years of struggle, which became interconnected with the Cold War, regional rivalries and then the American-led wars with Iraq in 1991 and 2003, the northern part of Iraq – which is predominantly Kurdish – is now an autonomous region. Since 2013, autonomous Kurdish cantons have also emerged in northern Syria, in the wake of the wider civil war there whilst the allied Kurdish nationalist movement that had hitherto sought a state in the eastern part of Turkey now officially seeks a democratic con-federal settlement. The future status of these territories and relationships between them and their neighbours (which include the insurgent 'Islamic State' in Iraq and Syria that was established in 2014, the Turkish state, which will be a century old in 1923, Iran and the weakened central governments in Iraq and Syria) remain uncertain and pose challenges to established concepts of nationhood, sovereignty and territory (Paasche and Sidaway 2015).

won a decisive majority, thus replacing effective military rule since 1962 with a fledgling democracy, there are likely to be peaceful changes to the political landscape, although key ethnic parties and ethnic armed organizations still prefer a federal nation-state to a union where politics is dominated by the ethnic Burman or Bamar majority population. Globally, there a numerous other examples of de facto states (Pegg 1998; Bacheli *et al*. 2004), such as Somaliland (Srebrnik 2004), Abkhazia (O Loughlin *et al*. 2011) and the Turkish Republic of Northern Cyprus (Navaro-Yashin 2005, 2012), as well as bi- or 'multinational' territories, such as Bosnia-Herzegovina (Dahlman and Ó Tuathail 2005; Ó Tuathail and Dahlman 2006). Such cases reveal the truly complex nature of the historical, cultural and political geographies that complicate and sometimes contradict territorial nation-statehood.

Two 'multinational' communist countries, namely Yugoslavia and the Soviet Union, sought to regulate nationalism by assigning citizens to one of a number of constituent national identities. This sometimes involved inventing nationalities to rationalize and simplify more complex tribal and religious identities, whilst asserting that these should be subservient to an overarching sense of Soviet or Yugoslav identity which coincided with the boundaries of the USSR or of Yugoslavia. So, for example, in the USSR, people could be declared on their identity documents as having one of a number of officially recognized nationalities (Uzbek, Latvian or Russian, for example), but they would also and supposedly above all be citizens of the USSR. In due course, it was in part because of local nationalist challenges to wider Soviet and Yugoslav affiliations that the USSR and Yugoslavia collapsed in the early 1990s.

Many of those self-identified nations without their own state (the Kurds are an example, see Case study 22.1; as are Palestinians, Basques, Karen and Tibetans, to name a few) claim either the right to one or at least a high level of self-rule or autonomy. And frequently, smaller recognized national identities within a multinational state (such as Scotland in the United Kingdom or Quebec in Canada) become the basis for claims that they should enjoy full statehood. In many cases too, either the central state or some other community with another affiliation resists. There are numerous examples of this, including the complex case of Northern Ireland, where most Catholics (Republicans) would wish to see the province united with the rest of the Irish Republic (which itself successfully broke away from the British colonial empire earlier in the twentieth century). Most Protestants (Unionists), who claim descent from settler populations from England and Scotland, wish to remain part of a 'United Kingdom' (see Case study 21.4).

The Irish case is just one of dozens of situations where conflicting nationalist and confessional (religious-cultural) logics collide, often with violent consequences. There is clearly something very powerful going on, whereby nationalist visions are linked with particular territories and conceptions of state. Yet, as Anderson (1983: 3) recognizes:

> But if the facts [of the existence of many and sometimes conflicting nationalisms] are clear, their explanation remains a matter of long-standing dispute. Nation, nationality, nationalism – all have proved notoriously difficult to define, let alone analyse. In contrast to the immense influence that nationalism has exerted on the modern world, plausible theory about it is conspicuously meagre. Hugh Seton-Watson, author of by far the best and most comprehensive English-language text on nationalism, and heir to a vast tradition of liberal historiography [theories of history writing] and social science, sadly observes: 'Thus I am driven to the conclusion that no "scientific definition has existed and exists".'

Readers may wish to 'prove' Seton-Watson's observation for themselves, by trying to come up with a universally valid definition of a nation. Faced with this task,

Case study 22.2

Zomia: highland resistance to nation-building and state-making

The map refers to a vast mountainous region of approximately 2.5 million square kilometres, spanning the boundaries of ten recognized nation-states, and sprawling across the designated 'world regional area' limits of 'South Asia', 'Central Asia', 'East Asia' and mainland 'South-east Asia' (Figure 22.2). This transnational highland zone is called 'Zomia' (based on a Tibeto-Burman term 'zomi'), a term invented and proposed by historian Willem van Schendel (2005: 284–5), who argues that 'much of Zomia resisted the projects of nation-building and state-making of the countries to which it belonged'. Part of the reason for this are the great many dispersed 'national minority' groupings, such as Naga, Akha, Lahu, Hmong, Lisu, Shan and Kachin, as well as numerous other groups, each with their own peculiar socio-ecological adaptations to highland life, and cultural, linguistic and religious affinities that are distinct from dominant 'national' languages and religions. Similar communities (the four towns indicated on the map) – just a short distance apart – fall into four states and macro-regions.

James C. Scott (2009) has produced an 'anarchist history of upland Southeast Asia', revealing the connected but often antagonistic co-evolution of hill and valley across much of Zomia. He argues that 'Zomia coheres as a region not by political unity, which it utterly lacks, but by comparable patterns of diverse agriculture, dispersal, mobility and egalitarianism' (Scott 2008: 12). Scott (2009) reveals that, over long periods of time, many groups of people viewed the uplands as economic, cultural and political 'refuges' from interfering and hierarchical lowland state authorities. Thus, historically, many people migrated to these areas in order to escape, evade or resist state interference. These spaces of state 'evasion', 'resistance' and 'refuge' were ultimately partitioned into various national geo-bodies following the nineteenth and early twentieth century rivalries and boundary-making activities of imperial powers, and the adoption of modern political geography by dominant indigenous polities, and subsequent post-colonial nationalist elites (Winichakul 1996).

The arbitrary and abrupt nature of geopolitical boundaries generated tensions between central states and the upland groups, who have frequently been regarded as suspicious, backward, primitive and uncooperative 'minorities', and, occasionally, as security threats by lowland state authorities (van Schendel 2005; Michaud 2009; Scott 2009). In the modern

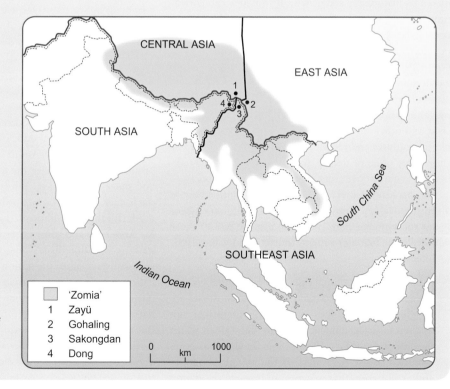

Figure 22.2 A map of Zomia.

Source: adapted from van Schendal (2005b)

Legend:
- ☐ 'Zomia'
- 1 Zayü
- 2 Gohaling
- 3 Sakongdan
- 4 Dong

history of these nation-states, Zomia has been characterized by 'a high incidence of regionalist and separatist movements, "non-state spaces", and discursive battles around concepts such as "tribe" and "indigenous people"' (van Schendel 2005: 285). Central territorial states have sought to extend administrative control into the uplands of Zomia through various 'development projects', forced resettlement of highland groups, campaigns aimed to extend settled farming into higher lands, religious conversions, spatial extensions of central bureaucratic administration and infrastructure such as roads, making these 'spaces of evasion' more accessible over time.

'Zomia' is part of a new conceptual map proposed by scholars to address relative academic neglect in 'area imagination', which helps us to break free of our rigid national geographic imaginaries, particularly with regard to the histories, ethnographies and geographies of mobile groups (Ludden 2003), the politics of place and belonging of so-called 'minorities' (Michaud 2010), and the complex interrelated, transitional and transient dimensions of borderscapes (Rajaram and Grundy-Warr 2007). We need to be critical of reifying 'national geo-bodies' and pay attention to myriad pre-existing and contemporary transnational social and political formations that challenge the map of nation-states.

students will often work through a long list of characteristics ascribed to nationality. But it seems that exceptions can always be found. Language is a favoured criterion, but then many languages are spoken by more than one 'nation' (English is an example) and some 'nation-states' (Switzerland, Belgium or Mozambique, for example) contain substantial communities speaking different languages. Religion is sometimes chosen, but the same objections apply. Ethnicity and 'race' turn out to be problematic criteria, favoured by racists of all stripes, and often part of the basis for national identities, but susceptible to the obvious and undeniable point that everywhere is much too mixed up historically and genetically for such categorizations to be watertight. Besides, some nationalisms have come to celebrate their multiracial and multicultural composition, as in the 'melting pot' United States or the 'rainbow nation' of South Africa. 'Culture' usually crops up as a criterion. Yet (as Chapter 13 has indicated), cultures are always (though of course to varying degrees) heterogeneous and contested. Think, for example, of age, gender, class and other variations and the coexistence of multiple sub-cultures and identities (which, as Chapter 21 has shown, are often related to distinctive 'local' territorialities) that characterize every supposedly 'national society'.

All this leads Anderson to declare that nations are in a sense 'imagined communities'. This imaginary status is not to deny that they are not in a sense real to those who feel they belong to them. Indeed, Anderson (1983: 6–7) feels that:

> In fact, all communities larger than primordial villages of face-to-face contact (and perhaps even those) are imagined. Communities are to be distinguished, not by their falsity/genuineness, but by the style in which they are imagined . . . Finally, it is imagined as community, because regardless of the actual inequality and exploitation that may prevail in each, the nation

is always conceived as a deep, horizontal comradeship. Ultimately it is this fraternity that makes it possible, over the past two centuries, for so many millions of people, not so much to kill, as willingly to die for such limited imaginings.

Within all this is a profound territorial link between the nation and the state. The state claims to be a sovereign expression of the nation – bound to it and to a particular place. That is, it has territorial limits. The nation-state has a geography, which is charted, demarcated, mapped and represented to the 'national population' in their school atlases and geography lessons. Such a system of 'national' geographical representation is always combined with an historical vision, a grand narrative of 'national history', often assuming that the nation is ancient, even primeval.

Yet Anderson and other critical accounts of nationalism stress that it is very much a modern ideology. For what makes mass nationalism possible are certain socio-economic and technical transformations, notably the arrival of media and national educational systems. Schooling, newspapers, and later radio and television all help to promote and popularize the idea that people belong to and share in the nation. Whilst others have emphasized the longer historical roots of many nationalisms in pre-modern ethnic affiliations (for example, Smith 1988), for Anderson and most other critical observers, what is striking is nationalism's relative modernity. Even where nationalists imagine the nation as ancient, such an imagination is itself more often than not predominantly a nineteenth- and twentieth-century phenomenon. At a pinch, nationalism might be traced to the seventeenth century. But the ideology of the nation-state was not anywhere very evident before then. So whilst someone might talk about a thousand years (or more) of, for example, English or British, Korean or Indian national history, they

Plate 22.2 'Nation' imagined as race.

(Everett Historical/Shutterstock)

conveniently forget that English or British, Korean and Indian nationalisms are relatively modern concepts, much less than a thousand years old.

The tendency for nationalists is to 'reinvent the past', to pick out selective moments from the past, or to manipulate history (Hobsbawm 1996), whether this is in banal ways through the national curriculum of schools or through deliberate propaganda to mobilize the masses. Whilst history is undoubtedly significant, the nationalist brew would be incomplete without ancestral connections to 'homeland' and to particular places. In other words, territory is central to nationalism, and this is often why whenever there are divergent nationalist claims to one piece of land, extreme violence often follows. Indeed, the terrible forms of so-called 'ethnic cleansing' witnessed in the former Yugoslavia in the 1990s are illustrations of recent nationalist extremism and the significance of historical imaginations concerning territorial-political and cultural identity.

Nationalist narratives and claims are not always linked to such violent actions. At times they may be rather more rhetorical or theatrical. Graham E. Clarke (1996: 231–2) raises a particular Nepalese example:

> [I]n the 1960s in Kathmandu the sole national newspaper carried articles, no doubt read tongue in cheek by some educated Nepalese, arguing that since Lumbini, the birthplace of the historical Buddha (Gautama), was located some few five miles north of the current southern border, that Buddha was therefore Nepalese and not Indian.

All of this relates to the important issue of how we deal with things like space and identity in history. As Morris-Suzuki (1996: 42) writes:

> The nation . . . casts a long shadow backwards on our vision of the past, and channels our perceptions into a particular spatial framework. In my bookcase, I have a volume on the history of Thailand since the tenth

century, which, considering the repeated political and cultural realignments within the space we now label 'Thailand', seems only a little more bizarre than its neighbour on the shelf, a history of the Soviet Union from palaeolithic times to World War II.

There has been a strong tendency to see nations and nationalisms as essentially being derived from American and European prototypes. It is important to challenge the idea that nationhood is a nationalist project originating in the West that was simply implanted onto the rest of the world without significant transformations in the various cultural, ethnic and religious contexts it touched. African, Middle Eastern or Asian variants of nationalism or constructions of statehood are far more than simply colourful (or failed) replicas of the European–American model(s). To be sure, imported idioms and motifs from Europe and America have been important; for example, the official state language in a fair number of former colonies is that of the old colonial power. And European (and less often United States) imperialism has provided an important backdrop to the trajectory of nationalisms in Africa and Asia, not least because the anti-colonial nationalists themselves were often educated in Western institutions and adopted concepts such as self-determination, national liberation and territorial sovereignty in their political struggles against the colonial powers. Yet whilst 'globalizing' capitalism and especially imperialism are part of the picture, African, Middle Eastern and Asian nationalisms are also (like those of Europe and the Americas) rooted in local historical trajectories. In many cases these are of much longer vintage, often based on sophisticated cultural, religious and ethnic tapestries, some of the main patterns of which have subsequently been appropriated or (re)invented as pre-colonial 'national' histories.

Thus, we should perhaps think in terms of multiple histories and geographies of nations and states, and not just of particular European or American modular forms. The influential Bengali intellectual Partha Chatterjee (1993) has persuasively argued against the imagining of Indian national identity through the lens of the colonial power and stresses the 'essential' inner or spiritual domains of culture that were never colonized, never European. Furthermore, there are different coexisting national voices or 'fragments' – among women, peasants, elite, castes, outcasts, and so on – each with its separate discourse. As Stein Tønnesson and Hans Antlöv (1996: 32) put it:

> When the national idea entered Asia it could not be implemented without mediation, hence transformation, by indigenous agencies in particular settings. There were existing and alternative ideas with which

European-style nationalism interacted and inter-mixed . . . the nationalist ideas were invested with local qualities, meanings and nuances which could not be found in Europe. People had their own views on what constituted a legitimate social order, and such views could not be ignored by the modernizing leaders of the anti-colonial struggles.

As well as different cultural 'forms of the nation', we may also consider different gendered perspectives of nationalism and nation-states. Although Chatterjee's (1993) arguments are quite specific to the South Asian case, they do reveal the coexistence of different voices, men and women, and this relates to the point about nationalism and constructions of nation-statehood invoking different conceptions of 'manhood' and 'wom-anhood' more widely. Although there are immense histor-ical and geographical variations of this, there is a general tendency for women to be seen as particularly important transmitters of 'national culture' (for example, in the idea of a 'mother-tongue' language) (Yuval-Davis 1997) and as somehow the embodiment of the nation. McClintock (1994: 352) thus notes that:

> Nations are contested systems of cultural represen-tation that limit and legitimize people's access to the resources of the nation-state, but despite many nationalists' ideological investment in the idea of popular unity, nations have historically amounted to the sanctioned institutionalization of gender dif-ference. No nation in the world grants women and men the same access to the rights and resources of the nation-state.

Moreover, particular ideas of the 'family' are central to most imagined communities:

> Nations are frequently figured through the iconogra-phy of familial and domestic space. The term nation derives from [the Latin] natio: to be born. We speak of nations as 'motherlands' and 'fatherlands'. Foreigners 'adopt' countries that are not their native homes and are naturalized into the national 'family'. We talk of the 'Family of Nations', of 'homelands' and 'native' lands. In Britain, immigration matters are dealt with at the Home Office; in the United States, the president and his wife are called the First Family. Winnie Man-dela was, until her recent fall from grace, honoured as South Africa's 'Mother of the Nation'. In this way, despite their myriad differences, nations are symboli-cally figured as domestic genealogies.

In several European nationalisms (including 'British') one significance of this is that the sexist notion of women (usually grouped with children) supposedly as naturally inferior to men, or as requiring the protection of natu-rally more powerful men, frequently provided the prior backdrop to depicting hierarchies (between dominating and dominated classes, for example) within the nation as natural, like those of a family. A similar conception pro-vided part of the racist justification for overseas colonies. Peoples subject to colonial domination were often repre-sented in such racist terms as being equivalent to 'families' of black 'children' ruled by a 'benevolent' white father.

22.3 Constructing boundaries: upwards and outwards

States come in diverse shapes and sizes. But they all have boundaries (which, if they have a coastline, also extend into the sea and are governed by international protocols: see Stienberg 2001). The extract from Winichakul (1996) quoted at the start of this chapter noted how the 'ter-ritoriality' of the modern nation-state is of a bounded space: 'a certain portion of the earth's surface which can be easily identified'. Pre-modern dynastic realms and empires could make do with loose boundaries. But modern nation-states have felt it necessary to demarcate their boundaries, to iron out perceived irrationalities and anomalies, sometimes by going to war. In short, they have sought to nationalize and unify 'their' space and 'their' (national) populations and render them into known, sur-veyed and defensible sovereign territory and communi-ties. They also seek to order and frame 'nature'. In *The Nature of the State,* Whitehead *et al.* (2007) examine why a two-dimensional view of states is problematic, through foregrounding state-nature relations. A number of key issues emerge from 'excavating the political ecologies of the modern state' (the subtitle to their book). They cite the way that the Netherlands emerged as a nation-state through a dual process of building a global empire (extending to the Americas and South-east Asia) and reclaiming land from the sea as an example of how the regulation of nature is folded into a nation-state project. But similar examples can be found elsewhere in both pre-modern and contemporary states. Elden (2013: 49) likewise points to the significance of 'the political tech-nology of territory' with its associated 'biometrics and geo-metrics' used to 'secure the volume' in terms of both state security as well as environmental resource exploita-tion. In other words, state territory extends upwards into airspace and downwards into geological resources. For example, Biggs (2010) examines how successive states in Vietnam (pre-colonial, French colonial, national, regional and superpowers, such as the US during the Vietnam

War) have tried to extend their territorial, political and economic power over the 'fluid, volatile environment' of the Mekong delta. What he reveals is that nation-nature are constantly in some sort of flux, and that with every effort to contain, harness and transform nature, there are many ways in which the 'serpentine force' of the Cuu Long (Nine Dragons, the Vietnamese name for the Delta) is never entirely under full state control. Sea-level change, salt water intrusion, flooding, and siltation are all processes of change that require actions that make state-nature relations central to the logic of the nation-states, but also exceed their capacity and power.

The rise of geopolitics in the late nineteenth and early twentieth centuries represented a particular expression of these state-territorial rationalities (as Chapter 20 explored), with lots of ideas about nature folded into the arguments, but state rationalities have wider forms and deeper roots. The nineteenth-century invention and refinement of statistics (*state-istics* = the science of the state) and demography (*demos* = people, *graphy* = writing) and the establishment of geography (*geo* = earth, *graphy* = writing) as a university discipline and field of research are all part of this regime of knowledge and power where people are surveyed and made into subjects of nation-states. For states with land boundaries the occupation and official demarcation of the frontiers is an important part of this process.

Consider the example of the border that is often recognized as the oldest, more or less stable, still-existing border in the world, that between Spain and Portugal. The mutual recognition of the border between Spain and Portugal is usually traced in modern Spanish and (particularly) Portuguese history to the Treaty of Alcañices signed on 12 September 1297 (in fact, the date on the Treaty is 12 September 1335, but amongst other things, our conventions for counting years have altered since). The Treaty has acquired something of the status of a foundational text. In other words, it is interpreted as a kind of proof of the ancient historical basis of the nations concerned.

Yet the treaty was not signed in the name of states or 'nations'. Named after the Templar castle in which it was sealed and witnessed, the text of the treaty of Alcañices begins with the words 'In the name of God. amen.' and is signed in the presence of the Templars and other holy orders by those who describe themselves as:

> by the grace of God the King of Portugal and the Algarve and by the grace of God the King of Castille and Leon,

and has as its subject:

> towns, castles and lands, town boundaries, divisions and orderings . . . [disputes over which] have caused

many wars, homicides and excesses, as a consequence of which the lands of both [kingdoms] have been looted, burnt and ruined, weighing heavily on God . . . [and] because of our sins, risking the danger of losing them and them falling into the hands of our enemies in the faith and most gravely [causing] the violation of God's will and injury to the holy church of Rome and Christendom.

> (Cited in Martínez 1997: 15; our translation)

Moreover, the actual demarcation of the Portuguese–Spanish borderline had to wait until the nineteenth and twentieth centuries. Two formal delimitation treaties set out an agreed frontier and established mechanisms for its physical demarcation on the ground. But gone are 'amens' and references to 'the will of God'. Instead, the treaties (the first of 1864 for the northern half of the border and the second of 1926 for the southern half of the border) make reference to the need to impose order and well-defined demarcations, to 'eliminate the anomalous situation in which, in the shadow of ancient feudal traditions' (Tratado de Limites 1866: 1; our translation), some frontier areas (including a number of villages) were recognized as shared or common lands with usage rights by communities of both states/'nationalities'. Following the treaties, such areas were divided and the border, where not demarcated by a river, was marked on the ground by rectangular boundary stones every few hundred metres (although it took a couple of decades to put in place all the boundary markers and resolve local conflicts and differences over the 'fine-scale' division of lands). In other words, the Portuguese-Spanish case indicates how the epoch of modern nationalism (i.e. the nineteenth and twentieth centuries) saw what James Anderson (1995: 71) called:

> a territorialisation of politics, with a sharpening of differences at the borders of states and of nations between 'internal' and 'external', 'belonging' and 'not belonging', 'us' and 'them'.

By the same logic, or an extreme extension of it, minorities who do not 'fit in' sometimes have to be moved, murdered or deported – or, in the euphemisms of our times, 'cleansed' (see Sibley 1995). This has been associated with, for example, Nazi racial territorial visions of a Europe cleansed of Jews and Gypsies and an expanded racially pure Germany. The Nazi Holocaust represents an extreme case. But 'cleansing' or 'purification' of national space, amounting to the expulsion or murder of people defined as 'foreign' or 'alien', has been widespread in the twentieth century. There are examples from all continents: the creation of modern Turkey whose Armenian population were slaughtered in the second decade of the twentieth century (and which still has not resolved the status of its Kurdish minority); the creation of Israel in the 1940s, which was accompanied by the flight of indigenous Palestinian Arabs from territories deemed part of the new Jewish national state; the system of reservations for native Americans in the USA and Canada; the violent exchange of Muslim, Hindu and Sikh populations which accompanied the 1947 partition of India; the 1974 partition of Cyprus; the wars of the 1990s in the former Yugoslavia (see Case study 21.2); and the partition of Ireland. These logics have also produced calls for the modification of boundaries, sometimes resulting in violence and war. No continent has been without examples of such conflict and violence and it is probably impossible to find a state which has not at some time expelled people or murdered them in the name of some nation or other. Yet each nationalism must also be unique, establishing itself as different from others (even if the apparatuses of flags and anthems are superficially similar), constructing a sense of self against others who are defined as outside the imagined community. We will return to borders and borderlands in Section 22.5.

22.4 Nation-states as symbolic systems

As we have seen, the state is the bureaucratic expression of nationalism. This is not to say that a widespread sense of nationalism inevitably precedes the state. Indeed, what is often termed the state apparatus (everything from regulations governing schools, to tax inspectors and politicians) seeks to foster national subjectivities out of the frequently ambivalent and disparate array of identities contained by its boundaries. If, as has been argued by many, nationalism is akin to religion, then the state becomes its symbolic structure. When examining the superficially quite different cases of Australia and Sri Lanka, Bruce Kapferer (1988) claims that nationalism is itself a religion, owing to the fact that, as with most religious-like beliefs, nationalism demands the recognition (his word is 'reification', which means something more than this) of an all-encompassing entity (the nation). The nation fulfils the role of a sacred cause, something greater than any individual and something which may be worth dying for. The nation is the God or deity of the religion of nationalism and the state is its theology or temple. Moreover, as Herzfeld (1992: 37) notes:

> Every bureaucratic action affirms the theology of the state. Just as nationalism can be viewed as religion,

Plate 22.3 Representing the limits of the 'nation-state': boundary patrols.

(David R. Frazier Photolibrary, Inc./Alamy)

bureaucratic actions are its most commonplace rituals. There are other such everyday rituals: Hegel saw the reading of the morning newspaper as the secular replacement of prayer.

There are indeed many public rituals of nationality and statehood: coronations and remembrance days, military parades, national holidays, national prowess (or the lack of it) at football or the Olympics, swearing in of governments, state funerals. (Football in the United Kingdom is also revealing of the complexity of British nationalisms, and the existence of separate Scottish, English, Welsh and Northern Irish squads is a testimony to the limits to 'Britishness' and the endurance or 'revival' of other national affiliations.) In all these rituals, the nation is reaffirmed and the state performed and made to seem omnipresent, historical and real. Dramatic cultural or political events (as well as notable national sporting occasions, such as soccer World Cup or Olympic successes) covered by the media reinforce senses of national community. The events of 11 September 2001 were thus narrated in the United States as an 'attack on America'. It is also said, for example, that virtually every adult American alive at the time can recall where they were on hearing the news of the assassination of US President John F. Kennedy in 1963. Whilst his funeral, like that of Diana Spencer in 1997, became a global media spectacle, it was represented and felt most acutely as a kind of national loss.

But the nation-state also demands (like all effective religions) personal commitment and more minor ritualistic acts, many of which rest on a geographical imagination of inside and outside, belonging and otherness (see Taussig 1997). The anthropologist Michael Herzfeld (1992: 109) examines this theme and is worth quoting at some length:

> Nationalist ideologies are systems of classification. Most of them are very clear about what it takes to be an insider. That, at least, is the theory. In practice, however, divergent interpretations give the lie to such essentialist claims, as to take one prominent and current example, in the debate currently waging in Israel about the definition of a Jew. Such taxonomic [naming] exercises . . . are central to the very existence of the nation-state. All other bureaucratic classifications are ultimately calibrated to the state's ability to distinguish between insiders and outsiders. Thus . . . one can see in bureaucratic encounters a ritualistic enactment of the fundamental principles upon which the very apparatus of state rests. Seen in these terms, arguments about the number on a lost driver's license or an applicant's entitlement to social security do not simply challenge or reinforce the power of particular functionaries of state. They rehearse the logic of the state itself.

Not only that, but the whole exercise of state power gets taken for granted as the natural order of things. Only when many of those activities which are ascribed to the state are no longer carried out (in situations of war, for example) or when a person finds themselves on the wrong side of a state-sanctioned category (the wrong side of the boundary, the wrong side of the law) is the power (a power over life and death and thousands of lesser things) and the universality of the symbolic order of 'the state' revealed. The state claims the monopoly over these things. And for others to exercise judgment and to punish or to kill is 'to take the law into their own hands'. These things are reserved for the territorial state. But what if there is no state? Or as cultural anthropologist Bernhard Helander (2005: 193) asks: 'Who needs a State?' There are parts of the world where any semblance of effective state sovereignty has become so scattered, fragmented or ineffective in practice that other forms of rule and competing authority structures take over. For instance, Helander wrote about the complex power situations in Somalia affecting every single aspect of daily life, where 'any opinion expressed or action performed must always be positioned in the political landscape' of rival clans, warlords, and issues of ethnic, religious and cultural identity. In the contexts of atomistic and antagonistic power struggles we need to appreciate the local power configurations that enable communities to continue with everyday life in the absence of a meaningful state apparatus. Helander was critical of international organizations that tend to act too rashly in countries such as Somalia, often distributing massive sums of inappropriate aid according to the 'shifting agendas of foreign donors' and frequently without great familiarity with the nuances of the 'local' human, cultural and political landscape. Such perspectives would clearly be even more applicable in situations of failed international interventions creating uncertain and extremely dangerous regime changes, unpopular occupations, and an almost complete absence of any form of security for large segments of the population. This happened in parts of Iraq after the US-led invasion to depose the government of Saddam Hussein in 2003 and in Libya following uprising against Kaddafi and Western-led intervention to enable his overthrow in 2011. Arguably this was also the situation in Afghanistan in the 1980s, after the Soviet Union invaded to prop up a communist government in the capital city who faced rebellion in the more conservative countryside. Afghanistan then became a focus of Cold War geopolitical conflict (as was detailed in Chapter 20), laying the basis for many more years of confrontation, subsequent interventions (by the United States and its allies) and enduring state failure. In such situations, we may actually have to ask, 'What kind of State? Where and who are the authorities?'

Plate 22.4 Suvarnabhumi airport, Thailand – passport control signage.

(TCJ2020/Shutterstock)

22.5 Sovereigntyscapes: 'shadows', 'borderlands' and 'transnationalisms'

We have seen that the geographies of 'nations' and states do not always coincide (consider again the Kurdish case, described in Case study 22.1), and that national territorial histories are insufficient to account for ethno-histories, transnational identities and human mobilities (as illustrated in Case study 22.2). Thus sovereignty is rarely without contradictions or challenges from other states, potential states and nations. But how else might we think about the challenges to sovereignty and the historical and geographical complexity of nations? One way might be to think of political landscapes as 'sovereigntyscapes' (Sidaway 2003; Sidaway *et al.* 2005) containing varieties of countervailing tendencies, fragmented state sovereignty, ambiguous forms of sovereign control, and situations (such as Somalia, as noted above) where state authority may have collapsed or been replaced by various contending de facto forms of authority. Even when we consider the state as strong and central, we may view sovereignty as being 'graduated', whereby, as Aiwha Ong (1999: 217) observed, 'states make different subject populations, privileging one gender over the other, and in certain kinds of human skills, talents and ethnicities; it thus subjects different sectors of the population to different regimes of valuation and control.'

A variation on the theme of 'shadow networks' is to consider myriad cross-border connections between people that somehow circumvent or subvert state-centred rules and regulations. In some contexts, such as the European Union, cross-border links are actively fostered and promoted (along with a common market and internal freedom of capital and personal mobility) with the aim of fostering a supranational (beyond nation) community (Kramsch and Hooper 2004). In other cases (such as the USA–Mexican border) or places where there is large scale 'illegal' movement of people and goods, state power is defied or subverted. In this regard, Abraham and van Schendel (2005) draw upon a critical distinction between what states define as 'legal/illegal' and what ordinary people perceive as 'licit/illicit'. Thus many transnational movements of people, commodities and ideas are illegal because they defy the norms and rules of formal political authority, but they are quite acceptable, 'licit', in the eyes of the participants in these transactions and flows. Here the authors were not so concerned with the flows associated with big syndicates, but with the many 'microprocesses' and transactions that form 'everyday transnationality' in borderland spaces (van Schendel 2005: 55). Such transactions may involve kinship and family networks that were partitioned by superimposed boundaries,

Plate 22.5 War-making and with it a sense of shared struggle can be productive of national identity.
(Vacclav/fotolia)

but revived subsequently in new forms. We should try to avoid overly dualistic perspectives of 'trans-border' or 'transnational' flows, such as 'domestic/foreign', 'internal/external', 'legal/illegal', because by doing so, we would be perceiving flows entirely from rigid state-centred and fixed territorial positions. Even if we just consider state practices such as the enormous efforts of the US federal authorities in trying to keep 'illegal aliens' 'out' (Plate 22.3), there are many more countervailing actions at official, quasi-official, unofficial levels, trying to make sure that as many people 'get in' because of their enormous contributions to economic sectors (Andreas 2000).

Why is such work of relevance to ideas about 'nation' and the 'nation-state'? It is precisely the very everydayness of many cross-border interactions, movements and connections that raises big questions about the impression of solidity of spatially fixed notions of nationhood. Despite attempts to police them (indirectly resulting in the death of thousands of migrants in the recent decade as they seek to cross those fortified land-frontiers or are smuggled across dangerous maritime ones), the southern border of the United States and the maritime and land frontiers of many southern and eastern member states of the European Union exhibit similar porosity. Migrations have also produced significant transnational social networks, for example amongst Hispanics in the United States or Maghrebis in Europe or British and other Europeans in the settler-colonies of Australia and New Zealand.

22.6 Conclusions: the place of the nation-state?

There have never been so many states as there are today. In the nineteenth century a wave of new states (countries such as Argentina, Mexico, Bolivia) emerged in the Americas in revolt against Spanish and Portuguese empires. These American prototypes and the USA itself (which dates from 1776) provided an example to nationalists elsewhere in the colonial world. But it was not until the twentieth century that most of Africa and Asia could escape direct colonial domination. This frequently required violent 'national-liberation' struggles against entrenched resistance from the colonial powers and white settler populations and in due course, the United Nations became a key arbiter of such post-colonial projects. In the decades between about 1945 and 1975, dozens of new 'sovereign' states emerged in place of the old colonial map. The end of the Cold War saw a fresh crop, as the Soviet Union was succeed by 15 recognized sovereign states (and more that went unrecognized or are contested, such as Transnistria, along Moldova's border with Ukraine) and there have been several secessions since, yielding some universally recognized new states (such as Eritrea and South Sudan or most of those that succeed Yugoslavia) as well as others that are not universally recognized, such as Kosovo and some that operate as de facto states without any formal international recognition (such as Somaliland).

Yet, for many years the demise or decline of the state has been discerned or predicted, and such claims have of late become even more common in discourses about 'globalization'. These usually argue that the growing scale and power of transnational flows, particularly of capital (but also of people, ideas and religious affiliations, technologies and so on) is subverting the capacity of the state and weakening national identities. The nation-state is often described as being 'hollowed-out' or 'eroded'. In this view, the state no longer has the power to command, for example, the society and economy inside its boundaries that was once attributed to it. And such a 'hollowing out' is sometimes seen to point the way to a post-national world (or some kind of shared global culture in which national cultures are replaced by a more hybrid, but common global mixture).

Yuval-Davis (1997, reprinted in Brenner *et al.* 2003: 322) pointed to the lack of congruence between nations and states, arguing that there is often a lack of 'overlap between the boundaries of state citizens and "the nation"', which requires us to have a much more 'multi-layered' notion of people's citizenship needs, 'because people's membership in communities and polities is dynamic and multiple'. And, as we have seen, in recent years, the sovereignty of many states has also been questioned through imperial 'interventions' in the name of humanitarian intervention or the 'war on terror'.

Others object that transnational forces of 'globalization' are really nothing new and that capitalism in particular has shown itself to be able to coexist with states and nations and in symbiotic relationship with them. In other words, they reinforce each other. Moreover, 'globalization' is not only massively uneven (as we have seen in earlier chapters) but as likely to produce local backlashes as a universal culture of, say, the same fast food, drinks and soap operas and political orientations everywhere in the world. That is, the technologies of capitalism (particularly media) provide the preconditions for strengthening, rather than undermining, imagined communities of nationalism, while states still act to fine-tune the regulatory frameworks for continued capital accumulation (resorting where needed to force to suppress opposition). States still enact laws about business, trade unions, property rights and so on. Everywhere, buying a property or land or setting up a legal business requires some kind of registration with the state. No amount of globalization has ended this. However, instead of further entering the large and complex debates about the impacts of 'globalization' on nations and states, let us return to the conception of the state as a symbolic system, and as a complex of representations. The historian-philosopher and activist Michael Foucault (1979: 29) (see too Spotlight box 24.2) argued in one of his most famous essays that:

> We all know the fascination which the love, or horror, of the state exercises today; we know how much attention is paid to the genesis of the state, its history, its advance, its power and abuses, etc. . . . But the state, no more probably today than at any other time in its history, does not have this unity, this individuality, this rigorous functionality, nor, to speak frankly, this importance; maybe after all the state is no more than a composite reality and a mythicised abstraction, whose importance is a lot more limited than many of us think.

Hence, to recognize the state as, in part at least, a symbolic system is also to recognize that, as Rose and Miller (1992: 172) argue: '"the state" itself emerges as an historically variable linguistic device for conceptualizing and articulating ways of ruling'. In other words, things like the 'nation' and the 'state' are made real mainly in certain words, texts (including maps) and deeds, that is, in language and action. The nation-state is an historically specific way of governance that links land, nation, population and polity. Think again of the staging of those national sporting, political and cultural occasions, which bring the nation home, and the more mundane or bureaucratic acts of state, such as the display of maps in schools and public buildings or the action of showing a passport or filling in a form with your national (insurance, social security, registration or identity) number.

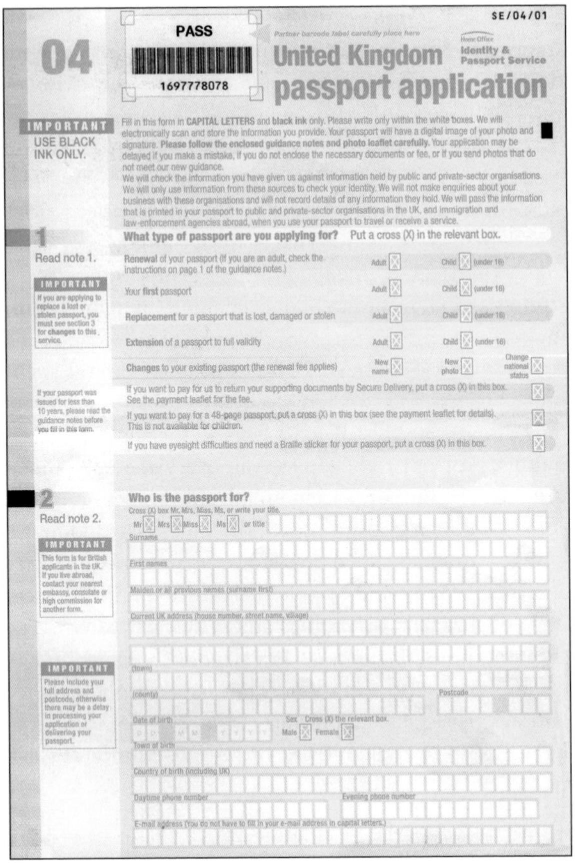
SE/04/01

04

PASS

1697778078

Partner barcode label carefully place here

Home Office Identity & Passport Service

United Kingdom passport application

IMPORTANT USE BLACK INK ONLY.

Fill in this form in **CAPITAL LETTERS** and **black ink** only. Please write only within the white boxes. We will electronically scan and store the information you provide. Your passport will have a digital image of your photo and signature. **Please follow the enclosed guidance notes and photo leaflet carefully.** Your application may be delayed if you make a mistake, if you do not enclose the necessary documents or fee, or if you send photos that do not meet our new guidance.

We will check the information you have given us against information held by public and private-sector organisations. We will only use information from these sources to check your identity. We will not make enquiries about your business with these organisations and will not record details of any information they hold. We will pass the information that is printed in your passport to public and private-sector organisations in the UK, and immigration and law-enforcement agencies abroad, when you use your passport to travel or receive a service.

1 Read note 1.

What type of passport are you applying for? Put a cross (X) in the relevant box.

Renewal of your passport (If you are an adult, check the instructions on page 1 of the guidance notes.) Adult ☒ Child ☒ (under 16)

Your **first** passport Adult ☒ Child ☒ (under 16)

Replacement for a passport that is lost, damaged or stolen Adult ☒ Child ☒ (under 16)

Extension of a passport to full validity Adult ☒ Child ☒ (under 16)

Changes to your existing passport (the renewal fee applies) New name ☒ New photo ☒ Change national status ☒

IMPORTANT If you are applying to replace a lost or stolen passport, you must see section 3 for **changes** to this service.

If you want to pay for us to return your supporting documents by Secure Delivery, put a cross (X) in this box. See the payment leaflet for the fee. ☒

If you want to pay for a 48-page passport, put a cross (X) in this box (see the payment leaflet for details). This is not available for children. ☒

If you have eyesight difficulties and need a Braille sticker for your passport, put a cross (X) in this box. ☒

If your passport was issued for less than 10 years, please read the guidance notes before you fill in this form.

2 Read note 2.

Who is the passport for?

Cross (X) box Mr, Mrs, Miss, Ms, or write your title.

Mr ☒ Mrs ☒ Miss ☒ Ms ☒ or title

Surname

First names

Maiden or all previous names (surname first)

Current UK address (house number, street name, village)

(town)

(county) Postcode

Date of birth D D M M Y Y Y Y Sex Cross (X) the relevant box. Male ☒ Female ☒

Town of birth

Country of birth (including UK)

Daytime phone number Evening phone number

E-mail address (You do not have to fill in your e-mail address in capital letters.)

IMPORTANT This form is for British applicants in the UK. If you live abroad, contact your nearest embassy, consulate or high commission for another form.

IMPORTANT Please include your full address and postcode, otherwise there may be a delay in processing your application or delivering your passport.

Plate 22.6 Identifying citizenship.

The political geographer Joe Painter (2006: 753) called this 'prosaic stateness', 'the mundane practices through which something which we label "the state" becomes present in everyday life'. According to Painter (2006: 753) therefore:

> Behind each of these registration numbers, licenses and certificates are yet more documents and records held in state archives tracking employment, earnings, criminal convictions, academic performance, visits to doctors and hospitals, ownership of vehicles and landed property and numerous other features of individuals' 'private' lives. If weighed down by anxieties about the scope of the state's knowledge of us, we repair to the local pub for a drink, we will find that the state decides when and where the pub can open, the possible sizes of our serving of beer, how much of its price goes in tax . . . how our drinks are labeled . . . hygiene required in the pub kitchen and the minimum wages paid to the staff.

He might have added that in many places states (including the USA during the 1920s' 'prohibition' era) have outlawed the sale or production of alcohol altogether and that all states seek (with varying degrees of coercion and persuasion and success) to regulate or proscribe the consumption of other intoxicants. In this, as in other aspects of their regulatory, ideological and coercive power, perhaps nation-states exist above all as systems of actions and beliefs – an 'imagination' if you like – which must be continually re-enacted, re-narrated and re-imagined as territorial sovereign spaces in order to seem important and real to us. Just as they have been here. And as they will be should you go to a pub, or perhaps even to a café, classroom or canteen instead.

Learning outcomes

Having read this chapter, you should understand that:

- Nations, nationalism and states are complex historically and geographically variable phenomena.
- Nationalism is an ideology (a system of beliefs) which holds that people have a primary identity to a particular nation and that such communities should be able to express themselves in a geographically defined state.
- Nations can be understood as a kind of imagined community. They are imagined because not all members of a national community can know each other.
- Such national imaginaries contain a geography, a mental map of national space and its boundaries.
- Nation-states embody particular ways of governing population, nature, territory and economy: these modes of governance are variable in space and time (the role of the state has and continues to change) – and new modes and scales (such as the supranational project of the European Union) of governance have emerged.
- National imaginaries are also gendered, for example in the idea of mothers as key transmitters of 'national culture' to the next generation.
- States can be understood as complex symbolic systems.

Further reading

Anderson, B. (1983) *Imagined Communities: Reflections on the Origin and Spread of Nationalism,* Verso, London. A revised (third) edition (2006) is available. Readable and rewarding. It is worth comparing Anderson (who stresses the modernity of nations and nationalism) with another theorist who argues that many nations do have much deeper historical roots:

Smith, A. (1988) *The Ethnic Origin of Nations,* Blackwell, Oxford.

For a rejoinder to Anderson that stresses the roles of colonial history and the United Nations in crafting nation-states, see:

Kelly, J. D. and Kaplan, M. (2001) *Represented Communities: Fiji and World Decolonization,* University of Chicago Press, Chicago, IL.

Nairn, T. (2003) [original 1977 reprinted 1981] *The Break-up of Britain,* Common Ground Publishing, Altona and Big Thinking Edinburgh (2003 edition). The earlier editions can usually be found in libraries and a section of the 2003 one is also online. A classic study of the twists and turns of the British state and its English, Welsh, Scottish and Irish allies and opponents. It is worth reading in tandem with Gilroy, P. (2002) [originally 1987] *There Ain't no Black in the Union Jack: The Cultural Politics of Race and Nation,* Routledge, London (2002 edition).

Taylor, P.J. and Flint, C. (2007) *Political Geography: World-Economy, Nation State and Locality,* Prentice Hall, Harlow. Now in its fifth edition, this text may be consulted for further ideas on most political geography topics, including a treatment of nations and nationalism.

For accounts of how borders are changing, yet sometimes attitudes towards them as somehow 'natural' persist, compare:

Amoore, L. (2006) Biometric borders: Governing mobilities in the war on terror, *Political Geography,* 25, 336–51.

Fall, J.J. (2010) Artificial states? On the enduring geographical myth of natural borders, *Political Geography,* 29, 140–7.

For an argument about (and case-study exemplifying) how state borders can productively be studied, see:

Megoran, N. (2006) For ethnography in political geography: experiencing and re-imagining Ferghana Valley boundary closures, *Political Geography,* 26(10), 622–40.

For two engrossing studies of border-making in South-east Asia, see:

Baird, I.G. (2010) Different views of history: shades of irredentism along the Laos-Cambodia border, *Journal of Southeast Asian Studies,* 41(2), 187–213.

Harris, I. (2010) Rethinking Cambodian political discourse on territory: genealogy of the Buddhist ritual boundary (sīmā), *Journal of Southeast Asian Studies,* 41(2), 215–39.

The second one of these is particularly suggestive on how deep-seated cultural and political practices interact with modern assumptions of sovereignty to produce a situation where: 'From Independence onwards the status of the national border has grown into a grand obsession and Cambodia's political elites have, usually as a means of whipping up nationalist sentiment and the fear of being swallowed up, chanted the same basic mantra to the effect that the border is continually being violated by neighbouring states' (pp. 216–17).

For more general reviews of scholarship on borders:

Diener, A. C. and Hagen, J. (2009) Theorizing borders in a 'borderless world': globalization, territory and identity, *Geography Compass,* 3(3), 1196–216. See too their (2012) *Borders: A Very Short Introduction* (Oxford University Press). For a guide to further literature, see: Sidaway, J.D. (2015) Mapping border studies, *Geopolitics,* 20(1), 214–22.

For accounts of death and suffering at the external borders of the EU, see:

Van Houtum, H. (2010) Human blacklisting: the global apartheid of the EU's external border regime, *Environment and Planning D: Society and Space,* 28, 957–76. Since this was published, the scale of death and suffering has increased.

THE GEOGRAPHIES OF CITIZENSHIP

Chapter 23

Richard Yarwood

Topics covered

- Citizenship
- Nation-state
- Activism and active citizenship
- Human Rights

23.1 Introduction: citizenship and place

Citizenship matters. Without it you are unable to access easily many basic rights such as education or welfare benefits. It is a precondition of being able to work and move legally within and between countries. Being a citizen may also foster a feeling of belonging or even a sense of duty and a desire to serve a wider community. Citizenship is also geographical; it is something that is only given meaning when it is put in a spatial context. You are a citizen of a place, be it a formally recognized country or an informal community. You may also see yourself as a citizen of the world, keen to engage in international politics or actions aimed at tackling global issues such as climate change or unfair trade. At the same time, local places and sites provide a context for you to act as a citizen, be it through voting, writing to a councillor or simply taking part in many aspects of everyday life. This said, citizenship often operates in the background of life, subtle and unremarkable until it is disturbed. Perhaps you only consider it when presenting a passport at a border control (Plate 23.1) or if your rights are threatened in some way. When this slumbering giant is awoken, it can provoke protest, activism and even revolution. No wonder, therefore, that geographers are starting to take the idea more seriously and examine its social and political significance.

Citizenship traditionally referred to the relationship between an individual and a political unit. With this association comes an obligation for a person to fulfil particular duties and the state to assure certain rights. For example, in some states a citizen has an obligation to undertake national service, perhaps in the form of military duty. In turn, citizens have recourse to certain political, social and civic rights that are determined and enforced by national and international law.

Plate 23.1 Citizenship is most often associated with membership of a nation-state.

(Jan Mika/Shutterstock)

Yet, these seemingly straightforward statements belie that citizenship is a contested idea (Spotlight box 23.1). It is far from a universally agreed concept and, instead, is continually being disputed, renegotiated and redefined. Take, for example, the citizenship tests that have been introduced by many countries to prescribe what would-be citizens should know about the daily life, history, politics and tradition of their adoptive state. The Australian test tends to focus on European and Aboriginal histories with little attention given to the significance of Asian influences on Australian daily life. In the UK politicians have debated the relative merits of including questions on the UK's history over ones on current political-legal structures. And in any case, can a series of multiple-choice questions really get the essence of what it means to be a citizen? More often they advocate a particular view of citizenship, usually reflecting rather prescribed nationalistic ideas. Despite efforts to fix citizenship through tests, the idea is far too evasive to be captured in this way. Similarly, policies that have introduced various citizenship 'lessons',

Spotlight box 23.1

Defining citizenship?

Citizenship traditionally refers to a person's relationship with a nation-state. It defines who is or isn't a member of a country and the rights and duties associated with that membership. But citizenship refers to more than a set of laws that define a person's rights and duties in relation to a nation-state. Anderson *et al.* (2008) describe it as 'people's senses of belonging in relation to places near and far; senses of responsibility for the ways in which these relations are shape; and a

sense of how individual and collective action helps to shape the world in which we live'. Understandings of citizenship require consideration of the ways in which political structures shape, and are shaped by, personal identities, institutional structures, everyday actions and symbolic landscapes. Barker (2010) refers to citizenship as an 'unstable outcome of ongoing struggles'. It is therefore difficult to pin down, both as a concept and a lived reality. It is the contested, multiscalar and, perhaps, ephemeral nature of citizenship that makes it of interest to geographers.

'duties', 'service' and 'charters' have been criticized for following a particular vision of citizenship. Yet what is viewed as 'good' or acceptable citizenship is subject to contest (Staeheli 2011). There are stark differences, for example, between 'activist' citizens who seek to challenge governments, often through civil disobedience or direct action, and an 'active' citizen who responds to government calls to undertake voluntary work to replace services once provided by the state (Spotlight box 23.2).

These contrasts are important as different normative theories of citizenship can be used to evaluate gaps between what rights citizens are entitled to and the gap

Spotlight box 23.2

Electoral geographies, citizenship and beyond

Formal structures of government and governance reveal much about citizenship and the ability of individuals to engage with decision making and democracy at local and national scales (Plate 23.2). Universal suffrage is considered a key political right, and the right to vote has been fought for, sometimes using other civil rights including freedom of speech and the right to protest (see Case study 23.1, for example). It would be naïve, though, to assume that a universal right to vote implies equality amongst citizens. Geographers have critically examined electoral systems and the social and political outcomes of their organization (Johnston 2005). In some cases, electoral boundaries can be manipulated through practices such as gerrymandering (altering electoral boundaries to suit particular political parties) to influence the outcome of elections. Governments may also seek to allocate goods and services to particular places to solicit or reward support.

Other authors have examined how minority groups continue to be excluded from electoral politics (Secor 2004). Women, for example, are under-represented in positions of power; the young are less likely to vote and, conversely, parties may favour welfare benefits aimed at older votes, such as free travel on public transport, as they are deemed more likely to vote and, hence, influence the outcome of an election. It has been suggested that a disenfranchisement of some groups from electoral politics has contributed to a stratified decline in electoral turnout. In the UK's 2015 General Election, the comedian Russell Brand stated he would not vote in protest against a political system that has created a 'disillusioned underclass' and encouraged young people to do the same (although he later changed his mind and voiced his support of the Labour Party). Other commentators have also questioned who politicians are serving and whether multi-national cooperations now have more influence than democratically elected politicians. Noreena Hertz commented, 'as citizens we must make it clear to government that unless government focuses on people as well

Plate 23.2 Voting in elections is an important political right, yet many groups, including women and the young, are frequently under-represented in electoral politics.

(Asianet-Pakistan/Shutterstock)

as business . . . we will continue to scorn representative democracy, and will chose to shop and protest rather than vote' (Hertz 2001: 212). Others have argued that as many citizens do not participate in any political actions, a closer focus on social citizenship is required (MacKian 1995).

Much attention has been given to new structures of governance that combine governmental and non-governmental organizations and whether they offer 'active citizens' new or better opportunities to participate more fully in local decision making (Painter and Jeffrey 2009). Other geographers have paid attention to actions outside formal political structures that seek to challenge rather than comply with state readings of citizenship. The scope, nature and significance of these actions ranges from local, tactical protests to globalized campaigns that use space as part of a broader strategy of resistance (Spotlight box 23.3).

between these in reality. We might assume, for example, that all citizens should be treated equally but many people continue to be excluded from full citizenship in *de jure* (legal) or *de facto* (actual) terms on the basis of race, sexuality, gender, disability, age, wealth and other forms of social labelling (Smith 1989b). Studies of citizenship not only draw attention to social inequalities but the political structures that cause it and, significantly, how they can be challenged and changed. For example, the language of rights may be used to contest racism, exploitation in the workplace, or poor access to services (Tonts and Larson 2002). New forms of political engagement, such as women's cooperatives in the majority world, can form a platform for new voices to be heard and empowered.

Understandings of geography and citizenship are deeply and mutually intertwined. Citizenship 'marks a point of contact between social, cultural and political geography' (Smith 2000: 83) and challenges us to think across our various sub-disciplines. At the same time, citizenship requires an appreciation of geography. Its multi-scalar nature (Painter 2002) means that 'geography as a discipline is uniquely placed to work through what citizenship may mean at a wide diversity of levels' (Askins and Fuller 2006: 4). This chapter explores the exciting relationship between geography and citizenship across a series of spaces from the local to the global. It starts by considering the nation-state, which is still seen by many as the bedrock of citizenship.

23.2 Bounded citizenship

Citizenship has been described as a bounded concept (Isin 2012). This is in two ways. First, citizenship is widely defined as membership of a political community that has formally recognized boundaries (Smith 2000). In other words, citizenship is territorial and *bound into* the dimensions of a particular geographical unit. Second, citizenship might be thought of as 'social glue' that binds people to each other and a territory. It promotes feelings of belonging, identity, duty and entitlement.

Over time, the territories of citizenship have changed (Painter and Philo 1995). The idea originated in the Classical period, which, in turn, influenced ideas and practices of citizenship in the West (Bellamy 2008). Greek citizenship, for example, was associated with the territory of a particular city-state and could not be transferred to another. The duties of citizenship were onerous and required an active contribution to public life through political, civil, legal and military service. Classical citizenship was exclusive: to be a citizen of Athens was to be male, over 20, born to an Athenian citizen family, a

warrior, a patriarch and an owner of slaves. Although contemporary citizenship aims to be inclusionary and more equitable, exclusion continues to cast a 'long shadow' across the concept (Bellamy 2008). For example, despite universal suffrage in the West, the geographies of elections reveal much about social difference and power (Spotlight box 23.2).

Contemporary citizenship emerged with and continues to be strongly associated with the Western nation-state (Turner 2012) and, for most, is simply conferred by birth within the territory of a state (*jus soli* or 'law of the soil') or through family or ethnic descent (*jus sanguinis* or 'law of the blood') (Bauder 2014). These categories can be subject to contest. In 2004, a referendum in the Republic of Ireland led to an amendment of its constitution to remove citizenship from any future Irish-born children of immigrant parents (Tormey 2007). The favouring of *jus sanguinis* over *jus soli* reflected concerns about a perceived increase in immigration, especially by asylum seekers, and 'baby tourism.' Tormey (2007) suggested that the referendum succeeded as its advocates successfully positioned citizenship as 'a moral regime' with foreign nationals, their offspring and foetuses as 'suspect patriots'.

Being a citizen of a country contributes to its sense of national identity and is an important part of state-building (Jones *et al.* 2004). It confers a sense of membership that, like membership of any organization, determines what someone is entitled to (rights) and what he or she is expected to contribute (duties). Precisely how citizenship has been defined and practised has varied over time and space, reflecting a state's political and social history (Case study 23.1).

T.H. Marshall's (1950) key essay 'Citizenship and social class' outlined the growth of civil, political and social rights over time in Britain (Table 23.1). Marshall noted that the development of a national set of rights brought with it a shift in the geographical focus of citizenship, from the local to the national. Thus, national institutions and bureaucracies replaced local charities in the provision of social rights. Marshall argues that as the institutions responsible for these rights became remote, citizens needed to employ experts or intermediaries to recognize and realize the rights afforded to them. Offices of the welfare state, for example, advise upon and deliver (or increasingly deny) social benefits to those in need of them. It has been suggested that this has led to a 'thin' or passive form of Liberal citizenship, one where the citizen expects rights to be delivered to him or her by the state rather than contributing to their delivery (Desmoyers-Davis 2001). Other forms of citizenship have developed in other places. Republican models, for example, have led to 'thicker', more active form of citizenship that places greater emphasis on the duties of citizens. These ideals

Case study 23.1

The complex citizenship of Hong Kong

In 1997 Hong Kong ceased to be a Crown Colony of the United Kingdom and reverted to the authority of the People's Republic of China. In accordance with the 1984 Sino-British Joint Declaration, which guaranteed continuity in its capitalist economy and lifestyle for 50 years after the hand-over (Kean 2010), Hong Kong has been run as a Special Administrative Region (SAR) of China.

Under British rule, efforts were made to pacify the people of Hong Kong in light of 'Maoist' influences from mainland China: citizenship was regarded by many 'as a matter of holding passports and enjoying some degree of civil liberties' (Shiu-Hing 2001: 127). After 1984 more Hong Kong residents began to demand and apply rights of political participation. In part this reflected a feeling by many citizens who felt that self-determination was being denied to them by both the British and Chinese states.

Yet many of Hong Kong's residents, particularly the skilled or wealthy, have sought to use citizenship as a personal strategy. There has been large-scale immigration to countries that offered dual citizenship, such as Canada or Australia, especially in times of perceived crisis. This form of transnational citizenship is seen by some as offering 'an escape route' if the autonomy of the region is ever threatened. Pivotal events have led to periods of net emigration, including the signing of the Sino-British Joint Declaration in 1984, the Tiananmen Square massacre in 1989, the outbreak of the SARS virus in 2003 and the global financial crisis in 2009. Yet Hong Kong also experienced immigration from China that became the subject of progressively tighter legislation. Currently some 'one-way' permits are offered to those from China with skills and qualifications in the information technology and financial service sectors rather than those who might become a burden upon the welfare system.

The current citizenship of Hong Kong is complex. In *de jure* terms Hong Kong citizens are citizens of China but the 'one county, two systems' paradox means that Hong Kong's citizens enjoy political and civil rights that have not been afforded to citizens in the rest of China – such as the right to travel, protest and read a free press. Many citizens identity more strongly with Hong Kong than China, refusing to acknowledge the Chinese national day and resenting political interventions from Beijing (Degolyer 2001).

This said, there is also a strong faction that supports closer ties with Beijing.

In September 2014, Hong Kong's Central District and other areas of the city were occupied by students protesting for democratic reform. More precisely, the protests centred on proposals to reform the election of Hong Kong's Chief Executive in 2017. Although the principal of universal suffrage had been agreed by the Chinese Government, in August 2015 Beijing ruled that voters would have a choice of three pre-approved candidates. This prompted the formation of the 'Occupy Central' movement to campaign for pan-democracy. Their actions were essentially part of a tactical protest in aid of specific rights, and so differs from the wider Occupy movement (Case study 23.4), which sought wider reforms of the capitalist economy. Both, however, used the tactical occupation of symbolic space to bring supporters together and draw maximum attention to their causes.

Occupy Central held marches, conducted an unofficial ballot (in which nearly 800,000 people voted to oppose the reforms) and proposed an occupation of the Central District on 1 October 2014, China's National Day. In the event, the occupation was prompted by students who had organized a boycott of lectures. As numbers grew, Occupy Central activists joined the students. There were efforts to break up the occupation by riot police using tear gas. In response, protestors deployed umbrellas, usually carried as protection against the sun, which soon became the symbol of the movement. The robust response by authorities also prompted greater numbers to join the protests and a largely peaceful stand-off occurred with the authorities. Indeed, the BBC reported how polite and well-ordered the event was with protestors acting as 'good citizens' by tidying litter, doing homework and apologizing for the disruption. Although illegal, the protest was 'allowed' to take place relatively peacefully, reflecting Hong Kong's autonomous position. Protests by students in Tiananmen Square in 1989 were violently repressed by the Chinese security forces with the loss of an estimated 2,000–3,000 lives. These events remind us that rights are rarely given away but represent the outcome of struggle between citizen and state.

Hong Kong's position as a global city made direct intervention from the Chinese government less likely: to do so would damage a valuable and developing territorial and trading asset. While occupations occurred in various places in Hong Kong, the main one centred on the Central Financial District. This was not only to cause maximum disruption to global business but also because the area had become strongly associated with Hong Kong's emergent post-colonial identity (Law 2002). The symbolic space (Plate 23.3) of the Central District was subverted using street art, slogans and a sense of carnival to draw attention to Occupy' Central's demands. Over time, people dissipated from the protest sites although there were interventions from Hong Kong's police. The situation remains fluid and it remains to be seen how protestors and the authorities (of both Hong Kong and China) will respond in the longer term to popular demands for democratic reform in Hong Kong.

Plate 23.3 The Occupy Central protest in Hong Kong. The site of the protest was chosen for its symbolism as well as its connections with the global economy and, thus, media.

(coloursinmylife/Shutterstock)

Table 23.1 The development of rights in the UK

	Timescale	Significance	Evidenced in
Civil rights	18th century	'Necessary for individual freedom-liberty of the person, freedom of speech, thought and faith, the right to own property and to conclude valid contracts and the right to justice'.	Courts and judicial system
Political rights	19th century	'The right to participate in the exercise of political power, as a member of a body invested with political authority or as an elector of the members of such a body'.	Parliament and local government
Social rights	20th century	'A modicum of economic welfare and security to the right to share to the full the social heritage and to live the life of a civilised being according to the standards prevailing in the society'	Education, social welfare provision

Source: after Marshall (1950[1992]), all quotes on p.8

reflect a wariness of state power and, instead, favour self-governance and self-determination at the local level. Republican citizenship is significant in the USA (Staeheli 2005), where participation is encouraged through town-hall meetings, religious congregations, and participation in voluntary and civic groups (Turner 2002).

Both of these models are based on the experiences of Western countries and ideas of citizenship have tended to reflect European values (Isin 2005: 35). This is in part because the nation-state emerged from the European geo-political arena. As European powers colonized other parts of the world, the European model of state-citizenship was imposed on them (Isin 2002, 2005). The nature of Imperial Citizenship ranged widely. At the one extreme were exclusionary and paternalistic ideas. Thus indigenous Australians were not granted citizenship until 1968 (when they were also included in the census for the first time). Prior to this indigenous Australians were *wards*, not citizens, of the state and with very few rights. They were unable

to marry, work or travel without the permission of the state; sale of alcohol, land and property was prohibited; mobility was restricted; and parents had no legal rights over their children. Other forms of Imperial Citizenship attempted to provide equal rights for colonized peoples. Prior to 1983, Citizens of the UK and Colonies had the right to work and live in Britain as well as to hold a British passport and vote in UK elections. Ultimately, though, Imperial Citizenship was unable to reconcile forms of citizenship based on kinship and community (found in many non-Western countries) with individualistic notions of citizenship based on political rights (Gorman 2006).

In many places, tensions remain between forms of citizenship based on nation-states and other associations based on kinship, tribes and belief. This has led Isin (2012: 567) to conclude that it is now 'difficult to imagine citizenship merely as nationality or membership in the nation-state'. It is important to move beyond Western definitions and linguistics to appreciate how citizenship plays out in different cultural settings. McEwan argues that the concept of citizenship is 'unable to recognize either the political relevance of gender or of non-western perspectives and experiences' (2005: 971). Her work in South Africa draws attention to the ways in which marginalized people, including women, the young and unemployed youths, have carved out alternative spaces away from traditional, male-dominated political assemblies from which they can be heard. Other authors have also pointed to the growing importance of places above and between nation-states to citizenship (Desforges *et al*. 2005), as the next section examines.

23.3 Beyond boundaries

For some groups of people wider opportunities to travel, work and live *between* states have led to what has been termed 'transnational' citizenship, which draws on the rights and identities of more than one country (Ho 2008). In 2013, there were over 231 million migrants on a global level and, between 2000 and 2013, these numbers increased by 2.2 per cent (UN 2013). Migration has not only accelerated but has become increasingly differentiated, with multiple forms and entry points reflecting social difference at a global scale. On the one hand, this so-called 'Age of Migration' (Castles and Miller 2009) has loosened the moorings of citizenship from the nation-state but, on the other, has led to increased efforts to assert the significance of the nation-state as the primary determinant of citizenship.

It has been argued that new and significant forms of international migration and mobility are indicative of new forms of transnational citizenship (Samers 2010). **Transnationalism**, as the name suggests, recognizes that ideas and practices of citizenship cross national boundaries and flow between their borders, rather than being confined by them. By implication, the nation-state becomes less significant in the determination and regulation of citizenship (Case study 23.2).

Yet, transnationalism has also prompted responses from nation-states. States experiencing net emigration have attempted to redefine citizenship for their own advantage. Mexico, for example, has sought to extend citizenship to emigrants in order to benefit economically from its citizens who have moved abroad (Escobar 2006). Indeed, more people than ever before hold dual citizenship (Sassen 2002), reflecting a response by states to claim mobile citizens as their own.

Many states have also sought to reassert national sovereignty and citizenship. In many countries quotas on numbers of migrants, stringent border security, the streamlining of removal processes, confinement of asylum seekers, citizenship tests, a lack of welfare support and the withdrawal of rights to work all represent a fortification of state boundaries and make it harder for migrants to achieve citizenship. Such policies have sought to stratify citizenship and migration. Samers (2010) identifies a continuum that encompasses full citizens of a single nation-state; dual, transnational and cosmopolitan citizens with varying rights and duties; denizenship; and, finally, illegal residents and aliens with few or no rights.

In contrast to the 'super rich', 'super-mobile' citizens, temporary and 'illegal' migrants can suffer economic

Case study 23.2

Transnational citizenship in the European Union

The 1992 Maastricht Treaty established the precedent of European Citizenship that was awarded to citizens of its member states in addition to their already-held national citizenship. This meant, for example, that a citizen of France also became a citizen of the European Union super-state (Ferbrache and Yarwood 2015). With this status came the right for most EU citizens to live, work and move between the states of the EU (most but not all: following expansion in 2004 and 2006 many member states restricted the right of citizens from accession states to migrate and work in their territories). European citizens availing themselves of these rights have contributed to the development of transnational business networks, wider forms of

political participation and the growth of employment markets across Europe (Favell 2003). Strüver (2005) also found that regular cross-border movements of Dutch citizens living in a German border town identified as being transnational European citizens rather than of one nation. In some circumstances transnational citizenship has allowed physical, imaginative and communicative travel between countries to the extent that it is getting harder to distinguish places of origin from places of settlement. Instead, they are simultaneously linked in economic, cultural and emotional ways (Ho 2008).

There is, however, growing resistance to this form of transnational European citizenship, witnessed by a surge in right-wing populist political parties that are seeking to withdraw their nation-states from Europe and European political influence.

exploitation social hostility with few rights. The United Nations Refugee Agency has estimated that there are ten million people without a state, with no legal recourse to education, travel, work, healthcare and even a home as these often depend on having formal identification. Statelessness can arise from changes in state borders and instances where a person's parents have migrated to a state that does not permit nationality to be passed to children. States may also seek to revoke citizenship as, for example, has been discussed recently by some Western states in response to those who have travelled to support terrorist organizations.

Transnational practices and ideas have opened up the possibility of new spaces of citizenship but this form of citizenship remains the preserve of a few. If, as Cresswell (2009) contends, the right to be mobile is an significant aspect citizenship, then it continues to be denied to many.

23.4 Local citizenship: activist citizens

Mobility is an important signifier of citizenship but, for many people, citizenship is something that is played out in the localities where they live. Staeheli (2005: 196–7) comments that 'while nation-states may be where the formal standing as citizen is vested, it is largely through localities that the horizontal bonds of citizenship operate' to mobilize citizens and create identity. Thus, voting in local elections, writing to counsellors, engaging in planning enquiries, participating as governors of schools or campaigning for local services all offer opportunities for citizens to engage with the running of affairs in their locality and, in doing so, to exercise their political and civic rights.

Increasingly citizens are also expected to have a duty to participate in their localities (Cheshire and Woods 2009). Over recent years many Western neoliberal governments have developed policies aimed at encouraging 'active citizenship' or voluntary activity to provide or support local services. Examples include involving local citizenry in policing (Yarwood and Edwards 1995) (Plate 23.4), the provision of health care (Barnett and Barnett 2003), welfare (Conradson 2003) and housing (Yarwood 2002). New Zealand has followed these principles to such a degree that it has been regarded as 'a social laboratory of the world' (Tennant *et al.* 2008: 26).

The impact of these reforms has been geographically uneven, reflecting differences in local participation and community leadership. Some communities, usually middle-class ones, are better placed to organize and help themselves. This may lead to more parochial forms of citizenship in which vocal, well-organized and compliant local communities are granted more rights and duties than residents who are unable or unwilling to volunteer

Plate 23.4 Neighbourhood Watch is a voluntary crime prevention scheme in the UK that has embodied state-led ideas of active citizenship. It has found favour largely in middle-class areas.

(Bikeworldtravel/Shutterstock)

(Desforges *et al.* 2005). This can lead to a view that sees local communities, rather than deeper social or political forces, as the cause and solution of local problems (Rose 1996). Depending on how communities respond, they may be judged and rewarded with, or denied, further funding (Desforges *et al.* 2005).

In another development, many charities have been obliged to 'professionalize' their activities in order to win government funding or contracts (Milligan and Fyfe 2005). This is so much so that large, cooperatist charities have emerged that get most of the their funding from government rather than private donations. Jenifer Wolch (1990) referred to this as 'the Shadow State', reflecting that voluntary groups now do the government's work but appear separate from it.

Governments pursuing **active citizenship** policies have been criticized for passing the buck of welfare provision to the voluntary sector, reflecting a shift from Liberal to more Republican forms of citizenship (Case study 23.3). This said, those who volunteer often do so out of an ethical desire to help others rather than government policy or institutional mission statements (Cloke *et al.* 2007). Places such as soup kitchens give volunteers opportunities to act on personal, political, religious and altruistic beliefs.

Case study 23.3

Food banks: the dilemma of ethical citizenship

There has always been a 'moving frontier' between the state and voluntary sector in the provision of social welfare (Mohan 2003). Its position varies over time and space but, recently, it has been argued that the frontier has shifted away from the state and towards the third sector as a result of neoliberal reforms that have seen governments withdraw from the provision of social welfare. These debates have been encapsulated by a growing reliance on charity-run food banks in many countries.

Food banks originated in North America but are now found in most parts of the world. They are run by charities with the aim of distributing food directly or indirectly (via other charities) to people in need.

In many countries there has been a phenomenal increase in the numbers of people asking for support from food banks, especially following the 2007 recession. In the UK, the Trussell Trust estimate that they provided 913,138 people with food in 2013–14, compared to 25,889 in 2008–9 (see Trussell Trust website, www.trusselltrust.org/stats). The charity established its first food bank in 2004; it now has 423 with an average of two new ones opened each week. The European Food Banks states that it distributed 402,000 tons of food to 5.7 million people in 2013. According to Freedom America, one in seven families rely on food banks and associated food distribution programmes.

Food banks are intended as an emergency response to those without food. In the UK, food is only distributed to people who have been referred to a food bank from professionals such as doctors, social workers, the police or the Child Support Agency. This entitles them to three days of food that is intended to fill a gap caused by, say, a delay in welfare payments. Although food banks are intended as a stop-gap measure to supplement rather than replace the welfare state, critics have suggested that an insidious creep is occurring towards these kinds of charities providing more permanent forms of welfare (Cooper *et al.* 2014). For many, the increasing enrolment of food banks into the state welfare provision represent an abrogation of government responsibility (Cloke 2011) and a shift away from universal rights towards reliance on local charity. The growth of food banks not only points to the uneven terrain of citizenship, where the right to food seems unobtainable to many, but also a view that the voluntary sector are being given increased responsibility, even for fundamental issues such as hunger (Plate 23.5).

That said, many of those who volunteer to provide welfare are far from neoliberal policy dupes or apologists but, instead, act out of concerns driven by beliefs or ideals. Indeed, the space of the food bank or soup-run allows citizens to act on personal ideals of care. Cloke *et al.* (2007: 1095) have termed this a form of 'ethical citizenship' in which people volunteer 'because they *wanted* to rather than because they felt *obliged* to'. In some cases, these activities have been viewed as a form of resistance by drawing attention to gaps in welfare provision and challenging the state policies (Conradson 2003; Staeheli 2013). In Philadelphia, for example, there has been a long-standing conflict between organizers of soup-runs and the Mayor, who has repeatedly tried to ban them from public places. Although volunteering has become increasingly politicized, the ethics and motivations of individual citizen-volunteers remains important. An emphasis on the individual citizen (Staeheli 2011, 2013) and acknowledging his or her political and ethical entanglements with community, however imagined, is crucial to understanding how local places are shaped by citizen action.

Plate 23.5 Soup kitchens and food banks offer opportunities for people to act upon ethical and humanitarian convictions but may also reflect the state's withdrawal from social welfare provision.

(Radiokafka/Shutterstock)

23.5 Activist citizens and transnational networks

Active citizenship has been criticized for promoting duties over rights, volunteering above political participation and, implicitly or otherwise, supporting the neoliberal roll-back of the state. By contrast, it is possible to trace a range of 'deviant' actions that also use local sites to challenge state and corporatist power to assert social and political rights. In contrast to active citizenship, which is largely focused on changing neighbourhoods, activist citizenship is global in its concerns and reach (Parker 1999) (see Spotlight box 23.3).

The growth of **'New' Social Movements (NSMs)** reflect a feeling, popularized in books such as *No Logo* by Naomi Klein (2001), that conventional politics is failing to fulfil citizens' political rights. It is argued that

free-trade and deregulation have diminished the power of state governments and, consequently, the significance of electoral politics. As some multi-national corporations now have more power and wealth than many nation-states, they are more likely to respond to customers than citizens. In response, activist citizens have developed new forms of political action (Jones *et al.* 2004) that operate outside conventional political channels. Direct action, protest and consumer pressure are used to pursue economic, social, political and environmental goals (Routledge 2003).

NSMs are characterized by fluid alliances between diverse sets of people with various identities, affiliations and motivations that find expression in a particular campaign or form of resistance. Thus, a protest against the use of child labour might be supported by faith groups with a concern about social justice; trade unions seeking to improve employment rights; NGOs

---

Spotlight box 23.3

Active and activist citizens

Gavin Parker (1999) illustrates clearly the difference between 'active' and 'activist' citizenship (Table 23.2). 'Active' citizenship operates at spatial scales below the nation-state – neighbourhood, community and locality are emphasized – but generally in support of the state and its policies. Hence Parker describes them as 'good' in the sense that they obey laws and use formally recognized channels for action.

By contrast, activist citizens challenge the state and other institutions. They often mistrust authority and feel obliged to voice their concerns outside its formal apparatus using various forms of direct action that range in intensity, duration and legitimacy; from violent direct action to mundane acts of everyday consumption. Engin Isin (2008: 38) summarizes these differences in citizenship aptly:

> we contrast 'activist citizens' with 'active citizens' who act out already written scripts. While activist citizens engage in writing scripts and creating the scene, active citizens follow scripts and participate in scenes that are already created. While activist citizens are creative, active citizens are not.

They are labelled 'deviant' in the sense that they may depart from the law. What constitutes 'good' citizenship

Table 23.2 Citizen protest and action

Activist	Littoral zone	Active
'Deviant' citizen	⟷	'Good' citizen
'Protest'	⟷	'Participation'
'Negative'	⟷	'Positive'
Outside	⟷	Inside
Direct action	⟷	Due process
Unstable	⟷	Stabilized
Illegal/not legitimized	⟷	Legal/ legitimized
Visible	⟷	Obscured

Source: after Parker (1999)

is, of course, hugely subjective and reflects political and ethical standpoints. It reminds us that citizenship is not a static term but a contested one.

Although Table 23.2 is useful in drawing out different types of citizen action, it should not be thought of as a rigid binary. People may display both kinds of behaviour, depending on spatial and political context. One thing that is remarkable about New Social Movements is their ability to enrol a range of citizens, from Anarchist to Zapatista, into specific causes.

Case study 23.4

The Occupy movement

The Occupy movement started in Wall Street, New York in September 2011. Using the slogan 'We are the 99%', the Occupy movement drew attention to the dispropor-tional amount of wealth held by just 1 per cent of the population. Inspired in part by popular uprisings against authoritarian regimes in the Middle East (referred to in the media as the 'Arab Spring'), but using global activ-ist networks and social media, other occupations were established in 952 other cities in 81 countries. Occupa-tions centred on the spaces associated with or close to urban financial centres including La Defense in Paris, the Beurs World Trade Centre in Rotterdam and Dame Street in Dublin. All were organized, peaceful, leaderless and informal, establishing agreed norms of behaviour and cooperation. Sites were linked electronically and used commons symbols, notably the 'We are the 99%' logo and Guy Fawkes masks (Plate 23.6) based on the film V for Vendetta. Globally coordinated days of action were used to show solidarity and mirror the international reach of the corporations and individuals they opposed.

As well as wealth redistribution, Occupy also called for a reform of banking, a reduction in the political influ-ence of corporations, an end to austerity measures, job creation and democratic reform. Camps were supported by a wide range of interest groups that had a common grievance with laissez-faire capitalism and its conse-quences. These included trade unions, activist groups,

Plate 23.6 Occupy Wall Street was one site in a global protest by activists seeking to draw attention to social and economic inequality. The Guy Fawkes mask became a world-wide symbol of the movement.

(Daryl Lang/Shutterstock)

faith groups, politicians, academics and musicians. Marxist geographer David Harvey spoke at a number of meetings, encouraging anti-wealth (as opposed to anti-poverty) protests. By the end of 2012, protestors had been evicted from their sites by governments using legal injunctions enforced by the police. The Occupy movement continues to exist as an informally organized global network that draws attention to the inequalities caused by modern capitalism.

with a focus on protecting young people; Marxists seeking to resist free-trade capitalism and so on. These alliances extend across borders as activists in different countries share information and coordinate actions. These often crystallize in specific sites chosen for their symbolic meaning or potential to maximize the impact of a protest (Case study 23.4).

Peter Jackson (2010b: 139) also contends that glo-balized flows of ideas and cultures are leading to a form of transnational 'cultural citizenship'. Faith, politics, ethnicity and cultural practices may, for example, play a greater role in shaping identity as a citizen than loyalty to a nation. Desforges *et al.* (2005: 444) sum up these trends succinctly and optimistically:

> it is the connections to strangers without – living, working and dying – in other places that form some of the most important, and potentially liberating, new geographies of citizenship in the contemporary world.

23.6 Citizenship and everyday places

The study of active and activist citizens implies that citizenship involves some form of conscious engagement with politics and/or wider society. Yet, for many people citizenship is something that is rarely thought about; it might be acknowledged when crossing a border, reflected upon when living in another country or drawn upon when rights are lost. Sara MacKian (1995: 212) has argued that more attention should be given to citizens who are simply living out their daily lives rather than choosing 'to sit on committees or to shake boxes on flag days'.

Geographers have turned their attention to the importance of everyday spaces, such as shops, parks and schools, to the practice of citizenship in daily life. Painter and Philo (1995:195) have argued that:

> If people cannot be present in public spaces (streets, squares, parks, cinemas, churches, town halls) without

feeling uncomfortable, victimized and basically 'out of place', then it must be questionable whether or not these people can be regarded as citizens at all.

As was noted in the discussion of territoriality in Chapter 21, women, for example, may sometimes feel excluded from some public spaces, especially at night, due to the threat of sexual assault; gay people may feel it necessary to hide their sexuality in 'public'; and religious, 'racial' or ethnic difference may be the target of victimization, verbal or physical assault. In addition, those with physical disabilities may be unable to access sites, young people can be excluded from public space by curfews and the elderly may find it harder to find employment.

Although legislation has been enshrined to ensure equality, there is often a gap between *de jure* (legal) rights and whether these are manifest in daily life (*de facto*) (Smith 1989b). To take one example, Bell and Binnie (2000: 10) suggest that 'all citizenship is sexual citizenship' but it is often assumed to 'hetronormative' (i.e heterosexuality is the hegemonic norm) (Bell and Binnie 2006). Sexuality impacts on the right to marry or form civil partnerships; practice religion; work, including service in the military; migrate; travel; adopt children; participate in public events; and express national identity. Even where legislation has improved the rights of sexual minorities, for example in countries where same-sex marriage is legal, homophobic abuse may still occur on a de facto level and in particular institutional settings. Hubbard (2013), for example, outlines how two gay men were excluded from a London pub despite national legislation to ensure equality in terms of sexuality.

Some geographers have also drawn attention to the importance of non-public spaces in the formation of citizenship. Feminist scholars, for example, have noted that domestic spaces have often been ignored in the study of citizenship yet provide an important context for establishing and asserting women's and children's rights (Lister 2003; Chouinard 2009). Institutional spaces can also be important as they can attempt to shape the practice of what is viewed as 'good citizenship'. Schools and youth groups (Pykett 2009; Mills 2013) are particularly significant here, sometimes reflecting a view that children are 'citizens in making' (rather than citizens already) that need instruction so that they will be useful to society. Landscapes reflect citizenship idea through the ordering of buildings, monuments, open spaces, vistas and views (Jones *et al.* 2004); this is often linked to ideas of the nation-state (as Chapter 22 documented). In France, for example, through the twentieth century, the idea of a national identity was strengthened by the flying of a national flag (the tricolour), the use of the Gallic Coq as a national symbol, the construction of state buildings in prominent urban spaces and the erection of national war

memorials in public spaces (Baker 2012). In the second half of the twentieth century, the advent of postcolonial states in the wake of the decline of European imperialism led to the proliferation of such national symbols and rites of citizenship – such as national anthems, school and university systems, armies, as well as passport agencies and embassies. After the collapse of the Soviet Union (see Chapter 20) yielded 15 successor states, each new state had to establish norms, laws and symbols of citizenship, often raising thorny questions about who belonged and who would be refused citizenship and deemed a 'foreigner', since borders and citizenship rules had changed, even though they might still be living in the place where they were born.

Although the study of citizenship has traditionally concerned itself with political engagement in public spaces, it is clear that citizenship is about more than this. Citizenship is also about the way that people engage with spaces on an 'ordinary' basis (Steaheli *et al.* 2012). Although the formal rules and regulations that define citizenship are important, so too are the everyday negotiated practices that constitute belonging to a particular state or community. Thus, interactions in schools, homes, shops, nurseries and community groups help to establish migrants and their families as visible and valuable citizens in wider society (Bauder 2014). For example, Dominican immigrant shopkeepers were able to overcome anti-immigration sentiments in predominantly African-American and Puerto-Rican neighbourhoods of Philadelphia through daily negotiations with customers. Practices included flexible pricing, stocking 'boutique' services and allowing the shop to be used as a site of interaction between 'old' and 'new' groups of residents (Pine 2010).

The emphasis on cultural as well as political forms of citizenship have reflected a spatial shift in its study, from central, political spaces to everyday and sometimes marginal places. Indeed, Bullen and Whitehead (2005: 499) consider that the:

> contribution of geography to the study of citizenship has been . . . a changing spatial focus concerning where citizens are to be found – from the town hall to the ghetto; the public square to the private home; the city to the edge community.

23.7 Conclusions

This chapter has introduced the idea of citizenship and examined its significance across a range of geographical scales. Although traditional associations between individuals and the nation-state continue to have significance, it is clear that citizenship is more than this.

A person's identity as a citizen is not simply a reflection of national belonging but, rather, is shaped by a whole series of local and global cultural influences that are played out on a daily basis upon a range of scales (Jackson 2010b). It is a fluid idea that is not only defined by political engagement but, for some, *is* political engagement (Isin 2002). At the same time, others have also pointed to citizenship as being simply able to participate in everyday life, often in a political ways. This diversity is what makes the study of citizenship of interest to geographers. It pulls together social, cultural and political geographies to produce rounded, but not holistic, views of society and space. To quote from my own book, *Citizenship*:

> The idea of citizenship underpins concerns between individual identity and performance and understandings of broader political structures that shape, and are shaped, by these contexts. It offers a chance to bridge the personal and performative aspects of the cultural turn with the structural and institutional foci of political and social geography within variously and fluid spaces and places.
>
> (Yarwood 2014)

It does so across a multiple and coexisting range of scales, from the global to the local. Thus, a householder who chooses to recycle goods is simultaneously engaging with his or her state though the local council (who may provide a recycling service), as well with global initiatives to improve sustainability, and at the same time is acting in the private space of his or her home.

Geographers have not only engaged with citizenship academically but have also performed them through personal and varied forms of political and social engagements (Fuller and Kitchen 2004). The inclusion of citizenship in introductory textbooks such as this marks a recognition of its essential geography (Anderson *et al.* 2008: 39). To paraphrase Cloke *et al.* (2005: 603): citizenship matters, you matter, your citizenship matters. Having been introduced to geographies of citizenship, how and *where* will you practise citizenship for yourself?

Learning outcomes

Having read this chapter, you should be able to:

- Show how ideas of citizenship are contested over time and space.
- Illustrate the significance of citizenship to contemporary society using a range of international case studies.
- Appreciate how geography and citizenship are linked.
- Demonstrate how citizenship is played out at various scales, from the local to the global.

Further reading

For much more on the geographies of citizenship:
Yarwood, R. (2014) *Citizenship,* Routledge, London.
These journal articles provide critical and thoughtful discussions on the importance of studying citizenship using geographical perspectives:
Anderson, J., Askins, K., Cook, I., Desforges, L., Evans, J., Fannin, M., Fuller, D., Griffiths, H., Lambert, D., Lee, R., MacLeavy, J., Mayblin, L., Morgan, J., Payne, B., Pykett, J., Roberts, D. and Skelton, T. (2008) What is geography's contribution to making citizens?, *Geography,* 93, 34–9.

Desforges, L., Jones, R. and Woods, M. (2005) New geographies of citizenship, *Citizenship Studies,* 9, 439–51.

Painter, J. and Philo, C. (1995) Spaces of citizenship: an introduction, *Political Geography,* 14, 107–20.

Staeheli, L. (2011) Political geography: where's citizenship?, *Progress in Human Geography,* 35, 393–400.

The journal *Citizenship Studies* provides multidisciplinary perspectives on citizenship. There is no dedicated journal to geography and citizenship but special issues of geography journals on citizenship have included:

Political Geography, 14(2) (1995) The spaces of citizenship.

Journal of Historical Geography, 22(4) (1996) Geographical education and citizenship.

Urban Geography, 24(2) (2003) Cities and citizenship.

Space and Policy, 9(1) (2005) Geographies of citizenship.

Citizenship Studies, 9(5) (2006) New geographies of citizenship.

Political Geography, 25(8) (2006) Geographies of sexual citizenship.

ACME: An International E-Journal for Critical Geographies, 7(2) (2008) Geographies of everyday citizenship.

Geography, 95(3) (2010) Designing identity: exploring citizenship through geographies of identity.

Environment and Planning D: Society and Space, 30(1) (2012) Citizenship without community.

Any student of citizenship should study Marshall's classic essay and responses to it:

Marshall, T. (1950) *Citizenship and Social Class,* Pluto, London, 3–54. Cambridge University Press, Cambridge.

The following texts provide good introductions to different political formations of citizenship:

Bellamy, R. (2008) *A Very Short Introduction to Citizenship,* Oxford University Press, Oxford.

Isin, E and Turner, B (eds) (2002) *Handbook of Citizenship Studies,* Sage, London.

GLOBAL GOVERNANCE

Chapter 24

Klaus Dodds and Chih Yuan Woon

Topics covered

- Defining and understanding governance

- The relationship between governance, territory and power

- The governance regimes for maritime spaces and their associated environments

24.1 Conceptualizing governance

The term governance, derived from the Greek verb *kubernan,* suggests notions of steering and/or piloting. Governance as a term is, on the face of it, a source of reassurance. Actions involving steering and piloting connote a sense of in-control, predictability and stability. But there are occasions where the very institutions and structures that (partially) govern our lives (such as international regulations) appear powerless and inadequate to cope with the events at hand. For example, in June 2013, Singaporean and Malaysian officials reported extreme levels of air pollution, with forest fires in neighbouring Indonesia widely blamed for creating a transnational haze over South-east Asia. It was not the first time a pollution haze has affected those countries, as in 1997–8 and 2006 when once again Indonesian illegal logging practices and associated forest fires were cited as the primary source (Jones 2006). Even though these affected nations have entered into a legally binding agreement, via ASEAN (the Association of Southeast Asian Nations), to intervene against the haze problem, the seeming inability of the Indonesian government to control management practices in large and remote forested areas of the archipelago stimulated intense debates about an apparent lack of and forms of national governance as well as the inability of regional treaties in governing individual states' actions (see Nurhidayah *et al.* 2014). Moreover, it also raised questions about complicity and whether neighbouring countries, via their companies, were involved in attempts to circumvent restrictions on burning (Varkkey 2014).

Likewise, when severe disasters such as flooding and earthquakes affect communities, we gain further insights into what the geography (and lack) of governance looks and feels like – it can be devastating, as the people of the Philippines discovered when typhoon Haiyan struck and killed over 6,000 people in November 2013 and devastated vast swathes of the country and its infrastructure (Plate 24.1). Whilst it is easy to attribute blame to 'natural' weather phenomenon, claims abound that the dysfunction of proper governing mechanisms (e.g. absence of a clear disaster preparedness program and political corruption that distorts relief missions) also accentuated the (unequal) impacts of the disaster (see Keister 2013). Over 1 million people were left homeless and some 6 million were displaced. In its aftermath, over 40 countries supported the UN effort alongside an array of non-governmental organizations in attempting to both respond to the initial destruction and implement recovery and rebuilding programmes as well as to support the displaced (McCall 2014). The relationship between natural catastrophes and governance is complex therefore and disasters have also frequently offered opportunities for

Plate 24.1 Typhoon Haiyan, Philippines 2013.
(fotomuhabiri/fotolia)

states to extend their role and may become catalysts in the reordering of society and politics. It has been argued that only war offers greater potential to achieve such reconfigurations (Guyot-Réchard 2015).

Moreover, there are other ways in which governance manifests itself. For scholars working in fields like political geography and related disciplines such as International Relations (IR), governance refers to a system of rules, norms, codes, regulations and compliance mechanisms designed to regulate human activity, especially at the global level (Herod *et al.* 1998; Held and McGrew 2002; Sparke 2006). However, the mere identification of 'global governance' presents an important challenge to dominant strands of IR and their depictions of the international arena which focus on states, as the dominant actors, and how they 'navigate' and 'steer' their way in the global arena in order to maximise their interests (Donnelly 2000; Goldin 2013).

However, critics of this view (which is known as realism in IR) argue that states, societies and markets are embedded and implicated with one another, across a range of geographical scales. It is apparent, moreover, that even if states remain the primary political actors there is not only a great deal of variation within the interstate community but also a range of other organizations facilitating, respecting and obstructing 'global governance' (for earlier reflections on colonial governance, see Chapter 8). The list would include non-governmental organizations, inter-governmental organizations, corporations and/or criminal cartels. Likewise, it no longer seems plausible to adhere to a rigid distinction between the domestic and the foreign. As John Agnew (1994) rightly cautions, such a domestic/foreign polarity constitutes the 'territorial trap' whereby there is a neglect of the changing significance and meanings of states in different historical-geographical circumstances. Indeed, states might well continue to enjoy formal sovereignty over their national territories, but they are also deeply affected by the contemporary transnational flows and global capital markets. The financial crisis of 2008–10 (and subsequent 'austerity'), for example (see Plate 24.2), duly demonstrated how the notion of the state as a territorial container was being challenged, while ideas pertaining to the safeguarding of 'national economies' and 'national interests' were constantly (re)produced by political leaders and senior figures in financial authorities like the Bank of England, US Federal Reserve and European Central Bank who were eager to convey the impression that they were in 'control'.

We might, at this stage, make a fundamental distinction between two kinds of political-territorial world orders. There is an idealized order, which in the international system is composed of states, which enjoy de jure sovereignty over their national territories. This intricate link between sovereignty and territory is often traced back to the Treaty of Westphalia (1648) between European sovereigns, whereby there is an international codification of the basic principles of territorial integrity, border inviolability and supremacy of the state. Alternatively, there is a functional order that is rather more complicated which holds the de facto view that states, for example, do not enjoy complete and absolute authority over their territorial domains. This might manifest itself in all kinds of ways from an inability to impose law and order on parts of their 'national territory' (as described in Chapter 22) to an inability to stop others interfering with the territorial integrity of a country (for example, in 2014, Russia annexed the Crimean peninsula and destabilized eastern Ukraine, with many observers arguing that Russia was seeking to extend its international borders into Ukrainian territory). As John Agnew (2005b; 2009) claims, sovereignty is never complete and/or absolute – rather than assuming sovereignty as fixed and naturally tied in to the nation-state and territory, attention should be given to how sovereignty can function on different geographical scales and can be shared by multiple actors (Jessop 2002; Brenner 2004).

In this chapter we explore a number of themes and issues germane to a discussion on global governance mindful of those *idealized* and *functional* senses of world order. But we will do so from some potentially unusual vantage

Plate 24.2 Financial crisis, 2008.
(Toby Melville/Reuters)

points, namely the Arctic and the South China Sea where there is no shortage of material pertaining to states and political leaders eager to perform, protect and exclude in the name of governance (as detailed in Chapter 20). It might seem odd to investigate maritime spaces but in doing so we will be able to reflect on how governance has been understood and implemented in watery environments. In so doing, we recall that 70 per cent of our planet is composed of water and that the seas and oceans are complex spaces claimed by coastal states, traversed by commercial traffic, fished and exploited for its resources, and enrolled in legal frameworks, strategic planning and defence arrangements by local states, international organizations such as the UN Food and Agricultural Organization, and extra-territorial powers alike.

Initially, we consider why there has been an upsurge of reflection on global governance, with due reverence given to some relevant contextual and theoretical perspectives. Thereafter, the governance of the Arctic and the South China Sea are used as examples of how the regulation of these maritime spaces have become embedded in an ever more complex matrix of states, non-governmental organizations, and international governmental bodies including the United Nations (see Spotlight box 24.1). Finally, the chapter concludes with how governance questions remind us of the importance of accountability, access and authority in the contemporary world.

Spotlight box 24.1

United Nations

The UN has 193 member states, a figure that includes the vast majority of the world's sovereign states. Established in 1945, it was meant to succeed the League of Nations, to facilitate 'cooperation in international law, international security, economic progress, social progress, human rights and achievement of world peace' (UN website). The League of Nations was an inter-governmental organization whose primary goals, as stated in its Covenant, included preventing war through collective security, disarmament and settling international disputes through negotiation and arbitration. However, the onset of the Second World War demonstrated that the League had failed in its primary purpose. There were many reasons for this failure. The USA had refused to join – following political debate and lack of consensus over the League in the US Senate. It has also been pointed out that the structural weakness of the organization – many decisions required the unanimous consent of the entire Assembly which made conclusive and swift action difficult – culminated in its eventual demise (see Gill 1996; Pollock 2003). The inspiration for the formation of the UN thus stems from the wish for a more effective organization for the managing of world affairs.

Headquartered in New York, the UN has six major elements: the General Assembly (the debating chamber), the Security Council (addressing resolutions pertaining to peace and security), the Secretariat (providing support for the UN), the UN Trusteeship Council (inactive), the International Court of Justice (based in The Hague), and the Economic and Social Council (promoting international economic development and cooperation). There are also other major agencies associated with the UN, including the World Health Organization, the World Food Programme and UN Children's Fund. The current Secretary-General is the former South Korean diplomat, Ban Ki-Moon, who took over the post in 2007 (see Plate 24.3).

Plate 24.3 UN Secretary General, Ban Ki-Moon.
(kisa kuyruk/Shutterstock)

The organization is funded by assessed subscriptions from member states. The regular two-year budget of the UN and its specialized agencies are funded by assessments – the General Assembly approves the regular budget and determines how much each member state has to give. This is broadly based on the relative economic capabilities of various countries, as evaluated by their Gross National Income, taking into account adjustments for external debt and low per capita income (UN website). Given that the Assembly has established the principle that the UN should not be overly dependent on any one member to finance its operations, there is a 'ceiling' rate, setting the maximum amount a state can contribute to the budget.

24.2 Theorizing global governance

In the last decade or so, terms like governance have become associated for many Western viewers with television reports of political leaders, global corporations and international financial organizations such as the World Bank (see Chapter 8). G7/8/20 meetings around the world in places like Genoa, London, Seattle and Toronto further cement an impression of the rich and powerful gathering to manage the world (see Plate 24.4). In close proximity, it is common to find individuals and social movements taking to the streets of those aforementioned cities protesting against global economic and political integration, and highlighting the persistence of inequality (Klein 2007). The Occupy movement, a social movement of anti-austerity protestors, has targeted particular sites of international governance and in particular the European Central Bank and World Bank, for the explicit

Plate 24.4 Recent G20/G7 meeting.
(Anadolu Agency/Getty Images)

purpose of drawing attention to how governance gets made in and through particular places.

But global governance is increasingly being theorized through the optics of climate change as well, especially as it relates to how contemporary capitalism is complicit in continued environmental degradation, greenhouse gas emission and fossil fuel production and consumption. In her provocative book, *This Changes Everything*, the Canadian author Naomi Klein (2014) argues that our ability to act decisively with regard to climate change mitigation is constrained by ideological and structural forces. She argues that, 'we have not done the things that are necessary to lower emissions because these things fundamentally conflict with deregulated capitalism ... We are stuck because the actions that would give us the best chance of averting catastrophe – and would benefit the vast majority – are extremely threatening to an elite minority that has a stranglehold over our economy, our political process, and most of our major media outlets' (Klein 2014: 18). For this critic, governance is effectively 'captured' by self-interested political and financial elites. All of this placed further pressure on those attending the 2015 UN Climate Change Conference in Paris to secure meaningful progress on greenhouse emission reduction.

In discussing global governance, we need to address two different constituencies. First, we should provide some contextual detail to these aforementioned activities. Why, for example, is it now so common for high-level meetings between the G7 and G20 to attract such protests, violence and even death? Second, how have theorists explored the nature of governance with reference to world order? Who, for example, benefits from good governance?

In an earlier phase, the 1980s and 1990s, governance was a subject matter more often reserved for discussions of the global South (Sheppard and Nagar 2004; Slater 2004). Indeed, as Williams *et al.* (2009: 3) rightly note, this period has seen the global South being constantly represented 'as a collection of place and peoples in need of external (i.e. Northern) intervention'. Under the euphemism of 'good governance', it was argued by international institutions like the World Bank and leading states such as the USA that public decision making would be better served if state bureaucracies were reduced, legal systems reformed, accountability improved, formal democracy and democratic institutions entrenched and market led reforms implemented. For the critics of good governance, these reforms were empowered by a neoliberal economic vision, which placed a premium on a reform package designed to make Southern economies more 'accessible' to foreign direct investment and corporations (Harvey 2005). As Roberts' *et al.* (2003: 887) put it, neoliberal idealism, bolstered by the 'simple master narrative about the inexorable force of economic globalization' upheld the idea that the universal extension of the virtues of openness, transparency and integration inherent in free markets would ultimately bring

'worldwide peace and prosperity'. Premised on a market-driven approach in shaping the political and economic priorities of the state, neoliberalism is unequivocally represented as a force that will lift the whole world out of poverty as more and more communities embrace and partake in the workings of the capitalist global economy (Tickell and Peck 2003). Thus, the critics complained that underlying claims to good governance was actually a disciplinary impulse (a form of governmentality, see Spotlight box 24.2) in which governments and their national populations were trained to operate in new ways, with the incentive being that they were more likely to attract additional aid and investment (Larner 2003; Watts 2003). In this sense, governance came with certain caveats and stringent conditions.

It was no accident that good governance debates and structural adjustment coincided with the decline of the Cold War and the intensification of a sense of global interdependence (see Chapter 8). To put it bluntly, Northern states were still eager to control further aid packages, while at the same time take advantage of new economic opportunities in emerging markets, especially with the demise of the Soviet Union and Cold War networks and relations (see Chapter 21). For Southern states, especially those with weak economies and limited control over their national territories, these kinds of demands were accepted as part of what was termed 'structural adjustment'. For instance, many Latin American nations including Mexico, Argentina and Brazil implemented both internal and external changes (notably privatization and deregulation and the reduction of trade barriers) in the 1980s so that they could qualify for loans from IMF and the World Bank to 'save' their debt-ridden economies. Furthermore, international institutions asserted further control in the late 1990s when the subject matter of corruption was addressed. Countries such as Kenya that were judged to be aberrant for a period of time had funding support suspended (see Chapter 17).

In the aftermath of the 11 September 2011 attacks on the United States, this good governance trend was supplemented by further financial and military pressures. Fearful of a repeat of 9/11, the USA led attempts by the international community to control more closely financial flows and, at the same, intervene in the global South if concerns were expressed that some countries and regions might harbour terrorists and their terror networks. This concern for 'quasi-states' (as Interational Relations theorist Robert Jackson (1993) had termed them) and 'weak states' manifested itself in the invasion of Afghanistan and Iraq and surveillance and other military initiatives elsewhere. For example, the firm belief that Philippines' susceptibility to transnational terrorist networks due to its government's weak

Spotlight box 24.2

Governmentality

Developed by the French philosopher and historian Michel Foucault (see Plate 24.5) in a series of essays delivered at the College de France in the late 1970s and early 1980s, it addresses the ways in which subjects are governed via a series of techniques and rationalities. In so doing, it considers how governments attempt to manage their populations. Foucault himself described it as the 'art of government' and suggested that authorities might control populations in a manner whereby particular understandings of how to behave and act become simply accepted without contestation. Neoliberal governmentality, for instance derives its power in part from the image of the absentee state and the acceptance of market mechanisms as the best way to allocate resources. However, as Peck (2004) cautions, the *practical content* of neoliberal reform strategies is often quite 'interventionist', albeit in different ways. In his words, neoliberal imperatives are always melded with 'a range of paternalist, authoritarian, developmentalist and socio-democratic state form, together with the concomitant ascendancy of (appropriately elastic) notions of governmentality'. Hence beyond the clichés of more market/less state, the neoliberal script actually suggestively encompasses a wide range of proactive state strategies designed to refashion state–economy relations around a new constellation of elite, managerial and financial interests. In this formulation, there is a restructuring (rather than 'rolling back') of state responsibilities and spatialities – contemporary phenomena like the proliferation of NGOs, many of which

Plate 24.5 Michel Foucault.
(Jean-Pierre Fouchet/Getty Images)

are organized, financed or co-opted by national governments or international agencies, many of which deliver services and operationalize discourses that were once the privileged province of nation-states and their local outposts, signifying that the clean lines once imagined to exist between the national state and the offshore world, or between bureaucracy and civil society have become increasingly complicated (Ferguson and Gupta 2002; Brenner *et al.* 2003). What this means is that there is no one simple outcome to neoliberal governmentality, comprising a series of unified and fully integrated market-oriented policies; the focus is placed instead on how these 'neoliberal' processes are mediated and played out in different historical-geographical circumstances.

control over peripheral islands with ongoing separatist insurgencies has led to the USA deploying armed forces (in tandem with those of the Philippines) in the name of dealing with such potential threats (Glassman 2005; Woon 2009). Thus, it can be seen that countering terrorism, promoting market-led reform and geopolitical realignment in the aftermath of the Cold War have all played their parts in reshaping contemporary global governance. For the critics, including the protestors that gathered at some G20 meetings (and those in the Occupy movement, which was examined in Chapters 21 and 23), these transformations have deepened market hegemony and arguably reduced the capacity of many countries to manage their own affairs.

Making sense of these kinds of changes has attracted a range of theoretical perspectives, and we can only briefly review the major ones. For disciplines such as International Relations (IR), a consideration of governance is never far removed from the central concern of order. For a theorist such as Hedley Bull (1995), order in world politics was epitomized by 'concerns [for] the pattern or disposition of international activity that sustains the elementary, primary or universal goals of the system and society of states'. These goals included: the preservation of the system, the maintenance of peace, and the upholding of the sovereign independence of states. For other theorists, order has also been understood as embracing both the production and preservation of stability and regular patterns of behaviour within the system of states and, as a consequence, the promotion of cooperative behaviour (Elster 1989).

This understanding of order remains influential but the nature of that order might, and indeed does, vary over time and space. For some theorists, the long-term stability of any world order depends on the role of a hegemonic party (Gilpin 1989, Cox 2001). In this conception, **hegemony**, denoting the political, economic, cultural and especially *ideological* dominance that one group, state or class has over others, is widely seen as the necessary condition for harnessing stability in the global arena. Hegemony is not simply domination, but relates to the capacity to persuade others that the system as a whole is also in their interests. As such, interest is devoted to the role of the United States in the post-1945 era in shaping and maintaining a new international economic and political order based on ideas such as free trade and economic liberalization. While a hegemonic state might enjoy extraordinary military and other power capabilities, its influence lies in part in its capacity to persuade

others that the prevailing system should be preserved. This approach has enjoyed renewed popularity in recent years because of interest in the growing importance of China (connected with the debates described in the closing section of Chapter 20) and debate about whether this might lead to a new hegemonic power replacing *Pax Americana*. Some have argued that a decline of American power and the rise of new challengers might be seen not simply as a putative transition from one hegemon to another, but a change in the very nature of hegemony, from one of states closely connected with their ruling classes to a more dispersed pattern (see Figure 24.1), whereby 'What binds these diverse regions and actors together is a shared commitment to an ideology of market economics and a growing recognition that territoriality alone is not a secure basis for economic or geopolitical power' (Agnew and Corbridge 1995: 205–7).

Others have explored world orders on the premise that stability is ensured by a so-called balance of power. This is largely based on what IR calls a realist understanding of world politics, which posits that states are

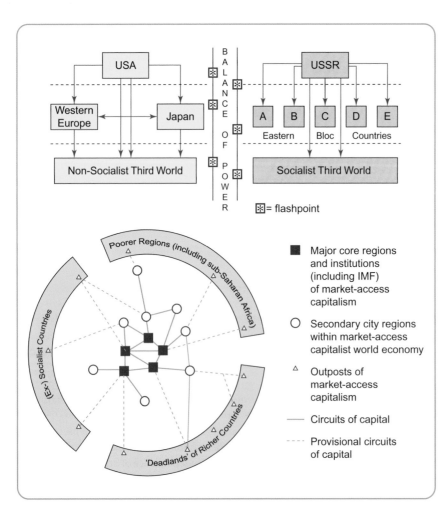

Figure 24.1 Diagrammatic representation of *hegemony* during (above) and (below) after the Cold War.

Source: based on Agnew and Corbridge (1995)

constantly in the processing of negotiating their relations with one another, and that this occurs against a backdrop in which there is no single overreaching authority (the UN is itself an expression of the member states, not above them). The international system is judged to be anarchical because there is no effective world government. So, as a consequence, states have to coexist with one another, sometimes uneasily. In so doing, if there is a stable world order then it is likely to be balanced by two or more states acting as restraining influences. So, according to this concept, the Cold War era was comparatively stable because the Soviet Union and the USA counterbalanced one another. What matters under this approach is a concern for power projection and the economic and military strengths of states. Of course these different forms of power and governance may coexist, albeit with the emphasis between them and their relative significance evolving.

As we have noted, from this vantage point, the United Nations is not considered to be any kind of substitute for the absence of world government. Fundamentally, the UN is a collective of individual member states, which currently stands at 193. Realists tend to be sceptical about the nature and scope of the authority of this international body. This scepticism is in part rooted in the experiences of the League of Nations, which proved unable to prevent conflict in the inter-war period, and the experience of the Cold War where the superpowers both routinely marginalized the UN when it did not suit their purposes. Critics of contemporary US foreign policy would also note that the Bush administration was eager to by-pass any restraints imposed by the UN General Assembly when it came to seeking authorization for the US-led invasion of Iraq in 2003.

Finally, other scholars have considered how states work together to create something akin to an international society. Mindful of a lack of world government and inspired by the writings of Immanuel Kant (Spotlight box 24.3) and his studies of 'perpetual peace', these analysts consider how governance is addressed through restraint and cooperation. How do sovereign states seek to avoid confrontation and exercise restraint? One answer is by building 'thick relationships' that emphasize mutual interdependence and universally accepted norms. For these authors, the creation of the United Nations and later regional blocs such as the European Union (EU) is emblematic of this trend of seeking to promote interdependence and cooperation. In particular, the EU has frequently been utilized as a case study to exemplify how multi-level governance has functioned to enable the formation of interlocking and collaborative networks between various nation-states (Paasi 2003, 2009; Bialasiewicz *et al.* 2005). For instance, Sbargia's

(2000) claim that EU possesses a multi-level governance system is premised on the observation that overlapping competencies among multiple levels of government and the interaction of political actors across those levels exist within the regional bloc. Concurring that member state executives, while powerful, are only one set among a variety of actors in the European polity, Leitner *et al.* (2002), on the other hand, exemplify how transnational networks among cities and regions in the EU are good examples of new political relations emerging across national boundaries, but situated at subnational political scale. According to them, the 'horizontal collective action among cities and regions, forged around a common agenda of mutual advantage [crosses] – and may challenge – the hierarchical relations between different scales of political governance (local, regional, national and supranational)' (Leitner *et al.* 2002: 296–7) (see too Chapter 14 and Spotlight box 20.3).

Subsequent work informed by the Kantian tradition has investigated further the manner in which like-minded states create international regimes for the purpose of sharing certain rules, values and norms in the apparent absence of a world authority. Indeed, the initial justification put forth by the Bush administration to invade Iraq in 2003 was premised on the claim that the country possessed weapons of mass destruction (WMDs). However, when these alleged WMDs were not found on Iraqi soil, the argument shifted to the notion that the Saddam regime was a dictatorship, and abusive of human rights (see Dalby 2003; Flint and Falah 2004). In both cases, while many members of that American administration were sceptical of the UN, they still wanted nonetheless the imprimatur of the UN Security Council. And the subsequent arguments about the legality of the US-led invasion of Iraq were rooted, on all sides, in competing arguments about international law and the scope of existing UN resolutions addressing Iraq's behaviour regarding weapons of mass destruction and human rights abuses. The debate was also mired in accusations that Iraq's substantial oil reserves were an important strategic consideration within the Bush administration (see Chapter 5 and Le Billon and El Khatib 2004).

Governance, in this sense, is a *shared* if imperfect project in which states (and the emphasis often remains on these actors) seek to embed and develop an international society. For Kantians, the existence of democratic/republican states was considered to be critical to the long-term viability of such an international society not least because it was believed that democracies were less likely to wage war on one another. But in a world where not all states are democracies (and the democratic spectrum is a broad one), theorists disagree about what kinds of conditions improve stability and order.

Spotlight box 24.3

Immanuel Kant

Immanuel Kant (see Plate 24.6) was an eighteenth-century philosopher who wrote an essay in 1795 entitled 'Perpetual peace: a philosophical sketch'. Kant outlines what he calls some 'preliminary articles' necessary for more pacific relations between states including 'No independent states, large or small, shall come under the dominion of another state by inheritance, exchange, purchase, or donation'. He then outlined what he called three definitive articles which would provide the necessary foundation for peace itself: every state should be republican, the 'law of nations' would function amongst a federation of free states and a law of world citizenship would be based on universal hospitality. Kant talked about republican not democratic states, which would be defined by representative government and that legislature will be separated from the executive branch of the government. He also does not regard that republican governments are sufficient by themselves to produce peace; rather he envisages some kind of league of nations and freedom of emigration that would be necessary to manage human affairs (Archibugi 1995; Kleingeld 2004). It is perhaps unsurprising then that observations have been made that the EU is in some ways Kantian, given how its regional structures and integrative (economic and immigration) policies are largely indicative of Kant's model of a 'federation' of states (Elden and Bialasiewicz 2006; Wolin 2010). This is contrary to the USA's (generally realist) view of the world, in which the absence of an effective world government signifies that the USA has to take the lead in maintaining peace and order in an otherwise anarchical geopolitical scene. Such a distinction, according to scholars like

Plate 24.6 Immanuel Kant.

(Juulijs/fotolia)

Balibar (2003), was most clearly seen in the post-9/11 era whereby (the majority of) Europe's attachment to international laws and norms to deal with 'terrorism' is contrasted to America's enhanced world role in this transformed security condition.

At a systemic level, there is broad agreement that the development of multilateral institutions and institutionalized cooperation has been tremendously important in shaping contemporary global governance. Whether it is expressed through the United Nations and/or organizations such as the World Bank and IMF, states and non-state actors alike are embedded in a whole raft of obligations and restraints ranging from global human rights to international trade law and intellectual property rights. While the United States might be unrivalled as a military power, it is also deeply dependent on others for its economic and financial stability. Indeed, as noted earlier, the effects of the 'good governance' developments

were to further entrench a particular global order – one that is perhaps best understood as a neoliberal one, empowered by shared values, norms and rules designed to ease global exchange. But the notion of 'shared' should not blind us to the fact this is an imposed project. Governance, as Richard Ashley (1987) once noted, is via imposition – imposing rules, silencing others and their knowledge, practices and projects.

Whatever understanding of governance we choose to adopt, it is never divorced from fundamental questions of power and knowledge. The manner in which the world appears to be organized and managed is not a natural condition of global life. The prevailing global economic order, based on neoliberal capitalism and good governance strategies, is a human creation. The rules, norms and values selected to regulate that order are also imposed. This in turn shapes public debate about, for instance, feasible policy options. Some policies and practices appear more 'reasonable', such as cutting public spending in the aftermath of a financial crisis, and those that seek to challenge those policies are often presented as iconoclastic and disruptive, such as activists, students and trade unionists. The prevailing norms and mechanisms of governance work to promote particular agendas, and geographers are increasingly mindful of how those 'structures' of governance impact, in highly differential ways, upon communities and places around the world.

Let us now turn to the case studies of the Arctic and South China Sea to find some evidence of how institutions, networks and processes associated with governance shape these two increasingly contested oceanic spaces. We focus on these two examples not to suggest that they are in any way unique or exceptional. Rather, in line with growing acknowledgements that seas and their associated maritime geographies can provide important geopolitical insights (Steinberg 2001; Steinberg and Gerhardt 2015), we argue that there is plenty of evidence to be gathered about how their governance works, according to prevailing norms and values associated with the contemporary neoliberal economic and political order.

24.3 Governing the Arctic Ocean

In the last decade, the changing physical conditions in the Arctic region have generated scores of commentaries (see, for example, Johnson 2010; Young 2012), and captured the attention of states and other organizations including the EU. One event often cited as transformative in that regard was the 2007 planting of the Russian flag on the bottom of the central Arctic Ocean. Images of an underwater submersible gently dropping the titanium flagpole into place were widely circulated in national and global media networks (Dodds 2010). For Russian audiences, the flag planting exercise was widely interpreted as indicative of national prowess and technological sophistication even if the expedition itself was privately funded by a Swedish benefactor. For others, including senior Canadian political officials, the expedition and flag planting ceremony was judged to be provocative and unnecessary. While international lawyers noted that such an activity had little to no international legal significance, political scientists and journalists were penning evaluations of the resource and strategic significance of the Arctic in the post-Cold War era, while raising the spectre of ungovernability (Anderson 2009; Emmerson 2010; Spotlight box 24.4 and Chapter 5).

This flag planting episode brought to the fore both the changing geopolitical representation of the Arctic and, relatedly, the governance of the Arctic, and specifically the role of international cooperation between and beyond states. Six years after the flag planting episode, however, the geographical imaginaries surrounding the Arctic were altered substantially when five 'Asian states' namely China, India, South Korea, Japan and Singapore became observers to the Arctic Council and in so doing encouraged a broadside of media commentary reflecting on the growing role of these countries and what that might mean for cooperation and indeed competition (see Solli et al. 2013). Almost inevitably, China's role in the Arctic was scrutinized most closely with concern raised by some that Chinese financial and political investments might destabilize existing governance arrangements.

Spotlight box 24.4

Defining the Arctic

Definitions of the Arctic region vary from those based on biological, climatic and/or geographical factors, such as the Arctic Circle and/or political criteria. The Arctic Council's definition includes all oceans and territories north of the Arctic Circle and adjacent territories in Siberia and North America, and southern oceanic regions in the Atlantic and Bering Strait (see Figure 24.2). All eight members of the Arctic Council are typically described as 'Arctic states', namely Canada, Denmark/Greenland, Finland, Iceland, Norway, Russia, Sweden and the United States. Of those eight, five are described as Arctic Ocean coastal states (Canada, Denmark/Greenland, Norway, Russia and the United States) because of their geographical proximity to the Arctic Ocean and the rights they acquire under the terms of the United Nations Convention on the Law of the Sea.

Source: *http://web.arcticportal.org/uploads/UQ/3a/UQ3aTSHhcNfq8-OjsuoQtg/CAFFpolitical.jpg*

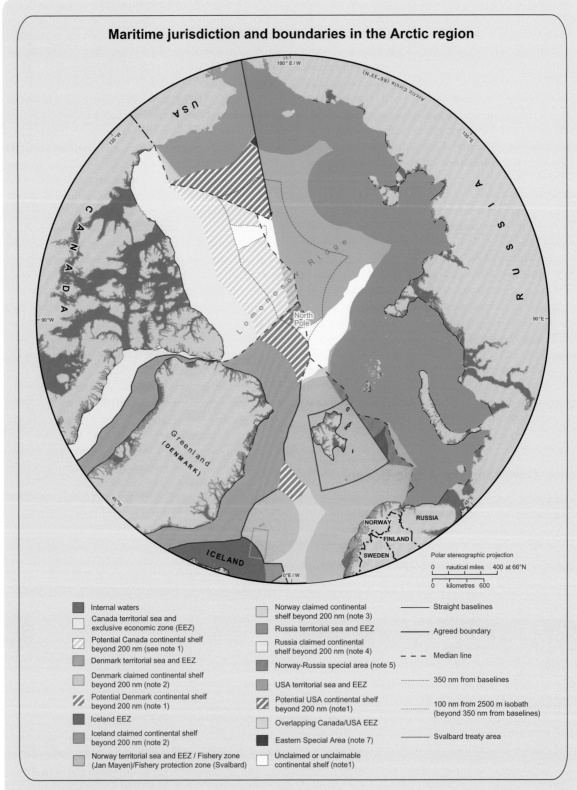

Maritime jurisdiction and boundaries in the Arctic region

Legend	
Internal waters	Norway claimed continental shelf beyond 200 nm (note 3)
Canada territorial sea and exclusive economic zone (EEZ)	Russia territorial sea and EEZ
Potential Canada continental shelf beyond 200 nm (see note 1)	Russia claimed continental shelf beyond 200 nm (note 4)
Denmark territorial sea and EEZ	Norway-Russia special area (note 5)
Denmark claimed continental shelf beyond 200 nm (note 2)	USA territorial sea and EEZ
Potential Denmark continental shelf beyond 200 nm (note 1)	Potential USA continental shelf beyond 200 nm (note1)
Iceland EEZ	Overlapping Canada/USA EEZ
Iceland claimed continental shelf beyond 200 nm (note 2)	Eastern Special Area (note 7)
Norway territorial sea and EEZ / Fishery zone (Jan Mayen)/Fishery protection zone (Svalbard)	Unclaimed or unclaimable continental shelf (note1)

Straight baselines
Agreed boundary
Median line
350 nm from baselines
100 nm from 2500 m isobath (beyond 350 nm from baselines)
Svalbard treaty area

Polar stereographic projection

0 nautical miles 400 at 66°N

0 kilometres 600

Figure 24.2 Map of the Arctic.

Source: based on map produced by the International Boundaries Research Group (IBRU) at Durham University. Original and notes are at: *www.durham.ac.uk/ibru/resources/arctic*

The two strands (i.e. geopolitics and governance) are closely inter-related because debates over polar governance have followed on from a sense in which the Arctic is in a state of physical and geopolitical flux (Johnson 2010; Dodds and Nuttall 2015). To put it simply, during the Cold War, while the Arctic was indisputably a frontline between the USA and the Soviet Union, it was a region in which the presence of thick sea ice acted as a physical barrier to movement and extra-territorial interest – it was a space of 'thin governability'. The Arctic Ocean, while accessible, was not characterized by the kind of accessibility that might have been taken for granted in the other maritime spaces such as the Mediterranean and South China Sea. Both the Soviets and the US navies developed polar strategies predicated on the belief that each side would seek to contain the movement of their enemies' submarine fleets in particular and were not concerned about Korean, Chinese and Japanese shipping operators, for example.

The dominant Cold War conceptualization of Artic security was, therefore, based on containment (as part of the wider Cold War geopolitics examined in Chapter 20) rather than territorial transgression. As part of this containment exercise, both sides conducted an assortment of underwater, drifting ice and aerial surveillance operations of the kind depicted in films such as *Ice Station Zebra* (1968) and *The Hunt for Red October* (1990) (see Plate 24.7). One immediate consequence of such activities was to ensure that the Arctic Ocean was a highly militarized space with little to no evidence of cooperation among the Soviet Union and the four coastal states in particular, namely the USA, Canada, Denmark and Norway. With four out of the five Arctic Ocean coastal states being members of NATO, this sense of the Arctic as a geopolitical frontline was well founded.

As the Cold War declined, the dominant geopolitical representation of the Arctic shifted. In part, this was due to the improvement of relations between the previously opposing sides. After Mikhail Gorbachev's noted speech in 1987 calling for the Arctic to be a 'zone of peace', concerted efforts were made to improve relations between the five Arctic Ocean coastal states and neighbouring countries such as Finland, Iceland and Sweden. One manifestation of this rapprochement was the creation in 1996 of the Arctic Council (AC), which was designed to improve cooperation over matters of mutual concern including environmental management and shipping. Polar governance was entering a new phase but a period nonetheless dominated

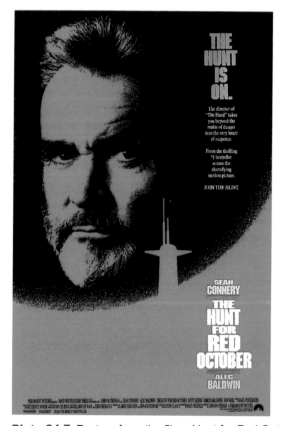

Plate 24.7 Posters from the films *Hunt for Red October* (1990) and *Ice Station Zebra* (1968).
(Courtesy of Everett Collection/Rex Shutterstock)

by states and their security-led agendas. Hence, rather than a straightforward 'rolling back' of the state, contemporary governmentality functions through a restructuring of state's role and responsibilities – participation in an interstate forum whereby negotiations of positions and agendas are made vis-à-vis other relevant actors.

The AC is an intergovernmental organization. It is intended to aid and abet Arctic states in areas of common interest. Notably, all parties agreed that any discussions involving military and security matters would be avoided even though the Cold War was considered to be finished. On a more progressive note, however, indigenous peoples and organizations such as the Sami Council were invited to be permanent participants of the Arctic Council. Underlying the creation of the Arctic Council was a sense in which the members involved recognized that the logic of containment was neither sufficient nor desirable in the changed geopolitical circumstances. Instead the Arctic has been understood as a weakly governed space needing effective spatial administration.

Apart from the apparently obvious point that the superpowers were no longer so threatening to one another (with the Arctic as a major theatre of operations), a key driver of change has been the spectre of climate change (Johnson 2010; Steinberg and Gerhardt 2015). While serving as an indicator of global environmental change, melting sea ice was widely identified as indicative of greater accessibility in a political and material sense. Politically, the Arctic Ocean has attracted more interest from national governments, corporations, scientific communities, indigenous peoples and media networks. The 2007 flag planting episode coinciding as it did with satellite images of an apparently ice-free North West Passage encouraged a maelstrom of media speculation about an apparent 'scramble for the pole'. Materially, a more accessible Arctic Ocean raises the spectre of further resource extraction in areas such as oil and gas (see Plate 24.8), alongside other activities such

Plate 24.8 Oil/gas extraction in the Arctic.

(Leonid Ikan/fotolia)

as fishing, tourism and trans-polar shipping routes, with their apparent promise of cutting thousands of nautical miles for those seeking to move freight from East Asia to Europe (Powell 2008).

This interest in spatial administration manifests itself in the interest shown by political actors, including the European Union (EU), in examining a variety of governance options. At present, Arctic Ocean governance is shaped by three key factors – the Arctic Council, the Law of the Sea and a host of regional regimes such as fisheries agreements. The Arctic Council (AC) is a soft-law institution, meaning that it is largely advisory and lacking in a permanent secretariat, for example (McIver 1997; Bloom 1999). It does not have any legal competence. It cannot demand that member states restrain from, for example, drilling offshore for oil and gas. Organizationally, the Arctic Council has attached to its permanent membership so-called observer states such as Britain, and now new observer states such as China, South Korea and Singapore. These 'observer states' cannot shape the agenda of the annual meetings but they are allowed to attend a certain amount of the formal business of the member states and contribute to the work of the AC. Permanent participants such as indigenous peoples' groups (e.g. Inuit Circumpolar Council, Sami Council, Aleut International Association) also attend the meetings of the AC but do not have voting rights.

Since its creation in 1996, the AC arguably demonstrates something that is considered axiomatic by realist scholars, namely that states tend to veer towards self-interested behaviour. One of the central reasons why the AC is a soft-law institution is that the five Arctic Ocean coastal states in particular were reluctant to agree to a more substantial treaty-based international regime, as found in Antarctica. Notwithstanding concerns about the growing accessibility of the Arctic Ocean, and the mounting interest from parties geographically remote from the region, the states concerned have sought to improve and indeed strengthen cooperation with one another in specific areas such as shipping, search and rescue, and environmental cooperation.

The United States and Russia have at times been reluctant to strengthen the remit of the AC. Smaller states such as Norway, Denmark and Sweden have shown a willingness to strengthen the AC. Between 2006 and 2012, the three Nordic countries agreed to create a semi-permanent secretariat in Tromso, which later became permanent in 2013 onwards. This move to improve the coordination and networking capacity of the AC was, in very large part, driven by growing interest in the forum from outside parties. As the Arctic states recognized at a ministerial meeting in Greenland in 2011, there was more of a need to be seen to be generating more 'Arctic governance'. A new legally binding measure on search and rescue was signed and in 2013 another agreement on oil spill response was also negotiated at the same time new observers were admitted with new rules and criteria governing their behaviour were published.

The second major element in the governance of the Arctic Ocean lies in the provisions of the Law of the Sea Convention (LOSC) (see Plate 24.9). For the five Arctic Ocean coastal states, the LOSC regulates large sways of the Arctic Ocean by acknowledging a series of jurisdictions exists, ranging from the 12 nautical mile wide territorial sea, the 24 nautical mile wide contiguous zone and a 200 nautical mile wide exclusive economic zone in which coastal states enjoy sovereign rights when it comes to the exploitation of resources (Steinberg 2001; Dodds 2010). As Article 56 notes:

In the exclusive economic zone, the coastal State has:

(a) sovereign rights for the purpose of exploring and exploiting, conserving and managing the natural resources, whether living or non-living, of the waters superjacent to the seabed and of the seabed and its subsoil, and with regard to other activities for the economic exploitation and exploration of the zone, such as the production of energy from the water, currents and winds

Moreover, under Articles 76 and 77, coastal states can seek to extend their sovereign rights over extended continental shelves (ECS). Interested parties, including all the Arctic Ocean coastal states barring the USA (which has not acceded to the LOSC), have (or will have) submitted geological and oceanographic materials to the Commission on the Limits of the Continental Shelf (CLCS) based within the United Nations in New York. If accepted by the CLCS, coastal states are allowed to identify ECS and extend their sovereign rights over potentially thousands

Plate 24.9 Signing of the Law of the Sea Convention in 1982.

(UN Photo)

of square miles of seabed. The implications for the Arctic Ocean are considerable – it is likely that the five coastal states will enjoy collectively sovereign rights to explore and exploit the natural resources of virtually the entire maritime region and anything left over will be classified as 'The Area' and thus under the auspices of the International Seabed Authority.

So the notion that there is a wild 'scramble for resources' in the Arctic Ocean is misplaced in one sense. There is no 'scramble' because there is no need to 'scramble' (Dodds 2013). In 2008, the five Arctic Ocean coastal states in the so-called Ilulissat Declaration re-affirmed their commitment to respect the Law of the Sea as the primary mechanism for ensuring cooperation in the Arctic Ocean and thus rejecting calls for any kind of Arctic Treaty. Non-coastal states, under the terms of LOSC, enjoy rights of innocent passage in these particular maritime zones, subject to some regulatory rights of coastal states. Innocent passage, under Article 19 of the LOSC, is defined as:

Passage is innocent so long as it is not prejudicial to the peace, good order or security of the coastal State. Such passage shall take place in conformity with this Convention and with other rules of international law.

This right to innocent passage, alongside a growing commercial interest in trans-polar shipping routes, in large part explains the interests of the EU, South Korea, Singapore, Japan and China, for example. The EU Commission in 2008 outlined the EU's interests in the Arctic and the European Parliament called for the EU Commission to develop an Arctic policy in 2009. Shipping and fishing have been identified as core interests, and Denmark, Finland and Sweden are EU member states, and, at one stage, it was even possible that Iceland might have emerged as a fourth EU member state with distinct Arctic interests.

The third element shaping contemporary Arctic Ocean governance is a patchwork of national and regional fisheries management organizations such as the North East Atlantic Fisheries Commission, the North Atlantic Salmon Conservation Organization, the North Atlantic Conference and the North Atlantic Fisheries Ministers' Conference. With the 'opening up' of the Arctic Ocean in the coming decades, as a consequence of sea ice thinning, a number of Arctic states and others including the EU Commission have called for further multilateral mechanisms to be developed for the purpose of managing Arctic fisheries. One suggestion in particular has been to create an Arctic Regional Fisheries Management Organization for the purpose of coordinating such efforts across the Arctic Ocean. In 2014, the five Arctic Ocean coastal states held a meeting in Greenland to discuss the need to develop in advance agreement on how to manage central

Arctic Ocean fisheries, if and when this maritime area becomes more accessible and more attractive to commercial fishing, especially if fish stocks migrate northwards due to warming waters further south.

Looking ahead, the future governance of the Arctic Ocean is likely to be largely determined by, on the one hand, the continued existence of the AC and, on the other hand, by the provisions of the LOSC. Neither Russia nor the United States appears willing to act in hegemonic ways, although Russian involvement in eastern Ukraine in 2014 raised the possibility that a new 'Cold War' might once again encapsulate the Arctic region. They and smaller Arctic states such as Norway and Denmark/Greenland benefit from this 'pooling' arrangement and there has been a great deal of governance talk emphasizing how the Arctic should be 'contained' and or 'insulated' from crises further south.

The eight Arctic states have effectively agreed to abide by particular rules, customs, values and norms, while at the same developing their own national strategies for 'their' part of the Arctic. They have also been emphatic in their rejection of a proposal by the EU Commission in 2008 to create an Arctic Treaty, along the lines of the 1959 Antarctic Treaty. One reason for this initiative was to encourage the Arctic states to collaborate more closely with extra-territorial actors such as the EU and to work towards transforming the Arctic Ocean into a zone of peace and cooperation. For the five Arctic Ocean coastal states there is little or no apparent incentive to agree to any further treaty development. Each, in their different way, is eager to protect its sovereign rights in the Arctic Ocean without neglecting to cooperate in areas of mutual interests such as fishing. But all of this can also be a delicate project as issues such as energy exploitation, shipping and fishing alongside military/strategic considerations all have the capacity to be divisive.

Contemporary governance in the Arctic Ocean reminds us of two things. First, states do tend, as realists would note, to articulate their interests in the Arctic in national terms. An emphasis on national security, resource control and maritime surveillance is common to all the major policy pronouncements of the five coastal states (e.g. Canada's Northern Strategy of 2007). Second, however, states and non-states are able to cooperate with one another and to create regimes and mechanisms (albeit with limited powers) to encourage information exchange, cooperation and negotiation. The establishment of international norms and conventions help to arbitrate the different interests of relevant parties so that issues pertaining to the Arctic can be debated and resolved in a peaceful and orderly manner. Third, indigenous groups and organizations have become more active in demanding greater autonomy in terms of regional governance and future resource exploitation. In Greenland, for example, the Danish government agreed, after a referendum in 2008, to further autonomy and the awarding of resource rights to the population there. So oil and gas exploration off the coast of Greenland in the future might provide a new revenue stream for eventual independence from Denmark, as might aluminium smelting – but this is controversial, with critics fearing that Greenland will become dependent on multinational corporations and their strategies, not to mention the whimsical nature of global markets (Nuttall 2008). Moreover, indigenous groups help to unite the native peoples who may be artificially divided by national territorial borders so that a platform is available for them to articulate their concerns. A good case in point is the Inuit Circumpolar Conference whereby Inuit living in USA, Russia and Canada often come together to actively elicit responsibility on the part of the Arctic states to deal with the issue of climate change so that a sustainable living environment can be made available to the indigenous communities (Osofsky 2006/2007).

24.4 Governing the South China Sea

The Arctic Ocean and the South China Sea are very different in terms of their geography, climate and geostrategic importance. Yet there has been no lack of comparisons made between these two seascapes, primarily because of their commonality stemming from the presence of rich natural resources and the competition to exploit them (VanderZwaag and Vu 2012; Storey 2013b; Taylor 2014). Indeed the South China Sea – the second largest semi-enclosed sea in the world which is bordered by China and eight other ASEAN states – is not only a crucial conduit for more than a quarter of the world's trade volume (Schofield 2009) but it is also home to a large number of assets, notably maritime living resources as well as oil and gas reserves (Rosenberg 2009; Nguyen Dang 2013).

Whilst the presence of valuable resources in the Arctic and the South China Sea have arguably led to disputing claims in these two regions, the scope of such claims has differed greatly, however. In the whole of the vast Arctic area, there is only one piece of territory that is being disputed: Hans Island, a 1.3 km^2 atoll in the Nares Straits that is claimed by both Denmark and Canada. The scenario in the South China Sea is far more complex, whereby multiple parties contest entire archipelagos. The Paracels, a group of some 30 small islands, reefs and shoals situated to the central north of the South China Sea, forms the subject of a bilateral dispute between Vietnam and China (including Taiwan). Further south, China, Taiwan and Vietnam assert sovereignty over all the atolls in the Spratly Islands, while the Philippines, Malaysia and Brunei claim part of the group. A more recent island sovereignty dispute, which has nevertheless garnered international attention, is that between China and the Philippines over the ring-shaped Scarborough Reef, which comprises several rocks to the North of the Spratly Islands. Similarly, for maritime boundary disputes, the situation in the South China Sea has proved much more challenging as compared to the Arctic. The two disputed areas in the High North of the Arctic (between Canada and America in the Beaufort Sea and between Canada and Denmark in the Lincoln Sea) are relatively small and neither has generated serious frictions in bilateral relations. However, in the South China Sea, China's maritime boundary claims have been expansive, overlapping with the EEZs of all the littoral states.

In analyzing the multiple disputes in the South China Sea, many commentators have pointed to China's uncompromising stance as being the main source of the problems. In justifying its claims, China has often referred back to official Chinese maps to indicate a discontinuous nine-dash line that encloses approximately 80 per cent of the South China Sea (see Figure 24.3). This U-shape line first appeared in a map in 1914 drawn by Chinese cartographer Hu Jin Jie (Zou 1999) – part of the claims

considered in the closing section of the chapter – and it was originally confirmed by China in 1947 with 11 dashes entitled 'Locations of the South China Sea Islands' (Xue 2014). The Chinese authorities subsequently removed two dashes in the Gulf of Tonkin in 1953. Although China has never officially clarified what the nine-dash line denotes, it appears that Beijing is not only claiming sovereignty over the atolls within the line but also 'historical rights' to maritime resources. In 2013 Zhiguo Gao – a Chinese judge on the UN's International Tribunal on the Law of the Sea – published a co-authored academic article which argued that the nine-dash line was justified under international law and had 'become synonymous with a claim of sovereignty over the island groups that always belonged to China and with an additional Chinese claim of historical rights of fishing, navigation, and other marine activities (including the exploitation of resources, mineral or otherwise) on the islands and in the adjacent waters' (Gao and Jia 2013: 108). However, the nine-dash line significantly cuts into the maritime claims of the Philippines, Brunei, Malaysia, Indonesia and Vietnam, who argue that it violates their sovereign right to develop maritime resources provided for under the LOSC.

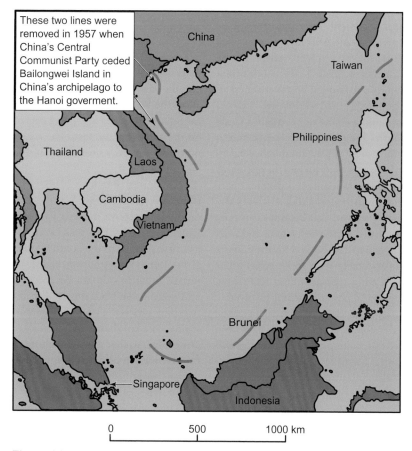

Figure 24.3 Map of China's 'nine-dash line'.

To negotiate these territorial and boundary disagreements, several governing frameworks have been conceived and adopted, but they are not without their limitations. As with the Arctic case, contestants in the South China Sea have vowed to settle their differences in accordance with the LOSC. However, China's commitment to existing international legal regimes has remained questionable. For instance, few non-Chinese legal experts believe that the nine-dash line promulgated by China is compatible with the LOSC, and in January 2013 the Philippines formally challenged such a cartographic imagination of the South China Sea. Despite China's refusal to participate in the proceedings, the case is ongoing and the Arbitral Tribunal is set to issue a verdict. However, even if the Tribunal rules that the nine-dash line is incompatible with the LOSC, Beijing seems set to ignore the ruling, leaving the problem unsolved.

The governance of the South China Sea has also been approached through the diplomatic, cooperative route, whereby official negotiations have been taking place between ASEAN and China. The initial result of this process is the 2002 Declaration on the Conduct of Parties in the South China Sea, which serves as a confidence building measure to prevent possible conflicts that might arise from island disputes in the area. The implementation of this political document, however, is long and daunting (it took nine years for ASEAN and China to agree to the Guidelines for the implementation of the Declaration of the Conduct of Parties in the South China Sea), with many scholars questioning its effectiveness in reducing tensions over the disputed islands (see Nguyen 2003). ASEAN is now urging China to negotiate a Code of Conduct in the South China Sea, which is expected to be binding and contain more stringent compliance mechanisms, but this has been met with lukewarm responses from Chinese officials. The fundamental problem here is that Beijing rejects multilateral talks vis-à-vis the ASEAN forum, insisting instead that disputes can only be resolved bilaterally – that is between China and each of the claimants on a one-to-one basis. However, many ASEAN members are extremely wary about direct bilateral engagements with a big regional player like China because of the asymmetrical power relations involved.

Lastly, a more proactive governance approach coming in the form of joint development of resources have been mooted. According to this 'solution', claimant states will put aside their territorial claims to engage in a cooperative undertaking in the exploration and exploitation of resources (particularly hydrocarbon ones). On the surface, such a proposal is attractive given that it will help to ease tensions by creating a win–win situation through all parties having access to the valuable maritime assets. A practical implementation of this approach is the Joint Marine Seismic Undertaking (JSMU) between oil corporations of China, the Philippines and Vietnam in 2005. Once hailed as a 'historic event' or a 'breakthrough' in the cooperation amongst the actors involved in the Spratly Islands dispute, the JSMU is stillborn, however. No concrete results were being registered and no follow-up actions have been undertaken upon the completion of the project. According to Schofield and Storey (2011), the shortcomings of such a cooperative venture are fully revealed insofar as it is a highly sensitive issue, with claimant states remaining adamant that they have undisputed sovereignty over the area in question.

Summarizing the preceding discussion, it can be seen that there are significant differences in the ways in which the Arctic states and South China Sea claimants approach their maritime disputes. As pointed out in the previous section, Arctic actors have subscribed to the principles of neoliberal governmentality by appealing to and relying on international laws and conventions to govern and address their disagreements in an orderly manner. This resolution pathway has proved to be untenable in the South China Sea, however, given that cooperation through legal and developmental regimes is arguably marred by what realists describe as the maximization of individual state's interests and agendas. Under such circumstances, it is hardly surprising that pessimistic overtures have emerged to characterize the future of politics in the South China Sea. Specifically, there have been contentions that the rapid modernization of China's navy and the expansion of its civilian maritime agencies will allow the Beijing government to increase its presence in the South China Sea and bring coercive pressures to bear on the smaller claimants. The rise of Chinese military power will in turn provide a catalyst for regional military modernization programs, notably in Vietnam and the Philippines (Bateman 2014). Others have argued that some ASEAN states such as the Philippines may hinge on the USA's 'pivot' to Asia Pacific to create a common front with America so as to counterbalance China's assertive actions in the South China Sea (Bhattacharaya 2014). But as Storey (2013b) rightly points out, such militaristic initiatives do not get to the root of the problem and getting the USA involved in the South China Sea will only provoke a more belligerent and uncooperative China. The key then is to return all parties to the negotiating table, so that a sustainable and plausible governing framework can be derived to resolve the disputes in the region. Such a framework, according to Storey, has to be outcome-oriented rather than process-driven and will need to factor in a cooperative ethos through adherence to international legal regimes, especially the LOSC, as well as establishing effective conflict management and crisis-prevention mechanisms.

24.5 Conclusion

In both the Arctic and the South China Sea, the governance regimes are changing in large part because of their further integration into the contemporary neoliberal world order. But this is throwing up tensions between states and non-state organizations. In the Arctic, a limited number of coastal states are attempting to cement their sovereign rights, while others such as China are eager to 'open up' the Arctic Ocean to trans-polar shipping routes and resource exploitation. In the South China Sea, a 'more assertive' China is widely viewed as reshaping interactions and dynamics amongst claimant states, thereby raising critical questions for multilateral governance in the region. International law and protocols are emerging as increasingly important mechanisms for ensuring that these potential flashpoints are addressed in an orderly manner. And by orderly, we mean not only in a non-violent manner but also in ways that minimize disruptions to commercial activities and investment. Following Foucault, this is in line with neoliberal governmentality whereby international conventions help to arbitrate the different positions and interests of states so that consensual partnerships and collaborative efforts can be harnessed to deal with various issues pertaining to these two maritime spaces. Without suggesting the determinacy of such an outcome, sovereign states in the Arctic and the South China Sea have also been eager to remind international audiences that they are determined to protect their interests, militarily if necessary.

But debates about governance should not be restricted to states alone and their sovereign rights. One danger of focusing on world order and global governance is that we give states a kind of privilege they don't merit. States and their claims to sovereignty don't just exist – they are actively produced. Likewise claims to governance are just claims – they will have to be constantly negotiated with other state and non-state actors in the global arena. This is especially pertinent given that many contemporary issues can no longer be confined within the limits of national territorial boundaries nor can a singular state authority adequately deal them with. A good case in point is the regulation of 'global commons' (e.g. oceans and the atmosphere) whereby the role of the international community is essential in collectively governing the resources that are vital to the sustenance of life. Alternatively, concerns have also been raised with regards to the trans-national impacts arising from increased mobilities of people, goods and corporations in this globalizing era. It is then hardly surprising that inter-governmental organizations such as the UN and EU have functioned as governance regimes in facilitating dialogues and meaningful cooperation to tackle these 'problems'. For instance, the cross-border danger posed by infectious diseases such as the deadly Ebola and Middle East Respiratory Syndrome (MERS) outbreaks in recent years has led to the reiteration of the importance of the UN, non-governmental organizations (NGOs) and states in coordinating joint efforts to deal with such dangers. More widely, NGOs have frequently become key agents in networks of governance. A good example would be the protests enacted by Greenpeace to critique the lacklustre commitments of many states in dealing with climate change. In this sense, governance is never emblematic of a natural state of affairs. It is a complex social process that involves multiple actors often with conflicting agendas. This makes governance a highly contested endeavour and closely bound up with issues of power – it is not only capable of being supported but can also be resisted, rejected or even overthrown.

As the previous chapters reminded us, therefore, we are talking here in large part about how we, as human beings, choose to organize our affairs. Ideas about space, place, knowledge, power, international relations, governance and order are critical here and embedded within human cultures. Those ideas are then put to work and continue to inform and influence the ways in which we understand the world around us including our relationship with others. All of this is, of course, profoundly geographical.

Learning outcomes

Having read this chapter you should understand:

- The term governance and the manner in which it has been understood within geography and related disciplines such as International Relations.
- The term international order and how we might make a distinction between functional and idealized orders.
- In the 1980s and 1990s governance was strongly associated with reforming government and economy in the global South, especially in the light of concerns over debt.
- Governmentality is a term developed in the writings of Michel Foucault addressing the 'art of government' and the way in which populations are organized and managed.

- The Arctic is undergoing a fundamental 'state change' and provides an interesting example of evolving governance and changing physical properties of the Arctic (e.g. melting sea ice) are provoking different debates about future governance.
- The governance of the South China Sea through legal regimes, joint development efforts and diplomatic negotiations has met with widespread obstacles.
- Future governance will depend on future governmentalities and how ideas about space, power, knowledge and order are mobilized. These relate to changing forms and patterns of hegemony.

Further reading

Agnew, J (2005) *Hegemony: The New Shape of Global Power,* Temple University Press, Philadelphia, PA. A very good overview of how the international system has evolved especially in the post 1945 era.

See too this paper for an argument for the importance of thinking about power and authority beyond the conventional focus of many on the exclusive role of states:

Agnew, J (1994) The territorial trap: the geographical assumptions of international relations theory, *Review of International Political Economy,* 1(1), 53–80.

Fifteen years on from the original publication, a set of essays published in *Geopolitics* revisited Agnew's arguments. As the introduction to that set notes:

> Attempts to anchor states (both heuristically and practically) within readily definable territorial boundaries tend to obscure the intensity of the very trans-border flows which themselves secure the functioning of those states within their claimed territorial unit.
>
> (Reid-Henry 2010: 753)

See: Reid-Henry, S. (2010) 'The territorial trap fifteen years on', *Geopolitics,* 15(4), 752–6, as well as other essays in the special section of *Geopolitics* that this introduces.

On the Artic and South China Sea:

Anderson, A. (2009) *After the Ice: Life, Death and Politics in the New Arctic,* Virgin Books, London. Written by a former editor of *New Scientist,* this book explores likely changes to the Arctic in the next 20–30 years.

Borgerson, S. (2007) Arctic meltdown, *Foreign Affairs,* 87, 63–77. An influential essay, which set the tone of much of the alarmist debate about potential changes to the Arctic.

Dodds, K (2013) The Ilulissat Declaration (2008): The Arctic States, 'Law of the Sea', and Arctic Ocean, *SAIS Review,* 33, 45–55. The article considers why the Arctic coastal states felt it necessary to issue a declaration affirming their sovereignty in the maritime Arctic.

Dodds, K. and M. Nuttall (2016) *Scramble for the Polar Regions? The Contemporary Geopolitics of the Arctic and Antarctic Polity,* Cambridge University Press, Cambridge. This book addresses contemporary geopolitical challenges facing the Arctic and Antarctic, and how resource exploitation and speculation are placing further pressures on governance arrangements.

Emmerson, C. (2010) *The Future History of the Arctic,* Bodley Head, London. An accomplished account of the geopolitical dynamics at play in the contemporary Arctic.

Hayton, B. (2014) *The South China: The Struggle for Power in Asia,* Yale University Press, New Haven.

Huang, J. and Billo, A. (eds) (2014) *Territorial Disputes in the South China Sea: Navigating Rough Waters,* Palgrave Macmillan, New York. An edited volume that disentangles the legal, historical and governance aspects of the South China Sea territorial and boundary disputes.

Steinberg, P., Tasch, J. and Gerhardt, H. (2015) *Contesting the Arctic: Rethinking Politics in the Circumpolar North,* I.B. Tauris, London. A survey of how the Arctic region has been drawn into intense debates about sovereignty and stewardship.

Wu, S. and Hong, N. (eds) (2014) *Recent Developments in the South China Sea Dispute: The Prospect of a Joint Development Regime* Routledge, Abingdon. An excellent set of essays that consider the future possibilities for governing the South China Sea.

On Foucault:

Crampton, J. and Elden, S. (eds) (2007) *Space, Knowledge and Power: Foucault and Geography* Ashgate, Aldershot. A compendium that highlights geographical readings of Foucault, with notions such as governmentality, power, knowledge and discourses duly interrogated.

Huxley, M. (2008) Space and government: governmentality and geography, *Geography Compass,* 2(5), 1635–58.

Rose-Redwood, R. (2008) Governmentality, geography and the geo-coded world, *Progress in Human Geography,* 30, 469–86. Two useful papers that summarize how Foucault's notion of governmentality has been engaged by geographers.

A range of writings on governance:

Goldin, I. (2013) *Divided Nations: Why Global Governance is Failing, and What We can do About it,* Oxford University Press, Oxford. A powerful polemic from an author who was involved in global governance projects and offers a thoughtful reflection on what needs to change to make globalization sustainable.

Klein, N. (2007) *The Shock Doctrine: The Rise of Disaster Capitalism,* Metropolitan Books, New York. An argument about how economic and natural disasters are used to reshape states and societies in ways that favour the powerful.

Kjaer, A. (2004*) Governance: A Key Concept,* Sage, London. A short accessible guide to some of the different meanings associated with the term governance.

Sinclair, T. (2004) *Governance: Critical Concepts in Political Science,* Routledge, London. A very clearly written account of the concept of governance by a political scientist.

Sparke, M. (2006) Political geography: political geographies of globalization (2): governance, *Progress in Human Geography,* 30, 1–16. A good review article on how governance has been conceptualized within political geography, with particular focus on issues of neoliberalism, power and globalization.

Taylor, P.J. (2005) New political geographies: global civil society and global governance through world city networks, *Political Geography,* 24, 703–30. An analysis of the intersections between a variety of networks: state agencies, NGOs and cities.

Whitman, J. (ed.) (2009) *Palgrave Advances in Global Governance,* Palgrave, Basingstoke. This explores the different ways of understanding global governance depending in part on whether one addresses the role of the state, economic sectors, international organizations and non-state actors.

Useful websites

www.un.org/   The official website of the United Nations.

www.europa.eu/   The official website of the European Union.

www.globalgovernancewatch.org/   The right-wing American Enterprise Institute runs a Global Governance Watch.

www.globalgovernance.eu/   The home of the Global Governance Institute, an independent think-tank based in Brussels.

www.eui.eu/Projects/GGP/Home.aspx   European University Institute Global Governance Programme.

www.arctic-council.org/   The home of the Arctic Council.

www.tni.org/   The Transnational Institute, a network of scholars and activists originally set up with support from the Institute of Policy Studies, www.ips-dc.org/.

Glossary

A

Abjection the process by which we seek to repress that which we regard as unclean, improper, impure or dangerous. In geographic terms, abject material tends to be located in marginal spaces which become repositories for those things which are regarded as threatening the social body.

Active citizenship voluntary action, often at the instigation of governments, aimed at improving local communities.

Activism political activism that is strategic in nature and may go beyond conventional or formal political channels.

Agglomeration the concentration of productive activities in a particular region.

Agribusiness large-scale, capital-intensive, agricultural businesses incorporating supply, production and processing capacities.

Agri-food system the highly integrated system of agricultural production which involves both upstream (e.g. suppliers) and downstream (e.g. processing) industries.

Alternative food networks a reaction to conventional (e.g. supermarket-dominated) food chains, in which local and/or organic foods are marketed through alternative outlets such as farmers' markets, box schemes and home deliveries.

Anthropocentric a way of understanding the value of the environment which prioritizes humans as having the most value. In other words the environment is only useful as a resource for humans. In this approach humans do not have any responsibility to ensure the environmental sustainability of our actions.

Apartheid the policy of spatial separation on racial grounds employed in South Africa under National Party rule between the late 1940s and early 1990s.

Appropriationism the replacement of agricultural inputs with industrial alternatives. It forms a key process in the industrialization of the agri-food system.

B

Balance of payments (BOP) the difference in value between a country's inward and outward payments for goods, services and other transactions.

Balkanization progressive subdivision of a region into small political units.

Bands societies of hunter–gatherers typically numbering up to 500 individuals. See Spotlight box 1.1.

Billion thousand million.

Biodiversity the variability among living organisms from all sources including terrestrial, marine and other aquatic ecosystems and the ecological complexes of which they are part; this includes diversity within species, between species and of ecosystems.

Biomass plant and animal residue burnt to produce heat.

Biosphere that part of the earth's surface, extending from the uppermost part of the earth's rocky core (lithosphere or geosphere) to the lower atmosphere, including the hydrosphere. The biosphere corresponds to and sustains the domain of life.

Biotechnology a branch of technology concerned with the industrial production of living organisms and their biological processes.

Birth rate number of babies born per thousand population per year; known as the crude birth rate.

Bottom-up development economic and social changes brought about by activities of individuals and social groups in society rather than by the state and its agents.

Bounded applied to the behaviour of decision makers whose access to information, for example, is constrained by financial resources or time. They also have a limited capacity to process the information that they are able to obtain and they will also be constrained (bounded) by the environment within which their behaviour is taking place. Bounded cultures may be regarded as reactions to perceived threats to local cultures, entailing a strong assertion of the latter. These can create a level of local fragmentation, with a parochial, nostalgic, inward-looking sense of local attachment and cultural identity. Bounded cultures generally involve very clear definitions of 'insiders' and 'outsiders' in the creation of a sense of belonging.

Brand boomerang where the stories companies add to their goods through branding are contested by other stories – often about the social relations of production – brought to public attention by journalists, NGOs, filmmakers, artists, activists and others.

Branding an important means by which the worlds of the producer and the consumer are mediated; marketing and advertising that adds to a company's goods stories of particular associations, awarenesses, loyalties, origins and perceived qualities. See *commodity fetishism*.

Brundtland Report published in 1987, it adopted the position that it was possible to pursue economic growth without compromising the environment and introduced the first widely used definition of sustainable development: 'development which meets the needs of the present without compromising the ability of future generations to meet their own needs'.

Buyer-driven commodity chain a chain in which the nature of production (e.g. salmon farming) is shaped or driven by powerful 'downstream' actors such as distributors and retailers.

C

CAP Common Agricultural Policy of the European Union.

Capital money put into circulation or invested with the intent of generating more money. See Spotlight box 18.2.

Capitalism an historically specific economic system in which production and distribution are designed to accumulate capital and create profit. The system is characterized by the separation of those who own the means of production from those who work for them.

Chiefdom social formation based on societies characterized by the internal and unequal differentiation of both power and wealth and organized around the principle of kinship. See Spotlight box 1.3.

Citizenship traditionally used to describe the relationship between an individual and a nation-state, including what rights and duties he or she can expect. The definition now encompasses wider, more fluid and often contested relationships with other political units.

City-states urban regions having political jurisdiction and control over a specific territory. A form of social organization associated with some of the earliest states.

Civic food networks food networks that are run and organised by civic groups (e.g., charities, NGOs).

Civilization refers to an advanced form of social development characterized by such things as urban life, commercial activity, writing systems and philosophical thought.

Class social distinctions between groups of people linked to their material conditions and social status.

Clean development mechanism (CDM) a mechanism whereby industrialized countries can earn credits towards their own greenhouse gas reduction targets by investing in emission-reducing projects in the developing world. Part of the aim is to aid economic growth in developing countries without a commensurate increase in greenhouse gas emissions. At the same time this benefits the industrialized countries; such assistance is often cheaper than reducing their own emissions.

Climate change a change in climate that is attributed directly or indirectly to human activity that alters the composition of the global atmosphere and which is in addition to natural climate variability observed over comparable time periods. Includes temperature rise, sea-level rise, precipitation changes, droughts and floods.

Climate migration a subset of environmental migration whereby persons or groups of persons are forced to move because of gradual changes in the natural environment, such as extreme weather events, droughts, water scarcity or sea-level rise (see also environmental migration).

Cluster a localized concentration of similar and interlinked economic activities.

Cold War a period extending from 1945 to the late 1980s during which two ideologically opposed blocs emerged within the world system, both with nuclear capabilities. The first was headed principally by the USA while the other was dominated by the Soviet Union.

Command economy an economic system characterized by state-led central planning of economic activity combined with the simultaneous suppression of market-type relations.

Commodity a good or service produced through the use of waged labour and sold in exchange for money.

Commodity fetishism how the relationships between the lives of commodities' consumers and producers are made invisible by advertising imagery which places their meanings, values and qualities in other imagined geographies. See also *follow the thing*.

Communism a political theory attributed to the works of Karl Marx and Friedrich Engels. Communism is characterized by the common ownership of the means of production. The foundations for full communism were supposed to be laid during a transitional period, known as socialism. The Soviet Union was the first state to be ruled by an avowedly communist government, from 1917 to 1991.

Community food scheme a site of resistance to the industrialization of agriculture, in which the local community retains control and where consumers get seasonal, fresh food at a price that supports farmers who use sustainable practices.

Comparative advantage in economic geography, refers to an advantage held by a nation or region in the production of a particular set of goods or services. See Spotlight box 14.4.

Competitive advantage exists when a firm can deliver the same benefits as competitors but at lower cost (cost advantage). A firm may also deliver benefits that are greater than those of competing products (differentiation advantage).

Conditional reserve those (mineral or ore) deposits that have already been discovered but that are not economic to work at present-day price levels with currently available extraction and production technologies.

Consumption a cultural-economic process; a placed and place-creating experience. The utilization of goods and services produced by economic processes, fostered by the retailing sector through marketing, advertising and branding. A process which, for every consumer, has a 'back story' – what shaped our buying of this or that – and an 'afterlife' – how we actively use the things we buy. A process implicated in many other aspects of our lives, including our senses of self-identity and caring relationships with others near and far. A process involving not only *shopping* but also entanglements in sociotechnical systems that produce our heating and lighting, for example.

Contact zone the space in which transculturation takes place – where two different cultures meet and inform each other, often in highly asymmetrical ways.

Containment the Western strategy of encircling the Soviet Union and its allies during the Cold War.

Core according to Wallerstein, the core refers to those regions of the capitalist world economy characterized by the predominance of core processes associated with relatively high wages, advanced technology and diversified production. See Spotlight box 2.1.

Counterurbanization population increases in rural areas beyond the commuting range of major urban areas.

Cultural capital the possession of taste, style or attitude that can be converted, in many instances, into financial capital. In the post-industrial economy, where ideas are a global currency, cultural capital is a lucrative commodity.

Cultural dupe a type of consumer described in some accounts as being pacified and seduced by advertising, an easily manipulated person following materialistic desires. See also *prosumer*.

Culture a system of shared meanings often based around such things as religion, language and ethnicity that can exist on a number of different spatial scales (local, regional, national, global, among communities, groups, or nations). Cultures are embodied in the material and social world, and are dynamic rather than static, transforming through processes of cultural mixing or transculturation. See Spotlight box 13.1.

Culture jamming tactics such as media hacking, information warfare, 'terror-art' and graffiti, which aim to invest advertisements, newscasts and other media artefacts produced by powerful agencies and organizations with subversive meaning.

D

DDT a chemical pesticide banned by many countries in the 1970s as a pollutant, which is a probable human carcinogen and causes damage to internal organs.

De-coupled payments subsidy payments made to farmers (e.g. CAP single farm payment) that are not linked to production levels.

Deep ecology An environmental approach which asks us to consider humans not only as part of nature but of equal value to non-human entities. This is a holistic vision whereby all human and non-human entities are interconnected and interdependent. A holistic perspective enables us to understand that if we upset one element, it will have an impact on all other elements.

Defensive localism a process where consumers purchase local foods to support local farmers and the local economy, irrespective of their quality and whether they are produced organically or conventionally.

Deforestation the removal of forests from an area.

Deindustrialization refers to a relative decline in industrial employment. It may also refer to an absolute decline in industrial output as well as employment.

Demarginalization the process whereby a marginal or stigmatized space becomes 'normalized', and its population incorporated into the mainstream.

Demographic transition model traces the shift from high birth and death rates to low ones.

Dependency a viewpoint or theory of development which argues that global inequality is explained by the patterns of exploitation of the periphery by the capitalist core, established during the colonial period and perpetuated by neo-colonial economic relations in recent times. The dependency theorists' recommendation for poorer countries is to de-link from the global economy.

Dependency approaches explanations of the the economic development of a state that are shaped by political, economic or cultural influences that are external to that state. Typically dependency involves two sets of states described as dominant/dependent, centre/periphery or metropolitan/satellite.

Depopulation the reduction of population in an area through out-migration or a reduction in the birth rate below the death rate.

Derivatives contracts between two entities that specify rights/obligations based on (hence 'derived' from) the performance of some other currency, commodity or service. They often include swaps, options, futures and mortgage-backed securities. They can be used to hedge against risk, or to provide leverage.

Diaspora literally, the scattering of a population; originally used to refer to the dispersal of Jews in AD 70, now used to refer to other population dispersals, voluntary and non-voluntary. Evokes a sense of exile and homelessness.

Diaspora space the spaces inhabited not only by those who have migrated and their descendants, but also by those who are conceptualized as indigenous or 'native'. Similar to contact zone – a meeting point of different cultures.

Discourse social and cultural theorists understand discourse to be the dominant meanings that are attached to a linguistic term or utterance.

Displaced persons refugees who have no obvious homeland.

Division of labour the separation of tasks in the production process and their allocation to different groups of workers.

E

Earth Summit the UN Conference on Environment and Development held in Rio de Janeiro in 1992. A total of 178 countries negotiated a global strategy centrally concerned with sustainable development.

Ecocatastrophism the prediction of impending environmental disasters, often as a result of human actions.

Ecocentrism a way of understanding the value of the environment which critiques the priorities of anthropocentrism and suggests that non-human entities have intrinsic value.

Ecological democratization an approach that suggests that the only way to achieve environmentally sustainable practices is to value participation and justice in environmental decision-making. Thus, this approach requires extensive citizen participation and the development of democratic institutions to tackle environmental issues at all scales.

Ecological modernization an environmental management approach that argues that economic growth does not need to be slowed to ensure environmental protection. It does not undermine the limits to growth thesis entirely, but suggests that we can 'reorient' economic growth and use technological solutions for environmental problems, thus overcoming the environmental impact of growth. It is a very weak interpretation of sustainable development that allows for a reformist response where the current dominance of free-market capitalism is not challenged.

Economies of scale occur when mass production of a good (product) results in a lower average cost for each item. Economies of scale occur within a firm, such as using expensive equipment more intensively, or outside the firm as a result of its location, such as the availability of a local pool of skilled labour or good transport links.

Edge city (exopolis) a term referring to an area with city-like functions usually arising on the edge of an already urbanized area or conurbation and heavily dependent on fast communications systems. Edge cities are regarded as symptomatic of the most recent phase of urbanization.

Electronic/digital money a payment system in which money is stored on a card and can be used to make, typically small, purchases, often simply by briefly holding the card at a contact point. Many universities and large companies use such cards in their canteens and for other services. Increasingly, public transport companies use these stored-value contactless smartcards as well, e.g. London's *Oyster Card*.

Emerging markets refers to those markets that are perceived to have a substantial growth potential. The term is often used in relation to selected countries of the former Soviet Union, Asia, Latin America and Africa.

Emotional labour workers are expected to display certain emotions, often in line with the goals of their employer or organization, as part of their job.

Empire an extended territorial political unit or state built up, often by force, under a supreme authority. Empires usually involve rule over alien or subject peoples.

Energy mix the balance between various sources of energy in primary energy consumption.

Energy ratio the relationship between energy consumption and economic growth in an economy:

$$\text{Energy ratio} = \frac{\text{Rate of change in energy consumption}}{\text{Rate of change in economic growth (GDP)}}$$

A value greater than 1 indicates that the amount of energy required to create an additional unit of GDP is increasing; a value less than 1 suggests the reverse.

Entitlements the set of all commodity bundles over which a person can establish command given the legal, political, economic and social arrangements of the community in which they live.

Environmental Kuznets Curve illustrates the hypothetical relationship between measures of environmental degradation and per capita income. Shaped rather like an upside-down U, the curve shows environmental degradation (e.g. pollution) increasing with rising wealth up to a certain point, beyond which higher income per capita leads to a reversal of damage. There is evidence that this theory applies to some environmental problems but not others.

Environmental migration defined by the International Organization for Migration as persons or groups of persons who, for compelling reasons of sudden or progressive changes in the environment that adversely affect their lives or living conditions, are obliged to leave their habitual homes, or choose to do so, either temporarily or permanently, and who move either within their country or abroad.

Environmentalism a broad term incorporating the concerns and actions in aid of the protection and preservation of the environment.

Ethical consumption where consumption is seen as a realm for political agency, a process that is not only generated by consumers being informed about the origins of commodities, but also by consumers' diverse personal and collective histories of wider ethical reflection and behaviour. A process which looks to extend consumption's 'close to home' caring relationships to those making the things we buy and share.

Ethnicity refers to the process through which groups are recognized as possessing a distinct collective cultural identity. See also *race and racism*.

EU European Union.

Exchange the process of interchange of goods and services between individuals, groups and/or organizations, whether involving money or not. Can also refer more broadly to social interactions.

Export processing zone a small closely defined area which possesses favourable trading and investment conditions created by a government to attract export-orientated industries.

F

Factors of production refers to those elements necessary for the effective functioning of the production process and typically includes land, labour and capital.

Fair trade attempts to overcome the injustices of free trade by guaranteeing producers a fair price and thus improving their lifestyles. Coffee, tea, bananas and chocolate are among the major fair trade products.

Fascism a term used particularly to describe the nationalistic and totalitarian regimes of Benito Mussolini (Italy, 1922–45), Adolf Hitler (Germany, 1933–45) and Francisco Franco (Spain, 1939–75).

Fast food a quick and accessible way to eat food; epitomized by McDonald's, it is usually eaten out of the home and out of our hands.

Fertility rates the number of live births per thousand women of child-bearing age.

Feudalism a hierarchical social and political system common in Europe during the medieval period. The majority of the population were engaged in subsistence agriculture while simultaneously having an obligation to fulfil certain duties for the landholder. At the same time the landholder owed various obligations (fealty) to his overlord.

Financial exclusion the processes that prevent disadvantaged social groups from gaining access to the financial system.

Financialization refers to the growing influence of capital markets, their intermediaries and processes in contemporary economic and political life.

Follow the thing an approach whose aim is to appreciate the social relationships between producers and consumers by tracing the lives of individual commodities from farm to fork, from factory to home, etc. See also *commodity fetishism*.

Food chain the route traced by particular foodstuffs from 'farm to fork'. Food chains involve a number of production, processing, distribution and consumption nodes, and the connecting links between them.

Food desert a place, usually in inner cities or remote rural areas, where access to fresh, affordable and healthy food is poor.

Food miles a term used to describe the distance that food travels from the point of production to the place of consumption. As well as distance, the mode of transport (e.g. air vs. ferry freight) is an important consideration.

Food regimes distinct relationships discerned between patterns of international food production and consumption and the developing capitalist system.

Food security when all people, at all times, have physical, social and economic access to sufficient, safe and nutritious food that meets their dietary needs and food preferences for an active and healthy life.

Fordism a regime of accumulation involving mass production and consumption. Named after Henry Ford (1863–1947), Fordism is known for a differentiated division of labour, assembly-line production and affordable mass-produced consumer goods.

Fordist or 'organized' capitalism a form of capitalism that reached its zenith during the period 1945 to 1973. It was characterized by the dominance of extractive and manufacturing industries, large-scale manufacture, mass-production and a significant level of state involvement. See Spotlight box 3.1.

Foreclosure or repossession is a legal process in which a lender attempts to recover the balance of a mortgage loan from a borrower who has stopped making payments, ultimately resulting in the sale of the house or apartment used as the collateral for the loan.

G

Gated communities residential developments protected by a range of mechanisms such as security gates, walls, private security guards and intercom systems.

Gemeinschaft a form of community said to be common in traditional societies (as distinct from industrial societies) and associated with notions of stability and informal personal contact.

Gender refers to socially constructed ideas of difference between men and women.

Gender division of labour a division of labour constructed around gender in which particular tasks and occupations are deemed to be male or female activities.

Gendered space the ways in which certain spaces are seen to be occupied exclusively or predominantly by either males or females.

Genetic modification (GM) human manipulation of genetic material (plant, animal and human) to create altered organisms.

Gentrification the process by which middle- and upper-class incomers displace established working-class communities. Often associated with new investment in the built environment, gentrification may be small-scale and incremental (i.e. instigated by individual incomers), or be associated with major redevelopment and regeneration schemes.

Geographies of exclusion the spatial processes by which a powerful grouping consciously seeks to distance itself from other less powerful groupings.

Geopolitics a term that has been used to refer to many things, including a tradition of representing space, states and the relations between them; also emphasizing the strategic importance of particular places.

Gesellschaft a form of association common in urban-based industrial societies (as distinct from traditional societies) and associated with non-permanent and utilitarian social relationships.

Ghetto refers to very high concentrations of people drawn from a particular ethnic or cultural background living in specific parts of an urban area. The term is now commonly associated with notions of deprivation, unemployment and social exclusion.

Global cities the term 'global city' was popularized by the sociologist Saskia Sassen in her 1991 book *The Global City* and is taken to refer to a small number of cities that serve as the command and control centres of the global economy. These cities possess a concentration of financial and business services linked to the multinational corporations that control the activities and organization of the global economy, and which are often conspicuously clustered in their downtown business districts. Global cities are also characterized by increasing social polarization as a result of a growing division in occupational and income opportunities, with growth in both high-skilled and low-skilled employment.

Global production networks the extensive webs of intra-, inter- and extra-firm connections through which commodities are produced, distributed, sold and consumed.

Global warming an increase in the temperature of the Earth's surface caused by trapping infrared radiation in carbon dioxide, increased amounts of which are produced by burning fossil fuels.

Globalized or 'disorganized' capitalism a form of capitalism identifiable since the mid-1970s. It is characterized by a relative decline in the importance of extractive and manufacturing industries, together with a relative increase in the importance of services. There is also an increasing tendency for the production process to be dominated by small-scale and flexible forms of organization. See Spotlight box 3.3.

Globalization a contested term relating to transformation of spatial relations that involves a change in the relationship between space, economy and society.

GM See genetic modification.

Governance the way in which power operates through the relationships between different organizations.

Green revolution a large increase in crop production in developing countries achieved by the use of fertilizers, pesticides and high-yield crop varieties.

Greenhouse gases gases that trap thermal radiation in the Earth's atmosphere, acting as a kind of blanket, leading to warming of the global climate system. Common greenhouse gases include carbon dioxide, methane and nitrous oxide.

Gross domestic product (GDP) the value left after removing the profits from overseas investments and those profits from the economy that go to foreign investors.

Gross national product (GNP) a broad measure of an economy's performance; it is the value of the final output of goods and services produced by the residents of an economy plus primary income from non-residential sources.

H

Heartland identified by the British geographer Halford Mackinder (1904) as the zone in East-Central Europe and Siberia, control of which would be a key to world domination. The term has since been appropriated by Latin American geopolitics.

Hegemony term derived from the work of Antonio Gramsci which refers to the ability of a dominant group to exert or maintain control through a combination of overt and subtle mechanisms.

Heritage according to UNESCO, 'heritage is our legacy from the past, what we live with today, and what we pass on to future generations. Our cultural and natural heritage are both irreplaceable sources of life and inspiration'. In human geography the focus is often on rural and urban heritage landscapes, frequently regarded as playing a formative role in the maintenance of national identity.

Heterogenization the way in which social forms that are conceived, controlled and put in place by corporations – e.g. McDonald's restaurants – become multiply localized in different places and cultures – e.g. McDonald's in Russia. See also *homogenization*.

High-value foods includes such foods as fruit, vegetables, poultry and shellfish. World trade in high-value foods has increased markedly during the past two decades.

Homogenization the effects that some academics say consumer culture has on places around the world. Social forms conceived, controlled and put in place by corporations – e.g. McDonald's restaurants – which are said to be the same wherever they are located. See also *heterogenization*.

Horizontal integration occurs when two companies, within the same industry and at the same stage of production, merge.

Hybridity refers to groups as a mixture of local and non-local influences; their character and cultural attributes are a product of contact with the world beyond a local place. See Case study 13.4.

Hypersegregation a term used to describe extreme residential segregation, such as that experienced by African-Americans in the USA.

Hypothetical resources those resources that might be expected to be found in the future in areas that have only been partially surveyed and developed.

I

Imaginary geographies the ideas and representations that divide the world into spaces with particular meanings and associations. These exist on different scales (e.g. the imaginaries that divide the world into a developed core and less developed peripheries, or the imagined divide between the deprived inner city and the affluent suburbs).

Imperialism a relationship of political, and/or economic, and/or cultural domination and subordination between geographical areas.

Indigenous peoples those peoples native to a particular territory that was later colonized, particularly by Europeans.

Industrial revolution a term that is often taken to refer to the marked transformation of productive forces, initially within the British economic system, between the mid-eighteenth and mid-nineteenth centuries. It resulted in the movement of Britain from a largely rural-based economy to one that was dominated by manufacturing and industrial production. Such a transformation resulted in substantial social, political as well as economic changes.

Industrialization of agriculture (see also agribusiness) a process whereby methods commonly associated with the manufacturing industry are increasingly incorporated into farming, e.g. specialization of labour, assembly-line production systems.

Infant mortality rate (IMR) number of deaths of persons aged under 1 per 1,000 live births.

Informal economy those parts of the economy which operate beyond official recognition and outside formal systems of control and, often, of remuneration.

Informal settlements also known as shanty towns or squatter settlements, these are sections of a city where poor people have moved in, often illegally or unofficially, and have constructed improvised housing using informal means and scrap materials: often plywood corrugated metal and sheets of plastic. They are usually built on the periphery of cities and often do not have proper sanitation, electricity, or other services. Informal settlements are mostly found in the major cities of developing nations in the global South and result from a combination of intense rural to urban migration pressures coupled with a lack of provision of affordable housing for low-income urban households.

Inherent value the value something has for someone, but not as means to a further end.

Instrumental value the value which something has for someone as a means to an end.

International division of labour a term referring to the tendency for particular countries and regions of the globe to specialize in particular types of economic activity.

International Monetary Fund (IMF) international financial institution that originated from the 1944 Bretton Woods Conference. Its main roles include regulating international monetary exchange and controlling fluctuations in exchange rates in order to alleviate balance of payments problems.

Intrinsic value simply the value something has. No appeal needs to be made to those for whom it has value.

Islam a monotheistic religion founded by the prophet Muhammad in the seventh century AD. Today there are two predominant divisions within Islam, the Sunni and Shi'i.

Islamophobia a prejudice against those who identify as Muslim, fuelled by post-9/11 discourses of Islamic fundamentalism and terrorist threat. Taking a variety of forms in the urban West, this can be interpreted as merely the latest inflection of a long-standing Orientalist discourse that contrasts Western democracy with Arab 'barbarism'.

K

Kondratieff cycle a term used to describe the cycles of boom and bust evident within the capitalist system since the mid-eighteenth century. Named after the Russian scholar N.D. Kondratieff.

Kyoto Protocol the agreed outcome of a meeting of 160 nations in Kyoto, Japan, in 1997 whereby many developed nations agreed to limit their greenhouse gas emissions relative to the levels emitted in 1990.

L

Legitimacy with regard to nation-states, a term meaning that the majority of people accept the rule of law of the governing political organizations.

Less developed countries (LDCs) countries at a disadvantage in today's global competitive environment because their comparative advantage in cheap labour or natural resource endowments has become subordinated to knowledge-based factors. LDCs suffer from poor productive capacities and competitiveness.

Life expectancy (at birth) average number of years of life expected on the basis of age-specific mortality schedules for the specified year.

Limits to growth the belief that there are natural limits to economic growth, which if exceeded will lead to environmental catastrophe.

Local Agenda 21 (LA21) the implementation by local administrations of sustainable development practices as defined in Agenda 21, an outcome of the Earth Summit, Rio de Janeiro, 1992.

Locality a place or region of sub-national spatial scale.

Low impact living (LIL) a deep green vision where humans minimize their environmental impact in all aspects of their daily lives.

M

Market-based states modern states where the market is the dominant means by which land, labour, capital and goods are exchanged and has a major influence over social and political organization.

Marxism a form of socialism and mode of analysis derived from the teachings of Karl Marx (1818–83).

Marxism regards capitalism as an inherently unjust system with the capitalists (those who own the means of production) exploiting the proletariat (those who must sell their labour in order to live). It aims to replace capitalism with a fairer system, socialism maturing into communism.

Mega-cities giant metropolises with populations of at least 10 million people. Also used by Manuel Castells to describe large cities in which some people are connected to global information flows while others are disconnected and information poor. This use of the term serves to highlight the problems associated with mega-cities in that they are large, highly unequal and beset by problems such as slum housing, pollution and urban sprawl, but also often lack the economic and political power of global cities and therefore the resources to adequately address their problems.

Merchant capitalism refers to an early phase of capitalist industrial development dominant in the larger urban regions of Europe from the late fifteenth century. Merchants were the principal actors engaged in both the provision of capital and the movement and trade of goods (predominantly bulky staples such as grain and manufactured goods).

Mergers occur when two firms agree to form a new company.

Modernism a term typically associated with the twentieth-century reaction against realism and romanticism within the arts. More generally, it is often used to refer to a twentieth-century belief in the virtues of science, technology and the planned management of social change.

Modernity refers to a period extending from the late sixteenth and early seventeenth centuries (in the case of Europe) to the mid to late twentieth century characterized by the growth and strengthening of a specific set of social practices and ways of doing things. It is often associated with capitalism and notions such as progress.

Monopoly in theory, exists in an industry when one firm produces all the output of a market; in practice varies between countries. In the United Kingdom, for example, any one firm that has 25 per cent of the market is considered to hold a monopoly.

Monopsony in theory exists in an economy when one firm or individual purchases all of the output in a given sector. An agribusiness company can gain a geographical monopsony over a given area through the use of contracts that prevent sale of produce to other parties.

Moral panic a term describing periodic episodes of concern about the threat of a particular group to the nation-state. Moral panics are normally fuelled by sensationalist media reporting, and are generally diffused by the state through policies which aim to counteract this imagined threat.

More developed countries (MDCs) countries with significant competitive advantages in today's globalizing economy. They have well-developed, increasingly knowledge-based and strongly interconnected manufacturing and service sectors that provide a significant proportion of employment and contribute to significant national and individual wealth. Indices such as literacy levels, incomes and quality of life are high and these countries exercise considerable political influence at the global scale. Examples are the United Kingdom, the United States, Germany and France.

Multiculturalism refers to a belief or policy that endorses the principle of cultural diversity and supports the right of different cultural and ethnic groups to retain distinctive cultural identities. It has often been criticized for being too symbolic and not politically radical enough in challenging racism.

N

Nationalism the ideology and sentiment of belonging to a 'nation' and the claim that the 'nation' should be expressed in a 'state'.

Nation-state and state a symbolic system of institutions claiming sovereignty over a bounded territory.

Negative equity is when the amount of an outstanding loan is greater than the market value of the asset for which the loan was provided, e.g. a house.

Neoliberalism an economic doctrine promoting market-led growth, deregulation and the privatization of state-owned enterprises.

Neo-Malthusian the belief that environmental problems are a consequence of population growth, following the arguments set out by Thomas Malthus in the late eighteenth century.

New economic geography (NEG) an economic geography that recognizes the importance of culture as an influence on economic processes and outcomes. In this way it draws attention to the culturalization of the economy in contrast to the economization of culture.

New industrial districts (NIDs) areas that specialize in a particular industry because of external economies which result from specialization.

New international division of labour (NIDL) the global shift of economic activity that occurs when the process of production is no longer constructed primarily around national economies.

New social movements fluid and informal groupings of political activists. They may encompass a diversity of interests, backgrounds and political viewpoints.

New World Order the notion of a Western-led post-Cold War structure of global power, which sanctions intervention.

Newly agriculturalizing countries (NACs) developing countries (e.g. Brazil, China, Kenya) where productivist farming systems have relocated, particularly for the production of high-value foods for export.

Newly industrialized countries (NICs) countries where there has been a relatively recent and significant shift away from primary activities towards manufacturing production. Examples are South Korea and Mexico.

NGO non-governmental organization.

Non-governmental organization (NGO) an organization formed by members of the public and one that has no government connections.

Non-renewable (stock) resources those resources, mainly mineral, that have taken millions of years to form. Their availability is therefore finite as there is no possibility of their stock being replenished on a time-scale of relevance to human society.

O

Overpopulation used to suggest that the finite resources of a particular area will run out if the population expands beyond a given point. Similar to the idea of a carrying capacity, that there is a limit beyond which environmental degradation occurs.

P

Palaeolithic the stage in the development of human society when people obtained their food by hunting, fishing and gathering wild plants, as opposed to engaging in settled agriculture. Also referred to as the Early Stone Age.

Participatory democracy a form of governance that encourages involvement of all people in political decision-making, as opposed to representative democracy.

Passive solar heating the use of sunlight to heat buildings through building design. This involves collecting sunlight through south-facing windows made of special glazing, using building materials with high heat storage capacity (e.g. brick walls and tile floors), and other design features that help to absorb and transmit heat, and protect from overheating.

Pastoral nomadism a form of social organization that is based on livestock husbandry for largely subsistence purposes. Pastoral nomads are characterized by a high level of mobility which allows them to search continually for new pastures in order to maintain their herds of animals.

Patriarchy system of gendered power relations through which men exercise power over women.

Peasant the term has had a number of different interpretations over the years and in different parts of the world. In general it usually refers to those individuals whose livelihood is largely dependent on the land and on rural subsistence-type activities. The term 'peasant' is usually reserved for those living in organized states, thus distinguishing them from band and tribal members, and so on.

Periphery according to Wallerstein, refers to those regions of the world capitalist economy characterized by low wages, simple technology and limited production.

Peri-urban those areas of land lying at the edge of urban areas and forming an interface between urban and rural areas. These areas are often referred to as rurban zones or the rural-urban fringe and are characterised by the intermingling of rural and urban land uses. The term originates from the French word périurbanisation.

Permaculture an environmental approach inspired by nature's patterns to create sustainable human habitats. It is based around three core principles – earth care (working with nature and designing systems that draw upon natural systems for inspiration), people care (looking after ourselves on a community and individual level through cooperation and mutual support) and fair shares (ensuring we only consume our share of the earth's resources).

Personal space the apparent desire by humans to have a pocket of space around them and into which they tend to resent others intruding without invitation.

Political economy an approach to social study that emphasizes the political/social construction and consequences of economic activity.

Post-Fordism production system comprises a mix of different ways of organizing production at a number of spatial scales. Common to all these types of production is some form of flexible production.

Postmodernism a philosophy that holds that the traits associated with twentieth-century modernism, such as belief in the possibility of managing social change according to sets of agreed principles, are now in retreat in the face of increasing individualism, pluralism and eclecticism.

Post-productivist transition a term used to describe the movement away from productivist agricultural systems. This new phase of agricultural production is characterized by extensive and diversified patterns of farming and the growing importance of non-agricultural activities in the countryside, for example, recreation.

Poverty the condition of possessing an income insufficient to maintain a minimal standard of living. Definitions of poverty are culturally specific, and thus relative to the social norms and expectations endemic to a given nation-state. However, the condition of absolute poverty (i.e. lacking the income to maintain a minimum diet) is acknowledged worldwide.

Power geometry the ways in which different social groups/individuals are placed in relation to the forces of globalization, enabling some to benefit and others to be disadvantaged.

Predatory lending a sub-set of subprime lending; a type of price discrimination making use of unsuitable loans designed to exploit vulnerable and unsophisticated borrowers.

Prehistoric societies societies that have left no written records.

Primary energy the energy in the basic fuels or energy sources used, e.g. the energy in the fuel fed into conventional power stations.

Primary sector comprises economic activities that exploit naturally occurring resources.

Pro-environmental behaviour (PEB) behaviour that reduces the negative impact of one's actions on the natural and built world, compared to alternatives.

Proto-industrialization refers to the early phase of capitalist industrial development in Europe. Characteristics of this period include a significant level of rural-based industrial activity and a low level of technological application in the production process.

Prosumer a type of consumer who not only uses commodities supplied to them, but completes them, creatively reworks them and/or makes them anew. See also *cultural dupe*.

Proven (proved) reserves those deposits of a resource that have already been discovered and are known to be economically extractable under current demand, price and technological conditions.

Q

Quality of life a composite measure that reflects individual preferences that include, for example, education, health, entertainment, living environment.

Quality turn the idea that local/alternative foods are of higher quality than products produced under conventional farming systems; in this way, quality is inextricably linked to locality.

Quaternary sector economic activities, mainly business enterprises, involved with the processing and exchange of information.

R

Race refers to the division of human beings into supposedly recognizable groups based predominantly on physical characteristics.

Racialized space the ways in which certain spaces are seen to be occupied exclusively or predominantly by a particular 'racial' or ethnic group.

Racism practices and attitudes that display dislike or antagonism towards people seen as belonging to particular ethnic groups. Social significance is attached to culturally constructed ideas of difference.

Refugees persons who flee to a foreign country to escape danger or persecution because of war, or religious or political reasons.

Relational approaches a term referring to a range of approaches that are concerned more with the network as a unit of analysis than the spatial unit. Despite considerable diversity between approaches, relational approaches focus primarily on the connections that exist between places and things. Particularly influential in recent iterations of urban and economic geography.

Relocalization (of food) refers to the renewed interest in foods of local and regional provenance, in which the link between 'product' and 'place' is emphasized and often formalized through a system of quality assurance or quality labels. Such locally distinctive quality food products are sold in regional and national markets.

Renewable energy energy sources such as winds, waves and tides that are naturally replenished and cannot be used up.

Renewable (flow) resources those resources that are naturally renewed within a sufficiently short time-span to be of use to human society. The continued availability of such resources is increasingly dependent upon effective management.

Replacement rate number of babies that an average woman should have to replace her generation, given prevailing levels of mortality (2.1 per woman in post-transition societies).

Representative democracy a form of governance that limits involvement of people in political decision-making to representatives often voted into positions of power by the broader public.

Residential segregation the ways in which, most obviously in urban areas, housing patterns can be observed where people live in areas divided along class or ethnic lines. In some instances this is conscious policy, in others it results from the interaction of social and economic processes.

Resource a substance in the physical environment that has value or usefulness to human beings and is economically feasible and socially acceptable to use.

Retroliberalism an approach to economic policy visible in parts of the Western world in the 2010s that sees a return to classical liberal views concerning the central role of the nation state in facilitating the free-market, modernizing the infrastructure of the economy and increasing the global reach of domestic corporations through trade diplomacy and aid.

Right to Food a human right recognised in the Universal Declaration of Human Rights and the International Covenant on Economic, Social and Cultural Rights. It requires signatory governments to respect, protect and fulfil their citizens' rights to adequate and sufficient food consistent with cultural traditions.

Romantic movement artistic, literary and philosophical movement that originated in the eighteenth century as a backlash against industrialization.

Rurality functionalist, critical political economy and social representation approach for distinguishing between rural and urban economy and society.

Rural–urban fringe refers to the zone where rural and urban land uses meet and intermix around the edges of urban areas. While some regard the rural urban fringe as a transition zone between the city and the countryside, others argue that it represents a distinctive landscape type in its own right. This zone has long been regarded as problematic in planning and management terms. It is typically regarded as lacking aesthetic quality and being dominated by the functional landscape elements of the urban infrastructure, the transport and distribution networks of the city and low-grade rural land.

S

Second global shift offshoring of service functions; the first global shift involved the offshoring of manufacturing functions.

Second industrial revolution a term sometimes used to account for the profound technological and accompanying social changes that affected industrial capitalism from the late nineteenth century. During this period Britain's industrial might was challenged by Germany and the USA.

Secondary mortgage market the market where investment banks, other financial institutions, and the two major US-government sponsored enterprises, Freddie Mac and Fannie Mae, repackage mortgages as securities to sell to institutional investors in national and global capital markets.

Secondary sector comprises economic activities that transform primary sector outputs into useable goods.

Securities tradable financial assets of any kind. Include bonds and banknotes (debt securities), company and other stocks traded (equity securities), futures, options and swaps (derivatives). Most securities are traded on exchanges regulated by national jurisdictions such as the US Securities and Exchange Commission (SEC) or the Financial Conduct Authority (UK).

Securitization the process of taking localized, non-standard and opaque assets like mortgages and transforming them into transparent and liquid securities that can be easily exchanged on global markets.

Semi-periphery according to Wallerstein, refers to those regions of the world capitalist economy which, while exploiting the periphery, are themselves exploited by the core countries. Furthermore, they are characterized by the importance of both core and peripheral processes.

Sense of place the feelings, emotions and attachments to a locality by residents (past or present), which may be articulated in art, literature, music or histories, or may become part of individual or group memory.

Services work done as an occupation or business for other individuals or businesses that brings about a change in the condition of a person or of a good belonging to some economic unit which does not produce or modify physical goods.

Sexuality refers to social differences linked to sexual identity and behaviour.

Shopping the experiencing of retail spaces, seeing and being seen by other shoppers within them, a social activity that may or may not involve buying things.

Simulacrum a copy without an original. An example might be Disneyland's 'Main Street', which represents an ideal American high street, but is not modelled on an original.

Slow food promoted as an anti- 'fast food' culture, slow food aims to decelerate the food consumption experience and celebrate the cultural connections surrounding local cuisines and traditional products. The slow-food movement aims to embed food in the local territory and culture.

Social construct a social concept or idea (such as race, class, gender or age) that is institutionalized and normalized within a culture to the extent that people behave as if it were a 'real' or a pre-social given.

Social constructionism a sociological theory of knowledge which claims that meanings and truths are established socially through habitual use and institutionalization. In opposition to realism, which regards truths as pre-given and objective, social constructionism recognises that individuals and groups participate in the creation of their realities through the way in which they perceive things and events.

Social embeddedness the idea that economic behaviour is embedded in, and mediated by, a complex and extensive web of social relations. Trust and regard are examples of such social relations.

Social exclusion the various ways in which people are excluded (economically, politically, socially, culturally) from the accepted norms within a society.

Social movement comprised of individuals, groups and organizations united by a common purpose or goal.

Spatial divisions of labour the concentration of particular sectors or production tasks in specific geographic areas.

Spatial interaction a term used to indicate interdependence between geographical areas. Covers the movement of people, goods, information and money between places.

Spatial relations the ways in which people are connected across geographic space through economic, social, cultural or political processes.

Speculative resources those resources that might be found in unexplored areas which are thought to have favourable geological conditions.

State a political unit having recognizable control (claiming supreme power) over a given territory. Unlike earlier social formations like bands and tribes, states have always based their power on their ability to control a specified territory and its inhabitants.

Stigma a term describing the condition of possessing a 'spoiled' or discredited identity.

Structural adjustment programmes loans designed to foster structural adjustment in LDCs by promoting market-led growth and a reduction in government intervention in the economy.

Structuralism a theory, evolved in Latin America in the 1940s and 1950s, which argues that the relative position of a given economy vis-à-vis the global economy is a function of the nature of the manner of insertion of that economy historically. Changing the fortunes of an economy therefore requires state intervention to alter its structure.

Studentification an increase in the student population in a residential area, principally associated with student renting in the private sector, though also associated with newly built off-campus accommodation developed by private investors. A widely noted phenomenon in those countries where students in higher education tend to live away from home, it is sometimes associated with gentrification, but has markedly different social and environmental outcomes.

Subculture a subdivision of a dominant culture or an enclave within it with a distinct integrated network of behaviour, beliefs and attitudes.

Substitutionism refers to the increased use of non-agricultural raw materials characterized by the replacement of food and fibre with industrial alternatives. It forms a key process in the industrialization of the agri-food system.

Subprime loan a high-cost loan designed for borrowers with poor credit or higher default risk, but also sold to borrowers with a good credit history.

Subprime mortgage loan to someone who may, as a result of unemployment or divorce for example, find it difficult to maintain regular repayments. These loans are offered on less favourable terms, such as a higher interest rate, in order to cover the higher credit risk. Because many sub-prime loans were packaged into mortgage-backed securities that ultimately defaulted they contributed to the 2007 financial crisis.

Subsumption a process whereby an agribusiness TNC increases its control over farming by offering contracts to farmers to provide 'raw materials' for its food-manufacturing activities.

Suburbanization, suburbs suburbanization describes the growth of areas on the fringes of major cities. Whilst residents of metropolitan regions have often tended to work within the central urban area, they have frequently chosen to live in satellite communities called suburbs and commute to work via car or mass transit systems. Suburbs are therefore most frequently viewed as residential areas, either being part of a city or separate residential communities within commuting distance of a city. In physical form they represent a mix of urban and rural elements and most have a lower population density than inner city neighbourhoods. Often considered dull and homogeneous in character, more recently research has highlighted the diverse and changing nature of suburbs with an increasing range of urban populations and activities evident in outer or edge of city locations.

Sustainability, sustainable development terms whose usage and meanings have grown exponentially in recent years since their original discussion in the 1987 Brundtland Report. At their most basic they refer to the idea that development can continue in ways that respects the needs of future generations. There is considerable debate though concerning how sustainability and these needs can be defined and measured. Often sustainability has come to refer to economic or social sustainability rather than just environmental sustainability. As sustainability discourses have proliferated it is fair to say that the meaning of sustainability and sustainable development have become less clear and subject to political manipulation. The terms have come to invoke a degree of cynicism amongst many radical/critical geographers.

Sustainable intensification This term is attributed to concerns about global food security. It evokes the idea that there is a need to achieve higher yields from the same acreage without damaging the environment. Advocates argue this can be achieved through science and technology innovations.

T

Territoriality a term used to describe an expression of ownership and control by an individual, group or state over a particular area of land in order to achieve particular ends.

Territory a recognizable region (area of land or sea) occupied and controlled by an individual, group or state.

Tertiary sector comprises economic activities engaged in enabling the exchange and consumption of goods and services (often referred to as the service sector).

Third World a rather vague term used to describe those regions of the world in which levels of development, as understood by such measures as GDP, are significantly below those of the economically more advanced regions. The term is increasingly seen as an inadequate description of the prevailing world situation since it disguises a significant amount of internal differentiation.

TNCs see transnational corporations.

Traceability in economic geography refers to the ability to determine the origin of agricultural foodstuffs.

Tradition an inherited, established or customary way of thinking, behaving or doing something, characteristic of persons in a particular family, group or society.

Transatlantic Trade and Investment Partnership (TTIP) a proposed free trade and investment agreement between the European Union and the United States.

Transculturation the ways in which subordinated or marginal groups select and invent from dominant cultures; although such groups cannot control what emanates from the dominant culture, they do determine to varying extents what they absorb into their own and what they use it for.

Transgression a term describing actions that breach social expectations of what is appropriate in a particular place. Deliberate transgression may thus constitute an act of resistance.

Transnational corporations (TNCs) major business organizations that have the power to coordinate and control operations in more than one country. They are the primary agents of globalization in, for example, the agri-food sector. See Spotlight box 14.2.

Transnationalism multiple ties and interactions linking people or institutions across the borders of nation-states and measured, for example, as flows of capital, people, information and images.

Travellers formerly referred to as 'gypsies', persons that are nomadic in lifestyle living in mobile homes of various types that are moved around from time to time.

Tribe a type of social formation usually said to be stimulated by the development of agriculture. Tribes tend to have a higher population density than bands and are also characterized by an ideology of common descent or ancestry. See Spotlight box 1.2.

U

Underclass a term referring to poorer, more marginalized groups in society who are seen to experience multiple deprivation.

Urban myths long-standing partial, at times stereotypical, images or impressions of the urban that are deeply ingrained within cultures and present throughout different historical periods. Often constructed in opposition to rural myths and implicated in moral debates about different ways of life associated with the rural and the urban.

Urban revanchism literally, the process of 'revenge' by which middle-class citizens take back the city from the marginal groups whom they portray as taking it from them. In practice, this is promoted by urban policies promoting law and order on the city streets and excluding those who do not fit in with the middle-class consumer ambience vital to the success of urban gentrification.

Urbanization refers to the increasing importance of the urban relative to the total population. It is initially stimulated by the movement of people from rural to urban areas.

V

Value-adding activity sequential steps in a production process that enhances the saleable value of a commodity.

Vertical disintegration a process whereby segments of the production process (usually in a vertically integrated business) are subcontracted out to smaller-scale producers.

Vertical integration occurs when firms at different stages of the production chain merge together.

W

World Bank international financial institution established in 1944. Its main role is to provide development funds to LDCs in the form of loans and technical assistance.

World systems theory Immanuel Wallerstein's conceptualization of the changing nature of the world socio-economic system into three distinct historical categories.

WTO World Trade Organization.

Bibliography

A

Aalbers, M.B. (2009) Geographies of the financial crisis, *Area*, **41**, 34–42.

Aalbers, M.B. (ed.) (2012a) *Subprime Cities: The Political Economy of Mortgage Markets*, Wiley-Blackwell, Oxford.

Aalbers, M.B. (2012b) Socializing space and politicizing financial innovation/destruction: some observations on Occupy Wall Street, *Belgeo*, **1–2**, http://belgeo.revues.org/6155.

Aalbers, M.B. (2015) Corporate financialization, in Castree, N. *et al.* (eds) *The International Encyclopaedia of Geography: People, the Earth, Environment, and Technology*, Wiley, Oxford.

Aas, F.K. (2007) *Globalization and Crime*, Sage, London.

Abraham, I. and van Schendel, W. (2005) *Illicit Flows and Criminal Things, States, Borders, and the Other Side of Globalization*, Indiana University Press, Bloomington and Indianapolis, IN.

Abrahamsen, R. (2000) *Disciplining Democracy: Development Discourse and Good Governance in Africa*, Zed Books, London.

ActionAid (2009) *Assessing the Alliance for Green Revolution in Africa*, ActionAid International, Johannesburg.

ActionAid International (2015) *Real Aid: An Agenda for Making Aid Work*, ActionAid, London, www.actionaid.org/sites/files/actionaid/real_aid.pdf.

Affifi, T. and Jäger, J. (eds) (2010) *Environment, Forced Migration and vulnerability*, Springer, Berlin.

Aggarwal, R., Kaushal, M., Kaur, S. and Farmaha, B. (2009) Water resource management for sustainable agriculture in Punjab, India, *Water Science and Technology*, **60**(11), 2905–11.

Agnew, J. (1994) The territorial trap: the geographical assumptions of international relations theory, *Review of International Political Economy*, **1**, 53–80.

Agnew, J. (2005a) Sovereignty regimes: territoriality and state authority in contemporary world politics, *Annals of the Association of American Geographers*, **95**(2), 437–61.

Agnew, J. (2005b) *Hegemony: The New Shape of Global Power*, Temple University Press, Philadelphia, PA.

Agnew, J. (2007) No borders, no nation: making Greece in Macedonia, *Annals of the Association of American Geographers*, **97**(2), 398–422.

Agnew, J. (2009) *Globalization and Sovereignty*, Rowan and Littlefield, Lanham, MD.

Agnew, J. (2010a) Emerging China and critical geopolitics: between world politics and Chinese particularity, *Eurasian Geography and Economics*, **51**(5), 569–82.

Agnew, J. (2010b) Still trapped in territory?, *Geopolitics*, **15**(4), 779–84.

Agnew, J. and Corbridge, S. (1995) *Mastering Space: Hegemony, Territory and International Political Economy*, Routledge, London.

AGRA *see* Alliance for a Green Revolution in Africa.

Ahluwalia, P. (2001) *Politics and Post-colonial Theory: African Inflections*, Routledge, London.

Akzin, B. (1964) *State and Nation*, Hutchinson, London.

Alland, A. (Jr) (1972) *The Human Imperative*, Columbia University Press, New York.

Alliance for a Green Revolution in Africa (AGRA) (2010) Statement on plant breeding and genetic engineering, Alliance for a Green Revolution in Africa, www.agra-alliance.org/section/about/genetic_engineering [accessed 12 October 2010].

Alvarez-Rivadulla, M.J. (2007) Golden ghettos: gated communities and class segregation in Montevideo, Uruguay, *Environment and Planning A*, **39**, 47–63.

Alvesson, M. (2000) Social identity and the problem of loyalty in knowledge-intensive companies, *Journal of Management Studies*, **37**(8), 1101–23.

Amin, A. (ed.) (1994) *Post-Fordism: A Reader*, Blackwell, Oxford.

Amin, A. (2002) *Ethnicity and the Multicultural City: Living with Diversity*, Report for Department of Transport, Local Government and the Regions, University of Durham.

Amin, A. (2004) Regions unbound: towards a new politics and place, *Geografiska Annaler B*, **86**(1), 31–42.

Amin, A. (2010) The remainders of race, *Theory, Culture and Society*, **27**(1), 1–23.

Amin, A. and Cohendet, P. (2004) *Architectures of Knowledge: Firms, Capabilities, and Communities*, Oxford University Press, Oxford.

Amin, A. and Thrift, N. (2002) *Cities: Reimagining the Urban*, Polity Press, Cambridge.

Amin, A. and Thrift, N. (2004) *The Blackwell Cultural Economy Reader*, Blackwell, Oxford.

Amiti, M. and Wei, S.J. (2004) *Fear of Service Outsourcing: Is it justified?*, International Monetary Fund Working Paper, WP/04/186.

Anderson, A. (2009) *After the Ice: Life, Death and Politics in the New Arctic*, Virgin Books, London.

Anderson, B. (1983) *Imagined Communities: Reflections on the Origins and Spread of Nationalism*, Verso, London.

Anderson, J. (1986) Nationalism and geography, in Anderson, J. (ed.) *The Rise of the Modern State*, Harvester, Brighton, 113–26.

Anderson, J. (1995) The exaggerated death of the nationstate, in Anderson, J., Brook, C. and Cochrane, A. (eds) (1995) *A Global World? Re-ordering Political Space,* Oxford University Press and the Open University, Oxford, 65–112.

Anderson, J. (2010) *Understanding Cultural Geography: Places and Traces,* Routledge, London.

Anderson, J. (2015) *Understanding Cultural Geography: Places and Traces,* 2nd edition, Routledge, London.

Anderson, J., Askins, K., Cook, I. *et al.* (2008) What is geography's contribution to making citizens? *Geography,* **93,** 34–39.

Anderson, K. (1991) *Vancouver's Chinatown: Racial Discourse in Canada 1875–1980,* McGill-Queens University Press, Montreal.

Anderson, K. (2000) 'The beast within': race, humanity and animality, *Environment and Planning D: Society and Space,* **18,** 301–20.

Andreas, P. (2000) *Border Games: Policing the US–Mexico Divide,* Cornell University Press, Ithaca, NY.

Andreasson, S. (2005) Orientalism and African Development Studies: the 'reductive repetition' motif in theories of African underdevelopment, *Third World Quarterly,* **26**(6), 971–86.

Anonymous (2012) 'The agony and the ecstasy of Steve Jobs', presented by Stage Force, seacoastonline.com, 14 June, www.seacoastonline.com/article/20120614/ENTERTAIN/206140321?template=printart [accessed 12 March 2015].

Antonisch, M. (2009) *Geopolitica*: the 'geographical and imperial consciousness' of fascist Italy, *Geopolitics,* **14,** 256–77.

Appadurai, A. (2003) Sovereignty without territoriality: notes for a postnational geography, in Low, S.M. and Lawrence-Zúñiga, D. (eds) *The Anthropology of Space and Place,* Blackwell, Oxford, 337–49.

Apple (2010a) Apple launches iPad, *Apple.com,* 27 January, www.apple.com/pr/library/2010/01/27ipad .html [accessed 4 August 2010].

Apple (2010b) Apple sells one million iPads, *Apple.com,* 3 May, www.apple.com/pr/library/2010/05/03ipad.html [accessed 4 August 2010].

Apple (2010c) iPad available in nine more countries on May 28, *Apple.com,* 7 May, www.apple.com/pr/library/2010/05/07ipad.html [accessed 4 August 2010).

Archibugi, D. (1995) Immanuel Kant, cosmopolitan law and peace, *European Journal of International Relations,* **1,** 429–56.

Ardener, S. (1995) Women making money go round: ROSCAs revisited, in Ardener, S. and Burman, S. (eds) *Money Go-Rounds: The Importance of Rotating Savings and Credit Associations for Women,* Berg, Oxford.

Ardener, S. and Burman, S. (eds) (1995) *Money Go-Rounds: The Importance of Rotating Savings and Credit Associations for Women,* Berg, Oxford.

Arenas, I. (2014) Assembling the multitude: material geographies of social movements from Oaxaca to Occupy, *Environment and Planning D: Society and Space,* **32**(3), 433–49.

Argent, N. (2002) From pillar to post? In search of the post-productivist countryside in Australia, *Australian Geographer,* **33,** 97–114.

Arrighi, G. (1994) *The Long Twentieth Century: Money, Power, and the Origins of our Times,* Verso, New York.

Arvidsson, A. (2006) *Brands: Meaning and Value in Media Culture,* Routledge, London.

Asheim, B., Coenen, L. and Vang, J. (2007) Face-to-face, buzz, and knowledge bases: sociospatial implications for learning, innovation, and innovation policy, *Environment and Planning C,* **25**(5), 655.

Ashley, R. (1987) Untying the sovereign state, *Millennium,* **17,** 227–62.

Ashlin, A. and Ladle, R. (2006) Environmental science adrift in the blogosphere, *Science,* **312,** 201.

Ashton, P. (2009) An appetite for yield: the anatomy of the subprime mortgage crisis, *Environment & Planning A,* **41,** 1420–41.

Askins, K. and Fuller, D. (2006) *Citizenship and Geography: The 'Geographies of Citizenship'*, Geographical Association, Sheffield, www.geography.org.uk/download/GA_AUCWGJan07ViewpointGuide.pdf, [accessed 9 July 2012].

Atkin, S. and Valentine, G. (eds) (2014) *Approaches to Human Geography,* 2nd edition, Sage, London and Thousand Oaks, New Delhi.

Atkins, P. and Bowler, I. (2001) *Food in Society: Economy, Culture and Geography,* Arnold, London.

Atkinson, A. (1991) *Principles of Political Ecology,* Belhaven, London.

Atkinson, A. (2007a) Cities after oil – 1: 'sustainable development' and energy futures, *City,* **11**(2), 201–13.

Atkinson, A. (2007b) Cities after oil – 2: background to the collapse of 'modern' civilisation, *City,* **11**(3), 293–312.

Atkinson, A. (2008) Cities after oil – 3: collapse and the fate of cities, *City,* **12**(1), 79–106.

Atkinson, R. and Blandy, S. (2006) *Gated Communities,* Routledge, London.

Atkinson, R. and Flint, J. (2004) Fortress UK? Gated communities, the spatial revolt of the elite and time-space trajectories of segregation, *Urban Studies,* **19**(6), 875–92.

Auty, R. (1979) World within worlds, *Area,* **11,** 232–5.

Auty, R. (1993) *Sustaining Development in Mineral Economies: The Resource Case Thesis,* Routledge, London.

Auty, R. (2001) *Resource Abundance and Economic Development,* Oxford University Press, Oxford.

AVERT (2014) *Universal Access to HIV Treatment,* AVERT, www.avert.org/universal-access-hiv-treatment.htm [accessed 10 April 2015].

Avery, R.B., Brevoort, K.P. and Canner, G.B. (2006) Higher-priced home lending and the 2005 HMDA data, *Federal Reserve Bulletin,* **92,** 123–66.

B

Bacheli, T., Bartmann, B. and Srebrnik, H.F. (2004) *De Facto States: The Quest for Sovereignty,* Routledge, London and New York.

Bachmann, V. and Sidaway, J. (2009) Zivilmacht Europa: a critical geopolitics of the European Union as a global power, *Transactions of the Institute of British Geographers,* **34**(1), 94–109.

Bagaeen, S. and Uduku, O. (eds) (2010) *Gated Communities: Social Sustainability and Historical Gated Developments,* Earthscan, London.

Bagemihl, B. (1999) *Biological Exuberance: Animal Homosexuality and Natural Diversity,* Martin's Press, New York.

Baker, A. (2012) Forging a national identity for France after 1789: the role of landscape symbols, *Geography,* **97,** 22–8.

Bakewell, O. (2011) Migration and development in sub-Saharan Africa, in Phillips, N. (ed.) *Migration in the Global Political Economy,* Lynne Rienner, Boulder, CO, www.imi.ox.ac.uk/publications/migration-and-development-in-sub-saharan-africa/@@/download/file [accessed 2 May 2015].

Bakhtin, M. (1984) *Rabelais and his World* (trans. Helen Iswolsky), Indiana University Press, Bloomington, IN.

Balibar, E. (2003) Whose power? Whose weakness? On Robert Kagan's critique of European ideology, *Theory and Event,* 6.

Ballinger, P. (2003) *History in Exile: Memory and Identity at the Borders of the Balkans,* Princeton University Press, Princeton, NJ.

Banrffalo, R. (1996) *Interview with David Harvey: The Politics of Social Justice,* www.uky.edu/AS/SocTheo/DisClosure/Harveydi.htm.

Bărbulescu, H. (2012) Constructing the Roma people as societal threat: the Roma expulsions from France, *European Journal of Science and Theology,* **8**(1), 279–89.

Baringhorst, S., Kneip, V. and Niesyto, J. (eds) (2009) *Political Campaigning on the Web,* Bielefeld Verlag.

Barker, K. (2010) Biosecure citizenship: politicising symbiotic associations and the construction of biological threat, *Transactions of the Institute of British Geographers,* **35,** 350–63.

Barling, D., Sharpe, R. and Lang, T. (2008) *Rethinking Britain's Food Security.* November. Report prepared for The Soil Association, Bristol.

Barnard, A. (ed.) (2004) *Hunter-Gatherers in History, Archaeology and Anthropology,* Berg, Oxford.

Barnes, T. and Farish, M. (2006) Between regions: science, militarism, and American geography from World War to Cold War, *Annals of the Association of American Geographers,* **96**(4), 858–63.

Barnes, T. and Minca, C. (2013) Nazi spatial theory: the dark geographies of Carl Schmitt and Walter Christaller. *Annals of the Association of American Geographers,* **103**(3), 669–87.

Barnet, R.J. (1973) *Roots of War: The Men and Institutions behind US Foreign Policy,* Penguin, Harmondsworth.

Barnett, C., Cloke, P., Clarke, N. and Malpass, A. (2005) Consuming ethics: articulating the subjects and spaces of ethical consumption, *Antipode,* **37**(1), 23–45.

Barnett, C., Cloke, P., Clarke, N. and Malpass, A. (2011) *Globalizing Responsibility: The Political Rationalities of Ethical Consumption,* Wiley Blackwell, Oxford.

Barnett, D. (1998) *London: Hub of the Industrial Revolution: A Revisionary History: 1775–1825,* Tauris Academic Studies, London.

Barnett, J. (2007) The geopolitics of climate change, *Geography Compass,* **1**(6), 1361–75.

Barnett, R. and Barnett, P. (2003) If you want to sit on your butts you'll get nothing! – community activism in response to threats of rural hospital closure in southern New Zealand, *Health and Place,* **9,** 59–71.

Barthes, R. (1972) *Mythologies,* Paladin, London.

Bassin, M. (1987) Race contra space: the conflict between German Geopolitik and National Socialism, *Political Geography Quarterly,* **6,** 115–34.

Bateman, S. (2014) Sovereignty as an obstacle to effective oceans governance and maritime boundary making-the case of the South China Sea, in Schofield, C., Lee, S. and Kwon, M-S. (eds) *The Limits of Maritime Jurisdiction,* Brill, Leiden, 201–24.

Bater, J.H. (1986) Some recent perspectives on the Soviet city, *Urban Geography,* **7,** 93–102.

Batterbury, S. and Warren, A. (2001) Desertification, in Smelser, N. and Baltes, P. (eds), *International Encyclopœdia of the Social and Behavioral Sciences,* Elsevier Press, Amsterdam, 3526–29.

Bathelt, H and Gluckler, J (2003) Toward a relational economic geography, *Journal of Economic Geography,* 3, 117–44.

Bauder, H. (2014) Domicile citizenship, human mobility and territoriality, *Progress in Human Geography,* **38**(1), 91–106.

Bauman, Z. (2011) Interview: Zygmunt Bauman on the UK riots, *Social Europe Journal,* Online Edition, www.social-europe.eu/2011/08/interview-zygmunt-bauman-on-the-uk-riots/.

Bayley, C. (1989) *Atlas of the British Empire,* Hamlyn, London.

BBC *see* British Broadcasting Corporation.

Beaumont, C. (2010) Foxconn suicide rate is lower than in the US, says Apple's Steve Jobs, *Daily Telegraph,* 2 June, www.telegraph.co.uk/technology/steve-jobs/7796546/Foxconn-suicide-rate-is-lower-than-in-the-US-says-Apples-Steve-Jobs.html [accessed 5 August 2010].

Beaverstock, J.V., Hubbard, P. and Short, J.R. (2004) Getting away with it? Exposing the geographies of the super-rich, *Geoforum,* **35,** 401–7.

Beddington, J. (2009) *Food, Energy, Water and the Climate: A Perfect Storm of Global Events?,* Government Office for Science, London, www.bis.gov.uk/assets/bispartners/goscience/docs/p/perfect-storm-paper.pdf [accessed 12 May 2011].

Beddington, J. (2010) Food security: contributions from science to a new and greener revolution, *Philosophical Transactions of the Royal Society B,* **365,** 61–71.

Bedford, T. (1999) Ethical consumerism, consumption, identity and ethics, unpublished PhD thesis, University of London, London.

Belasco, W. (2008) *Food: The Key Concepts,* Berg Publishers, Oxford.

Bell, D. and Binnie, J. (2000) *The Sexual Citizen,* Polity Press, Oxford.

Bell, D. and Binnie, J. (2004) Authenticating queer space: citizenship, urbanism and governance, *Urban Studies* **41**(9), 1807–20.

Bell, D. and Binnie, J. (2006) Geographies of sexual citizenship, *Political Geography*, **25**, 869–73.

Bell, D. and Jayne, M. (2006) *Small Cities: Urban Experience Beyond the Metropolis*, Routledge, Abingdon.

Bell, D. and Valentine, G. (eds) (1995) *Mapping Desire: Geographies of Sexualities*, Routledge, London.

Bell, M. (1994) Images, myths and alternative geographies of the Third World, in Gregory, D., Martin, R. and Smith, G. (eds) *Human Geography: Society, Space and Social Science*, Macmillan, London, 174–99.

Bellamy, R. (2008) *A Very Short Introduction to Citizenship*, Oxford University Press, Oxford.

Benko, G. and Strohmayer, U. (2004) *Human Geography: A History for the Twenty-First Century*, Arnold, London.

Benton, L. (1995) Will the real/reel Los Angeles please stand up? *Urban Geography*, **16**, 144–64.

Benton, T. (ed.) (2010) *Understanding Heritage and Memory*, Manchester University Press, Manchester.

Benton-Short, L. (2007) Bollards, bunkers, and barriers: securing the National Mall in Washington, DC, *Environment and Planning D: Society and Space*, **25**(3), 424–46.

Benton-Short, L. and Short, J.R. (2008) *Cities and Nature*, Routledge, London.

Berdahl, D. (1998) *Where the World Ended: Re-unification and Identity in the German Borderland*, University of California Press, Berkeley, CA.

Beresford, M.W. (1988) *East End, West End: The Face of Leeds during Urbanisation 1684–1842*, Thoresby Society, Leeds.

Berger, J. (1990) *Ways of Seeing*, Penguin, London.

Berger, M.T. (2001) The post-cold war predicament: a conclusion, *Third World Quarterly*, **22**, 1079–85.

Berger, P. and Luckmann, T. (1966) *The Social Construction of Reality: A Treatise in the Sociology of Knowledge*, Anchor Books, Garden City, New York.

Berndt, C. and Boeckler, M. (2009) Geographies of circulation and exchange: Constructions of markets, *Progress in Human Geography*, 33(4), 535–51.

Berzoets, J. (2011) The Soviet Union in Angola: Soviet and African perspectives on the failed socialist transformation, *Vestnik: The Journal of Russian and Asian Studies*, Issue 9 (Spring), www.sras.org/the_soviet_union_in_angola.

Betjeman, J. (1937) *Continual Dew*, John Murray, London.

Betts, V. (2002) Geographies of youth, religion and identity in (post-)socialist Cuba, unpublished PhD thesis, University of Birmingham.

Bhabha, H.K. (1994) *The Location of Culture*, Routledge, London.

Bhattacharya, A. (2014) *South China Sea: China's Renewed Confrontation and ASEAN options*, Institute of Peace and Conflict Studies Article, 28 May 2014, www.ipcs.org/article/china/south-china-sea-chinas-renewed-confrontation-and-asean-options-4469.htm.

Bialasiewicz, L. (2012) Off-shoring and out-sourcing the Borders of Europe: Libya and EU Border Work in the Mediterranean, *Geopolitics*, **17**(4), 843–66.

Bialasiewicz, L., Elden, S. and Painter, J. (2005) The constitution of EU territory, *Comparative European Politics*, **3**, 333–63.

Biggs, D. (2010) *Quagmire: Nation-Building and the Nature of the Mekong Delta*, Silkworm Books, Chiang Mai.

Bilgin, P. (2007) Only strong states can survive in Turkey's geography: the uses of geopolitical truths in Turkey, *Political Geography*, **26**(7): 740–56.

Birks, H. (1997) Environmental change in Britain: a long-term paleoecological perspective, in Mackay, A. and Murlis, J. (eds) *Britain's Natural Environment: A State of the Nation Review*, Ensis, London, 23–8.

BIS (2008) Statistics on exchange traded derivatives, www.bis.org.

Bivens J. (2003) *Updated Employment Multipliers for the U.S. Economy*, Working paper, Economic Policy Institute, www.epi.org/page/-/old/workingpapers/epi_wp_268.pdf [accessed 24 December 2014].

Black, J. (1998) *Maps and Politics*, Reaktion, London.

Blakkisrud, H. and Kolstø, P. (2011) From secessionist conflict toward a functioning state: processes of state- and nation-building in Transnistria, *Post-Soviet Affairs*, **27**(2), 178–210.

Blaut, J.M. (1993) *The Colonizer's Model of the World: Geographical Diffusionism and Eurocentric History*, Guilford Press, New York and London.

Blinder, A.S. (2006) Offshoring: the next industrial revolution, *Foreign Affairs*, Mar/Apr, 113–28.

Bloom, E. (1999) Establishment of the Arctic Council, *The American Journal of International Law*, **93**, 712–22.

Bluestone, B. and Harrison, B. (1982) *The Deindustrialization of America*, Basic Books, New York.

Blunden, J. (1995) Sustainable resources?, in Sarre, P. and Blunden, J. (eds) *An Overcrowded World: Population, Resources and Environment*, Oxford University Press and Open University, Oxford, 161–213.

Blunt, A. and Dowling, R. (2006) *Home*, Routledge, London.

Blunt, A. and Wills, J. (2000) *Dissident Geographies: An Introduction to Radical Ideas and Practice*, Prentice Hall, Harlow.

Bobek, H. (1962) The main stages in socio-economic evolution from a geographical point of view, in Wagner, P.L. and Mikesell, M.W. (eds) *Readings in Cultural Geography*, University of Chicago Press, Chicago, IL, 218–47.

Boersma, K., Langen, H. and Smets, P. (2013) Paradoxes of studentification: social mix versus gentrification in a disadvantaged neighborhood in Amsterdam East, *Open Urban Studies Journal*, 6(1), 40–9.

Bone, R. (2009) *The Canadian North: Issues and Challenges*, Oxford University Press, Don Mills, Ontario.

Bonnett, A. (2003) Geography as the world discipline: connecting popular and academic geographical imaginations, *Area*, **35**, 55–63.

Booth, K. (1999) Cold wars of the mind, in Booth, K. (ed.) *Statecraft and Security: The Cold War and Beyond*, Cambridge University Press, Cambridge, 29–55.

Borden, I. (2001) *Skateboarding, Space and the City: Architecture and the Body*, Berg, Oxford.

Borgerson, S. (2007) Arctic meltdown, *Foreign Affairs,* **87,** 63–77.

Bosco, F. J. (2006) Actor-network theory, networks and relational approaches in human geography, in Aitken, S. and Valentine, G. (eds) *Approaches to Human Geography,* Sage, London, 136–46.

Boserüp, E. (1990) *Economic and Demographic Relationships in Development,* Johns Hopkins University Press, Baltimore, MD.

Bourdieu, P. (1984) *Distinction,* Routledge & Kegan Paul, London.

Boyd, D. and Ellison, N. (2007) *Social Network Sites: Definition, History, and Scholarship,* Guilford College, Greensboro, NC, www.guilford.edu/about_guilford/services_and_administration/library/libguide_images/boyd.pdf.

BP (2015) *BP Statistical Review of World Energy June 2015,* BP, London.

Bradshaw, M.J. (2009) The geopolitics of global energy security, *Geography Compass,* **3**(5), 1920–37.

Bradshaw, M. (2014) *Global Energy Dilemmas: Energy Security, Globalization and Climate Change,* Polity Press, Cambridge.

Bradshaw, M., Frogatt, A., McGlade, C. and Spiers, J. (2015) Fossil fuels: reserves, cost curves, production and consumption, in Ekins, P., Bradshaw, M. and Watson, J. (eds) *Global Energy: Issue, Potentials and Policy Implications,* Oxford University Press, Oxford, 244–61.

Brah, A. (1996) *Cartographies of Diaspora: Contesting Identities,* Routledge, London.

Braun, B. (2002) *The Intemperate Rainforest: Nature, Culture and Power on Canada*'s *West Coast,* University of Minnesota Press, Minneapolis, MN.

Brautigam, D. (2009) *The Dragon's Gift: The Real Story of China in Africa,* Oxford University Press, Oxford.

Breheny, M. (1995) The compact city and transport energy consumption, *Transactions of the Institute of British Geographers NS,* **20**(1), 81–101.

Brenner, N. (2004) *New State Spaces: Urban Governance and the Rescaling of Statehood,* Oxford University Press, New York.

Brenner, N., Jessop, B., Jones, M. and MacLeod, G. (eds) (2003) *State/Space: A Reader,* Blackwell Publishing, Malden, MA.

Breward, C., Crang, P. and Crill, R. (eds) (2010) *British Asian Style: Fashion and Textiles/Past and Present,* V&A Publishing, London.

Bridge, G. and Le Billon, P. (2012) *Oil,* Polity Press, Cambridge.

British Broadcasting Corporation (BBC) (2006) *Oslo Gay Animal Show Draws Crowds,* http://news.bbc.co.uk/1/hi/world/europe/6066606.stm.

British Broadcasting Corporation (BBC) (2015) The Mediterranean's deadly migrant routes, www.bbc.com/news/world-europe-32387224 [accessed 15 May 2015].

Brooks, R. and Simon, R. (2007) Subprime debacle traps even very credit-worthy, *Wall Street Journal,* 3 December, A1.

Broome, R. (2002) *Aboriginal Australians: Black Responses to White Dominance, 1788–2001,* 3rd edition, Allen & Unwin, Crows Nest, NSW.

Brown, L.R. (2011) *World on the Edge: How to Prevent Environmental and Economic Collapse,* W.W. Norton & Company, New York.

Browne, K. and Lim, J. (2010) Trans lives in the 'gay capital of the UK', *Gender, Place and Culture,* **17**(5), 615–33.

Browne, K., Lim, J. and Brown, G. (eds) (2007) *Geographies of Sexualities: Theory, Politics and Practice,* Ashgate, Aldershot.

Bryman, A. (1995) *Disney and his Worlds,* Routledge, London.

Bryson, J.R. (2000) Spreading the message: management consultants and the shaping of economic geographies in time and space, in Bryson, J.R., Daniels, P.W., Henry, N.D. and Pollard, J.S. (eds) *Knowledge Space, Economy,* Routledge, London, 157–75.

Bryson, J.R. (2007) A 'second' global shift? The offshoring or global sourcing of corporate services and the rise of distanciated emotional labour, *Geografiska Annaler,* **89B**(1), 31–44.

Bryson, J.R. (2009) Economic geography: business services, in Kitchin R. and Thrift N. (eds) *International Encyclopedia of Human Geography,* Elsevier, Amsterdam, 368–74.

Bryson, J.R. (2010) Service innovation and manufacturing innovation: bundling and blending services and products in hybrid production systems to produce hybrid products, in Gallouj F. (ed.) *Handbook on Innovation in Services,* Edward Elgar, Cheltenham, 679–700.

Bryson, J.R. and Daniels, P.W. (eds) (2015a) *The Handbook of Service Business: Management, Marketing, Innovation and Internationalisation,* Edward Elgar, Cheltenham.

Bryson, J.R. and Daniels, P.W. (2015b), Service business: growth, innovation, competitiveness, in Bryson, J.R. and Daniels, P.W. (eds) *The Handbook of Service Business: Management, Marketing, Innovation and Internationalisation,* Edward Elgar, Cheltenham, 1–21.

Bryson, J.R. and Henry, N.D. (2005) The global production system: from Fordism to post Fordism, in Daniels, P.W. et al. *Human Geography: Issues for the 21st Century,* Prentice Hall, London, 313–36.

Bryson, J.R. and Rusten, G. (2005) Spatial divisions of expertise: knowledge intensive business service firms and regional development in Norway, *The Service Industries Journal,* **25**(8) 959–77.

Bryson, J.R. and Rusten, G. (2006) Spatial divisions of expertise and transnational 'service' firms: aerospace and management consultancy, in Harrington, J.W. and Daniels, P.W. (eds) *Knowledge-based Services, Internationalisation and Regional Development,* Aldershot, Ashgate, 79–100.

Bryson, J.R. and Rusten, G. (2008) Transnational corporations and spatial divisions of 'service' expertise as a competitive strategy: the example of 3M and Boeing, *The Service Industries Journal,* **28**(3), 307–323.

Bryson, J.R. and Rusten, G. (2011), *Design Economies and the Changing World Economy: Innovation, Production and Competitiveness,* Routledge, London.

Bryson, J.R. and Wellington, C. (2003) Image consultancy in the United Kingdom: recipe knowledge and recreational employment, *The Service Industries Journal,* **23**(1) 59–76.

Bryson, J.R., Clark, J. and Vanchan, V. (2015) *Handbook of Manufacturing Industries in the World Economy,* Edward Elgar, Cheltenham.

Bryson, J.R., Daniels, P.W. and Warf, B. (2004) *Service Worlds: People, Organizations, Technologies,* Routledge, London.

Bryson, J.R., McGuinness, M. and Ford, R.G. (2002) Chasing a loose and baggy monster: almshouses and the geographies of charity, *Area, 34*(1), 48–58.

Bryson, J.R., Taylor, M. and Cooper, R. (2008) Competing by design, specialization and customization: manufacturing locks in the West Midlands (UK), *Geografiska Annaler: Series B, Human Geography,* **90**(2), 173–86.

Bull, H. (1995) *The Anarchical Society,* Oxford University Press, Oxford.

Bullard, R.D. (1990) *Dumping in Dixie: Race, Class and Environmental Quality,* Westview Press, Boulder, Co.

Bullen, A. and Whitehead, M. (2005) Negotiating the networks of space, time and substance: a geographical perspective on the sustainable citizen, *Citizenship Studies, 9,* 499–516.

Bunyard, P. and Morgan-Grenville, F. (eds.) (1987) *The Green Alternative,* Methuen, London.

Burgess, E.W., Park, R.E. and McKenzie, R.D. (1925) *The City,* University of Chicago Press, Chicago, IL.

Butler, T. (2007) For gentrification?, *Environment and Planning A, 39*(1), 162–81.

Butler, T. and Lees, L. (2006) Super-gentrification in Barnsbury, London: globalization and gentrifying global elites at the neighbourhood level, *Transactions of the Institute of British Geographers, NS, 31*(4), 467–87.

Butlin, R.A. (1993) *Historical Geography, Through the Gates of Time and Space,* Edward Arnold, London.

Buzan, B. (2006) Will the 'global war on terrorism' be the new Cold War? *International Affairs,* **82**(6) 1101–18.

Byrne, D. (2001) *Understanding the Urban,* Palgrave, London.

C

Cairns, K. (2013) Youth, dirt and the spatialisation of subjectivity: an intersectional approach to white rural imaginaries, *Canadian Journal of Sociology,* **38**(4), 623–46.

Caldwell, M.L. (2004) Domesticating the French fry: McDonald's and consumerism in Moscow, *Journal of Consumer Culture,* **4**, 5–26.

Calhoun, C. (2002) The class consciousness of frequent travellers: towards a critique of actually existing cosmopolitanism, in Vertovec, S. and Cohen, R. (eds) *Conceiving Cosmopolitanism: Theory, Context and Practice,* Oxford University Press, Oxford, 86–109.

Callahan, W. (2010) *China: The Pessoptimist Nation,* Oxford University Press, Oxford and New York.

Calvocoressi, P. (1991) *World Politics since 1945,* Longman, London.

Cameron, A. (2007) Geographies of welfare and exclusion: reconstituting the 'public', *Progress in Human Geography, 31*(4), 519–26.

Campbell, C. (1987) *The Romantic Ethic and the Spirit of Modern Consumerism,* Blackwell, Oxford.

Carapico, S. (1985) Yemeni agriculture in transition, in Beaumont, P. and McLachlan, K. (eds) *Agricultural Development in the Middle East,* John Wiley & Sons, Chichester, 241–54.

Carley (1999) Neighbourhoods – building blocks of national sustainability, *Town and Country Planning,* February, 58–60.

Carneiro, A. de M. (1990) *Descrição da Fortaleza de Sofala e das mais da Índia,* Fundação Oriente, Lisbon.

Carolan, M. (2011) *The Real Cost of Cheap Food,* Earthscan, Abingdon.

Carr, J. (2010) Legal geographies – skating around the edges of the law: urban skateboarding and the role of law in determining young peoples' place in the city, *Urban Geography, 31*(7), 988–1003.

Carroll, R. (1998) The chill east wind at your doorstep, *The Guardian,* 28 October, 2–3.

Carson, R. (1962) *Silent Spring,* Hamish Hamilton, London.

Carter, D. (1988) *The Final Frontier: The Rise and Fall of the American Rocket State,* Verso, London and New York.

Carter, N. (2001) *The Politics of the Environment: Ideas, Activism, Policy,* Cambridge University Press, Cambridge.

Caspian Revenue Watch (2003) *Caspian Oil Windfalls: Who Will Benefit?,* The Open Society Institute, New York, www.revenuewatch.org/reports.

Castells, M. (1997) *The Power of Identity,* Blackwell, Malden, MA.

Castells, M. (2009) *The Rise of the Network Society: the Information Age, Economy, Society and Culture,* 2nd edition, Wiley-Blackwell, Oxford.

Castles, S. and Miller, M. (2009) *The Age of Migration: Population Movements in the Modern World,* Guilford Press, New York.

Castree, N. (2005) *Nature,* Routledge, London.

Castree, N (2011) Commentary: the future of geography in English universities, *The Geographical Journal,* **177**(4), 294–99.

Central Intelligence Agency (CIA) (2014) *The World Factbook,* CIA, Washington, DC, www.cia.gov/library/publications/resources/the-world-factbook/index.html.

Champion, A. (1999) Urbanisation and counterurbanisation, in Pacione, M. (ed.) *Applied Geography: Principles and Practice,* Routledge, London, 347–57.

Chan, J. (2010) *Dying Young: Suicide and China's Booming Economy,* Students and Scholars Against Corporate Misbehaviour, Hong Kong.

Chandler, J. (ed.) (1993) *John Leland's Itinerary,* Sutton, Stroud.

Chaney, D. (1990) Subtopia in Gateshead, the Metro-Centre as a cultural form, *Theory, Culture and Society,* 7, 49–68.

Charlesworth, A., Stenning, A., Guzik, R. and Paszkowski, M. (2006) 'Out of place' in Auschwitz? Contested development in post-war and post-socialist OŚięcim, *Ethics, Place and Environment,* **9**(2) 149–72.

Chatham House (2008) *Rising Food Prices: Drivers and Implications for Development,* A Chatham House Report, Chatham House, London.

Chatham House (2009) *Food Futures: Rethinking UK Strategy,* A Chatham House Report, Chatham House, London.

Chatterjee, P. (1993) *The Nation and its Fragments: Colonial and Postcolonial Histories,* Princeton University Press, Princeton, NJ.

Chatterton, P. and Pickerill, J. (2010) Everyday activism and transitions towards post-capitalist worlds, *Transactions of the Institute of British Geographers,* **35**(4), 475–90.

Cheshire, L. and Woods, M. (2009) Citizenship and governmentality, rural, in Kitchen, R. and Thrift, N. (eds) *International Encyclopedia of Human Geography,* Elsevier, London, 113–18.

Chiesura, A. (2003) The role of urban parks for the sustainable city, *Landscape and Urban Planning,* **68**(1), 129–38.

Child, J.C. (1985) *Geopolitics and Conflict in South America: Quarrels among Neighbours,* Praeger, New York.

Chouinard, V. (2009) Citizenship, in Kitchen, R. and Thrift, N. (eds) *International Encyclopedia of Human Geography,* Elsevier, London, 107–112.

Christaller, W. (1966) *Central Places in Southern Germany* (trans. by C.W. Baskin), Prentice Hall, Englewood Cliffs, NJ.

Christie, L. (2007) Crime scene: foreclosure, *CNN Money,* 19 November, http://money.cnn.com/2007/11/16/real_estate/suprime_and_crime/index.htm?cnn=yes.

Christopherson, S. (2008) Beyond the self-expressive creative worker: an industry perspective on entertainment media, *Theory, Culture and Society,* **25**(7–8), 73–95.

Christopherson, S. and Clark, J. (2007) *Remaking the Region: Power, Labor, and Firm Strategies in the Knowledge Economy,* Routledge Press, New York.

Chung, R. (1970) Space–time diffusion of the demographic transition model: the twentieth-century patterns, in Demko, G.J., Rose, H.M. and Schnell, G.A. (eds) *Population Geography: A Reader,* McGraw-Hill, New York.

CIA *see* Central Intelligence Agency

Clark, I. (2011) China and the United States: a succession of hegemonies?, *International Affairs,* **87**(1), 13–28.

Clarke, G.E. (1996) Blood, territory and national identity in Himalayan states, in Tønnesson, S. and Antlöv, H. (eds) *Asian Forms of the Nation,* Curzon, Richmond, 205–36.

Clarke, N. (2008) From ethical consumerism to political consumption, *Geography Compass,* **2**(6), 1870–84.

Clarke, N., Barnett, C., Cloke, P. and Malpass, A. (2007) Globalising the consumer: doing politics in an ethical register, *Geoforum,* **26**(3), 231–49.

Clifford, J. (1992) Travelling cultures, in Grossberg, L., Nelson, C. and Treichler, P. (eds) *Cultural Studies,* Routledge, London.

Clifford, N. and Valentine, G. (eds) (2010) *Key Methods in Geography,* 2nd edition, Sage, London.

Cloke, P.J. (2000) Rural, in Johnston, R.J., Gregory, D., Pratt, G. and Watts, M. (eds) *The Dictionary of Human Geography,* Blackwell, Oxford, 718.

Cloke, P.J. (2005a) Conceptualising rurality, in Cloke, P., Marsden, T. and Mooney, P. (eds) *Handbook of Rural Studies,* Sage, London.

Cloke, P.J. (2005b) The country, in Cloke, P.J., Crang, P. and Goodwin, M. (eds), *Introducing Human Geographies,* 2nd edition, Arnold, London.

Cloke, P. (2011) Emerging postsecular reapproachment in the contemporary city, in J. Beaumont and C. Baker (eds) *Postsecular City,* Continuum, London, 237–53.

Cloke, P., Crang, P. and Goodwin, M. (eds) (2005) *Introducing Human Geographies,* Arnold, London.

Cloke, P., Crang, P. and Goodwin, M. (2014) Foundations, in Cloke, P., Crang, P. and Goodwin, M. (eds) *Introducing Human Geographies,* 3rd edition, Routledge, Abindon, 1–6.

Cloke, P., Crang, P., Goodwin, M., Painter, J. and Philo, C. (2002) *Practicing Human Geography,* Sage, London.

Cloke, P., Johnsen, S. and May, J. (2007) Ethical citizenship? Volunteers and the ethics of providing services for homeless people, *Geoforum,* **38**, 1089–101.

Cloke, P., Philo, C. and Sadler, D. (1991) *Approaching Human Geography: An Introduction to Contemporary Human Geography,* Paul Chapman Publishing, London.

Cloke, P.J., Marsden, T. and Mooney, P. (eds) (2006) *Handbook of Rural Studies,* Sage, London.

Clover, C. (1999), Dreams of the Eurasian heartland: the reemergence of geopolitics, *Foreign Affairs,* **78**(2), 9–13.

Coafee, J., Murakami Wood, D. and Rogers, P. (2009) *The Everyday Resilience of the City: How Cities Respond to Terrorism and Disaster,* Palgrave Macmillan, Basingstoke.

Cochrane, A. (2007) *Understanding Urban Policy: A Critical Approach,* Blackwell, Oxford.

Coe, N.M. (2011) Unpacking globalisation: changing geographies of the global economy, in Lee, R., Leyshon, A., McDowell, L. and Sunley, P. (eds) *The Compendium of Economic Geography,* Sage, London.

Coe, N.M. (2012) Geographies of production II: a global production networks A-Z, *Progress in Human Geography,* **36**, 389–402.

Coe, N.M., Kelly, P.F. and Yeung, H. (2013) *Economic Geography: A Contemporary Introduction,* 2nd edition, Wiley, New Jersey.

Coleman-Jensen, A., Nord, M. and Singh, A. (2013) *Household Food Security in the United States,* Economic Research Report No. 155, United States Department of Agriculture, Washington, DC, www.ers.usda.gov/media/1183208/err-155.pdf.

Coll, S. (2004) *Ghost Wars: The Secret History of the CIA, Afghanistan and Bin Laden from Soviet Invasion to September 10, 2001,* Penguin, New York and London.

Collier, P. (2008) The politics of hunger: how illusion and greed fan the food crisis, *Foreign Affairs,* **87**(6), 67–79.

Connell, J. (2006) The taste of paradise: selling Fiji and Fiji water, *Asia Pacific Viewpoint,* **47**, 342–50.

Connell, J. (2008) Niue: embracing a culture of migration, *Journal of Ethnic and Migration Studies,* **34**(6), 1021–40.

Connelly, J. and Smith, G. (2003) *Politics and the Environment: From Theory to Practice,* 2nd edition, Routledge, London.

Connor, W. (1994) *Ethnonationalism: The Quest for Understanding*, Princeton University Press, Princeton, NJ.

Conradson, D. (2003) Doing organisational space: practices of voluntary welfare in the city, *Environment and Planning A*, **35**, 1975–1992.

Constance, D.H., Martinez, F., Aboites, G. and Bonanno, A. (2013) The problems with poultry production and processing, in James, H.S. (ed.) *Ethics and Economics of Agrifood Competition*, Springer, New York, 155–76.

Convery, I. and O'Brien, V. (2012) Gypsies, travellers and place: a co-ethnography, in Convery, I, Corsane, G and Davis, P. (eds) *Making Sense of Place. Multidisciplinary Perspectives*, Boydell Press, Woodbridge, 43–53.

Conzen, M.P. (1990) *The Making of the American Landscape*, Unwin Hyman, Boston, MA.

Cook, I. *et al.* (2006) Geographies of food: following, *Progress in Human Geography*, **30**(5), 655–66.

Cook, I. *et al.* (2008) Geographies of food: mixing, *Progress in Human Geography*, **32**, 821–33.

Cook, I. *et al.* (2010) iPad suicides timeline, followthethings.com, www.followthethings.com/ipadsuicidestimeline 2010.shtml [accessed 12 March 2015].

Cook, I. (2011a) Kino Eye, followthethings.com, www.followthethings.com/kinoeye.shtml [accessed 12 March 2015].

Cook, I. (2011b) Mange tout, followthethings.com, www.followthethings.com/mangetout.shtml [accessed 12 March 2015].

Cook, I. (2011c) The luckiest nut in the world, followthethings.com, www.followthethings.com/luckiestnut.shtml [accessed 12 March 2015].

Cook, I. (2011d) iPhone 3G – already with pictures! (aka 'iPhone Girl') followthethings.com, http://followthethings.com/iphonegirl.shtml [accessed 12 March 2015].

Cook, I. and Crang, P. (1996) The world on a plate: culinary culture, displacement and geographical knowledges, *Journal of Material Culture*, **1**(2), 131–53.

Cook, I. and Woodyer, T. (2012) Lives of things, in Barnes, T.J., Peck, J. and Sheppard, E. (eds) *The Wiley-Blackwell Companion to Economic Geography*, Wiley-Blackwell, Chichester, 226–41.

Cook, I., Crang, P. and Thorpe, M. (1999) Eating into Britishness: multicultural imaginaries and the identity politics of food, in Roseneil, S. and Seymour, J. (eds) *Practising Identities*, Macmillan, London, 223–48.

Cook, I., Crang, P. and Thorpe, M. (2000a) Regions to be cheerful, culinary authenticity and its geographies, in Cook, I., Crouch, D., Naylor, S. and Ryan, J. (eds) *Cultural Turns/Geographical Turns*, Longman, London, 109–39.

Cook, I., Crang, P. and Thorpe, M. (2000b) 'Have you got the customer's permission?' Category management and circuits of knowledge in the UK food business, in Bryson, J., Daniels, P., Henry, N. and Pollard, J. (eds) *Knowledge, Space, Economy*, Routledge, London, 242–60.

Cook, I., Crang, P. and Thorpe, M. (2004) Tropics of consumption: getting with the fetish of 'exotic' fruit?, in Hughes, A. and Reimer, S. (eds) *Geographies of Commodities*, Routledge, London.

Cook, I., Crouch, D., Naylor, S. and Ryan, J. (eds) (2000c) *Cultural Turns/Geographical Turns*, Prentice Hall, London.

Cook, I., Evans, J., Griffiths, H., Morris, B., Wrathmell, S. *et al.* (2007) 'It's more than just what it is': defetishising commodities, changing pedagogies, mobilising change, *Geoforum*, **38**(6), 1113–26.

Cook, I., Hobson, K., Hallett IV, L. *et al.* (2011) Geographies of food: afters, *Progress in Human Geography*, **35**(1), 104–20.

Cooke, B. and Kothari, U. (2001) *Participation: The New Tyranny?* Zed, London.

Cooper, N., Purcell, S. and Jackson, R. (2014*) Below the Breadline: The Relentless Rise of Food Poverty in Britain*, Church Action on Poverty, The Trussell Trust and Oxfam, UK.

Corbridge, S. (ed.) (1995) *Development Studies: A Reader*, Edward Arnold, London.

Corner, A., Parkhill, K., Pidgeon, N. and Vaughan, N. (2013) Messing with nature? Exploring public perceptions of geoengineering in the UK, *Global Environmental Change*, **23**(5), 938–47.

Cosgrove, D. (1994) Contested global visions, *Annals of the Association of American Geographers*, **84**, 270–94.

Cosgrove, D. (2001) *Apollo's Eye: A Cartographic Genealogy of the Earth in the Western Imagination*, Johns Hopkins University Press, Baltimore.

Cowen, M.P. and Shenton, R.W. (1996) *Doctrines of Development*, Routledge, London.

Cox, E., Ryan-Collins, J., Squires, P. and Potts, R. (2010) *Re-imagining the High Street: Escape from Clone Town Britain*, New Economics Foundation, London.

Cox, M. (2001) The new liberal empire: US power in the twenty-first century, *Irish Studies in International Affairs*, **12**, 39–56.

Crampton, J. (2014) The power of maps, in Cloke, P., Crang, P. and Goodwin, M. (eds) *Introducing Human Geographies*, 3rd edition, Routledge, London, 192–202.

Crampton, J. and Elden, S. (eds) (2007) *Space, Knowledge and Power: Foucault and Geography*, Ashgate, Aldershot.

Crang, M. (1998) *Cultural Geography*, Routledge, London.

Crang, P. (1997) Cultural turns and the (re)constitution of economic geography, in Lee, R. and Wills, J. (eds) *Geographies of Economies*, Arnold, London, 3–15.

Crang, P. and Ashmore, S. (2009) The transnational spaces of things: South Asian textiles in Britain and the grammar of ornament, *European Review of History*, **16**, 655–78.

Crang, P., Dwyer, C. and Jackson, P. (2003) Transnationalism and the spaces of commodity culture, *Progress in Human Geography*, **27**, 438–56.

Crawford, M. (1992) The world in a shopping mall, in Sorkin, M. (ed.) *Variations on a Theme Park: The New American City and the End of Public Space*, Noonday, New York.

Crawford, M. (2004) The world in a shopping mall, in Miles, M., Hall, T. and Borden, I. (eds) *The City Cultures Reader*, 2nd edition, Routledge, London.

Cresswell, T. (1996) *In Place/Out of Place: Geography, Ideology and Transgression,* University of Minnesota Press, Minneapolis, MN.

Cresswell, T. (2004) *Place: A Short Introduction,* Blackwell, Oxford.

Cresswell, T. (2009) The prosthetic citizen: new geographies of citizenship, *Political Power and Social Theory,* **20,** 259–73.

Crewe, L. (2008) Ugly beautiful? Counting the cost of the global fashion industry, *Geography,* **93**(1), 25–33.

Crone, P. (1986) The tribe and the state, in Hall, J.A. (ed.) *States in History,* Basil Blackwell, Oxford, 48–77.

Crone, P. (2003) *Pre-Industrial Societies: Anatomy of the Pre-Modern World,* Oneworld, Oxford.

Cronon, W. (1991) *Nature's Metropolis: Chicago and the Great West,* W.W. Norton, New York.

Cronon, W. (1996) *Uncommon Ground: Toward Reinventing Nature,* Norton, New York.

Crosby, A.E. (2004) *Ecological Imperialism: the Biological Expansion of Europe, 900–1900,* Cambridge University Press, Cambridge.

Crouch, D.P., Garr, D.J. and Mundigo, A.I. (1982) *Spanish City Planning in North America,* MIT Press, Cambridge, MA.

Crum, R.E. and Gudgin, G. (1977) *Non-production Activities in UK Manufacturing Industry,* Commission of the European Communities, Brussels.

Crump, J.R. (2004) Producing and enforcing the geography of hate: race, housing segregation, and housing related hate crimes in the United States, in Flint, C. (ed.) *Spaces of Hate: Geographies of Discrimination and Intolerance in the USA,* Routledge, New York, 227–44.

Crush, J. (1995) Imagining development, in Crush, J. (ed.) *Power of Development,* Routledge, London, 1–26.

Curry, J. and Kenney, M. (2004) The organizational and geographic configuration of the personal computer value chain, in Kenney, M. and Florida, R. (eds) *Locating Global Advantage: Industry Dynamics in the International Economy,* Stanford University Press, Stanford, 113–41.

Cybriwsky, R. and Ford, L. (2001) Jakarta, *Cities,* **18,** 199–210.

D

D'Silva, J. and Webster, J. (eds) (2010) *The Meat Crisis: Developing More Sustainable Production and Consumption,* Earthscan, London.

Dahlman, C. and Ó Tuathail, G. (2005) Broken Bosnia: the localized geopolitics of displacement and return in the two Bosnian places, *Annals of the Association of American Geographers,* **95,** 644–62.

Dake, K. and Thompson, M. (1999) Making ends meet, in the household and on the planet, *GeoJournal,* **47,** 417–24.

Dalby, S. (2003) Geopolitics, the Bush doctrine and war in Iraq, *Arab World Geographer,* **6,** 7–18.

Daniels, P.W. (1975) *Office Location: An Urban and Regional Study,* G. Bell, London.

Daniels, P.W. and Bryson, J.R. (2002) Manufacturing services and servicing manufacturing: changing forms of production in advanced capitalist economies, *Urban Studies,* **39**(5–6), 977–91.

Daniels, P.W. and Bryson, J.R. (2005) Sustaining business and professional services in a second city region: the case of Birmingham, UK, *The Service Industries Journal,* **25**(4), 505–24.

Daniels, S. (2011) Geographical imagination, *Transactions of the Institute of British Geographers NS,* **36**(2), 182–7.

Darwin, J. (2007) *After Tamerlane: The Rise and Fall of Global Empires,* Penguin, Harmondsworth.

Davidson, M. and Lees, L. (2010) New-build gentrification: its histories, trajectories, and critical geographies, *Population, Space and Place,* **16**(5), 395–411.

Davies, G. (1994) *A History of Money: From Ancient Times to the Present Day,* University of Wales Press, Cardiff.

Davies, G. (2000) Narrating the natural history unit, *Geoforum,* **31,** 539–51.

Davies, J., Sandström, S., Shorrocks, A. and Wolff, E. (2006) *World Distribution of Household Wealth.* London: Foreign Press Association and United Nations Secretariat, presentation 5 December.

Daviron, B. and Ponte, S. (2005) *The Coffee Paradox: Global Markets, Commodity Trade and the Elusive Promise of Development,* Zed Books, London.

Davis, A., Hirsch, D., Iwanaga, R., Iwata, M., Shigekawa, J., Uzuki, Y. and Yamada, A. (2014) Comparing the minimum income standard in the UK and Japan: methodology and outcome, *Social Policy and Society,* **13**(01), 89–101.

Davis, J. and Goldberg, R. (1957) *A Concept of Agribusiness,* Harvard University Press, Boston, MA.

Davis, M. (1990) *City of Quartz: Excavating the Future in Los Angeles,* Verso, London.

Davis, M. (1995) Fortress Los Angeles: The militarization of urban space, in Kasinitz, P. (ed.) *Metropolis: Centre and Symbol of our Times,* Macmillan, Basingstoke, 355–68.

Davis, M. (1998) *Ecology of Fear: Los Angeles and the Imagination of Disaster,* Metropolitan Books, New York.

Davis, M. (2000) *Late Victorian Holocausts,* Verso, London.

Davis, M (2006) *Planet of Slums,* London, Verso.

Deane, P. and Cole, W. (1962) *British Economic Growth 1688–1959,* Cambridge University Press, Cambridge.

Dear, M. (2000) *The Postmodern Urban Condition,* Blackwell: Malden, MA.

Dear, M. and Flusty, S. (1998) Postmodern urbanism, *Annals of the Association of American Geographers,* **88**(1), 50–72.

Dear, M. and Flusty, S. (2002) The resistable rise of the LA school, in Dear, M. (ed.) (2002) *From Chicago to L.A.: Making Sense of Urban Theory,* Sage, Thousand Oaks, CA, 3–16.

Dedrick, J., Kraemer, K.L. and Linden, G. (2010) Who profits from innovation in global value chains? A study of the iPod and notebook PCs, *Industrial and Corporate Change,* **19**(1), 81–116.

Deffeyes, K.S. (2001) *Hubbert's Peak: The Impending World Oil Shortage*, Princeton University Press, Princeton, NJ.

Defra (2008) *Synthesis Report on the Findings from Defra's Pre-feasibility Study into Personal Carbon Trading*, Department for Environment, Food and Rural Affairs, London, www.teqs.net/Synthesis.pdf [accessed 8 January 2015].

Degolyer, M. (2001) Conditional citizenship: Hong Kong people's attitudes toward the new motherland, *Citizenship Studies*, 5(2), 165–83.

Del Casino, V.J. (2009) *Social Geography. A Critical Introduction*, Wiley-Blackwell, Chichester.

Delaney, D. (2005) *Territory: A Short Introduction*, Blackwell, Malden.

Delaney, D. (2009) Territory and territoriality, in, Kitchin, R. and Thrift, N. (eds) *International Encyclopedia of Human Geography*, Elsevier, Oxford.

Demeritt, D. (1998) Science, social constructivism and nature, in Castree, N. and Braun, B. (eds) *Remaking Reality: Nature at the Millennium*, Routledge, London, 173–93.

Demeritt, D. (2002) What is the social construction of nature? *Progress in Human Geography*, 26, 767–90.

Denevan, W. (1992) The pristine myth: the landscapes of the Americas in 1492, *Annals of the Association of American Geographers*, 82, 369–85.

Dennis, R. (1984) *English Industrial Cities of the Nineteenth Century*, Cambridge University Press, Cambridge.

Department of the Built Environment (2014) *Employment Trends in the City of London*, DBE, London.

Department of Work and Pensions (2011) *Households Below Average Income: An Analysis of the Income Distribution 1994/95–2009/10*, HMSO, London.

Derudder, B. and Wilcox, F. (2005) An appraisal of the use of airline data in assessing the world city network: a research note on data, *Urban Studies*, 42(13), 2371–88.

Dery, M. (2010) *Culture Jamming: Hacking, Slashing and Sniping in the Empire of Signs*, 2nd edition, Open Magazine Pamphlet Series, Open Magazine.

Desai, V. and Potter, R. (eds) (2014) *The Arnold Companion to Development Studies*, 3rd edition, Arnold, London.

Desforges, L. (1998) 'Checking out the planet': global representations/local identities and youth travel, in Skelton, T. and Valentine, G. (eds) *Cool Places: Geographies of Youth Cultures*, Routledge, London, 174–91.

Desforges, L., Jones, R. and Woods, M. (2005) New geographies of citizenship, *Citizenship Studies*, 9, 439–51.

Desmoyers-Davis, T. (2001) *Citizenship in Modern Britain*, Cavendish, London.

Destouni, G. and Frank, H. (2010) Renewable energy, *Ambio*, 39, 18–21.

Deutschmann, C. (2011) Limits to Financialization, *European Journal of Sociology*, 52, 347–89.

Devall, B. and Sessions, G. (1985) *Deep Ecology: Living as if Nature Mattered*, Peregrine Smith Books, Salt Lake City, UT.

DeVerteuil, G. (2013) Where has NIMBY gone in urban social geography?, *Social & Cultural Geography*, 14(6), 599–603.

Diamond, J. (1997), *Guns, Germs and Steel*, Norton, New York.

Dicken, P. (2003) *Global Shift: Reshaping the Global Economic Map in the 21st Century*, 4th edition, Sage, London.

Dicken, P. (2007) *Global Shift: Reshaping the Global Economic Map in the 21st Century*, 5th edition, Sage, London.

Dicken, P. (2015) *Global Shift: Mapping the Changing Contours of the World Economy*, 7th edition, Sage, London.

Dicken, P. and Lloyd, P. E. (1990) *Location in Space: Theoretical Perspectives in Economic Geography*, Harper & Row, New York.

Dicken, P., Kelly, P.F., Olds, K. and Yeung, H. W-C. (2001) Chains and networks, territories and scales: towards a relational framework for analysing the global economy, *Global Networks*, 1(2), 89–112.

Dickenson, J., Gould, B., Clarke, C., Mather, S., Prothero, M., Siddle, D., Smith, C. and Thomas-Hope, E. (1996) *A Geography of the Third World*, Routledge, London.

Dietz, S. and Adger, W.N. (2003) Economic growth, biodiversity loss and conservation effort, *Journal of Environmental Management*, 68(1), 23–35.

Dikeç, M. (2006) The badlands of the republic: revolts, the French state and questions of the banlieues, *Environment and Planning D*, 24, 159–63.

Dikeç, M. (2007) *Badlands of the Republic: Space, Politics, and French Urban Policy*, Blackwell, RGS/IBG Book Series, Oxford.

Dinda, S. (2004) Environmental kuznets curve hypothesis: a survey, *Ecological Economics*, 49(4), 431–55.

Dittmer, J. (2005) Captian America's empire: reflections on identity, popular culture and post-9/11 geopolitics, *Annals of the Association of American Geographers*, 95(3), 626–43.

Dobb, M. (1946; 1963) *Studies in the Development of Capitalism*, Routledge & Kegan Paul, London.

Dobson, A. (2001) *Green Political Thought*, 3rd edition, Routledge, London.

Dodds, K. (1997) *Geopolitics in Antarctica: Views from the Southern Ocean Rim*, Wiley, Chichester.

Dodds, K. (2006) Popular geopolitics and audience dispositions: James Bond and the Internet Movie Database, *Transactions of the Institute of British Geographers*, 31(2), 116–30.

Dodds, K. (2010) Flag planting and finger pointing: the law of the sea, the Arctic and the political geographies of the outer continental shelf, *Political Geography*, 29, 63–73.

Dodds, K. (2011) Sovereignty watch: resources, sovereignty and territory in contemporary Antarctica, *Polar Record*, in press.

Dodds, K, (2013) The Ilulissat Declaration (2008): the Arctic states, 'Law of the Sea,' and Arctic Ocean, *SAIS Review*, 33, 45–55.

Dodds, K. (2014) *Geopolitics: A Very Short Introduction*, 2nd edition, Oxford University Press, Oxford.

Dodds, K. and Nuttall, M. (2015) *Scramble for the Polar Regions? The Contemporary Geopolitics of the Arctic and Antarctic*, Polity Press, Cambridge.

Dodds, K., Kuus, M. and Sharp J. (2013) *The Ashgate Research Companion to Critical Geopolitics,* Ashgate, Farnham.

Dodge, M. and Kitchin, R. (2000) *The Atlas of Cyberspace,* Continuum, London.

Dodgshon, R.A. (1987) *The European Past: Social Evolution and Spatial Order,* Macmillan, Basingstoke.

Dodgshon, R.A. (1998) *Society in Time and Space: A Geographical Perspective on Change,* Cambridge University Press, Cambridge.

Dodgshon, R.A. and Butlin, R.A. (eds) (1990) *An Historical Geography of England and Wales,* 2nd edition, Academic Press, London.

Dodson, B. (2010) Locating xenophobia: debate, discourse, and everyday experience in Cape Town, South Africa, *Africa Today,* 56(3), 2–22.

Doherty, B. (2002) *Ideas and Actions in the Green Movement,* Routledge, London.

Domosh, M. (2015) Practising development at home: race, gender, and the 'development' of the American South, *Antipode,* 47(4), 915–41.

Donnelly, J. (2000) *Realism and International Relations,* Cambridge University Press, Cambridge.

Dorling, D. (2004) *The Human Geography of the UK,* London, Sage.

Dorling, D. (2011) *Roads, Casualties and Public Health: the Open Sewers of the 21st Century,* PACTS' 21st Westminster Lecture, Parliamentary Advisory Council for Transport Safety, London, www.dannydorling.org/?page_id=1916.

Dorling, D. (2013) *Population 10 Billion: The Coming Demographic Crisis and How to Survive It,* Constable, London.

Dorling, D. and Fairbairn, D. (1997) *Mapping: Ways of Representing the World,* Prentice Hall, Harlow.

Dorling, D. and Lee, C. (2014) Inequality constitutes a particular place, Chapter 7 in Pritchard, D. and Pakes, F. (eds) *Riot, Unrest and Protest on the Global Stage,* Palgrave Macmillan, Basingstoke, 115–31.

Dorling, D. and Rees, P. (2003) A nation still dividing: the British census and social polarisation 1971–2001, *Environment and Planning A,* 35, 1287–313.

Dorling, D. and Rees, P. (2004) A nation dividing? Some interpretations of the question, *Environment and Planning A,* 36, 369–73.

Dorling, D. and Shaw, M. (2000) Life chances and lifestyles, in V. Gardiner and H. Matthews (eds) *The Changing Geography of the UK,* London, Routledge, 230–60.

Douglas, M. and Isherwood, B. (1996) *The World of Goods: Towards an Anthropology of Consumption,* 2nd edition, Routledge, London.

Doyle, T. (2005) *Environmental Movements in Majority and Minority Worlds: A Global Perspective,* Rutgers University Press, London.

Doyle, T. and McEachern, D. (2001) *Environment and Politics,* 2nd edition, Routledge, London.

Doyle, T. and McEachern, D. (2007) *Environment and Politics,* 3rd edition, Routledge, London.

Driver, F. (2014) Imaginative geographies, in Cloke, P., Crang, P. and Goodwin, M. (eds) *Introducing Human Geographies,* 3rd edition, Routledge, Abingdon, Oxon, pp. 234–48.

du Gay, P. (1996) *Consumption and Identity at Work,* Sage, London.

Duncan, J.S., Johnson, N.C. and Schein, R. (eds) (2004) *A Companion to Cultural Geography,* Blackwell, London.

Dunlap, R.E. and McCright, A.M. (2008) A widening gap: republican and democratic views on climate change, *Environment,* 50, 26–35.

Dunn, K.M. (2001) Representations of Islam in the politics of mosque development in Sydney, *Tijdschrift voor Economische en Sociale Geografi,* 92, 291–308.

Duruz, J. (2005) Eating at the borders: culinary journeys, *Environment and Planning D: Society and Space,* 23, 51–69.

Dutta, S. (2014) Asian cricket in the UK embraces change, Cricinfo.com, 4 June, www.espncricinfo.com/england/content/story/749755.html [accessed 15 October 2015].

DWP *see* Department of Work and Pensions.

Dwyer, C.L. (2006) Fabrications of India: transnational fashion networks, in Breward, C. and Gilbert, D. (eds) *Fashion's World Cities,* Berg, Oxford, 217–33.

Dwyer, C. and Crang, P. (2002) Fashioning ethnicities: the commercial spaces of multiculture, *Ethnicities,* 2, 410–30.

Dwyer, C. and Jackson, P. (2003) Commodifying difference: selling EASTern fashion, *Environment and Planning D: Society and Space,* 21, 269–91.

Dymski, G.A. (2010) Confronting the quadruple crisis, *Geoforum,* 41, 837–40.

E

Eddington, R. (2006) *The Eddington Transport Study,* HM Government, London, www.thepep.org/ClearingHouse/docfiles/Eddington.Transport.Study%20-%20Rod.pdf [accessed 21 November 2014].

EIA (Energy Information Administration) (2010) *International Energy Outlook 2010,* EIA, Washington, DC.

Ekbladh, D. (2002) 'Mr. TVA': grass-roots development, David Lillienthal, and the rise and fall of the Tennessee Valley Authority, *Diplomatic History,* 26, 335–74.

Ekbladh, D. (2010a) Meeting the challenge from totalitarianism: the Tennessee Valley Authority as a global model for liberal development, 1933–1945, *International History Review,* 32, 47–67.

Ekbladh, D. (2010b) *The Great American Mission: Modernization and the Construction of an American World Order,* Princeton University Press, Princeton, NJ.

Ekins, P., Bradshaw, M. and Watson, J. (eds) (2015) *Global Energy: Issue, Potentials and Policy Implications,* Oxford University Press, Oxford.

Elden, S. (2009) *Terror and Territory: The Spatial Extent of Sovereignty,* University of Minnesota Press, Minneapolis, MN.

Elden, S. (2010) Land, terrain, territory, *Progress in Human Geography,* 34(6), 799–817.

Elden, S. (2013) *The Birth of Territory,* The University of Chicago Press, Chicago, IL.

Elden, S. and Bialasiewicz, L. (2006) The new geopolitics of division and the problem of a Kantian Europe, *Review of International Studies*, **32**, 623–44.

Elster, J. (1989) *Nuts and Bolts for the Social Sciences*, Cambridge University Press, Cambridge.

Elster, J. (1989) *Nuts and Bolts for the Social Sciences*, Cambridge University Press, Cambridge.

Emmerson, C. (2010) *The Future History of the Arctic*, Bodley Head, London.

Engelen, E. and Faulconbridge, J. (2009) Introduction: financial geographies-the credit crisis as an opportunity to catch economic geography's next boat?, *Journal of Economic Geography*, **9**, 587–95.

Engels, F. (1845) *The Condition of the Working Class in England*, 1987 edition, Penguin, London and New York.

Enloe, C. (1983) *Does Khaki Become You? The Militarisation of Women's Lives*, Pluto Press, London.

Enloe, C. (1989) *Bananas, Beaches and Bases: Making Feminist Sense of International Politics*, University of California Press, Berkeley, CA.

Enloe, C. (1993) *The Morning After: Sexual Politics at the End of the Cold War*, University of California Press, Berkeley, CA.

Enloe, C. (2000) *Maneuvers: The International Politics of Militarizing Women's Lives*, University of California Press, Berkeley, CA.

Enloe, C. (2004) *The Curious Feminist: Searching for Women in a New Age of Empire*, University of California Press, Berkeley, CA.

Enloe, C. (2007) *Globalization and Militarism: Feminists Make the Link*, Rowan & Littlefield, Lanham, MD.

Epstein, G. and Jayadev, A. (2005) The rise of rentier incomes in OECD countries: financialization, central bank policy and labor solidarity, in G. Epstein (ed.) *Financialization and the World Economy*, Edward Elgar, Cheltenham, 46–74.

Equiano, O. (1789) *The Interesting Narrative of the Life of Olaudah Equiano, or Gustavus Vassa, the African*, London.

Ereaut, G. and Segnit, N. (2006) Warm words: how are we telling the climate story and can we tell it better?, www .ippr.org.uk/members/download.asp?f=%2Fecomm%2F files%2Fwarm%5Fwords%2Epdf.

Ericksen, P. (2008) Conceptualizing food systems for global environmental change research, *Global Environmental Change*, **18**, 234–45.

Escobar, A. (1995) *Encountering Development*, Princeton University Press, Princeton, NJ.

Escobar, C. (2006) Migration and citizen rights: the Mexican case, *Citizenship Studies*, **10**, 503–522.

Escobar, A. (2011) *Encountering Development: The Making and Unmaking of the Third World*, 2nd edition, Princeton University Press, Princeton, NJ.

Esposito, J.L. (ed.) (1995) *The Oxford Encyclopedia of Islam in the Modern World*, Oxford University Press, New York.

European Wind Energy Association (EWEA) (2014) *Wind in Power: 2014 European Statistics*, February 2015, EWEA, Brussels, www.ewea.org/fileadmin/files/library/publications/statistics/EWEA-Annual-Statistics-2014.pdf [accessed 22 October 2015].

Eurostat (2011) *Annual National Accounts, Aggregates and Employment*, Eurostat, Brussels.

Evans, R.L. (2007) *Fuelling our Future: An Introduction to Sustainable Energy*, Cambridge University Press, Cambridge.

F

Fairbairn, D. and Dorling, D. (1997) *Mapping and mapmaking: new approaches to the teaching of cartography*, Proceedings of the 18th International Cartography Conference, Stockholm, 23–27 June, 4, 1955–1962.

FAO *see* Food and Agriculture Organization.

Favell, A. (2003) Games without frontiers? Questioning the transnational social power of migrants in Europe, *Archives Europeennes De Sociologie*, **44**, 397–427.

Fawcett, T. (2010) Personal carbon trading: a policy ahead of its time?, *Energy Policy*, **38**, 6868–76.

Featherstone, M. (1995) *Undoing Culture: Globalization, Postmodernism and Identity*, Sage, London.

Featherstone, M., Lash, S. and Robertson, R. (eds) (1995) *Global Modernities*, Sage, London.

Ferbrache, F and Yarwood, R (2015) Britons abroad or European citizens? The negotiation of (trans)national space and citizenship by British migrants in France, *Geoforum*, **62**, 73–83.

Ferguson, J. and Gupta, A. (2002) Spatializing states: towards an ethnography of neoliberal governmentality, *American Ethnologist*, **29**, 981–1002.

Feygina, I., Jost, J.T. and Goldsmith, R.E. (2010) System justification, the denial of global warming, and the possibility of 'system-sanctioned change', *Personality and Social Psychology Bulletin*, **36**, 326–8.

Fields, G. (2004) *Territories of Profit*, Stanford Business Books, Stanford.

Fineman, S. (ed.) (2000) *Emotion in Organization*, Sage, London.

Fitter, R. and Kaplinsky, R. (2001) Who gains from product rents as the coffee market becomes more differentiated? A value chain analysis, *IDS Bulletin Paper*, IDS Sussex.

FitzSimmons, M. (1986) The new industrial agriculture: the regional differentiation of specialty crop production, *Economic Geography*, **62**, 334–53.

FitzSimmons, M. (1997) Restructuring, industry and regional dynamics, in Goodman, D. and Watts, M. (eds) *Globalising Food*, Routledge, London, 158–68.

Flint, C. and Falah, G.W. (2004) How the United States justified its war on terrorism: prime morality and the construction of a 'just war', *Third World Quarterly*, **25**, 1379–99.

Florida, R. (2002) *The Rise of the Creative Class and How It's Transforming Work, Leisure and Everyday Life*, Basic Books, New York.

Flowerdew, R. and Martin, D. (2005) *Methods in Human Geography: A Guide for Students Doing a Research Project*, 2nd edition, Longman, Harlow.

Flusty, S. (2004) *De-Coca-Colonization: Making the Globe from the Inside Out*, Routledge, New York.

Fold, N. and Pritchard, B. (eds) (2005) *Cross-continental Food Chains*, Routledge, London.

Foley, R. (1995) *Humans Before Humanity: An Evolutionary Perspective*, Blackwell, Oxford.

Food and Agriculture Organization (FAO) (1996) Rome declaration on world food security, *World Food Summit*, FAO, Rome.

Food and Agriculture Organization (FAO) (2005) *The State of Food Insecurity*, FAO, Rome.

Food and Agriculture Organization (FAO) (2006) *Food Security: Policy Brief*, FAO, Rome, ftp://ftp.fao.org/es/ESA/policybriefs/pb_02.pdf.

Food and Agriculture Organization (FAO) (2010) *The State of Food Insecurity in the World: Addressing Food Insecurity in Protracted Crises*, FAO, Rome.

Forest, B. (1995) West Hollywood as symbol: the significance of place in the construction of a gay identity, *Environment and Planning D: Society and Space,* **13**, 133–57.

Foresta, R.A. (1992) Amazonia and the politics of geopolitics, *Geographical Review*, 8(2), 128–42.

Foster, W., Cheng, Z., Dedrick, J. and Kraemer, K.L. (2006) *Technology and Organizational Factors in the Notebook Industry Supply Chain,* The Personal Computer Industry Center, University of California, Irvine, www.pcic.merage.uci.edu/papers.asp [accessed 29 August 2011].

Fotheringham, S.A., Brunsdon, C. and Charlton, M. (2000) *Quantitative Geography: Perspectives on Spatial Data Analysis,* Sage, London and Thousand Oaks, New Delhi.

Foucault, M. (1979) On governmentality, *Ideology and Consciousness*, **6**, 5–29.

Frank, A. (1966) The development of underdevelopment, *Monthly Review*, 18(4), 17–31.

Frank, A.G. (1997) The Cold War and me, *Bulletin of Concerned Asian Scholars,* **29**, available at www.rrojasdatabank.into/agfrank/syfrank.htm [accessed 7 December 2011].

Frank, A.G. (1998) *ReOrient: Global Economy in the Asian Age*, University of California Press, Berkeley, CA.

Frank, A.G. and Dutt, A.K. (2002) The development of underdevelopment, *The International Library of Critical Writings in Economics*, **140**(1), 97–111.

Fraser, G. (2014) Scapegoating immigrants is the oldest trick in the book, *The Guardian*, 7 November, www.theguardian.com/commentisfree/belief/2014/nov/07/scapegoating-immigrants-oldest-trick-in-book.

Freeman, C. (2000) *High Tech and High Heels in the Global Economy*, Duke University Press, Durham, NC.

Freeman, M. (1986) Transport, in Langton J. and Morris, R.J. (eds) *Atlas of Industrializing Britain, 1780–1914,* Methuen, London and New York.

Freidberg, S. (2003) Cleaning up down South: supermarkets, ethical trade and African horticulture, *Social and Cultural Geography*, **4**, 27–44.

Freidberg, S. (2014) Footprint technopolitics, *Geoforum,* **55**(0), 178–89.

Friedberg, S. (2004) *French Beans and Food Scares: Culture and Commerce in an Anxious Age,* Oxford University Press, Oxford.

Friedman, J. (1997) Global crises, the struggle for cultural identity and intellectual porkbarrelling: cosmopolitans versus locals, ethnics and nationals in an era of dehegemonisation, in Werbner, P. and Modood, T. (eds) *Debating Cultural Hybridity. Multi-Cultural Identities and the Politics of Anti-Racism,* Zed, London, 70–89.

Friedman, J. and Rowlands, M.J. (1977) Notes towards an epigenetic model of the evolution of civilization, in Friedman, J. and Rowlands, M.J. (eds) *The Evolution of Social Systems,* Duckworth, London, 201–76.

Friedman, T.L. (1999) It's a small world, *Sunday Times,* 28 March, Section 5.

Friedman, T.L. (2005) *The World is Flat: A Brief History of the Globalized World in the Twenty-first Century,* Allen Lane, London

Friedmann, H. (1993) The political economy of food, *New Left Review*, **197**, 29–57.

Friedmann, H. and McMichael, P. (1989) Agriculture and the state system: the rise and decline of national agricultures, 1870 to the present, *Sociologia Ruralis*, **29**, 93–117.

Friedmann, J. (1966) *Regional Development Policy: A Case Study of Venezuela,* MIT Press, Cambridge, MA.

Friend, T. (2003) *Indonesian Destinies,* The Belknap Press of Harvard University Press, Cambridge, MA.

Friends of the Earth (2006) What kind of world do you want? *Friends of the Earth Limited,* June.

French, S., Leyshon, A. and Thrift, N. (2009) A very geographical crisis: the making and breaking of the 2007–2008 financial crisis, *Cambridge Journal of Regions, Economy and Society,* **2**, 287–302.

Fröbel, F., Heinrichs, J. and Kreye, O. (1980) *The New International Division of Labour,* Cambridge University Press, Cambridge.

Fukuyama, F. (1992) *The End of History and the Last Man,* Penguin, London.

Fuller, D. and Kitchin, R. (eds) (2004) *Radical Theory/Critical Praxis: Making a Difference Beyond the Academy?,* Praxis (e) Press, Vernon and Victoria.

Furtado, C. (1964) *Development and Underdevelopment,* University of California Press, Berkeley, CA.

Fyfe, N. (1991) The police, space and society: the geography of policing, *Progress in Human Geography,* 15(3), 249–67.

G

Gad, G. and Holdsworth, D.W. (1987) Corporate capitalism and the emergence of the high-rise office building, *Urban Geography,* **8**, 212–31.

Gaffikin, F. and Nickson, A. (1984) *Jobs Crisis and the Multi-Nationals,* Birmingham Trade Union Group for World Development, Birmingham.

Gál, A. (2009) 'Future Bangalores? The increasing role of Central and Eastern Europe in services offshoring', available at: http://papers.ssrn.com/sol3/papers.cfm?abstract_id=1334165.

Gallent, N. (2006) The rural-urban fringe: a new priority for planning policy?, *Planning Practice and Research*, **21**(3), 383–93.

Gallent, N. and Anderson, J. (2007) Representing England's rural-urban fringe, *Landscape Research*, **32**(1), 1–21.

Gandy, M. (2002) *Concrete and Clay: Re-working Nature in New York City*, MIT Press, New York.

Gao, Z.G. and Jia, B.B. (2013) The nine-line dash in the South China Sea: history, status and implications, *The American Journal of International Law*, **107**, 98–124.

Garbin, D. and Millington, G. (2012) Territorial stigma and the politics of resistance in a Parisian banlieue: La Courneuve and beyond. *Urban studies*, **49**(10), 2067–83.

Gardner, B. (2013) *Global Food Futures: Feeding the World in 2050*, Bloomsbury, London.

Garland, J. and Chakraborti, N. (2004) England's green and pleasant land? Examining racist prejudice in a rural context, *Patterns of Prejudice*, **38**(4), 383–98.

Garland, J. and Chakraborti, N. (2006) 'Race', space and place: examining identity and cultures of exclusion in rural England, *Ethnicities*, **6**(2), 159–77.

Garland, J. and Chakraborti, N. (2009) Identity, 'otherness' and the impact of racist victimization in the English countryside, in Iganski, P. (ed.) *The Consequences of Hate Crime*, Greenwood, Westport, CT, 143–59.

Garner, R. (2000) *Environmental Politics: Britain, Europe and the Global Environment*, 2nd edition, Macmillan, London.

Gary, I. and Karl, T.L. (2003) *Bottom of the Barrel: Africa's Oil Boom and the Poor*, Catholic Relief Services, www.catholicrelief.org/africanoil.cfm.

Gates, D. (2005) Boeing 787: parts from around world will be swiftly integrated, *Seattle Times*, 11 September.

Gautier, C. (2008) *Oil, Water, and Climate: An Introduction*, Cambridge University Press, Cambridge.

Gentleman, A. (2014) What is it like to live on Britain's most expensive street?, *The Guardian*, 7 April.

Gereffi, G. (1994) The organisation of buyer-driven global commodity chains: how US retailers shape overseas production networks, in Gereffi, G. and Korzeniewicz, M. (eds) *Commodity Chains and Global Development*, Praeger, Westport, 95–122.

Gereffi, G. (2001) Shifting governance structures in global commodity chains, with special reference to the Internet, *American Behavioural Scientist*, **44**, 1616–37.

Gereffi, G. and Fernandez-Stark, K. (2010) *The Offshore Services Value Chain: Developing Countries and the Crisis*, The World Bank, Policy Research Working Paper 5262.

Gereffi, G., Humphrey, J. and Sturgeon, T. (2005) The governance of global value chains, *Review of International Political Economy*, **12**, 78–104.

Ghazvinian, J. (2007) *Untapped: The Scramble for Africa's Oil*, Harcourt, London.

Gibbon, P. and Ponte, S. (2005) *Trading Down: Africa, Value Chains, and the Global Economy*, Temple University Press, Philadelphia.

Gibson, C. (2009) Geographies of tourism: critical research on capitalism and local livelihoods, *Progress in Human Geography*, 1–8.

Giddens, A. (1991) *The Constitution of Society*, Polity Press, Cambridge.

Giddens, A. (2001) *Sociology*, Polity Press, Cambridge.

Giersch, P. (2001) A motley throng: social change on Southwest China's early modern frontier: 1700–1800, *The Journal of Asian Studies*, **60**(1), 67–94.

Giles, B.D. (1987) *A History of Geography at Birmingham, 1926–1986*, University of Birmingham.

Giles, C. and Goodall, I.H. (1992) *Yorkshire Textile Mills, 1770–1930*, HMSO, London.

Gill, G. (1996) *The League of Nations from 1929 to 1946*, Avery Publishing Group, New York.

Gill, G. (1996) *The League of Nations from 1929 to 1946*, Avery Publishing Group, New York.

Gills, B.K. (2011) Going south: capitalist crisis, systemic crisis, civilisational crisis, *Third World Quarterly*, **31**(2), 169–84.

Gilman, N. (2003) *Mandarins of the Future: Modernization Theory in Cold War America*, Johns Hopkins University Press, Baltimore, OH.

Gilmartin, M. (2008) Migration, identity and belonging, *Geography Compass*, **2**(6), 1837–52.

Gilmore, R.W. (2007) *Golden Gulag: Prisons, Surplus, Crisis and Opposition in Globalizing California*, University of California Press, Berkeley, CA.

Gilpin, R. (1989) *The Political Economy of International Relations*, Princeton University Press, Princeton, NJ.

Gilroy, P. (2000) *Between Camps: Nations, Cultures and the Allure of Race*, Penguin, London.

Gilroy, P. (2002) [originally 1987] *There Ain't no Black in the Union Jack: The Cultural Politics of Race and Nation*, Routledge, London (2002 edition).

Glassman, J. (2005) The 'war on terrorism' comes to Southeast Asia, *Journal of Contemporary Asia*, **35**, 3–28.

Glassner, M.I. (1993) *Political Geography*, John Wiley, New York.

Glasze, G., Webster, C. and Frantz, K. (2006) *Private Cities: Global and Local Perspectives*, Routledge, Abingdon.

Gleeson, B. (1998) The social space of disability in colonial Melbourne, in Fyfe, N. (ed.) *Images of the Street*, Routledge, London, 93–110.

Glennie, P. and Thrift, N. (1992) Modernity, urbanism and modern consumption, *Environment and Planning D: Society and Space*, **10**, 423–43.

Godfray, C J., Crute, I., Haddad, L. *et al.* (2010) The future of the global food system, *Philosophical Transactions of the Royal Society B*, **365**, 2769–77.

Goetz, A.M. and Sen Gupta, R. (1996) Who takes the credit: gender, power, and control over loan use in rural credit programs in Bangladesh, *World Development*, **24**, 45–63.

Gold, J.R. and Revill, G. (2004) *Representing the Environment*, Routledge, London.

Goldin, I. (2013) *Divided Nations: Why Global Governance is Failing, and What We Can Do About It*, Oxford University Press, Oxford.

Goldman, R. and Papson, S. (1998) *Nike Culture: The Sign of the Swoosh*, Sage, London.

Goodman, D. (2003) The quality 'turn' and alternative food practices: reflections and agenda, *Journal of Rural Studies*, **19**, 1–7.

Goodman, D. and Redclift, M. (1991) *Refashioning Nature: Food Ecology and Culture,* Routledge, London.

Goodman, D. and Watts, M. (eds) (1997) *Globalising Food,* Routledge, London.

Goodman, D., DuPuis, E. and Goodman, M. (2012) *Alternative Food Networks: Knowledge, Practice, and Politics,* Routledge, Abingdon.

Goodman, D., Sorj, B. and Wilkinson, J. (1987) *From Farming to Biotechnology: A Theory of Agro-industrial Development,* Blackwell, Oxford.

Goodman, M.K. (2004) Reading fair trade: political ecological imaginary and the moral economy of fair trade foods, *Political Geography,* **23**, 891–915.

Goodman, M.K., Maye, D. and Holloway, L. (2010) Ethical foodscapes: premises, promises and possibilities, *Environment and Planning A,* **42**, 1782–96.

Goodrum, A. (2005) *The National Fabric: Fashion, Britishness, Globalization,* Berg, Oxford.

Goodwin, M. (1995) Poverty in the city, you can raise your voice, but who is listening?, in Philo, C. (ed.) *Off the Map: The Social Geography of Poverty in the UK,* Child Poverty Action Group, London, 134–54.

Gordon, D., Mack, J., Lansley, S., Main, G., Nandy, S., Patsios, D. and Pomati, M. (2013) *The Impoverishment of the UK: PSE UK first results–living standards,* University of Bristol, Bristol.

Gore, A. (2006) *An Inconvenient Truth: The Planetary Emergency of Global Warming and What We Can Do About It,* Bloomsbury Publishing, London.

Gorman, D (2006) *Imperial Citizenship: Empire and the Question of Belonging,* Manchester University Press, Manchester.

Goss, J. (1993) The magic of the mall: form and function in the retail built environment, *Annals of the Association of American Geographers,* **83**, 18–47.

Goss, J. (1999a) Consumption, in Cloke, P., Crang, P. and Goodwin, M. (eds) *Introducing Human Geographies,* Arnold, London, 114–21.

Goss, J. (1999b) Once upon a time in the commodity world, an unofficial guide to the Mall of America, *Annals of the Association of American Geographers,* **89**, 45–75.

Goss, J. (2006) Geographies of consumption: the work of consumption, *Progress in Human Geography,* **30**(2), 237–49.

Gottdiener, M. (1982) Disneyland: a utopian urban space, *Urban Life,* **11**, 139–62.

Gottdiener, M. (1997) *The Theming of America: Dreams, Visions and Commercial Spaces,* Westview Press, Boulder, CO.

Gottman, J. (1973) *The Significance of Territory,* University Press of Virginia, Charlottesville, VA.

Gould, P. and Pitts, F.R. (eds) (2002) *Geographical Voices: Fourteen Autobiographical Essays,* Syracuse University Press, Syracuse, NY.

Gowan, T. (2010) *Hobos, Hustlers and Backsliders: Homeless in San Francisco,* University of Minnesota Press, Minneapolis, MN.

Graham, B.J., Ashworth, G.J. and Tunbridge, J.E. (2000) *A Geography of Heritage: Power, Culture and Economy,* Arnold, London.

Gray, K. and Murphy, C.N. (2013) Introduction: rising powers and the future of global governance, *Third World Quarterly,* **34**(2), 183–93.

Green, A. (1997) Income and wealth, in Pacione, M. (ed.) *Britain's Cities: Geographies of Division in Urban Britain,* Routledge, London, 78–102.

Green, F. and Sutcliffe, B. (1987) *The Profit System: The Economics of Capitalism,* Penguin, London.

Gregory, D., Johnston, R.J., Pratt, G., Watts, M. and Whatmore, S. (eds) (2009) *The Dictionary of Human Geography,* 5th edition, Wiley-Blackwell, Oxford.

Gregson, N. (2007) *Living with Things: Ridding, Accommodation, Dwelling,* Sean Kingston Publishing, Wantage.

Grenville, K. (2006) *The Secret River,* Canongate Press, London.

Groves, P.A. (1987) The northeast and regional integration, 1800–1860, in Mitchell, R.D. and Groves, P.A. (eds) *North America: The Historical Geography of a Changing Continent,* Hutchinson, London.

Grundy-Warr, C. and Dean, K. (2011) Not peace, not war: the myriad spaces of sovereignty, peace and conflict in Myanmar/Burma, in Kirsch, S. and Flint, C. (eds) *Reconstructing Conflict: Integrating War and Post-War Geographies,* Ashgate, Farnham, 91–114.

Guthman, J. (2004) Back to the land: the paradox of organic food standards, *Environment and Planning A,* **36**, 511–28.

Guthman, J. (2011) *Weighing In: Obesity, Food Justice and the Limits of Capitalism,* University of California Press, Berkeley, CA.

Guyot-Réchard, B. (2015) Reordering a border space: relief, rehabilitation, and nation-building in northeastern India after the 1950 Assam earthquake, *Modern Asian Studies,* in press.

Gwynne, R.N., Klak, T. and Shaw, D.J.B. (2003) *Alternative Capitalisms: Geographies of Emerging Regions,* Arnold, London.

H

Hackley, C. (2010) *Advertising and Promotion: An Integrated Marketing Communications Approach,* 2nd edition, Sage, London.

Hagen, J.B. (2006) *Preservation Tourism and Nationalism: the Jewel of the German Past* Ashgate, Aldershot.

Haggett, P. (1972) *Geography: A Modern Synthesis,* Harper & Row, New York, Evanston, San Francisco, London.

Hall, E.T. (1959) *The Silent Language,* Doubleday, Garden City, NY.

Hall, P. (ed.) (1966) *Von Thünen's Isolated State,* Pergamon, Oxford.

Hall, P. (2014) *Cities of Tomorrow: an Intellectual History of Urban Planning and Design since 1880,* 4th edition, Wiley-Blackwell, Chichester.

Hall, P. and Pain, K. (2006) *The Polycentric Metropolis: Learning from Mega-city Regions in Europe,* Earthscan, London.

Hall, P. and Pfeiffer, U. (2000) *Urban Future 21: A Global Agenda for 21st Century Cities,* Spon, London.

Hall, S. (1992) The West and the rest: discourse and power, in Hall, S. and Gieben, B. (eds) *Formations of Modernity,* Open University Press, Milton Keynes, 275–331.

Hall, S. (1995) New cultures for old, in Massey, D. and Jess, P. (eds) *A Place in the World? Places, Cultures and Globalization,* Oxford University Press, Oxford, 175–213.

Hall, S. (1996) The meaning of new times, in Morley, D. and Chen, K.-H. (eds) *Stuart Hall: Critical Dialogues in Cultural Studies,* Routledge, London, 223–37.

Hall, T. (2003) Car-ceral cities: social geographies of everyday urban mobility, in Miles, M. and Hall, T. (eds) *Urban Futures: Critical Commentaries on Shaping the City,* Routledge, London, 92–105.

Hall, T. and Barrett, H. (2012) *Urban Geography,* 4th edition, Routledge, Abingdon.

Hall, T. and Hubbard, P. (1996) The entrepreneurial city: new urban politics, new urban geographies?, *Progress in Human Geography,* **20**(2), 153–74.

Hall, T. and Hubbard, P. (eds) (1998) *The Entrepreneurial City: Geographies of Politics, Regime and Representation,* Chichester, Wiley.

Hall, T., Toms, P., McGuinnes, M., Parker, C. and Roberts, N. (2015) Where's the geography department? The changing administrative place of geography in British universities, *Area,* **47**, 1, 56–64.

Halvorsen, S. (2015) Encountering Occupy London: boundary making and the territoriality of urban activism, *Environment and Planning D: Society and Space.*

Hamilton, N. and Chincilla, N.S. (2001) *Seeking Community in a Global City: Guatemalans and Salvadorans in Los Angeles,* Temple University Press, Philadelphia, PA.

Hammett, D. (2009) Local beats to global rhythms: coloured student identity and negotiations of global cultural imports in Cape Town, South Africa, *Social and Cultural Geography,* **10**(4), 403–19.

Hanley, L. (2011) Invisible forcefields surround our estates, *The Guardian,* 11 August, www.theguardian .com/commentisfree/2011/aug/11/invisible-forcefield-regeneration-estates [accessed 20 April 2015].

Hanson, S. and Pratt, G. (1995) *Gender, Work and Space,* Routledge, London.

Haraway, D. (1989) *Primate Visions: Gender, Race and Nature in the World of Modern Science,* Routledge, New York.

Hardie, M. and Banks, A. (2014) *The Changing Shape of UK Manufacturing,* Office for Natioanl Statistics, London.

Harding, J. (2010) What we're about to receive, *London Review of Books,* **32**(9), 13 May, 3–8.

Harding, N. (2010) Can you look her in the iPad?, *The Independent,* 9 June, www.independent.co.uk/life-style/gadgets-and-tech/features/can-you-look-her-in-the-ipad-1994894.html [accessed 12 March 2015].

Harley, J.B. (1988) Maps, knowledge and power, in Cosgrove, D. and Daniels, S. (eds) *The Iconography of Landscape,* Cambridge University Press, Cambridge, 277–312.

Harper, S. (2005) *Ageing Societies,* Hodder Arnold, London.

Harris, C. and Ullman, E. (1945) The nature of cities, *Annals of the American Academy of Political Science,* **242**, 7–17.

Harris, D.R. (1989) An evolutionary continuum of plant–animal interaction, in Harris, D.R. and Hillman, G.C. (eds) *Foraging and Farming: The Evolution of Plant Exploitation,* Unwin Hyman, London, 11–26.

Harris, D.R. (1996a) Introduction: themes and concepts in the study of early agriculture, in Harris, D.R. (ed.) *The Origins and Spread of Agriculture and Pastoralism in Eurasia,* UCL Press, London, 1–9.

Harris, D.R. (1996b) The origins and spread of agriculture and pastoralism in Eurasia: an overview, in Harris, D.R. (ed.) *The Origins and Spread of Agriculture and Pastoralism in Eurasia,* UCL Press, London, 552–70.

Harris, F. (ed.) (2004) *Global Environmental Issues,* John Wiley and Sons, Chichester.

Harrison, S. (2009) Physical geography and human geography, in Kitchin, R., Thrift, N., *et al.* (eds) *The International Encyclopedia of Human Geography,* Elsevier, Oxford, 163–8.

Hart, G. (2001) Development critiques in the 1990s: culs de sac and promising paths, *Progress in Human Geography,* **25**, 649–58.

Hartwick, E. (1998) Geographies of consumption: a commodity-chain approach, *Environment and Planning D: Society and Space,* **16**, 423–37.

Harvey, D. (1973) *Social Justice and the City,* Arnold, London.

Harvey, D. (1974) Population, resources and the ideology of science, *Economic Geography,* **50**, 256–77.

Harvey, D. (1982) *The Limits to Capital,* Blackwell, Oxford.

Harvey, D. (1985a) *The Urbanization of Capital: Studies in the History and Theory of Capitalist Urbanization,* Blackwell, Oxford.

Harvey, D. (1985b) Money, time, space and the city, in Harvey, D. (ed.) *The Urban Experience,* Johns Hopkins University Press, Baltimore, MD.

Harvey, D. (1989) *The Condition of Postmodernity: An Enquiry into the Origins of Cultural Change,* Blackwell, Oxford.

Harvey, D. (2003) *The New Imperialism,* Oxford University Press, Oxford.

Harvey, D. (2005) *The New Imperialism,* Oxford University Press, Oxford.

Harvey, D. (2006) *Spaces of Global Capitalism: Towards a Theory of Uneven Capitalist Development,* Verso, London.

Harvey, D. (2014) *Seventeen Contradictions and the End of Capitalism,* Profile Books, London.

Haskell, T.L. (1985a) Capitalism and the origins of the humanitarian sensibility, part 1, *American Historical Review,* **90**, 339–61.

Haskell, T.L. (1985b) Capitalism and the origins of the humanitarian sensibility, part 2, *American Historical Review,* **90**, 547–66.

Hastings, A. and Dean, J. (2003) Challenging images: tackling stigma through estate regeneration, *Policy and Politics,* **31**, 171–84.

Haughton, G. and Hunter, C. (1994) *Sustainable Cities,* Regional Studies Association, London.

Hay, I. and Muller, S. (2012) 'That tiny, stratospheric apex that owns most of the world' – exploring geographies of the super-rich, *Geographical Research,* **50**(1), 75–88.

Haylett, C. (2001) Illegitimate subjects? Abject whites, neoliberal modernisation and middle class multiculturalism, *Environment and Planning D: Society and Space,* **19**(3), 351–70.

Hayward, K. (2004) *City Limits: Crime, Consumer Culture and the Urban Experience,* Glasshouse Press, London.

He, S. (2014) Consuming urban living in 'villages in the city': studentification in Guangzhou, China, *Urban Studies,* doi: 10.1177/0042098014543703.

Hebdige, D. (1979) *Subculture: The Meaning of Style,* Methuen, London.

Hebdige, D. (1987) Object as image: the Italian scooter cycle, in *Hiding in the Light: On Images and Things,* Comedia/Routledge, London, 77–115.

Hecht, S. and Cockburn, A. (1989) *The Fate of the Forest: Developers, Destroyers and Defenders of the Amazon,* Verso, London and New York.

Hedberg, D., Kullander, S. and Frank, H. (2010) The world needs a new energy paradigm, *Ambio,* **39**, 1–10.

Heilbronner, R.L. (1972) *The Economic Problem,* 3rd edition, Prentice Hall, Englewood Cliffs, NJ.

Heisenberg, W. (1958) *Physics and Philosophy: The Revolution in Modern Science,* Harper, New York.

Helander, B. (2005) Who needs a state? Civilians, security and social services in north-east Somalia, in Richards, P. (ed.) *No Peace, No War: An Anthropology of Contemporary Armed Conflict,* Ohio University Press, Athens, OH, 193–202.

Held, D. and McGrew, A. (eds) (2002) *Governing Globalization,* Polity Press, Cambridge.

Held, D. and McGrew, A. (2007) *Globalization/Anti-globalization: Beyond the Great Divide,* Polity Press, Cambridge.

Held, D., McGrew, D., Goldblatt, D. and Perraton, J. (1999) *Global Transformations: Politics, Economics and Culture,* Polity Press, Cambridge.

Helm, D. (ed.) (2007) *The New Energy Paradigm,* OUP, Oxford.

Hendrickson, M.K. and Heffernan, W.D. (2002) Opening spaces through relocalization: locating potential resistance in the weaknesses of the global food system, *Sociologia Ruralis,* **42**, 347–69.

Hendrikse, R.P. and Sidaway, J.D. (2010) Neoliberalism 3.0, *Environment and Planning A,* **42**, 2037–42.

Hepple, L. (1986) The revival of geopolitics, *Political Geography Quarterly,* **5**, 521–36.

Hepple, L. (1992) Metaphor, geopolitical discourse and the military in South America, in Barnes, T.J. and Duncan, J.S. (eds) *Writing Worlds,* Routledge, London, 136–54.

Herb, G.H. (1989) Persuasive cartography in Geopolitik and national socialism, *Political Geography Quarterly,* **8**, 289–303.

Herbert, S.K. (1997) *Policing Space: Territoriality and the Los Angeles Police Department,* University of Minnesota Press, Minneapolis.

Herbert, S.K. (2006) *Citizens, Cops, and Power: Recognizing the Limits of Community,* University of Chicago Press, Chicago, IL.

Herf, J. (1984) *Reactionary Modernism: Technology, Culture and Politics in Weimar and the Third Reich,* Cambridge University Press, Cambridge.

Herod, A., Ó Tuathail, G., Roberts, S. (eds) (1998) *An Unruly World: Globalization, Governance and Geography,* Routledge, London.

Hertz, N. (2001) *The Silent Takeover: Global Capitalism and the Death of Democracy,* William Heinemann, London.

Herzfeld, M. (1992) *The Social Production of Indifference: Exploring the Symbolic Roots of Western Bureaucracy,* University of Chicago Press, Chicago, IL.

Heske, H. (1986) German geographical research in the Nazi period, *Political Geography Quarterly,* **5**, 267–81.

Hettne, B. (1995) *Development Theory and the Three Worlds,* 2nd edition, Longman, London.

Hewitt, R. (2010) *Map of a Nation. A Biography of the Ordnance Survey,* Granta, London.

Hickman., L. (2013) Jeremy Grantham on population growth, China and climate sceptics, *The Guardian,* online, 15 April 2013, www.theguardian.com/environment/blog/2013/apr/15/jeremy-grantham-population-china-climate.

Hickman, M. (2010a) A gadget to die for? Concern over human cost overshadows iPad launch, *The Independent,* 27 May, www.independent.co.uk/news/world/asia/concern-over-human-cost-overshadows-ipad-launch-1983888.html [accessed 4 August 2010].

Hickman, M. (2010b) A cautionary tale of corporate hubris and high-handedness, *The Independent,* 16 July, www.independent.co.uk/opinion/commentators/martin-hickman-a-cautionary-tale-of-corporate-hubris-and-high-handedness-2027810.html [accessed 5 August 2010].

Hill, T.P. (1977) On goods and services, *Review of Income and Wealth,* **23**, 315–38.

Hinchliffe, S. (1996) Helping the earth begins at home: the social construction of socio-environmental responsibilities, *Global Environmental Change,* **6**, 53–62.

Hinchliffe, S. (2007) *Space for Nature,* Sage, London.

Hinchliffe, S. and Belshaw, C. (2003) Who cares? Values, power and action in environmental contests, in Hinchliffe, S., Blowers, A. and Freeland, J. (eds) *Understanding Environmental Issues,* John Wiley and Sons, Chichester, 89–126.

Hinchliffe, S., Kearnes, M.B., Degen, M. and Whatmore, S. (2005) Urban wild things: a cosmopolitical experiment, *Environment and Planning D: Society and Space,* **23**(5), 643–58.

Hinchliffe, S.J. (2007) *Geographies of Nature,* London, Sage.

Hindess, B. and Hirst, P. (1975) *Pre-Capitalist Modes of Production,* Routledge & Kegan Paul, London.

Hinrichs, C.C. (2000) Embeddedness and local food systems: notes on two types of direct agricultural market, *Journal of Rural Studies,* **16**, 295–303.

Hinrichs, C. (2014) Transitions to sustainability: a change in thinking about food systems change?, *Agriculture & Human Values,* **31**(1), 143–55.

Hirschmann, A.O. (1958) *The Strategy of Economic Development*, Yale University Press, New Haven, CT.

Ho, E. (2008) Citizenship, migration and transnationalism: a review and critical interventions, *Geography Compass*, 2, 1286–300.

Hobsbawm, E. (1995), *The Age of Extremes: The Short Twentieth Century, 1914–1991*, Abacus, London.

Hobsbawm, E.J. (1996) Ethnicity and nationalism in Europe today, in Balakrishnan, G. (ed.) *Mapping the Nation*, Verso, London, 255–66.

Hochschild, A.R. (1983) *The Managed Heart: Commercialization of Human Feeling*, University of California Press, London.

Hodge, J. and Haltrecht, J. (2009) *BedZED Seven Years On: The Impact of the UK's Best Known Eco-village and its Residents*, Bioregional, London.

Hoggart, K., Lees, L. and Davies, A. (2002) *Researching Human Geography*, Arnold, London.

Hoggart, R. (1957) *The Uses of Literacy: Aspects of Working Class Life*, Chatto and Windus, London.

Holdar, S. (1992) The ideal state and the power of geography: the life-work of Rudolf Kjellen, *Political Geography*, 11, 307–23.

Holloway, S.L. (2005) Articulating otherness? White rural residents talk about gypsy-travellers, *Transactions of the Institute of British Geographer*, NS, 30, 351–67.

Holloway, S. and Valentine, G. (eds) (2000) *Children's Geographies: Playing, Living, Learning*, Routledge, London.

Holmberg, T. (2005) Questioning 'the number of the beast': Constructions of humanness in a Human Genome Project (HGP) narrative, *Science as Culture*, 14, 23–37.

Homburger, E. (1994) *The Historical Atlas of New York City*, Henry Holt, New York.

Hoogevelt, A. (1997) *Globalisation and Postcolonialism*, Macmillan, London.

hooks, b. (1984) *Feminist Theory: From Margins to Centre*, South End Press, Boston, MA.

Hopma, J. and Woods, M. (2014) Political geographies of 'food security' and 'food sovereignty', *Geography Compass*, 8(11), 773–84.

Horton, J. and Kraftl, P. (2014) *Cultural Geographies. An Introduction*, Routledge, London.

House of Commons Environment, Food and Rural Affairs Committee (2009) *Securing Food Supplies up to 2050: The Challenges Faced by the UK*, Fourth Report of Session 2009–09, Vol. 1, House of Commons, London.

Howell, R.A. (2012) Living with a carbon allowance: the experiences of Carbon Rationing Action Groups and implications for policy, *Energy Policy*, 41, 250–8.

Howell, R.A. (2013) It's *not* (just) 'the environment, stupid!' Values, motivations, and routes to engagement of people adopting lower-carbon lifestyles, *Global Environmental Change*, 23(1), 281–90.

Hoyt, H. (1939) *The Structure and Growth of Residential Neighbourhoods in American Cities*, Federal Housing Administration, Washington, DC.

Hsu, J-Y. and Saxenian, A. (2000) The limits of guanxi capitalism: transnational collaboration between Taiwan and the USA, *Environment and Planning A*, 32, 1991–2005.

Hubbard, P. (1999) *Sex and the City: Geographies of Prostitution in the Urban West*, London, Ashgate.

Hubbard, P. (2006) *City*, Routledge, London.

Hubbard, P. (2008) Regulating the social impacts of studentification: a Loughborough case study, *Environment and Planning A*, 40(2), 323–41.

Hubbard, P. (2009) Geographies of studentification and purpose-built student accommodation: leading separate lives?, *Environment and Planning A*, 41, 1903–23.

Hubbard, P. (2012) *Cities and Sexualities*, Routledge, London.

Hubbard, P. (2013) Kissing is not a universal right: sexuality, law and the scales of citizenship, *Geoforum*, 49, 224–32.

Hubbard, P. (2016) *Contested Cities: Class, Gentrification and the Battle for the High Street*, Palgrave, Basingstoke.

Hudson, R. (2004) Conceptualising geographies and their economies: spaces, flows and circuits, *Progress in Human Geography*, 28(4), 447–71.

Hughes, A. (2000) Retailers, knowledges and changing commodity networks: the case of the cut flower trade, *Geoforum*, 31, 175–90.

Hughes, A. (2005) Corporate strategy and the management of ethical trade: the case of the UK food and clothing retailers, *Environment and Planning A*, 37(7), 1145–63.

Hughes, A. (2007) Supermarkets and the ethical/fair trade movement: making space for alternatives in mainstream economies?, in Burch, D. and Lawrence, G. (eds) *Supermarkets and Agri-food Supply Chains*, Edward Elgar, Cheltenham.

Hughes, A. and Reimer, S. (eds) (2004) *Geographies of Commodity Chains*, Routledge, London.

Hughes, B. (2010) *Too Many Of Whom and Too Much Of What? What the New Population Hysteria Tells us About the Global Economic and Environmental Crisis, and its Causes*, A No One Is Illegal discussion paper, www.noii.org.uk/2010/01/13/too-many-of-whomand-too-much-of-what/.

Hughes, C. (2011) Reclassifying Chinese nationalism: the geopolitik turn, *Journal of Contemporary China*, 20(71), 601–20.

Hugo, G. (2007) Population geography, *Progress in Human Geography*, 31(1), 77–88.

Hulme, M. (2004) A change in the weather? Coming to terms with climate change, in Harris, F. (ed.) *Global Environmental Issues*, John Wiley and Sons, Chichester, 21–44.

Hulme, M. (2009) *Why We Disagree About Climate Change: Understanding Controversy, Inaction and Opportunity*, Cambridge University Press, Cambridge.

Humphrey, J. (2007) Forty years of development research: transformations and reformations, *IDS Bulletin*, 38, 14–19.

Huntington, S.P. (1993) The clash of civilizations? *Foreign Affairs*, 72, 22–49.

Hutnyk, J. (1997) Adorno at Womad: South Asian crossovers and the limits of hybridity-talk, in Werbner, P. and Modood, T. (eds) *Debating Cultural Hybridity: Multi-cultural Identities and the Politics of Anti-racism*, Zed, London, 106–36.

Hutton, D. and Connors, L. (1999) *A History of the Australian Environment Movement,* Cambridge University Press, Melbourne.

Hyde, F.E. (1973), *Far Eastern Trade: 1860–1914,* Adam and Charles Black, London.

Hyndman, J. (2003) Beyond either/or: a feminist analysis of September 11th, *ACME: An International E-Journal for Critical Geographies,* **2**, 1–13, www.acme-journal.org.

Hyndman, J. (2007) Feminist geopolitics revisited: body counts in Iraq, *The Professional Geographer,* **59**, 35–46.

Hyndman, J. (2010) The question of 'the political' in critical geopolitics: querying the 'child soldier' in the 'war on terror', *Political Geography,* **29**, 247–56.

I

IEA (International Energy Agency) (2006) *World Energy Outlook 2006,* OECD/IEA, Paris.

IEA (International Energy Agency) (2014) *World Energy Outlook 2014,* IEA, Paris.

IEA, UNDP and UNIDO (2010) *Energy Poverty: How to Make Modern Energy Access Universal?,* OECD/IEA, Paris.

Iizuka, M. and Katz, J. (2015) Globalisation, sustainability and the role of institutions: the case of the Chilean salmon industry, *Tijdschrift voor Economische en Sociale Geografie,* **106**(2), 140–53.

Ilbery, B. and Maye, D. (2005) Alternative (shorter) food supply chains and specialist livestock products in the Scottish–English borders, *Environment and Planning A,* **37**, 823–44.

Ilbery, B. and Maye, D. (2010) Agricultural restructuring and changing food networks in the UK, in Coe, N. and Jones, A. (eds) *Reading the Economy: The UK in the 21st Century,* Sage, London, 166–80.

Illeris, S. (2007) The nature of services, in Bryson, J.R. and Daniels, P.W. (eds) *The Handbook of Service Industries,* Edward Elgar, Cheltenham.

Immergluck, D. (2009) *Foreclose: High-risk Lending, Deregulation, and the Undermining of America's Mortgage Market,* Cornell University Press, Ithaca, NY.

Ince, A., Featherstone, D., Cumbers, A., MacKinnon, D. and Strauss, K. (2015) British jobs for British workers? Negotiating work, nation, and globalization through the Lindsay oil refinery disputes, *Antipode,* **47**(1), 139–57.

Ingilby (2002) Are animals gay? Available at: www.funtrivia.com/ubbthreads/showthreaded.php?Cat=0&Number=34605&page=6.

Ingram, A. (2001) Alexander Dugin: geopolitics and neofascism in post-Soviet Russia, *Political Geography,* **20**(8), 1029–51.

International Assessment of Agricultural Knowledge, Science and Technology for Development (AASTD) (2009) *International Assessment of Agricultural Knowledge, Science and Technology for Development,* Executive Summary of the Synthesis Report, Island Press.

International Communications Union (2014) *Yearbook of Statistics: Telecommunications/ICT Indicators, 2004-2013,* ITU, Paris, www.internetworldstats.com/stats.htm [accessed 12 December 2014].

International Council for Local Environmental Initiatives (2002) *Second Local Agenda 21 Survey.* Published as UN Dept of Economic and Social Affairs, Background Paper 15 for the 2nd Preparatory Conference for the World Summit on Sustainable Development, DESA/DSD/PC2/BP15, www.iclei.org/rioplusten/finalrdocument.pdf.

International Monetary Fund (IMF) (2013) *World Economic Outlook,* IMF, Washington, DC.

IPCC (2013) *Climate Change 2013: The Physical Science Basis,* WMO/UNEP, Geneva.

IPCC (2014) *Climate Change 2014 Synthesis Report: Summary for Policymakers,* IPCC, Geneva.

Irwin, W. (1996) *The New Niagara: Tourism, Technology, and the Landscape of Niagara Falls, 1776–1917,* Pennsylvania State University, College Park, PA.

Isin, E. (2002) Citizenship after orientalism, in Isin, E. and Turner, B. (eds) *Handbook of Citizenship Studies,* Sage, London, 117–28.

Isin, E. (2005) Citizenship after orientalism: Ottoman citizenship, in Keyman, F. and Icduygu, A. (eds) *Challenges to Citizenship in a Globalising World,* Routledge, London, 31–52.

Isin, E. (2008) Theorising acts of citizenship, in Isin, E. and Nielson, G. (eds) *Acts of Citizenship,* Zed Books, London, 15–43.

Isin, E. (2012) *Citizens Without Frontiers: Inaugural Lecture,* www.oecumene.eu/files/oecumene/Enginpercent20Isinpercent20Inauguralpercent207percent20Februarypercent202012.pdf [accessed 12 September 2012].

ITU see International Telecommunications Union.

J

Jackson, P. (1999) Commodity culture: the traffic in things, *Transactions of the Institute of British Geographers, NS,* **24**, 95–108.

Jackson, P. (2002) Commercial cultures: transcending the cultural and the economic, *Progress in Human Geography,* **26**, 3–18.

Jackson, P. (2004) Local consumption cultures in a globalizing world, *Transactions of the Institute of British Geographers,* **29**(2), 165–78.

Jackson, P. (2010a) Food stories: consumption in an age of anxiety, *Cultural Geographies,* **17**, 147–65.

Jackson, P. (2010b) Citizenship and the geographies of everyday life, *Geography,* **95**, 139–40.

Jackson, P. and Taylor, J. (1996) Geography and the cultural politics of advertising, *Progress in Human Geography,* **19**, 356–71.

Jackson, P., Dwyer, C. and Thomas, N. (2007) Consuming transnational fashion in London and Mumbai, *Geoforum,* **38**(5), 908–24.

Jackson, R. (1993) *Quasi-States: Sovereignty, International Relations and the Third World,* Cambridge University Press, Cambridge.

James, A. (2007) Everyday effects, practices and causal mechanisms of 'cultural embeddedness': learning from Utah's high tech regional economy, *Geoforum,* **38**, 393–413.

Jarosz, L. (2009) Energy, climate change, meat, and markets: mapping the coordinates of the current world food crisis, *Geography Compass,* 3(6), 2065–83.

Jessop, B. (2002) *The Future of the Capitalist State,* Polity Press, Cambridge.

Jeswani, H.K., Wehrmeyer, W. and Mulugetta, Y. (2008) How warm is the corporate response to climate change? Evidence from Pakistan and the UK, *Business Strategy and the Environment,* 18, 46–60.

Jiang, R. (2004) *Lang Tu Teng* [Wolf Totem], Changjiang Wenyi Chubanshe, Wuhan.

Joffé, G. (1987) Frontiers in North Africa, in Blake, G.H. and Schofield, R.N. (eds) *Boundaries and State Territory in the Middle East and North Africa,* MENAS Press, Berkhamsted.

Johnson, L. (2010) The fearful symmetry of Arctic climate change: accumulation by degradation, *Environment and Planning D: Society and Space,* 28, 828–47.

Johnson, N. (2003) *Ireland, the Great War and the Geography of Remembrance,* Cambridge University Press, Cambridge.

Johnson, W. (2013) *River of Dark Dreams: Slavery and Empire in the Cotton Kingdom,* Harvard University Press, Cambridge, OH.

Johnston, J. (2011) Creating human geography in the English-speaking world, in Agnew, J. and Duncan, J. (eds) *The Wiley-Blackwell Companion to Human Geography,* Wiley Blackwell, Oxford, 89–113.

Johnston, R. (2005) Anglo-American electoral geography: same roots and same goals, but different means and ends?, *Professional Geography,* 57, 580–7.

Johnston, R. (2007) Commentary: on duplicitous battle-ground conspiracies, *Transactions of the Institute of British Geographers,* 32, 435–8.

Johnston, R., Poulsen, M. and Forrest, J. (2015) Increasing diversity within increasing diversity: the changing ethnic composition of London's neighbourhoods, 2001–2011, *Population, Space and Place,* 21(1), 38–53.

Johnston, R.J. and Sidaway J.D. (2015) *Geography and Geographers: Anglo-American Human Geography since 1945,* 7th edition, Arnold, London.

Jones, A. (2014). Geographies of production, I: relationality revisited and the 'practice shift' in economic geography. *Progress in Human Geography,* 38(4), 605–15.

Jones, D.S. (2006) ASEAN and transboundary haze pollution in southeast Asia, *Asia-Europe Journal,* 4, 431–46.

Jones, G. and Hollier, G. (1997) *Resources, Society and Environmental Management,* Paul Chapman, London.

Jones, H. (1990) *Population Geography,* 2nd edition, Paul Chapman, London.

Jones, M., Jones, R. and Woods, M. (2004) *An Introduction to Political Geography: Space, Place and Politics,* Routledge, London.

Jones, M., Jones, R., Woods, M., Whitehead, M., Dixon, D. and Hannah, M. (2015) *An Introduction to Political Geography: Space, Place and Politics,* 2nd edition, Routledge, London.

Jones, O. (2012) *Chavs: The Demonization of the Working Class,* Verso, London.

Jones, R. (2007) *People/States/Territories: The Political Geographies of British State Formation,* Blackwell, Oxford.

Jonsson, A-K. and Nilsson, A. (2014) Exploring the relationship between values and pro-environmental behaviour: the influence of locus of control, *Environmental Values,* 23, 297–314.

Journal of Rural Studies (2009) De-centring White Ruralities: Ethnicity and Indigeneity, special issue of *Journal of Rural Studies,* 25(4).

Jurgens, U. and Gnad, M. (2002) Gated communities in South Africa: experiences from Johannesburg, *Environment and Planning B: Planning and Design,* 29, 337–53.

Justice, C. (2012) *The Death of Outsourcing,* KPMG International, Houston, TX.

K

Kadercan, B. (2015) Triangulating territory: a case for pragmatic interaction between political science, political geography, and critical IR, *International Theory,* 7(1), 125–61.

Kapferer, B. (1988) *Legends of People, Myths of State: Violence, Intolerance and Political Culture in Sri Lanka and Australia,* Smithsonian Institution Press, Washington, DC.

Kaplan, M. (2007) Fijian water in Fiji and New York: local politics and a global commodity, *Cultural Anthropology,* 22, 685–706.

Kaplinsky, R. (2005) *Globalization, Poverty and Inequality,* Polity Press, Cambridge.

Kay, C. (2001) Reflections on rural violence in Latin America, *Third World Quarterly,* 22, 5.

Kay, C. (2008) Reflections on Latin American rural studies in the neoliberal globalization period: a new rurality?, *Development and Change,* 39(6), 915–43.

Kaye, H.J. (1984) *The British Marxist Historians,* Polity Press, Cambridge.

Kean, R. (2001) Appendix: Hong Kong chronology, *CitizenshipStudies,* 5(2), 221–32.

Kearns, A. and Mason, P. (2013) Defining and measuring displacement: is relocation from restructured neighbourhoods always unwelcome and disruptive?, *Housing Studies* 28(2) 177–204.

Keay, J. (1993) *The Honourable Company: A History of the English East India Company,* Harper Collins, London.

Keister, J. (2013) Political dysfunction in the Philippines is hurting Haiyan's victims, *The Washington Post,* 15 November.

Keivani, R. and Werna, E. (2001) Refocusing the housing debate in developing countries from a pluralist perspective, *Habitat International,* 25(2), 191–208.

Kelleher, W. and Cook, I. (2014a) Cries for help found in Primark clothes (a.k.a. 'labelgate'), *followthethings.com,* www.followthethings.com/primarkcriesforhelp.shtml [accessed 12 March 2015].

Kelleher, W. and Cook, I. (2014b) The letter in the Saks Fifth Avenue shopping bag, *followthethings.com,* www.followthethings.com/saksbagletter.shtml [accessed 12 March 2015].

Kelly, P. (1984) *Fighting for Hope,* Chatto and Windus, London.

Kelly, P. (1997) *Checkerboards and Shatterbelts: The Geopolitics of South America,* University of Texas Press, Austin.

Kenna, T. and Dunn, K. (2009) The virtuous discourse of private communities, *Geography Compass,* 3(2), 797– 816.

Kennedy, J.F. (1962) Commencement address to Yale University, 11 June, New Haven, Connecticut.

Kershaw, I. (2000) *The Nazi Dictatorship: Problems and Perspectives of Interpretation,* 4th edition, Arnold, London.

Kessler, J. and Appelbaum, R. (1998) The growing power of retailers in producer-driven commodity chains: a 'retail revolution' in the US automobile industry?, unpublished manuscript, Department of Sociology, University of California at Santa Barbara, CA.

Keyes, C.F. (1995) *The Golden Peninsula: Culture and Adaptation in Mainland Southeast Asia,* University of Hawaii Press, Honolulu.

Kim, Y.-H. (2008) Global-local, in Hall, T., Hubbard, P. and Short, J.R. (eds) *The Sage Companion to the City,* Sage, London, 123–37.

Kinzer, S. (2006) *Overthrow: America's Century of Regime Change from Hawaii to Iraq,* Times Books, New York.

Kipling, R. (1912) *Rudyard Kipling's Verse: Definitive Edition,* Hodder & Stoughton, London.

Kirwan, J. (2006) The interpersonal world of direct marketing: examining conventions of quality at UK farmers' markets, *Journal of Rural Studies,* 22, 301–12.

Kirwan, J., Ilbery, B., Maye, D. and Carey, J. (2013) Grassroots social innovations and food localisation: an investigation of the Local Food programme in England, *Global Environmental Change,* 23, 830–7.

Kjaer, A. (2004) *Governance: A Key Concept,* Sage, London.

Klare, M. (2002) *Resource Wars: The New Landscape of Global Conflict,* Henry Holt and Company LLC, New York.

Klare, M. (2004) *Blood and Oil: How America's Thirst for Petrol is Killing Us,* Penguin, London.

Klare, M. (2008) *Rising Powers, Shrinking Planet,* Metropolitan Books, New York.

Klein, N. (2000) *No Logo: Taking Aim at the Brand Bullies,* Flamingo, New York and London.

Klein, N. (2001) *No Logo: No Space, No Choice, No Jobs,* Flamingo, London.

Klein, N. (2007) *The Shock Doctrine: The Rise of Disaster Capitalism,* Metropolitan Books, New York.

Klein, N. (2014) *This Changes Everything,* Allen Lane, London.

Kleingeld, P. (2004) Approaching perpetual peace: Kant's defence of a League of States and his ideal of a World Federation, *European Journal of Philosophy,* 12, 304–25.

Kleinhans, R. (2003) Displaced but still moving upwards in the housing career? Implications of forced residential relocation in the Netherlands, *Housing Studies* 18(4) 473–99.

Kleveman, L. (2003) *The New Great Game: Blood and Oil in Central Asia,* Atlantic Books, London.

Klingmann, A. (2007) *Brandscapes: architecture in the experience economy,* MIT Press: Cambridge, MA.

Klopper, C. (2010) Intercultural musicianship: a collective and participatory form of music exchange across the globe, *Australian Journal of Music Education,* 1(1), 48–57.

Kneafsey, M., Holloway, L., Cox, R., Dowler, L., Venn, L. and Tuomainen, L. (2008) *Reconnecting Consumers, Producers and Food: Exploring Alternatives,* Berg Publishers, Oxford.

Knowles, A. K., Cole, T. and Giordano, A. (2014) *Geography of the Holocaust,* Indiana University Press, Bloomington, IL.

Knox, P. and Agnew, J. (1994) *The Geography of the World Economy,* 2nd edition, Edward Arnold, London.

Knox, P. and Agnew, J. (2004) *The Geography of the World Economy,* 4th edition, Edward Arnold, London.

Knox, P. and Pinch, S. (2010) *Urban Social Geography: An Introduction,* 6th edition, Pearson, Harlow.

Knox, P., Agnew, J. and McCarthy, L. (2014) *The Geography of the World Economy: An Introduction to Economic Geography,* 6th edition, Taylor and Francis, London.

Kobayashi, A. and Peake, L. (2000) Racism out of place: thoughts on whiteness and an antiracist geography in the new millennium, *Annals of the Association of American Geographers,* 90, 392–403.

Kondratieff, N.D. (1925) The major economic cycles, *Voprosy Konjunktury,* 6, 28–79; an English translation is to be found in *Lloyds Bank Review* (1978), 129, 41–60.

Kong, L. (2007) The promises and prospects of geography in higher education, *Journal of Geography in Higher Education,* 31(1), 13–7.

Korten, D.C. (1998) Your mortal enemy, *The Guardian,* 21 October, 4–5.

Koter, M. (1990) The morphological evolution of a nineteenth-century city centre: Lódz, Poland, 1825–1973, in Slater, T.R. (ed.) *The Built Form of Western Cities,* Leicester University Press, Leicester and London.

KPMG International (2012) *The Death of Outsourcing,* KPMG International, Houston, TX.

Kramsch, O. and Hooper, B. (2004) (eds) *Cross-Border Governance in the European Union,* Routledge, London.

Krippner, G. (2011) *Capitalizing on Crisis: The Political Origins of the Rise of Finance,* Harvard University Press Cambridge, MA.

Kwan, M.P. (2013) Beyond space (as we knew it): toward temporally integrated geographies of segregation, health, and accessibility: space–time integration in geography and GIScience, *Annals of the Association of American Geographers,* 103(5), 1078–86.

L

Landes, D.S. (1969) *The Unbound Prometheus,* Cambridge University Press, Cambridge.

Landman (2010) Gated minds, gated places: the impact and meaning of hard boundaries in South Africa, in Bagaeen, S. and Uduku, O. (eds) (2010) *Gated Communities: Social Sustainability and Historical Gated Developments,* Earthscan, London, 49–61.

Langley, P. (2003) *The Everyday Life of Global Finance,* International Political Economy Group Working Paper No. 5, University of Manchester, Manchester.

Langton, J. (1984) The industrial revolution and the regional geography of England, *Transactions of the Institute of British Geographers, NS,* **9**, 145–67.

Langton, J. and Morris, R.J. (eds) (1986) *Atlas of Industrializing Britain, 1780–1914,* Methuen, London and New York.

Langton, M. (1998) *Burning Questions: Emerging Environmental Issues for Indigenous Peoples in Northern Australia,* Centre for Indigenous Natural and Cultural Resource Management, Northern Territory University, Darwin.

Larner, W. (2003) Neoliberalism?, *Environment and Planning D: Society and Space,* **21**, 509–12.

Lash, S. and Urry, J. (1987) *The End of Organized Capitalism,* Polity Press, Cambridge.

Lash, S. and Urry, J. (1994) *Economies of Signs and Space,* Sage, London.

Latham, A. (2008) Cities (2002): Ash Amin and Nigel Thrift, in Hubbard, P., Kitchin, R. and Valentine, G. (eds) *Key Texts in Human Geography,* London, Sage, 215–23.

Laurence, J. (1997) The poor of Britain are going hungry, *The Independent,* 11 June, 7.

Laurie, N., Dwyer, C., Holloway, S. and Smith, F. (1999) *Geographies of New Femininities,* Longman, Harlow.

Law, L. (2002) Defying disappearance: cosmopolitan public spaces in Hong Kong *Urban Studies,* **39**, 1625–45.

Lawler, S. (2005) Disgusted subjects: the making of middle-class identities, *The Sociological Review,* **53**(3), 429–46.

Lawrence, F. (2008) *Eat Your Heart Out,* Penguin, London.

Lawton, R. (1989) Introduction: aspects of the development and role of great cities in the Western world in the nineteenth century, in Lawton, R. (ed.) *The Rise and Fall of Great Cities,* Belhaven, London.

Laxton, P. (1986) Textiles, in Langton, J. and Morris, R.J. (eds) *Atlas of Industrializing Britain, 1780–1914,* Methuen, London and New York, 106–13.

Le Billon, P. (2007) Geographies of war: perspectives on 'resource wars', *Geography Compass,* **1**(2), 163–82.

Le Billon, P. and El Khatib, F. (2004) From free oil to 'freedom oil': terrorism, war and US geopolitics in the Persian Gulf, *Geopolitics,* **9**, 109–37.

Le Heron, R.B. (1993) *Globalised Agriculture,* Pergamon Press, London.

Lee, R. (2000) Radical and postmodern? Power, social relations and regimes of truth in the social construction of alternative economic geographies, *Environment and Planning A,* **32**, 991–1009.

Lee, R. (2003) The demographic transition: three centuries of fundamental change, *Journal of Economic Perspectives,* **17**, 167–90.

Lee, R. (2006) The ordinary economy: tangled up in values and geography, *Transactions of the Institute of British Geographers, NS,* **31**, 413–32.

Lee, R.B. (1968) What hunters do for a living, or how to make out on scarce resources, in Lee, R.B. and DeVore, I. (eds) *Man the Hunter,* Aldine Press, Chicago, IL, 30–48.

Lees, L. (2008) Gentrification and social mixing: towards an inclusive urban renaissance?, *Urban Studies,* **45**, 2449–70.

Lees, L. (2014) The urban injustices of New Labour's 'New Urban Renewal': the case of the Aylesbury Estate in London, *Antipode,* **46**(4), 921–47.

Lees, L., Slater, T. and Wyly, E. (2013) *Gentrification,* Routledge, London.

Lei, G. (2005) Realpolitik nationalism: International sources of Chinese nationalism, *Modern China,* **31**(4), 487–514.

Leicht, K.T. and Fennell, M.L. (1997) The changing organizational context of professional work, *Annual Review of Sociology,* **23**, 215–31.

Leitner, H., Pavlik, C. and Sheppard, E. (2002) Networks, governance and the politics of scale: inter-urban networks and the European Union, in Herod, A. and Wright, M. (eds) *Geographies of Power: Placing Scale,* Blackwell Publishing, Malden, MA, 274–303.

Lemanski, C. and Oldfield, S. (2009) The parallel claims of gated communities and land invasions in a southern city: polarised state responses, *Environment and Planning,* **41**(3), 634–48.

Lemon, J.T. (1987) Colonial America in the eighteenth century, in Mitchell, R.D. and Groves, P.A. (eds) *North America: The Historical Geography of a Changing Continent,* Hutchinson, London.

Lester, A. (1999) Historical geographies of imperialism, in Graham, B. and Nash, C. (eds) *Modern Historical Geographies,* Prentice Hall, Harlow.

Lester, A. (2002) Obtaining the 'due observance of justice': the geographies of colonial humanitarianism, *Environment and Planning D: Society and Space,* **20**, 277–93.

Levinson, M. (2013), *Job Creation in the Manufacturing Revival* (7–5700), Congressional Research Service, Washington DC.

Levy, F. and Murnane, R.J. (2004) *The New Division of Labour: How Computers are Creating the Next Job Market,* Princeton University Press, Princeton, NJ.

Lewin, A.Y. and Peeters, C. (2006) Offshoring work: business hype or the onset of fundamental transformation?, *Long Range Planning,* **39**, 221–39.

Lewis, G. (1990) Community through exclusion and illusion: the creating of social worlds in an American shopping mall, *Journal of Popular Culture,* **24**, 121–36.

Lewis, M. (1990) *Liar's Poker: Rising Through the Wreckage on Wall Street,* Penguin Books, London.

Lewis, T. and Potter, E. (eds) (2011) *Ethical Consumption: A Critical Introduction,* Routledge, London.

Lewontin, R. (1993) *Biology as Ideology: The Doctrine of DNA,* Harper Perennial, New York.

Ley, D. and Olds, K. (1999) World's fairs and the culture of consumption in the contemporary city, in Anderson, K. and Gale, F. (eds), *Cultural Geographies,* 2nd edition, Longman, Sydney, 221–40.

Leyshon, A. (1995) Annihilating space? The speed up of communications, in Allen, J. and Hamnett, C. (eds) *A Shrinking World?,* Oxford University Press, Oxford.

Leyshon, A. and Thrift, N. (1994) Access to financial services and financial infrastructural withdrawal: problems and policies, *Area,* **26,** 268–75.

Leyshon, A. and Thrift, N. (1997) *Money Space: Geographies of Monetary Transformation,* Routledge, London.

Leyshon, M. (2008) The betweenness of being a rural youth: inclusive and exclusive lifestyles, *Social and Cultural Geography,* 9(1), 1–26.

Li, X. (ed.) (2010) *The Rise of China and the Capitalist World Order,* Ashgate, Surrey.

Lien, M. (2000) Imagined cuisines: nation and market as organizing structures in Norwegian food marketing, in Jackson, P., Lowe, M., Miller, D. and Mort, F. (eds) *Commercial Cultures: Economies, Practices, Spaces,* Berg, Oxford, 153–73.

Lister, R. (2003) *Citizenship: Feminist Perspectives,* 2nd edition, Palgrave, Basingstoke.

Little, J. (2002) Rural geography: rural gender identity and the performance of masculinity and femininity in the countryside, *Progress in Human Geography,* **26**(5), 665–70.

Little, J. and Leyshon, M. (2003) Embodied rural geographies: developing research agendas, *Progress in Human Geography,* **27**(3), 257–72.

Little, R., Maye, D. and Ilbery, B. (2010) Collective purchase: loving local and organic foods beyond the niche market, *Environment and Planning A,* **42,** 1797–813.

Littler, J. (2008) *Radical Consumption: Shopping for Change in Contemporary Culture,* Open University Press, Maidenhead.

Livingston, D. (2011) Teleshopping AK-47, followthethings.com, www.followthethings.com/teleshopping.shtml [accessed 12 March 2015].

Livingstone, D. (1992) *The Geographical Tradition: Issues in the History of a Contested Enterprise,* Blackwell, Oxford.

Liu, X. (2015) Take the new Silk Road as an opportunity not a threat, *Financial Times,* 10 May, 9.

Logan, J.R. (2013) The persistence of segregation in the 21st century metropolis, *City & Community,* **12**(2), 160–8.

Logan, J.R. and Stults, B.J. (2011) *The Persistence of Segregation in the Metropolis: New Findings from the 2010 Census,* US2010 Project Report, www.s4.brown.edu/us2010/Data/Report/report2.pdf.

Lowenthal, D. (1994) European and English landscapes as national symbols, in Hooson, D. (ed.) *Geography and National Identity,* Blackwell, Oxford, 15–38.

Ludden, (2003) Presidential address: maps in the mind and the mobility of Asia, *The Journal of Asian Studies,* **62**(4), 1057–78.

Luttwak, E. (1990) From geopolitics to geoeconomics, *National Interest,* **20,** 17–24.

Luttwak, E. (2012) *The Rise of China vs. the Logic of Strategy,* Belknap Press, USA.

Lutz, W., Goujon, A., Samir, K.C. and Sanderson, W. (2007) *Vienna Yearbook of Population Research 2007,* OAW, Wien, www.oeaw.ac.at/vid/publications/VYPR2007/VYPR2007.shtml [accessed 2 May 2015].

M

Macdonald, C.L. and Sirianni, C. (1996) *Working in the Service Economy,* Temple University Press, Philadelphia.

MacKian, S. (1995) 'That great dust-heap called history': recovering the multiple spaces of citizenship, *Political Geography,* **14,** 209–16.

Mackinder, H. (1904) The geographical pivot of history, *Geographical Journal,* **23,** 421–44.

Mackinder, H. (1919) *Democratic Ideals and Reality: A Study in the Politics of Reconstruction,* Constable, London.

Mackinnon, D. and Cumbers, A. (2011) *Introduction to Economic Geography: Uneven Development, Globalization and Place,* 2nd edition, Pearson, London.

Macnaghten, P. and Urry, J. (1998) *Contested Natures,* Sage, London.

Madge, C. (2014a) Living through, living with and living on: creative cathartic methodologies, cancerous spaces and a politics of compassion, *Social and Cultural Geography,* doi: 10.1080/14649365.2014.990498.

Madge, C. (2014b) On the creative re(turn) to geography: poetry, politics and passion, *Area,* **46**(2), 178–85.

Maffesoli, M. (1996) *The Time of the Tribes: The Decline of Individualism in Mass Society,* translated by Don Smith, Sage, London.

Maguire, E.R., Burgoine, T. and Monsivais, P. (2015) Area deprivation and the food environment over time: a repeated cross-sectional study on takeaway outlet density and supermarket presence in Norfolk, UK, 1990–2008, *Health & Place,* doi:10.1016/j.healthplace.2015.02.012.

Mahajan, S. (ed.) (2005) *Input–Output Analysis: 2005,* Office for National Statistics, London.

Mahon, R. (1987) From Fordism to?: new technology, labour markets and unions, *Economic and Industrial Democracy,* **8,** 5–60.

Maisels, C.K. (1993) *The Emergence of Civilization,* Routledge, London.

Maitland, B. (1985) *Shopping Malls, Planning and Design,* Construction Press, London.

Malbon, B. (1997) Clubbing, consumption, identity and the spatial practices of every-night life, in Skelton, T. and Valentine, G. (eds) *Cool Places,* Routledge, London, 266–86.

Malbon, B. (1999) *Clubbing,* Routledge, London.

Malone, A. and Jones, R. (2010) Revealed: inside the Chinese suicide sweatshop where workers toil in 34-hour shifts to make your iPod, *The Daily Mail,* 11 June, www.dailymail.co.uk/news/article-1285980/Revealed-Inside-Chinese-suicide-sweatshop-workers-toil-34-hour-shifts-make-iPod.html [accessed 4 August 2010].

Malthus, T. (1798) *Essay on the Principle of Population,* J. Johnson, London.

Mann, C.C. (2011) *1493: How Europe's Discovery of the Americas Revolutionized Trade, Ecology and Life on Earth,* Granta, London.

Mann, P. (1965) *An Approach to Urban Sociology,* Routledge, London.

Marcuse, H. (1964) *One-Dimensional Man,* Abacus, London.

Markit (2011) *Markit/CIPS UK Manufacturing PMI™,* www.markit.com, 4 January.

Markusen, A. (2006) Urban development and the politics of a creative class: evidence from a study of artists, *Environment and planning A,* 38(10), 1921.

Marquez, P. (2005) *Dying Too Young: Addressing Premature Mortality and Ill Health Due to Non-Communicable Diseases and Injuries in the Russian Federation,* The World Bank, Europe and Central Asia Human Development Department.

Marsden, T., Banks, J. and Bristow, G. (2000) Food supply chain approaches: exploring their role in rural development, *Sociologia Ruralis,* 40, 424–38.

Marsh, D.C. (1977) *The Changing Structure of England and Wales: 1871–1961,* Routledge and Kegan Paul, London.

Marsh, G.P. (1869) *Man and Nature; or, Physical Geography as Modified by Human Action,* C. Scribner & Co., New York.

Marshall, G. (2007) *Carbon Detox: Your Step-by-step Guide to Getting Real About Climate Change,* Gaia Books, London.

Marshall, T. (1950[1992]) Citizenship and social class, in Marshall, T. and Bottomore, T. (eds) *Citizenship and Social Class,* Pluto, London, 3–54.

Marston, S.A., Liverman, D.M., Del Casino, V. and Robbins, P. (2011) *World Regions in Global Context: People, Places and Environments,* 4th edition, Prentice Hall, Upper Saddle River, NJ.

Marston, S.A., Knox, P., Liverman, D., Del Casino, V. and Robbins, P. (2013) *World Regions in Global Context: People, Places, and Environments,* 5th edition, Prentice Hall, Upper Saddle River, NJ.

Martin, A. (2007) Trouble in China is good news for American Toy Manufacturers, *New York Times,* 15 August.

Martin, L.L. and Mitchelson, M.L. (2009) Geographies of detention and imprisonment: Interrogating spatial practices of confinement, discipline, law, and state power, *Geography Compass,* 3(1), 459–77.

Martin, R. (2010) The local geographies of the financial crisis: from the housing bubble to economic recession and beyond, *Journal of Economic Geography,* 11(4), 587–618.

Martin, R.L. (1994) Stateless monies, global financial integration and national economic autonomy: the end of geography?, in Corbridge, S., Martin, R. and Thrift, N. (eds) *Money, Power and Space,* Blackwell, Oxford, 253–78.

Martin, R.L. (1999a) The new 'geographical turn' in economics: some critical reflections, *Cambridge Journal of Economics,* 23, 65–91.

Martin, R.L. (1999b) The new economic geography of money, in Martin, R.L. (ed.) *Money and the Space Economy,* Wiley, Chichester, 3–27.

Martin, R.L. (ed.) (1999c) *Money and the Space Economy,* Wiley, Chichester.

Martínez, M. (1997) *Olivenza y el tratado de Alcañices,* Ayuntamiento de Olivenza.

Marx, K. (1867) *Das Kapital;* translated into English as *Capital,* 3 vols, International Publishers, New York (1967) and Penguin, London (1976).

Marx, K. (1973) *Gründrisse: Foundations of the Critique of Political Economy,* Penguin, London.

Massey, D. (1984) *Spatial Division of Labour: Social Structures and the Geography of Production,* Macmillan, London.

Massey, D. (1993) Power-geometry and a progressive sense of place, in Bird, J., Curtis, B., Putnam, T., Robertson, G. and Tickner, L. (eds) *Mapping the Futures: Local Cultures, Global Change,* Routledge, London, 59–69.

Massey, D. (1994) *Space, Place and Gender,* Polity, Cambridge.

Massey, D. (2009) Concepts of space and power in theory and in political practice, *Documents d'Anàlisi Geogràfica,* 55, 15–26.

Massey, D. and Jess, P. (eds) (1995a), *A Place in the World? Places, Cultures and Globalization,* Oxford University Press, Oxford.

Massey, D. and Jess, P. (1995b) The contestation of place, in Massey, D. and Jess, P. (eds) *A Place in the World? Places, Cultures and Globalization,* Oxford University Press, Oxford, 133–74.

Mather, A.S. and Chapman, K. (1995) *Environmental Resources,* Longman, London.

Mattelart, A. (1979) *Multinational Corporations and the Control of Culture,* Harvester Press, Brighton.

Mawby, R.I. and Yarwood, R. (eds) (2011) *Rural Policing and Policing the Rural: A Constable Countryside?,* Ashgate, Farnham.

Mawdsley, E. (2012) *From Recipients to Donors: Emerging powers and the Changing Development Landscape,* Zed Books, London.

Maye, D. and Ilbery, B. (2006) Regional economies of local food production: tracing food chain links between 'specialist' producers and intermediaries in the Scottish-English borders, *European Urban and Regional Studies,* 13(4), 337–54.

Maye, D. and Kirwan, J. (2010) Alternative food networks, sociology of agriculture and food, entry for *Sociopedia.isa,* Sage, London.

Maye, D. and Kirwan, J. (2013) Food security: a fractured consensus, *Journal of Rural Studies,* 29(1), 1–6.

Maye, D., Holloway, L. and Kneafsey, M. (eds) (2007) *Alternative Food Geographies: Representation and Practice,* Elsevier, Oxford.

McCall, C. (2014) Scars of typhoon Haiyan still run deep 1 year on, *The Lancet,* 384, 1656–7.

McCarthy, C., Rodriguez, A., Buendia, E., Meacham, S., David, S., Godina, H., Supriya, K. and Wilson-Brown, C. (1997) Danger in the safety zone: notes on race, resentment and the discourse of crime violence and suburban security, *Cultural Studies,* 11, 274–95.

McCarthy, J. (2005) Rural geography: multifunctional rural geographies – reactionary or radical?, *Progress in Human Geography,* 29, 773–82.

McCarthy, J. (2006) Rural geography: alternative rural economies: the search for alterity in forests, fisheries, food, and fair trade, *Progress in Human Geography*, **30**(6), 803–11.

McCarthy, S. (1999) The fabulous kingdom of gay animals, available at www.salon.com/it/feature/1999/03/cov_15featurea.html [accessed 18 December 2006].

McClintock, A. (1994) *Imperial Leather: Race, Gender and Sexuality in the Colonial Context*, Routledge, London.

McConnell, F. (2010) The fallacy and the promise of the territorial trap: sovereign articulations of geopolitical anomalies, *Geopolitics*, **15**(4), 762–8.

McCormick, J. (1989) *The Global Environmental Movement*, Belhaven Press, London.

McCormick, J. (1991) *British Politics and the Environment*, Earthscan, London.

McDonald, D.A. (2002) What is environmental justice?, in McDonald, D.A. (ed.) *Environmental Justice in South Africa*, Ohio University Press, Athens, OH, 1–12.

McDowell, L. (1999) *Gender, Identity and Place: Understanding Feminist Geographies*, Polity Press, Cambridge.

McDowell, L. (2007) Gender divisions of labour: sex, gender, sexuality and embodiment in the service sector, in Bryson, J. R. and Daniels, P. W. (eds) *The Handbook of Services*, Edward Elgar, Cheltenham, 395–408.

McDowell, L. (2009) *Working Bodies: Interactive Service Employment and Workplace Identities*, Wiley-Blackwell, Chichester.

McEwan, C. (2005) New spaces of citizenship? Rethinking gendered participation and empowerment in South Africa, *Political Geography*, **24**, 969–91.

McGuigan, J. (2009) *Cool Capitalism*, Pluto Press, London.

McGuinness, M. (2000) Geography matters? Whiteness and contemporary geography, *Area*, **32**, 225–30.

McIntosh, L. and D. Maddox (2008) Salmond fury at 'bunch of spivs' behind bank crisis, *News.Scotsman.com*, http://news.scotsman.com/latestnews/Salmond-fury-at-39bunch-of.4503240.jp [accessed 26 October 2010].

McIver, J. (1997) Environmental protection, indigenous rights and the Arctic Council: rock, paper, scissors on the ice?, *The Georgetown International Environmental Law Review*, **10**, 147–68.

McKeon, B. (2010) Apple's rotten core, *Irish Times*, 12 June, www.irishtimes.com/newspaper/weekend/2010/0612/1224272334457.html [accessed 5 August 2010].

McKibben, B. (1999) *The End of Nature*, Random House, New York.

McMahon, R.J. (2001) Introduction: the challenge of the Third World, in Hahn, P.L. and Heiss, M.A. (eds) (2001) *Empire and Revolution: The United States and the Third World since 1945*, Ohio State University Press, Columbus, OH, 1–16.

McMichael, P. (2009) A food regime analysis of the 'world food crisis', *Agriculture and Human Values*, **26**, 281–95.

McNeill, J. (2000) *Something New Under the Sun: An Environmental History of the Twentieth Century*, Penguin Books, London.

Meadows, D. H., Meadows, D. I., Randers, J. and Behrens III, W. W. (1972) *The Limits to Growth: A Report to the Club of Rome*, Universe Books, New York.

Mearsheimer, J. (2010) The gathering storm: China's challenge to US power in Asia, *Chinese Journal of International Politics*, **3**(4), 381–96.

Megoran, N. (2006) For ethnography in political geography: experiencing and re-imagining Ferghana Valley boundary closures, *Political Geography*, **26**(10), 622–40.

Megoran, N. and Sharapova, S. (eds) (2012) *Halford Mackinder and the International Relations of Central Asia*, Hurst, London.

Meinig, D. W. (1986) *The Shaping of America. A Geographical Perspective on 500 Years of History: Atlantic America, 1492–1800*, Yale University Press, New Haven and London.

Merchant, C. (2005) *Radical Ecology*, 2nd edition, Routledge, London.

Meyer, D. R. (1990) The new industrial order, in Conzen, M. P. (ed.) *The Making of the American Landscape*, Unwin Hyman, London and Winchester, MA.

Michaelis, L. (2007) Consumption behavior and narratives about the good life, in Moser, S.C. and Dilling, L. (eds) *Creating a Climate for Change: Communicating Climate Change and Facilitating Social Change*, Cambridge University Press, New York, 251–65.

Michaud, J. (2009) Handling mountain minorities in China, Vietnam and Laos: from history to current concerns, *Asian Ethnicity*, **10**(1), 25–49.

Michaud, J. (2010) Editorial – Zomia and beyond, *Journal of Global History*, **5**, 187–214.

Middleton, N. (2003) *The Global Casino: An Introduction to Environmental Issues*, 3rd edition, Arnold, London.

Miles, D. (2006) *The Tribes of Britain*, Phoenix, London.

Miller, D. (1995) Consumption as the vanguard of history, a polemic by way of an introduction, in Miller, D. (ed.) *Acknowledging Consumption: A Review of New Studies*, Routledge, London, 1–57.

Miller, D. (1997) Coca-Cola, a black sweet drink from Trinidad, in Miller, D. (ed.) *Material Cultures*, UCL Press, London.

Miller, D. (1998) *A Theory of Shopping*, Polity, Cambridge.

Miller, D. (2001) The poverty of morality, *Journal of Consumer Culture*, **1**(2), 225–43.

Miller, D. (2010) Why clothing is not superficial, in *Stuff*, Polity Press, Cambridge, 12–41.

Miller, D. (2011) *Tales from Facebook*, Polity, Cambridge.

Miller, D. and Woodward, S. (eds) (2010) *Global Denim*, Berg, Oxford.

Miller, J.C. (2014) Malls without stores (MwS): the affectual spaces of a Buenos Aires shopping mall, *Transactions of the Institute of British Geographers, NS*, **39**, 14–25.

Miller, R. (2013) Save our state: a decade of writing on jurisdiction and sovereignty in east and west Asia, *International Journal of Middle East Studies*, **45**(1), 149–60.

Milligan, C. and Fyfe, N.R. (2005) Preserving space for volunteers: exploring the links between voluntary welfare organisations, volunteering and citizenship, *Urban Studies*, **42**, 417–33.

Millington, A. C., Mutiso, S. K., Kirkby, J. and O'Keefe, P. (1989) African soil erosion: nature undone and the limitations of technology, *Land Degradation and Rehabilitation*, 1, 279–90.

Mills, S. (2013) 'An instruction in good citizenship': scouting and the historical geographies of citizenship education, *Transactions of the Institute of British Geographers*, 38, 120–34.

Millstone, E. and Lang, T. (2008) *The Atlas of Food*, 2nd edition, Earthscan, London.

Mintel (2004) *Nightclubs*, Mintel Market Intelligence, London.

Mintel (2006) *Nightclubs*, Mintel Market Intelligence, London.

Mitchell, D. (1996) Public space and the city, *Urban Geography*, 17, 127–31.

Mitchell, D. (2000) *Cultural Geography: A Critical Introduction*, Blackwell, Oxford.

Mitchell, D. (2005) The S.U.V. model of citizenship: floating bubbles, buffer zones, and the rise of the 'purely atomic' individual, *Political Geography*, 24(1), 77–100.

Mitchell, J.B. (ed.) (1962) *Great Britain: Geographical Essays*, Cambridge University Press, Cambridge.

Mitchell, R.D. and Groves, P.A. (eds) (1987) *North America: The Historical Geography of a Changing Continent*, Hutchinson, London.

Mitchell, W.C. (1937) *The Backward Art of Spending Money and Other Essays*, McGraw-Hill, New York.

Mohan, J. (2000) Geographies of welfare and social exclusion, *Progress in Human Geography*, 24, 291–300.

Mohan, J. (2003) Voluntarism, municipalism and welfare: the geography of hospital utilization in England in 1938, *Transactions of the Institute of British Geographers*, 28, 56–74.

Monrreal, S. (2008) A novel, spicy delicacy: tamales, advertising and late nineteenth century imaginative geographies of Mexico, *Cultural Geographies*, 15, 449–70.

Mooney, P.H. and Hunt, S.A. (2009) Food security: the elaboration of contested claims to a consensus frame, *Rural Sociology*, 74, 469–97.

Moore, M. (2010) Factory suicides force China to rethink ethos, *Daily Telegraph*, 26 May.

Moore, R.I. (ed.) (1981) *The Hamlyn Historical Atlas*, Hamlyn, London and New York.

Moran, D. (2004) Exile in the Soviet forest: 'special settlers' in northern Perm Oblast, *Journal of Historical Geography*, 30, 395–413.

Moran, D. (2015) *Carceral Geography: Spaces and Practices of Incarceration*, Ashgate, Aldershot.

Moretti, E. (2013) *The New Geography of Jobs*, Mariner Books, Boston, MA.

Morgan, K. and Sonnino, R. (2010) The urban foodscape: world cities and the new food equation, *Cambridge Journal of Regions, Economy and Society*, 3, 209–24.

Morgan, K., Marsden, T. and Murdoch, J. (2006) *Worlds of Food: Place, Power and Provenance in the Food Chain*, Oxford University Press, Oxford.

Morley, D. (2000) *Home Territories: Media, Mobility and Identity*, Routledge, London.

Morris, C. and Kirwan, J. (2010) Food commodities, geographical knowledges and the reconnection of production and consumption: the case of naturally embedded food products, *Geoforum*, 41, 131–43.

Morris, C., Kirwan, J. and Lally, R. (2014) Less meat initiatives: an initial exploration of a diet-focused social innovation in transitions to a more sustainable regime of meat provisioning, *International Journal of Sociology of Agriculture and Food*, 21(2), 189–208.

Morris-Suzuki, T. (1996) The frontiers of Japanese identity, in Tønnesson, S. and Antlöv, H. (eds) *Asian Forms of the Nation*, Curzon, Richmond, 41–66.

Mountjoy, A.B. (1976) Worlds without end, *Third World Quarterly*, 2, 753–7.

Mountz, A. (2009) Border, in Gallaher, C., Dahlman, C.T., Gilmartin, M., Mountz, A. and Shirlow, P. (eds) *Key Concepts in Political Geography*, Sage, London, 198–209.

Moyo, D. (2009) *Dead Aid: Why Aid Is Not Working and How There Is a Better Way for Africa*, Allen Lane, London.

Mukherjee, A. (2008) The audio-visual sector in India, in Barrowclough, D. and Kozul-Wright, Z. (eds) *Creative Industries and Developing Countries*, Routledge, London.

Mukherjee, R. and Banet-Weiser, S. (eds) (2012) *Commodity Activism*, NYU Press, New York.

Murdoch, J. (2006) *Post-structuralist Geography: A Guide to Relational Space*, Sage, London.

Murphy, A.B. (2012) Entente territorial: Sack and Raffestin on territoriality, *Environment and Planning D: Society and Space*, 30(1), 159–72.

Murphy, A.B. (2013) Territory's continuing allure, *Annals of the Association of American Geographers*, 103(5), 1212–26.

Murray, W.E. (2006) Neo-feudalism in Latin America? Globalisation, agribusiness, and land re-concentration in Chile, *Journal of Peasant Studies*, 33, 646–77.

Murray, W.E. (2008) Neoliberalism, rural geography and the global south, *Human Geography*, 1(1), 33–8.

Murray, W.E. and Overton, J. (2014) *Geographies of Globalization*, 2nd edition, Routledge, New York and London.

Murray, W.E. and Overton, J. (2015) Retroliberalism and the new aid regime of the 2010s, *Progress in Development Studies*, forthcoming.

Murray, W.E. and Terry, J.P. (2004) Niue's place in the Pacific, in Terry, J.P. and Murray, W.E. (eds) *Niue Island: Geography on the Rock of Polynesia*, INSULA, UNESCO, Paris.

Mutersbaugh, T. (2005) Fighting standards with standards: harmonization, rents, and social accountability in certified agrofood networks, *Environment and Planning A*, 37, 2033–51.

N

Naess, A. (1973) The shallow and the deep: long-range ecological movement, *Inquiry*, 16, 95–100.

Nagel, C. (2002) Geopolitics by another name: immigration and the politics of assimilation, *Political Geography*, 21, 971–87.

Narlikar, A. (2013) India rising: responsible to whom?, *International Affairs*, **89**(3), 595–614.

Nash, C.J. (2013) Queering neighbourhoods: politics and practice in Toronto, *ACME* **12**(9), 193–219.

National Research Council (2000) *Beyond Six Billion: Forecasting the World's Population*, National Academy Press, Washington, DC.

National Statistics Online (NSO) (2004) *Family Expenditure Survey*, HMSO, London.

Natter, W. (2003) Geopolitics in Germany 1919–1945, in Agnew, J., Mitchell, K. and Toal, G. (eds) *A Companion to Political Geography*, Blackwell, Oxford, 197–203.

Nature (2010) How to feed a hungry world (Editorial), *Nature*, **466**, 531–2.

Nava, M., Blake, A., MacRury, I. and Richards, B. (eds) (1997) *Buy This Book: Studies in Advertising and Consumption*, Routledge, London.

Navaro-Yashin, Y. (2005) Confinement and imagination: sovereignty and subjectivity in a quasi-state, in Hansen, T.B. and Stepputat, F. (eds) *Sovereign Bodies: Citizens, Migrants and States in a Postcolonial World*, Princeton University Press, Princeton, 103–19.

Navaro-Yashin, Y. (2012) *The Make-Believe Space: Affective Geography in a Post-War Polity*, Duke University Press, Durham and London.

Nayak, A. (2006) Displaced masculinities: chavs, youth and class in the post-industrial city, *Sociology*, **40**(5), 813–31.

Nayak, A. and Jeffrey A. (2011) *Geographical Thought: An Introduction to Ideas in Human Geography*, Pearson Education, Harlow.

Neilson, J. and Pritchard, B. (2009) *Value Chain Struggles: Institutions and Governance in the Plantation Districts of South India*, Wiley-Blackwell, Oxford.

Nellemann, C., MacDevette, M., Manders, T. *et al.* (eds) (2009) *The Environmental Food Crisis – The Environment's Role in Averting Future Food Crises: A UNEP Rapid Response Assessment*, United Nations Environment Programme, Arendal, Norway.

Nelson, L. and Seager, J. (2004) *A Companion to Feminist Geography*, Blackwell, Oxford.

Newman, P., Beatley, T. and Boyer, H. (2009) *Resilient Cities: Responding to Peak Oil and Climate Change*, Island Press, Washington, DC.

Nguyen, H.T. (2003) The 2002 Declaration on the Conduct of Parties in the South China Sea: a note, *Ocean Development and International Law*, **34**, 279–85.

Nguyen Dang, T. (2013) Cooperation in the South China Sea: from dispute management to ocean governance, http://nghiencuubiendong.vn/en/conferences-and-seminars-/hoi-thao-quoc-te-4/782-cooperation-in-the-south-china-sea-from-dispute-management-to-ocean-governance-by-nguyen-dang-thang [accessed 20 December 2014].

Nixon, S. (1997) Circulating culture, in du Gay P (ed.) *Production of Culture/Cultures of Production*, Sage, London, 177–234.

Nord, M., Andrews, M. and Carlson, S. (2009) *Household Food Security in the United States, 2008*, Economic Research Report 83, United States Department of Agriculture, Economic Research Service, Washington DC, www.ers.usda.gov/Publications/ERR83/ERR83.pdf.

Nostrand, R.L. (1987) The Spanish borderlands, in Mitchell, R. D. and Groves, P. A. (eds) *North America: The Historical Geography of a Changing Continent*, Hutchinson, London.

Nurhidayah, L., Lipman, Z. and Alam, S. (2014) Regional environmental governance: an evaluation of the ASEAN legal framework for addressing transboundary haze pollution, *Australian Journal of Asian Law*, **15**, Article 6.

Nuttall, M. (2008) Climate change and the warming politics of autonomy, *Indigenous Affairs*, **1**, 44–51.

O

Ó Gráda, C. (2007) Making famine history, *Journal of Economic Literature*, **45**(1), 5–38.

Ó Tuathail, G. (1996a) *Critical Geopolitics: The Politics of Writing Global Space*, Routledge, London.

Ó Tuathail, G. (1996b) An anti-geopolitical eye: Maggie O'Kane in Bosnia, 1992–3, *Gender, Place and Culture*, **3**(2), 177–85.

Ó Tuathail, G. (1998) Postmodern geopolitics? The modern geopolitical imagination and beyond, in Ó Tuathail, G. and Dalby, S. (eds) *Rethinking Geopolitics*, Routledge, London, 16–38.

Ó Tuathail, G and Dahlman, C. (2006) 'The West Bank of the Drina': land allocation and ethnic engineering in Republika Srpska, *Transactions: Institute of British Geographers*, **95**, 644–62.

O'Brien, R. (1992) *Global Financial Integration: The End of Geography*, Royal Institute of International Affairs, Pinter Publishers, London.

O'Connor, A. (1976) Third World or one world, *Area*, **8**, 269–71.

O'Hara, M. (2014) *Austerity Bites, A Journey to the Sharp End of Cuts in the UK*, Policy Press, Bristol.

O'Loughlin, J. and van der Wusten, H. (1990) Political geography and panregions, *Geographical Review*, **80**, 1–20.

O'Loughlin, J., Kolossov, V. and Toal, G. (2011) Inside Abkhazia: survey of attitudes in a *de facto* state, *Post-Soviet Affairs*, **27**(1), 1–36.

O'Loughlin, J., Toal, G. and Kolossov, V. (2005) Russian geopolitical culture and public opinion: the masks of Porteus revisited, *Transactions of the Institute of British Geographers*, **30**(3), 322–35.

O'Reilly, K. and Crutcher, M.E. (2006) Parallel politics: the spatial power of New Orleans Labor Day parades, *Social and Cultural Geography*, **7**(2), 245–65.

O'Riain, S. (2004) The politics of mobility in technology driven commodity chains: developmental coalitions in the Irish software industry, *International Journal of Urban and Regional Research*, **28**, 642–63.

O'Riordan, T. (ed.) (2000) *Environmental Science for Environmental Management*, 3rd edition, Prentice Hall, Harlow.

Oakeshott, I. and Gourlay, C. (2006) Science told: hands off gay sheep, *Sunday Times*, London.

Obama, B. (2014) Remarks by the President on the Ebola Outbreak, www.whitehouse.gov/the-press-office/2014/09/16/remarks-president-ebola-outbreak [accessed 20 December 2014] .

Odell, P.R. (1989) Draining the world of energy, in Johnston, R.J and Taylor, P.J. (eds) *A World in Crisis?*, 2nd edition, Blackwell, Oxford.

OECD *see* Organization for Economic Co-operation Development

Ogborn, M. (1999) Historical geographies of globalisation, *c.* 1500–1800, in Graham, B. and Nash, C. (eds) *Modern Historical Geographies*, Prentice Hall, Harlow.

Ohnuki-Tierney, E. (1997) McDonald's in Japan: changing manners and etiquette, in Watson, J. L. (ed.) *Golden Arches East: McDonald's in East Asia*, Stanford University Press, Stanford, CA, 161–82.

Olli, E., Grendstad, G. and Wollebaek, D. (2001) Correlates of environmental behaviors: bringing back social context, *Environment and Behavior*, 33, 181–208.

Ong, A. (1999) *Flexible Citizenship: The Cultural Logics of Transnationality*, Duke University Press, Durham, NC.

Oppenheimer, S. (2012) *The Origins of the British: the New Prehistory of Britain*, Robinson, London.

Organization for Economic Co-operation and Development (OECD) (2005) *Potential Offshoring of ICT-intensive Using Occupations*, Working Party on the Information Economy, DSTA/ICC/IE(2004)19, OECD, Paris.

Organization for Economic Cooperation and Development (OECD) (2009) *OECD in Figures 2009*, OECD, Paris.

Organization for Economic Co-operation and Development (OECD) (2014a) Development aid rises but not for sub-Saharan Africa, *OECD Observer*, www.oecdobserver.org/news/fullstory.php/aid/4351/Development_aid_rises,_but_not_for_sub-Saharan_Africa.html.

Organization for Economic Co-operation and Development (OECD) (2014b) *Short Term Labour Market Statistics, 2014*, OECD, Paris, http://stats.oecd.org/index.aspx?queryid=38899\# [accessed 25 January 2015].

Organization for Economic Co-operation and Development/IEA (2014) *Key World Energy Statistics 2014*, OECD/IEA, Paris.

Osofsky, H. (2006/2007) The Inuit petition as a bridge? Beyond dialectics of climate change and indigenous people's rights, *American Indian Law Review*, 31, 675–97.

Oswalt, P. (ed.) (2004) *Schrumpfende Städte. Band 1: Internationale Untersuchung*, Hantje Cantz, Ostfildern-Ruit.

Overton, J. and Murray, W.E. (2011) Playing the scales: regional transformations and the differentiation of rural space in the Chilean wine industry, *Journal of Rural Studies*, 27(1), 63–72.

Overton, J. and Murray, W.E. (2014) Sovereignty for sale? Coping with marginality in the South Pacific – the example of Niue, *Hrvatski Geograkski Glasnik (Croatian Geographical Bulletin)*, 76(1), 5–25.

Overton, J. and Murray, W.E. (2016) Fictive place, *Progress in Human Geography*, forthcoming.

P

Paasche, T. and Sidaway J.D. (2015) Transecting security and space in Kurdistan, Iraq, *Environment and Planning A*, in press.

Paasche, T.F., Yarwood, R. and Sidaway, J.D. (2014) Territorial tactics: the socio-spatial significance of private policing strategies in Cape Town, *Urban Studies*, 51(8), 1559–75.

Paasi, A. (2003) Region and place: regional identity in question, *Progress in Human Geography*, 27, 475–85.

Paasi, A. (2009) The resurgence of the 'region' and 'regional identity': theoretical perspectives and empirical observations on regional dynamics in Europe, *Review of International Studies*, 35, 121–46.

Pacione, M. (2009) *Urban Geography: A Global Perspective*, 3rd edition, Routledge, London.

Packard, V. (1977) *The Hidden Persuaders*, Penguin, Harmondsworth.

Paddison, R. (2001) Studying cities, in Paddison, R. (ed.) *Handbook of Urban Studies*, London, Sage, 1–9.

Pain, R. (2009) Globalized fear? Towards an emotional geopolitics, *Progress in Human Geography*, 33(4), 466–86.

Pain, R. (2014) Everyday terrorism: Connecting domestic violence and global terrorism, *Progress in Human Geography*, 38(4), 531–50.

Pain, R. and Smith, S.J. (eds) (2008) *Fear: Critical Geopolitics and Everyday Life*, Ashgate, Aldershot.

Painter, J. (2002) Multilevel citizenship, identity and regions in contemporary Europe, in Anderson, J. (ed.) *Transnational Democracy: Political Spaces and Border Crossings*, Routledge, London, 93–110.

Painter, J. (2006) Prosaic geographies of stateness, *Political Geography*, 25, 752–74.

Painter, J. (2010) Rethinking territory, *Antipode*, 42(5), 1098–118.

Painter, J. and Jeffrey, A. (2009), *Political Geography*, 2nd edition, Sage, London.

Painter, J. and Philo, C. (1995) Spaces of citizenship: an introduction, *Political Geography*, 14, 107–20.

Pallot, J. (2005) Russia's penal peripheries: space, place and penalty in Soviet and post-Soviet Russia, *Transactions of the Institute of British Geographers*, 30(1), 98–112.

Pani, E. and Holman, N. (2013) A fetish and fiction of finance: unraveling the subprime crisis abstract?, *Economic Geography*, 90, 213–35.

Pantazis, C., Gordon, D. and Levitas, R.A. (eds) (2006) *Poverty and Social Exclusion in Britain: The Millennium Survey*, Policy Press, Bristol.

Park, C. (1994) *Sacred Worlds: An Introduction to Geography and Religion*, Routledge, London.

Parker, A. (2004) *Two-Speed Europe: Why 1 Million Jobs will Move Offshore*, Forrester Research, Cambridge, MA.

Parker, G. (1999) The role of the consumer-citizen in environmental protest in the 1990s, *Space and Polity*, 3, 67–83.

Parkin, J. (2013) B'eau Pal Water, followthethings.com, www.followthethings.com/beaupal.shtml [accessed 12 March 2015].

Parks, B.C. and Roberts, J.T. (2008) Inequality and the global climate regime: breaking the north–south impasse, *Cambridge Review of International Affairs*, **21**(4), 621–48.

Parrott, N., Wilson, N. and Murdoch, J. (2002) Spatializing quality: regional protection and the alternative geography of food, *European Urban and Regional Studies*, **9**, 241–61.

Patel, R. (2000) Urban violence: an overview, in Miles, M., Hall, T. and Borden, I. (eds) *The City Cultures Reader*, Routledge, London, 261–5.

Peach, C. (1996) Does Britain have ghettos?, *Transactions of the Institute of British Geographers*, **21**, 216–35.

Peach, W.N. and Constantin, J.A. (1972) *Zimmerman's World Resources and Industries,* 3rd edition, Harper & Row, London.

Pearce, F. (2003) Saving the world, plan B, *The New Scientist*, 13 December, 6–7.

Peck, J. (2004) Geography and public policy: constructions of neoliberalism, *Progress in Human Geography,* **28**, 392–405.

Peck, J. (2005) Struggling with the creative class, *International Journal of Urban and Regional Research*, **29**(4), 740–70.

Peck, J. (2012) Austerity urbanism: American cities under extreme economy, *Cities*, **16**(6), 626–55.

Peet, R. with Hartwick, E. (1999) *Theories of Development,* Guilford Press, London.

Pegg, S. (1998) *International Society and the De Facto State*, Ashgate, Aldershot.

Penrose, J. (2002) Nations, states and homelands: territory and territoriality in nationalist thought, *Nations and Nationalism,* **8**, 277–97.

Perkins, J.H. (1997) *Geopolitics and the Green Revolution: Wheat, Genes and the Cold War*, Oxford University Press, Oxford.

Peters, G.P., Minx, J.C., Weber, C.L. and Edenhofer, O. (2011) Growth in emission transfers via International trade from 1990 to 2008, *PNAS*, **108**(21), 8903–8.

Peterson Del Mar, D. (2012) *Environmentalism,* 2nd edition, Routledge, Abingdon.

Petty, W. (2004)[1678] *Essays on Mankind and Political Arithmetic,* Kessinger Publishing, Whitefish, MT.

Pfaff, J. (2010) Mobile phone geographies, *Geography Compass*, **4**(10), 1433–77.

Phillips, D. (2006) Parallel lives? Challenging discourses of British Muslim self-segregation in multicultural Britain, *Environment and Planning D: Society and Space,* **24**, 25–40.

Phillips, M. (2002) Distant bodies? Rural studies, political economy and post-structuralism, *Sociologia Ruralis,* **42**(2), 81–105.

Phillips, T. (2005) *After 7/7: Sleepwalking to Segregation,* website of Commission of Racial Equality, London.

Philo, C. (2008) Introduction, in Phlio, C. (ed.) The*ory and Methods in Human Geography,* Ashgate, Aldershot, xiii–xlix.

Phyne, J. and Mansilla, J. (2003) Forging linkages in the commodity chain: the case of the Chilean salmon farming industry, 1987–2001, *Sociologia Ruralis,* **43**(2), 108–27.

Pickerill, J. (2008) From wilderness to WildCountry: the power of language in environmental campaigns in Australia, *Environmental Politics,* **17**(1), 93–102.

Pickles, J. (2004) *A History of Spaces: Cartographic Reason, Mapping and the Geo-coded World,* Routledge, London and New York.

Pieterse, J.N. (2011) Global rebalancing: crisis and the East–South turn, *Development and Change,* **42**, 22–48.

Pieterse, J.N. and Parekh, B. (eds) (1995) *Decolonization of the Imagination: Culture, Knowledge and Power,* St Martins Press, London.

Pike, A. (2009a) Geographies of brands and branding, *Progress in Human Geography,* **33**(5), 619–45.

Pike, A. (2009b) Brand and branding geographies, *Geography Compass,* **3**(1), 190–213.

Pike, A. (2011) Placing brands and branding: a socio-spatial biography of Newcastle Brown Ale, *Transactions of the Institute of British Geographers, NS,* **36**, 206–22.

Piketty, T (2014) *Capital in the Twenty-first Century,* Belknap Press, Cambridge, MA.

Pile, S. (1999) The heterogeneity of cities, in Pile, S., Brook, C. and Mooney, G. (eds) *Unruly Cities?: Order/Disorder,* Routledge, London, 7–52.

Pinch, S. (1994) Social polarization: a comparison of evidence from Britain and the United States, *Environment and Planning A,* **25**, 779–95.

Pinch, S. and Henry, N. (1999) Paul Krugman's geographical economics, industrial clustering and the British motor sport industry, *Regional Studies,* **33**, 815–27.

Pine, A. (2010) The performativity of urban citizenship, *Environment and Planning A,* **42**, 1103–20.

Pine, B.J. and Gilmore, J.H. (1999) *The Experience Economy: Work is Theatre and Every Business a Stage,* Harvard Business School Press, Cambridge, MA.

Pinstrup-Andersen, P. (2009) Food security: definition and measurement, *Food Security,* **1**(1), 5–7.

Pletsch, C. (1981) The three worlds or the division of social scientific labour 1950–1975, *Comparative Studies in Society and History,* **23**, 565–90.

Poguntke, T. (1993) Goodbye to movement politics? Organisational adaption of the German Green Party, *Environmental Poli*tics, **2**, 379–404.

Political Geography (2006) Geographies as Sexual Citizenship, special issue of *Political Geography,* **25**(8).

Pollard, J.S., Oldfield, J., Randalls, S.C. and Thornes, J.E. (2008) Firm finances, weather derivatives and geography, *Geoforum,* **39**(2), 616–24.

Pollock, F. (2003) *The League of Nations,* The Lawbook Exchange, New Jersey.

Ponte, S. (2002) The 'latte revolution'?: regulation, markets and consumption in the global coffee chain, *World Development,* **30**, 1099–122.

Pool, H. (2011) Incest, blackmail, murder – but no minorities in Midsomer, please, we're English, *The Guardian,* 15 March.

Popke, E.J. (2001) Modernity's abject space: the rise and fall of Durban's Cato Manor, *Environment and Planning A,* **33**, 737–52.

Population Division of the Department of Economic and Social Affairs of the United Nations Secretariat (2012) *World Population Prospects: The 2012 Revision,* United Nations, New York.

Population Institute (2011) *From 6 Billion to 7 Billion: How Population Growth is Changing and Challenging the World,* Population Institute, www.populationinstitute.org/external/files/reports/from-6b-to-7b.pdf [accessed 15 April 2015].

Population Reference Bureau (2007) *Human Population: Fundamentals of Growth: Future Growth,* www.prb.org/Educators/TeachersGuides/HumanPopulation/FutureGrowth/TeachersGuide.aspx?p=1.

Population Reference Bureau (2014) *2014 World Population Data Sheet,* www.prb.org/pdf14/2014-world-population-data-sheet_eng.pdf [accessed 5 June 2015].

Porritt, J. (2009) Perfect storm of environmental and economic collapse are closer than you think, *guardian.co.uk,* 23 March, www.guardian.co.uk/environment/2009/mar/23/jonathon-porritt-recession-climate-crisis [accessed 12 May 2011].

Porter, M.E. (1990) *The Competitive Advantage of Nations,* Free Press, New York.

Potter, R.B. (1979) Perception of urban retailing facilities: an analysis of consumer information fields, *Geografiska Annaler,* **61B,** 19–27.

Potter, R. and Lloyd-Evans, S. (1998) *The City in the Developing* World, Longman, Harlow.

Potter, R.B., Binns, T., Elliott, J.A. and Smith, D. (2008) *Geographies of Development,* 3rd edition, Pearson Education, Harlow.

Poulsen, M., Forrest, J. and Johnston, R. (2002) From modern to post-modern?: contemporary ethnic residential segregation in four US metropolitan areas, *Cities,* **19**(3), 161–72.

Pounds, N.J.F. (1947) *An Historical and Political Geography of Europe,* Harrap, London.

Pounds, N.J.G. (1990) *An Historical Geography of Europe,* Cambridge University Press, Cambridge.

Pow, C.-P. (2011) Living it up: super-rich enclave and transnational elite urbanism in Singapore, *Geoforum,* **42**(3), 382–93.

Powell, K. H. (2014) In the shadow of the ivory tower: an ethnographic study of neighborhood relations, *Qualitative Social Work,* **13**(1), 108–26.

Powell, R. (2008) Configuring an 'Arctic Commons?', *Political Geography,* **27,** 827–32.

Power, A. and Tunstall, R. (1997) *Dangerous Disorder: Riots and Violent Disturbances in Thirteen Areas of Britain, 1991–92,* Joseph Rowntree Foundation, York.

Power, M. (2003) *Rethinking Development Geographies,* Routledge, London.

Power, M. (2007) Digitized virtuosity: video war games and post 9/11 cyber-detterence, *Security Dialogue,* **38**(2), 271–88.

Power, M. (2015) The rise of the BRICS, in Agnew, J., Secor, A., Mamadouh, V. and Sharp, J. (eds) *The Wiley Blackwell Companion to Political Geography,* Wiley-Blackwell, Chichester, 379–92.

Price, P.L. (2010) At the crossroads: critical race theory and critical geographies of race, *Progress in Human Geography,* **34**(2), 147–74.

Priestley, J.B. (1937) *English Journey,* William Heinemann, London.

Pritchard, B. (1998) The emergent contours of the third food regime: evidence from Australian dairy and wheat sectors, *Economic Geography,* **74**(1), 64–74.

Pritchard, B. and Choithani, C. (2014) Hunger games: changing targets and the politics of global nutrition, *The Conversation,* 26 September, https://theconversation.com/hunger-games-changing-targets-and-the-politics-of-global-nutrition-32045.

Programme Evaluation Organization (2005) *Performance Evaluation of Targeted Public Distribution System,* Planning Commission, New Delhi.

Progress in Human Geography, **24**(1), Classics in Human Geography revisited, 91–9.

Pykett, J. (2009) Making citizens in the classroom: an urban geography of citizenship education?, *Urban Studies,* **46,** 803–23.

R

Raban, J. (1990) *Hunting Mr Heartache,* Collins Harvill, London.

Radcliffe, S.A. (2006) Culture in development thinking: geographies, actors, and paradigms, in Radcliffe, S.A. (ed.) *Culture and Development in a Globalizing World: Geographies, Actors and Paradigms,* Routledge, London, 1–29.

Radcliffe, S. and Westwood, S. (1996) *Remaking the Nation: Place, Identity and Politics in Latin America,* Routledge, London.

Radical Routes (2006) *How to Work Out Your Ecological Footprint,* www.radicalroutes.org.uk/pub.html.

Raffestin, C. (2012) Space, territory and territoriality, *Environment and Planning D: Society and Space,* **30**(1), 121–41.

Rahnema, R. (1997) Introduction, in Rahnema, R. and Bawtree, V. (eds) *The Post-Development Reader,* Zed Books, London.

Rajaram, P.K. and Grundy-Warr, C. (2007) *Borderscape: Hidden Geographies and Politics at Territory's Edge,* University of Minnesota Press, Minneapolis, MN.

Ram, P., Mohanty, S.K. and Ram, U. (2009) Understanding the distribution of BPL cards: all-India and selected states, *Economic and Political Weekly,* **44**(7), 66–71.

Rawcliffe, P. (1998) *Environmental Pressure Groups in Transition,* Manchester University Press, Manchester.

Reddish, A. and Rand, M. (1996) The environmental effects of present energy policies, in Blunden, J. and Reddish, A. (eds) *Energy, Resources and Environment,* Open University and Hodder & Stoughton, London, 43–91.

Rees, J. (1985) *Natural Resources: Allocation, Economics and Policy,* 2nd edition, Routledge, London.

Rees, J. (1991) Resources and environment: scarcity and sustainability, in Bennett, R. and Estall, R. (eds) *Global*

Change and Challenge: Geography in the 1990s, Routledge, London, 5–26.

Rees, P., Martin, D. and Williamson, P. (eds) (2002) *The Census Data System,* Wiley, Chichester.

Rees, W. and Wackernagel, M. (2008) Urban ecological footprints: why cities cannot be sustainable – and why they are a key to sustainability, *Urban Ecology,* **V,** 537–55.

Reeves, R. (1999) Do we really need gay florists?, *Observer,* 8 August.

Reid, A. and Zheng, Y. (eds) (2009) *Negotiating Asymmetry: China's Place in Asia,* NUS Press, Singapore.

Reid-Henry, S.M. (2007) Exceptional sovereignty? Guantanamo Bay and the re-colonial present, *Antipode,* **39**(4), 627–48.

Reid-Henry, S. (2010) The territorial trap fifteen years on, *Geopolitics,* **15**(4), 752–6.

REN21 (2015) *Renewables 2015 Global Status Report,* REN21 Secretariat, Paris.

Renner, M. (2002) The Anatomy of Resource Wars, Worldwatch Paper No. 162, Earthwatch Institute, Washington, DC.

Renting, H., Marsden, T.K. and Banks, J. (2003) Understanding alternative food networks: exploring the role of short food supply chains in rural development, *Environment and Planning A,* **35,** 393–411.

Renting, H., Schermer, M. and Rossi, A. (2012) Building food democracy: exploring civic food networks and newly emerging forms of food citizenship, *International Journal of Sociology of Agriculture & Food,* **19**(3), 289–307.

Rhodes, C. (2014) *Manufacturing: Statistics and Policy, Economic Policy and Statistics Section,* House of Commons Library, London.

Rice-Oxley, M. and Mahmood, M. (2014) Migrants' tales: 'I feel for those who were with me. They got asylum in the sea', *The Guardian,* 20 October, www.theguardian .com/world/2014/oct/20/-sp-migrants-tales-asylum-sea-mediterranean [accessed 15 May 2015].

Rippon, M. (2014) What is the geography of geographical indications? Place, production methods and protected food names, *Area,* **46**(2), 154–62.

Rist, G. (1997) *The History of Development,* Zed, London.

Ritzer, G. (2000) *The McDonaldisation of Society,* 2nd edition, Pine Forge Press, Thousand Oaks, CA.

Ritzer, G. (2004) *The Globalization of Nothing,* Pine Forge/ Sage, London.

Ritzer, G. and Jurgenson, N. (2010) Production, consumption, presumption: the nature of capitalism in the age of the digital prosumer, *Journal of Consumer Culture,* **10**(1), 13–36.

Robbins, P. (2004) *Political Ecology,* Blackwell, Oxford.

Robbins, P., Hinstz, J. and Moore, S.A. (2014) *Environment and Society,* 2nd edition, Wiley-Blackwell, Oxford.

Roberts, S., Secor, A. and Sparke, M. (2003) Neoliberal geopolitics, *Antipode,* **35,** 886–97.

Roberts, S., Secor, A. and Sparke, M. (2003) Neoliberal geopolitics, *Antipode,* **35,** 886–97.

Robinson, D. (2013) 'In' crowd shuns nightclubs, *Financial Times,* 9 June, www.ft.com/cms/s/0/8c90d5f0-cf8b-

11e2-a050-00144feab7de.html\#axzz3VbYkegvP [accessed 27 March 2015].

Robinson, G. (2004) *Geographies of Agriculture,* Pearson, London.

Robinson, G.M. and Pobric, A. (2006) Nationalism and identity in post-Dayton Accords: Bosnia-Hercegovina, *Tijdschrift voor Economische en Sociale Geografie,* **97**(3), 237–52.

Robinson, J. (1997) The geopolitics of South African cities: states, citizens, territory, *Political Geography,* **16,** 365–86.

Robinson, J. (2006) *Ordinary Cities: Between Modernity and Development,* Routledge, Abingdon.

Roche, M. (2002) Rural geography: searching rural geographies, *Progress in Human Geography,* **26**(6), 823–29.

Rogers, R. (1999) *Towards an Urban Renaissance, Final Report of the Urban Task Force,* chaired by Lord Rogers of Riverside, E. and Spon, F.N., London.

Rollins, W.H. (1995) Whose landscape? Technology, Fascism and environmentalism on the National Socialist Autobahn, *Annals of the Association of American Geographers,* **85,** 494–520.

Roouum, D. (1995) *What is Anarchism?: An Introduction,* Freedom Press, London.

Rose, N. (1996) The death of the social? Re-figuring the territory of government, *Economy and Society,* **25,** 327–56.

Rose, N. and Miller, P. (1992) Political power beyond the state: problematics of government, *British Journal of Sociology,* **43,** 173–205.

Rosen, G. and Razin, E. (2009) The rise of gated communities in Israel: reflections on changing urban governance in a neo-liberal era, *Urban Studies,* **46**(8), 1702–22.

Rosenberg, D. (2009) Fisheries management in the South China Sea, in Bateman, S. and Emmers, R. (eds) *Security and International Politics in the South China Sea: Towards a Cooperative Management Regime,* Routledge, London, 61–79.

Rose-Redwood, R. (2008), Governmentality, geography and the geo-coded world, *Progress in Human Geography,* **30,** 469–86.

Ross, M. (2001) *Extractive Sectors and the Poor: An Oxfam America Report,* Oxfam, www.oxfamamerica.org/cirexport/ index.html.

Rössler, M. (1989) Applied geography and area research in Nazi society: central place theory and planning, *Environment and Planning D: Society and Space,* 7, 419–31.

Rostow, W.W. (1960) *The Stages of Economic Growth: A Non-Communist Manifesto,* Cambridge University Press, Cambridge.

Rostow, W.W. (1971) *The Stages of Economic Growth,* 2nd edition, Cambridge University Press, Cambridge.

Round. J. (2012) Demographic transformations, in Daniels, P., Bradshaw, M., Shaw, D. and Sidaway, J. (eds) *An Introduction to Human Geography: Issues for the 21st Century,* Prentice Hall, London, 87–110.

Routledge, P. (2003) Convergence space: process geographies of grassroots globalization networks, *Transactions of the Institute of British Geographers,* **28,** 333–49.

Rowe, M. (2014), Alien views, *Geographical Magazine*, August, http://geographical.co.uk/nature/wildlife/item/219 [accessed 20 April 2015].

Rowell, A., Marriott, J. and Stockman, L. (2005) *The Next Gulf: London, Washington and Oil Conflict in Nigeria*, Constable, London.

Royal Society of Public Health (2015) *Health on the High Street*, RSPH, London.

Rusten, G., Bryson, J.R. and Aarflot, U. (2007) Places through product and products through places: industrial design and spatial symbols as sources of competitiveness, *Norwegian Journal of Geography*, 61(3), 133–44.

Rutledge, I. (2006) *Addicted to Oil: America's Relentless Drive for Energy Security*, I. B. Tarus, London.

S

Saarinen, J. (2007) Cultural tourism, local communities and representations of authenticity: the case of Lesedi and Swazi cultural villages in Southern Africa, in Wishitemi, B., Spenceley, A. and Wels, H. (eds) *Culture and Community: Tourism Studies in Eastern and Southern Africa*, Rozenberg, Amsterdam.

Sachs, J.D. and Warner, A. M. (2001) Natural resources and economic development: the curse of natural resources, *European Economic Review*, 45, 827–38.

Sachs, W. (1992) *The Development Dictionary*, Zed Books, London.

Sack, R. (1986) *Human Territoriality: Its Theory and History*, Cambridge University Press, Cambridge.

Sack, R. (1992) *Place, Modernity and the Consumers World*, Johns Hopkins University Press, Baltimore, MD.

SACOM (2010) Appeal by concerned *Internat*ional scholars: create human labour standards at Foxconn. *SACOM.hk* 8 June (http://sacom.hk/lang_hk/國際學者的呼籲-在富士康創建人道的勞工標準並/[accessed 12 March 2015].

Sage, C. (2003) Social embeddedness and relations of regard: alternative 'good food' networks in south-west Ireland, *Journal of Rural Studies*, 19, 47–60.

Sage, C. (2012) *Environment and Food*. Routledge, London.

Sage, C. (2013) The interconnected challenges for food security from a food regimes perspective: Energy, climate and malconsumption, *Journal of Rural Studies*, 29, 71–80.

Said, E. (1978) *Orientalism*, Vintage Books.

Sakwa, R. (1999) *The Rise and Fall of the Soviet Union, 1917–1991*, Routledge, London.

Sakwa, R. (2015a) *Frontline Ukraine: Crisis in the Borderlands*, I.B. Tauris, London.

Sakwa, R. (2015b) The death of Europe? Continental fates after Ukraine, *International Affairs*, 91(3), 553–79.

Saldanha, A. (2002) Music tourism and factions of bodies, *Tourist Studies*, 2(1), 43–62.

Saldanha, A. (2011) The concept of race, *Geography*, 96(1), 27–33.

Salway, P. (ed.) (1984) Roman Britain, in *Oxford History of England*, Oxford University Press, Oxford.

Samers, M. (2010) *Migration*, Routledge, London.

Samir, K.C., Barakat, B., Goujon, A., Sanderson, W.C. and Lutz, W. (2010) Projection of populations by level of educational attainment, age and sex for 120 countries for 2005–2050, *Demographic Research*, 22, 383–472.

Sandercock, L. (1998) *Towards Cosmopolis: Planning for Multicultural Cities*, Wiley, Chichester.

Sandercock, L. (2003) *Cosmopolis 2: Mongrel Cities of the 21st Century*, Continuum, London.

Sandercock, L. (2006) Cosmopolitan urbanism: a love song to our mongrel cities, in Binnie, J., Holloway, J., Millington, S. and Young, C. (eds) *Cosmopolitan Urbanism*, Routledge, Abingdon, 37–52.

Santos, M. (1974) Geography, Marxism and underdevelopment, *Antipode*, 6, 1–9.

Sassen, S. (1991) *The Global City: New York, London, Tokyo*, Princeton University Press, Princeton, NJ.

Sassen, S. (1994) *Cities in a World Economy*, Pine Forge Press, London.

Sassen, S. (2001) *The Global City: New York, London, Tokyo*, updated 2nd edition, Princeton University Press, Princeton, NJ.

Sassen, S. (2002) Towards post-national and denationalized citizenship, in Isin, E. and Turner, B. (eds) *Handbook of Citizenship Studies*, Sage, London, 277–93.

Sassen, S. (2006) *Territory, Authority, Rights: From Medieval to Global Assemblages*, Princeton University Press, Princeton, NJ.

Saunders, D. (2010) *Arrival City: How the Largest Migration in History is Reshaping Our World*, William Heinemann, London.

Savage, M., Warde, A. and Ward, K. (2003) *Urban Sociology, Capitalism and Modernity*, Palgrave, Basingstoke.

Saxenian, A. (2006) *The New Argonauts: Regional Advantage in a Global Economy*, Harvard University Press, Cambridge, MA.

Sayer, A. and Walker, R. (1992) *The New Social Economy: Reworking the Division of Labour*, Blackwell, Oxford.

Sbargia, A. (2000) The European Union as a coxswain: governance by steering, in Pierre, J. (ed.) *Debating Governance: Authority, Steering and Democracy*, Oxford University Press, Oxford, 219–40.

Schama, S. (1995) *Landscape and Memory*, HarperCollins, London.

Schneiders, L. (2006) Is wilderness racist? *Chain Reaction*, Autumn, 25–7.

Schofield, C. (2009) Dangerous ground: a geopolitical overview of the South China Sea, in Bateman, S. and Emmers, R. (eds) *Security and International Politics in the South China Sea: Towards a Cooperative Management Regime*, Routledge, London, 7–25.

Schofield, C. and Storey, I. (2011) *The South China Sea Dispute: Increasing Stakes and Rising Tensions*, The Jamestown Foundation, USA.

Schumpeter, J. (1939) *Business Cycles: A Theoretical, Historical and Statistical Analysis of the Capitalist Process*, McGraw-Hill, London.

Schumpeter, J.A. (1942) *Capitalism, Socialism and Democracy*, Harper, New York.

Schuurman, F.J. (2001) Globalization and development studies: introducing the challenges, in Schuurman, F.J. (ed.) *Globalization and Development: Challenges for the 21st Century,* Sage, London, 3–16.

Schuurman, N. (2004) *GIS: A Short Introduction,* Blackwell, Oxford.

Schweik, S.M. (2009) *The Ugly Laws: Disability in Public,* New York, NYU Press.

Scott, A. (2004) A perspective on economic geography, *Journal of Economic Geography,* **4,** 479–99.

Scott, A. and Soja, E. (eds) (1996) *The City: Los Angeles and Urban Theory at the End of the Twentieth Century,* University of California Press, Berkeley, CA.

Scott, J.C. (2008) 'Stilled to silence at 500 metres': making sense of historical change in Southeast Asia, *IIAS Newsletter,* number 49, Autumn, 12–13.

Scott, J.C. (2009) *The Art of Not Being Governed: An Anarchist History of Upland Southeast Asia,* Yale University Press, New Haven, CT.

Secor, A (2004) Feminizing electoral geographies, in Staeheli, L., Kofman, E. and Peake, L. (eds) *Mapping Women, Making Politics: Feminist Perspectives on Political Geography,* Routledge, Abingdon.

Seel, B. and Plows, A. (2000) Coming live and direct: strategies of Earth First! in Seel, B., Patterson, M. and Doherty, B. (eds) *Direct Action in British Environmentalism,* Routledge, London, 112–32.

Sen, A. (1981) *Poverty and Famines: An Essay on Entitlement and Deprivation,* Oxford University Press, Oxford.

Sennett, R. (1994) *Flesh and Stone: The Body And The City In Western Civilization,* Penguin, London.

Service, E.R. (1971) *Primitive Social Organization,* 2nd edition, Random House, New York.

Seyfang, G. and Smith, A. (2007) Grassroots innovation for sustainable development: towards a new research and policy agenda, *Environmental Politics,* 16(4), 584–603.

Shabi, R. (2002) The e-waste land, *The Guardian,* 30 November.

Shakespeare, T. (1994) Cultural representations of disability: dustbins for disavowal, *Disability and Society,* 9, 283–99.

Shaw, K. (2008) Gentrification: what it is, why it is, and what can be done about it, *Geography Compass,* **2**(5), 1697–728.

Shaw, T.M., Cooper, A.F. and Chin, G.T. (2009) Emerging powers and Africa: implications for/from global governance, *Politikon,* 36(1), 27–44.

Sheppard, E. (2002) The spaces and times of globalization: place, scale, networks and positionality, *Economic Geography,* 78(3), 307–30.

Sheppard, E. and Barnes, T.J. (eds) (2000) *A Companion to Economic Geography,* Blackwell, Oxford.

Sheppard, E. and Nagar, R. (2004) From east–west to north–south, *Antipode,* **36,** 557–63.

Sheppard, E. and Nagar, R. (2004) From east-west to north-south, *Antipode,* 36, 557–63.

Sherratt, A. (ed.) (1980) *The Cambridge Encyclopaedia of Archaeology,* Cambridge University Press, Cambridge.

Shevky, E. and Bell, W. (1955) *Social Area Analysis,* Stanford University Press, Stanford, CA.

Shields, R. (1991) *Places on the Margin,* London, Routledge.

Shilling, C. (1993) *The Body and Social Theory,* Sage, London.

Shirlow, P. and Murtagh, B. (2006) *Belfast: Segregation, Violence and the City,* Pluto Press, London.

Shiu-Hing, L. (2001) Citizenship and participation in Hong Kong, *Citizenship Studies,* 5(2), 127–42.

Shiva, V. (1991) The Green Revolution in the Punjab, *The Ecologist,* 21(2), 57–60.

Shiva, V. (2002) *Water Wars: Privatization, Pollution, and Profit,* Pluto Books, London.

Short, J.R. (1996) *The Urban Order: An Introduction to Cities, Culture and Power,* Blackwell, Oxford.

Short, J.R. (2004) *Global Metropolitan: Globalizing Cities in a Capitalist World,* Routledge, New York.

Short, J.R. (2006) *Imagined Country,* Syracuse University Press, Syracuse, NY.

Short, J.R., Kim, Y-H., Kuus, M. and Wells, H. (1996) The dirty little secret of world city research: data problems in comparative analysis, *International Journal of Urban and Regional Research,* 20(4), 697–719.

Shove, E. (2003) *Comfort, Cleanliness and Convenience: The Social Organization of Normality,* Berg, Oxford.

Shove, E. and Walker, G. (2014) What is energy for? Social practice and energy demand, *Theory, Culture and Society,* **31**(5), 41–58.

Shubin, S. (2010) 'Where can a gypsy stop?' Rethinking mobility in Scotland, *Antipode,* 42(5), 494–524.

Shubin, S. (2011) 'Where can a Gypsy stop?' Rethinking mobility in Scotland, *Antipode,* 42(5).

Shurmer-Smith, P. (ed.) (2002) *Doing Cultural Geography,* Sage, London.

Shurmer-Smith, P. and Hannam, K. (1994) *Worlds of Desire, Realms of Power: A Cultural Geography,* Arnold, London.

Sibalis, M. (2004) Urban space and homosexuality: the example of the Marais, Paris 'Gay Ghetto', *Urban Studies,* 41(9), 1739–58.

Sibalis, M. (2004) Urban space and homosexuality: the example of the Marais, Paris 'Gay Ghetto', *Urban Studies,* 41(9), 1739–58.

Sibley, D. (1995) *Geographies of Exclusion: Society and Difference in the West,* Routledge, London.

Sibley, D. (1999) Creating geographies of difference, in Massey, D., Allen, J. and Sarre, P. (eds) *Human Geography Today,* Polity, Cambridge, 115–28.

Sidaway, J.D. (1998) What is in a Gulf? From the 'arc of crisis' to the Gulf War, in Ó Tuathail, G. and Dalby, S. (eds) *Rethinking Geopolitics,* Routledge, London and New York, 224–39.

Sidaway, J.D. (1999) American power and the Portuguese Empire, in Slater, D. and Taylor, P.J. (eds) *The American Century,* Blackwell, Oxford, 195–209.

Sidaway, J.D. (2000) Iberian geopolitics, in Dodds, K. and Atkinson, D. (eds) *Geopolitical Traditions: A Century of Geopolitical Thought,* Routledge, London, 118–49.

Sidaway, J.D. (2003) Sovereign excesses? Portraying post-colonial sovereigntyscapes, *Political Geography*, **22**, 157–78.

Sidaway, J.D. (2007) Enclave space: a new metageography of development?, *Area*, **39**(3), 331–9.

Sidaway, J.D. (2009) Shadows on the path: negotiating geopolitics on an urban section of Britain's South West Coast Path, *Environment and Planning D: Society and Space,* **27**(6), 1091–116.

Sidaway, J.D. (2010) 'One island, one team, one mission': geopolitics, sovereignty, 'race' and rendition, *Geopolitics,* **15**(4), 667–83.

Sidaway, J.D. (2012) Geographies of development: new maps? New visions?, *Professional Geographer,* **64**, 49–62.

Sidaway, J.D. (2015) Mapping border studies, *Geopolitics,* **20**(1), 214–22

Sidaway, J.D. and Power, M. (2005) The tears of Portugal: race and destiny in Portuguese geopolitical narratives, *Environment and Planning D: Society and Space,* **23**(4), 527–54.

Sidaway, J.D., Grundy-Warr, C. and Park, B.-G. (2005) Asian sovereignty scapes, Editorial, *Political Geography,* **24**, 779–83.

Silverstone, R., Hirsch, E. and Morley, D. (1992) Information and communication technologies and the moral economy of the household, in Silverstone, R. and Hirsch, E. (eds) *Consuming Technologies: Media and Information in Domestic Spaces,* Routledge, London, 9–17.

Simmel, G. (1978) *The Philosophy of Money,* Routledge & Kegan Paul, London.

Simmel, G. (1991) Money in modern culture, *Theory, Culture and Society,* **8**, 17–31.

Simmel, G. (2004) Metropolis and mental life, in Miles, M., Hall, T. and Borden, I. (eds) *The City Cultures Reader,* 2nd edition, Routledge, London, 12–19.

Simmons, I.G. (1996) *Changing the Face of the Earth: Culture, Environment, History,* 2nd edition, Blackwell, Oxford.

Simon, D. (2008) Urban environments: issues on the Peri-Urban fringe, *Annual Review of Environment and Resources,* **33**, 167–85.

Sinclair, T. (2004) *Governance: Critical Concepts in Political Science,* Routledge, London.

Singer, P. (2009) *Animal Liberation: The Definitive Classic of the Animal Movement* (updated edition), Harper Collins, New York. (First published 1975.)

Sisson, A. (2011) *More Than Making Things: A New Future for Manufacturing in a Service Economy,* The Work Foundation, Lancaster University, www.thework foundation.com/DownloadPublication/Report/284_284 _More%20than%20making%20things.pdf [accessed 27 January 2015].

Six, C (2009) The rise of postcolonial states as donors: a challenge to the development paradigm?, *Third World Quarterly,* **30**(6), 1103–21.

Skeggs, B. (1997) *Formations of Class & Gender: Becoming Respectable,* Sage, London.

Slater, C. (1995) Amazonia as Edenic narrative, in Worster, D. (ed.) *Uncommon Ground: Reinventing Nature,* Norton, New York, 114–59.

Slater, C. (2004) Marketing the rain forest: raw vanilla fragrance and the ongoing transformation of the jungle, *Cultural Geographies,* **11**, 165–80.

Slater, D. (1993) The geopolitical imagination and the enframing of development theory, *Transactions of the Institute of British Geographers, NS,* **18**, 419–37.

Slater, D. (1997) *Consumer Culture and Modernity,* Polity Press, Cambridge.

Slater, D. (2003) Beyond Euro-Americanism: democracy and post-colonialism, in Anderson, K., Domosh, M., Pike, S. and Thrift, N. (eds) *Handbook of Cultural Geography,* Sage, London, 420–32.

Slater, D. (2004) *Geopolitics and the Post-Colonial: Rethinking North–South Relations,* Blackwell, Malden, MA.

Smil, V. (1994) *Energy in World History,* Westview, Boulder, Co.

Smil, V. (2010) *Energy Transitions: History, Requirements, Prospects,* Praeger, Santa Barbara, CA.

Smith, A. (1776) *An Inquiry into the Nature and Causes of the Wealth of Nations,* edited by Skinner, A. (1974) Penguin, London.

Smith, A. (1977) *The Wealth of Nations,* edited by Skinner, A. Penguin, Harmondsworth.

Smith, A.D. (1988) *The Ethnic Origin of Nations,* Blackwell, Oxford.

Smith, B. (2007) *Good Governance and Development,* Macmillan, Basingstoke.

Smith, D.A. and Timberlake, M. (1995) Conceptualizing and mapping the structure of the world's city system, *Urban Studies,* **32**(2), 287–302.

Smith, D.M. (1995) *Geography and Social Justice,* Blackwell, Oxford.

Smith, D.P. and Holt, L. (2007) Studentification and 'apprentice' gentrifiers within Britain's provincial towns and cities: extending the meaning of gentrification, *Environment and Planning A,* **39**(1), 142–61.

Smith, D.P. and Hubbard, P. (2014) The segregation of educated youth and dynamic geographies of studentification, *Area,* **46**(1), 92–100.

Smith, F. (2001) Refiguring the geopolitical landscape: nation, 'transition' and gendered subjects in post-cold war Germany, *Space and Polity,* **5**, 213–35.

Smith, J.R., Louis, W.R., Terry, D.J., Greenaway, K.H., Clarke, M.R. and Cheng, X. (2012) Congruent or conflicted? The impact of injunctive and descriptive norms on environmental intentions, *Journal of Environmental Psychology,* **32**, 353–61.

Smith, M.D. (1996) The empire filters back: consumption, production, and the politics of Starbucks coffee, *Urban Geography,* **17**, 502–24.

Smith, N. (1984) Isiah Bowman: political geography and geopolitics, *Political Geography Quarterly,* **3**, 69–76.

Smith, N. (1996) *The New Urban Frontier: Gentrification and the Revanchist City,* Routledge, London.

Smith, N. (2002) New globalism, new urbanism, gentrification as global urban strategy, *Antipode,* **34,** 434–57.

Smith, N. (2003) *American Empire: Roosevelt's Geographer and the Prelude to Globalization,* University of California Press, Berkeley, CA.

Smith, S. (1989a) *The Politics of Race and Residence,* Polity, Cambridge.

Smith, S. (1989b) Space, society and citizenship: a human geography for the new times?, *Transactions of the Institute of British Geographers,* **14,** 144–57.

Smith, S. (2000) Citizenship, in Johnston,R., Gregory, K., Pratt, G. and Watts, M. (eds) *The Dictionary of Human Geography,* 4th edition, Blackwell, Oxford, 83–4.

Smith, S.J. (2005) Society–space, in Cloke, P., Crang, P. and Goodwin, M. (eds) *Introducing Human Geographies,* 2nd edition, Hodder Arnold, London, 18–33.

Smyth, W.J. (2006) *Map-making, Landscapes and Memory: A Geography of Colonial and Early Modern Ireland c. 1530–1750,* Cork University Press, Cork.

Sneddon, C. and Fox, C. (2011) The Cold War, the US Bureau of Reclamation, and the technopolitics of river basin development, 1950–1970, *Political Geography,* **30,** 450–60.

Snow, P. (1988) *The Star Raft: China's Encounter with Africa,* The Bath Press, London.

Sogge, D. (2002) *Give and Take: What's the Matter with Foreign Aid?,* Zed Books, London.

Soja, E. (1996) *Thirdspace: Journeys to Los Angeles and Other Real and Imagined Places,* Blackwell, Oxford.

Soja, E. (2000) *Postmetropolis: Critical Studies of Cities and Regions,* Blackwell, Oxford.

Soja, E.J. (1989) *Postmodern Geographies: The Reassertion of Space in Critical Social Theory,* Verso, London.

Solli, P., Rowe, E. and Lindgren, W. (2013) Coming into the cold: Asia's Arctic interests, *Polar Geography,* **36,** 253–70.

Soper, K. (1995) *What is Nature?,* Blackwell, Oxford.

Spain, D. (1992) *Gendered Spaces,* University of North Carolina Press, Chapel Hill, NC.

Sparke, M. (2006) Political geography: political geographies of globalization (2): governance, *Progress in Human Geography,* **30,** 1–16.

Spicker, P. (2006) *The Idea of Poverty,* Polity, Bristol.

Spillius, A. (2003) Dialing tone, *Telegraph Magazine,* 19 April, 38–43.

Spirn, A.W. (1997) The authority of nature: conflict and confusion in landscape architecture, in Wolschke-Bulmahn, J. (ed.) *Nature and Ideology: Natural Garden Design in the Twentieth Century,* Dumbarton Oaks Research Library and Collection, Washington, 249–61.

Spivak, G.C. (1985) Three women's texts and a critique of imperialism, *Critical Inquiry,* **12,** 243–61.

Squire, G. and Gill, A. (2011) 'It's not all heartbeat you know': policing domestic violence in rural areas, in Mawby, R.I. and Yarwood, R. (eds) *Rural Policing and Policing the Rural: A Constable Countryside?,* Ashgate, Farnham, 159–68.

Squires, G.D. (ed.) (2004) *Why the Poor Pay More: How to Stop Predatory Lending,* Praeger, Westport, CT.

Squires, P. (ed.) (2008) *ASBO Nation, The Criminalisation of Nuisance in Contemporary Britain,* Policy Press, Bristol.

Srebrnik, H.F. (2004) Can clans form nations? Somaliland in the making, in Bacheli, T., Bartmann, B. and Srebrnik, H.F. (eds) *De Facto States: The Quest for Sovereignty,* Routledge, London and New York, 210–31.

Staeheli, L. (2005) Editorial: Can American cities be sites of citizenship? What can we do about it?, *Urban Geography,* **26,** 197–9.

Staeheli, L. (2011) Political geography: where's citizenship?, *Progress in Human Geography,* **35,** 393–400.

Staeheli, L. (2013) The 2011 Antipode AAG lecture: Whose responsibility is it? Obligation, citizenship and social welfare, *Antipode,* **45,** 521–40.

Staeheli, L.A. and Mitchell, D. (2006) USA's destiny?: regulating space and creating community in American shopping malls, *Urban Studies,* **43**(5–6), 977–92.

Staeheli, L.A., Ehrkamp, P., Leitner, H. and Nagel, C.R. (2012) Dreaming the ordinary: daily life and the complex geographies of citizenship, *Progress in Human Geography,* **36**(5), 628–44.

Stamp, L.D. and Beaver, S. (1933) *The British Isles: A Geographic and Economic Survey,* Longman, London.

Stamp, L.D. and Beaver, S. (1963) *The British Isles: A Geographic and Economic Survey,* 5th edition, Longman, London.

Stannard, K. (2003) Earth to academia: on the need to reconnect university and school geography, *Area,* **25,** 316–22.

Stebbing, E.P. (1935) The encroaching Sahara: the threat to the West African colonies, *Geographical Journal,* 506–19.

Steg, L. and Sievers, I. (2000) Cultural theory and individual perceptions of environmental risks, *Environment and Behavior,* **32,** 250–69.

Steinberg, P.E. (2001) *The Social Construction of the Ocean,* Cambridge University Press, Cambridge.

Steinberg, T.P.J. and Gerhardt, H. (2015) *Contesting the Arctic: Rethinking Politics in the Circumpolar North,* I.B. Tauris, London.

Steinfeld, H., Gerber, P., Wassenaar, T., Castel, V., Rosales, M. and de Haan, C. (2006) *Livestock's Long Shadow: Environmental Issues and Options,* FAO, Rome.

Stern Review (2006) *Stern Review: The Economics of Climate Change,* HM Treasury, London.

Stevens, P. (2003) *Resource Impact – Curse or Blessing? A Literature Survey,* Centre for Energy, Petroleum and Mineral Law and Policy, electronic journal, www.cepmlp.org.

Stiglitz, J.E. and Charlton (2007) *Fair Trade for All: How Trade can Promote Development,* revised edition, Oxford University Press, Oxford.

Stobart, J. and Raven, N. (eds) (2004) *Towns, Regions and Industries: Urban and Industrial Change in the Midlands, c. 1700–1840,* Manchester University Press, Manchester.

Stöhr, W.B. and Taylor, D.R.F. (1981) *Development from Above or Below? The Dialectics of Regional Planning in Developing Countries,* John Wiley, Chichester.

Storey, D. (2012a) Heritage, culture and identity: the case of Gaelic games, in Hill, J., Moore, K. and Wood, J. (eds)

Sport, History and Heritage: An Investigation into the Public Representation of Sport, Boydell and Brewer, Martlesham, 223–34.

Storey, D. (2012b) *Territories: The Claiming of Space*, 2nd edition, Routledge, London.

Storey, D. (2013a) 'New' migrants in the British countryside, *Journal of Rural and Community Development*, 8(3), 291–302.

Storey, I. (2013b) Arctic lessons: What the South China Sea claimants can learn from cooperation in the high north, *ISEAS Perspective*, No. 65, www.iseas.edu.sg/documents/publication/ISEAS_Perspective_2013_65.pdf [accessed 20 December 2014].

Strange, S. (1999) *Mad Money: When Markets Outgrow Governments*, University of Michigan Press, Ann Arbor, MI.

Strüver, A (2005) Spheres of transnationalism within the European union: on open doors, thresholds and drawbridges along the Dutch–German border, *Journal of Ethnic and Migration Studies*, 31(2), 323–43.

Stuart, T. (2009) *Waste: Uncovering the Global Food Scandal*, Penguin, London.

Sturgis, P., Brunton-Smith, I., Kuha, J. and Jackson, J. (2014) Ethnic diversity, segregation and the social cohesion of neighbourhoods in London, *Ethnic and Racial Studies*, 37(8), 1286–309.

Stutz, F. P. and de Souza, A. R. (1998) *The World Economy: Resources, Location, Trade and Development*, 3rd edition, Prentice-Hall, Upper Saddle River, NJ.

Sugden, D. (1982) *Arctic and Antarctic*, Basil Blackwell, Oxford.

Sukarno, I. (1955) Modern History Sourcebook: President Sukarno of Indonesia: Speech at the opening of the Bandung conference, 18 April 1955, www.fordham.edu/halsall/mod/1955sukarno-bandong.html [accessed 7 April 2003].

Sum, N-L. and Ngai, P. (2005) Globalization and paradoxes of ethical transnational production: code of conduct in a Chinese workplace, *Competition and Change*, 9, 181–200.

Sumartojo, R. (2004) Contesting place: antigay and lesbian hate crime in Columbus, Ohio, in Flint, C. (ed.) *Spaces of Hate: Geographies of Discrimination and Intolerance in the USA*, Routledge, New York, 87–107.

Sundbo, J. (2015), Service and Experience, in Bryson, J.R. and Daniels, P.W. (eds) (2015) *The Handbook of Service Business: Management, Marketing, Innovation and Internationalisation*, Edward Elgar, Cheltenham, 205–22.

Sundbo, J. and Sorensen, F. (eds) (2013) *Handbook on the Experience Economy*, Elgar, Cheltenham.

Suri, V. and Chapman, D. (2008) Economic growth, trade and energy: implications for the environmental Kuznets curve, *Ecological Economics*, 25(2), 195–208.

Swaine, M. (2010) *America's Challenge: Engaging a Rising China in the Twenty-First Century*, Carnegie Endowment for International Peace, Washington, DC.

Swanton D, (2010) Sorting bodies: race, affect, and everyday multiculture in a mill town in northern England, *Environment and Planning A*, 42(10), 2332–50.

Swyngedouw, E. (2000) Authoritarian governance, power, and the politics of rescaling, *Environment and Planning D: Society and Space*, 18, 63–76.

Sybert, S. (2014) Taiko in Brazil: Japanese cultural diaspora and hybridization through percussion music, https//:scholarship.org.uc/item/8rc4w0d0.

T

Takahashi, L.M. and Dear, M.J. (1997) The changing dynamics of community opposition to human service facilities, *Journal of the American Planning Association*, 63, 79–93.

Takeuchi, K., Katoh, K., Nan, Y. and Kou, Z. (1995) Vegetation change in desertified Kerqin sandy lands, *Inner Mongolia/Geographical Reports*, Tokyo Metropolitan University, 30, 1–24.

Talbot, J. M. (2004) *Grounds for Agreement: The Political Economy of the Coffee Commodity Chain*, Rowman and Littlefield, Lanham, MD.

Tan, T. Y. and Kudaisya, G. (2002) *The Aftermath of Partition in South Asia*, Routledge, London.

Taussig, M. (1997) *The Magic of the State*, Routledge, London.

Taylor, I. (1997) Running on empty, *The Guardian*, 14 May, 2–6.

Taylor, J. (2014) Chinese behavior in the Arctic vs. the South China Sea, *Banyan Analytics*, www.anser.org/babrief_arcticscs [accessed 20 December 2014].

Taylor, P. (2004) *World City Network: A Global Urban Analysis*, Routledge, London.

Taylor, P.J. (1989) *Political Geography*, Longman, London.

Taylor, P.J. (1994) From heartland to hegemony: changing the world in political geography, *Geoforum*, 25, 403–17.

Taylor, P.J. (2005) New political geographies: global civil society and global governance through world city networks, *Political Geography*, 24, 703–30.

Taylor, P.J. and Flint, C. (2007) *Political Geography: World-Economy, Nation State and Locality*, 5th edition, Prentice Hall, Harlow.

Taylor, S. and Tyler, M. (2000) Emotional labour and sexual difference in the airline industry, *Work, Employment and Society*, 14(1), 77–95.

Tennant, M., O'Brien, M. and Sanders, J. (2008) *The History of the Non-profit Sector in New Zealand*, Office for the Community and Voluntary Sector, Wellington.

The Economist (1999) The Next Shock, *The Economist*, 4 March, 29, available from www.economist.com.

The Economist (2013) Welcome home: offshoring, *The Economist*, 19 January, 11–12.

The Guardian (2015) Life expectancy falls for older UK women, *The Guardian*, 7 April, www.theguardian.com/society/2015/apr/07/life-expectancy-falls-older-uk-women-public-health-england [accessed 5 May 2015].

The Times Archaeology of the World (1999) New edition, Times Books, London.

The Times Atlas of World History (1989) 3rd edition, Guild Publishing, London.

The Times Atlas of World History (1999) New edition, Times Books, London.

The Wilderness Society (2006) *A Fringe of Green: Protecting Australia's Forests and Woodlands,* www.wilderness .org.au/campaigns/forests/fringe/\#why-save.

TheCityUK (2014) *The UK as an International Financial Centre,* London: TheCityUK.

Thomas, D. and Middleton, N. (1994) *Desertification: Exploding the Myth,* Wiley, Chichester.

Thompson, E.P. (1963) *The Making of the English Working Class,* Penguin, London and New York.

Thompson, S. (2005) 'Territorialising' the school playground: deconstructing the geography of playtime, *Children's Geographies,* 3(1), 63–78.

Thomson, S. (2005) 'Territorialising' the primary school playground: deconstructing the geography of playtime, *Children's Geographies* 3(1), 63–78.

Thrift, N. (1996) New urban eras and old technological fears: reconfiguring the goodwill of electronic things, *Urban Studies,* 33(8), 1463–94.

Thrift, N. and Kitchin, R. (2008) *The International Encyclopedia of Human Geography,* Elsevier, London.

Tickell, A. (2003) Cultures of money, in Anderson, K., Domosh, M., Pile, S. and Thrift, N. (eds) *Handbook of Cultural Geography,* Sage, London, 116–30.

Tickell, A. and Peck, J. (2003) Making global rules: globalization or neoliberalization, in Peck, J. and Yeung, H. (eds) *Remaking the Global Economy,* Sage, London, 163–81.

Tiffin, M., Mortimore, M. and Gickuki, F. (1994) *More People, Less Erosion: Environmental Recovery in Kenya,* John Wiley, Chichester.

Tissot, S. and Poupeau, F. (2005) *La spatilisation des problems sociaux, Actes de la recherché en Sciences socials,* 159 (September), 4–9.

Toal, G. (2003) Re-asserting the regional: political geography and geopolitics in world thinly known, *Political Geography,* 22, 653–55.

Tobler, W. (1970) A computer simulating urban growth in the Detroit region, *Economic Geography,* 46, 234–40

Toennies, F. (1887) *Community and Society* (1957 edn), Michigan State University Press, East Lansing, MI.

Toje, A. (2005) The 2003 European Union security strategy: a critical appraisal, *European Foreign Affairs Review,* 10, 117–33.

Tokar, B. (1994) *The Green Alternative,* 2nd edition, R. and E. Miles, San Pedro, CA.

Tollefson, J. (2010) The global farm, *Nature,* 466, 554–6.

Tønnesson, S. and Antlöv, H. (1996) Asia in theories of nationalism and national identity, in Tønnesson, S. and Antlöv, H. (eds) *Asian Forms of the Nation,* Curzon, Richmond, 1–40.

Tonts, M. and Larsen, A. (2002) Rural disadvantage in Australia: a human rights perspective, *Geography,* 87, 132–41.

Topik, S. (2009) Historicizing commodity chains: five hundred years of the coffee global commodity chain, in Bair, J. (ed.) *Frontiers of Commodity Chain Research,* Stanford University Press, Stanford, CA, 37–62.

Tormey, A. (2007) 'Everyone with eyes can see the problem': moral citizens and the space of Irish nationhood, *International Migration,* 45, 69–100.

Tratado de Limites (1866) *Tratado de Limites entre Portugal e Espanha assinado em Lisboa aos 29 de Setembro de 1864,* Imprensa Nacional, Lisbon.

Traynor, I. (2015), Migrant crisis: EU plan to strike Libya networks could include ground forces, *The Guardian,* 13 May, www.theguardian.com/world/2015/may/13/migrant-crisis-eu-plan-to-strike-libya-networks-could-include-ground-forces [accessed 16 May 2015].

Tregear, A. (2011) Progressing knowledge in alternative and local food networks: critical reflections and a research agenda, *Journal of Rural Studies,* 27, 419–30.

Truman, H. (1949) *Public Papers of the President, 20 January,* US Government Printing Offices, Washington, DC.

Tuan, Yi-Fu (1999) *Who am I? An Autobiography of Emotion, Mind and Spirit,* University of Wisconsin Press, Madison, WI.

Tuan, Yi-Fu (2002) *Dear Colleague: Common and Uncommon Observations,* University of Minnesota Press, Minneapolis, MN.

Tucker, A. (2009) *Queer Visibilities: Space, Identity and Interaction in Cape Town,* Wiley-Blackwell, Chichester.

Tunander, O. (2001) Swedish-German geopolitics for a new century: Rudolf Kjellén's 'The State as Living Organism', *Review of International Studies,* 27, 451–63.

Turner, B. (2002) Religion and politics: the elementary forms of citizenship, in Isin, E. and Turner, B. (eds) *Handbook of Citizenship Studies,* Sage, London, 259–76.

Turner, B. (2012) National and social citizenship: some structural and cultural problems with modern citizenship, in Kyung-Sup, C. and Turner, B. *Contested Citizenship in East Asia: Development Politics, National Unity and Globalization,* Routledge, Abingdon, 15–42.

Turner, B.S. (2007) The enclave society: towards sociology of immobility, *European Journal of Social Theory,* 10(2), 287–303.

Tyler, I. (2013) *Revolting Subjects: Social Abjection and Resistance in Neoliberal Britain,* Zed Books, London.

U

UK Universities (2005) *Studentification: A Guide to Challenges, Opportunities and Good Practice.* UK Universities, London.

UN HABITAT (2009) *Planning Sustainable Cities: Global Report on Human Settlements 2009,* Earthscan, London.

UN Millennium Development Goals (2000) www.millennium goals.org/.

UN *see* United Nations.

UNAIDS (2010) *Getting to Zero: 2011–2015 Strategy,* Joint United Nations Programme on HIV/AIDS (UNAIDS), www.unaids.org/sites/default/files/sub_landing/files/JC2034_UNAIDS_Strategy_en.pdf.

UNAIDS (2013) *Access to Antiretroviral Therapy in Africa: Status Report on Progress towards the 2015 Targets,* United Nations, www.unaids.org/en/resources/documents/

2013/20131219_AccessARTAfricaStatusReportProgress towards2015Targets [accessed 10 April 2015].

UNHCR (2014) *Climate Change, Natural Disasters and Human Displacement: A UNHCR Perspective,* The UN Refugee Agency, www.unhcr.org/4901e81a4.html, [accessed 15 April 2015].

UNHCR (2015a) *25 Years of Global Forced Displacement: UNHCR Statistical Yearbook 2013,* United Nations Refugee Agency, www.unhcr.org/54cf9bd69.html [accessed 2 June 2015].

UNHCR (2015b) *UNHCR Boosts Presence in Greek Islands to Cope with Soaring Refugee Arrivals,* www.unhcr.org/557171779.html [accessed 15 May 2015].

Understanding Cities (1999) DD304, Open University, Milton Keynes.

UNCTAD *see* United Nations Conference on Trade and Development.

UNDP *see* United Nations Development Programme.

UNEP *see* United Nations Environment Programme.

UNESCO (2013) *Creative Economies,* UNESCO, www.unesco.org/culture/pdf/creative-economy-report-2013.pdf.

UN-HABITAT (2006) The state of the world's cities 2006/7, *The Millennium Development Goals and Urban Sustainability,* Earthscan, London.

UNICEF *see* United Nations Children's Fund.

United Nations (UN) (2001) *The State of the World's Cities: Istanbul,* Habitat Publications Unit, www.unhabitat.org/Istanbul+5/statereport.htm.

United Nations (UN) (2002) *Manual on Statistics on International Trade in Services,* United Nations, New York.

United Nations (UN) (2006) *World Urbanization Prospects: The 2005 Update,* United Nations, New York, www.un.org/esa/population/publications/WUP2005/2005wup.htm.

United Nations (UN) (2009) *World Urbanization Prospects: The 2008 Update,* United Nations, New York, www.un.org/esa/population/publications/wup2007/2007WUP_Highlights_web.pdf.

United Nations (UN) (2013) *World Population Prospects: The 2012 Revision, Highlights and Advance Tables,* United Nations, New York, http://esa.un.org/wpp/Documentation/pdf/WPP2012_HIGHLIGHTS.pdf [accessed 22 April 2015].

United Nations (UN) (2014a) *World Population Prospects: The 2012 Revision,* data available online from: http://esa.un.org/wpp/ [accessed 5 April 2015].

United Nations (UN) (2014b) *Dramatic Fall in Malaria Deaths Show Fight Against Disease Can Be Won,* United Nations News, www.un.org/apps/news/story.asp?NewsID=49548\#.VYhy1Pmqqkp [accessed 15 April 2015].

United Nations (UN) (2014c) *Millennium Development Goals Report 2014,* United Nations, New York.

United Nations (UN) (2014d) *World Urbanization Prospects: The 2014 Revision, Highlights,* United Nations, New York, http://esa.un.org/unpd/wup/Highlights/WUP2014-Highlights.pdf.

United Nations Children's Fund (UNICEF) (2013) *HIV and AIDS,* UNICEF Eastern and Southern Africa, www.unicef.org/esaro/5482_HIV_AIDS.html [accessed 17 April 2015].

United Nations Children's Fund (UNICEF) (2014), *Committing to Child Survival: A Promise Renewed – Progress Report 2014,* UNICEF, www.apromiserenewed.org/APR_2014_web_15Sept14.pdf [accessed 30 April 2015].

United Nations Conference on Trade and Development (UNCTAD) (2006) http://stats.unctad.org/FDI/TableViewer/tableView.aspx?ReportId=5 [accessed 31 December 2006].

United Nations Conference on Trade and Development (UNCTAD) (2009) *World Investment Report 2009,* UNCTAD, New York and Geneva.

United Nations Conference on Trade and Development (UNCTAD) (2013) *The rise of BRICS FDI and Africa,* www.safpi.org/sites/default/files/publications/webdiaeia2013d6_en.pdf [accessed 1 February 2014].

United Nations Conference on Trade and Development (UNCTAD) (2014) *Global Investment Trends Monitor,* No. 15, 28 January, http://unctad.org/en/PublicationsLibrary/webdiaeia2014d1_en.pdf [accessed 1 August 2014].

United Nations Development Programme (UNDP) (1998) *Human Development Report 1998,* Oxford University Press, Oxford.

United Nations Environment Programme (UNEP) (1999) *Global Environmental Outlook 2000,* UNEP-Earthscan Publications, London.

United Nations Development Programme (UNDP) (2009) *Human Development Report – Overcoming Barriers: Human Mobility and Development,* UNDP, Geneva, http://hdr.undp.org/en/media/HDR_2009_EN_Complete.pdf.

United Nations Population Division (1998) *Briefing Packet,* 1998 Revision of World Population Prospects.

United Nations Population Division (1999) *The World at 6 Billion,* United Nations, www.un.org/esa/population/publications/sixbillion/sixbillion.htm [accessed 15 April 2015].

United Nations Population Division (2012) *World Population Prospects: The 2012 Revision,* United Nations, New York.

United Nations Population Division (2015) *Population Indicators,* United Nations, http://esa.un.org/unpd/wpp/DVD.

United Nations World Tourism Organization (UNWTO) (2014) *World Tourism Highlights, 2014 Edition,* UNWTO, Madrid.

Urry, J. (2005) The place of emotions within place, in Davidson, J., Bondi, L. and Smith, M. (eds) *Emotional Geographies,* Ashgate, Aldershot, 77–86.

USDA (2015) *Trends in US Local and Regional Food Systems: A Report to Congress,* Economic Research Service, USDA, Washington, DC.

V

Valentine, G. (1989) The geography of women's fear, *Area,* **21**(4), 385–90.

Valentine, G. (1995) Out and about: geographies of lesbian landscapes, *International Journal of Urban and Regional Research,* **19**(1), 96–111.

Valentine, G. (2001) *Social Geographies: Space and Society,* Prentice Hall, Harlow.

Valkenier, E.K. (1983) *The Soviet Union and the Third World: An Economic Bind,* Praeger, New York.

van der Ploeg, J.D. (2010) The food crisis, industrialized farming and the imperial regime, *Journal of Agrarian Change,* **10**(1), 98–106.

van der Zee, H.I. (1982) *The Hunger Winter: Occupied Holland 1944–45,* Norman and Hobhouse, London.

VanderZwaag, D. and Vu, H.D. (2012) Regional cooperation in the South China Sea and the Arctic: lessons to be learned?, in Chircop A., Letalik, N., McDorman, T. and Rolston, S. (eds) *The Regulation of International Shipping: International and Comparative Perspectives,* Martinus Nijhoff Publishers, The Netherlands, 171–208.

van Schendel, W. (2005a) Spaces of engagement: How borderlands, illegal flows, and territorial states interlock, in Abrahams, I. and van Schendel, W. (eds) *Illicit Flows and Criminal Things,* Indiana University Press, Bloomington and Indianapolis, IN, 38–68.

Van Schendel, W. (2005b) Geographies of knowing, geographies of ignorance: jumping scale in Southeast Asia, in Kratoska, P.H., Raben, R. and Nordholt, H.S. (eds) *Locating Southeast Asia: Geographies of Knowledge and Politics of Space,* Singapore University Press, Singapore, 275–307.

Van Welsum, D. and Reif, X. (2005) *Potential Offshoring: Evidence from Selected OECD Countries,* OECD, DSTIICCP.

Varkkey, H. (2014) Regional cooperation, patronage and the ASEAN agreement on transboundary haze pollution, *International Environmental Agreements: Politics, Law and Economics,* **14,** 65–81.

Visser, G. (2003) Gay men, tourism and urban space: reflections on Africa's 'gay capital', *Tourism Geographies,* **5**(2), 168–89.

Visser, M. (1986) *Much Depends on Dinner,* Collier/Macmillan, New York.

Vom Hau, M., Scott, J. and Hulme, D. (2012) Beyond the BRICs: alternative strategies of influence in the global politics of development, *European Journal of Development Research,* **24,** 187–204.

von Braun, J. (2009) The food crisis isn't over, *Nature,* **456,** 701.

W

Wacquant, L. (2007) *Urban Outcasts: A Comparative Sociology of Advanced Marginality,* Polity Press, Cambridge.

Wacquant, L. (2009) *Punishing the Poor: The Neoliberal Government of Social Insecurity,* Duke University Press, Durham, NC.

Wacquant, L. (2010) Class, race and hyperincarceration in revanchist America, *Daedalus,* **139**(3), 74–90.

Wade, R. (2001) Winners and losers, *The Economist,* April, 79–82.

Walker, R. (1996) Another round of globalization in San Francisco, *Urban Geography,* **17,** 60–94.

Wall, D. (1999) *Earth First! and the Anti-roads Movement,* Routledge, London.

Wallace, D. and Wallace, R. (1998) *A Plague on Your Houses: How New York was Burned Down and How National Public Health Crumbled,* Methuen, London.

Wallace, D. and Wallace, R. (2000) Life and death in Upper Manhattan and the Bronx: toward an evolutionary perspective on catastrophic social change, *Environment and Planning A,* **32,** 1245–66.

Wallace, I. (1985) Towards a geography of agribusiness, *Progress in Human Geography,* **9,** 491–514.

Wallerstein, I. (1979) *The Capitalist World Economy,* Cambridge University Press, Cambridge.

Wallerstein, I. (1980) Imperialism and development, in Bergeson, A. (ed.) *Studies of the Modern World System,* Academic Press, New York.

Wallerstein, I. (1991) *Geopolitics and Geoculture: Essays on the Changing World System,* Cambridge University Press, Cambridge.

Wallerstein, I. (1994) Development: lodestar or illusion?, in Sklair, L. (ed.) *Capitalism and Development,* Routledge, London, 3–20.

Walton, G. (2015) Sarcasm gives call centres in Manila the Edge, *The Daily Telegraph,* 9 March.

Wang, Z. (2012) *Never Forget National Humiliation: Historical Memory in Chinese Politics and Foreign Relations,* Columbia University Press, New York.

Ward, D. (1987) Population growth, migration, and urbanization, 1860–1920, in Mitchell R. D. and Groves, P.A. (eds) *North America: The Historical Geography of a Changing Continent,* Hutchinson, London.

Ward, K., Binnie, J., Brown, G., Browne, K., Ingram, A., Isaacs, G., Leap, W. and Tucker, A. (2010) Review forum. Reading Andrew Tucker's Queer Visibilities: space, identity and interaction in Cape Town, *Political Geography,* **29**(8), 454–62.

Ward, S. (2004) *Planning and Urban Change,* Sage, London.

Warde, A. (2014) After taste: culture, consumption and theories of practice, *Journal of Consumer Culture,* **14**(3), 279–303.

Warhurst, C., Nickson, D., Witz, A. and Cullen, A. (2000) Aesthetic labour in interactive service work: some case study evidence from the 'new' Glasgow, *The Service Industries Journal,* **20**(3), 1–18.

Watney, S. (1987) *Policing Desire: Pornography, AIDS and the Media,* Methuen, London.

Watnick, M. (1952–3) The appeal of Communism to the peoples of underdeveloped areas, *Economic Development and Cultural Change,* **1,** 22–36.

Watson, J.L. (1997a) Introduction: transnationalism, localization, and fast foods in East Asia, in Watson J. L. (ed.) *Golden Arches East: McDonald's in East Asia,* Stanford University Press, Stanford, CA, 1–38.

Watson, J.L. (1997b) McDonald's in Hong Kong: consumerism, dietary change, and the rise of a children's culture, in Watson, J. L. (ed.) *Golden Arches East: McDonald's in East Asia,* Stanford University Press, Stanford, CA, 77–109.

Watson, S. and Gibson, K. (eds) (1995) *Postmodern Cities and Spaces,* Blackwell, Oxford.

Watts, D.C.H., Ilbery, B. and Maye, D. (2005) Making re-connections in agro-food geography: alternative systems of food provision, *Progress in Human Geography*, 29(1), 22–40.

Watts, M. (2003) Development and governmentality, *Singapore Journal of Tropical Geography*, 24, 6–34.

Weber, A. (1929) *Alfred Weber's Theory of the Location of Industries*, Chicago University Press, Chicago, IL.

Weigold, A. (1999) Famine management: the Bengal famine (1942–44) revisited, *South Asia*, 22(1), 63–77.

Weinrich, J. (1982) Is homosexuality biologically natural?, in Paul, W., Weinrich, J., Gonsiorek, J. and Hotvedt, M. (eds) *Homosexuality: Social, Psychological and Biological Issues*, Sage, Beverley Hills, CA, 197–208.

Wellington, C. and Bryson, J. R. (2001) At face value?: image consultancy, emotional labour and professional work, *Sociology*, 35(4), 933–46.

Werbner, P. (1997) Introduction: The dialectics of cultural hybridity, in Werbner, P. and Modood, T. (eds) *Debating Cultural Hybridity: Multi-Cultural Identities and the Politics of Anti-Racism*, Zed Books, London, 1–26.

Westad, O.A. (2006) *The Global Cold War: Third World Interventions and the Making of our Times*, Cambridge University Press, Cambridge.

Whatmore, S. (1995) From farming to agribusiness: the global agro-food system, in Johnston, R., Taylor, P. and Watts, M. (eds) *Geographies of Global Change*, Blackwell, Oxford, 36–49.

Whatmore, S. (2002) *Hybrid Geographies*, Routledge, London.

Whatmore, S. (2014) Nature and human geography, in Cloke, P., Crang, P. and Goodwin, M. (eds) *Introducing Human Geographies*, 3rd edition, Routledge, London, 152–62.

Whatmore, S., Stassart, P. and Renting, H. (2003) What's alternative about alternative food networks?, *Environment and Planning A*, 35, 389–91.

White, K., Haas, J.S. and Williams, D.R. (2012) Elucidating the role of place in health care disparities: the example of racial/ethnic residential segregation, *Health Services Research*, 47(3), 1278–99.

Whitehead, M., Jones, M. and Jones, R. (2007) *The Nature of the State: Excavating the Political Ecologies of the Modern State*, Oxford University Press, Oxford.

Whitman, J. (ed.) (2009) *Palgrave Advances in Global Governance*, Palgrave, Basingstoke.

WHO *see* World Health Organization.

Wiener, M. J. (1985) *English Culture and the Decline of the Industrial Spirit, 1850–1980*, Penguin, Harmondsworth.

Wiggins, S., Kirsten, J. and Llambi, L. (eds) (2010) The Future of Small Farms, special issue of *World Development*, 38(10), 1341–526.

Wilk, R. (2006) Bottled water: the pure commodity in the age of branding, *Journal of Consumer Culture*, 6, 303–25.

Wilkinson R and Pickett K (2010) *The Spirit Level: Why Equality is Better for Everyone*, Allen Lane.

Williams, C.C. (1996) Local exchange and trading systems: a new source of work and credit for the poor and unemployed?, *Environment and Planning A*, 28, 1395–415.

Williams, G., Meth, P. and Willis, K. (2009) *Geographies of Developing Areas: The Global South in a Changing World*, Routledge, Abingdon.

Williams, P. and Hubbard, P. (2001) Who is disadvantaged?: retail change and social exclusion, *International Review of Retail, Distribution and Consumer Research*, 11, 267–86.

Williams, R. (1973) *The City and the Country*, Chatto and Windus, London.

Williams, R. (1976) *Keywords: A Vocabulary of Culture and Society*, Fontana, London.

Willis, K. (2005) *Theories and Practices of Development*, Routledge, London.

Willis, P. (1990) *Uncommon Culture*, Open University Press, Milton Keynes.

Willis, R.P. (ed.) (2001) New Zealand in the 1990s, special edition of *Asia Pacific Viewpoint*, 42, 1.

Wilson, A. (1992) Technological utopias, world's fairs and theme parks, in Wilson, A. (ed.) *The Culture of Nature: North American Landscape from Disney to the Exxon Valdez*, Blackwell, Oxford, 157–90.

Wilson, A. (2002) *The Ukrainians: Unexpected Nation*, Yale University Press, New Haven and London.

Wilson, D. (2005) *Inventing Black-on-Black Violence: Discourse, Space, Representation*, Syracuse University Press, Syracuse.

Wilson, G.A. (2001) From productivism to post-productivism and back again?: exploring the (un) changed natural and mental landscapes of European agriculture, *Transactions of the Institute of British Geographers*, 26(1), 77–102.

Wilson, G. and Rigg, J. (2003) 'Post-productivist' agricultural regimes and the South: discordant concepts?, *Progress in Human Geography*, 27(6), 681–707.

Wilton, R. (1996) Diminished worlds?: the geography of everyday life with HIV/AIDS, *Health and Place*, 2, 69–83.

Winchester, H. and White, P. (1988) The location of marginalized groups in the inner city, *Environment and Planning D: Society and Space*, 6, 37–54.

Winchester, H.P.M., Kong, L. and Dunn, K. (2003) *Landscapes: Ways of Imagining the World*, Prentice Hall, Harlow.

Winchester, S. (2003) *Krakatoa: The Day the World Exploded*, Penguin Books, London.

Winichakul, T. (1995) *Siam Mapped: A History of the Geobody of a Nation*, University of Hawaii Press, Hawaii.

Winichakul, T. (1996) Maps and the formation of the geobody of Siam, in Tønnesson, S. and Antlöv, H. (eds) *Asian Forms of the Nation*, Curzon Press, Richmond, 67–91.

Winter, M. (2003) Embeddedness, the new food economy and defensive localism, *Journal of Rural Studies*, 19, 23–32.

Wirth, L. (1938) Urbanism as a way of life, *American Journal of Sociology*, 44, 1–24, reprinted in Hart, P. K. and Reiss, A. J. (eds) (1957) *Cities and Society*, Free Press, Chicago, IL.

Withers, C.W.J. and Mayhew, R.J. (2002) Rethinking 'disciplinary' history: geography in British universities, c. 1580–1887, *Transactions of the Institute of British Geographers*, **27**, 11–29.

Wolch, J. (1990) *The Shadow State: Government and Voluntary Sector in Transition*, The Foundation Centre, New York.

Wolch, J. (2002) Anima urbis, *Progress in Human Geography*, **26**(6), 721–42.

Wolf, E. R. (1966) *Peasants*, Prentice-Hall, Englewood Cliffs, NJ.

Wolfe, T. (1988) *Bonfire of the Vanities*, New York, Bantam.

Wolfe-Phillips, L. (1987) Why Third World?: origins, definitions and usage, *Third World Quarterly*, **9**, 1311–19.

Wolin, R. (2010) The idea of cosmopolitanism: from Kant to the Iraq war and beyond, *Ethics and Global Politics*, **3**, 143–53.

Wolters, O.W. (1982) *History, Culture, and Religion in Southeast Asian Perspectives*, Institute of Southeast Asian Studies, Singapore.

Women and Geography Study Group (1997) *Feminist Geographies: Explorations in Diversity and Difference*, Longman, Harlow.

Wood, A. and Welch, C. (1998) *Policing the Policemen: The Case for an Independent Evaluation Mechanism for the IMF*, Bretton Woods Project, Friends of the Earth US, London.

Wood, G. (1985) *Labelling in Development Policy: Essays in Honour of Bernard Schaffer*, Sage, London.

Woods, C. (1998) *Development Arrested: Race, Power and Blues in the Mississippi Delta*, Verso, London.

Woods, M. (2005) *Contesting Rurality: Politics in the British Countryside*, Ashgate, Oxford.

Woods, M. (2010) *Rural*, Routledge, New York and London.

Woods, M. (2012) *Rural Geography*, 2nd edition, Sage, London.

Woodward, K. (1997) Concepts of identity and difference, in Woodward, K. (ed.) *Identity and Difference*, Sage, London, 8–59.

Woodward, R. (2004) *Military Geographies*, Blackwell, Oxford.

Woodward, R. (2005) From military geography to militarism's geographies: disciplinary engagements with the geographies of militarism and military activities, *Progress in Human Geography*, **29**, 718–40.

Woodward, M.D. (2015) Ordos Municipality: a market-era resource boomtown, *Cities*, **43**, 115–32.

Woon, C.Y. (2009) A 'New Mecca for terrorism'?: unveiling the 'second front' in Southeast Asia, in Ingram, A. and Dodds, K. (eds) *Spaces of Security and Insecurity: Geographies of the War on Terror*, Ashgate, 85–108.

World Bank (2009) *World Development Report 2009*, World Bank, Washington, DC.

World Bank (2010) *World Development Report 2010: Development and Climate Change*, World Bank, Washington, DC.

World Bank (2015a) *Fertility Rate, Total (Births per Woman)*, The World Bank Data, http://data.worldbank.org/indicator/SP.DYN.TFRT.IN [accessed 5 May 2015].

World Bank (2015b) *International Migrant Stock, Total*, The World Bank Data, http://data.worldbank.org/indicator/SM.POP.TOTL [accessed 5 May 2015].

World Bank (2015c) *Life Expectancy at Birth, (Total) Years*, The World Bank Data, http://data.worldbank.org/indicator/SP.DYN.LE00.IN [accessed 5 May 2015].

World Bank (2015d) *World Development Indicators 2015*, World Bank, Washington, DC.

World Health Organisation (2011) *Number of Deaths Due to HIV/AIDS*, World Health Organisation, www.who.int/gho/hiv/epidemic_status/deaths_text/en/ [accessed 15 April 2015].

World Health Organisation (2014) *Estimated Adult and Child Deaths From AIDS, 2013 by WHO Region*, World Health Organisation, www.who.int/gho/hiv/epidemic_status/hiv_007.jpg [accessed 15 April 2015].

World Urbanization Prospects (2014) *The 2014 Revision, Highlights*.

Worldmapper (2015a) *Affected by Disasters*, map available from: www.worldmapper.org/display.php?selected=245 [accessed 22 June 2015].

Worldmapper (2015b) *Killed by Disasters*, map available from: www.worldmapper.org/display.php?selected=246 [accessed 22 June 2015].

Wright Mills, C. (1959) *White Collar Work: The American Middle Classes*, Oxford University Press, New York.

Wright, C. (2004) Consuming lives, consuming landscapes: interpreting advertisements for Cafedirect coffees, *Journal of International Development*, **16**(5), 665–80.

Wright, R. (1995) *The Color Curtain: A Report on the Bandung Conference*, Banner Books, New York.

Wrigley, N. and Lowe, M. (eds) (1996) *Retailing, Consumption and Capital: Towards the New Retail Geography*, Longman, Harlow.

Wrigley, N. and Lowe, M. (2002) *Reading Retail*, Arnold, London.

Wrigley, N., Warm, D. and Margetts, B. (2003) Deprivation, diet and food-retail access: findings from the Leeds 'food deserts' study, *Environment and Planning A*, **35**, 151–88.

WTO (2014) *World Trade Report 2014: Trade Development: Recent Trends and the Role of the WTO*, World Trade Organization, Geneva.

WTO (2014b) *International Trade Statistics 2014*, World Trade Organization, Geneva.

Wylie, J. (2007) *Landscape*, Routledge, London.

Wyly, E.K., Moos, M., Kabahizi, E. and Hammel, D. (2009) Cartographies of race and class: mapping the class-monopoly rents of American subprime mortgage capital, *International Journal of Urban and Regional Research*, **33**, 332–54.

X

Xing, Y. and Detert, N. (2010) *How the iPhone widens the United States trade deficit with the People's Republic of China*, ADBI Working Paper 257, Asian Development Bank Institute, Tokyo, www.adbi.org/working-paper/2010/12/14/4236.iphone.widens.us.trade.deficit.prc/.

Xue, WWWWG.F. (2014) The South China Sea: competing claims and conflict situations, in Schofield, C., Lee, S. and Kwon, M-S. (eds) *The Limits of Maritime Jurisdiction*, Brill, Leiden, 225–48.

Y

Yan, Y. (1997) McDonald's in Beijing: the localization of Americana, in Watson, J. L. (ed.) *Golden Arches East: McDonald's in East Asia*, Stanford University Press, Stanford, CA, 39–76.

Yang, C. (2009) Strategic coupling of regional development in global production networks: redistribution of Taiwanese personal computer investment from the Pearl River Delta to the Yangtze River Delta, China, *Regional Studies, 43*, 385–407.

Yang, Y. (2006) *The Taiwanese Notebook Computer Production Network in China: Implications for Upgrading of the Chinese Electronics Industry,* The Personal Computer Industry Center, University of California, Irvine, CA, www.pcic.merage.uci.edu/papers.asp [accessed 29 August 2011].

Yang, Y-R. and Coe, N.M. (2009) The governance of global production networks and regional development: a case study of Taiwanese PC production networks, *Growth and Change, 40*, 30–53.

Yarwood, R. (2002) Parish councils, partnership and governance: the development of 'exceptions' housing in the Malvern Hills District, England, *Journal of Rural Studies, 18*, 275–91.

Yarwood, R. (2007) The geographies of policing, *Progress in Human Geography, 31*(4), 447–65.

Yarwood, R. (2014) *Citizenship,* Routledge, London.

Yarwood, R. and Edwards, B. (1995) Voluntary action in rural areas: the case of neighbourhood watch, *Journal of Rural Studies, 11*, 447–459.

Yarwood, R. and Paasche, T. (2015) The relational geographies of policing and security, *Geography Compass, 9*(6), 362–70.

Yarwood, R. and Tyrrell, N. (2012) Why children's geographies?, *Geography, 97*(3), 123–8.

Yeandle, M. and Davies, N. (2013) *The Global Financial Centres Index 14,* Z/Yen, London.

Yergin, D. (2006) Ensuring energy security, *Foreign Affairs, 85*(2), 69–82.

Yeung, H.W. (2005) Rethinking relational economic geography, *Transactions of the Institute of British Geographers,* New Series, 30(1), 37–51.

Yiftachel, O. and Ghanem, A. (2005) Understanding ethnocratic regimes: the politics of seizing contested territories, *Political Geography, 23*(4), 647–76.

Young, M. and Willmott, P. (1962) *Family and Kinship in East London,* Pelican, London.

Young, O. (2012) Arctic tipping points: governance in turbulent times, *Ambio, 41*, 75–84.

Yuval-Davis, N. (1997) *Gender and Nation,* Sage, London.

Yuval-Davis, N. (2003) Citizenship, territoriality and the gendered construction of difference, in Brenner, N., Jessop, B., Jones, M. and MacLeod, G. (eds) *State/Space: A Reader,* Blackwell, Oxford, 309–25.

Z

Zalasiewicz, J., Williams, M., Haywood, A. and Ellis, M. (2011) The Anthropocene: a new epoch of geological time?, *Philosophical Transactions of the Royal Society of London A: Mathematical, Physical and Engineering Sciences, 369*(1938), 835–41.

Zelezny, L.C., Chua, P. and Aldrich, C. (2000) Elaborating on gender differences in environmentalism, *Journal of Social Issues, 56*(3), 443–57.

Zeng, J., Xiao, Y. and Breslin, S. (2015) Securing China's core interests: the state of the debate in China, *International Affairs 91*(2), 245–66.

Zhang, W.M. (2009) *Zhongguo Hai Quan* [China's Maritime Rights], Haijun Chubanshe, Beijing.

Zick Varul, M. (2008) Consuming the campesino: fair trade marketing between recognition and romantic commodification, *Cultural Studies, 22*(5), 654–79.

Zook, M.A. (2003) Underground globalization: mapping the space of flows of the internet adult industry, *Environment and Planning A, 35*(7), 1261–86.

Zou, K.Y. (1999) The Chinese traditional maritime boundary line in the South China Sea and its legal consequences for the resolution of the dispute over the Spratly islands, *International Journal of Marine and Coastal Law, 14*, 27–55.

Zukin, S. (1989) *Loft Living: Culture and Capital in Urban Change,* Rutgers University Press, Newark, NJ.

Zukin, S. (1995) *The Cultures of Cities,* Blackwell, Oxford.

Index

Note: page numbers in **bold** refer to definitions in the glossary